# CD-ROM animations and interactions . . . linked to specific text chapters

| ch. | animation/interaction |
|---|---|
| 3 | Feedback control of temperature animation |
| 3 | Subatomic particles interaction |
| 3 | Atomic number, mass number interaction |
| 3 | Ionic bonding animation |
| 3 | pH interaction |
| 3 | Carbon bonds animation |
| 3 | Mechanical work animation |
| 3 | Visible light interaction |
| 3 | Isotope animation |
| 3 | Half-life interaction |
| 3 | Positron-emission tomography (PET) animation |
| 3 | Energy flow animation |
| 3 | Total energy remains constant animation |
| 3 | Economic types interaction |
| 4 | Levels of organization interaction |
| 4 | Sun to earth animation |
| 4 | Matter recycling and energy flow animation |
| 4 | Linked processes animation |
| 4 | The role of organisms in an ecosystem animation |
| 4 | Diet of the red fox interaction |
| 4 | Prairie trophic levels interaction |
| 4 | Categories of food webs interaction |
| 4 | Energy flow in Silver Springs animation |
| 4 | Water cycle interaction |
| 4 | Carbon cycle animation |
| 4 | Nitrogen cycle interaction |
| 4 | Phosphorus cycle animation |
| 4 | Sulfur cycle animation |
| 4 | Hubbard Brook forest experiment animation |
| 5 | Stanley Miller's experiment animation |
| 5 | Evolutionary tree of life animation |
| 5 | Adaptive trait interaction |
| 5 | Change in moth population animation |
| 5 | Stabilizing selection animation |
| 5 | Disruptive selection animation |
| 5 | Modeling genetic drift interaction |

| ch. | animation/interaction |
|---|---|
| 5 | Evolutionary tree diagrams |
| 6 | Coastal breezes interaction |
| 6 | Climate and ocean currents map animation |
| 6 | Air circulation and climate animation |
| 6 | Air circulation interaction |
| 6 | Upwelling along western coasts animation |
| 6 | El Niño Southern Oscillation interaction |
| 6 | Greenhouse effect interaction |
| 6 | Increasing greenhouse gases interaction |
| 6 | Biomes map interaction |
| 6 | Interactions in prairie interaction |
| 6 | Interaction in a rainforest interaction |
| 7 | Ocean provinces graphic |
| 7 | Lake zonation interaction |
| 7 | Lake turnover interaction |
| 7 | Trophic nature of lakes interaction |
| 8 | Species diversity by latitude interaction |
| 8 | Area and distance effects interaction |
| 8 | How species interact interaction |
| 8 | Gause's competition experiment interaction |
| 8 | Succession interaction |
| 8 | Resources depletion and degradation interaction |
| 9 | Capture-recapture method interaction |
| 9 | Exponential growth animation |
| 9 | Life history patterns interaction |
| 10 | Geologic forces animation |
| 10 | Plate margins interaction |
| 10 | Soil profiles interaction |
| 11 | HIV replication animation |
| 11 | Life cycle of *Plasmodium* interaction |
| 12 | Current and projected population sizes by region interaction |
| 12 | Examples of age structure interaction |
| 12 | U.S. age structure interaction |
| 12 | Demographic transition model interaction |
| 13 | Tranferring genes into plants animation |
| 13 | Land use interaction |
| 14 | Properties of water animation |

| ch. | animation/interaction |
|---|---|
| 14 | Dissolution of sodium chloride animation |
| 14 | Threats to aquifers interaction |
| 14 | Effects of deforestation interaction |
| 15 | Energy use interaction |
| 15 | Chernobyl fallout interaction |
| 17 | Formation of photochemical smog |
| 17 | Thermal inversion and smog interaction |
| 17 | Acid deposition animation |
| 17 | Effect of air pollution in forests animation |
| 18 | Greenhouse effect interaction |
| 18 | Increase in greenhouse gases interaction |
| 18 | How CFCs destroy ozone animation |
| 19 | Stream pollution animation |
| 20 | Pesticide examples interaction |
| 22 | Humans affect biodiversity interaction |
| 22 | Habitat loss and fragmentation interaction |
| 23 | Biodiversity hot-spots interaction |
| 25 | San Francisco Bay region growth interaction |
| 26 | Two view of economics animation |

## Human activity interaction

In this CD-ROM interaction, students explore the effects of human activity on biodiversity, by clicking on each of 16 relationships for more information.

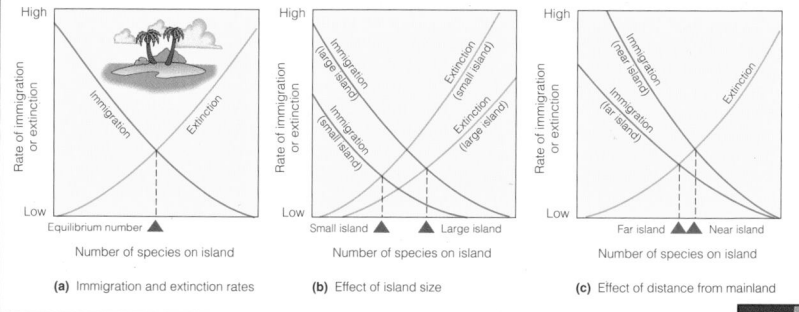

(a) Immigration and extinction rates  (b) Effect of island size  (c) Effect of distance from mainland

**Figure 8.6**  *The species equilibrium model or theory of island biogeography, developed by Robert MacArthur and Edward O. Wilson.*

## Equilibrium interaction

This interaction demonstrates the concept of species equilibrium in an understandable, intuitive way. Students are guided from Figure 8.6 in the book (above) to the CD-ROM interaction (at right) where they can change the size and distance of an island from the mainland and see for themselves how these changes affect the number of species on the island.

We start with a moderately-sized island some distance from the mainland. It has an intermediate level of species diversity. As before, dots will represent the different species. Use the controls to vary the size of the island and its distance from the mainland. Observe how these changes affect immigration rate, extinction rate, and the equilibrium number of species.

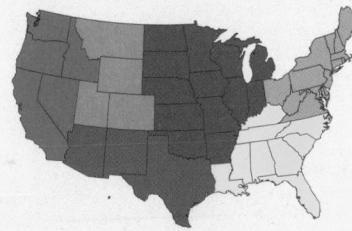

# Miller's worldwide best-seller and these seamlessly integrated resources . . . *what a team!*

LIVING IN THE ENVIRONMENT / THIRTEENTH EDITION / G. TYLER MILLER, JR.

**FREE CD-ROM with every new book!**

**Always up to date! The Book Web Site features the latest information on chapter topics!**

## Science-based, balanced, engaging and up to the minute!

With hundreds of new topics and illustrations, this 13th Edition gives students a dynamic platform for their study of the scientific laws, principles, and connections that are the basis of environmental science. Every chapter of this best-seller explores the latest environmental developments and reflects the major shifts in environmental science education that are taking place in this century. Your students will benefit from Miller's clear discussion of the basic science that makes environmental problems and their solutions understandable . . . his proven ability to get students involved in environmental issues . . . and his carefully balanced presentation of good and bad news and advantages and disadvantages of environmental technologies.

## Multimedia and online synergy!

Miller's *Living in the Environment* offers your course multimedia excitement and online immediacy that is unprecedented. Correlated chapter by chapter with the enclosed *Interactive Concepts in Environmental Science* CD-ROM, as well as with the book's continually updated Web site, and the InfoTrac® College Edition online library of periodicals, this 13th Edition keeps every class discussion current.

**Plus so many other great resources for your course.** For details, see pages 24–28 of this Preview.

**Turn the page for your quick tour** ▶▶

Preview

1

# Immerse your students in the excitement of this evolving discipline!

You are looking at the culmination of more than 32 years of research and teaching experience in environmental science. At 757 pages, this comprehensive science-based book uses basic scientific and ecological concepts, laws, and principles to enable students without prior scientific training to understand and think critically about environmental problems and solutions and form their own conclusions about controversial environmental issues.

Praised by instructors throughout the world, Miller's texts are used at a ratio of five to one over other environmental science textbooks!

This 13th Edition of *Living in the Environment* supports your lectures with the most talked-about and significant developments occurring today. In this book, you'll find:

- **New topics**—180 new or improved illustrations and 112 new topics
- **Basic science**—More effective and extensive coverage of basic science than any other book for this course
- **Balance**—Unparalleled presentation of good and bad environmental news and advantages and disadvantages of environmental technologies
- **Solutions**—Exceptional presentation and evaluation of solutions to environmental problems
- **Web links** for every chapter that direct students to an interactive Web site
- **New diagrams** that clarify solutions to environmental problems

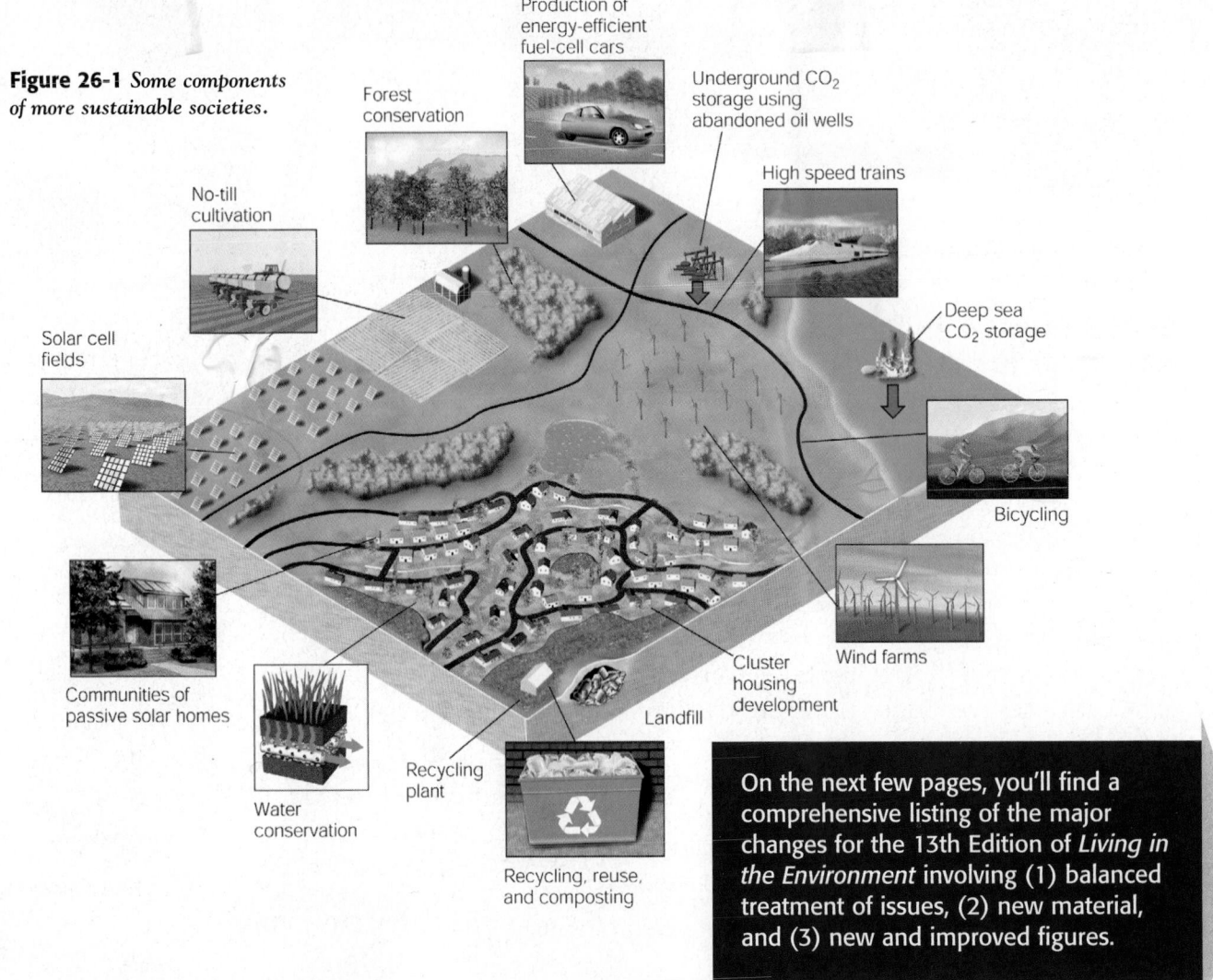

**Figure 26-1** *Some components of more sustainable societies.*

Production of energy-efficient fuel-cell cars

Forest conservation

Underground CO$_2$ storage using abandoned oil wells

High speed trains

No-till cultivation

Deep sea CO$_2$ storage

Solar cell fields

Bicycling

Communities of passive solar homes

Wind farms

Cluster housing development

Landfill

Water conservation

Recycling plant

Recycling, reuse, and composting

On the next few pages, you'll find a comprehensive listing of the major changes for the 13th Edition of *Living in the Environment* involving (1) balanced treatment of issues, (2) new material, and (3) new and improved figures.

## Chapter 1 – Environmental Problems, Their Causes, and Sustainability

**Balance:**

- Good and bad news about economic development (pp. 6–7)
- Environmental problems and their root causes (pp. 12–13)
- Are things getting better or worse? (pp. 13–14)
- Environmental worldviews (pp. 14–15)

**New Material:**

- New terms: gross national income (GNI) and gross national income in purchasing power parity (GNI PPP) (p. 4)
- Good and bad news about economic development (pp. 6–7)
- Update of indicators of globalization (pp. 7–8)
- Some harmful environmental effects of poverty (*Connections*, p. 8)
- Lessons from China (*Connections*, p. 15)

**New and Improved Illustrations:**

- Figure 1-3

## Chapter 2 – Environmental History: An Overview

**Balance:**

- Beneficial and harmful effects of the information and globalization revolution (pp. 24–25)
- Consequences of advanced industrial societies (*Connections*, p. 25)

**New Material:**

- Improved and updated timeline diagrams of U.S. environmental history (Figures 2-4, 2-7, 2-8, 2-9, 2-10, 2-11)
- Environmental record of the Bush administration (pp. 35–36)

**New and Improved Illustrations:**

- Figures 2-4 (improved), 2-7 (improved), 2-8 (improved), 2-9 (improved), 2-10 (improved), figure in Rachel Carson *Individuals Matter* box, 2-11 (improved), 2-11 (improved), and 2-12

**Figure 2-10** *Found in Chapter 2, these timelines—spanning from the 1870s to 2002—help students place important environmental events into perspective.*

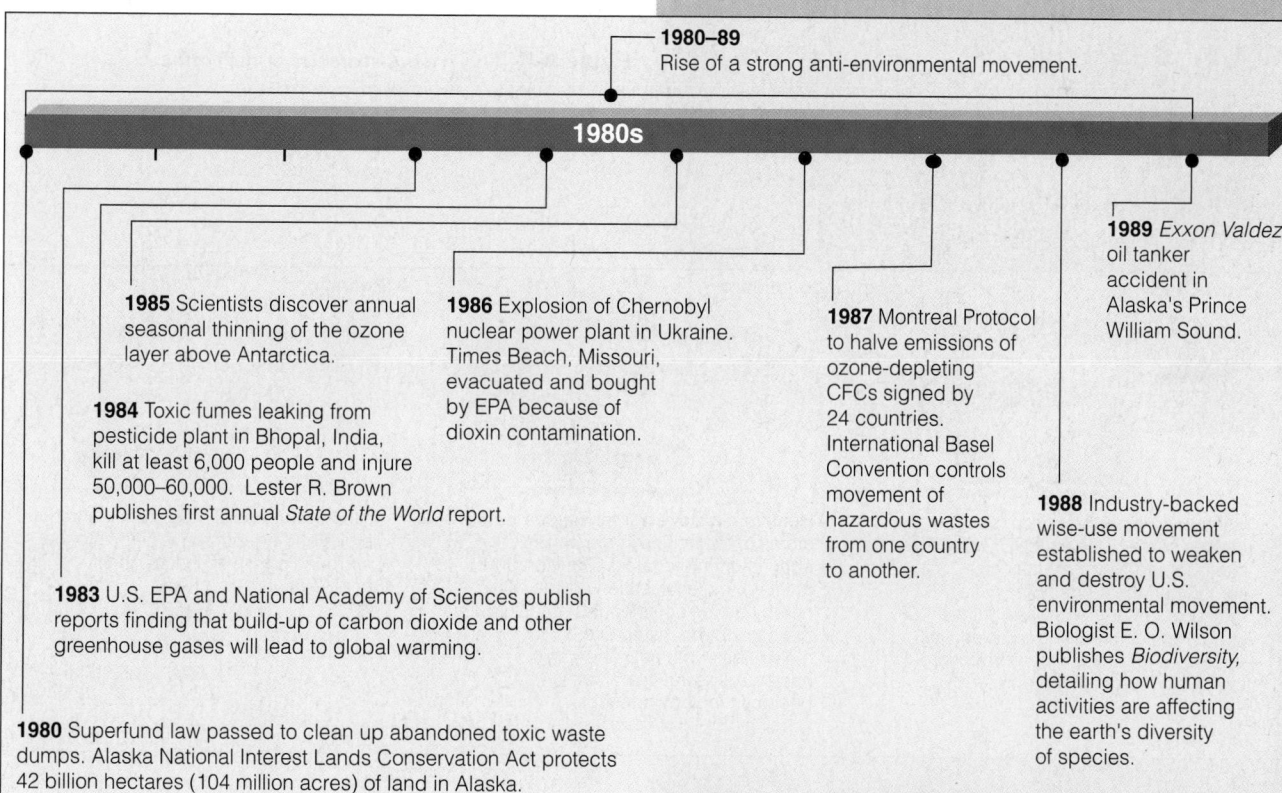

**1980–89**
Rise of a strong anti-environmental movement.

**1980s**

**1985** Scientists discover annual seasonal thinning of the ozone layer above Antarctica.

**1984** Toxic fumes leaking from pesticide plant in Bhopal, India, kill at least 6,000 people and injure 50,000–60,000. Lester R. Brown publishes first annual *State of the World* report.

**1983** U.S. EPA and National Academy of Sciences publish reports finding that build-up of carbon dioxide and other greenhouse gases will lead to global warming.

**1980** Superfund law passed to clean up abandoned toxic waste dumps. Alaska National Interest Lands Conservation Act protects 42 billion hectares (104 million acres) of land in Alaska.

**1986** Explosion of Chernobyl nuclear power plant in Ukraine. Times Beach, Missouri, evacuated and bought by EPA because of dioxin contamination.

**1987** Montreal Protocol to halve emissions of ozone-depleting CFCs signed by 24 countries. International Basel Convention controls movement of hazardous wastes from one country to another.

**1989** *Exxon Valdez* oil tanker accident in Alaska's Prince William Sound.

**1988** Industry-backed wise-use movement established to weaken and destroy U.S. environmental movement. Biologist E. O. Wilson publishes *Biodiversity*, detailing how human activities are affecting the earth's diversity of species.

## Chapter 3 – Science, Systems, Matter, and Energy

**Balance:**

- Scientific proof (p. 44)
- Frontier and consensus science (p. 44)
- Section 3-8 on matter and energy change laws and environmental problems (pp. 60–61)

**New Material:**

- Improved diagram of what scientists do (Figure 3-2, p. 41)
- Example of applying scientific method to an everyday situation (pp. 42–43)
- Improved discussion of inductive reasoning (pp. 43–44)
- Law of conservation of problems (p. 46)
- Plasma as a fourth state of matter (p. 50)
- Definition of radiation (p. 51)
- Nature of spectrum of electromagnetic radiation released by the sun (Figure 3-10, p. 52)
- Distinction between convection, conduction, and radiation (pp. 52–53 and Figure 3-11, p. 53)

**New and Improved Illustrations:**

- Figures 3-2 (improved), 3-6 (improved), 3-10, 3-11

## Chapter 4 – Ecosystems: Components, Energy Flow, and Matter Cycling

**New Material:**

- General updating

**New and Improved Illustrations:**

- Figures 4-1, 4-4, 4-5, 4-6 (improved), 4-8 (improved), 4-17, 4-31 (improved)

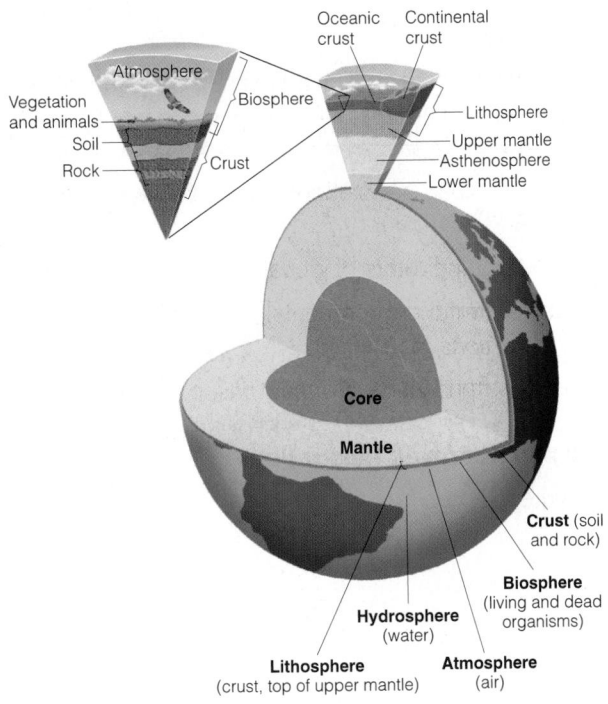

**Figure 4-6** *The general structure of the earth.*

**Figure 3-11** *Three ways in which heat can be transferred from one place to another.*

**Convection**

Heating water in the bottom of a pan causes some of the water to vaporize into bubbles. Because they are lighter than the surrounding water, they rise. Water then sinks from the top to replace the rising bubbles. This up and down movement (convection) eventually heats all of the water.

**Conduction**

Heat from a stove burner causes atoms or molecules in the pan's bottom to vibrate faster. The vibrating atoms or molecules then collide with nearby atoms or molecules, causing them to vibrate faster. Eventually, molecules or atoms in the pan's handle are vibrating so fast it becomes too hot to touch.

**Radiation**

As the water boils, heat from the hot stove burner and pan radiate into the surrounding air, even though air conducts very little heat.

## Chapter 5 – Evolution and Biodiversity: Origins, Niches, and Adaptation

**Balance:**

- Origin of life hypotheses (pp. 96–99)

**New Material:**

- Distinction between mass extinction and mass depletion based on new fossil evidence (p. 106)

**New and Improved Illustrations:**

- Figures 5-4 (improved), 5-5, 5-7 (improved)

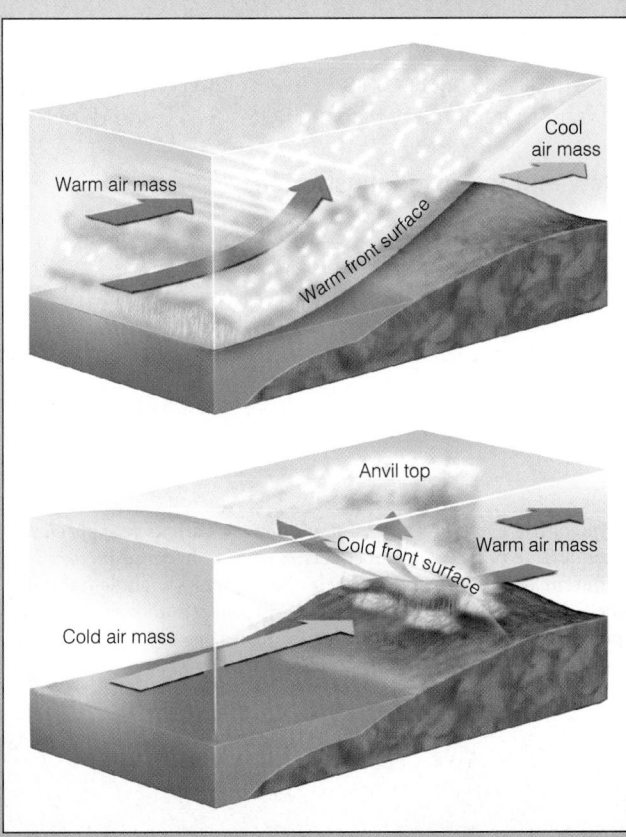

## Chapter 6 – Biogeography: Climate, Biomes, and Terrestrial Biodiversity

**New Material:**

- Expanded discussion of weather (Section 6-1, pp. 111–114)
- Warm and cold fronts (Figure 6-2, p. 111)
- Highs and lows (pp. 112–113)
- Tornadoes (p. 113 and Figure 6-3, p. 112)
- Tropical cyclones (p. 113 and Figure 6-4, p. 113)
- Formation of warm and cool ocean currents (Figure 6-12, p. 118)
- Distribution of deserts (Figure 6-23, p. 126)
- Human impact on deserts (Figure 6-26, p. 128)
- Distribution of grasslands (Figure 6-27, p. 129)
- Human impacts on grasslands (Figure 6-33, p. 134)
- Distribution of forests (Figure 6-35, p. 136)
- Human impact on forests (Figure 6-41, p. 141)
- Human impact on mountains (Figure 6-42, p. 141)

**New and Improved Illustrations:**

- Figures 6-2, 6-3, 6-4, 6-12, 6-13 (improved), 6-18 (improved), 6-22, 6-23, 6-26, 6-27, 6-33, 6-35, 6-41, 6-42

**Figure 6-2** *A warm front (top) occurs when an advancing mass of warm air meets and rises up over a retreating mass of more dense cool air. A cold front (bottom) is the boundary formed when a mass of cold air wedges beneath a retreating mass of less dense warm air.*

**Figure 6-22** *Generalized effects of altitude (left) and latitude (right) on climate and biomes. Parallel changes in vegetation type occur when we travel from the equator to the poles or from lowlands to mountaintops.*

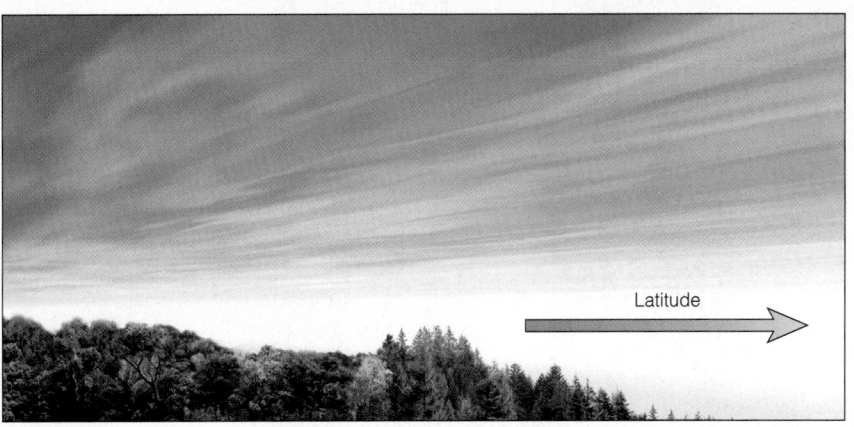

## Chapter 7 – Aquatic Ecology: Biodiversity in Aquatic Systems

### Balance:

- Threats to coral reefs (Figure 7-17, p. 155) and good news about coral reefs (*Connections*, p. 155)
- Good and bad news about the sustainability of aquatic ecosystems (pp. 162–163)

### New Material:

- Advantages and disadvantages of living in water (Figure 7-3, p. 146)
- Major ecological and economic services provided by marine systems (Figure 7-6, p. 147)
- Threats to coral reefs (Figure 7-17, p. 155)
- Effects of trawlers on ocean bottom life (Figure 7-18, p. 156)
- Major ecological and economic services provided by freshwater systems (Figure 7-19, p. 157)
- Impacts of humans on freshwater systems (pp. 160 and 162)

### New and Improved Illustrations:

- Figures 7-1, 7-2 (improved), 7-3, 7-6, 7-9, 7-12 (improved), 7-15, 7-17, 7-18, 7-19, 7-21 (improved), 7-22 (improved)

## Chapter 8 – Community Ecology: Structure, Species Interactions, Succession, and Sustainability

### Balance:

- How predictable is succession? (p. 184)
- Does species diversity increase ecosystem stability? (p. 185)
- Is there a balance of nature? (pp. 184–187)

### New Material:

- Life cycle of a frog (Figure in *Connections*, p. 171)
- Updated discussion of vanishing amphibians (*Connections*, pp. 170–171)
- Updating of information on sharks (*Case Study*, p. 176)
- Mutualistic relationship between fungi (mycorrhizae) and roots of many plants (Figures 8-12c and d, p. 179)

### New and Improved Illustrations:

- Figures 8-1, Figure in *Connections*, p. 171, 8-9 (improved), 8-12, 8-18 (improved)

**Figure 7-3** *Advantages and disadvantages of living in water.*

| Advantages | Disadvantages |
|---|---|
| Physical support from water bouyancy | Can tolerate a narrow range of temperatures |
| Fairly constant temperature | Exposure to dissolved pollutants |
| Nourishment from dissolved nutrients | Fluctuating population size for many species |
| Water availability | Dispersion separates many aquatic offspring from parents |
| Easy dispersement of organisms, larvae, and eggs | |
| Less exposure to harmful UV radiation | |
| Dilution and dispersion of pollutants | |

*Typical life cycle of a frog. Populations of various frog species can decline because of the effects of various harmful factors at different points in their life cycle. Such factors include habitat loss, drought, pollution, increased ultraviolet radiation, parasitism, disease, overhunting for food (frog legs), and nonnative predators and competitors.*

## Chapter 9 – Population Dynamics, Carrying Capacity, and Conservation Biology

**Balance:**

■ Controversy over effects of predation on controlling population size (pp. 194–195)

**New Material:**

■ Updating of population problems of the Southern Sea Otter (p. 190)

■ Population growth patterns of r-selected and K-selected species (Figure 9-9, p. 196)

**New and Improved Illustrations:**

■ Figures 9-1, 9-9

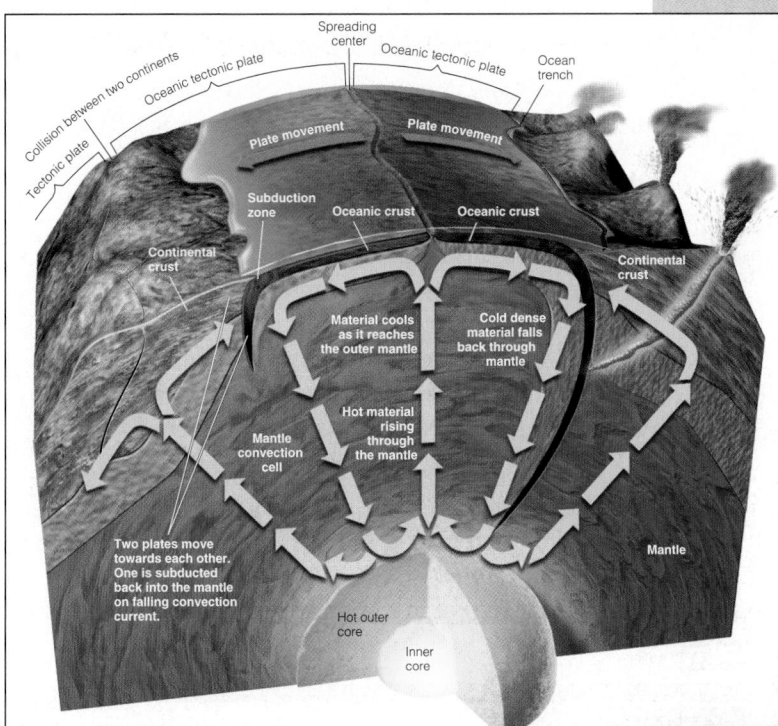

## Chapter 10 – Geology: Processes, Hazards, and Soils

**Balance:**

□ Benefits of volcanic eruptions (p. 212)

□ Controversy over the seriousness of soil erosion in the United States (pp. 219–220)

□ Good news about slowing soil erosion in the United States (*Case Study*, p. 223)

□ Inorganic versus organic fertilizers (pp. 225–226)

**New Material:**

□ New chapter opening discussion: the Mount St. Helens eruption (p. 203)

□ Details of tectonic plates (Figure 10-4, p. 206)

□ Erosion in northwest China (pp. 217–218)

□ Causes and consequences of desertification (Figure 10-21, p. 221)

□ Preventing and cleaning up salinization (Figure 10-24, p. 222)

□ Advantages and disadvantages of conservation tillage (Figure 10-25, p. 223)

**New and Improved Illustrations:**

□ Figures 10-4, 10-21, 10-24, 10-25

**Figure 10-4** *The earth's crust is made up of a series of rigid plates, called tectonic plates, which move around in response to forces in the mantle.*

**Figure 10-21** *Causes and consequences of desertification. Natural climate change also plays a role in desertification.*

# Chapter 11 – Risk, Toxicology, and Human Health

**Balance:**

- Synthetic vs. natural chemicals (p. 231)
- Good and bad news about infectious disease rates and deaths (p. 237)
- New do-it-yourself technique for disinfecting water (*Solutions*, p. 244)
- Acceptable risks (Figure 11-15, p. 246; Figure 11-17, p. 247; and Figure 11-18, p. 248)
- Limitations of risk analysis (pp. 248–249) and risk management (p. 249)
- Good news about human health (p. 250)

**New Material:**

- Update on death rates, health toll, and costs of smoking (p. 228)
- Update on hormonally active chemicals (*Connections*, p. 235)
- Types of pathogens (Figure 11-8, p. 236)
- How a virus reproduces (Figure 11-9, p. 237)
- How bacteria exposed to antibiotics develop genetic resistance (figure in *Spotlight*, p. 238)
- Update on HIV/AIDS (pp. 239–240)
- Global distribution of HIV (Figure 11-10. p. 240)
- Synergistic interactions among HIV/AIDS, tuberculosis, and hunger/malnutrition (Figure 11-11, p. 240)
- Deaths from various causes (Figure 11-17, p. 247)

**New and Improved Illustrations:**

- Figures 11-1 (improved), 11-8, 11-9, figure in *Spotlight* (p. 238), 11-10, 11-11, 11-13 (improved), 11-18

**Other Changes:**

- Moved this chapter into scientific principles and concepts part of the book

# Chapter 12 – The Human Population: Growth, Demography, and Carrying Capacity

**Balance:**

- Good and bad news on life expectancy (p. 261)
- Pro/Con of reducing births (p. 267)
- Conflict over immigration into the United States (*Case Study*, p. 268)
- Controversy over demographic transition for developing countries (p. 269)

**New Material:**

- Updating of population data
- Past and projected annual increase in the world's population (Figure 12-5, p. 256)
- U.S. population growth past and future (Figure 12-14, p. 260)
- Comparison of demographic data for the United States, Mexico, and Canada (Figure 12-15, p. 260)
- Effects of population decline from a rise in death rates in Africa (p. 261)
- Health care in China (p. 274)

**New and Improved Illustrations:**

- Figures 12-1, 12-2, 12-3 (updated), 12-4 (updated), 12-5, 12-6 (updated), 12-8 (updated), 12-9 (updated), 12-10 (updated), 12-11 (updated), 12-12 (updated), 12-13 (updated), 12-14, 12-15, 12-16 (improved), 12-17 (updated), 12-18 (updated), 12-21 (updated), figure in *Case Study* (p. 268, updated), 12-28 (updated)

**Figure 12-15** *Comparison of basic demographic data for the United States (red), Mexico (blue), and Canada (yellow). (Data from U.S. Census Bureau and Population Reference Bureau)*

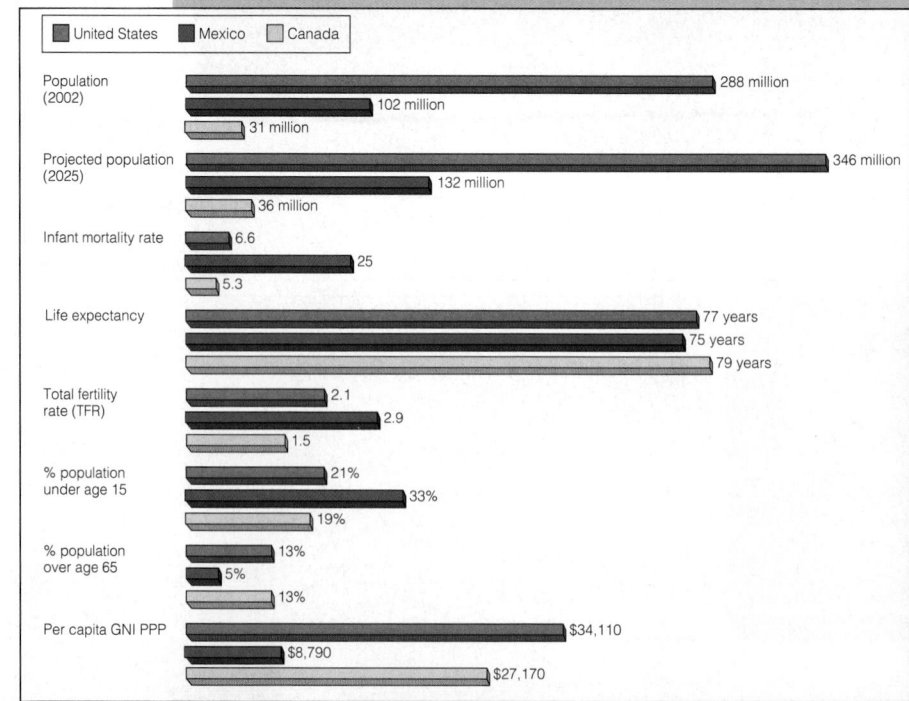

## Chapter 13 – Food Resources

**Balance:**

- Good and bad news about global food production (pp. 281, 284–285)
- Good and bad news about global undernutrition and malnutrition (pp. 285–286)
- Advantages/Disadvantages of traditional crossbreeding (pp. 289–290)
- Advantages/Disadvantages of genetically modified crops and food (pp. 290–291 and Figure 13-17, p. 292)
- Can China's population be fed? (*Case Study*, p. 293)
- Good and bad news about irrigated land (pp. 293–294)
- Advantages/Disadvantages of cultivating more land (pp. 294–295)
- Advantages/Disadvantages of aquaculture (pp. 305–307 and Figure 13-35, p. 307)
- Advantages/Disadvantages of government agricultural policies (pp. 307–308)

**New Material:**

- Fossil fuel inputs for various foods (Figure 13-4, p. 280)
- Ecological and economic services provided by croplands (Figure 13-5, p. 281)
- Tassas crop production method in Africa (p. 284)
- Average daily food intake per person (Figure 13-12, p. 287)
- Effects of global warming on food production (Figure 13-14, p. 289)
- Transgenomics as a technique for genetic engineering of crop plants (p. 290)
- Terminator genes (p. 291)
- Advantages/Disadvantages of genetically modified food (Figure 13-17, p. 292)
- Update on feeding China (*Case Study*, p. 293)
- Mad cow disease (p. 297)
- Fossil fuel inputs for harvesting various marine species (Figure 13-31, p. 303)
- Commercial fishing and the tragedy of the Commons (*Connections*, p. 305)
- New trends and research in aquaculture (p. 307)

**New and Improved Illustrations:**

- Figures 13-1, 13-4, 13-5, 13-10 (updated), 13-12, 13-14, 13-17, 13-31, 13-32 (updated), 13-36

## Chapter 14 – Water Resources

**Balance:**

- Advantages/Disadvantages of Egypt's Aswan Dam (Figure 14-9, p. 319 and *Case Study*, p. 321)
- Advantages/Disadvantages of China's Three Gorges Dam (pp. 320–321)
- Advantages/Disadvantages of withdrawing groundwater (pp. 324–325)
- Advantages/Disadvantages of floods (p. 332)
- Good news about drip irrigation (*Solutions*, p. 333)

**New Material:**

- Expanded chapter-opening discussion to include grain import wars (p. 312)
- Site of China's Three Gorges Dam (Figure 14-12, p. 320)
- Methods of reducing water waste in industries, homes, and businesses (Figure 14-20, p. 331)
- Xeriscaping example (Figure 14-21, p. 332)

**New and Improved Illustrations:**

- Figures 14-2 (improved), 14-7 (improved), 14-12, 14-20, 14-21

**Figure 13-36** *Components of more sustainable, low-throughput agriculture.*

| Increase | | Decrease |
|---|---|---|
| High-yield polyculture | | Soil erosion |
| Organic fertilizers | | Soil salinization |
| Biological pest control | | Aquifer depletion |
| Integrated pest management | | Overgrazing |
| Irrigation efficiency | | Overfishing |
| Perennial crops | | Loss of biodiversity |
| Crop rotation | | Loss of prime cropland |
| Use of more water-efficient crops | | Food waste |
| Soil conservation | | Subsidies for unsustainable farming and fishing |
| Subsidies for more sustainable farming and fishing | | Population growth |
| | | Poverty |

# Chapter 15 – Geologic Resources: Nonrenewable Mineral and Energy Resources

## Balance:

- Pro/Con of General Mining Law of 1872 (p. 347)
- Pro/Con of oil and natural gas development in the Arctic National Wildlife Refuge (p. 360)
- Advantages/Disadvantages of conventional oil (Figure 15-26, p. 361) and heavy oils (Figure 15-28, p. 361)
- Advantages/Disadvantages of natural gas (Figure 15-29, p. 362)
- Advantages/Disadvantages of coal (Figure 15-31, p. 364)
- Advantages/Disadvantages of gaseous and liquid fuels from coal (Figure 15-34, p. 365)
- Advantages/Disadvantages of nuclear power (Figure 15-38, p. 369 and Figure 15-39, p. 369)

## New Material:

- Chapter opening: bitter lessons from Chernobyl (p. 338)
- Global consumption of fossil fuels (Figure 15-13, p. 351)
- Trends in use of fossil fuels, nuclear power, and biomass (pp. 350–351)
- Past and projected energy consumption by fuels in the United States (pp. 351–352 and Figure 15-15, p. 352)
- Past and projected oil consumption by developed and developing nations (Figure 15-19, p. 355)
- Oil use in the United States (Case Study, pp. 356–357)
- Offshore oil drilling in the Gulf of Mexico (Figure 15-21, p. 357)
- Past and future U.S. oil production, consumption, and imports (Figure 15-23, p. 357)
- A brief history of oil (Spotlight, p. 359)
- Update on oil drilling in Alaska's Arctic National Wildlife Refuge (Pro/Con, p. 360)

- Boric acid corrosion in U.S. nuclear reactors (p. 368)
- Locations of U.S nuclear power plants (Figure 15-37, p. 368)
- Radioactive wastes stored at nuclear power plants (pp. 368–369)
- How safe are radioactive wastes stored at nuclear power plants? (Case Study, p. 371)
- What is the threat from "dirty" radioactive bombs? (p. 373)
- Update on storage of radioactive wastes underground at Yucca Flats site (Case Study, pp. 374–375)
- Pebble bed modular nuclear reactor (pp. 375–376 and Figure 15-42, p. 376)

## New and Improved Illustrations:

- Figures 15-12 (updated), 15-13, 15-15, 15-17 (improved), 15-19, 15-21, 15-22 (updated), 15-23, 15-26 (improved), 15-28 (improved), 15-29 (improved), 15-31 (improved), 15-34 (improved), 15-37, 15-42

**Figure 15-42** Pebble bed modular reactor (PBMR). *This is one of several new and smaller reactor designs that some nuclear engineers say should improve the safety of nuclear power and reduce its costs. This design reduces chances of a runaway chain reaction by encapsulating uranium fuels in tiny heat-resistant ceramic spheres instead of packing large numbers of fuel pellets into long metal rods.*

Each pebble contains about 10,000 uranium dioxide particles the size of a pencil point.

Pebble detail
- Silicon carbide
- Pyrolytic carbon
- Porous buffer
- Uranium dioxide

Graphite shell

Helium

Turbine
Generator

Pebble

Core

Reactor vessel

Recuperator

Water cooler

Hot water output

Cool water input

# Chapter 16 – Energy Efficiency and Renewable Energy

## Balance:

- Advantages/Disadvantages of hybrid and fuel cell cars (pp. 386–388)
- Advantages/Disadvantages of solar energy (Figure 16-16, p. 394)
- Advantages/Disadvantages of passive and active solar heating (Figure 16-20, p. 396)
- Advantages/Disadvantages of using solar energy to produce high-temperature heat and electricity (Figure 16-22, p. 398)
- Advantages/Disadvantages of solar cells (Figure 16-25, p. 400)
- Advantages/Disadvantages of hydropower (Figure 16-27, p. 401)
- Advantages/Disadvantages of wind power (p. 403 and Figure 16-30, p. 403)
- Advantages/Disadvantages of biomass (Figure 16-32, p. 404)
- Advantages/Disadvantages of hydrogen (pp. 405–409 and Figure 16-35, p. 409)
- Advantages/Disadvantages of geothermal energy (Figure 16-38, p. 410)
- Economics and energy resources (pp. 410–413)

## New Material:

- Two general principles for saving energy (p. 382)
- Average fuel economy of new vehicles sold in the United States, 1975–2001 (Figure 16-7, p. 386)
- Car size and car safety (p. 386)
- $CO_2$ emissions from cars powered by various types of engines (Figure 16-11, p. 388)
- Onboard auto fuel cell using sodium borohydride as source of hydrogen (p. 388)
- Hybrid cars versus fuel cells (p. 388 and Figure 16-11, p. 388)
- Real cost of gasoline in the United States (*Connections*, p. 388) and Figure 16-8, p. 386)
- Fuel cell bicycle and electric scooter (p. 389)
- New high-intensity fluorescent table lamp (p. 392)
- Good and bad news about increased use of renewable energy (p. 394)
- Update on hydrogen as energy source (Section 16-7, pp. 405–409)
- Hydrogen energy system and economy (Figure 16-34, p. 407)
- U.S. government research and development funding for various sources of energy (Figures 16-42, p. 413 and 16-43, p. 413)

## New and Improved Illustrations:

- Figures 16-7, 16-8 (updated), 16-11, 16-15 (improved), 16-16 (improved), 16-24, 16-25 (improved), 16-27 (improved), 16-32 (improved), 16-34, 16-35 (improved), 16-38 (improved), 16-42, 16-43 and Table 16-1 (updated)

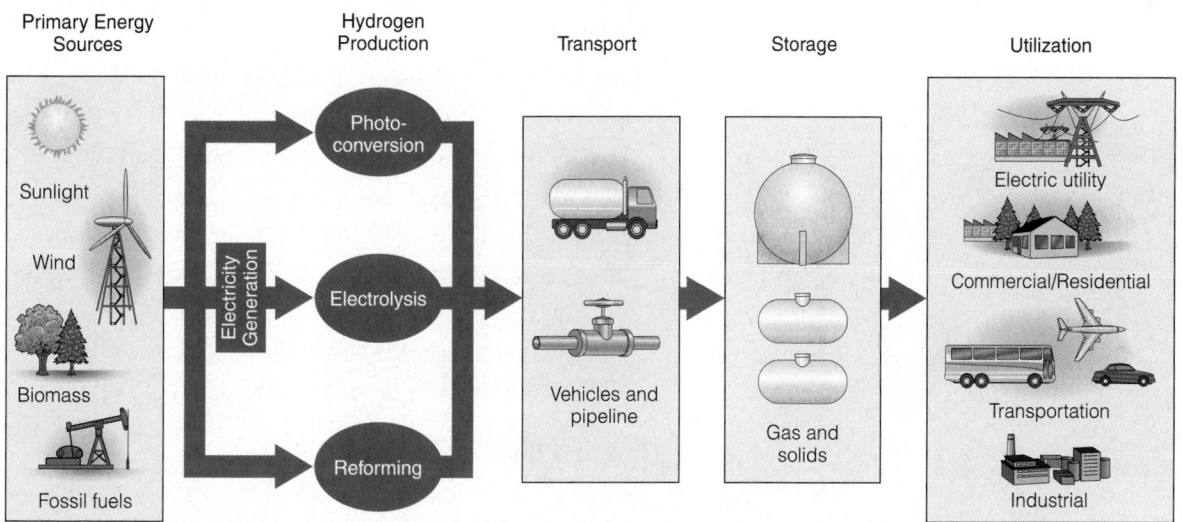

**Figure 16-34** *A hydrogen energy system. (Data from U.S. Department of Energy and the Worldwatch Institute)*

# Chapter 17— Air and Air Pollution

## Balance:

- Air pollution in the past (*Spotlight*, p. 423)
- Good and bad news about acid deposition in the United States (p. 433)
- Good and bad news about air pollution (pp. 439–440)
- Advantages/Disadvantages of emissions trading (p. 441)

## New Material:

- Satellite tracking of air pollutants (Figure 17-5, p. 421)
- What is the next step? (pp. 443–444)

## New and Improved Illustrations:

- Figures 17-1, 17-5, 17-7, 17-15 (improved)

# Chapter 18 — Climate Change and Ozone Loss

## Balance:

- Effects of human activities on climate (pp. 455–456)
- Factors affecting future climate change (pp. 456–460)
- Controversy over what to do about projected climate change (p. 465)
- Advantages/Disadvantages of use of the marketplace to reduce or prevent greenhouse gas emissions (pp. 466–467)
- Advantages/Disadvantages of removing $CO_2$ from the atmosphere (pp. 467–469)
- Controversy over Kyoto treaty (pp. 469–470)

## New Material:

- Update of effects of human activities on global warming (pp. 450–452)
- Top ten nations in terms of total and per capita $CO_2$ emissions (Figure 18-5, p. 451)
- Apparent connections between increases in (1) fossil fuel use, (2) atmospheric concentrations of $CO_2$, and (3) global temperature between 1970 and 2000 (Figure 18-6, p. 452)
- Temperature changes and floating ice losses in the Arctic (Figure 18-8, p. 453)
- Ice cover in Antarctica (Figure 18-9, p. 453)
- Effects of elevated levels of $CO_2$ on uptake of nitrate fertilizer (p. 459)
- Some possible beneficial effects of global warming (Figure 18-15, p. 460)
- Projected changes in precipitation patterns in this century as a result of global warming (Figure 18-17, p. 462)
- Effects of projected sea level rise by 2100 on cities and low-lying islands (Figure 18-19, p. 463)
- Removal of carbon dioxide from the atmosphere or from smokestacks and storing (sequestering) it in plants, deep underground reservoirs, and the deep ocean (Figure 18-21, p. 467)
- Effects of soil conservation on greenhouse gas emissions (Figure 18-22, p. 468)
- New Section 18-7 on what is being done to reduce greenhouse gas emissions (pp. 469–471)
- Update on controversy over Kyoto treaty (pp. 469–470)
- $CO_2$ emissions from different types of transportation (Figure 18-24, p. 471)
- Ways individuals can reduce their $CO_2$ emissions (Figure 18-25, p. 472)
- Expected effects of decreased levels of ozone in the stratosphere (Figure 18-31, p. 475)

## New and Improved Illustrations:

- Figures 18-1, 18-4 (updated), 18-5, 18-6, 18-8, 18-9, 18-12 (updated), 18-14 (improved), 18-15, 18-17, 18-19, 18-20 (improved), 18-21, 18-22, 18-24, 18-25, 18-27 (updated), 18-28 (updated), 18-29 (updated), 18-31

**Figure 18-21** *Possible methods for removing carbon dioxide from the atmosphere or from smokestacks and storing (sequestering) it in plants, deep underground reservoirs, and the deep ocean.*

# Chapter 19 – Water Pollution

## Balance:

- Good and bad news about stream pollution (pp. 487–488)
- Controversy over arsenic in drinking water (*Spotlight,* pp. 496–497)
- Can oceans take care of our wastes? (p. 496)
- Pro/Con of strengthening the U.S. Clean Water Act (p. 503)
- What should we do with sewage sludge? (pp. 505–506)
- Good and bad news about drinking water (pp. 507–508)

## New Material:

- Results of coliform bacteria test (Figure 19-2, p. 485)
- Point and non-point sources of water pollution (Figure 19-4, p. 486)
- Expanded discussion of lake pollution (Section 19-3, pp. 489–493)
- How much arsenic should we allow in drinking water? (*Spotlight*, pp. 496–497)
- The Baltic Sea (*Case Study*, p. 499)
- Methods for preventing and cleaning up excessive pollution of coastal waters (Figure 19-15, p. 502)
- What is the next step? (pp. 509–510)

## New and Improved Illustrations:

- Figures 19-2, 19-4, 19-10, figure in *Spotlight* (p. 496), figure in *Case Study* (p. 499), 19-15

# Chapter 20 – Pesticides and Pest Control

## Balance:

- Advantages of pesticides (pp. 514–516) and disadvantages of pesticides (pp. 516–518)
- Advantages/Disadvantages of alternatives to conventional pesticides (pp. 520–523)

## New Material:

- Pesticide use on cut flowers (p. 514)

## New Illustration:

- Figure 20-1

**Figure 19-10** *Principal sources of groundwater contamination in the United States.*

# Chapter 21 — Solid and Hazardous Waste

## Balance:

- Solid waste options (pp. 528–531; Figure 21-3, p. 528; and Figure 21-4, p. 530)
- Centralized recycling of mixed wastes (p. 537 and Figure 21-8, p. 538) vs. separating solid wastes for recycling (pp. 537–538)
- Advantages/Disadvantages of recycling (pp. 538–539)
- Advantages/Disadvantages of recycling plastics (p. 541)
- Advantages/Disadvantages of phytoremediation (p. 542)
- Advantages/Disadvantages of incineration (pp. 543–544 and Figure 21-11, p. 543)
- Advantages/Disadvantages of landfills (pp. 544–545 and Figure 21-13, p. 545)
- Advantages/Disadvantages of deep well disposal (p. 545 and Figure 21-14, p. 545)
- Advantages/Disadvantages of surface impoundments (p. 546 and Figure 21-15, p. 546)
- Good and bad news about lead pollution (p. 548)

## New Material:

- Terrorism and release of toxic chemicals from industrial plants (p. 528)
- A black day on Bhopal (*Case Study*, p. 528)
- Industrial ecosystem in Kalundborg, Denmark (Figure 21-5, p. 532)
- Economic importance of the recycling industry in the United States (p. 539)
- Chemical methods for detoxifying hazardous wastes (p. 542)
- Using a plasma torch to detoxify hazardous wastes (pp. 542–543)
- Threats from toxic mercury (pp. 549-551 and Figure 21-19, p. 550)
- Update on brownfields (pp. 553–554)
- Update on the Superfund Law and cleanup (p. 553 and *Solutions*, p. 554)

## New and Improved Illustrations:

- Figures 21-5, figure in *Individuals Matter* box (p. 534), 21-14 (improved), 21-15 (improved), 21-19

**Figure 21-5** Industrial ecosystem *in Kalundborg, Denmark, reduces waste production by mimicking a natural food web by having the wastes of one business become the raw materials for another business.*

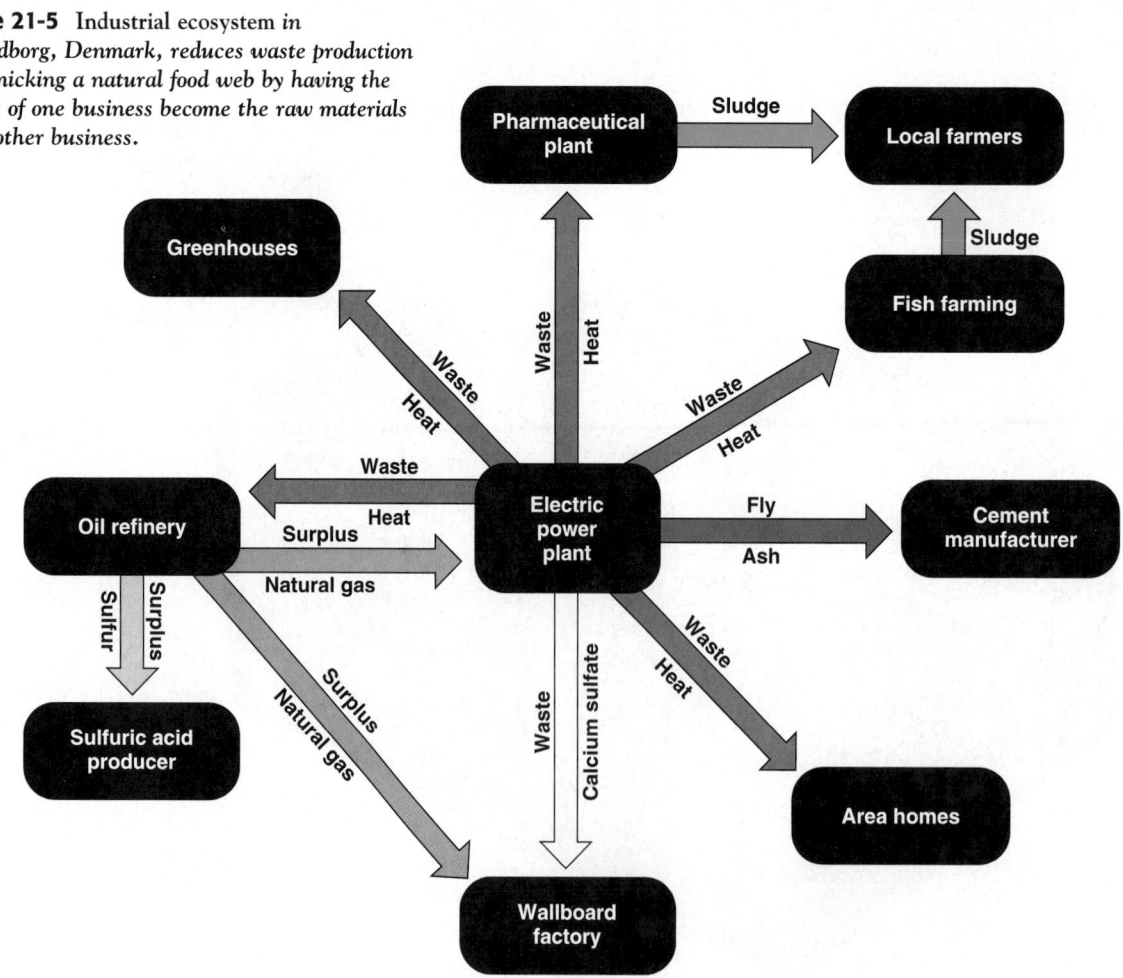

# Chapter 22 – Sustaining Wild Species

**Balance:**

- Good and bad news about endangered species in the United States (Figure 22-3, p. 562)
- Controversy over extinction rates (p. 567–568)
- Should we put a price on nature? (*Spotlight*, p. 571)
- Advantages/Disadvantages of kudzu (*Connections*, p. 577)
- Controversy over ivory sales ban (pp. 580–581)
- Should the Endangered Species Act be strengthened or weakened? (pp. 584–585)
- Which species should we protect? (p. 585)
- Advantages/Disadvantages of zoos (pp. 587–588)
- Controversy over sport hunting (pp. 589–590)
- Controversy over snow geese (*Connections*, p. 591)

**New Material:**

- Update on premature extinction of species because of human activities (pp. 561–562, 567–568)
- Ten most threatened species of U.S. songbirds (Figure 22-15, p. 574)
- Nonnative species in the United States (Figure 22-17, p. 576)
- Kudzu expansion in the United States (figure in Connections, p. 577)
- Killing invader species that stowaway in the ballast water of ships (*Individuals Matter*, p. 580)

**New and Improved Illustrations:**

- Figures 22-7 (improved), 22-15, 22-17, and 22-21

**Figure 22-17** *Some nonnative species that have been deliberately or accidentally introduced into the United States.*

## Chapter 23 – Sustaining Terrestrial Biodiversity: The Ecosystem Approach

**Balance:**

- How should public lands be used? (pp. 597–598)
- Use of public rangelands (p. 598 and *Individuals Matter*, p. 599)
- Advantages/Disadvantages of different tree harvesting methods (pp. 602–604)
- Good and bad news about the world's forests (p. 604)
- Should there be more tree plantations? (pp. 605–606)
- Should some forests be allowed to burn? (pp. 607–608)
- Good and bad news about the U.S. forests (p. 609)
- How should national forests be managed? (pp. 609–611)
- How rapidly are tropical forests being cleared? (p. 612)
- Design of nature reserves (pp. 623–624)
- Should more wilderness be protected? (*Case Study*, p. 628)
- Controversy over ecological restoration (pp. 630–631)

**New Material:**

- Global forest cover (Figure 23-6, p. 599)
- Distribution of the world's forest by major ecological zone (Figure 23-8, p. 600)
- Deforestation in the 1990s (p. 604 and Figure 23-15, p. 605)
- Gypsy moth infestation in the United States (Figure 23-16, p. 607)
- Charter forest proposal (pp. 610–611)
- The downward spiral of tropical forest degradation (*Connections*, p. 616)
- Conservation concession (pp. 616–617)
- Ways to protect tropical forests (Figure 23-23, p. 617)
- New park system in Brazil (p. 621)
- Four principles for carrying out ecological restoration (p. 629)
- What is the next step? (p. 630)

**New and Improved Illustrations:**

- Figures 23-1, figure in *Individuals Matter* (p. 599), 23-6, 23-7, 23-8, 23-10, 23-15, 23-16, 23-19, 23-23, figure in *Individuals Matter* (p. 619)

## Chapter 24 – Sustaining Aquatic Biodiversity

**Balance:**

- Controversy over commercial whaling (pp. 643–646)
- Dealing with beach erosion (pp. 647–648)
- Fishery access (pp. 649–650 and *Spotlight*, p. 650)
- Good and bad news on wetlands protection in the United States (p. 651)
- Protecting Lake Baikal (*Case Study*, p. 654)
- Management of the Columbia River basin (pp. 656–657)

**New Material:**

- Update on human impacts on aquatic biodiversity (pp. 637–640)
- Update on commercial whaling (p. 646)
- Update on zebra mussel infiltration (Figure 24-13, p. 655)

**New and Improved Illustrations:**

- Figures 24-1, 24-13 (improved)

| Prevention | | Restoration |
|---|---|---|
| Protect most diverse and endangered areas | | Reforestation |
| Educate settlers about sustainable agriculture and forestry | | Rehabilitation of degraded areas |
| Phase out subsidies that encourage unsustainable forest use | | Concentrate farming and ranching on already-cleared areas |
| Add subsidies that encourage sustainable forest use | | |
| Protect forests with *debt-for-nature* swaps, *conservation easements*, and *conservation concessions* | | |
| Certify sustainably grown timber | | |
| Reduce illegal cutting | | |
| Reduce poverty | | |
| Slow population growth | | |

**Figure 23-23** *Solutions: ways to protect forests and use them more sustainably.*

# Chapter 25 – Sustainable Cities: Urban Land Use and Management

**Balance:**

- Good and bad news about urban problems in the United States (pp. 664–665)
- Advantages/Disadvantages of urban areas (pp. 668–671)
- Pro/Con of motor vehicles (pp. 672–674)
- Advantages/Disadvantages of motor scooters (Figure 25-14, p. 674)
- Advantages/Disadvantages of bicycles (Figure 25-15, p. 674)
- Advantages/Disadvantages of mass transit rail systems (Figure 25-16, p. 675)
- Advantages/Disadvantages of rapid rail systems (Figure 25-17, p. 675)
- Advantages/Disadvantages of bus systems (Figure 25-19, p. 676)

**New Material:**

- Urban population in developed and developing countries (Figure 25-3, p. 662)
- Rural-to-urban shift in the United States (Figure 25-5, p. 664)
- Major urban regions in the United States (Figure 25-6, p. 665)
- Urban sprawl in Las Vegas, Nevada (Figure 25-7, p. 665)
- Advantages/Disadvantages of motor scooters (Figure 25-14, p. 674)
- Advantages/Disadvantages of bicycles (Figure 25-15, p. 674)
- Advantages/Disadvantages of mass transit rail systems (Figure 25-16, p. 675)
- Advantages/Disadvantages of rapid rail systems (Figure 25-17, p. 675)
- Advantages/Disadvantages of bus systems (Figure 25-19, p. 676)
- Mass Transit in the United States (*Case Study*, p. 677)
- Bus system in Curitiba, Brazil (figure in *Solutions* box, p. 679)

**New and Improved Illustrations:**

- Figures 25-1, 25-2 (improved), 25-3, 25-5, 25-6 (improved), 25-7, 25-14, 25-15, 25-16, 25-17, 25-19, figure in *Solutions* (p. 679), 25-22

# Chapter 26 – Economics, Environment, and Sustainability

**Balance:**

- Importance of natural resources (p. 690)
- Advantages/Disadvantages of global market economy (p. 693)
- Conventional vs. ecological economists (pp. 693-695; Figure 26-6, p. 694; and Figure 26-7, p. 695)
- Full-cost pricing (pp. 697–700)
- Controversy over discount rates (p. 702)
- Advantages/Disadvantages of benefit-cost analysis (p. 702)
- Regulation vs. market forces (pp. 703–706 and Table 26-1, p. 706)
- Tax burden vs. tax shifting (p. 704 and *Solutions*, p. 705)
- Pro/Con of tradable pollution and resource rights (pp. 704–705)
- Good and bad news about poverty (p. 707)

**New Material:**

- Principles for shifting to more environmentally sustainable economies (Figure 26-14, p. 710)
- Shifts in types of businesses during this century (Figure 26-15, p. 711)

**New and Improved Illustrations:**

- Figures 26-1, 26-9 (updated), 26-13 (updated), 26-14, 26-15

**Figure 26-14** *Major principles for shifting to more environmentally sustainable economies or eco-economies during this century.*

| Economics | Environmentally Sustainable Economy (Eco-Economy) | Resource Use and Pollution |
|---|---|---|
| Reward (subsidize) earth-sustaining behavior | | Reduce resource use and waste by refusing, reducing, reusing, and recycling |
| Penalize (tax and do not subsidize) earth-degrading behavior | | Improve energy efficiency |
| Tax pollution and waste instead of wages and profits | | Rely more on renewable solar and geothermal energy |
| Use full-cost pricing | | Shift from a carbon based (fossil fuel) economy to a solar–hydrogen based economy |
| Sell more services instead of more things | | |
| Do not deplete natural capital | | |
| Live off income from natural capital | | **Ecology and Population** |
| Reduce poverty | | Mimic nature |
| | | Preserve biodiversity |
| | | Repair ecological damage |
| | | Stabilize population by reducing fertility |

## Chapter 27 – Politics, Environment, and Sustainability

**Balanced:**

- Regulatory takings issue (*Case Study*, p. 725)
- Controversy over global free trade (pp. 733–737)
- Good and bad news about international environmental efforts (pp. 731–733)
- Improving environmental laws and regulations (*Solutions*, p. 736)

**New Material:**

- The regulatory takings controversy (*Case Study*, p. 725)
- Update on global conservation and environmental groups (p. 727)
- Good and bad news about international environmental efforts (pp. 731–733)
- Goals of global and national environmental NGOs (*Solutions*, p. 737)

## Chapter 28 – Environmental Worldviews, Ethics, and Sustainability

**Balance:**

- Differing environmental views (pp. 742–747 and Figure 28-3, p. 743)
- Crisis vs. tapestry models of environmental problems (p. 747)

**New Material:**

- New chapter opening on Biosphere 2 (p. 741)
- *Guest Essay* by Noel Perrin on green colleges (p. 752)

**New and Improved Illustrations:**

- Figure 28-1, 28-3

**Figure 28-3** *Comparison of two opposing environmental worldviews.*

**Environmental Worldviews**

**Planetary Management**

As the planet's most important species, we are in charge

Resources are unlimited

All economic growth is good and is unlimited

Our success depends on managing the world's life-support systems for our benefit

**Environmental Wisdom**

All species are important and we are not in charge

The earth's resources are limited and should not be wasted

Some forms of economic growth are environmentally beneficial and some are environmentally harmful

Our success depends on learning how the earth sustains itself and integrating such scientific lessons from nature (environmental wisdom) into the ways we think and act

# Leading-edge coverage of the basic science that makes environmental topics meaningful

Since its first edition, *Living in the Environment* has led the way in using scientific laws, principles, models, and concepts to help students clarify complex environmental topics such as global warming, ozone depletion, biodiversity loss, energy options and policies, and others. Forty percent (303 pages) of this 13th Edition is devoted to explaining basic scientific concepts that are essential to your students' understanding of environmental issues. This includes 212 pages of text in Chapters 3 through 11 (listed below) and an additional 91 pages integrated throughout the text that reinforces and supplements the material covered in Part II.

## Part II: Scientific Principles and Concepts:

Chapter 3    Science, Systems, Matter, and Energy

Chapter 4    Ecosystems: Components, Energy Flow, and Matter Cycling

Chapter 5    Evolution and Biodiversity: Origins, Niches, and Adaptation

Chapter 6    Biogeography: Climate, Biomes, and Terrestrial Biodiversity

Chapter 7    Aquatic Ecology: Biodiversity in Aquatic Systems

Chapter 8    Community Ecology: Structure, Species Interactions, Succession, and Sustainability

Chapter 9    Population Dynamics, Carrying Capacity, and Conservation Biology

Chapter 10    Geology: Processes, Hazards, and Soils

Chapter 11    Risk, Toxicology, and Human Health

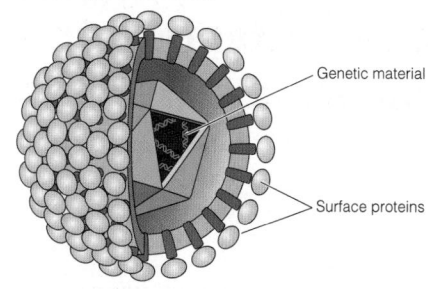

A typical virus consists of a shell of proteins surrounding genetic material

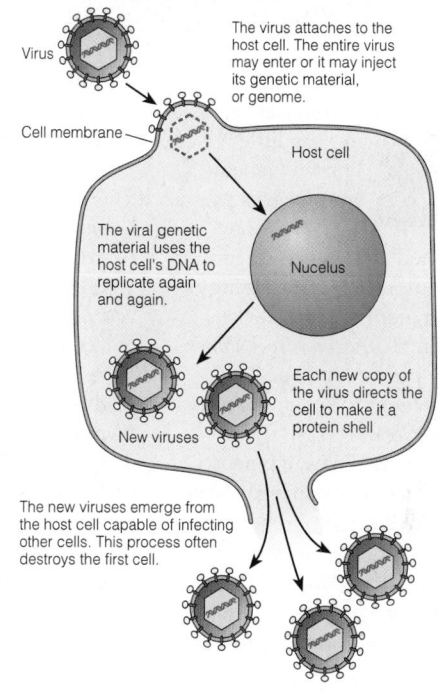

**Figure 11-9** *How a virus reproduces. (American Medical Association)*

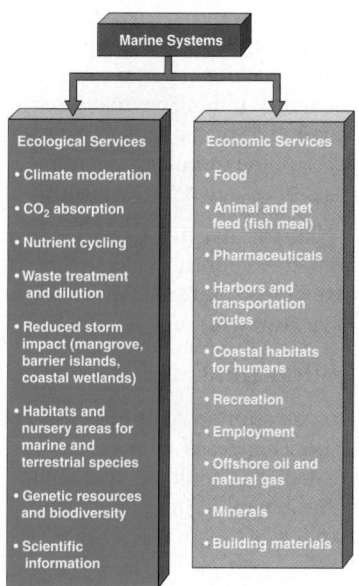

**Figure 7-6** *Major ecological and economic services provided by marine systems.*

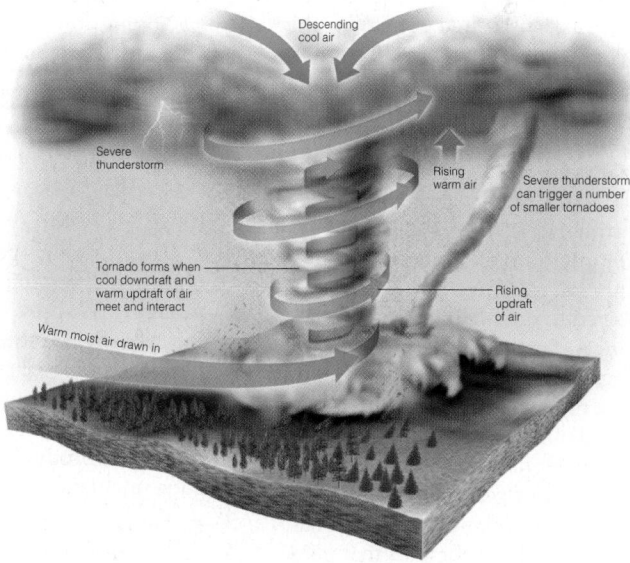

**Figure 6-3** *Formation of a tornado or twister. Although twisters can form any time of the year, the most active tornado season in the United States is usually March through August. Each year more than 800 tornadoes strike the United States. Meteorologists cannot predict with great accuracy when and where most tornadoes will form.*

**Science Based**

19

# Unbiased attention to different viewpoints . . . unequalled in other texts

With the help of dozens of reviewers and copy editors, Miller has diligently scoured every sentence for even a hint of bias. In addition, throughout the book, this acclaimed environmental scholar consistently includes discussion of a variety of viewpoints—helping students to think critically and evaluate the issues for themselves.

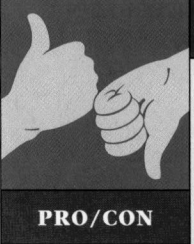

**Balanced and Fair**

## Controversy over the General Mining Law of 1872

**PRO/CON**

Some people have gotten rich by using the little known General Mining Law of 1872. This law was designed to **(1)** encourage mineral exploration and mining of gold, silver, copper, zinc, nickel, uranium, and other *hardrock minerals* on U.S. public lands and **(2)** help develop the then sparsely populated West.

Under this 1872 law, a person or corporation can assume legal ownership of parcels of land on essentially all U.S. public land except parks and wilderness areas by *patenting* it. This involves **(1)** declaring the belief that the land contains valuable hardrock minerals, **(2)** spending $500 to improve the land for mineral development, **(3)** filing a claim, **(4)** paying an annual fee of $100 for each 8 hectares (20 acres) to maintain the claim whether or not a mine is in operation, and, if desired, **(5)** paying the federal government $6–12 per hectare ($2.50–5.00 an acre) for the land. Once purchased, the land can be used, leased, or sold for essentially any purpose.

So far, public lands containing an estimated $240–385 billion (adjusted for inflation) of publicly owned mineral resources have been transferred to private interests at 1872 prices. Domestic and foreign mining companies operating under this law remove mineral resources worth at least $2–3 billion per year on once-public land they bought at very low prices.

In addition, the Congressional Budget Office estimates that mining companies remove hardrock minerals worth at least $650 million per year from public land that has not been transferred to private ownership.

*Hardrock mining companies also pay no royalties on the minerals they extract from such lands.* In contrast, **(1)** oil and natural gas companies pay a gross royalty of 12.5% and **(2)** coal companies a gross royalty of 8–12.5% on the wholesale price of the resources they remove from public lands. Congress has also given hardrock mining companies tax breaks worth an estimated $823 million between 2002 and 2012.

No provision in the 1872 law requires mining companies to pay for environmental cleanup of any damage they cause to these lands and nearby water resources. Cleanup costs for land and streams damaged by 557,000 abandoned hardrock mines (Case Study, p. 345) and open pits (mostly in the West) will cost U.S. taxpayers an estimated $33–72 billion.

Mining companies defend the 1872 law. They point out that

- They must invest large sums of money (often $100 million or more) to locate and develop an ore site before they make any profits from mining hardrock minerals.

- Their mining operations **(1)** provide high-paying jobs to miners, **(2)** supply vital resources for industry, **(3)** stimulate the national and local economies, **(4)** reduce trade deficits, and **(5)** save American consumers money on products produced from such minerals.

- Paying royalties on their profits and requiring them to pay cleanup costs would force them to move their mining operations to other countries.

For decades, environmentalists have been trying, without success, to have this law revised to protect taxpayers and the environment by

- Permanently banning the patenting (sale) of public lands but allowing 20-year leases of designated public land for hardrock mining.

- Requiring mining companies to pay a *gross* royalty of 8–12% on the wholesale value of all minerals removed from public land—similar to what oil, natural gas, and coal companies pay. Hardrock mining companies want to **(1)** continue paying no royalties or **(2)** if the law is changed pay no more than a 5% *net* royalty based on gross sales minus production costs—a system that would yield a much lower return on sales of these minerals owned jointly by all taxpayers.

- Making mining companies legally and financially responsible for environmental cleanup and restoration of each site or charging them an additional mining fee to help pay for cleanup costs. Currently, mining companies are required to post bonds to cover 100% of the estimated cleanup costs in case they go bankrupt.

Canada, Australia, South Africa, and other countries that are major extractors of hardrock minerals have laws with such requirements.

**Critical Thinking**

Do you support or oppose the three major changes that environmentalists believe should be made in the U.S. General Mining Law of 1872? Explain.

# 25 clarifying diagrams present advantages and disadvantages of environmental technologies

| Projected Advantages | | Projected Disadvantages |
|---|---|---|
| Need less fertilizer | | Irreversible and unpredictable genetic and eco-logical effects |
| Need less water | | Harmful toxins in food from possible plant cell mutations |
| More resistant to insects, plant dis-ease, frost, and drought | | New allergens in food |
| Faster growth | | Lower nutrition |
| Can grow in slightly salty soils | | Increased evolution of pesticide-resistant insects and plant diseases |
| Less spoilage | | Creation of herbicide-resistant weeds |
| Better flavor | | Harm beneficial insects |
| Less use of con-ventional pesticides | | Lower genetic diversity |
| Tolerate higher levels of herbicide use | | |

**Figure 13-17** *Projected advantages and disadvantages of genetically modified crops and foods.*
From *Living in the Environment*, 13th Edition, p. 292

| Advantages | | Disadvantages |
|---|---|---|
| Large fuel supply | | High cost (even with large subsidies) |
| Low environmental impact (without accidents) | | Low net energy yield |
| Emits 1/6 as much $CO_2$ as coal | | High environmental impact (with major accidents) |
| Moderate land disruption and water pollution (without accidents) | | Catastrophic accidents can happen (Chernobyl) |
| Moderate land use | | No acceptable solution for long-term storage of radioactive wastes and decommissioning worn-out plants |
| Low risk of accidents because of multiple safety systems (except in 35 poorly designed and run reactors in former Soviet Union and Eastern Europe) | | Spreads knowledge and technology for building nuclear weapons |

**Figure 15-38** *Advantages and disadvantages of using nuclear power to produce electricity. This evaluation includes the entire nuclear fuel cycle.*
From *Living in the Environment*, 13th Edition, p. 369

| Advantages | | Disadvantages |
|---|---|---|
| Can be produced from water | | Not found in nature |
| Low environmental impact | | Energy is needed to produce fuel |
| No $CO_2$ emissions | | Negative net energy |
| Good substitute for oil | | Nonrenewable if generated by fossil fuels or nuclear power |
| Competitive price if environmental and social costs are included in cost comparisons | | High costs (but expected to come down) |
| Easier to store than electricity | | Short driving range for current fuel cell cars |
| Safer than gasoline and natural gas | | No distribution system in place |
| High efficiency (65–95%) in fuel cells | | |

**Figure 16-35** *Advantages and disadvantages of using hydrogen as a fuel for vehicles and for providing heat and electricity.*
From *Living in the Environment*, 13th Edition, p. 409

| Advantages | | Disadvantages |
|---|---|---|
| Affordable | | Little protection in an accident |
| Produce no pollution | | Do not protect riders from bad weather |
| Quiet | | Not practical for trips longer than 8 kilometers (5 miles) |
| Require little parking space | | Can be tiring (except for electric bicycles) |
| Easy to maneuver in traffic | | Lack of safe bike parking |
| Take few resources to make | | |
| Very energy efficient | | |
| Provide exercise | | |

**Figure 25-15** *Advantages and disadvantages of bicycles.*
From *Living in the Environment*, 13th Edition, p. 674

# Good/bad news . . . advantages and disadvantages . . . helping students analyze and decide for themselves

Throughout this book, Miller intersperses "good news/bad news" sections, which give students concise, readable summaries of the positive and negative aspects of environmental issues and technologies. In addition, Miller includes thorough discussions that not only focus specifically on the advantages and disadvantages but also engage students in considering all sides and taking an informed stand.

**What Are the Major Advantages and Disadvantages of Solar Energy?** Figure 16-16 (p. 394) lists some of the advantages and disadvantages of making a shift to greatly increased use of direct solar energy and indirect forms of solar energy such as wind. Like fossil fuels and nuclear power (Chapter 15), each renewable energy alternative has a mix of advantages and disadvantages, as discussed in the remainder of this chapter.

Here is some *good news* about the increased use of renewable energy:

- In 2001, the European Union (EU) adopted a law requiring its member countries to get 12% of their total energy and 22% of their electricity from renewable energy by 2010.

- A 2001 joint study by the American Council for an Energy Efficient Economy, the Tellus Institute, and the Union of Concerned Scientists showed how renewable energy could provide 20% of U.S. energy and save consumers $440 billion by 2020.

- In 2001, voters overwhelmingly approved a $100 million bond issue aimed at **(1)** making San Francisco, California, the nation's top urban producer of solar power and wind power and **(2)** using these renewable forms of energy to supply about 25% of the energy used by the city's schools and government buildings.

- According to Royal Dutch Shell International Petroleum, renewable energy could account for 50% of the world's energy production by 2050.

The *bad news* is that solar and wind power currently provide only about 1% of the world's commercial energy—mostly because they have received and continue to receive much lower government tax breaks, subsidies, and research and development funding than fossil fuels and nuclear power.

From *Living in the Environment*, 13th Edition, p. 393–394

**Is It Feasible to Recycle Plastics?** Plastics are various types of polymer molecules made by chemically linking monomer molecules (petrochemicals) produced mostly from oil and natural gas (Figure 21-9).

Currently, only about 7% by weight of all plastic wastes and 10% of plastic containers in the United States are recycled, for the following reasons:

- Plastics are very difficult to isolate from other wastes because they **(1)** occur in so many different and often difficult-to-identify forms of resins, **(2)** sometimes consist of composites or laminated layers of different plastics, and **(3)** contain stabilizers and other chemicals that must be removed before recycling.

- Recovering individual plastic resins does not yield much material because only small amounts of any given resin are used per product.

- The price of oil is so low (Figure 15-22, p. 357) that the cost of virgin plastic resins (except for PET, used mostly in plastic drink bottles) is about 40% lower than that of recycled resins.

Thus mandating that plastic products contain a certain amount of recycled plastic resins is **(1)** unlikely to work and **(2)** could hinder the use of plastics in reducing the resource content and weight (Solutions, p. 533) of many widely used items such as plastic bags, bottles, and other containers.

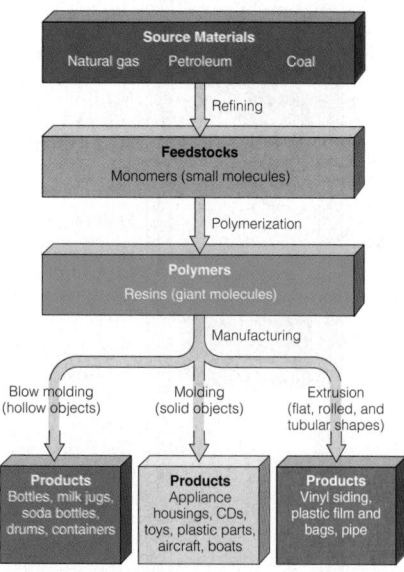

**Figure 21-9** *How plastics are made.*

From *Living in the Environment*, 13th Edition, p. 541

**Balanced and Fair**

# Spotlight, Connections, and Solutions boxes link concepts and encourage critical thinking

## A Brief History of Oil

In 1859, the world's first commercial oil well was drilled in Titusville, Pennsylvania. This was the beginning of the *Age of Oil*, which now supplies most of the world's energy (Figure 15-12, left). *We are not running out of oil, but many energy experts expect that by 2059—some 200 years after oil was discovered—we will probably begin shifting to increased dependence on natural gas and possibly hydrogen by 2100* (Figure 15-16).

Here are some milestones in the Age of Oil:

- **1905:** Oil supplies 10% of U.S. energy.
- **1925:** United States produces 71% of the world's oil.
- **1930:** Because of an oil glut, oil sells for 10¢ a barrel.
- **1953:** U.S. oil companies account for about half of the world's oil production and the United States is the world's leading oil exporter.
- **1955:** United States has 20% of the world's estimated oil reserves.
- **1960:** OPEC formed so developing countries, with most of the world's known oil and projected oil supplies, can get a higher price for their oil.
- **1961:** U.S.-proven oil reserves reach a peak and begin to decline.

- **1970:** U.S. oil production peaks and begins to decline.
- **1973:** United States uses 30% of the world's oil, imports 36% of this oil, and has only 5% of the world's proven oil reserves.
- **1973–1974:** OPEC reduces oil imports to the West and bans oil exports to the U.S. because of its support for Israel in the 18-day Yom Kippur War with Egypt and Syria. World oil prices rise sharply (Figure 15-22) and lead to **(1)** double-digit inflation in the United States and many other countries and **(2)** a global economic recession.
- **1975:** Production of estimated U.S. oil reserves peaks.
- **1979:** Iran's Islamic Revolution shuts down most of Iran's oil production
- **1981:** Ir global oil p (Figure 15-
- **1983:** Fa cuts its oil
- **1985:** U tion begins duction is r enough to **(** of oil or **(2)** on oil impo decreases t reducing oi other energ
- **August** States and

Gulf War to protect Saudi Arabia and Kuwait oil supplies after Iraq invades Kuwait.

- **2001:** OPEC has 67% of world oil reserves and produces 40% of the world's oil. U.S. has only 3% of oil reserves, used 26% of the world's oil production, and imported 55% of its oil.
- **2010:** U.S. could be importing at least 61% of the oil it uses as consumption continues to exceed production (Figure 15-23).
- **2010–2030:** Production of oil from the world's estimated oil reserves is expected to peak. Oil prices expected to increase gradually as the demand for oil increasingly exceeds the supply—unless the world decreases demand by

**Spotlight** boxes highlight and give insights into key environmental problems and concepts.

**Connections** boxes help students understand connections in nature and among environmental concepts, problems, and solutions.

## Using the Internet to Save Energy and Paper and Reduce Global Warming

According to a 2000 report by researchers at the Center for Energy and Climate Solutions, increasing use of the Internet is saving energy and material resources by

- Allowing more employees to work at home.
- Allowing a reduction in retail, manufacturing, warehouse, and commercial office space. Some online companies keep no merchandise in warehouses and have it shipped to customers directly from manufacturers. For example, Amazon.com uses 1/16 as much energy per unit of floor space to sell a book as a regular store.
- Using less energy to get products from sellers to consumers. Sending a package by overnight air uses about 40% less fuel than driving round trip to the mall to get the product. Shipping by

rail saves even more energy. However, shipping a larger number of packages to individuals instead of bulk shipments to businesses causes a huge increase in packaging.

- Reducing the energy, paper, and materials used to produce, package, and market consumer items such as computer software and music CDs by downloading them.
- Reducing energy used in transporting goods by using Internet-based systems to auction off empty shipping space on trucks, aircraft, and trains.

The resulting energy savings also reduce air pollution and $CO_2$ emissions by reducing fossil fuel use. Paper production (a highly energy- and resource-intensive industry) is expected to decrease as **(1)** consumers use the Internet to download software and view magazines, newspapers, research articles, telephone directories, encyclopedias, and books, **(2)** con-

sumers and businesses send more e-mail and less mail and reports by using envelopes and packages, and **(3)** easily updated online catalogs replace paper catalogs.

Although this book is printed on paper, I used no paper in preparing it for the publisher. Instead, the manuscript was sent to the publisher electronically as attachments to e-mail messages. Copyediting of the manuscript was also done via e-mail attachments.

This and other books are still being printed on paper. However, we can envision a day not too far away when we can read and interact with most textbooks on websites maintained by book publishers or individual authors.

### Critical Thinking

What types of environmental harm might be increased by greatly expanded use of the Internet to sell more and more goods in the global marketplace?

## Principles of Sustainability: Learning from Nature

Here are four basic ecological lessons or principles of sustainability derived from observing how nature works:

- *Most ecosystems use renewable solar energy as their primary source of energy.* Thus a sustainable society would be powered mostly by current sunlight, not ancient sunlight stored as polluting fossil fuels.
- *Ecosystems replenish nutrients and dispose of wastes by recycling chemicals.* There is almost no waste in nature because the waste outputs and decomposed remains of one organism are resource inputs for

other organisms. Thus a sustainable society would emphasize **(1)** preventing and reducing waste and **(2)** recycling and reusing resources (Figure 3-21, p. 61).

- *Biodiversity **(1)** helps maintain the sustainability and ecological functioning of ecosystems and **(2)** serves as a source of adaptations to changing environmental conditions.* Thus a sustainable society emphasizes conserving biodiversity by protecting ecosystems and preventing the premature extinction of species.
- *In nature there are always limits to population growth and resource consumption.* The population size and growth rate of all species are controlled by their interactions with

other species and with their nonliving environment, especially resource availability. Thus a sustainable society emphasizes reducing **(1)** births to control population growth and **(2)** resource consumption to prevent environmental overload and depletion of natural resources.

### Critical Thinking

List two ways in which human activities violate each of these four principles of sustainability. In what ways does your lifestyle violate these principles? Would you be willing to change these practices? What beneficial and harmful effects would such changes have on your lifestyle?

**Solutions** boxes summarize a variety of solutions to environmental problems proposed by various analysts. "Critical Thinking" questions at the end of each box encourage students to evaluate proposed solutions so they can make informed decisions. In addition to inclusion in these boxes, discussion of solutions—along with an emphasis on helping students think objectively about each issue—is interspersed throughout the book. In all, Miller includes 245 pages devoted to listing and evaluating solutions.

**Connections and Solutions**

23

# This book's new interactive Web site . . . for topic-by-topic enrichment!

## www.info.brookscole.com/miller13

From the screen for each text chapter, the following resources are just a click away:

- Chapter outline
- Chapter summary
- Learning objectives
- Hypercontent linking students to related Web sites for news, research, and images
- Flash cards that help students master terms and concepts
- A multiple-choice practice quiz that students can use to test themselves on chapter material
- Pro/Con sections that expose students to a variety of viewpoints on environmental issues
- A guide to related InfoTrac® College Edition articles by region of the U.S., maximizing use of the world-class InfoTrac College Edition online library (see facing page for details)
- Crossword puzzles featuring chapter material
- A glossary that students can use to test themselves on chapter material
- References listing major books and articles related to chapter material

### The Miller site is also linked to these important resources at the Biology Resource Center:

- **BioUpdates and EcoUpdates**—These engaging reviews—five to six each month—present current articles on appealing environmental and biological topics plus some original articles

- **Critical Thinking via Global Linking**—Poses questions arising from current developments in the field and provides hyperlinks to helpful sites

- **Links to the Best General Biology and Environmental Science Web Sites,** including government sites and virtual museums

- **Relevant Newsgroups** to keep you abreast of specialized information

- **Career Center**—offering information about careers in biology and environmental science

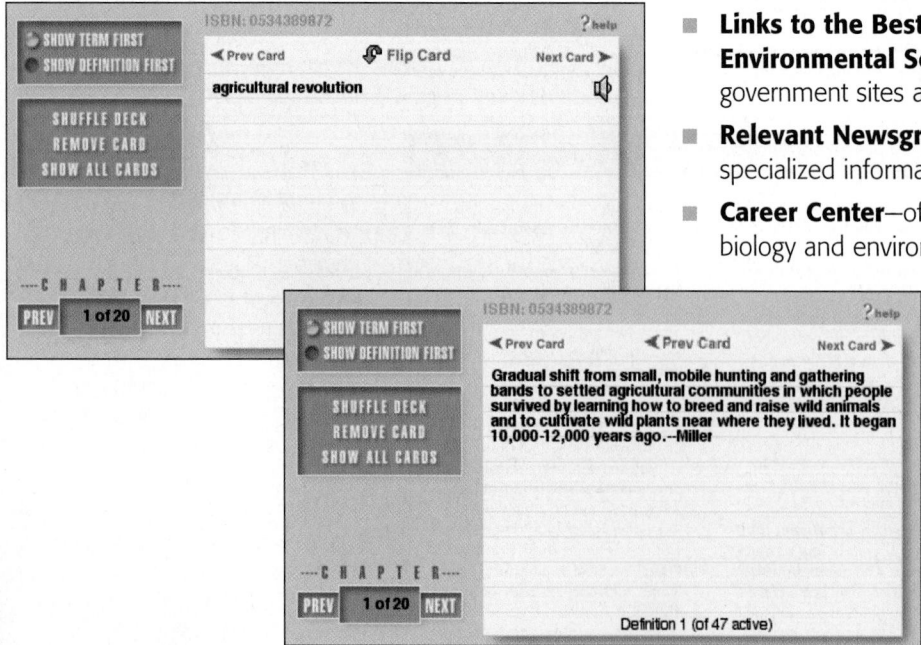

**Online Resources**

24

# InfoTrac® College Edition . . . FREE online access to complete articles from thousands of periodicals

Packaged FREE with every new copy of Miller's *Living in the Environment*, this online library gives students access to complete articles—not just abstracts—from thousands of popular and scholarly periodicals dating back as far as 22 years. When you adopt this 13th Edition of Miller's text, both you and your students will receive personal identification numbers that allow free, unlimited use of InfoTrac College Edition for the duration of one academic term.

## Chapter-by-chapter integration with this text

Every chapter of this text contains key search words and article titles for two recent InfoTrac College Edition articles. It's a great way for students to practice their research skills.

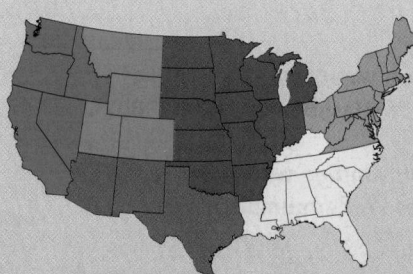

**Articles organized by state and region for local study!**
*Online Regional Articles for Environmental Science* are correlated to each chapter in Miller's text and are organized by state and region—West, Southwest, Rocky Mountains, Midwest, East, and South—so students can study environmental science at the local level. All drawn from InfoTrac College Edition's current library, these regional articles can be conveniently accessed at **www.info.brookscole.com/miller13**

## FREE! Student Guide to InfoTrac College Edition

Located on the Brooks/Cole Resource Center site, this online guide correlates each chapter in the book to articles from InfoTrac College Edition. It includes an introduction to the database, electronic readings for each chapter, and critical thinking questions.

### Just a few of the thousands of periodicals available from InfoTrac College Edition

Air/Water Pollution Report
Alternatives
Alternatives Journal
American Forests
American Naturalist
American Scientist
Audubon
Business and the Environment
Buzzworm
Buzzworm's Earth Journal
Clean Water Report
Conservation Matters
Conservationist
Discover
Duke Environmental Law & Policy Forum
Earth Island Journal
Ecological Applications
Ecological Monographs
Ecologist
Ecology
Ecology Law Quarterly
Endangered Species Bulletin
Endangered Species Update
Energy & Environmental Management
Environment
Environment Bulletin
Environment Action Magazine
Environmental & Planning Law Journal
Environmental Design & Construction
Environmental Law
Environmental Technology

EPA Journal
Global Environmental Change Report
Ground Water
Ground Water Monitor
Habitat (Australia)
Hazardous Waste News
International Solar Energy Intelligence Report
International Wildlife
Journal of Environmental Development
Journal of Environmental Education
Journal of Wildlife Law & Policy
Journal of Soil & Water Conservation
Management of World Wastes
National Parks
National Wildlife
New York State Conservationist
Nuclear Waste News
Pesticide & Toxic Chemical News
Pollution Engineering
Science News
Science Weekly
Science World
Scientist
UCLA Journal of Environmental Law & Policy
Waste Age
Waste News
Wilderness
World Wastes

InfoTrac College Edition is available exclusively from Thomson • Brooks/Cole and only available to colleges and universities. Publications are subject to change.

**Online Resources**

# WebTutor™ Advantage . . . Online teaching and tutorial support available on WebCT and Blackboard

*WebTUTOR™ Advantage*

## Takes the pain out of creating and managing homework—with ready-made questions and automatic grading.

With the rich tutorial material in *WebTutor Advantage*, you'll never again have to spend time creating paper handouts or grading homework. You can assign pre-formatted, text-specific content as is or alter the sequence to customize lessons. For your students, these tutorials, quizzes, flashcards with audio, and animations comprise a rich online study toolbox that reinforces and clarifies what they read in the text.

## Helps students better prepare for your lectures!

Assign the easy-to-navigate tutorial material and interactive quizzes as homework *before* you lecture on a topic. Students work through exercises, get immediate feedback—and come better prepared to class.

## Eases your load with automatic grading!

Students' responses are automatically graded, with the results appearing in your gradebook. You can track students' progress, assess problem areas, and address the issues in lectures.

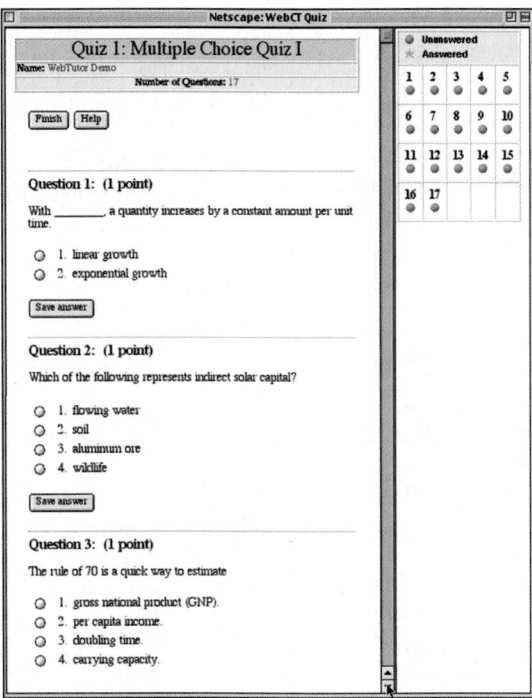

**Gives every student a front-row seat for discussion!** Instructors who have tried *WebTutor Advantage* love the way it allows students—even those in very large classes—to actively participate in class discussions online. This student-to-student interaction has enormous potential to enhance each student's experience with course content.

**Course management and online communication with students is a breeze!** With *WebTutor Advantage*, you can provide virtual office hours, post your syllabi, and set up threaded discussions. *WebTutor Advantage* includes a course calendar, real-time chat, and an integrated e-mail system.

**WebTutor Advantage on WebCT: 0-534-39801-4**
**WebTutor Advantage on Blackboard: 0-534-39802-2**

### To bundle *WebTutor Advantage* with every student book, use these order numbers:

■ Miller's *Living in the Environment*, 13th Edition with *WebTutor Advantage* on WebCT: **0-534-42757-X**

■ Miller's *Living in the Environment*, 13th Edition with *WebTutor Advantage* on Blackboard: **0-534-43163-1**

> Extend your reach beyond the classroom.
> Try *WebTutor Advantage* today at
> **http://e.thomsonlearning.com**

# Multimedia Manager for Environmental Science: A Microsoft® PowerPoint® Link Tool 0-534-39806-5

**Put visuals to work in your lectures with the ultimate presentation tool.**
Your lectures will never be the same—or more engaging. This full-featured presentation tool includes more than 650 images and nearly 100 animations and interactions.

**Preparation in a Snap**—A complete *PowerPoint®* file for each chapter includes an overview slide with all illustrations in thumbnail form. From this single snapshot, select, copy, and paste the slides you want to use right onto your lecture slide, all while staying in *PowerPoint*.

**Quick Links to Animations**—If a slide has a green button, just click on it to show a related animation. Then move to the next slide, without ever having to leave *PowerPoint*.

**Select and Enlarge an Illustration**—This unique feature lets you select a piece of a figure and enlarge it to add emphasis or show more detail. Combine a figure with another illustration, or draw on it; for instance, by circling it.

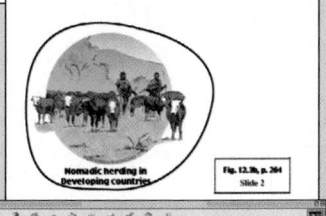

**Present Art Step-by-Step**—Slides contain art divided into sections, allowing you to introduce material in manageable segments. Just click to show one part of a diagram at a time rather than all at once.

**Edit Labels**—You can edit or remove labels, because every label is in a text box. No other presentation tool has this feature.

**Use Un-Labeled Art for Testing**—A separate file includes text art with line "leaders" but without labels. Ideal for testing purposes!

**Get a Head Start with Lecture Templates**—Save time prepping lectures with *PowerPoint* templates that integrate art and key concept points. They're included on the CD-ROM along with all the other art and animations.

### Electric and Hybrid Cars
- Rechargeable battery systems
- Hybrid electric-internal combustion engine
- Fuel cells

**Also Enclosed . . . Quick-time movies from CNN® to jump start your lectures!**
Enclosed with *Multimedia Manager*, you'll find an additional CD-ROM featuring many quick-time video segments of environmental news footage from CNN. These one-to-six-minute segments have been carefully selected from current CNN footage to complement your presentations. *To receive the complete 5-CD-ROM set of CNN videos, see next page for details.*

**Also available to enhance your lectures . . .**

## Transparency Acetates and Masters

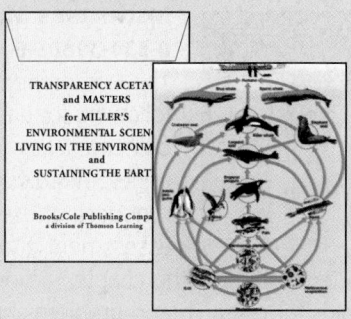

Includes approximately 100 color acetates of line art from Miller's text and nearly 600 black-and-white master sheets of key diagrams for making overhead transparencies.
**0-534-39805-7**

**Presentation Tools**

# Even more instructor tools to ease your teaching load!

**CNN® Today: Environmental Science Video Series**

Now available in a 5-Volume CD-ROM set as well as on separate video-cassettes, these CNN videos contain high-interest news stories about environmental topics that will spark lively class discussion and generate a deeper understanding the importance of environmental science in our day-to-day lives. Ask your Thomson• Brooks/Cole representative for video policy by adoption size.

5-Volume CD-ROM Set: **0-534-39931-2**
Or these individual videocassettes:
  1998 Edition, Volume I: **0-534-55341-9**
  1999 Edition, Volume II: **0-534-52321-8**
  2000 Edition, Volume III: **0-534-52322-6**
  2001 Edition, Volume IV: **0-534-38596-6**
  New! Volume V: **0-534-39793-X**

**Turner Learning Videos for Environmental Science**
**In the Shadow of the Shuttle: Protecting Endangered Species**
  VHS: **0-534-53039-7**
**Costa Rica: Science of the Rainforest**
  VHS: **0-534-53040-0**

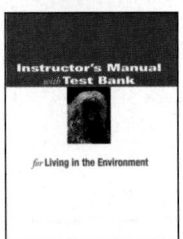

**Instructor's Manual with Test Bank**
**0-534-39803-0**
This comprehensive manual includes the following for each text chapter: concept maps, objectives, key terms, suggested term paper topics, interdisciplinary activities and projects, synopses of useful films and videos, assessment questions that evaluate students' understanding of the chapter, action-oriented term paper topics, topics for research and problem-solving, laboratory skills, and computer skills—as well as an extensive selection of multiple-choice test questions, also organized by chapter.

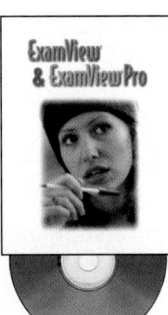

**ExamView® Testing and Assessment Software . . . *includes online testing*!**
For Windows and Macintosh: **0-534-39804-9**
Expand your range of assessment and tutorial capabilities—and save yourself time in the process. With *ExamView*, you can easily create and customize tests. The program's Quick Test Wizard guides you step by step through the process of creating a test in minutes.

## And these useful student tools . . .

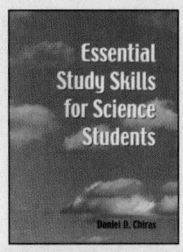

**Essential Study Skills for Science Students**
*by Daniel D. Chiras.* Available FREE when packaged with Miller's text! Written specifically to help students do their best in your science course, this book includes chapters on developing good study habits; sharpening memory; getting the most out of lectures, labs, and reading assignments; improving test-taking abilities; and becoming a critical thinker. **0-534-37595-2**
(To order packaged with Miller's *Living in the Environment*, 13th Edition: **0-534-43172-0**)

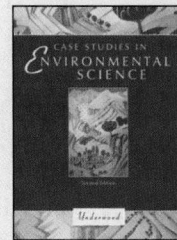

**Case Studies in Environmental Science, Second Edition**
*by Larry Underwood.* The author presents 12 case studies offering a range of views on environmental issues such as land use, alternate energy resources, soil conservation, wildlife management, acid rain, air quality, toxic wastes, and others. The case studies focus on eight geographic regions in the U.S. and Canada, emphasizing their wider applicability. Thought-provoking questions, commentaries, and readings are included to stimulate discussion and encourage students to investigate the issues in more detail. 424 pages. Paperbound. **0-03-031582-4**
(To order packaged with Miller's *Living in the Environment*, 13th Edition: **0-534-43190-9**)

**Exploring Water Resources: GIS Investigations for the Earth Sciences**
*by Michelle Hall-Wallace, Christian J. Schaller, C. Scott Walker & Larry P. Kendall.* This useful guide (including FREE ArcView® GIS software) helps even the novice users tap into the power of ArcView® to explore, manipulate, and analyze large data sets. **0-534-39156-7**
(To order packaged with Miller's *Living in the Environment*, 13th Edition: **0-534-43199-2**)

Video and Testing Resources

# Student tested, professor approved

Miller's texts have been used by more than two million students at more than half of the nation's colleges and universities. The following list represents those schools who have adopted one of Miller's texts, including *Environmental Science*, 9th Edition; *Living in the Environment*, 12th Edition; and *Sustaining the Earth*, 5th Edition.

**Alabama -**
Athens State University
Auburn University
Auburn University-Montgomery
Calhoun State Community College
Gadsden State Community College
Heritage Christian University
Jacksonville State University
Miles College
Samford University
Southeast College of Technology
Spring Hill College
Tuskegee University
University of Alabama-Birmingham
University of Alabama-Huntsville
University of Alabama-Tuscaloosa
University of North Alabama
University of South Alabama

**Alaska -**
Embry-Riddle Aeronautical University
Sheldon Jackson College
University of Alaska-Anchorage
University of Alaska-Fairbanks

**Arizona -**
Arizona State University
Arizona Western College
Central Arizona College-Signal Peak
Cochise College
Grand Canyon University
Northern Arizona University
Pima Community College-Downtown
Pima Community College-West
The Art Institute of Phoenix
University of Arizona
Western International University
Yavapai College

**Arkansas -**
Arkansas State University
Arkansas Tech University
Harding University
Henderson State University
Ouachita Technical College
University of Arkansas-Fayetteville
University of Arkansas-Little Rock
University of Arkansas Community College of Batesville
University of Central Arkansas
University of the Ozarks

**California -**
Azusa Pacific University
Barstow College
Biola University
Cabrillo College
California International University
California Polytechnic State University-Pomona
California Polytechnic State University-San Luis Obispo
California State University-Chico
California State University-Dominguez Hills
California State University-Fresno
California State University-Fullerton
California State University-Long Beach
California State University-Los Angeles
California State University-Northridge
California State University-Sacramento
California State University-San Bernardino
Cerro Coso Community College
Chapman University
City College of San Francisco
Claremont Graduate School
Coastline Community College
College of Marin
College of San Mateo
College of the Canyons
Compton Community College

Cosumnes River College
Crafton Hills College
Cuesta College
Cuyamaca College
Cypress College
De Anza College
Devry University
Dominican College of San Rafael
Foothill College
Fresno City College
Fresno Pacific University  Gavilan Community College
Glendale Community College
Golden West College
Grossmont College
Hartnell College
Heald College
Kelsey Jenney College
Las Positas College
Long Beach City College
Los Angeles Harbor College
Los Angeles Valley College
Los Medanos College
Mendocino College
Merced College
Merritt College
Mission College
Mount San Antonio College
Mount San Jacinto College
MTI College of Business and Technology
National University
Notre Dame de Namur University
Orange Coast College
Pacific Union College
Peralta Junior College
Platt College
Reedley College
Riverside Community College-Norco
Riverside Community College-Riverside City
Sacramento City College
Saint Mary's College of California
San Bernardino Valley College
San Diego Mesa College
San Diego State University
San Francisco State University
San Jose City College
San Jose State University
Santa Barbara City College
Santa Clara University
Santa Monica College
Santiago Canyon College
Shasta College
Sierra College
Solano Community College
Sonoma State University
Southwestern College
University of California-Davis
University of California-Los Angeles
University of California-Santa Barbara
University of La Verne
University of Redlands
University of San Diego
University of San Francisco
University of Southern California
University of the Pacific
Ventura College
West Los Angeles College
West Valley College
Westwood College of Technology
Yuba College

**Colorado -**
Aims Community College-Greeley
Arapahoe Community College
Colorado College
Colorado State University
Community College of Denver
Fort Lewis College

Naropa University
University of Colorado-Boulder
University of Denver
University of Northern Colorado
University of Southern Colorado

**Connecticut -**
Central Connecticut State University
Connecticut College
Eastern Connecticut State University
Fairfield University
Goodwin College
Middlesex Community Technical College
Norwalk Community College
Quinnipiac University
Trinity College
University of Bridgeport
University of Connecticut
University of Hartford

**Delaware -**
Wesley College

**District of Columbia -**
American University
George Washington University
Howard University
Southeastern University
Trinity College

**Florida -**
Barry University-Miami
Beacon College
Brevard Community College-Cocoa
Brevard Community College-Melbourne
Brevard Community College-Palm Bay
Broward Community College-Davie
City College of Miami
Eckerd College
Edison Community College-Fort Myers
Edison Community College-Naples
Edison Community College-Punta Gorda
Florida Community College-Deerwood
Florida Community College-Downtown
Florida Community College-Kent
Florida Community College-North
Florida Community College-South
Florida Gulf Coast University
Florida Institute of Technology
Florida International University
Florida Memorial College
Florida Southern College
Gulf Coast Community College
Hillsborough Community College-Dale Mabry
International Academy of Design
International College-Fort Myers
International College-Naples
Johnson and Wales University
Manatee Community College
Miami-Dade Community College-InterAmerican
Miami-Dade Community College-Kendall
New College of Florida
Nova Southeastern University
Palm Beach Community College
Palm Beach Community College-Central
Pasco-Hernando Community College
Rollins College
Saint Petersburg Junior College
Seminole Community College
Tampa Technical Institute
University of Central Florida
University of Florida
University of Miami
University of South Florida
University of Tampa
Valencia Community College-West

**Georgia -**
Albany State College
Armstrong Atlantic State University
Brewton-Parker College
Darton College
Gainesville College
Georgia Military College
Georgia Perimeter College-Clarkston
Georgia Perimeter College-Decatur
Georgia Perimeter College-Dunwoody
Georgia Perimeter College-Lawrenceville
Georgia Southern University
Georgia State University
Kennesaw State University
Mercer University
North Georgia College
Oxford College of Emory University
Savannah College of Art and Design
Southern Polytechnic State University
State University of West Georgia
Truett McConnell College
University of Georgia
Valdosta State University

**Hawaii -**
Chaminade University
Hawaii Pacific University
University of Hawaii-Hilo

**Idaho -**
Albertson College of Idaho
Boise State University
North Idaho College
University of Idaho

**Illinois -**
Aurora University
Black Hawk College
Bradley University
Carl Sandburg College-Galesburg
Chicago State University
College of DuPage
Columbia College
Elmhurst College
Heartland Community College
Highland Community College
Illinois State University
Judson College
Kaskaskia College
Kendall College
Kishwaukee College
Knox College
Lake Forest College
Lake Land College
Lewis and Clark Community College
Lewis University
Lincoln College
Lincoln College at Normal
Loyola University-Lake Shore
McHenry County College
McKendree College
Monmouth College
Northeastern Illinois University
Northern Illinois University
Oakton Community College
Richland Community College
Robert Morris College
Rock Valley College
Roosevelt University
Saint Xavier University
School of the Art Institute of Chicago
Southern Illinois University-Carbondale
Southern Illinois University-Edwardsville
Southwestern Illinois College
Southwestern Illinois College-Granite
Trinity International University
University of Chicago
University of Illinois-Chicago
Wabash Valley College
Western Illinois University
William Rainey Harper College

**Indiana -**
Ancilla College
Ball State University
Calumet College of Saint Joseph
Franklin College
Indiana University-Bloomington
Indiana University-East

Indiana University-Northwest
Indiana University-South Bend
Indiana University-Southeast
Ivy Tech State College
Ivy Tech State College-Northwest
Oakland City University-Branchville
Purdue University-Calumet
Purdue University-Fort Wayne
Purdue University-Indianapolis
Taylor University
University of Evansville
University of Indianapolis
University of Notre Dame
University of Southern Indiana
Valparaiso University

**Iowa -**
Buena Vista University
Clinton Community College
Dordt College
Drake University
Graceland University
Grinnell College
Iowa Central Community College
Iowa Lakes Community College
Iowa State University
Iowa Wesleyan College
Iowa Western Community College-Council Bluffs
Loras College
Marshalltown Community College
Marycrest International University
Mount Saint Clare College
Muscatine Community College
Northeast Iowa Community College-Calmar
Northwestern College
Scott Community College
Southwestern Community College
University of Dubuque
University of Iowa
University of Northern Iowa
Upper Iowa University

**Kansas -**
Baker University
Butler County Community College
Kansas State University
Kansas Wesleyan University
University of Kansas
Washburn University
Wichita State University

**Kentucky -**
Berea College
Cumberland College
Eastern Kentucky University
Elizabethtown Community College
Hazard Community College
Jefferson Community College
Lindsey Wilson College
Maysville Community College
Owensboro Community College
Paducah Community College
Prestonsburg Community College
Saint Catharine College
Somerset Community College
Union College
University of Kentucky
University of Louisville

**Louisiana -**
Delgado Community College-City Park
Grambling State University
Louisiana College
Louisiana State University-Baton Rouge
Louisiana State University-Shreveport
Louisiana Technical College
Louisiana Technical College-Abbeville
Louisiana Technical College-Ferriday
Louisiana Technical College-Lake Providence
Louisiana Technical College-Opelousas
Louisiana Technical College-Reserve
Louisiana Technical University
McNeese State University
Nicholls State University
Nuñez Community College
Southeastern Louisiana University
University of Louisiana at Lafayette
University of New Orleans

**Maine -**
Saint Joseph's College
University of Maine-Farmington
University of New England
University of New England-Westbrook College
University of Southern Maine

**Maryland -**
Bowie State University
College of Notre Dame of Maryland
College of Southern Maryland
Columbia Union College
Goucher College
Hagerstown Business College
Hood College
Johns Hopkins University
McDaniel College
Montgomery College-Germantown
Montgomery College-Rockville
Montgomery College-Takoma Park
Morgan State University
University of Maryland-Baltimore County
University of Maryland-College Park
University of Maryland-Eastern Shore
Washington College

**Massachusetts -**
Atlantic Union College
Babson College
Berkshire Community College
Brandeis University
Bristol Community College
Bunker Hill Community College
Cape Cod Community College
Curry College
Emerson College
Greenfield Community College
Hampshire College
Holyoke Community College
Lasell College
Massachusetts College of Liberal Arts
New England College of Finance
North Shore Community College
Northeastern University
Northern Essex Community College
Roxbury Community College
Salem State College
Springfield Technical Community College
Stonehill College
University of Massachusetts-Amherst
University of Massachusetts-Dartmouth
Wellesley College
Western New England College

**Michigan -**
Albion College
Alma College
Andrews University
Baker College-Owosso
Bay Mills Community College
Central Michigan University
Cleary College
Cornerstone College
Eastern Michigan University
Ferris State University
Grand Rapids Community College
Grand Valley State University
Henry Ford Community College
Kellogg Community College
Lake Michigan College
Lansing Community College
Marygrove College
Michigan State University
Michigan Technological University
Mid-Michigan Community College-Harrison
Northwestern Michigan College
Oakland Community College-Auburn Hills
Oakland Community College-Highland Lakes
Oakland Community College-Orchard Ridge
Oakland Community College-Southfield
Oakland University
Saginaw Valley State University
Saint Clair County Community College
Schoolcraft College
Siena Heights University
Spring Arbor College
University of Michigan-Dearborn
Wayne State University

**Minnesota -**
Alexandria Technical College
Bemidji State University
Bethel College
Central Lakes College-Brainerd
College of Saint Catherine
Dakota County Technical College
Duluth Business University
Fond Du Lac Community College
Hibbing Community College
Itasca Community College
Metropolitan State University
Minnesota School of Business
Minnesota State University-Moorhead
Minnesota West Community and Technical College
Normandale Community College
Rasmussen Business College
Rasmussen College-Saint Cloud
Saint Cloud State University
Saint John's University
Saint Mary's University
Saint Paul Technical College
University of Minnesota-Twin Cities
University of Saint Thomas
Winona State University

**Mississippi -**
Alcorn State University
Itawamba Community College
Jackson State University
Mississippi College
Mississippi University for Women
Northeast Mississippi Community College

**Missouri -**
Drury College
Jefferson College
Lindenwood University
Maryville University of Saint Louis
Mineral Area College
Park University
Saint Louis University
Southwest Missouri State University
Truman State University
University of Missouri-Rolla
University of Missouri-St Louis
Webster University

**Montana -**
Dawson Community College
Montana State University-Havre
University of Great Falls
University of Montana

**Nebraska -**
Bellevue University
Chadron State College
Concordia University
Dana College
Mid-Plains Community College
Nebraska Wesleyan University
University of Nebraska-Lincoln
University of Nebraska-Omaha

**Nevada -**
Great Basin College
Morrison University
University of Nevada-Reno
Western Nevada Community College

**New Hampshire -**
Colby Sawyer College
College for Lifelong Learning-North Country Region
Daniel Webster College
Dartmouth College
Franklin Pierce College
Hesser College
Keene State College
McIntosh College
Plymouth State College
Saint Anselm College
Southern New Hampshire University
University of New Hampshire

**New Jersey -**
Bergen Community College
Brookdale Community College
Burlington County College
Camden County College

Centenary College
College of Saint Elizabeth
County College of Morris
Cumberland County College
Devry College of Technology
Drew University
Felician College
Georgian Court College
Kean University
Mercer County Community College
Middlesex County College
Montclair State University
New Jersey City University
New Jersey Institute of Technology
Ocean County College
Ramapo College of New Jersey
Raritan Valley Community College
Rider University
Rowan University
Rutgers, The State University of New Jersey-New Brunswick
Rutgers, The State University of New Jersey-Newark
Saint Peters College
Stockton College of New Jersey

**New Mexico -**
Albuquerque Technical Vocational Institute
College of Santa Fe
Northern New Mexico Community College
Santa Fe Community College
University Of New Mexico

**New York -**
Adirondack Community College
Binghamton University
Bryant and Stratton Business Institute-Albany
Bryant and Stratton Business Institute-Liverpool
Bryant and Stratton Business Institute-Rochester
Bryant and Stratton Business Institute-Syracuse
Cazenovia College
City University of New York-Bronx Community College
City University of New York-College of Staten Island
City University of New York-Medger Evers College
City University of New York-Queens College
City University of New York-York College
Clinton Community College
College of Saint Rose
Concordia College
Daemen College
Dutchess Community College
Fordham University
Hartwick College
Ithaca College
LeMoyne College
Long Island University-C.W. Post
Long Island University Southampton College
Manhattanville College
Maria College
Marist College
Marymount College
Mercy College
Mohawk Valley Community College
Nassau Community College
New York Institute of Technology-Central Islip
New York Institute of Technology-Manhattan
New York Institute of Technology-Old Westbury
New York School of Interior Design
New York University
North Country Community College-Saranac Lake
North Country Community College-Ticonderoga
Orange County Community College
Pace University-New York
Pace University-Westchester
Pace University-White Plains
Paul Smith's College of Arts and Sciences
Polytechnic University-Brooklyn
Roberts Wesleyan College
Rochester Institute of Technology
Rockland Community College
Saint John Fisher College
Saint Lawrence University
Schenectady County Community College
Skidmore College
State University of New York-Empire State College
State University of New York-Farmingdale
State University of New York-Genesee
State University of New York-Institute of Technology
State University of New York-Oneonta
State University of New York-Plattsburgh

State University of New York-Purchase
State University of New York-Stony Brook
State University of New York-Canton
State University of New York-Cortland
State University of New York-Buffalo
State University of New York-Fredonia
Suffolk Community College-Ammerman
Tompkins Cortland Community College
University at Albany
Utica College
Wagner College
Wells College

**North Carolina -**
Appalachian State University
Belmont Abbey College
Brevard College
Brunswick Community College
Caldwell Community College
Catawba College
Coastal Carolina Community College
Davidson College
Durham Technical Community College
East Carolina University
Gardner-Webb University
Guilford College
Guilford Technical Community College
High Point University
Lenoir Community College
Lenoir-Rhyne College
Meredith College
North Carolina State University
Pamlico Community College
Pfeiffer University
Queens University
Randolph Community College
Rowan-Cabarrus Community College
Salem College
University of North Carolina-Chapel Hill
University of North Carolina-Charlotte
University of North Carolina-Pembroke
University of North Carolina-Wilmington
Vance-Granville Community College
Wake Technical College
Wingate University

**North Dakota -**
Embry-Riddle Aeronautical University
Jamestown College
Mayville State University
North Dakota State University-Fargo
Turtle Mountain Community College
University of Mary

**Ohio -**
Ashland University
Baldwin Wallace College
Bowling Green State University
Bowling Green State University-Firelands
Cedarville University
Denison University
Devry Institute of Technology
Lakeland Community College
Marietta College
Miami University-Hamilton
Miami University-Middletown
Miami University-Oxford
Mount Union College
Mount Vernon Nazarene University
Ohio State University
Ohio University
Ohio University-Eastern
Ohio Wesleyan University
Stark State College
University of Akron
University of Cincinnati
Washington State Community College
Wittenberg University
Xavier University
Youngstown State University

**Oklahoma -**
Bacone College
East Central University
Northeastern State University
Oklahoma City University
Oklahoma State University-Stillwater
Rogers State University
Rose State College

Tulsa Community College-Metro
University Center at Tulsa

**Oregon -**
Columbia Gorge Community College
Linfield College
Marylhurst University
Mount Hood Community College
Oregon Institute of Technology
Portland Community College-Sylvania
Portland State University
Southern Oregon University
Southwestern Oregon Community College
University of Oregon
Willamette University

**Pennsylvania -**
Alvernia College
Bloomsburg University
Bucknell University
Bucks County Community College
California University of Pennsylvania
Carnegie Mellon University
Chatham College
Chestnut Hill College
Community College of Beaver County
Community College of Philadelphia
Delaware County Community College
DeSales University
Dickinson College
Drexel University
East Stroudsburg University
Edinboro University
Elizabethtown College
Franklin and Marshall College
Geneva College
Gettysburg College
Harrisburg Area Community College-Wildwood
Juniata College
Kutztown University
LaSalle University
Lehigh University
Luzerne County Community College
Millersville University
Muhlenberg College
Neumann College
Northampton Community College
Pennsylvania State University-Altoona
Pennsylvania State University-Berks
Pennsylvania State University-Lehigh Valley
Pennsylvania State University-New Kensington
Pennsylvania State University-Schuylkill
Pennsylvania State University-State College
Philadelphia University
Pittsburgh Institute of Mortuary Science
Reading Area Community College
Robert Morris University
Saint Joseph's University
Shippensburg University
Slippery Rock University
Susquehanna University
Temple University
Thiel College
University of Pittsburgh-Bradford
University of Pittsburgh-Pittsburgh
University of Pittsburgh-Titusville
University of Scranton
Valley Forge Military Academy and College
Villanova University
Waynesburg College
West Chester University
Westminster College
Westmoreland County Community College
Widener University
Wilson College

**Rhode Island -**
Brown University
Community College of Rhode Island
Johnson and Wales University
New England Institute of Technology
Providence College
Salve Regina University
University of Rhode Island

**South Carolina -**
Clemson University
Florence-Darlington Technical College
Francis Marion University

Johnson and Wales University
Lander University
Presbyterian College
Trident Technical College
University of South Carolina-Beaufort
University of South Carolina-Columbia
Wofford College

**South Dakota -**
Huron University
South Dakota State University

**Tennessee -**
Austin Peay State University
Belmont University
Carson Newman College
Chattanooga State Technical Community College
Cleveland State Community College
East Tennessee State University
Freed-Hardeman University
Middle Tennessee State University
Roane State Community College-Harriman
Roane State Community College-Oak Ridge
Southern Adventist University
Trevecca Nazarene University
University of Tennessee-Knoxville

**Texas -**
Austin College
Austin Community College-Rio Grande
Baylor University
Collin County Community College-Preston Ridge
Eastfield College
Houston Community College-Central
Lamar University
Lee College-Baytown
McMurry University
Midwestern State University
North Lake College
Northwood University
Palo Alto College
Saint Edward's University
Sam Houston State University
San Antonio College
Southern Methodist University
Stephen F. Austin State University
Tarrant County College-Northeast
Tarrant County College-Northwest
Tarrant County College-Southeast
Texarkana College
Texas Agricultural and Mechanical University-
   College Station
Texas Agricultural and Mechanical University-
   Commerce
Texas State Technical College-Harlingen
Texas Wesleyan University
Texas Woman's University
Tyler Junior College
University of Houston-University Park
University of Houston-Clear Lake
University of Houston-Downtown
University of North Texas
University of Texas-Arlington
University of Texas-Austin
University of Texas-Pan-American
University of Texas-San Antonio

**Utah -**
Brigham Young University
Latter Day Saints Business College
Salt Lake Community College
Utah Valley State College
Weber State University

**Vermont -**
Community College of Vermont-Brattleboro
Johnson State College
Landmark College
Middlebury College
Southern Vermont College
University of Vermont

**Virginia -**
Averett College
Averett University-Danville
Bridgewater College
Bryant and Stratton College
Ferrum College
George Mason University

Hollins University
Longwood College
Lord Fairfax Community College
Lynchburg College
Old Dominion University
Paul D. Camp Community College
Piedmont Virginia Community College
Randolph-Macon College
Saint Leo University
University of Richmond
Virginia Military Institute
Virginia Polytechnic Institute
Virginia State University
Virginia Union University
Virginia Western Community College

**Washington -**
Bellevue Community College
Big Bend Community College
Central Washington University
City University
Clark College
Everett Community College
North Seattle Community College
Northwest College
Peninsula College
Pierce College at Fort Steilacoom
Seattle Central Community College
Seattle University
Shoreline Community College
Skagit Valley College
South Seattle Community College
Spokane Community College
Spokane Falls Community College
Tacoma Community College
Trinity Lutheran College
University of Washington
Walla Walla College
Walla Walla Community College
Washington State University
Western Washington University
Whatcom Community College
Whitman College

**West Virginia -**
Bluefield State College
Glenville State College
Greenbrier Community College
Huntington Junior College of Business
Mountain State University
University of Charleston
West Liberty State College
West Virginia Northern Community College
West Virginia University-Morgantown
West Virginia University-Parkersburg

**Wisconsin -**
Beloit College
Blackhawk Technical College
Carthage College
Concordia University
Marian College of Fond du Lac
Mid-State Technical College-Wisconsin Rapids
Milwaukee Area Technical College
Milwaukee Area Technical College-West
Naes College of the Menominee
Northland College
University of Wisconsin-Madison
University of Wisconsin-Marinette
University of Wisconsin-Milwaukee
University of Wisconsin-Platteville
University of Wisconsin-River Falls
University of Wisconsin-Sheboygan
University of Wisconsin-Stevens Point
University of Wisconsin-Superior
University of Wisconsin-Washington
University of Wisconsin-Waukesha
Viterbo College

**Wyoming -**
Northwest College
University of Wyoming

# Living in the Environment

# Living in the Environment

*Principles, Connections, and Solutions*

THIRTEENTH EDITION

## G. TYLER MILLER, JR.

*President, Earth Education and Research*

*Adjunct Professor of Human Ecology*
*St. Andrews Presbyterian College*

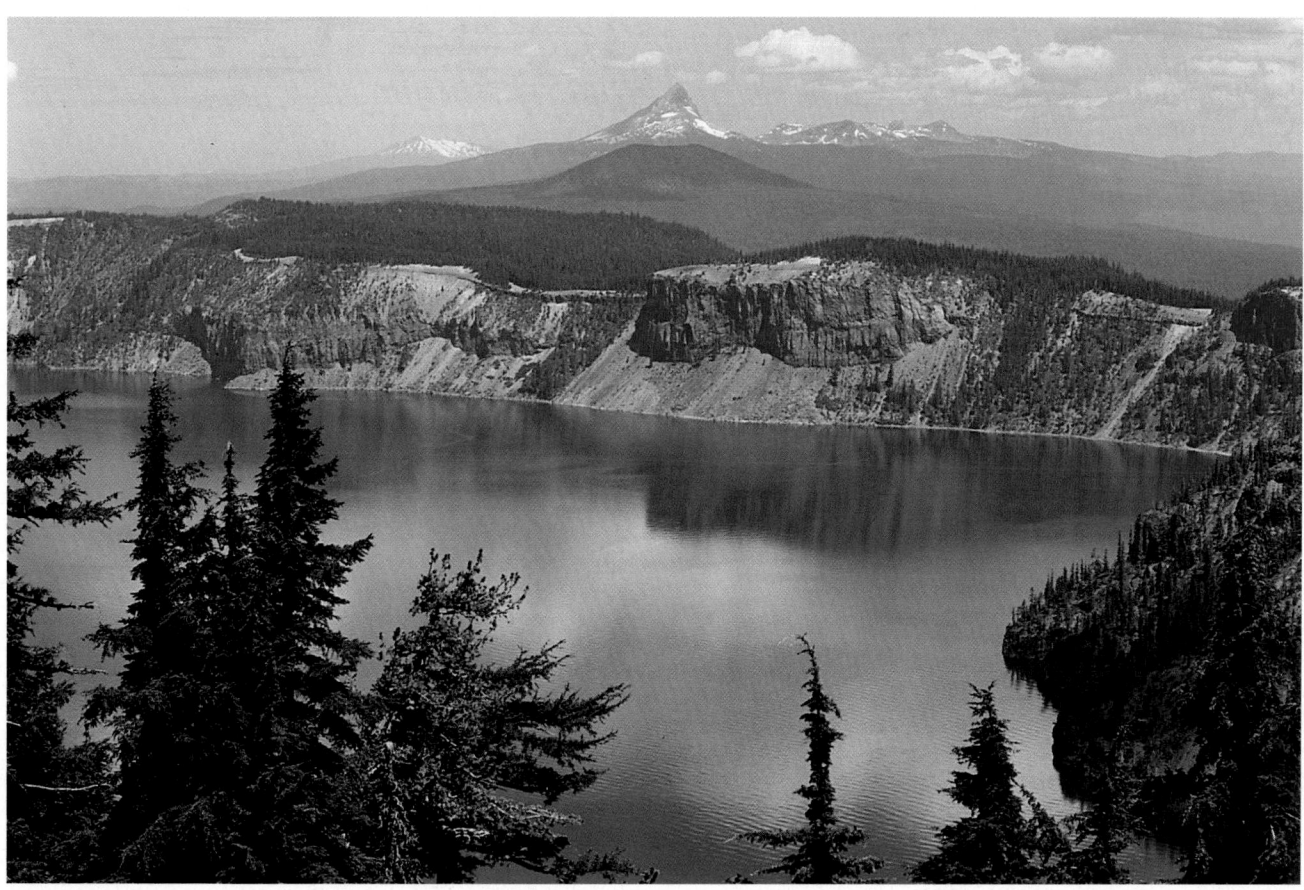

**THOMSON**

**BROOKS/COLE**

Australia • Canada • Mexico • Singapore • Spain • United Kingdom • United States

**THOMSON**

**BROOKS/COLE**

Publisher: *Jack Carey*
Assistant Editor: *Suzannah Alexander*
Editorial Assistant: *Jana Davis*
Technology Project Manager: *Keli Sato Amann*
Marketing Manager: *Ann Caven*
Marketing Assistant: *Sandra Perin*
Advertising Project Manager: *Linda Yip*
Print/Media Buyer: *Karen Hunt*
Production Management, copyediting,
   and composition: *Thompson Steele, Inc.*
Permissions Editor/Photo Researcher: *Linda L. Rill*
Interior Illustration: *Precision Graphics; Sarah Woodward; Darwin and
   Vally Hennings; Tasa Graphic Arts, Inc.; Alexander Teshin Associates;
   John and Judith Waller; Raychel Ciemma; Victor Royer, Electronic
   Publishing Services, Inc., and J/B Woolsey Associates*
Cover Image: *Snow monkey, or Japanese red-faced macaque, Japan,
   Natural Exposures/Daniel J. Cox*
Text and Cover Printer: *Transcontinental Printing/Interglobe*

Title Page Photograph: *Crater Lake, Oregon (Jack Carey)*
Part Opening Photographs
Part I: *Composite satellite view of Earth.* © *Tom Van Sant/
   The GeoSphere Project*
Part II: *Endangered green sea turtle.* © *David B. Fleetham/Tom Stacks
   Associates*
Part III: *Sunset. NOAA Corps Collection, photo by Commander John
   Bortniak, NOAA Corps (ret).*
Part IV: *Area of forest in Czechoslovakia killed by acid deposition and
   other air pollutants.* © *Silvestris Fotoservice/Natural History
   Photographic Agency*
Part V: *Highly endangered Florida panther.* © *George Gentry/Fish &
   Wildlife Service*
Part VI: *Antipollution demonstration by Louisiana residents against
   Monsanto Chemical Company.* © *Sam Kittner/Sipa Press*

**Brooks/Cole-Thomson Learning**
511 Forest Lodge Road
Pacific Grove, CA 93950
USA

**Asia**
Thomson Learning
5 Shenton Way #01-01
UIC Building
Singapore 068808

**Australia**
Nelson Thomson Learning
102 Dodds Street
South Melbourne, Victoria 3205
Australia

**Canada**
Nelson Thomson Learning
1120 Birchmount Road
Toronto, Ontario M1K 5G4
Canada

**Europe/Middle East/Africa**
Thomson Learning
High Holborn House
50/51 Bedford Row
London WC1R 4LR
United Kingdom

**Latin America**
Thomson Learning
Seneca, 53
Colonia Polanco
11560 Mexico D.F.
Mexico

**Spain**
Paraninfo Thomson Learning
Calle/Magallanes, 25
28015 Madrid, Spain

For more information about our products, contact us at:
Thomson Learning Academic Resource Center
1-800-423-0563
For permission to use material from this text, contact us by:
**Phone:** 1-800-730-2214
**Fax:** 1-800-730-2215
**Web:** http://www.thomsonrights.com

Library of Congress Control Number: 2002106327

Student Edition with InfoTrac College Edition: ISBN 0-534-39798-0

Student Edition without InfoTrac College Edition: ISBN 0-534-39807-3

International Student Edition: ISBN 0-534-27411-0
(Not for sale in the United States)

Annotated Instuctor's Edition: ISBN: 0-534-39799-9

# For Instructors and Students

**How Did I Become Involved with Environmental Problems?** In 1966, I heard a scientist give a lecture on the problems of population growth and pollution. Afterward I went to him and said, "If even a fraction of what you have said is true, I will feel ethically obligated to give up my research on the corrosion of metals and devote the rest of my life to research and education on environmental problems and solutions. Frankly, I do not want to believe a word you have said, and I am going into the literature to try to show that your statements are either untrue or grossly distorted."

After 6 months of study I was convinced of the seriousness of these and other environmental problems. Since then, I have been studying, teaching, and writing about them. This book summarizes what I have learned in more than three decades of trying to understand environmental principles, problems, connections, and solutions.

**What Is My Philosophy of Education?** In our lifelong pursuit of knowledge, I believe we should do three things:

- *Question everything and everybody,* as any good scientist does.
- *Develop a list of principles, concepts, and rules to serve as guidelines in making decisions,* and continually evaluate and modify this list on the basis of experience. This is based on my belief that the key goal of education is to learn how to sift through mountains of facts and ideas to find the few that are most useful and worth knowing. We need to be *wisdom seekers,* not information vessels. This takes a firm commitment to learning how to think logically and critically. This book is full of facts and numbers, but they are useful only to the extent that they lead to an understanding of key ideas, scientific laws, concepts, principles, and connections.
- *Interact with what you read as a way to sharpen your critical thinking skills.* I do this by marking key sentences and paragraphs with a highlighter or pen. I put an asterisk in the margin next to an idea I think is important and double asterisks next to an idea I think is especially important. I write comments in the margins, such as *Beautiful, Confusing, Misleading,* or *Wrong.* I fold down the top corner of pages with highlighted passages and the top and bottom corners of especially

important pages. This way, I can flip through a book and quickly review the key passages. I urge you to interact in such ways with this book.

**What Are the Major Trends in Environmental Science Education?** This is a *science-based* book designed for introductory courses on environmental science. It is an *interdisciplinary* study of how nature works and how things in nature are interconnected.

This thirteenth edition continues my efforts to emphasize the following major shifts in environmental science education that have taken place over the past 25 years and are expected to accelerate in this century:

- *Increased emphasis on science-based approaches to understanding and solving environmental problems.* Since its first edition, this book has led the way in using scientific laws, principles, models, concepts and critical thinking to help us **(1)** understand environmental and resource problems and their possible solutions and **(2)** see how these concepts, problems, and solutions are connected. The first edition had four chapters on basic scientific concepts when other books had a single chapter. In this thirteenth edition, nine chapters (one more than in the last edition) and 303 pages are devoted to the treatment of scientific principles and concepts—far more than in any other introductory environmental science text of this size. This emphasis on basic science will become increasingly important throughout this century. I have introduced only the concepts and principles necessary for understanding the material in the book, and I have tried to present them simply but accurately.

- *Increased emphasis on solutions.* The emphasis in this century is on finding and implementing scientific, technological, economic, and political solutions to environmental problems. This text has stressed solutions as a major theme for many years. In this new edition, 245 pages are devoted to presenting and evaluating solutions to environmental problems—far more than in any other introductory environmental science textbook of this size.

- *Greater emphasis on prevention solutions.* Since its first edition, this book has categorized solutions to environmental problems that various analysts have proposed as either **(1)** *input* (prevention) solutions such as pollution prevention and waste reduction or **(2)** *output* (cleanup) solutions such as pollution control and waste management. Both approaches are needed, but so far most emphasis has been on output or management solutions. There is a growing awareness of the need to put more emphasis on input or prevention approaches.

- *More emphasis on decentralized micropower.* I highlight the shift from large centralized sources of electricity (mostly coal and nuclear plants) to a dispersed array of smaller micropower plants, including gas turbines, solar-cell arrays, wind turbines, and fuel cells. This shift is under way and will accelerate during this century.

- *Greater integration of economics and environment.* I emphasize the increased use of emissions trading, environmental accounting, full-cost pricing, phasing in environmentally friendly government subsidies, and evolving eras of environmental management in businesses. This trend discussed in Chapter 26 (p. 690) is under way and is expected to increase rapidly during this century.

To help ensure that the material is accurate and up to date, I have consulted more than 10,000 research sources in the professional literature and about the same number of Internet sites. I have also benefited from the more than 250 experts and teachers (see list on pp. x–xii) who have provided detailed reviews of this and my other three books in this field.

**How Have I Attempted to Achieve Balance?** Some environmental issues are controversial. The challenge for an author is to give a fair and balanced presentation of **(1)** opposing viewpoints, **(2)** advantages and disadvantages of various technologies and proposed solutions to environmental problems, and **(3)** good and bad news about environmental problems. This allows you to make up your own mind about important environmental issues. Studying a subject as important as environmental science and ending up with no conclusions, opinions, and beliefs means that both the teacher and student have failed. However, such conclusions should be based on using critical thinking to evaluate opposing ideas and solutions to environmental problems.

A few examples of my efforts to provide a balanced presentation are **(1)** the pros and cons of reducing birth rates (p. 267), **(2)** the Pro/Con box on oil development in the Arctic National Wildlife Refuge (p. 360), **(3)** Section 18-4 (pp. 457–460; Figure 18-15, p. 460, and Figure 18-16, p. 461) on global warming, **(4)** advantages and disadvantages of pesticides (Section 20-2, pp. 515–516 and Section 20-3, pp. 516–518), and **(5)** diagrams summarizing the advantages and disadvantages of various technological solutions to environmental problems (such as Figure 13-17, p. 292; Figure 15-26, p. 361; Figure 16-35, p. 409; Figure 21-13, p. 545); and Figure 25-17, p. 675.

**What Are Some Key Features of This Book?** This book is *science based, solution oriented,* and *flexible.* About 40% of the book is devoted to providing a *scientific foundation,* 30% to *environmental problems,* and 30% to *solutions* to these problems.

The book is divided into six major parts (see Brief Contents, p. xiii). After the introductory chapters in Part I and the scientific principles and concepts chapters in Part II have been covered, the rest of the book can be used in virtually any order. In addition, most chapters and many sections within these chapters can be moved around or omitted to accommodate courses with different lengths and emphases.

Each chapter begins with a brief *case study* designed to capture interest and set the stage for the material that follows. In addition to these 28 case studies, 65 other case studies are found throughout the book (some in special boxes and others within the text); they provide a more in-depth look at specific environmental problems and their possible solutions. Fourteen *Guest Essays* present the point of view of an individual environmental researcher or activist point of view, which readers can evaluate using the Critical Thinking questions.

Other special boxes found in the text include **(1)** *Pro/Con boxes* that present both sides of a few highly controversial environmental issues, **(2)** *Connections boxes* that show connections in nature and among environmental concepts, problems, and solutions, **(3)** *Solutions boxes* that summarize a variety of solutions to environmental problems proposed by various analysts, **(4)** *Spotlight boxes* that highlight and give insights into key environmental problems and concepts, and **(5)** *Individuals Matter boxes* that describe what people have done to help solve environmental problems. To encourage critical thinking and integrate it throughout the book, all boxes (except Individuals Matter) end with Critical Thinking questions.

This book is an integrated study of environmental problems, connections, and solutions. The five integrated themes are **(1)** *biodiversity and natural resources (ecosystem services),* **(2)** *sustainability,* **(3)** *connections in nature,* **(4)** *pollution prevention,* and **(5)** *the importance of individuals working together to solve problems to environmental advantage.*

I hope you will start by looking at the brief table of contents (p. xiii) to get an overview of this book.

This book has 706 illustrations, 180 of them new to this edition. These illustrations are designed to present complex ideas in understandable ways and to relate learning to the real world.

I have not cited specific sources of information within the text. This is rarely done for an introductory-level text in any field, and it would interrupt the flow of the material. Instead, on the website material for each chapter you will find **(1)** readings, **(2)** Internet site references, and **(3)** references to complete articles that can be accessed online on the *InfoTrac* supplement available free to qualified users of this book. These sources **(1)** back up most of the content of this book and **(2)** serve as springboards to further information and ideas. Placing these references on the website also allows me to update them regularly.

Instructors wanting a shorter book covering this material with a different emphasis and organization can use one of my three other books written for various types of environmental science courses: **(1)** *Environmental Science,* 9th edition (542 pages, Brooks/Cole, 2003), **(2)** *Sustaining the Earth: An Integrated Approach,* 6th edition (349 pages, Brooks/Cole, 2004), and **(3)** *Essentials of Ecology,* 2nd edition (276 pages, Brooks/Cole, 2004).

**What Are the Major Changes in the Thirteenth Edition?** Detailed changes by chapter are listed in the annotated material in the insert provided with the instructor's version of this book and on this book's website. Major changes include the following:

## CONTENT

- Updated and revised material throughout the book.

- 180 new or improved illustrations.

- Expanded coverage of weather and climate in Chapter 6.

- Movement of the chapter on Risk, Toxicology, and Health (Chapter 11) into Part II on Scientific Principles and Concepts to consolidate treatment of scientific principles and allow instructors more flexibility in treatment of chapters and topics.

- Addition of 112 new topics. See the insert provided with the instructor's version of this book and this book's website for a detailed list of these topics listed by chapter. Examples include the following:

  - Good and bad news about economic development (pp. 6–7)

  - Harmful environmental effects of poverty (Spotlight, p. 8)

  - Transfer of energy by convection, conduction, and radiation (Figure 3-11, p. 53)

  - Expanded treatment of weather (pp. 111–114)

  - Life cycle of frogs (figure in box on p. 170)

- Brief history of oil (Spotlight, p. 359)

- How Safe Are Radioactive Wastes Stored at Nuclear Power Plants? (Case Study, p. 371)

- Threat from dirty radioactive bombs (p. 373)

- Possible beneficial effects of global warming for people in some areas (Figure 18-15, p. 460)

- Carbon sequestration for reducing carbon dioxide emissions (pp. 467–469 and Figure 18-21, p. 467)

- Arsenic levels in drinking water (Spotlight, pp. 496–497)

- Water pollution in the Baltic Sea (Case Study, p. 499)

- Terrorism and release of toxic chemicals from industrial plants (p. 528)

- Use of plasma torch to detoxify hazardous chemicals (pp. 542–543)

- Threat from toxic mercury (pp. 549–551 and Figure 21-19, p. 550)

- Urban sprawl in Las Vegas, Nevada (Figure 25-7, p. 665)

- New Guest Essay by Noel Perrin (see pp. 752–753)

## LEARNING AIDS

- Greater use of numbered and bulleted lists to make the information as accessible as possible and help students comprehend and review key material.

- New CD-ROM: *Interactive Concepts in Environmental Science* integrates concept summaries and almost 100 engaging animations and interactions based on figures from the text with flashcards and quizzing on the Web.

**In-Text Study Aids** Each chapter begins with a few general questions to reveal how it is organized and what students will be learning. When a new term is introduced and defined, it is printed in boldface type. A glossary of all key terms is located at the end of the book.

Questions are used as titles for all subsections so readers know the focus of the material that follows. In effect, this is a built-in set of learning objectives.

Each chapter ends with **(1)** a set of Review Questions covering *all* of the material in the chapter as a study guide for students and **(2)** a set of questions to encourage students to think critically and apply what they have learned to their lives. The Critical Thinking questions are followed by several projects that individuals or groups can carry out.

**Internet and Online Study Aids**   Qualified users of this textbook have free access to the *Brooks/Cole Biology and Environmental Science Resource Center.* Access the online resource material for this book by logging on at

www.info.brookscole.com/miller13

At this website you will find the following material for each chapter:

- Flash Cards, which allow you to test your mastery of the Terms and Concepts to Remember for each chapter.

- Tutorial Quizzes, which provide a multiple-choice practice quiz.

- Student Guide to InfoTrac, which will lead you to Critical Thinking Projects that use InfoTrac College Edition as a research tool.

- References, which lists the major books and articles consulted in writing this chapter.

- A brief What You Can Do list addressing key environmental problems.

- Hypercontents, which takes you to an extensive list of websites with news, research, and images related to individual sections of the chapter.

Qualified adopters of this textbook also have access to *WebTutor Toolbox on WebCT* at

http://e.thomsonlearning.com

It provides access to a full array of study tools, including flashcards (with audio), practice quizzes, online tutorials, and web links.

Students using *new* copies of this textbook also have free and unlimited access to *InfoTrac College Edition.* This fully searchable online library gives users access to complete environmental articles from several hundred periodicals dating back over the past four years. Each chapter ends with two practice exercises to help students learn how to navigate this valuable source of information.

Other student learning tools include:

- A new CD-ROM: *Interactive Concepts in Environmental Science* that integrates concept summaries and almost 100 engaging animations and interactions based on figures from the text with flashcards and quizzing on the Web. The front endpapers list all the animations.

- *Essential Study Skills for Science Students* by Daniel D. Chiras. This books includes chapters on **(1)** developing good study habits, **(2)** sharpening memory, **(3)** getting the most out of lectures, labs, and reading assign-

ments, **(4)** improving test-taking abilities, and **(5)** becoming a critical thinker. Your instructor can have this book bundled FREE with your textbook.

- *Laboratory Manual by C. Lee Rocket and Kenneth J. Van Dellen.* This manual includes a variety of laboratory exercises, workbook exercises, and projects that require a minimum of sophisticated equipment.

**Supplementary Materials for Instructors**   The following supplementary materials are available to instructors adopting this book:

- *Multimedia Manager.* This CD-ROM, free to qualified adopters, allows you to **(1)** create custom lectures using over 2,000 pieces of high-resolution artwork, images, and Quick Time movies from the CD and the web, **(2)** assemble database files, and **(3)** create Microsoft PowerPoint® lectures using text slides and figures from the textbook. This program's editing tools allow **(1)** slides to be moved from one lecture to another, **(2)** modification or removal of figure labels and leaders, **(3)** insertion of your own slides, **(4)** saving slides as JPEGs, and **(5)** preparation of lectures for use on the Web.

- *Transparency Masters and Acetates.* Includes **(1)** 100 color acetates of line art and **(2)** nearly 600 black and white master sheets of key diagrams for making overhead transparencies. Free to qualified adopters.

- *CNN® Today Videos.* These videos, updated annually, contain short clips of news stories about environmental news. Qualified adopters can receive one video free each year for 3 years. These videos are now available to professors electronically for classroom presentation as well  as on videotape.

- Two videos, **(1)** *In the Shadow of the Shadow of the Shuttle: Protecting Endangered Species,* and **(2)** *Costa Rica: Science in the Rainforest,* are available to adopters.

- *Instructor's Manual with Test Bank.* Free to qualified adopters.

- *ExamView.* Allows you to **(1)** easily create and customize tests, **(2)** see them on the screen exactly as they will print, and **(3)** print them out.

**Help Me Improve This Book**   Let me know how you think this book can be improved; if you find any errors, bias, or confusing explanations, please e-mail them to me at

mtg89@hotmail.com

Most errors can be corrected in subsequent printings of this edition rather than waiting for a new edition.

**Acknowledgments** I wish to thank the many students and teachers who **(1)** responded so favorably to the 12 editions of *Living in the Environment*, the 9 editions of *Environmental Science*, and the 5 editions of *Sustaining the Earth* and **(2)** corrected errors and offered many helpful suggestions for improvement. I am also deeply indebted to the more than 250 reviewers, who pointed out errors and suggested many important improvements in the various editions of these three books. Any errors and deficiencies left are mine.

The members of the talented production team, listed on the copyright page, have made vital contributions as well. My thanks also go to production editors Hal Humphrey at Brooks/Cole and Andrea Fincke at Thompson Steele, Thompson Steele's page layout artist Bonnie Van Slyke, Brooks/Cole's hard-working sales staff, and Keli Amann and her talented colleagues who developed the multimedia and the website material associated with this book.

I also thank Paul M. Rich for his help with some of the chapters on basic ecology in the eleventh edition of this book; C. Lee Rockett and Kenneth J. Van Dellen for developing the *Laboratory Manual* to accompany this book; Jane Heinze-Fry for her work on concept mapping, *Environmental Articles, Critical Thinking and the Environment: A Beginner's Guide,* and the *Internet Booklet*; Richard K. Clements for his excellent work on the *Instructor's Manual* and the two InfoTrac exercises found at the end of each chapter; and the people who have translated this book into six different languages for use throughout much of the world.

My deepest thanks go to Jack Carey, biology publisher at Brooks/Cole, for his encouragement, help, 36 years of friendship, and superb reviewing system. It helps immensely to work with the best and most experienced editor in college textbook publishing.

I dedicate this book to the earth that sustains us and to Kathleen Paul Miller, my wife and research assistant.

*G. Tyler Miller, Jr.*

# Guest Essayists and Reviewers

**Guest Essayists** The following are authors of Guest Essays: **(1) Robert D. Bullard,** professor of sociology and director of the Environmental Justice Resource Center at Clark Atlanta University; **(2) Herman E. Daly,** senior research scholar at the School of Public Affairs, University of Maryland; **(3) Lois Marie Gibbs,** director, Center for Health, Environment, and Justice; **(4) Garrett Hardin,** professor emeritus of human ecology, University of California, Santa Barbara; **(5) Paul G. Hawken,** environmental author and business leader; **(6) Jane Heinze-Fry,** author, teacher, and consultant in environmental education; **(7) Amory B. Lovins,** energy policy consultant and director of research, Rocky Mountain Institute; **(8) Lester W. Milbrath,** director of the research program in environment and society, State University of New York at Buffalo; **(9) Peter Montague,** director, Environmental Research Foundation; **(10) Norman Myers,** tropical ecologist and consultant in environment and development; **(11) David W. Orr,** professor of environmental studies, Oberlin College; **(12) Noel Perrin,** adjunct professor of environmental studies, Dartmouth College; **(13) Andrew C. Revkin,** environmental author and environmental reporter for the *New York Times*; and **(14) Nancy Wicks,** ecopioneer and director of Round Mountain Organics.

**Cumulative Reviewers** Barbara J. Abraham, Hampton College; Donald D. Adams, State University of New York at Plattsburgh; Larry G. Allen, California State University, Northridge; Susan Allen-Gil, Ithaca College; James R. Anderson, U.S. Geological Survey; Mark W. Anderson, University of Maine; Kenneth B. Armitage, University of Kansas; Samuel Arthur, Bowling Green State University; Gary J. Atchison, Iowa State University; Marvin W. Baker Jr., University of Oklahoma; Virgil R. Baker, Arizona State University; Ian G. Barbour, Carleton College; Albert J. Beck, California State University, Chico; W. Behan, Northern Arizona University; Keith L. Bildstein, Winthrop College; Jeff Bland, University of Puget Sound; Roger G. Bland, Central Michigan University; Grady Blount II, Texas A&M University, Corpus Christi; Georg Borgstrom, Michigan State University; Arthur C. Borror, University of New Hampshire; John H. Bounds, Sam Houston State University; Leon F. Bouvier, Population Reference Bureau; Daniel J. Bovin, Université Laval; Michael F. Brewer, Resources for the Future, Inc.; Mark M. Brinson, East Carolina University; Dale Brown, University of Hartford; Patrick E. Brunelle, Contra Costa College; Terrence J. Burgess, Saddleback College North; David Byman, Pennsylvania State University, Worthington–Scranton; Lynton K. Caldwell, Indiana University; Faith Thompson Campbell, Natural Resources Defense Council, Inc.; Ray Canterbery, Florida State University; Ted J. Case, University of San Diego; Ann Causey, Auburn University; Richard A. Cellarius, Evergreen State University; William U. Chandler, Worldwatch Institute; F. Christman, University of North Carolina, Chapel Hill; Preston Cloud, University of California, Santa Barbara; Bernard C. Cohen, University of Pittsburgh; Richard A. Cooley, University of California, Santa Cruz; Dennis J. Corrigan; George Cox, San Diego State University; John D. Cunningham, Keene State College; Herman E. Daly, University of Maryland; Raymond F. Dasmann, University of California, Santa Cruz; Kingsley Davis, Hoover Institution; Edward E. DeMartini, University of California, Santa Barbara; Charles E. DePoe, Northeast Louisiana University; Thomas R. Detwyler, University of Wisconsin; Peter H. Diage, University of California, Riverside; Lon D. Drake, University of Iowa; David DuBose, Shasta College; Dietrich Earnhart, University of Kansas; T. Edmonson, University of Washington; Thomas Eisner, Cornell University; Michael Esler, Southern Illinois University; David E. Fairbrothers, Rutgers University; Paul P. Feeny, Cornell University; Richard S. Feldman, Marist College; Nancy Field, Bellevue Community College; Allan Fitzsimmons, University of Kentucky; Andrew J. Friedland, Dartmouth College; Kenneth O. Fulgham, Humboldt State University; Lowell L. Getz, University of Illinois at Urbana–Champaign; Frederick F. Gilbert, Washington State University; Jay Glassman, Los Angeles Valley College; Harold Goetz, North Dakota State University; Jeffery J. Gordon, Bowling Green State University; Eville Gorham, University of Minnesota; Michael Gough, Resources for the Future; Ernest M. Gould Jr., Harvard University; Peter Green, Golden West College; Katharine B. Gregg, West Virginia Wesleyan College; Paul K. Grogger, University of Colorado at Colorado Springs; L. Guernsey, Indiana State University; Ralph Guzman, University of California, Santa Cruz; Raymond Hames, University of Nebraska, Lincoln; Raymond E. Hampton, Central Michigan University; Ted L. Hanes, California State University, Fullerton; William S. Hardenbergh, Southern Illinois University at Carbondale; John P. Harley, Eastern Kentucky University; Neil A. Harriman, University of Wisconsin, Oshkosh; Grant A. Harris, Washington State University; Harry S. Hass, San Jose City College; Arthur N. Haupt, Population Reference Bureau; Denis A. Hayes, environmental consultant; Stephen Heard, University of Iowa; Gene Heinze-Fry, Department of Utilities, Commonwealth of Massachusetts; Jane Heinze-Fry, environmental educator; John G. Hewston, Humboldt State University; David L. Hicks, Whitworth College; Kenneth M. Hinkel, University of Cincinnati; Eric Hirst, Oak Ridge National Laboratory; Doug Hix, St. Andrews Presbyterian College, University of Hartford; S. Holling, University of British Columbia; Donald Holtgrieve, California State University, Hayward; Michael H. Horn, California State University, Fullerton; Mark A. Hornberger, Bloomsberg University; Marilyn Houck, Pennsylvania State University; Richard D. Houk, Winthrop College; Robert J. Huggett, College of William and Mary; Donald Huisingh, North Carolina State University; Marlene K. Hutt, IBM; David R. Inglis, University of Massachusetts; Robert Janiskee, University of South Carolina; Hugo H. John, University of Connecticut; Brian A. Johnson, University of Pennsylvania, Bloomsburg; David I. Johnson, Michigan State University; Mark Jonasson, Crafton Hills College; Agnes Kadar, Nassau Community College; Thomas L. Keefe, Eastern Kentucky University; Nathan Keyfitz, Harvard University; David Kidd, University of New Mexico; Pamela S. Kimbrough; Jesse Klingebiel, Kent School; Edward J. Kormondy, University of Hawaii–Hilo/West Oahu College; John V. Krutilla, Resources for the Future, Inc.; Judith Kunofsky, Sierra Club; E. Kurtz; Theodore Kury, State University of New York at Buffalo; Steve Ladochy, University of Winnipeg; Mark B. Lapping, Kansas State University; Tom Leege, Idaho Department of Fish and Game; William S. Lindsay, Monterey Peninsula College; E. S. Lindstrom, Pennsylvania State University; M. Lippiman, New York University Medical Center; Valerie A. Liston, University of Minnesota; Dennis Livingston, Rensselaer Polytechnic Institute; James P. Lodge, air pollution consultant; Raymond C. Loehr, University of Texas at Austin; Ruth Logan, Santa Monica City College; Robert D. Loring, DePauw University; Paul F. Love, Angelo State University; Thomas Lovering, University of California, Santa Barbara; Amory B. Lovins, Rocky Mountain Institute; Hunter Lovins, Rocky Mountain Institute; Gene A. Lucas, Drake University; Claudia Luke; David Lynn; Timothy F. Lyon, Ball State University; Stephen Malcolm, Western Michigan University; Melvin G. Marcus, Arizona State University; Gordon E. Matzke, Oregon State University; Parker Mauldin, Rockefeller Foundation; Marie McClune, The Agnes Irwin School (Rosemont, Pennsylvania); Theodore R. McDowell, California State University; Vincent E. McKelvey, U.S. Geological Survey; Robert T. McMaster, Smith College; John G. Merriam, Bowling Green State University; A. Steven Messenger, Northern Illinois University; John Meyers, Middlesex Community College; Raymond W. Miller,

Utah State University; Arthur B. Millman, University of Massachusetts, Boston; Fred Montague, University of Utah; Rolf Monteen, California Polytechnic State University; Ralph Morris, Brock University, St. Catherine's, Ontario, Canada; Angela Morrow, Auburn University; William W. Murdoch, University of California, Santa Barbara; Norman Myers, environmental consultant; Brian C. Myres, Cypress College; A. Neale, Illinois State University; Duane Nellis, Kansas State University; Jan Newhouse, University of Hawaii, Manoa; Jim Norwine, Texas A&M University, Kingsville; John E. Oliver, Indiana State University; Carol Page, copy editor; Eric Pallant, Allegheny College; Charles F. Park, Stanford University; Richard J. Pedersen, U.S. Department of Agriculture, Forest Service; David Pelliam, Bureau of Land Management, U.S. Department of Interior; Rodney Peterson, Colorado State University; Julie Phillips, De Anza College; William S. Pierce, Case Western Reserve University; David Pimentel, Cornell University; Peter Pizor, Northwest Community College; Mark D. Plunkett, Bellevue Community College; Grace L. Powell, University of Akron; James H. Price, Oklahoma College; Marian E. Reeve, Merritt College; Carl H. Reidel, University of Vermont; Charles C. Reith, Tulane University; Roger Revelle, California State University, San Diego; L. Reynolds, University of Central Arkansas; Ronald R. Rhein, Kutztown University of Pennsylvania; Charles Rhyne, Jackson State University; Robert A. Richardson, University of Wisconsin; Benjamin F. Richason III, St. Cloud State University; Ronald Robberecht, University of Idaho; William Van B. Robertson, School of Medicine, Stanford University; C. Lee Rockett, Bowling Green State University; Terry D. Roelofs, Humboldt State University; Christopher Rose, California Polytechnic State University; Richard G. Rose, West Valley College; Stephen T. Ross, University of Southern Mississippi; Robert E. Roth, Ohio State University; Arthur N. Samel, Bowling Green State University; Floyd Sanford, Coe College; David Satterthwaite, I.E.E.D., London; Stephen W. Sawyer, University of Maryland; Arnold Schecter, State University of New York at Syracuse; Frank Schiavo, San Jose State University; William H. Schlesinger, Ecological Society of America; Stephen H. Schneider, University of California, Berkeley; Clarence A. Schoenfeld, University of Wisconsin, Madison; Henry A. Schroeder, Dartmouth Medical School; Lauren A. Schroeder, Youngstown State University; Norman B. Schwartz, University of Delaware; George Sessions, Sierra College; David J. Severn, Clement Associates; Paul Shepard, Pitzer College and Claremont Graduate School; Michael P. Shields, Southern Illinois University at Carbondale; Kenneth Shiovitz; F. Siewert, Ball State University; E. K. Silbergold, Environmental Defense Fund; Joseph L. Simon, University of South Florida;

William E. Sloey, University of Wisconsin, Oshkosh; Robert L. Smith, West Virginia University; Val Smith, University of Kansas; Howard M. Smolkin, U.S. Environmental Protection Agency; Patricia M. Sparks, Glassboro State College; John E. Stanley, University of Virginia; Mel Stanley, California State Polytechnic University, Pomona; Norman R. Stewart, University of Wisconsin, Milwaukee; Frank E. Studnicka, University of Wisconsin, Platteville; Chris Tarp, Contra Costa College; Roger E. Thibault, Bowling Green State University; William L. Thomas, California State University, Hayward; Shari Turney, copyeditor; John D. Usis, Youngstown State University; Tinco E. A. van Hylckama, Texas Tech University; Robert R. Van Kirk, Humboldt State University; Donald E. Van Meter, Ball State University; Gary Varner, Texas A&M University; John D. Vitek, Oklahoma State University; Harry A. Wagner, Victoria College; Lee B. Waian, Saddleback College; Warren C. Walker, Stephen F. Austin State University; Thomas D. Warner, South Dakota State University; Kenneth E. F. Watt, University of California, Davis; Alvin M. Weinberg, Institute of Energy Analysis, Oak Ridge Associated Universities; Brian Weiss; Margery Weitkamp, James Monroe High School (Granada Hills, California); Anthony Weston, State University of New York at Stony Brook; Raymond White, San Francisco City College; Douglas Wickum, University of Wisconsin, Stout; Charles G. Wilber, Colorado State University; Nancy Lee Wilkinson, San Francisco State University; John C. Williams, College of San Mateo; Ray Williams, Rio Hondo College; Roberta Williams, University of Nevada, Las Vegas; Samuel J. Williamson, New York University; Ted L. Willrich, Oregon State University; James Winsor, Pennsylvania State University; Fred Witzig, University of Minnesota at Duluth; George M. Woodwell, Woods Hole Research Center; Robert Yoerg, Belmont Hills Hospital; Hideo Yonenaka, San Francisco State University; Malcolm J. Zwolinski, University of Arizona.

# Brief Contents

### PART I
## HUMANS AND SUSTAINABILITY: AN OVERVIEW   1

1   Environmental Problems, Their Causes, and Sustainability   2
2   Environmental History: An Overview   21

### PART II
## SCIENTIFIC PRINCIPLES AND CONCEPTS   39

3   Science, Systems, Matter, and Energy   40
4   Ecosystems: Components, Energy Flow, and Matter Cycling   64
5   Evolution and Biodiversity: Origins, Niches, and Adaptation   95
6   Biogeography: Climate, Biomes, and Terrestrial Biodiversity   110
7   Aquatic Ecology: Biodiversity in Aquatic Systems   144
8   Community Ecology: Structure, Species Interactions, Succession, and Sustainability   165
9   Population Dynamics, Carrying Capacity, and Conservation Biology   190
10   Geology: Processes, Hazards, and Soils   203
11   Risk, Toxicology, and Human Health   228

### PART III
## HUMAN POPULATION, RESOURCES, AND SUSTAINABILITY   253

12   The Human Population: Growth, Demography, and Carrying Capacity   254
13   Food Resources   277
14   Water Resources   312
15   Geologic Resources: Nonrenewable Mineral and Energy Resources   338
16   Energy Efficiency and Renewable Energy   380

### PART IV
## ENVIRONMENTAL QUALITY AND POLLUTION   417

17   Air and Air Pollution   418
18   Climate Change and Ozone Loss   446
19   Water Pollution   483
20   Pesticides and Pest Control   512
21   Solid and Hazardous Waste   525

### PART V
## SUSTAINING BIODIVERSITY AND CITIES   559

22   Sustaining Wild Species   560
23   Sustaining Terrestrial Biodiversity: The Ecosystem Approach   594
24   Sustaining Aquatic Biodiversity   634
25   Sustainable Cities: Urban Land Use and Management   661

### PART VI
## ENVIRONMENT AND SOCIETY   689

26   Economics, Environment, and Sustainability   690
27   Politics, Environment, and Sustainability   716
28   Environmental Worldviews, Ethics, and Sustainability   741

**Appendices**   A1

**Glossary**   G1

**Index**   I1

# Detailed Contents

NASA

## PART I

## HUMANS AND SUSTAINABILITY: AN OVERVIEW   1

### 1   Environmental Problems, Their Causes, and Sustainability   2

*Living in an Exponential Age   2*

1-1   Living More Sustainably   3

Spotlight: *Cast of Players in the Environmental Drama*   3

Guest Essay: *Natural Capital* by Paul G. Hawken   16

1-2   Population Growth, Economic Growth, Environmentally Sustainable Development, and Globalization   4

Spotlight: *Current Exponential Growth of the Human Population*   5

Connections: *Some Harmful Environmental Effects of Poverty*   8

1-3   Resources   9

Connections: *Free-Access Resources and the Tragedy of the Commons*   11

Connections: *Lessons from China*   15

1-4   Pollution   10

1-5   Environmental Problems: Causes and Connections   12

1-6   Is Our Present Course Sustainable?   13

Solutions: *Some Guidelines for Working with the Earth*   18

### 2   Environmental History: An Overview   21

*Near Extinction of the American Bison   21*

2-1   Cultural Changes and the Environment   22

Connections: *Consequences of the Agricultural Revolution*   24

Connections: *Consequences of Advanced Industrial Societies*   25

2-2   Environmental History of the United States: The Tribal and Frontier Eras   25

2-3   Environmental History of the United States: The Early Conservation Era (1832–1960)   26

Individuals Matter: *Alice Hamilton*   28

Spotlight: *How Should Public Land Resources Be Used? Preservationists vs. Conservationists*   32

2-4   Environmental History of the United States: The Environmental Era (1960–2002)   29

Individuals Matter: *Rachel Carson*   33

2-5   Case Study: Aldo Leopold and His Land Ethic   36

## PART II

## SCIENTIFIC PRINCIPLES AND CONCEPTS   39

### 3   Science, Systems, Matter, and Energy   40

*Two Islands: Can We Treat This One Better?   40*

3-1   Science and Critical Thinking   41

Guest Essay: *Critical Thinking and Environmental Studies* by Jane Heinze-Fry   42

Connections: *What Is Harming the Robins?*   44

3-2   Models and Behavior of Systems   44

3-3   Matter: Forms, Structure, and Quality   47

3-4   Energy: Forms and Quality   51

3-5   Physical and Chemical Changes and the Law of Conservation of Matter   54

Spotlight: *Keeping Track of Atoms*   54

3-6   Nuclear Changes   55

3-7   Two Laws Governing Energy Changes   59

3-8   Connections: Matter and Energy Change Laws and Environmental Problems   60

**4   Ecosystems: Components, Energy Flow, and Matter Cycling   64**

*Have You Thanked the Insects Today?*   *64*

4-1   The Nature of Ecology   65

Connections: *Microbes: The Invisible Rulers of the Earth*   65

4-2   The Earth's Life-Support Systems   68

4-3   Ecosystem Concepts and Components   70

4-4   Connections: Food Webs and Energy Flow in Ecosystems   76

4-5   Primary Productivity of Ecosystems   80

4-6   Connections: Matter Cycling in Ecosystems   82

Case Study: *Effects of Deforestation on Nutrient Cycling*   90

4-7   How Do Ecologists Learn About Ecosystems?   89

4-8   Ecosystem Services and Sustainability   92

**5   Evolution and Biodiversity: Origins, Niches, and Adaptation   95**

*Earth: The Just-Right, Resilient Planet*   *95*

5-1   Origins of Life   96

Spotlight: *How Did Life First Evolve?*   99

5-2   Evolution and Adaptation   100

Spotlight: *What Is Artificial Selection?*   100

5-3   Ecological Niches and Adaptation   103

Spotlight: *Cockroaches: Nature's Ultimate Survivors*   105

5-4   Speciation, Extinction, and Biodiversity   104

Guest Essay: *The Future of Evolution* by Norman Myers   108

**6   Biogeography: Weather, Climate, Biomes, and Terrestrial Biodiversity   110**

*Connections: Blowing in the Wind*   *110*

6-1   Weather: A Brief Introduction   111

6-2   Climate: A Brief Introduction   115

6-3   Biomes: Climate and Life on Land   122

6-4   Desert Biomes   125

6-5   Grassland, Tundra, and Chaparral Biomes   128

6-6   Forest Biomes   134

6-7   Mountain Biomes   141

6-8   Lessons from Geographic Ecology   141

**7   Aquatic Ecology: Biodiversity in Aquatic Systems   144**

*Why Should We Care About Coral Reefs?*   *144*

7-1   Aquatic Environments: Types, Components, and Limiting Factors   145

Spotlight: *Biofiltration*   149

7-2   Saltwater Life Zones   147

Connections: *Coral Partners May Enhance Reef Survival*   155

7-3   Freshwater Life Zones   156

7-4   Sustainability of Aquatic Life Zones   162

Temperate deciduous forest, Fall, Rhode Island

Temperate deciduous forest, Winter, Rhode Island

Hawaiian monk seal's mouth caught in plastic

## 8 Community Ecology: Structure, Species Interactions, Succession, and Sustainability   165

*Flying Foxes: Keystone Species in Tropical Forests   165*

8-1   Community Structure: Appearance and Species Diversity   166

8-2   General Types of Species   169

Connections: *Why Are Amphibians Vanishing?   170*

Connections: *Why Should We Care About Alligators?   173*

8-3   Species Interactions: Competition and Predation   172

Case Study: *Why Are Sharks Important Species?   176*

8-4   Symbiotic Species Interactions: Parasitism, Mutualism, and Commensalism   178

8-5   Ecological Succession: Communities in Transition   180

8-6   Ecological Stability and Sustainability   184

## 9 Population Dynamics, Carrying Capacity, and Conservation Biology   190

*Sea Otters: Are They Back from the Brink of Extinction?   190*

9-1   Population Dynamics and Carrying Capacity   191

9-2   The Role of Predation in Controlling Population Size   192

Case Study: *Wolf and Moose Interactions on Isle Royale   197*

9-3   Reproductive Patterns and Survival   195

9-4   Conservation Biology: Sustaining Wildlife Populations   198

9-5   Human Impacts on Ecosystems: Learning from Nature   199

Connections: *Ecological Surprises   200*

Solutions: *Principles of Sustainability: Learning from Nature   201*

## 10 Geology: Processes, Hazards, and Soils   203

*The Mount St. Helens Eruption   203*

10-1   Geologic Processes   204

10-2   Internal and External Earth Processes   205

10-3   Minerals, Rocks, and the Rock Cycle   209

10-4   Natural Hazards: Earthquakes and Volcanic Eruptions   210

10-5   Soil Resources: Formation and Types   212

10-6   Soil Erosion and Degradation   216

Case Study: *The Dust Bowl*

10-7   Solutions: Soil Conservation   222

Case Study: *Slowing Soil Erosion in the United States   223*

## 11 Risk, Toxicology, and Human Health   228

*The Big Killer   228*

11-1   Risk, Probability, and Hazards   229

11-2   Toxicology   229

11-3   Chemical Hazards   233

Connections: *Are Hormonally Active Chemicals a Health Threat?   235*

Rocky Mountain Institute, Colorado

An earth-sheltered house in the United States

11-4 Biological Hazards: Disease in Developed and Developing Countries  236

Spotlight: *Are We Losing Ground in Our War Against Infectious Bacteria?*  238

Case Study: *The Global Tuberculosis Epidemic*  241

Solutions: *Producing an Edible Hepatitis B Vaccine*  242

Solutions: *Improving Health Care in Developing Countries*  244

11-5 Risk Analysis  245


**P A R T   I I I**

**POPULATION, RESOURCES, AND SUSTAINABILITY  253**


12 **The Human Population: Growth, Demography, and Carrying Capacity  254**

*Slowing Population Growth in Thailand  254*

12-1 Factors Affecting Human Population Size  255

12-2 Population Age Structure  263

12-3 Solutions: Influencing Population Size  267

Case Study: *Immigration in the United States*  268

Guest Essay: *Moral Implications of Cultural Carrying Capacity* by Garrett Hardin  272

12-4 Case Studies: Slowing Population Growth in India and China  271

12-5 Cutting Global Population Growth  274

13 **Food Resources  277**

*Perennial Crops on the Kansas Prairie  277*

13-1 How Is Food Produced?  278

13-2 Producing Food by Green-Revolution and Traditional Techniques  281

13-3 Food Production, Nutrition, and Environmental Effects  284

Solutions: *Saving Children*  289

Case Study: *Can China's Population Be Fed?*  293

13-4 Increasing World Crop Production  289

Spotlight: *Shrinking the World's Genetic Plant Library*  295

13-5 Producing More Meat  296

Connections: *Some Environmental Consequences of Meat Production*  299

Spotlight: *Endangered Riparian Zones*  300

Gary Milburn/Tom Stack & Associates

Cotton-top tamarin

13-6 Catching and Raising More Fish 301

Connections: *Commercial Fishing and the Tragedy of the Commons* 305

13-7 Government Agricultural Policy 307

13-8 Solutions: Sustainable Agriculture 308

## 14 Water Resources 312

***Water and Grain Import Wars in the Middle East* 312**

14-1 Water's Importance and Unique Properties 313

14-2 Supply, Renewal, and Use of Water Resources 314

14-3 Too Little Water 317

14-4 Using Dams and Reservoirs to Supply More Water 318

Case Study: *Egypt's Aswan High Dam: Blessing or Disaster?* 321

Case Study: *The Colorado River Basin* 322

14-5 Transferring Water from One Place to Another 322

Case Study: *The Aral Sea Water Transfer Disaster* 324

14-6 Tapping Groundwater, Converting Salt Water to Fresh Water, Seeding Clouds, and Towing Icebergs 324

Case Study: *Mining Groundwater: The Shrinking Ogallala Aquifer* 327

14-7 Using Water More Efficiently 328

Spotlight: *Water Rights in the United States* 329

Solutions: *The Promise of Drip Irrigation* 333

Spotlight: *Running Short of Water in Las Vegas, Nevada* 334

14-8 Too Much Water 332

Connections: *Living Dangerously on Floodplains in Bangladesh* 335

14-9 Solutions: Achieving a More Sustainable Water Future 335

Christmas tree plantation, North Carolina

## 15 Geologic Resources: Nonrenewable Mineral and Energy Resources 338

***Bitter Lessons from Chernobyl* 338**

15-1 Nature and Formation of Mineral Resources 339

15-2 Finding and Removing Nonrenewable Mineral Resources 341

15-3 Environmental Effects of Extracting, Processing, and Using Mineral Resources 343

Case Study: *Some Environmental Effects of Gold Mining* 345

Pro/Con: *Controversy Over the General Mining Law of 1872* 347

15-4 Supplies of Mineral Resources 346

Solutions: *Mining with Microbes* 349

15-5 Evaluating Energy Resources 349

15-6 Oil 354

Spotlight: *A Brief History of Oil* 359

Pro/Con: *Should Oil and Gas Development Be Allowed in the Arctic National Wildlife Refuge?* 360

15-7 Natural Gas 362

15-8 Coal 363

15-9 Nuclear Energy 365

Case Study: *How Safe Are Radioactive Wastes Stored at Nuclear Power Plants?* 371

Case Study: *Underground Storage of High-Level Radioactive Wastes in the United States* 374

Mutualism between oxpeckers and a rhinoceros

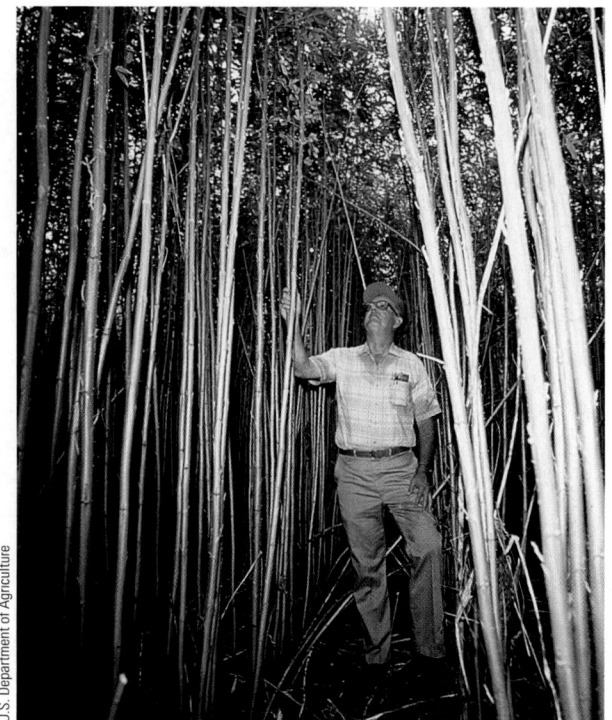

Fast growing Kenaf for making paper, Texas

## 16 Energy Efficiency and Renewable Energy 380

*The Coming Energy-Efficiency and Renewable-Energy Revolution* 380

16-1 The Importance of Improving Energy Efficiency 381

Guest Essay: *Technology Is the Answer (But What Was the Question?)* by Amory B. Lovins 384

16-2 Ways to Improve Energy Efficiency 383

Connections: *The Real Cost of Gasoline in the United States* 388

Guest Essay: *Living Lightly on the Earth at Round Mountain Organics* by Nancy Wicks 390

Connections: *Using the Internet to Save Energy and Paper and Reduce Global Warming* 393

16-3 Using Solar Energy to Provide Heat and Electricity 393

16-4 Producing Electricity from Moving Water and from Heat Stored in Water 400

16-5 Producing Electricity from Wind 401

16-6 Producing Energy from Biomass 403

16-7 The Solar–Hydrogen Revolution 405

Spotlight: *Producing Hydrogen from Green Algae Found in Pond Scum* 408

16-8 Geothermal Energy 409

16-9 Entering the Age of Decentralized Micropower 410

16-10 Solutions: A Sustainable Energy Strategy 412

## PART IV
## ENVIRONMENTAL QUALITY AND POLLUTION 417

## 17 Air and Air Pollution 418

*When Is a Lichen Like a Canary?* 418

17-1 The Atmosphere 419

17-2 Outdoor Air Pollution 420

Spotlight: *Air Pollution in the Past: The Bad Old Days* 423

17-3 Photochemical and Industrial Smog 423

17-4 Regional Outdoor Air Pollution from Acid Deposition 428

17-5 Indoor Air Pollution 434

17-6 Effects of Air Pollution on Living Organisms and Materials 437

Spotlight: *Health Dangers from Fine Particles* 440

17-7 Solutions: Preventing and Reducing Air Pollution 439

## 18 Climate Change and Ozone Loss 446

*A.D. 2060: Green Times on Planet Earth* 446

18-1 Past Climate Change and the Natural Greenhouse Effect 447

18-2 Climate Change and Human Activities 448

18-3 Projecting Future Changes in the Earth's Climate 454

Spotlight: *How Do Climate Models Work?* 456

18-4 Factors Affecting Changes in the Earth's Average Temperature 457

18-5 Some Possible Effects of a Warmer World 460

Connections: *Global Warming, Kirtland's Warblers, and Adélie Penguins* 463

18-6 Solutions: Dealing with the Threat of Climate Change 464

Solutions: *Energy Efficiency to the Rescue* 465

Boll weevil

Solutions: *Organic Farming and No-Till Cultivation to the Rescue* 468

18-7 What Is Being Done to Reduce Greenhouse Gas Emissions? 469

18-8 Ozone Depletion in the Stratosphere 472

Connections: *The Cancer You Are Most Likely to Get* 478

18-9 Solutions: Protecting the Ozone Layer 476

Individuals Matter: *Ray Turner and His Refrigerator* 479

## 19 Water Pollution 483

### *Learning Nature's Ways to Purify Sewage 483*

19-1 Types, Effects, and Sources of Water Pollution 484

Case Study: *Hurricanes, Hog Farms, and Water Pollution in Eastern North Carolina* 487

19-2 Pollution of Freshwater Streams 489

Individuals Matter: *Tracking Down the Pfiesteria Cell from Hell* 489

19-3 Pollution of Freshwater Lakes 489

19-4 Groundwater Pollution and Its Prevention 493

Spotlight: *How Much Arsenic Should We Allow in Drinking Water?* 496

19-5 Ocean Pollution 496

Case Study: *The Baltic Sea* 499

Solutions: *Bring Back the Oysters* 501

19-6 Solutions: Preventing and Reducing Surface Water Pollution 502

Solutions: *Using Wetlands to Treat Sewage* 507

Wind farm, California

19-7 Drinking Water Quality 507

Individuals Matter: *Using UV Light, Horseradish, and Slimes to Purify Water* 508

## 20 Pesticides and Pest Control 512

### *Along Came a Spider 512*

20-1 Pesticides: Types and Uses 513

20-2 The Case for Pesticides 514

20-3 The Case Against Pesticides 515

Spotlight: *How Effective Have Pesticides Been in Reducing Crop Losses?* 517

20-4 Pesticide Regulation in the United States 518

Connections: *What Goes Around Can Come Around* 518

20-5 Other Ways to Control Pests 520

## 21 Solid and Hazardous Waste 525

### *There Is No "Away": Love Canal 525*

21-1 Wasting Resources 526

Case Study: *Mining and Smelting Waste in Montana* 527

Case Study: *A Black Day in Bhopal* 529

21-2 Producing Less Waste and Pollution 528

Guest Essay: *We Have Been Asking the Wrong Questions About Wastes* by Lois Marie Gibbs 530

Solutions: *Doing More with Less: Increasing Resource Productivity* 533

21-3 Solutions: Cleaner Production and Selling Services Instead of Things 531

Monoculture cropland, California

Individuals Matter: *Ray Anderson* 534

Guest Essay: *Cleaner Production: A New Environmentalism for the 21st Century* by Peter Montague 536

21-4 Reuse 534

Solutions: *What Kind of Grocery Bags Should We Use?* 535

21-5 Recycling 535

Solutions: *Using Composting to Recycle Biodegradable Wastes* 539

Case Study: *Recycling, Reuse, and Waste Reduction in Germany* 540

21-6 Case Studies: Recycling Wastepaper and Plastics 540

21-7 Detoxifying, Burning, Burying, and Exporting Wastes 542

Individuals Matter: *Using Landfill Methane to Heat a School* 545

21-8 Case Studies: Lead, Mercury, Chlorine, and Dioxins 548

21-9 Hazardous-Waste Regulation in the United States 552

Spotlight: *Using Honeybees to Detect Toxic Pollutants* 553

Solutions: *How Can the Superfund Law Be Improved?* 554

21-10 Solutions: Achieving a Low-Waste Society 555

22-3 Why Should We Care About Biodiversity? 568

Spotlight: *What Is the Economic Value of the Earth's Ecological Services?* 571

Connections: *Biophilia* 572

22-4 Extinction Threats from Habitat Loss and Degradation 572

Case Study: *The Plight of Migrating Birds* 575

22-5 Extinction Threats from Nonnative Species 574

Connections: *Deliberate Introduction of the Kudzu Vine* 577

Case Study: *The Termite from Hell* 579

Individuals Matter: *Killing Invader Species and Saving Shipping Companies Money* 580

22-6 Extinction Threats from Hunting and Poaching 579

22-7 Other Extinction Threats 581

22-8 Protecting Wild Species from Depletion and Extinction: The Research and Legal Approach 582

Spotlight: *Accomplishments of the Endangered Species Act* 586

22-9 Protecting Wild Species from Depletion and Extinction: The Sanctuary Approach 586

22-10 Wildlife Management 588

Connections: *What Should Be Done About Snow Geese?* 591

PART V

SUSTAINING BIODIVERSITY AND CITIES 559

22 Sustaining Wild Species 560

*The Passenger Pigeon: Gone Forever* 560

22-1 Human Impacts on Biodiversity 561

22-2 Species Extinction 563

Case Study: *Bats Are Getting a Bad Rap* 567

23 Sustaining Terrestrial Biodiversity: The Ecosystem Approach 594

*Who Is Afraid of the Big Gray Wolf?* 594

23-1 Land Use in the World and the United States 595

Individuals Matter: *The Eco-Rancher* 599

23-2 Managing and Sustaining Forests 598

Solutions: *Certifying Sustainably Grown Timber* 606

U.S. Geological Survey

Mt. St. Helens before volcano eruption

U.S. Geological Survey

Mt. St. Helens after volcano eruption

NOAA Corps Collection/Photographer: Commander John Bortniak, NOAA Corps. (ret.)

Coral reef sanctuary, Tortugas Marine Ecological Reserve, Florida Keys

23-3  Forest Resources and Management in the United States  608

23-4  Tropical Deforestation and the Fuelwood Crisis  612

Solutions: *The Incredible Neem Tree*  614

Connections: *The Downward Spiral of Tropical Forest Degradation*  616

Solutions: *Sustainable Agriculture and Forestry Tropical Forests*  618

Individuals Matter: *Kenya's Green Belt Movement*  619

Individuals Matter: *New Stoves Help Save India's Forests and Improve Women's Health*  620

23-5  Managing and Sustaining National Parks  619

23-6  Establishing, Designing, and Managing Nature Reserves  621

Solutions: *Parks in Costa Rica*  622

Solutions: *The Nature Conservancy*  623

Solutions: *Biosphere Reserves*  625

Case Study: *The U.S. National Wilderness Preservation System*  628

23-7  Ecological Restoration  629

Individuals Matter: *Ecological Restoration of a Tropical Dry Forest in Costa Rica*  630

## 24  Sustaining Aquatic Biodiversity  634

*Connections: Can Lake Victoria Be Saved?  634*

24-1  The Importance of Aquatic Biodiversity  635

24-2  Human Impacts on Aquatic Biodiversity  637

Spotlight: *Invasion of Wetlands by Purple Loosestrife*  640

24-3  Protecting and Sustaining Marine Biodiversity  640

Case Study: *Near Extinction of the Blue Whale*  643

24-4  Managing and Sustaining the World's Marine Fisheries  649

Spotlight: *Managing Fisheries with Individual Transfer Quotas*  650

24-5  Protecting, Sustaining, and Restoring Wetlands  651

Individuals Matter: *Restoring a Wetland*  652

24-6  Protecting, Sustaining, and Restoring Lakes and Rivers  653

Case Study: *Protecting Lake Baikal*  654

## 25  Sustainable Cities: Urban Land Use and Management  661

*The Ecocity Concept in Davis, California  661*

25-1  Urbanization and Urban Growth  661

Spotlight: *The Urban Poor*  663

25-2  Urban Resource and Environmental Problems  668

Connections: *How Can Reducing Crime Help the Environment?*  671

25-3  Transportation and Urban Development  671

Pro/Con: *Good and Bad News About Motor Vehicles*  673

Case Study: *Mass Transit in the United States*  677

Solutions: *Curitiba, Brazil*  678

25-4  Urban Land-Use Planning and Control  676

Solutions: *Ecological Land-Use Planning*  681

Solutions: *Land-Use Planning in Oregon*  683

Dan Kline/Visuals Unlimited

Wolf spider

25-5 Solutions: Making Urban Areas More Livable and Sustainable 682

Case Study: *Tapiola, Finland* 683

Guest Essay: *The Ecological Design Arts* by David W. Orr 684

## PART VI
## ENVIRONMENT AND SOCIETY 689

## 26 Economics, Environment, and Sustainability 690

*How Important Are Natural Resources?* 690

26-1 Economic Resources and Systems and Environmental Problems 691

Solutions: *Appropriate Technology* 696

Guest Essay: *The Steady-State Economy in Outline* by Herman E. Daly 698

26-2 Monitoring Economic and Environmental Progress 695

26-3 Harmful External Costs and Full-Cost Pricing 698

26-4 The Economics of Pollution Control and Resource Management 700

26-5 Using Regulations and Market Forces to Improve Environmental Quality 703

Solutions: *Shifting the Tax Burden from Wages and Profits to Pollution and Waste* 705

Spotlight: *What Is Good Environmental Management?* 707

26-6 Reducing Poverty to Improve Environmental Quality and Human Well-Being 708

Solutions: *Microloans to the Poor* 709

26-7 Making the Transition to More Environmentally Sustainable Economies 710

Case Study: *How Is Germany Investing in the Future and the Earth?* 712

Connections: *Jobs and the Environment* 713

## 27 Politics, Environment, and Sustainability 716

*Rescuing a River* 716

27-1 Politics and Environmental Policy 717

27-2 Developing and Influencing Environmental Policy 717

Solutions: *Election Finance Reform* 721

Individuals Matter: *Environmental Careers* 724

27-3 Case Study: *Environmental Policy in the United States* 719

Solutions: *Types of Environmental Laws in the United States* 724

27-4 Environmental Law 723

Case Study: *The Regulatory Takings Controversy* 725

Spotlight: *SLAPPs: Intimidating Environmental Activists* 726

27-5 Environmental and Anti-Environmental Groups and Claims 727

Guest Essay: *Environmental Justice for All* by Robert D. Bullard 728

Individuals Matter: *Environmental Action on Campuses* 732

Guest Essay: *Covering the Environment* by Andrew C. Revkin 734

Solutions: *Improving Environmental Laws and Regulations* 736

27-6 Global Environmental Policy 731

Solutions: *Goals of National and Global Environmental NGOs* 737

Solutions: *Improving Trade Agreements* 738

## 28 Environmental Worldviews, Ethics, and Sustainability 741

*Biosphere 2: A Lesson in Humility* 741

28-1 Environmental Worldviews in Industrial Societies 742

28-2 Life-Centered Environmental Worldviews 743

Connections: *Why Should We Care About Future Generations?* 745

Spotlight: *Deep Ecology* 746

28-3 Solutions: Living More Sustainably 747

Guest Essay: *Envisioning a Sustainable Society* by Lester W. Milbrath 748

Individuals Matter: *Mindquake: Evaluating One's Environmental Worldview* 750

Connections: *Learning from the Earth* 751

Guest Essay: *Green Colleges* by Noel Perrin 752

Spotlight: *What Are Our Basic Needs?* 754

## Appendices

1    Units of Measurement   A1

2    Some Basic Chemistry   A2

3    Classifying and Naming Species   A5

## Glossary   G1

## Index   I1

# PART I

# HUMANS AND SUSTAINABILITY: AN OVERVIEW

*The environmental crisis is an outward manifestation of a crisis of mind and spirit. There could be no greater misconception of its meaning than to believe it is concerned only with endangered wildlife, human-made ugliness, and pollution. These are part of it, but more importantly, the crisis is concerned with the kind of creatures we are and what we must become in order to survive.*

LYNTON K. CALDWELL

# 1 ENVIRONMENTAL PROBLEMS, THEIR CAUSES, AND SUSTAINABILITY

## Living in an Exponential Age

Once there were two kings who enjoyed playing chess, with the winner claiming a prize from the loser. After one match, the winning king asked the losing king to pay him by placing one grain of wheat on the first square of the chessboard, two on the second, four on the third, and so on. The number of grains was to double each time until all 64 squares were filled.

The losing king, thinking he was getting off easy, agreed with delight. It was the biggest mistake he ever made. He bankrupted his kingdom and still could not produce the incredibly large number of grains of wheat he had promised. In fact, it is probably more than all the wheat that has ever been harvested!

This fictional story illustrates **exponential growth,** in which a quantity increases by a fixed percentage of the whole in a given time. As the losing king learned, exponential growth is deceptive. It starts off slowly, but after only a few doublings it grows to enormous numbers because each doubling is more than the total of all earlier growth. If plotted on a graph, continuing exponential growth eventually yields a graph shaped like the letter *J* (Figure 1-1).

Here is another example. Fold a piece of paper in half to double its thickness. If you could do this 42 times, the stack would reach from the earth to the moon, 386,400 kilometers (240,000 miles) away. If you could double it 50 times, the folded paper would almost reach the sun, 149 million kilometers (93 million miles) away!

Six important environmental issues are **(1)** *population growth,* **(2)** *increasing resource use,* **(3)** *global climate change,* **(4)** *premature extinction of plants and animals,* **(5)** *pollution,* and **(6)** *poverty.* All these issues are interconnected and are growing exponentially.

For example, between 1950 and 2002, the world's population increased from 2.5 billion to 6.2 billion. Unless death rates rise sharply, it may reach 8 billion by 2028, 9 billion by 2050, and 10–14 billion by 2100 (Figure 1-1). Global economic output, much of it environmentally damaging, is a rough measure of resource use. It has increased sevenfold since 1950.

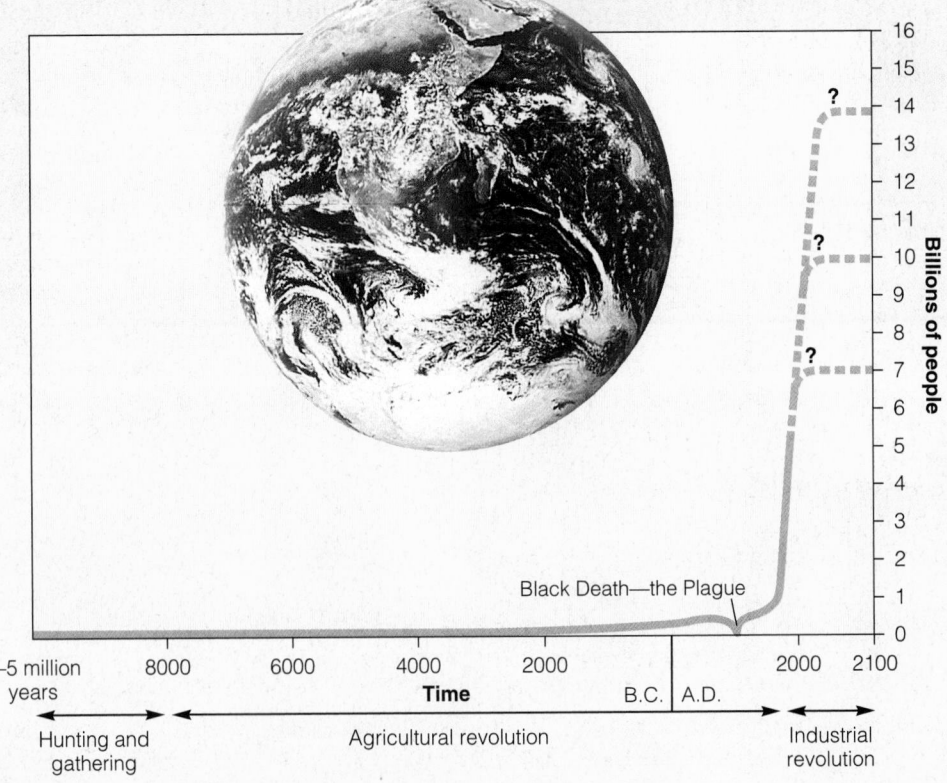

**Figure 1-1** The *J*-shaped curve of past exponential world population growth, with projections to 2100. Notice that exponential growth starts off slowly, but as time passes the curve becomes increasingly steep. The current world population of 6.2 billion people is projected to reach 7–14 billion people sometime during this century. (This figure is not to scale.) (Data from World Bank and United Nations; photo courtesy of NASA)

*Alone in space, alone in its life-supporting systems, powered by inconceivable energies, mediating them to us through the most delicate adjustments, wayward, unlikely, unpredictable, but nourishing, enlivening, and enriching in the largest degree—is this not a precious home for all of us? Is it not worth our love?*

BARBARA WARD AND RENÉ DUBOS

This chapter presents an overview of **(1)** environmental problems, **(2)** their causes, **(3)** controversy over their seriousness, and **(4)** ways we can live more sustainably. It discusses these questions:

- What are natural resources, and why are they important? What is an environmentally sustainable society?

- How fast is the human population increasing?

- What is the difference between economic growth and economic development? What are some harmful environmental effects of poverty?

- What are the earth's main types of resources? How can they be depleted or degraded?

- What are the principal types of pollution? How can pollution be reduced and prevented?

- What are the basic causes of today's environmental problems? How are these causes connected?

- Is our current course sustainable? What is environmentally sustainable development? How can we live more sustainably?

## 1-1 LIVING MORE SUSTAINABLY

**What Is the Difference Between Environment, Ecology, and Environmental Science?** **Environment** is everything that affects a living organism (any unique form of life). **Ecology** is a biological science that studies the relationships between living organisms and their environment.

This textbook is an introduction to **environmental science.** It is an interdisciplinary science that uses concepts and information from *natural sciences* such as ecology, biology, chemistry, and geology and *social sciences* such as economics, politics, and ethics to help us understand **(1)** how the earth works, **(2)** how we are affecting the earth's life-support systems (environment), and **(3)** how to deal with the environmental problems we face. Many different groups of people are concerned about environmental issues (Spotlight, right).

**What Keeps Us Alive?** Our existence, lifestyles, and economies depend completely on the sun and the earth, a blue and white island in the black void of space (Figure 1-1). To economists *capital* is wealth used to sustain a business and to generate more wealth. By analogy, we

**SPOTLIGHT**

## Cast of Players in the Environmental Drama

The cast of major characters you will encounter in this book include the following:

- **Ecologists,** who are biological scientists studying relationships between living organisms and their environment.

- **Environmental scientists,** who use information from the physical sciences and social sciences to **(1)** understand how the earth works, **(2)** learn how humans interact with the earth, and **(3)** develop solutions to environmental problems.

- **Conservation biologists,** who in the 1970s created a multidisciplinary science to **(1)** investigate human impacts on the diversity of life found on the earth (biodiversity) and **(2)** develop practical plans for preserving such biodiversity.

- **Environmentalists,** who **(1)** are concerned about the impact of people on environmental quality and **(2)** believe some human actions are degrading parts of the earth's life-support systems for humans and many other forms of life. Some of their beliefs and proposals for dealing with environmental problems are based on scientific information and concepts and some are based on their social and ethical environmental beliefs (environmental worldviews). Environmentalists are a broad group of people from different economic groups (rich, middle-class, poor) and with different political persuasions (ranging from conservative to liberal).

- **Preservationists,** concerned primarily with setting aside or protecting undisturbed natural areas from harmful human activities.

- **Conservationists,** concerned with using natural areas and wildlife in ways that sustain them for current and future generations of humans and other forms of life.

- **Restorationists,** devoted to the partial or complete restoration of natural areas that have been degraded by human activities.

Many people consider themselves members of several of these groups.

### Critical Thinking

Which, if any, of these groups do you most identify with? Why?

can think of **(1)** energy from the sun as **solar capital** and **(2)** the planet's air, water, soil, wildlife, forests, rangelands, fisheries, minerals, and natural purification, recycling, and pest control processes as **natural resources** or **natural capital** (Guest Essay, p. 16). **Solar energy** is defined broadly to include direct sunlight and indirect forms of solar energy such as **(1)** wind power, **(2)** hydropower (energy from flowing water), and **(3)** biomass (direct solar energy converted to chemical energy stored in biological sources of energy such as wood).

**What Is an Environmentally Sustainable Society?** An environmentally sustainable society satisfies the basic needs of its people for food, clean water, clean air, and shelter into the indefinite future without **(1)** depleting or degrading the earth's natural resources and **(2)** thereby preventing current and future generations of humans and other species from meeting their basic needs. *Living sustainably* means **(1)** living off the natural income replenished by soils, plants, air, and water and **(2)** not depleting the earth's endowment of natural capital that supplies this income (Guest Essay, p. 16).

For example, imagine you inherit $1 million. Invest this capital at 10% interest per year, and you will have a sustainable annual income of $100,000 without depleting your capital. If you spend $200,000 a year, your $1 million will be gone early in the 7th year; even if you spend only $110,000 a year, you will be bankrupt early in the 18th year.

The lesson here is a very old one: *Protect your capital.* Deplete your capital, and you move from a sustainable to an unsustainable lifestyle.

The same lesson applies to the earth's natural capital. Environmentalists and many leading scientists believe we are living unsustainably by depleting and degrading the earth's endowment of natural capital at an accelerating rate as our population (Figure 1-1) and demands on the earth's resources and life-sustaining processes increase exponentially.

Other analysts do not believe we are living unsustainably. They contend that **(1)** environmentalists have exaggerated the seriousness of population and environmental problems, and **(2)** any population, resource, and environmental problems we face can be overcome by human ingenuity and technological advances.

## 1-2 POPULATION GROWTH, ECONOMIC GROWTH, DEVELOPMENT, AND GLOBALIZATION

**How Rapidly Is the Human Population Growing?** The increasing size of the human population is an example of exponential growth (Figures 1-1 and 1-2 and Spotlight, p. 5). The main reason for the rapid growth of the earth's human population over the past 100 years has been a much greater drop in death rates (mostly because of increases in food supplies and bet-

**World Population Reached**

1 billion in 1804
2 billion in 1927 (123 years later)
3 billion in 1960 (33 years later)
4 billion in 1974 (14 years later)
5 billion in 1987 (13 years later)
6 billion in 1999 (12 years later)

**World Population May Reach**

7 billion in 2013 (14 years later)
8 billion in 2028 (15 years later)
9 billion in 2050 (22 years later)

**Figure 1-2** World population milestones. (Data from United Nations Population Division, *World Population Prospects, 1998*)

ter health and sanitation) than in birth rates.

One measure of population growth is **doubling time:** the number of years it takes for a population growing at a specified rate to double its size. A quick way to calculate doubling time is to use the **rule of 70:** 70/percentage growth rate = doubling time in years (a formula derived from the basic mathematics of exponential growth). For example, in 2002 the world's population grew by 1.28%. If that rate continues, the earth's population will double in about 55 years (70/1.28 = 54.7 or about 55 years).

Some *good news* is that the exponential rate of annual population growth slowed from 2.1% in 1963 to 1.28% in 2002. The *bad news* is that the world's population is still growing exponentially at a rapid rate and is projected to increase from 6.2 billion to 8–14 billion people sometime during this century (Figure 1-1).

**What Is Economic Growth?** Almost all countries seek **economic growth:** an increase in their capacity to provide people with goods and services. This increase is accomplished by population growth (more consumers and producers), more consumption per person, or both.

Economic growth usually is measured by an increase in several indicators:

- **Gross national income (GNI)**—formerly called **gross national product (GNP):** the market value in current dollars of all goods and services produced *within* and *outside* a country during a year plus net income earned abroad by a country's citizens.

- **Gross national income in purchasing power parity (GNI PPP):** The market value of a country's GNI in terms of the goods and services it would buy in the United States. This is a better way to compare the standards among countries.

- **Gross domestic product (GDP):** the market value in current dollars of all goods and services produced *within* a country during a year.

- **Gross world product (GWP):** the market value in current dollars of all goods and services produced in the world during a year.

- **Per capita GNI**—formerly called **per capita GNP:** the GNI divided by the total population at mid-year. It gives the average slice of the economic pie per person.

- **Per capita GNI in purchasing power parity (per capita GNI PPP):** the GNI PPP divided by the total population at mid-year. This is a better way to make comparisons of people's economic welfare among countries.

**What Is Economic Development?** Economic development is the improvement of living standards by economic growth. The United Nations classifies the world's countries as economically developed or developing based primarily on their degree of industrialization and their per capita GNI (Figure 1-3).

The **developed countries** (with a total population of 1.2 billion people) include the United States, Canada, Japan, Australia, New Zealand, and all the countries of Europe. Most are highly industrialized

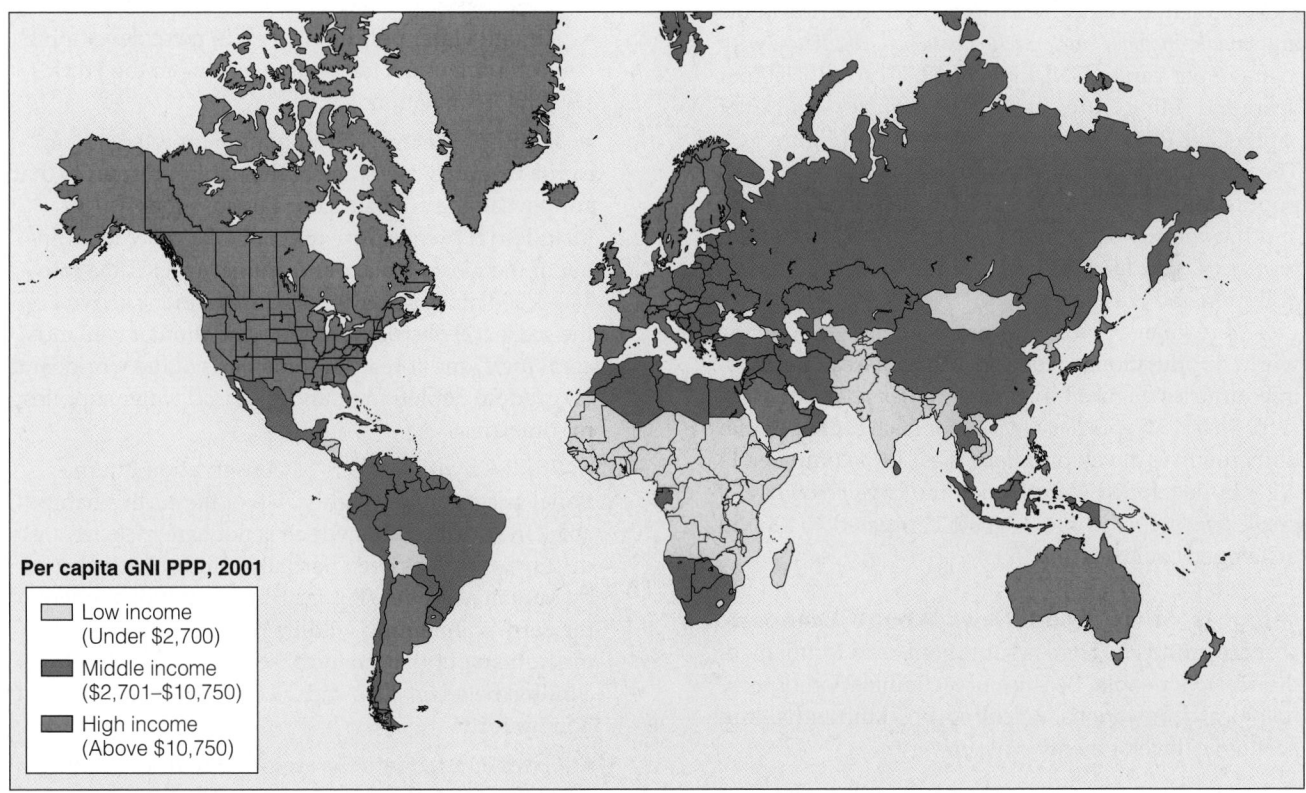

**Per capita GNI PPP, 2001**

☐ Low income (Under $2,700)

■ Middle income ($2,701–$10,750)

■ High income (Above $10,750)

**Figure 1-3** Degree of economic development as measured by per capita gross national income in purchasing power parity (per capita GNI PPP) in 2001. (Data from United Nations and the World Bank)

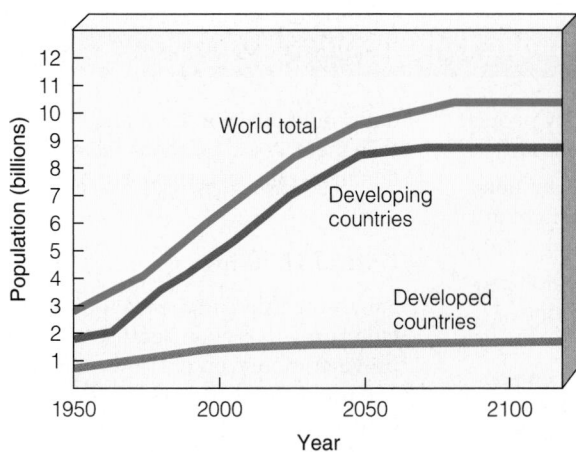

**Figure 1-4** Past and projected population size for developed countries, developing countries, and the world, 1950–2120. More than 95% of the addition of 3.6 billion people between 1990 and 2030 is projected to occur in developing countries. (Data from United Nations)

and have high average per capita GNI PPPs (above $10,750 per year, except for industrialized countries in eastern Europe and some in northern and southern Europe). These countries, with 19% of the world's population, **(1)** have about 85% of the world's wealth and income, **(2)** use about 88% of its natural resources, and **(3)** generate about 75% of its pollution and waste.

All other nations (with a total population of 5 billion people) are classified as **developing countries,** most of them in Africa, Asia, and Latin America. Some are *middle-income, moderately developed countries* with average per capita GNI PPPs of $2,701 to $10,750 per year and others are *low-income countries* with per capita GNI PPPs less than $2,701 per year (Figure 1-3). The developing countries with 81% of the world's population **(1)** have about 15% of the world's wealth and income, **(2)** use about 12% of the world's natural resources, and **(3)** produce about 25% of the world's pollution and waste.

More than 95% of the projected increase in the world's population is expected to take place in developing countries (Figure 1-4), *where 1 million people are added every 5 days.* The primary reason for such rapid population growth in developing countries (1.6% compared to 0.1% in developed countries) is the *large percentage of people who are under age 15* (33% compared to 18% in developed countries in 2002).

**What Is Some Good News About Economic Development?** Here is some *good news* for many of the world's people. Because of a combination of technological innovations, scientific breakthroughs, and economic development

- Between 1900 and 2002, global life expectancy at birth more than doubled from 33 to 67 years

(76 in developed countries and 65 in developing countries).

- Between 1955 and 2002, the world's average infant mortality during the first year of life dropped by **(1)** 60% in developed countries and **(2)** 40% in developing countries.

- Global food production has outpaced population growth since 1978.

- Since 1950 the percentage of rural families in developing countries with access to safe drinking water has increased from 10% to almost 75%.

- We have learned how to produce more goods with less raw materials.

- Since 1970 levels of most major air and water pollutants have been reduced in most of the world's developed countries.

**What Is Some Bad but Challenging News About Economic Development?** Here is some *bad environmental news* that challenges us to do better:

- Average life expectancy in developing countries is 11 years less than in developed countries.

- Infant mortality in developing countries is more than eight times higher than in developed countries.

- The harmful environmental effects of industrialized food production may eventually limit future food production unless there is a shift to more sustainable ways to produce food.

- Air and water pollution levels in most developing countries are much too high according to the World Health Organization.

- Because of increased population growth and per capita resource use, some of the natural resources that support all life are being used unsustainably. This includes **(1)** premature extinction of a growing number of the world's plant and animal species at a rate 100–1,000 times faster than before humans arrived on the scene, **(2)** destruction or degradation of wetlands, coral reefs, and forests in some parts of the world, and **(3)** gradual depletion of underground water supplies in some areas.

- Studies by researchers at Conservation International suggest that roughly 73% of the earth's habitable land surface (that which is not bare rock, ice, or drifting sand) has been partially or heavily disturbed by human activities (Figure 1-5). What will happen to the earth's remaining wildlife habitats and species if the human population increases from 6.2 billion to 8 billion between 2002 and 2028 and perhaps to 9 billion by 2050?

- Gases emitted into the atmosphere from burning fossil fuels and clearing forests could cause the world's climate to become warmer during this cen-

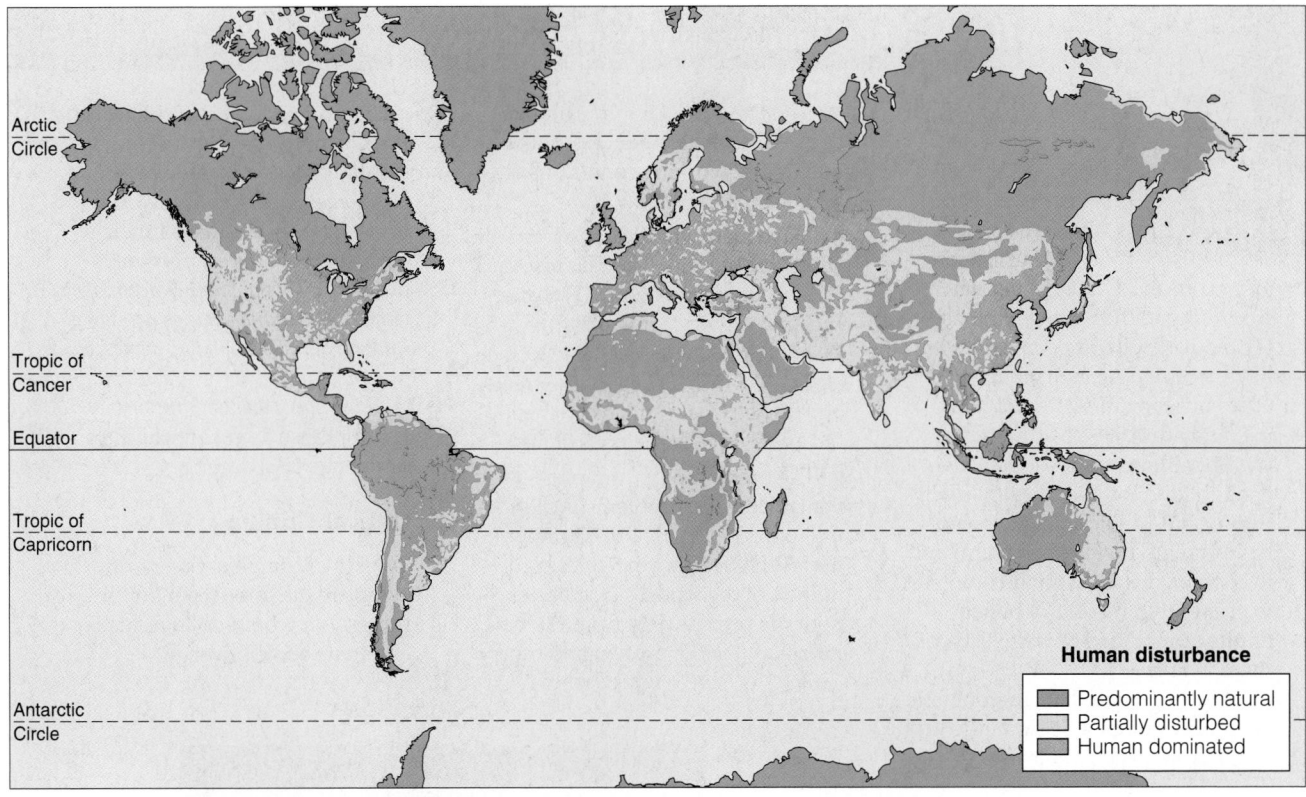

**Figure 1-5** Human disturbance of the earth's land area. (Data from Lee Hannah and David Lohse, *1993 Annual Report*, Washington, D.C.: Conservation International)

tury. Such *global warming* can cause environmental and economic disruption by **(1)** shifting areas where crops can be grown, **(2)** altering water supplies by shifting patterns of precipitation, **(3)** shifting where various plants and animals can survive, and **(4)** raising average sea levels, which can flood low-lying cities, islands, coral reefs, and coastal wetlands. Some countries will be winners and some (mostly poorer countries) will be losers in these projected climate shifts.

▪ An estimated 1.4 billion people in developing countries—roughly one of every four people on the planet—have an annual income of less than $370 (U.S.) per year. This income of roughly $1 (U.S.) per day is the World Bank's definition of **acute poverty** where people cannot meet their basic economic needs. According to a 2000 World Bank study, nearly half of humanity suffer from poverty and are trying to survive on less than $1–3 (U.S.) a day. About 70% of these people are women and children. Such *poverty* has a number of harmful health and environmental effects (Connections, p. 8).

▪ Despite enormous global economic growth since 1970, the gulf between the world's richest countries and poorest countries has widened dramatically. For example, today the average per capita GNI for the world's ten richest countries is more than 100 times

that for the world's ten poorest countries. At the individual level, the total wealth of the world's 200 richest people is greater than the combined wealth of about half or 3.1 billion of the world's people.

**What Is Globalization?** One of the major trends since 1950, and especially since 1970, is **globalization,** the process of global social, economic, and environmental change that leads to an increasingly integrated world.

Here are a few indicators of globalization:

*Economic*

▪ Between 1950 and 2002, the global economy grew from $6.6 trillion to $47 trillion.

▪ Between 1950 and 2002, international trade of goods and services increased from 5% to 16% of the gross world product.

▪ Between 1970 and 2002, the number of transnational corporations operating in three or more countries grew from 7,000 to about 60,000.

*Information and Communication*

▪ By 2002, roughly 550 million people (1 in every 11 people in the world) had Internet access on a global basis, a figure that is growing rapidly.

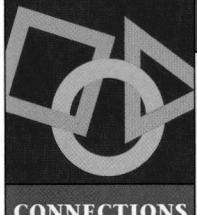

# Some Harmful Environmental Effects of Poverty

Daily life is a harsh struggle for the estimated one of every two people on the earth who try to survive on an income of $1–3 (U.S.) per day. According to the United Nations, **(1)** about 1.2 billion people do not have access to clean drinking water, adequate sanitation, decent housing, and adequate health care, **(2)** 790 million people do not have enough food for good health (see figure), **(3)** 2 billion people do not have enough fuel to keep warm and to cook food and do not have access to electricity, and **(4)** 854 billion adults cannot read or write (64% of them women).

*Poverty* is related to environmental quality and people's quality of life because poor people often

- Deplete and degrade local forests, soil, grasslands, wildlife, and water supplies for short-term survival. They do not have the luxury of worrying about long-term supplies of natural resources when their daily life is focused on getting enough food and water to survive.

- Live in areas with high levels of air and water pollution and with the greatest risk of natural disasters such as floods, earthquakes, hurricanes, and volcanic eruptions.

- Spend an average of 4–6 hours **(1)** *per day* searching for and carrying fuelwood and **(2)** *per week* drawing and carrying water.

- Must take jobs (if they can find them) that subject them to unhealthy and unsafe working conditions at very low pay.

- Have many children as a form of economic security. Their children **(1)** help them grow food, **(2)** gather fuel (mostly wood and dung), **(3)** haul drinking water, **(4)** tend livestock, **(5)** work, **(6)** beg in the streets, and **(7)** help them survive in their old age (typically their 50s or 60s).

- Die prematurely from preventable health problems. According to the World Health Organization (WHO), each year at least 10 million of the world's desperately poor die prematurely from **(1)** malnutrition (lack of protein and other nutrients needed for good health), **(2)** infectious diseases caused by drinking contaminated water and **(3)** increased susceptibility to infectious diseases because of their weakened condition from malnutrition. *This premature death of at least 27,400 human beings per day is equivalent to 69 jumbo jet planes, each carrying 400 passengers, accidentally crashing every day with no survivors. Half of those dying are children under age 5.*

## Critical Thinking

You are in charge of the world. What are the three most important things you would do to reduce or eliminate acute poverty?

John Bryson/Photo Researchers, Inc.

One in every three children under age 5, such as this Brazilian child, suffers from malnutrition. According to the World Health Organization, each day at least 13,700 children under age 5 die prematurely from malnutrition and infectious diseases, most from drinking contaminated water and a weakened condition from malnutrition—an average of 10 preventable deaths each minute.

---

- According to Forecasting International, by 2010 some 95% of the people in developed countries and 50% of those in developing countries will be online.

## Environmental Effects

- Since 1950, the number of species and infectious disease organisms (microbes) transported across international borders by trade and travel has increased significantly.

- Since 1950, many long-lived pollutants have been transferred across the globe by wind, rainfall patterns, ocean currents, and rivers. On an even larger scale, nations now face the global threats of **(1)** widespread ocean pollution, **(2)** depletion of ozone in the upper atmosphere (stratosphere) that keeps much of the sun's harmful ultraviolet radiation from reaching the earth's surface, and **(3)** global and regional climate change caused by chemicals released into the environment by human activities.

## 1-3 RESOURCES

**What Is a Resource?** From a human standpoint, a **resource** is anything obtained from the environment to meet human needs and wants. Examples include food, water, shelter, manufactured goods, transportation, communication, and recreation.

Some resources, such as solar energy, fresh air, wind, fresh surface water, fertile soil, and wild edible plants, are directly available for use. Other resources, such as petroleum (oil), iron, groundwater (water found underground), and modern crops, are not directly available. They become useful to us only with some effort and technological ingenuity. For example, petroleum was a mysterious fluid until we learned how to find, extract, and convert (refine) it into gasoline, heating oil, and other products that we could sell at affordable prices.

On our short human time scale, we classify the material resources we get from the environment as **(1)** *perpetual,* **(2)** *renewable,* or **(3)** *nonrenewable* (Figure 1-6).

**What Are Perpetual and Renewable Resources?** Solar energy is called a **perpetual resource** because on a human time scale it is renewed continuously. It is expected to last at least 6 billion years as the sun completes its life cycle.

On a human time scale, a **renewable resource** can be replenished fairly rapidly (hours to several decades) through natural processes as long as it is not used up faster than it is replaced. Examples are **(1)** forests, **(2)** grasslands, **(3)** wild animals, **(4)** fresh water, **(5)** fresh air, and **(6)** fertile soil.

However, renewable resources can be depleted or degraded. The highest rate at which a renewable resource can be used *indefinitely* without reducing its available supply is called its **sustainable yield.**

If we exceed a resource's natural replacement rate, the available supply begins to shrink, a process known as **environmental degradation.** Examples of such degradation include **(1)** urbanization of productive land, **(2)** waterlogging and salt buildup in soil, **(3)** excessive topsoil erosion, **(4)** deforestation, **(5)** groundwater depletion, **(6)** overgrazing of grasslands by livestock, **(7)** reduction in the earth's forms of wildlife (biodiversity) by elimination of habitats and species, and **(8)** pollution. A major cause of environmental degradation of renewable resources is a phenomenon known as the *tragedy of the commons* (Connections, p. 11).

**What Are Nonrenewable Resources?** Resources that exist in a fixed quantity or stock in the earth's crust are called **nonrenewable resources.** On a time scale of millions to billions of years, geological processes can renew such resources. However, on the

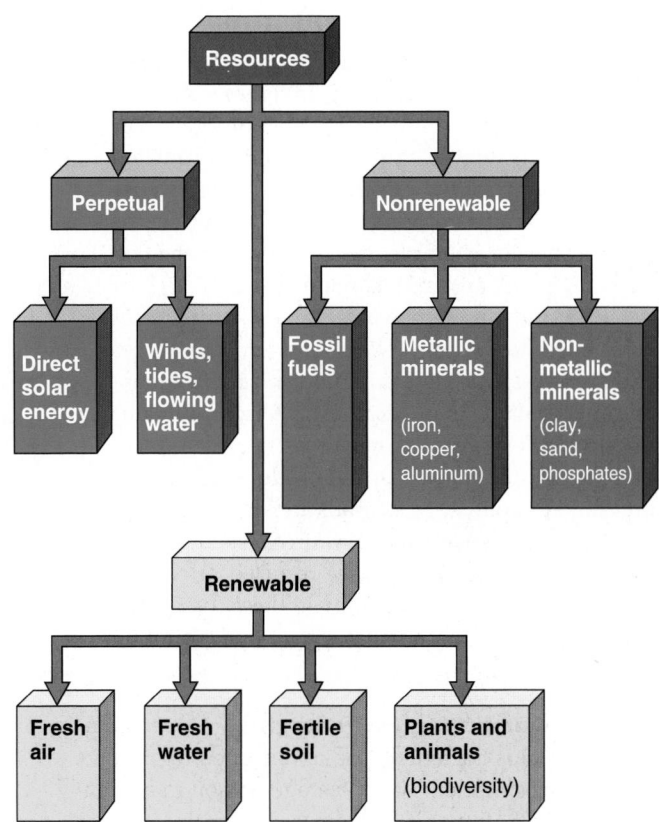

**Figure 1-6** Major types of material resources. This scheme is not fixed; renewable resources can become nonrenewable if used for a prolonged period at a faster rate than they are renewed by natural processes.

much shorter human time scale of hundreds to thousands of years, these resources can be depleted much faster than they are formed.

These exhaustible resources include **(1)** *energy resources* (such as coal, oil, and natural gas, which cannot be recycled), **(2)** *metallic mineral resources* (such as iron, copper, and aluminum, which can be recycled), and **(3)** *nonmetallic mineral resources* (such as salt, clay, sand, and phosphates, which usually are difficult or too costly to recycle) (Figure 1-6).

Figure 1-7 (p. 10) shows the production and depletion cycle of a nonrenewable energy or mineral resource. We never completely exhaust a nonrenewable mineral resource. However, such a resource becomes *economically depleted* when the costs of extracting and using what is left exceed its economic value. At that point, we have six choices: **(1)** try to find more, **(2)** recycle or reuse existing supplies (except for nonrenewable energy resources, which cannot be recycled or reused), **(3)** waste less, **(4)** use less, **(5)** try to develop a substitute, or **(6)** wait millions of years for more to be produced.

Some nonrenewable material resources, such as copper and aluminum, can be recycled or reused to extend supplies. **Recycling** involves collecting and reprocessing a resource into new products. For example, glass bottles can be crushed and melted to make new bottles or other glass items. **Reuse** involves using a resource over and over in the same form. For example, glass bottles can be collected, washed, and refilled many times.

Recycling nonrenewable metallic resources takes much less energy, water, and other resources and produces much less pollution and environmental degradation than exploiting virgin metallic resources. Reusing such resources takes even less energy and other resources and produces less pollution and environmental degradation than recycling.

Nonrenewable energy resources, such as coal, oil, and natural gas, cannot be recycled or reused. Once burned, the useful energy in these fossil fuels is gone, leaving behind waste heat and polluting exhaust gases.

**What Is Our Ecological Footprint?** An **ecological footprint** is the amount of land needed to produce the resources needed by an average person in a country. Largely as a result of increased human land use (Figure 1-5), and resource use per person, the environmental impact or *ecological footprint* of each person in developed countries is large compared to that in developing countries (Figure 1-8).

China and other developing countries hope to increase their total and per capita economic growth, which will increase the ecological footprints of their people (Connections, p. 15). According to William Rees and Mathis Wackernal, developers of the ecological footprint concept, it would take the land area of about three planet earths if all the world's 6.2 billion

**Figure 1-8** Relative ecological footprints of the United States, the Netherlands, and India. (Data from William Rees and Mathis Wackernagel)

people consumed the same amount of resources as each person in the United States.

## 1-4 POLLUTION

**What Is Pollution, and Where Do Pollutants Come From?** Any addition to air, water, soil, or food that threatens the health, survival, or activities of humans or other living organisms is called **pollution.** Pollutants can enter the environment **(1)** naturally (for example, from volcanic eruptions) or **(2)** through human (anthropogenic) activities (for example, from burning coal). Most pollution from human activities occurs in or near urban and industrial areas, where pollutants are concentrated. Industrialized agriculture also is a major source of pollution.

Some pollutants contaminate the areas where they are produced; others are carried by wind or flowing water to other areas. Pollution does not respect local, state, or national boundaries.

There are two types of pollutant sources:

- **Point sources,** where pollutants come from single, identifiable sources. Examples are the **(1)** smokestack of a coal-burning power plant, **(2)** drainpipe of a factory, or **(3)** exhaust pipe of an automobile.

- **Nonpoint sources,** where pollutants come from dispersed (and often difficult to identify) sources. Examples are **(1)** runoff of fertilizers and pesticides (from farmlands, golf courses, and suburban lawns and gardens) into streams and lakes and **(2)** pesticides sprayed into the air or blown by the wind into the atmosphere.

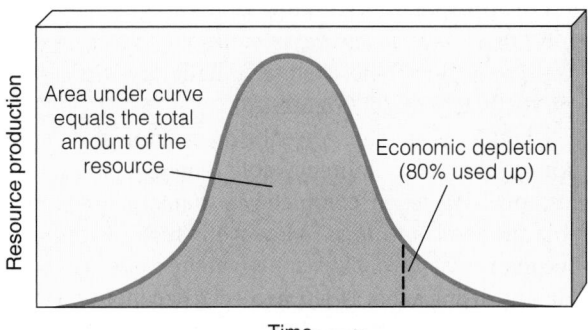

**Figure 1-7** Full production and exhaustion cycle of a nonrenewable resource such as copper, iron, oil, or coal. Usually, a nonrenewable resource is considered *economically depleted* when 80% of its total supply has been extracted and used. Normally, it costs too much to extract and process the remaining 20%.

**CONNECTIONS**

One cause of environmental degradation is the overuse of **common-property** or **free-access resources.** Such resources are owned by no one (or jointly by everyone in a country or area) but are available to all users at little or no charge.

Examples include (1) clean air, (2) the open ocean and its fish, (3) migratory birds, (4) wildlife species, (5) publicly owned lands (such as national forests, national parks, and wildlife refuges), (6) gases of the lower atmosphere, and (7) space.

In 1968, biologist Garrett Hardin called the degradation of renewable free-access resources the **tragedy of the commons.** It happens because each user reasons, "If I do not use this resource, someone else will. The little bit I use or pollute is not enough to matter, and such resources are renewable."

With only a few users, this logic works. However, the cumulative effect of many people trying to exploit a free-access resource eventually exhausts or ruins it. Then no one can benefit from it, and therein lies the tragedy.

Two solutions to this problem are to

- *Use free-access resources at rates well below their estimated sustainable yields or overload limits by reducing population, regulating access, or both.* This prevention approach is rarely used because (1) it entails establishing and enforcing regulations that restrict resource use or population growth, and (2) it is difficult and expensive to determine the sustainable yield of a forest, grassland, or animal population because such yields vary with weather, climate, and unpredictable biological factors.

- *Convert free-access resources to private ownership.* The reasoning is that owners of land or some other resource have a strong incentive to protect their investment. However, this approach is not practical for global common resources (such as the atmosphere, the open ocean, most wildlife species, and migratory birds) that cannot be divided up and converted to private property.

Experience shows another possibility. Just because a resource is easily available to a community does not always mean people have free and unregulated access to that resource. Many communities have established a set of rules and traditions to regulate and share their access to a common-property resource such as ocean fisheries, grazing lands, and forests.

### Critical Thinking

Give three examples of how you cause environmental degradation as a result of the tragedy of the commons. How should we deal with this problem? Explain.

---

It is much easier and cheaper to identify and control pollution from point sources than from widely dispersed nonpoint sources.

**What Types of Harm Do Pollutants Cause?** Unwanted effects of pollutants include the following:

- Disruption of life-support systems for humans and other species

- Damage to wildlife, human health, and property

- Nuisances such as noise and unpleasant smells, tastes, and sights

**Solutions: What Can We Do About Pollution?** We use two basic approaches to deal with pollution: (1) prevent it from reaching the environment or (2) clean it up if it does. **Pollution prevention** or **input pollution control** reduces or eliminates the production of pollutants. We can prevent (or at least reduce) pollution by following the five *R*s of resource use: *refuse (do not use), replace (find a less harmful sustitute), reduce (use less), reuse,* and *recycle.*

**Pollution cleanup** or **output pollution control** involves cleaning up pollutants after they have been produced. Environmentalists have identified three problems with relying primarily on pollution cleanup:

- *It is only a temporary bandage as long as population and consumption levels grow without corresponding improvements in pollution control technology.* For example, adding catalytic converters to car exhaust systems has reduced air pollution. But increases in the number of cars and in the total distance each travels have reduced the effectiveness of this cleanup approach.

- *It often removes a pollutant from one part of the environment only to cause pollution in another.* For example, we can collect garbage, but the garbage is then (1) burned (perhaps causing air pollution and leaving a toxic ash that must be put somewhere), (2) dumped into streams, lakes, and oceans (perhaps causing water pollution), or (3) buried (perhaps causing soil and groundwater pollution).

- *Once pollutants have entered and become dispersed into the environment at harmful levels, it usually costs too much to reduce them to acceptable levels.*

Both pollution prevention and pollution cleanup are needed. Environmentalists and some economists urge us to emphasize prevention because it works better and is cheaper than cleanup. As Benjamin Franklin observed long ago, "An ounce of prevention is worth a pound of cure." An increasing number of businesses have found that *pollution prevention pays.*

Governments can encourage both pollution prevention and pollution cleanup by

■ Using incentives such as various subsidies and tax write-offs.

■ Using regulations and taxes.

Most analysts believe a combination of both approaches is best because excessive regulation and too much taxation can cause a political backlash. Achieving the right balance is difficult.

## 1-5 ENVIRONMENTAL PROBLEMS: CAUSES AND CONNECTIONS

**What Are Key Environmental Problems and Their Basic Causes?**  We face a number of interconnected environmental and resource problems (Figure 1-9). The first step in dealing with these problems is to identify their underlying causes (Figure 1-10).

**How Are Environmental Problems and Their Causes Connected?**  Once we have identified environmental problems and their root causes, the next step is to understand how they are connected to one another. The three-factor model in Figure 1-11 is a starting point.

- Rapid population growth
- Unsustainable resource use
- Poverty
- Not including the environmental costs of economic goods and services in their market prices
- Trying to manage and simplify nature with too little knowledge about how it works

**Figure 1-10** Environmentalists have identified five basic causes of the environmental problems we face.

According to this simple model, the environmental impact (**I**) of population on a given area depends on three key factors: **(1)** number of people (**P**), **(2)** average resource use per person (affluence, **A**), and **(3)** the beneficial and harmful environmental effects of the technologies (**T**) used to provide and consume each unit of resource.

In developing countries, population size and the resulting degradation of potentially renewable resources (as the poor struggle to stay alive, Connections, p. 8) tend to be the key factors in total environmental impact (Figure 1-11, top). In such countries per capita resource use is low.

In developed countries, high rates of per capita resource use and the resulting high levels of pollution and environmental degradation per person usually are the key factors determining **(1)** overall environmental impact (Figure 1-11, bottom) and **(2)** a country's ecological footprint per person (Figure 1-8). For example, the average U.S. citizen consumes about 35 times as much as the average citizen of India and 100 times as much as the average person in the world's poorest countries. *Thus poor parents in a developing country would need 70–200 children to have the same lifetime resource consumption as 2 children in a typical U.S. family.*

Some forms of technology, such as polluting factories and motor vehicles and energy-wasting devices, increase environmental impact by raising the T factor in the equation. Other technologies, such as pollution control and prevention, solar cells, and energy-saving devices, lower environmental impact by decreasing the T factor in the equation. In other words, some forms of technology are *environmentally harmful* and some are *environmentally beneficial.* Figure 1-11 shows that ways to reduce our environmental impact are to **(1)** slow population growth, **(2)** decrease resource use and waste (especially by using resources more efficiently), **(3)** increase use of environmentally beneficial technologies, and **(4)** phase out environmentally harmful technologies.

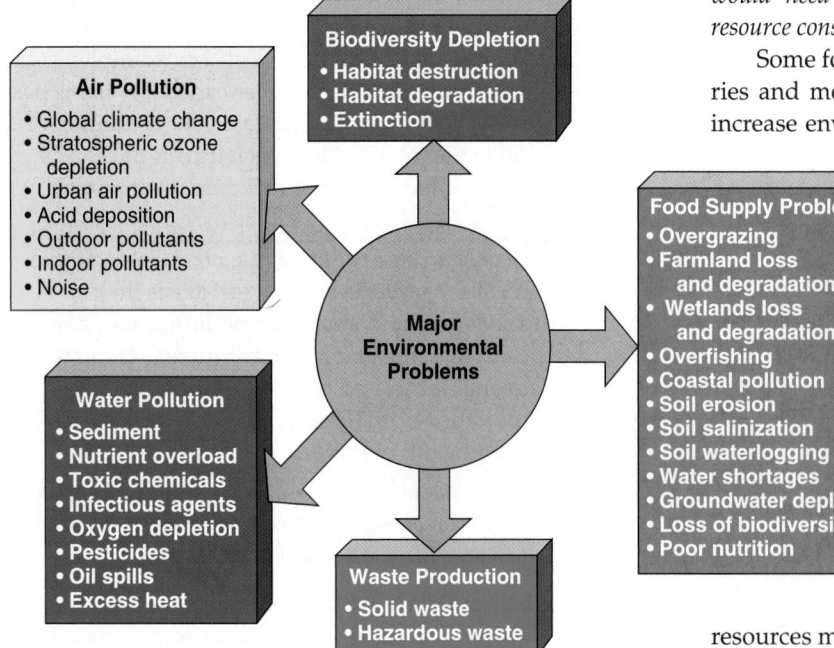

**Air Pollution**
- Global climate change
- Stratospheric ozone depletion
- Urban air pollution
- Acid deposition
- Outdoor pollutants
- Indoor pollutants
- Noise

**Biodiversity Depletion**
- Habitat destruction
- Habitat degradation
- Extinction

**Major Environmental Problems**

**Food Supply Problems**
- Overgrazing
- Farmland loss and degradation
- Wetlands loss and degradation
- Overfishing
- Coastal pollution
- Soil erosion
- Soil salinization
- Soil waterlogging
- Water shortages
- Groundwater depletion
- Loss of biodiversity
- Poor nutrition

**Water Pollution**
- Sediment
- Nutrient overload
- Toxic chemicals
- Infectious agents
- Oxygen depletion
- Pesticides
- Oil spills
- Excess heat

**Waste Production**
- Solid waste
- Hazardous waste

**Figure 1-9** Major environmental and resource problems.

**Developing Countries**

| Population (**P**) | X | Consumption per person (affluence, **A**) | X | Technological impact per unit of consumption (**T**) | = | Environmental impact of population (**I**) |

**Developed Countries**

**Figure 1-11** Simplified model of how three factors—population, affluence, and technology—affect the environmental impact of population in developing countries (top) and developed countries (bottom).

The three-factor model in Figure 1-11 can **(1)** help us understand how key environmental problems and some of their causes are connected and **(2)** guide us in seeking solutions to these problems. However, these problems involve a number of poorly understood interactions among many more factors than those in this simplified model, as outlined in Figure 1-12 (p. 14). For a more detailed model, see the inside back cover.

## 1-6 IS OUR PRESENT COURSE SUSTAINABLE?

**Are Things Getting Better or Worse?** Experts disagree about **(1)** how serious our population and environmental problems are and **(2)** what we should do about them. Some analysts believe human ingenuity and technological advances will allow us to **(1)** clean up pollution to acceptable levels, **(2)** find substitutes for any resources that become scarce, and **(3)** keep expanding the earth's ability to support more humans, as we have done in the past. They accuse most scientists and environmentalists of **(1)** exaggerating the seriousness of the problems we face and **(2)** failing to appreciate the progress we have made in improving quality of life and protecting the environment.

In contrast, environmentalists and many leading scientists contend we are disrupting the earth's life-support system for us and other forms of life at an accelerating rate, which if kept up could lead to serious environmental and economic harm. They are greatly encouraged by the progress we have made in increasing average life expectancy, reducing infant mortality, increasing food supplies, and reducing many forms of pollution. But they point out how much more we need to do to help make the earth more sustainable for present and future human generations and for other species that support us and other forms of life.

On November 18, 1992, some 1,680 of the world's senior scientists from 70 countries, including 102 of the 196 living scientists who are Nobel laureates, signed and sent an urgent warning to government leaders of all nations. According to this warning,

> *Our massive tampering with the world's interdependent web of life—coupled with the environmental damage inflicted by deforestation, species loss, and climate change—could trigger widespread adverse effects, including unpredictable collapses of critical biological systems whose interactions and dynamics we only imperfectly understand. . . . No more than one or a few decades remain before the chance to avert the threats we now confront will be lost and the prospects for humanity immeasurably diminished.*

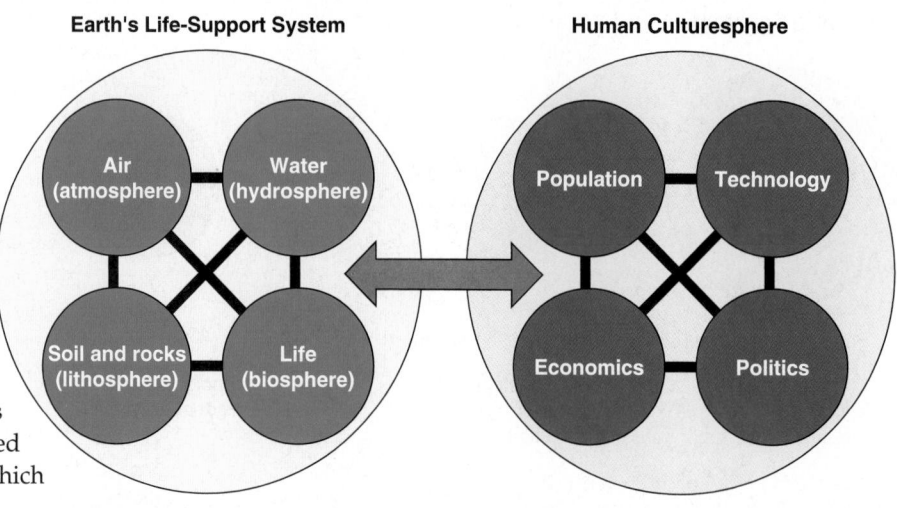

**Figure 1-12** Major components and interactions within and between the earth's life-support system and the human sociocultural system (culturesphere). The goal of environmental science is to learn as much as possible about these complex interactions.

**Earth's Life-Support System**

Air (atmosphere)
Water (hydrosphere)
Soil and rocks (lithosphere)
Life (biosphere)

**Human Culturesphere**

Population
Technology
Economics
Politics

Also in 1992, the U.S. National Academy of Sciences and the Royal Society of London, two of the world's leading scientific organizations, issued a joint report, their first ever, which began,

*If current predictions of population growth prove accurate and patterns of human activity on the planet remain unchanged, science and technology may not be able to prevent either irreversible degradation of the environment or continued poverty for much of the world. . . . Sustainable development can be achieved, but only if irreversible degradation of the environment can be halted in time.*

These warnings are not the views of a small number of scientists but the consensus of the mainstream scientific community, consisting of most of the world's key researchers on environmental problems.

The most useful answer to the question of whether things are getting better or worse is *both*. Some things are getting better and some are getting worse. We need to encourage environmentally beneficial trends and discourage environmentally harmful trends.

Our challenge is not to get trapped into confusion and inaction by listening primarily to

- *Technological optimists* who overstate the situation by telling us to be happy and not to worry because technological innovations and conventional economic growth and development will lead to a wonderworld for everyone.

- *Environmental pessimists* who overstate the problems to the point where our environmental situation seems hopeless. According to the noted conservationist Aldo Leopold (p. 36), "I have no hope for a conservation based on fear."

**Whom Should We Believe? A Clash of Environmental Worldviews** Conflicts over how serious our environmental problems are and what we should do about them arise mostly out of differing **environmental worldviews: (1)** how people think the world works, **(2)** what they think their role in the world should be, and **(3)** what they believe is right and wrong environmental behavior (**environmental ethics**).

People with widely differing environmental beliefs or worldviews can take the same data, be logically consistent, and arrive at quite different conclusions because they start with different assumptions and values.

Many different environmental worldviews exist, but most are variations of two major opposing ones.

Most people in today's industrial consumer societies have a **planetary management worldview,** which has become increasingly common in the past 50 years. According to this view, human beings, as the planet's most important and dominant species, can and should manage the planet mostly for their own benefit.

The basic environmental beliefs of this worldview include the following:

- *We are in charge of nature.*

- *There is always more.* The earth has an unlimited supply of resources for use by us through science and technology. If we deplete a resource, we will find substitutes. To deal with pollutants, we can invent technology to clean them up, dump them into space, or move into space ourselves. If we extinguish other species, we can use genetic engineering to create new and better ones.

- *All economic growth is good, and the potential for global economic growth is essentially limitless.*

- *Our success depends on how well we can understand, control, and manage the earth's life-support systems for our benefit.*

All or most aspects of this worldview are widely supported because it is said to be the primary driving force behind the major improvements in the human condition since the beginning of the industrial revolution about 275 years ago.

Another environmental worldview, known as the **environmental wisdom worldview,** is based on the following major beliefs, which are the opposite of those making up the planetary management worldview:

- *Nature does not exist just for us and we only think we are in charge.* We need the earth, but the earth does not need us.

- *There is not always more.* The earth's resources are **(1)** limited, **(2)** should not be wasted, and **(3)** should be used efficiently and sustainably for us and other species.

- *Some forms of technology and economic growth are environmentally beneficial and should be encouraged, but some are environmentally harmful and should be discouraged.*

- *Our success depends on (1) learning how the earth sustains itself and adapts to ever-changing environmental conditions and (2) integrating such scientific lessons from nature (environmental wisdom) into the ways we think and act.*

**What Is Environmentally Sustainable Economic Development?** A growing number of analysts have called for a shift during this century from an emphasis on traditional economic development fueled by economic growth of essentially any type to an emphasis on **environmentally sustainable economic development.** This type of development uses **(1)** economic rewards (government subsidies, tax breaks, and emissions trading) to *encourage* environmentally beneficial and sustainable forms of economic development and **(2)** economic penalties (government taxes and reg-

ulations) to *discourage* environmentally harmful and unsustainable forms of economic growth.

According to Lester R. Brown, an environmental leader:

> *Some good news is that there is a growing worldwide recognition outside the environmental community that the economy we now have cannot take us where we want to go. Three decades ago, only environmental activists were speaking out on the need for a change to a more environmentally sustainable economy. Now the ranks of activists have broadened to include CEOs of major corporations, government ministers, prominent scientists, and intelligence agencies.*
>
> *The goal is to develop a new type of economy to replace our eventually unsustainable fossil fuel–based, automobile-centered, throwaway economy. This new eco-economy is a solar-powered, bicycle- and rail-centered, reuse and recycle economy that uses energy, water, land, and materials much more efficiently and wisely than we do today. In addition to helping sustain the earth's life-support systems, such an economy can lead to greater economic security, healthier lifestyles, and a worldwide improvement in the human condition.*

Implementing an *environmental or sustainability revolution* over the next 50 years involves shifting our efforts from

- Pollution cleanup to pollution prevention (cleaner production).

---

## Connections: Lessons from China

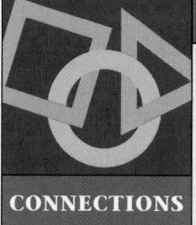

**CONNECTIONS**

China is the world's most populous country, with almost 1.3 billion people. Since 1980, it has also been the world's fastest growing economy—expanding more than fourfold between 1980 and 2002.

As incomes in China have risen, so has consumption of resources. Suppose that China could shift to the meat-based, fossil fuel–based, automobile-centered, high resource use and waste economy found in the United States. Environmental leader Lester R. Brown has estimated the following impacts on global resource consumption if per capita Chinese consumption of key

resources reached U.S. per capita levels:

- If China switched to an automobile economy and consumed oil at the U.S. rate, its annual oil consumption would be greater than what the entire world now produces each year.

- If China's per capita consumption of fossil fuels reached U.S. levels, global emissions of carbon dioxide would double and accelerate projected global warming.

- If annual per capita paper consumption in China reached the U.S. level, China would need more paper each year than the world currently produces.

According to Lester R. Brown, China is showing us why **(1)** it and

other industrializing countries cannot follow the industrialized model of today's industrialized countries, **(2)** the economies of the world's industrialized countries cannot be sustained in the long run, and **(3)** there is an urgent need for developed and developing countries alike to shift to more environmentally sustainable economies or eco-economies.

### Critical Thinking

What do you believe would be the three most important effects on your lifestyle if **(a)** we shifted to an environmentally sustainable economy over the next 50 years and **(b)** we do not shift to such an economy? Explain.

*Paul G. Hawken*

*Paul G. Hawken understands both business and ecology. In addition to founding Smith & Hawken, a retail company known for its environmental initiatives, he has written seven widely acclaimed books, including* Growing a Business *(1987),* The Ecology of Commerce *(1993),* Factor 10, The Next Industrial Revolution *(1998, with Amory and Hunter Lovins), and* Natural Capitalism *(1999, with Amory and Hunter Lovins). He produced and hosted* Growing a Business, *a series for public television shown nationwide on 210 stations and now shown in 115 countries.* The Ecology of Commerce *was hailed as the best business book of 1993 and one of the most important books of the 20th century. In 1987,* Inc. *magazine named Hawken one of the 12 best entrepreneurs of the 1980s, and in 1995 he was named by the* Utne Reader *as one of the 100 visionaries who could change our lives.*

Great ideas, in hindsight, seem obvious. The concept of natural capital is such an idea. *Natural capital* is the myriad necessary and valuable resources and ecological processes that we rely on to produce our food, products, and services.

The concept of natural capital is not a new one. Economists have long noted that natural capital is a factor in industrial production, but a marginal factor.

A new view is emerging: Our economic systems cannot long endure without taking the flow of renewable and nonrenewable resources [Figure 1-6] through economies into account. This revision of neoclassical economics, yet to be accepted by most mainstream academicians, provides business and public policy with a powerful new tool for the continued prosperity of business and the preservation and restoration of the earth's living natural systems.

Most Americans are filled with cornucopian fantasies of technological prowess, where human ingenuity bypasses natural limits and creates unimagined abundance. Optimism easily intertwines with the belief that nanotechnology, biotechnology, computers, and technologies yet to be developed will eliminate hunger, disease, and want.

Dreams of alleviating human suffering are worthy. However, they usually overlook the absolute necessity of fertile soil, ocean fisheries, a stable climate, biological diversity, and pure water, all of which we are degrading and none of which can be created by any human-made technology known or imagined.

In our pursuit of dominance over the natural world, we have not taken into account the basic principle that industrialism, for all its sophistication, is enormously inefficient with respect to resource use, energy use, and waste production. The hypotheses and theories of neoclassical economists originated in a time of resource abundance. Today it is difficult for many of these economists to understand that the success of linear industrial systems based on increasing economic growth by increasing the rate of flow of materials and energy through economic systems has laid the groundwork for the next stage in economic evolution.

This shift is profoundly biological. It involves incorporating the cycling of material resources that supports natural systems into our ways of making things and our ways of dealing with the waste matter produced by our current linear industrial systems. This shift is going to happen because cyclical industrial systems work better than linear ones. They close the loop and reincorporate wastes as part of the production cycle. There are no landfills in a cyclical society.

If there is so much inefficiency in our current system, why is it not more apparent? The inefficiencies are

- Waste disposal (mostly burial and burning) to waste prevention and reduction.

- Protecting species to protecting the places (habitats) where they live.

- Environmental degradation to environmental restoration.

- Increased resource use to more efficient (less wasteful) resource use.

- Population growth to population stabilization by decreasing birth rates.

The Solutions box (p. 18) gives some guidelines that various analysts have suggested for living more sustainably by working with the earth.

This chapter has presented an overview of the problems most environmentalists and many of the world's most prominent scientists believe we face and

their root causes. It has also summarized the controversy over how serious environmental problems are and described two opposing environmental worldviews. The rest of this book presents a more detailed analysis of these problems, the controversies they have created, and solutions proposed by analysts.

Try not to be overwhelmed or immobilized by the *bad environmental news* because there is also some *great environmental news.* We **(1)** have made immense progress in improving the human condition and dealing with many environmental problems, **(2)** are learning a great deal about how nature works and sustains itself, and **(3)** have numerous scientific, technological, and economic solutions available to deal with the environmental problems we face, as you will learn in this book.

The challenge is to make creative use of our economic and political systems to implement such masked by a financial system in which money, prices, and markets give us inaccurate information. Markets are not giving us correct information about how much our suburbs, cars, and plastic drinking water bottles truly cost based on the environmental harm they cause.

Instead, we are getting warning signals from the beleaguered airsheds and watersheds, the overworked and eroded soils, the life-degrading inner cities and rural counties, the breakdown of stability worldwide, and the conflicts based on shortages of water and some other resources in parts of the world. These feedbacks from nature are providing the information that our prices should give us but do not.

Prices do not give us good information for a simple reason: *improper accounting*. Natural capital has never been placed on the balance sheets of companies or the countries of the world. To paraphrase G. K. Chesterton, it could fairly be said that capitalism might be a good idea, but we have not tried it yet. Capitalism cannot be fully attained or practiced until we have an accurate balance sheet, as any accounting student will tell us.

As it stands, our economic system is based on accounting principles that would bankrupt a company. When natural capital is placed on the balance sheet, not as a free resource of infinite supply but as an integral and valuable part of the production process, everything changes. The nearly obsessive pursuit of improvement in *human productivity* becomes balanced by the need for improved *resource productivity*. Using more and more resources to make fewer people more productive flies in the face of what we need to improve our society and the environment. After all, it is people we have plenty of, so it is people we must use to reduce the flow of matter and energy resources through economies and the resulting pollution and loss of natural capital. Moving from linear industrial systems to cyclical ones that mimic nature accomplishes this.

Many people sincerely believe an economic system based on the integrity of natural systems is unworkable. To answer that concern, we may want to reverse the question and ask, "How have we created an economic system that tells us it is cheaper to destroy natural capital than to maintain it?" We know this is not the way to take care of our cars, houses, and bridges, but somehow we have managed to overlook a pricing system that discounts the future and sells off the past. Or to put it another way, "How did we create an economic system that confuses capital with income?"

Can we devise and implement a more rational economic system? I think so. It is right before us. It requires no new theories, only common sense. It is based on the simple but powerful proposition that *all capital must be valued*.

There may be no *right* way to value a forest or a river, but there is a *wrong* way, which is to give it little or no value. If we have doubts about how to value a 500-year-old tree, we need only ask how much it would cost to make a new one from scratch. Or a new river. Or a new atmosphere.

Our goal should be to estimate and integrate the worth of living systems into every aspect of our culture and commerce so that human systems mimic natural systems. Only if we do this can our cultures reflect growth and harmony rather than damage and discord.

**Critical Thinking**

If you were in charge of the world's economy, what are the three most important things you would do? Compare your answers with those of other members of your class.

solutions. This requires governments, businesses, and individuals to integrate social, economic, and environmental goals and policies in their decision making (Figure 1-13).

**Figure 1-13** Types of decision making in traditional and sustainable societies. The traditional decision making in most societies involves treating social, economic, and environmental issues separately (left). Environmentally sustainable development calls for integrating social, economic, and environmental issues and concepts to find *sustainable solutions* to problems (right).

**Traditional decision making**

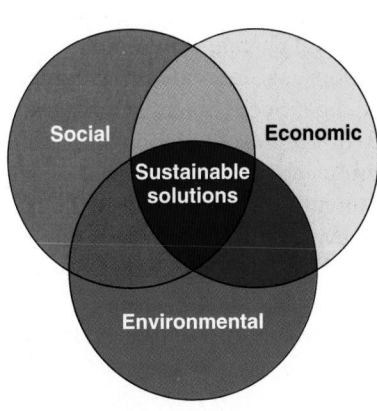

**Decision making in a sustainable society**

## Some Guidelines for Working with the Earth

**SOLUTIONS**

- Leave the earth in as good as or better shape than we found it.
- Take no more than we need.
- Try not to harm life, air, water, or soil.

- Sustain the variety of the earth's life-forms and the places (habitats) where they live (biodiversity).

- Help maintain the earth's capacity for self-repair and adaptation.

- Do not use renewable resources (soil, water, forests, grasslands, and wildlife) faster than they are replenished.

- Do not waste resources.

- Do not release pollutants into the environment faster than the earth's natural processes can dilute or recycle them.

- Emphasize pollution prevention and waste reduction.

- Slow the rate of population growth by decreasing birth rates.

- Have the market prices of all goods and services include all of their harmful environmental costs and thus tell the ecological truth.

- Reduce poverty.

See various chapters on the website for this book for specific ways you can work with the earth by trying to implement such guidelines.

### Critical Thinking

Which of these guidelines do you agree with and which do you disagree with? Why? Can you add any other guidelines?

---

*What's the use of a house if you don't have a decent planet to put it on?*

HENRY DAVID THOREAU

## REVIEW QUESTIONS

**1.** Define the boldfaced terms in this chapter.

**2.** What is *exponential growth?* Give two examples of exponential growth.

**3.** Distinguish among *environment, ecology,* and *environmental science.* Distinguish among *ecologists, environmental scientists, conservation biologists, environmentalists, preservationists, conservationists,* and *restorationists.*

**4.** Distinguish between *solar capital* and *natural capital (natural resources).*

**5.** What is an *environmentally sustainable society?* Distinguish between living on principal and living on interest, and relate this to the sustainability of **(a)** the earth's life-support system and **(b)** your lifestyle.

**6.** What is the main reason for the rapid growth of the world's population during the past 100 years? What are *doubling time* and the *rule of 70?* Use the rule of 70 to calculate how many years it would take for the population of a country to double if it was growing at 2% per year.

**7.** Define *economic growth, gross national income, gross national income purchasing power parity, gross domestic product, gross world product, per capita GNI, per capita GNI PPP,* and *economic development.* Distinguish between *developed countries* and *developing countries.*

**8.** List six pieces of *good news* about economic development. List nine pieces of *bad but challenging news* about economic development.

**9.** Why does it make sense for a poor family to have a large number of children? List six ways in which poverty is related to environmental quality, people's quality of life, and premature deaths of poor people.

**10.** Define *globalization* and list seven indicators of this phenomenon.

**11.** Distinguish among a *perpetual resource, renewable resource,* and *nonrenewable resource,* and give an example of each.

**12.** What are *sustainable yield* and *environmental degradation?* Give eight examples of environmental degradation.

**13.** Define and give three examples of *common-property resources.* What is the *tragedy of the commons?* Give three examples of this tragedy on a global scale, and explain how your lifestyle contributes to these examples. List three ways to deal with the tragedy of the commons.

**14.** Distinguish between a *physically depleted nonrenewable resource* and an *economically depleted nonrenewable resource.* Distinguish between *reuse* and *recycling.* Draw a depletion curve for a nonrenewable resource, and explain how recycling and reuse affect depletion time.

---

One key is to recognize that most economic and political change comes about as a result of individual actions and individuals acting together to bring about change. Social scientists suggest it only takes about 5–10% of the population of a country or of the world to bring about major social change. Anthropologist Margaret Mead summarized our potential for change: "Never doubt that a small group of thoughtful, committed citizens can change the world. Indeed, it is the only thing that ever has."

We live in exciting times during what might be called a *hinge of cultural history.* Indeed, if I had to pick a time to live, it would be the next 50 years as we face the challenge of developing more environmentally sustainable societies.

**15.** What is the *ecological footprint per person* and what useful information does it give us?

**16.** What is *pollution?* Distinguish between *point sources* and *nonpoint sources* of pollution. List three types of harm caused by pollution.

**17.** Distinguish between *pollution prevention (input pollution control)* and *pollution cleanup (output pollution control).* What are three problems with relying primarily on pollution cleanup? Why is pollution prevention better than pollution control? List two ways that governments can encourage both pollution prevention and pollution cleanup.

**18.** According to environmentalists, what are five basic causes of the environmental problems we face?

**19.** Describe a simple model of relationships between population, resource use per person, resource use technology, and overall environmental impact. How do these factors differ in developed and developing countries?

**20.** What is an *environmental worldview?* Distinguish between the *planetary management* and *environmental wisdom environmental worldviews.*

**21.** What is *environmentally sustainable economic development?* How does it differ from traditional economic growth and economic development?

**22.** List six major changes that environmentalists believe should take place over the next 50 years as part of an *environmental* or *sustainability revolution.* What are two important keys to bringing about such changes?

**23.** List 12 guidelines that environmentalists have suggested for working with the earth.

## CRITICAL THINKING

**1.** Do you believe the society you live in is on an unsustainable path? Explain. Do you believe it is possible for the society you live in to become a mostly sustainable society within the next 50 years? Explain.

**2.** Do you favor instituting policies designed to reduce population growth and stabilize **(a)** the size of the world's population as soon as possible and **(b)** the size of the population of the country where you live as soon as possible? Explain. If you agree that population stabilization is desirable, what three major policies would you implement to accomplish this goal?

**3.** Explain why you agree or disagree with the following propositions:
   **a.** The economic growth from high levels of resource use in developed countries provides money for more financial aid to developing countries for reducing pollution, environmental degradation, and poverty.
   **b.** Stabilizing population is not desirable because without more consumers, economic growth would stop.
   **c.** The world will never run out of renewable resources and most currently used nonrenewable resources because technological innovations will

produce substitutes, reduce resource waste, or allow use of lower grades of scarce nonrenewable resources.

**4.** List **(a)** three forms of economic growth you believe are environmentally unsustainable and **(b)** three forms you believe are environmentally sustainable.

**5.** When you read that at least 27,400 human beings die prematurely each day (19 per minute) from preventable malnutrition and infectious disease, do you **(a)** doubt whether it is true, **(b)** not want to think about it, **(c)** feel hopeless, **(d)** feel sad, **(e)** feel guilty, or **(f)** want to do something about this problem?

**6.** How do you feel when you read that **(1)** the average American consumes about 50 times more resources than the average Chinese citizen, **(2)** human activities lead to the premature extinction of at least 10 species per day, **(3)** humans have disturbed about 73% of the earth's habitable land (Figure 1-5, p. 7), and **(4)** human activities are projected to make the earth's climate warmer: **(a)** skeptical about their accuracy, **(b)** indifferent, **(c)** sad, **(d)** helpless, **(e)** guilty, **(f)** concerned, or **(g)** outraged? Which of these feelings help perpetuate such problems, and which can help alleviate these problems?

**7.** Do you agree or disagree with the five basic causes of environmental problems listed in Figure 1-10, p. 12? Explain. List any other root causes you believe should be added.

**8.** One of the tragic characters in Greek mythology is Cassandra. The god Apollo gave her the gift of being able to foretell the future but then added the curse that no one would believe her. Have the environmental problems we face been **(a)** overblown by prophets of doom (Cassandras) or **(b)** reduced in severity because enough people have listened to their warnings and acted to prevent the prophecies from coming true? Explain.

**9.** Explain why you agree or disagree with each of the following statements: **(a)** humans are superior to other forms of life, **(b)** humans are in charge of the earth, **(c)** all economic growth is good, **(d)** the value of other species depends only on whether they are useful to us, **(e)** because all species eventually become extinct we should not worry about whether our activities cause the premature extinction of a species, **(f)** all species have an inherent right to exist, **(g)** nature has an almost unlimited storehouse of resources for human use, **(h)** technology can solve our environmental problems, **(i)** I do not believe I have any obligation to future generations, and **(j)** I do not believe I have any obligation to other species.

**10.** Explain why you agree or disagree with each of the beliefs of **(a)** the planetary management worldview on p. 14 and **(b)** the environmental wisdom worldview on p. 15.

**11.** What are the basic beliefs of your environmental worldview? Are the beliefs of your environmental worldview consistent with your answers to question 9? Are your environmental actions consistent with your environmental worldview?

**12.** Do you believe your current lifestyle is sustainable? If your answer is no, explain why and list five things you could do now to make your lifestyle more sustainable. Which of these things do you actually plan to do?

## PROJECTS

**1.** What are the major resource and environmental problems in the city, town, or rural area where you live? Which of these problems affect you directly? Have these problems gotten better or worse during the last 10 years?

**2.** Roughly what percentages of key resources such as water, food, and energy used by your local community come from the following places: nearby, another state, or another country?

**3.** Make a list of the resources you truly need. Then make another list of the resources you use each day only because you want them. Finally, make a third list of resources you want and hope to use in the future. Compare your lists with those compiled by other members of your class, and relate the overall result to the tragedy of the commons (Connections, p. 11).

**4.** When the "World Scientists' Warning to Humanity" (p. 15) was released to the press, the television networks and major papers in the United States and Canada almost ignored it, with the *Washington Post* and the *New York Times* in the United States rejecting the story as not newsworthy. Use the library or Internet to see what the major news stories were in the *Washington Post* and the *New York Times* on November 18, 1992, and evaluate their importance relative to the "World Scientists' Warning to Humanity."

**5.** Use the library or the Internet to find out bibliographic information about *Lynton B. Caldwell, Barbara Ward, René Dubos,* and *Henry David Thoreau,* whose quotes appear at the beginning and end of this chapter.

**6.** Write two-page scenarios describing what your life and that of any children you choose to have might be like 50 years from now if **(a)** we continue on our present path or **(b)** we shift to more environmentally sustainable societies throughout most of the world.

**7.** Make a concept map of this chapter's major ideas using the section heads and subheads and the key terms (in boldface type). Look on the website for this book for information about making concept maps.

## INTERNET STUDY RESOURCES AND RESOURCES FOR FURTHER READING AND RESEARCH

The website for this book contains helpful study aids and many ideas for further reading and research. Log on to

www.info.brookscole.com/miller13

and click on the Chapter-by-Chapter area. Choose Chapter 1 and select a resource:

- Flash Cards allows you to test your mastery of the Terms and Concepts to Remember for this chapter.

- Tutorial Quizzes provides a multiple-choice practice quiz.

- Student Guide to InfoTrac will lead you to Critical Thinking Projects that use InfoTrac College Edition as a research tool.

- References lists the major books and articles consulted in writing this chapter.

- Hypercontents takes you to an extensive list of sites with news, research, and images related to individual sections of the chapter.

## INFOTRAC COLLEGE EDITION

Improve your skills with InfoTrac College Edition, a searchable online database of articles from more than 700 periodicals. Log on to

http://www.infotrac-college.com

or access InfoTrac through the website for this book. Try to find the following articles:

**1.** Clark, W. C. 2001. A transition toward sustainability. *Ecology Law Quarterly* 27: 1021. *Keywords:* "Clark" and "sustainability." This is a very comprehensive article that details how human society and its interaction with the environment must adjust to assure future sustainability.

**2.** Jones, K., A. Scholtz, and A. G. Lehmer. 2002. Rio+ 10′: Let the people be heard. *Earth Island Journal* 17: 12. *Keywords:* "Rio" and "sustainability" Ten years after the Rio Earth Summit, there appears to have been little action on the part of participating countries to realize the recommendation of the summit. In fact, we may actually be going in the other direction.

# 2 ENVIRONMENTAL HISTORY: AN OVERVIEW

## Near Extinction of the American Bison

In 1500, before Europeans settled North America, 30–60 million North American bison—commonly known as the buffalo—grazed the plains, prairies, and woodlands over much of the continent.

These animals were once so numerous that in 1832 a traveler wrote, "As far as my eye could reach the country seemed absolutely blackened by innumerable herds." A single herd on the move might thunder past for hours.

For centuries, several Native American tribes depended heavily on bison, and they typically killed only the animals needed for food, clothing, and shelter. The dried feces of these animals, known as "buffalo chips," were used as fuel. These Native Americans did not deplete the bison because they hunted only with lances and bows and arrows, and occasionally drove some bison over cliffs.

By 1906, however, the once vast range of the bison had shrunk to a tiny area, and the species had been driven nearly to extinction (Figure 2-1). How did this happen? First, settlers moving west after the Civil War upset the sustainable balance between Native Americans and bison. Several plains tribes traded bison skins to settlers for steel knives and firearms, which allowed them to kill more bison.

But it was the new settlers who caused the most relentless slaughter. As railroads spread westward in the late 1860s, railroad companies hired professional bison hunters—including Buffalo Bill Cody—to supply construction crews with meat. Passengers also gunned down bison from train windows for sport, leaving the carcasses to rot.

Commercial hunters shot millions of bison for their hides and tongues (considered a delicacy), leaving most of the meat to rot. "Bone pickers" collected the bleached bones that whitened the prairies and shipped them east to be ground up as fertilizer.

Farmers shot bison because they damaged crops, fences, telegraph poles, and sod houses. Ranchers killed them because they competed with cattle and sheep for pasture. The U.S. Army killed at least 12 million bison as part of its campaign to subdue the plains tribes by killing off their primary source of food.

Between 1870 and 1875, at least 2.5 million bison were slaughtered each year. Only 85 bison were left by 1892. They were given refuge in Yellowstone National Park and protected by an 1893 law that forbids the killing of wild animals in national parks.

In 1905, 16 people formed the American Bison Society to protect and rebuild the captive population. Soon thereafter, the federal government established the National Bison Range near Missoula, Montana. Today an estimated 200,000 bison survive, about 97% of them on privately owned ranches.

Some wildlife conservationists have suggested restoring large herds of bison on public lands in the North American plains. This idea has been strongly opposed by ranchers with permits to graze cattle and sheep on federally managed lands.

The history of humanity's relationships to the environment provides many important lessons that can help us deal with today's environmental problems and not repeat past mistakes.

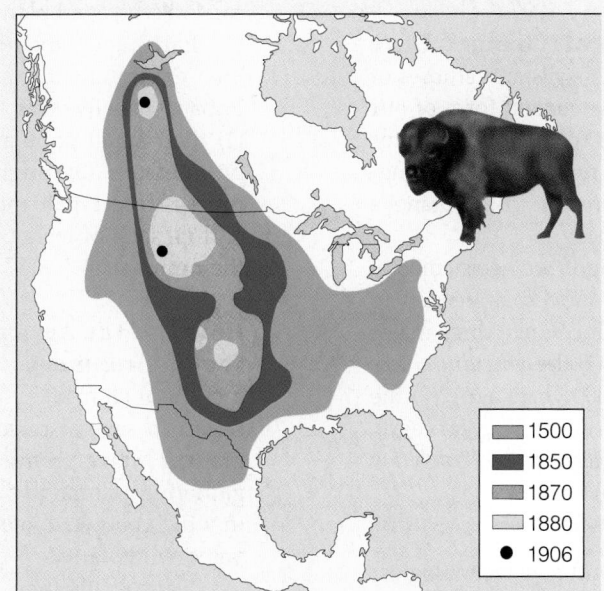

| | |
|---|---|
| ▨ | 1500 |
| ■ | 1850 |
| ▨ | 1870 |
| ▨ | 1880 |
| ● | 1906 |

**Figure 2-1** The historical range of the bison shrank severely between 1500 and 1906, mostly because of unregulated and deliberate overhunting.

*A continent ages quickly once we come.*

ERNEST HEMINGWAY

This chapter addresses the following questions:

- What major effects have hunter–gatherer societies, agricultural societies, and industrialized societies had on the environment? What might be the environmental impact of the current information and globalization revolution?

- What are the major phases in the history of land and wildlife conservation, public health, and environmental protection in the United States?

- What is Aldo Leopold's land ethic?

## 2-1 CULTURAL CHANGES AND THE ENVIRONMENT

**What Major Human Cultural Changes Have Taken Place?** Evidence from fossils and studies of ancient cultures suggests that the current form of our species, *Homo sapiens sapiens,* has walked the earth for only about 60,000 years (some recent evidence suggests 90,000–176,000 years), an instant in the planet's estimated 4.6-billion-year existence.

Until about 12,000 years ago, we were mostly hunter–gatherers who typically moved as needed to find enough food for survival. Since then, three major cultural changes have occurred: **(1)** the *agricultural revolution* (which began 10,000–12,000 years ago), **(2)** the *industrial revolution* (which began about 275 years ago), and **(3)** the *information and globalization revolution* (which began about 50 years ago).

These major cultural changes have

- Given us much more energy and new technologies with which to alter and control more of the planet to meet our basic needs and increasing wants.

- Allowed expansion of the human population, mostly because of increased food supplies and longer life spans.

- Increased our environmental impact because of increased resource use, pollution, and environmental degradation.

**How Did Ancient Hunting-and-Gathering Societies Affect the Environment** During most of our 60,000-year existence, we were **hunter–gatherers** who survived by collecting edible wild plant parts, hunting, fishing, and scavenging meat from animals killed by other predators. Our hunter–gatherer ancestors typically lived in small bands (of fewer than 50 people) who worked together to get enough food to survive. Many groups were nomadic, picking up their few possessions and moving seasonally from place to place to find enough food.

The earliest hunter–gatherers (and those still living this way today) survived through expert knowledge and understanding of their natural surroundings. They discovered **(1)** which plants and animals could be eaten and used as medicines, **(2)** where to find water, **(3)** how plant availability changed throughout the year, and **(4)** how some game animals migrated to get enough food. Because of a high infant mortality and an estimated average life span of 30–40 years, hunter–gatherer populations grew very slowly.

Advanced hunter–gatherers had a greater impact on their environment than did early hunter–gatherers. They **(1)** used more advanced tools and fire to convert forests into grasslands, **(2)** contributed to the extinction of some large animals (including the mastodon, saber-toothed tiger, giant sloth, cave bear, mammoth, and giant bison), and **(3)** altered the distribution of plants (and animals feeding on such plants) as they carried seeds and plants to new areas.

Early and advanced hunter–gatherers exploited their environment to survive. But their environmental impact usually was limited and local because of **(1)** their small population sizes, **(2)** low resource use per person, **(3)** migration, which allowed natural processes to repair most of the damage they caused, and **(4)** lack of technology that could have expanded their impact.

**How Has the Agricultural Revolution Affected the Environment?** Some 10,000–12,000 years ago, a cultural shift known as the **agricultural revolution** began in several regions of the world. It involved a gradual move from usually nomadic hunting-and-gathering groups to settled agricultural communities in which people domesticated wild animals and cultivated wild plants.

Plant cultivation probably developed in many areas, especially in the tropical forests of Southeast Asia, northeast Africa, and Mexico. People discovered how to grow various wild food plants from roots or tubers (fleshy underground stems). To prepare the land for planting, they cleared small patches of tropical forests by cutting down trees and other vegetation and then burning the underbrush (Figure 2-2). The ashes fertilized the often nutrient-poor soils in this **slash-and-burn cultivation.**

Early growers also used various forms of **shifting cultivation** (Figure 2-2), primarily in tropical regions. After a plot had been used for several years, the soil became depleted of nutrients or reinvaded by the forest. Then the growers cleared a new plot. They learned that each abandoned patch normally had to be left fallow (unplanted) for 10–30 years before the soil became fertile enough to grow crops again. While patches were regenerating, growers used them for tree crops, medicines, fuelwood, and other purposes. In this manner, most early growers practiced *sustainable cultivation.*

**Figure 2-2** The first crop-growing technique may have been a combination of slash-and-burn and shifting cultivation in tropical forests. This method is sustainable only if small plots of the forest are cleared, cultivated for no more than 5 years, and then allowed to regenerate for 10–30 years to renew soil fertility. Indigenous cultures have developed many variations of this technique and have found ways to use some former plots nondestructively while they are being regenerated.

These early farmers had fairly little impact on the environment because **(1)** their dependence mostly on human muscle power and crude stone or stick tools meant they could cultivate only small plots, **(2)** their population size and density were low, and **(3)** normally enough land was available so they could move to other areas and leave abandoned plots unplanted for the several decades needed to restore soil fertility. The gradual shift from hunting and gathering to farming had several significant effects (Connections, p. 24).

**How Has the Industrial Revolution Affected the Environment?** The next cultural shift, the **industrial revolution,** began in England in the mid-1700s and spread to the United States in the 1800s. It led to a rapid expansion in the production, trade, and distribution of material goods.

The industrial revolution represented a shift from dependence on **(1)** *renewable* wood (with supplies dwindling in some areas because of unsustainable cutting) and flowing water to **(2)** dependence on ma-

chines running on *nonrenewable* fossil fuels (first coal and later oil and natural gas). This led to a switch from small-scale, localized production of handmade goods to large-scale production of machine-made goods in centralized factories in rapidly growing industrial cities.

Factory towns grew into cities as rural people came to the factories for work. There they worked long hours under noisy, dirty, and hazardous conditions. Other workers toiled in dangerous coal mines. In these early industrial cities, coal smoke belching out of chimneys was so heavy that many people died prematurely of lung ailments. Ash and soot covered everything, and on some days the smoke was so thick that it blotted out the sun.

Fossil fuel–powered farm machinery, commercial fertilizers, and new plant-breeding techniques increased per acre crop yields. This helped protect biodiversity by reducing the need to expand the area of cropland to grow food. Because fewer farmers were needed, more people migrated to cities. With a larger

## Consequences of the Agricultural Revolution

Here are some of the beneficial and harmful effects of the agricultural revolution:

■ *Using domesticated animals to plow fields, haul loads, and perform other tasks increased the ability to expand agriculture and support more people.*

■ *People* **(1)** *cut down vast forests to supply wood for fuel and building materials,* **(2)** *plowed up large expanses of grassland to grow crops, and* **(3)** *built irrigation systems to transfer water from one place to another.* Such extensive land clearing degraded or destroyed the habitats of many wild plants and animals, causing or hastening their extinction.

■ *Soil erosion, salt buildup in irrigated soils, and overgrazing of grasslands by huge herds of livestock helped turn fertile land into desert; topsoil washed into streams, lakes, and irrigation canals.* This environmental degradation was a factor in the downfall of many great civilizations in the Middle East, North Africa, and the Mediterranean.

■ *People began accumulating material goods.* Nomadic hunter–gatherers could not carry many possessions in their travels, but farmers living in one place could acquire as much as they could afford.

■ *Farmers could grow more than enough food for their families.* They could store the excess for emergencies or use it to barter for other goods and services.

■ *Urbanization—the formation of villages, towns, and cities—became practical.* Some villages grew into towns and cities, which served as centers for trade, government, and religion. Towns and cities concentrated sewage and other wastes, polluted the air and water, and greatly increased the spread of diseases.

■ *Increased production and use of material goods created growing volumes of waste and pollution.*

■ *Conflict between societies became more common as ownership of land and water rights became a crucial economic issue.* Armies and their leaders rose to power and conquered large areas of land and water supplies. These rulers forced powerless people (slaves and landless peasants) to do the hard, disagreeable work of producing food and constructing irrigation systems, temples, and walled fortresses.

■ *The survival of wild plants and animals, once vital to humanity, became less important.* Wild animals, which competed with livestock for grass and fed on crops, became enemies to be killed or driven from their habitats. Wild plants invading cropfields became weeds to be eliminated.

### Critical Thinking

Would we be better off if agricultural practices had never been developed and we were still hunter–gatherers? Explain.

---

and more reliable food supply and longer life spans, the size of the human population began the sharp increase that continues today (Figure 1-1, p. 2, and Figure 1-2, p. 4).

After World War I (1914–18), more efficient machines and mass production techniques were developed. These technologies became the basis of today's advanced industrial societies in places such as the United States, Canada, Japan, Australia, and western Europe. Advanced industrial societies have provided numerous benefits along with environmental problems (Connections, p. 25).

**How Might the Information and Globalization Revolution Affect the Environment?** We are in the midst of a new cultural shift, the **information and globalization revolution,** in which new technologies such as the telephone, radio, television, computers, the Internet, automated databases, and remote sensing satellites mean we have increasingly rapid access to much more information on a global scale. Scientific information now doubles about every 12 years, and general information doubles about every 2.5 years. The World Wide Web contains at least 1 billion electronic pages and grows by roughly a million electronic pages per day.

This new cultural revolution can have beneficial and harmful environmental effects. On the *positive side,* today's information technologies

■ Help us understand more about how the earth, economies, and other complex systems work and how such systems might be affected by our actions.

■ Allow us to respond to environmental problems more effectively and rapidly.

■ Allow us to use remote sensing satellites to survey resources and monitor changes in the world's forests, grasslands, oceans, rivers, polar regions, cities, and other systems.

■ Enable us to develop sophisticated computer models and computer-generated maps of the earth's environmental systems.

■ Can reduce pollution and environmental degradation by substituting data for materials and energy and communication for transportation.

On the *negative side,* information technologies

■ Provide an overload of information.

■ Cause confusion, distraction, and a sense of hopelessness as we try to identify useful environmental information and ideas in a rapidly growing sea of information.

■ Increase environmental degradation and decrease cultural diversity as a globalized economy spreads over most of the earth and homogenizes the world's cultures.

## 2-2 ENVIRONMENTAL HISTORY OF THE UNITED STATES: THE TRIBAL AND FRONTIER ERAS

**What Happened During the Tribal Era?** The environmental history of the United States can be divided into four eras: **(1)** tribal, **(2)** frontier, **(3)** conservation, and **(4)** environmental.

During the *tribal era*, North America was occupied by 5–10 million tribal people for at least 10,000 years before European settlers began arriving in the early 1600s. These indigenous people, called Indians by the Europeans and now often called Native Americans, practiced hunting and gathering, burned and cleared fields, and planted crops. Because of their small populations and simple technology, they had a fairly low environmental impact.

With some exceptions, most Native American cultures had a deep respect for the land and its animals and did not believe in land ownership, as indicated by these quotes:

> *My people, the Blackfeet Indians, have always had a sense of reverence for nature that made us want to move through the world carefully, leaving as little mark behind as possible. (Jamake Highwater, Blackfoot)*

> *From our childhood we are taught that the animals and even the trees and other plants that we share a place with are our brothers and sisters. So when we speak of land, we are not speaking of property, territory, or even a piece of property upon which our houses sit and our crops are grown. We are speaking of something truly sacred. (Jimmie Durham, Cherokee)*

**What Happened During the Frontier Era (1607–1890)?** The frontier era began in the early 1600s when European colonists began settling North America. Faced with a continent containing seemingly inexhaustible forest and wildlife resources and rich soils, the early colonists developed a **frontier environmental worldview.** They viewed most of the continent as a wilderness to be conquered by clearing and planting and with vast resources. Forests were cleared not only for timber and cropland but also because they were seen as a hostile wilderness full of dangerous savages and wild beasts.

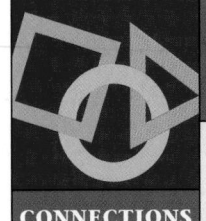

## CONNECTIONS

# Consequences of Advanced Industrial Societies

The *good news* is that advanced industrial societies provide a variety of benefits to most people living in them, including

■ Mass production of many useful and affordable products

■ A sharp increase in agricultural productivity

■ Lower infant mortality and longer life expectancy because of better sanitation, hygiene, nutrition, and medical care

■ A decrease in the rate of population growth

■ Better health, birth control methods, and education

■ Methods for controlling pollution

■ Greater average income and old-age security

However, the *bad news* is the resource and environmental problems we face today (Figure 1-9, p. 12), mostly because of the rise of advanced industrial societies.

### Critical Thinking

**1.** On balance, do you believe the advantages of the industrial revolution have outweighed its disadvantages? Explain.

**2.** What three major things would you do to reduce the harmful environmental impacts of advanced industrial societies?

This frontier environmental worldview contrasted sharply with that of some Native American cultures. According to Luther Standing Bear, a Sioux, "Only to the white man was nature a 'wilderness' and only to him was the land infested with 'wild animals' and 'savage' people. To us it was tame and bountiful."

Another factor accelerating settling of the continent and use of its resources was the transfer of vast areas of public land to private interests between 1850 and 1900. In 1850, the U.S. government owned about 80% of the total land area of the territorial United States. Tribal cultures occupied about 4% of the land, mostly in reservations designated by the government.

By 1900, more than half of the country's public land had been given away or sold cheaply to railroad, timber, and mining companies, land developers, states, schools, universities, and homesteaders to encourage settlement across the country. Under the Homestead Act of 1862, each qualified settler in the Great Plains was given 65 hectares (160 acres) of land free of charge.

This frontier environmental view prevailed for more than 280 years, until the government declared the frontier officially closed in 1890. However, this frontier environmental worldview remains part of American culture.

## 2-3 ENVIRONMENTAL HISTORY OF THE UNITED STATES: THE EARLY CONSERVATION ERA (1832–1960)

**Who Were Some Early Conservationists (1832–70)?** Between 1832 and 1870, some people became alarmed at the scope of resource depletion and degradation in the United States. They urged that part of the unspoiled wilderness on public lands owned jointly by all people (but managed by the government) be protected as a legacy to future generations.

Two of these early conservationists were *Henry David Thoreau* (1817–62) and *George Perkins Marsh* (1812–1939). Thoreau (Figure 2-3) was alarmed at the loss of numerous wild species from his native eastern Massachusetts. To gain a better understanding of nature, he built a cabin in the woods on Walden Pond near Concord, Massachusetts, lived there alone for 2 years, and wrote *Life in the Woods,* an environmental classic.

In 1864, George Perkins Marsh, a scientist and member of congress from Vermont, published *Man and Nature,* which helped legislators and influential citizens see the need for resource conservation. Marsh **(1)** questioned the idea that the country's resources were inexhaustible, **(2)** used scientific studies and case studies to show how the rise and fall of past civilizations were linked to the use and misuse of their resource base, and **(3)** formulated basic resource conservation principles we still use today.

**What Happened Between 1870 and 1930?** Between 1870 and 1930, a number of actions increased the role of the federal government and private citizens in resource conservation and public health (Figure 2-4). The *Forest Reserve Act of 1891* was a turning point in establishing the responsibility of the federal government for protecting public lands from resource exploitation.

In 1892, nature preservationist and activist *John Muir* (Figure 2-5) founded the Sierra Club. He became the leader of the *preservationist movement,* advocating the protection of large areas of wilderness on public lands from human exploitation, except for low-impact recreational activities such as hiking and camping. This idea was not enacted into law until 1964. He also proposed and lobbied for creation of a national park system on public lands, an idea that became law in 1916 (two years after his death).

**Figure 2-3** Henry David Thoreau (1817–62) was an American writer and naturalist who kept journals about his excursions into wild nature throughout parts of the northeastern United States and Canada and at Walden Pond in Massachusetts. He sought self-sufficiency, a simple lifestyle, and a harmonious coexistence with nature.

Mostly because of political opposition, effective protection of forests and wildlife did not begin until *Theodore Roosevelt* (Figure 2-6, p. 28), an ardent conservationist, became president. His term of office, 1901–9, has been called the country's *Golden Age of Conservation.* Some of his major contributions to conservation include the following:

- Persuading Congress to give the president power to designate public land as federal wildlife refuges
- Establishing the first federal refuge at Pelican Island off the east coast of Florida for preservation of the endangered brown pelican in 1903 and adding 35 more reserves by 1904
- Designating the Grand Canyon as one of the first 16 national parks
- More than tripling the size of the national forest reserves

In 1905, Congress created the *U.S. Forest Service* to manage and protect the forest reserves. Roosevelt appointed *Gifford Pinchot* (1865–1946) as its first chief. Pinchot pioneered scientific management of forest resources on public lands, using the principles of **(1)** *sustainable yield* (cutting trees no faster than they could regenerate) and **(2)** *multiple use* (using the lands for a variety of purposes, including resource extraction, recreation, and wildlife protection).

In 1906, Congress passed the *Antiquities Act,* which allows the president to protect areas of scientific or historical interest on federal lands as national monuments. Roosevelt then used this act to protect the Grand Canyon and other areas that would later become national parks.

In 1907, Congress, upset because Roosevelt had added vast tracts to the forest reserves, banned further executive withdrawals of public forests. On the day before the bill became law, Roosevelt defiantly reserved another 6.5 million hectares (16 million acres).

Early in the 20th century, the U.S. conservation movement split over how to use the beautiful Hetch

**1891–97** Timber cutting banned on large tracts of public land.

**1920–27** Public health boards established in most cities.

| 1870s | 1880s | 1890s | 1900s | 1910s | 1920s |

**1880** Killer fog in London kills 700 people.

**1893** Few remaining American bison given refuge in Yellowstone National Park.

**1918** Migratory Bird Act restricts hunting of migratory birds.

**1872** Yellowstone National Park established. American Forestry Association organized by private citizens to protect forests. American Public Health Association formed.

**1892** Sierra Club founded by John Muir to promote increased preservation of public land. Killer fog in London kills 1,000 people.

**1916** National Park Service Act creates National Park System and National Park Service.

**1915** Ecologists form Ecological Society of America.

**1870** First official wildlife refuge established at Lake Merritt, California.

**1891** Forest Reserve Act authorized the president to set aside forest reserves.

**1912** Public Health Service Act authorizes government investigation of water pollution.

**1911** Weeks Act allows Forest Service to purchase land at headwaters of navigable streams as part of National Forest System.

**1908** Swedish chemist Svante Arrhenius argues that increased emissions from burning fossil fuels will lead to global warming.

**1890** Government declares the country's frontier closed. Yosemite National Park established.

**1906** Antiquities Act allows president to set aside areas on federal lands as national monuments. Pure Food and Drug Act enacted.

**1905** U.S. Forest Service created. Audubon Society founded by private citizens to preserve country's bird species.

**1904** Child lead poisoning linked to lead-based paints.

**1903** First National Wildlife Refuge at Pelican Island, Florida, established by president Theodore Roosevelt.

**1902** Reclamation Act promotes irrigation and water development projects in arid West.

**1900** Lacey Act bans interstate shipment of birds killed in violation of state laws.

**Figure 2-4** Examples of the increased role of the federal government in resource conservation and public health and establishment of key private environmental groups, 1870–1930.

Hetchy Valley (in what is now Yosemite National Park) (Spotlight, p. 32). The *wise-use,* or *conservationist,* school, led by Roosevelt and Pinchot, believed all public lands should be managed wisely and scientifically to provide needed resources. The *preservationist* school, led by Muir (Figure 2-5), wanted wilderness areas on public lands to be left untouched. This controversy over use of public lands continues today.

In 1916, Congress passed the *National Park Service Act,* which **(1)** declared the parks were to be maintained in a manner that leaves them unimpaired for future generations and **(2)** established the National Park Service (within the Department of the Interior) to manage the system. Under its first head, Stephen T. Mather (1867–1930), the dominant park policy was to

**Figure 2-5** John Muir (1838–1914) was a geologist, explorer, and naturalist. He spent 6 years studying, writing journals, and making sketches in the wilderness of California's Yosemite Valley and then went on to explore wilderness areas in Utah, Nevada, the Northwest, and Alaska. He was largely responsible for establishing Yosemite National Park in 1890. He also founded the Sierra Club and spent 22 years lobbying actively for conservation laws.

**Figure 2-6** Theodore ("Teddy") Roosevelt (1858–1919) was a writer, explorer, naturalist, avid birdwatcher, and 26th president of the United States. He was the first national political figure to bring the issues of conservation to the attention of the American public. According to many historians, he has contributed more than any other president to natural resource conservation in the United States.

encourage tourist visits by allowing private concessionaires to operate facilities within the parks.

During the early 1900s, women such as *Jane Addams* (1860–1935) and *Alice Hamilton* (Individuals Matter, below) led efforts to improve public health (Figure 2-4).

After World War I (1914–18), the country entered a new era of economic growth and expansion. During the Harding, Coolidge, and Hoover administrations, the federal government promoted increased resource removal from public lands at low prices to stimulate economic growth.

President Hoover went even further and proposed that the federal government return all remaining federal lands to the states or sell them to private interests for economic development. But the Great Depression (1929–41) made owning such lands unattractive to state governments and private investors.

**What Happened Between 1930 and 1960?** A second wave of national resource conservation and improvements in public health began in the early 1930s (Figure 2-7) as President *Franklin D. Roosevelt* (1882–1945) strove to bring the country out of the Great Depression. Massive federal government programs designed to provide jobs and restore the environment included

- Low-cost purchase of large tracts of public land from cash-poor landowners.

- The *Civilian Conservation Corps* (CCC), established in 1933 to put 2 million unemployed people to work **(1)** planting trees, **(2)** developing and maintaining parks and recreation areas, **(3)** restoring silted waterways, **(4)** building levees and dams for flood control, **(5)** controlling soil erosion, and **(6)** protecting wildlife.

- Establishing the *Tennessee Valley Authority* (TVA) to provide jobs, replant forests, and build dams for flood control and hydroelectric power in the economically depressed Tennessee Valley.

## Alice Hamilton

INDIVIDUALS MATTER

Alice Hamilton (1869–1970) was the country's first influential expert in industrial medicine. After graduating from medical school, she became professor of pathology at the Woman's Medical School of Northwestern University in Chicago, Illinois. She became interested in the neglected and poorly understood field of industrial medicine after hearing numerous stories about health hazards in stockyards and factories.

Hamilton began investigating various hazardous industries. Despite little information, company resistance, and workers' failure to report health problems for fear of losing their jobs, Hamilton's persistence and resourcefulness as a researcher paid off. During the next several decades she became the country's leading investigator of occupational hazards.

In 1919, Hamilton was appointed assistant professor of industrial medicine at Harvard University, the first teaching appointment of a woman at this institution. In the 1920s, she published her classic text *Industrial Poisons in the United States* and became the country's most effective advocate for investigating and dealing with the environmental consequences of industrial activity.

Four decades before the widespread concern about pesticides and other industrial chemicals in the 1960s and 1970s, Hamilton was warning workers of their exposure to a variety of new chemicals whose effects on human health were unknown.

She unsuccessfully opposed the use of tetraethyl lead in gasoline in the 1920s, arguing that no exposure to lead is safe. Her position was vindicated in the late 1980s, when tetraethyl lead was phased out of gasoline in the United States. Her efforts were also instrumental in the introduction of workers' compensation laws.

Alice Hamilton was a strong advocate of *pollution prevention*. In a 1925 article she expressed the hope "that the day is not far off when we shall take the next step and investigate a new danger in industry before it is put to use, before any fatal harm has been done."

Alice Hamilton (1869–1970) was the first and foremost expert on industrial disease in the United States.

**Figure 2-7** Some important conservation and environmental events between 1930 and 1960.

- Building and operating many large dams in the arid western states, including Hoover Dam on the Colorado River, to provide jobs, flood control, cheap irrigation water, and cheap electricity for industry.

- Enacting the Soil Conservation Act of 1935, which established the *Soil Erosion Service* as part of the Department of Agriculture to correct the enormous erosion problems that had ruined many farms in the Great Plains states. Its name was later changed to the *Soil Conservation Service*, and it is now called the *Natural Resources Conservation Service*.

Federal resource conservation and public health policy during the 1940s and 1950s changed little, mostly because of preoccupation with World War II (1941–45) and economic recovery after the war.

Between 1933 and 1960, improvements in public health included **(1)** establishment of public health boards and agencies at the municipal, state, and federal levels, **(2)** increased public education about health issues, **(3)** introduction of vaccination programs, and **(4)** a sharp reduction in waterborne infectious disease, mostly because of improved sanitation and garbage collection.

## 2-4 ENVIRONMENTAL HISTORY OF THE UNITED STATES: THE ENVIRONMENTAL ERA (1960–2002)

**What Happened During the 1960s?** A number of important milestones in American environmental history occurred during the 1960s (Figure 2-8, p. 30). In 1962, biologist *Rachel Carson* (1907–64) published *Silent Spring*, which documented the pollution of air, water, and wildlife from pesticides such as DDT (Individuals Matter, p. 33). This influential book helped broaden the concept of resource conservation to include preservation of the *quality* of the air, water, soil, and wildlife.

Many historians mark this wake-up call as the beginning of the modern **environmental movement,** in which a growing number of citizens organized to demand that political leaders enact laws and develop policies to **(1)** curtail pollution, **(2)** clean up polluted environments, and **(3)** protect pristine areas from environmental degradation.

In 1964, Congress passed the *Wilderness Act,* inspired by the vision of John Muir more than 80 years earlier. The act authorized the government to protect

**Figure 2-8** Some important environmental events during the 1960s.

undeveloped tracts of public land as part of the National Wilderness System, unless Congress later decides they are needed for the national good. Land in this system is to be used only for nondestructive forms of recreation such as hiking and camping.

Between 1965 and 1970, the emerging science of *ecology* received widespread media attention. At the same time, the popular writings of biologists such as *Paul Ehrlich, Barry Commoner,* and *Garrett Hardin* awakened people to the interlocking relationships among population growth, resource use, and pollution (Figure 1-11, p. 13).

During that same period, a number of events increased public awareness of pollution (Figure 2-8). The public also became aware that pollution and loss of habitat were endangering well-known wildlife species such as the North American bald eagle, grizzly bear, whooping crane, and peregrine falcon.

During the 1969 U.S. *Apollo* mission to the moon, the astronauts photographed the earth from space, and we saw our tiny blue and white planet in the black void of space (Figure 1-1, p. 2). This widely publicized photo led to the development of the *spaceship-earth environmental worldview*, reminding us that we had better take care of the earth because it the only home we have.

**What Happened During the 1970s?** Media attention, public concern about environmental problems, scientific research, and action to address these concerns grew rapidly during the 1970s, sometimes called the *first decade of the environment*. Figure 2-9 summarizes some important events during this decade.

The first annual *Earth Day* was held on April 20, 1970. During this event, proposed by Senator *Gaylord Nelson* (born 1916), some 20 million people in more than 2,000 communities took to the streets to heighten awareness and to demand improvements in environmental quality.

President *Richard Nixon* (1913–94) responded to the rapidly growing environmental movement by **(1)** establishing the *Environmental Protection Agency* (EPA) in 1970 and **(2)** supporting passage of the *Endangered Species Act of 1973*, which greatly strengthened the role of the federal government in protecting endangered species.

An eye-opening event occurred in 1973 when the Arab members of the Organization of Petroleum Exporting Countries (OPEC)* reduced oil exports to the West and banned oil shipments to the United States because of its support for Israel in the 18-day Yom Kippur War with Egypt and Syria. This *OPEC oil embargo,* lasting until March 1974, sharply raised the

*OPEC was formed in 1960 so developing countries with much of the world's known and projected oil supplies could get a higher price for this resource. Today its members are Algeria, Indonesia, Iran, Iraq, Kuwait, Libya, Nigeria, Qatar, Saudi Arabia, the United Arab Emirates, and Venezuela. In 1973, OPEC produced 56% of the world's oil and supplied about 84% of all oil imported by other countries.

price of crude oil. The result was **(1)** double-digit inflation in the United States and many other countries, **(2)** high interest rates, **(3)** soaring international debt, and **(4)** a global economic recession. In 1979, a second reduction in oil supplies and a sharp price increase occurred when Iran's Islamic Revolution shut down most of Iran's oil production.

In 1978, the *Federal Land Policy and Management Act* gave the *Bureau of Land Management (BLM)* its first real authority to manage the public land under its control, 85% of which is in 12 western states. This law angered a number of western interests whose use of these lands was restricted for the first time. In the late 1970s, a coalition of ranchers, miners, loggers, developers, farmers, some elected officials, and others launched a political campaign known as the *sagebrush rebellion* against government regulation of the use of public lands. Its primary goal was to remove most

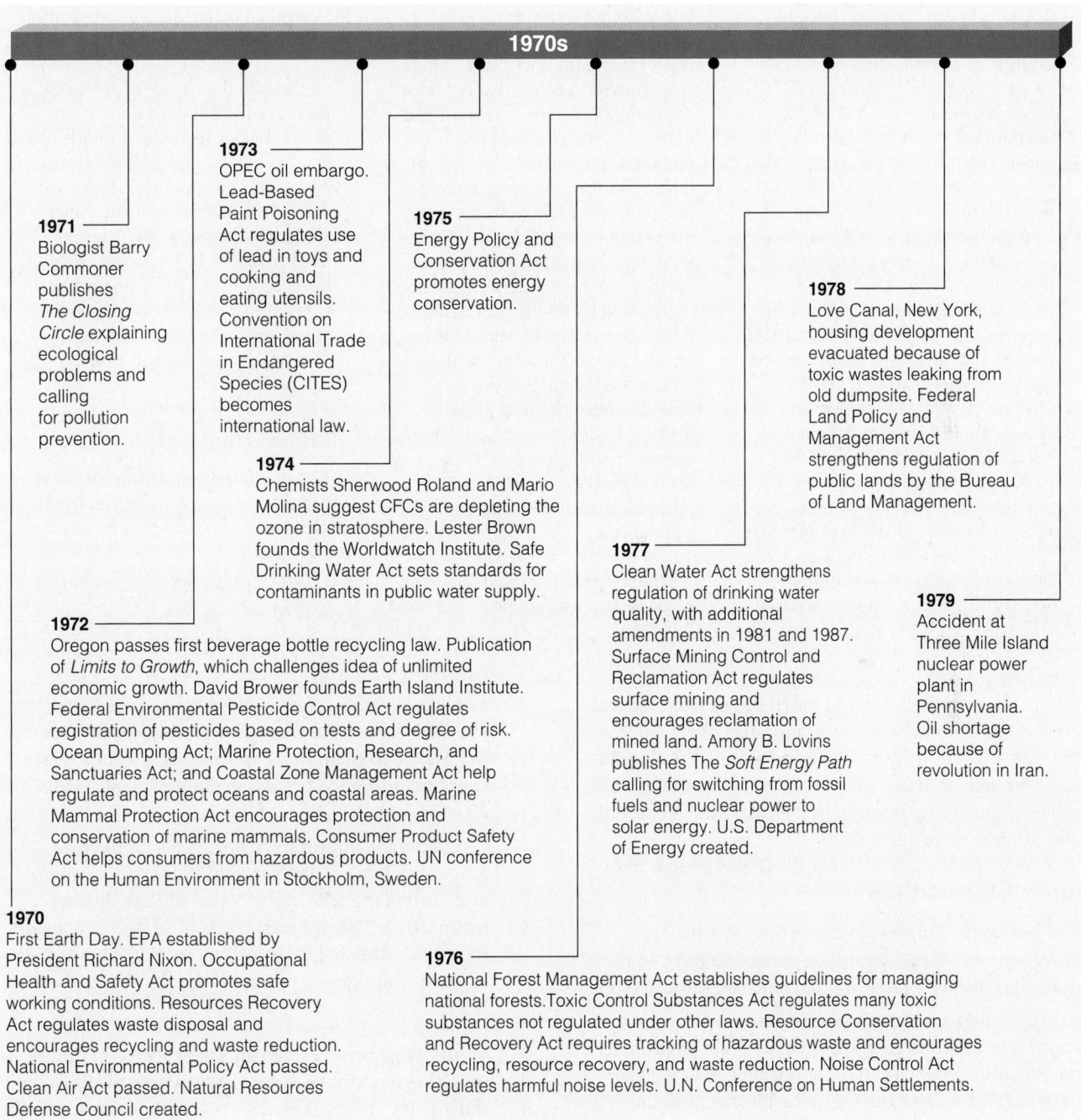

**1970s**

**1971**
Biologist Barry Commoner publishes *The Closing Circle* explaining ecological problems and calling for pollution prevention.

**1973**
OPEC oil embargo. Lead-Based Paint Poisoning Act regulates use of lead in toys and cooking and eating utensils. Convention on International Trade in Endangered Species (CITES) becomes international law.

**1975**
Energy Policy and Conservation Act promotes energy conservation.

**1978**
Love Canal, New York, housing development evacuated because of toxic wastes leaking from old dumpsite. Federal Land Policy and Management Act strengthens regulation of public lands by the Bureau of Land Management.

**1974**
Chemists Sherwood Roland and Mario Molina suggest CFCs are depleting the ozone in stratosphere. Lester Brown founds the Worldwatch Institute. Safe Drinking Water Act sets standards for contaminants in public water supply.

**1977**
Clean Water Act strengthens regulation of drinking water quality, with additional amendments in 1981 and 1987. Surface Mining Control and Reclamation Act regulates surface mining and encourages reclamation of mined land. Amory B. Lovins publishes The *Soft Energy Path* calling for switching from fossil fuels and nuclear power to solar energy. U.S. Department of Energy created.

**1979**
Accident at Three Mile Island nuclear power plant in Pennsylvania. Oil shortage because of revolution in Iran.

**1972**
Oregon passes first beverage bottle recycling law. Publication of *Limits to Growth*, which challenges idea of unlimited economic growth. David Brower founds Earth Island Institute. Federal Environmental Pesticide Control Act regulates registration of pesticides based on tests and degree of risk. Ocean Dumping Act; Marine Protection, Research, and Sanctuaries Act; and Coastal Zone Management Act help regulate and protect oceans and coastal areas. Marine Mammal Protection Act encourages protection and conservation of marine mammals. Consumer Product Safety Act helps consumers from hazardous products. UN conference on the Human Environment in Stockholm, Sweden.

**1970**
First Earth Day. EPA established by President Richard Nixon. Occupational Health and Safety Act promotes safe working conditions. Resources Recovery Act regulates waste disposal and encourages recycling and waste reduction. National Environmental Policy Act passed. Clean Air Act passed. Natural Resources Defense Council created.

**1976**
National Forest Management Act establishes guidelines for managing national forests.Toxic Control Substances Act regulates many toxic substances not regulated under other laws. Resource Conservation and Recovery Act requires tracking of hazardous waste and encourages recycling, resource recovery, and waste reduction. Noise Control Act regulates harmful noise levels. U.N. Conference on Human Settlements.

**Figure 2-9** Some important environmental events during the 1970s, sometimes called the *environmental decade.*

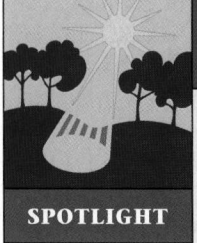
## How Should Public Land Resources Be Used? Preservationists vs. Conservationists

In 1901, conservationists, led by Gifford Pinchot and San Francisco mayor James D. Phelan, proposed to dam the Tuolumne River running through Hetch Hetchy Valley to supply drinking water for San Francisco. Preservationists, led by John Muir (Figure 2-5), were opposed.

After a bitter 12-year battle, Pinchot's views won, and in 1913 the dam was built and the valley was flooded. Today the controversy continues, with preservationists pressing to have the dam removed.

*Preservationists* would keep large areas of public lands untouched so they can be enjoyed today and passed on unspoiled to future generations. After Muir's death in 1914, preservationists were led by forester *Aldo Leopold* (Figure 2-12, p. 36), who said the role of the human species should be to protect nature, not conquer it (Section 2-5, p. 36).

Another effective supporter of wilderness preservation was *Robert Marshall* (1901–39) of the U.S. Forest Service. In 1935, he and Leopold founded the Wilderness Society. More recent preservationist leaders include **(1)** *David Brower* (1912–2000), former head of the Sierra Club and founder of both Friends of the Earth and Earth Island Institute, and **(2)** *Howard Zahniser* (1906–64), who as head of the Wilderness Society helped draft the Wilderness Act of 1964 and lobby Congress for its passage.

In contrast, *conservationists* see wilderness and other public lands as resources to be used to enhance the nation's economic growth and to provide the greatest benefit to the greatest number of people. In their view the government should protect these lands from harm by managing them efficiently and scientifically, using the principles of sustainable yield and multiple use.

Roosevelt and Pinchot thought conservation experts should form an elite corps of resource managers within the federal bureaucracy. Shielded from political pressure, they could develop scientific management strategies. Pinchot angered Muir and other preservationists when he stated his "wise-use" principle:

*The first great fact about conservation is that it stands for development.*

*There has been a fundamental misconception that conservation means nothing but the husbanding of resources for future generations. There could be no more serious mistake.... The first principle of conservation is the use of the natural resources now existing on this continent for the benefit of the people who live here now.*

Despite their basic differences, both groups opposed delivering public resources into the hands of a few for private profit. Both groups have been disappointed. Since 1910 rights to extract water and minerals, graze livestock, and harvest trees from public lands routinely have been given away or sold by Congress at below-market prices to large corporate farms, ranches, mining companies, and timber companies.

### Critical Thinking

**1.** Why do the conservationist and preservationist philosophies lead to different management practices for public lands?

**2.** Which philosophy do you favor? Explain.

---

public lands in the western United States from federal ownership and management and turn them over to the states. Then the plan was to persuade state legislatures to sell or lease the resource-rich lands at low prices to ranching, mining, timber, land development, and other private interests.

When *Jimmy Carter* (born 1924) was president between 1977 and 1981, he

- Persuaded Congress to create the *Department of Energy* to develop a long-range energy strategy to reduce the country's heavy dependence on imported oil.

- Appointed a number of competent and experienced administrators, drawn heavily from environmental and conservation organizations, to key posts in the EPA, the Department of the Interior, and the Department of Energy.

- Consulted with environmental leaders on environmental and resource policy matters.

- Helped create a *Superfund* as part of the *Comprehensive Environment Response, Compensation, and Liability Act of 1980* to clean up abandoned hazardous waste sites, including the Love Canal near Niagara Falls, New York.

- Used the Antiquities Act of 1906 to triple the amount of land in the National Wilderness System and double the area in the National Park System (primarily by adding vast tracts in Alaska). He used the Antiquities Act to protect more public land in all 50 states from development than any other president.

**What Happened During the 1980s?** Figure 2-10 (p. 34) summarizes some key environmental events during the 1980s. During this decade, farmers and ranchers and leaders of the oil, automobile, mining, and timber industries, who opposed many of the environmental laws and regulations developed in the issues such as global warming and global biodiversity protection.

During the 1990s, the anti-environmental movement strengthened because of (1) continuing support from its backers and (2) the 1994 federal election, which gave Republicans (many of whom were generally unsympathetic to environmental concerns) a majority in Congress.

For the most part, the 1990s were disappointing to environmentalists. They had to spend much of their time and funds (1) fighting efforts to discredit the environmental movement and to weaken or eliminate most environmental laws passed during the 1960s and 1970s and (2) countering claims by anti-environmental groups that major environmental problems such as global warming and ozone depletion are hoaxes or not very serious.

But during the 1990s,

- Many newer, smaller, and mostly local grassroots environmental organizations sprang up, mostly to deal with environmental threats in their local communities.

- Interest in environmental issues increased on many college campuses.

- Environmental studies programs at colleges and universities expanded.

- Awareness of important environmental issues such as sustainability, population growth, biodiversity protection, and threats from global warming increased.

In 2001, George W. Bush (born 1946) became president. Like President Reagan in the 1980s, he

- Appointed to key federal positions people who opposed or wanted to weaken many existing environmental and public and land use laws and policies.

- Did not consult seriously with environmental groups and leaders in developing his policies.

- Greatly increased private energy and mineral development and timber cutting on public lands.

- Cut federal funding for research on energy conservation and renewable energy resources and

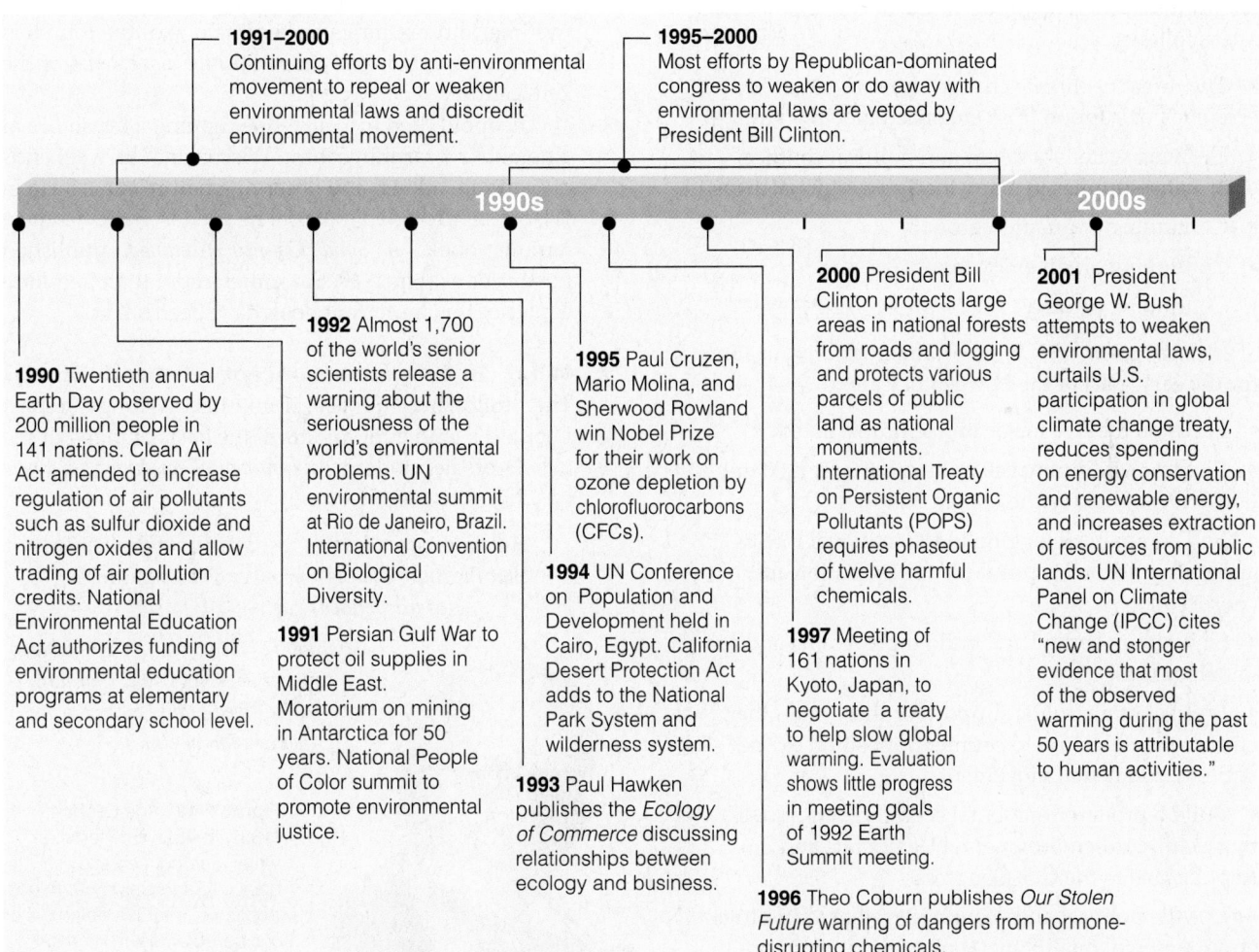

**1991–2000** Continuing efforts by anti-environmental movement to repeal or weaken environmental laws and discredit environmental movement.

**1995–2000** Most efforts by Republican-dominated congress to weaken or do away with environmental laws are vetoed by President Bill Clinton.

**1990s**

**2000s**

**1990** Twentieth annual Earth Day observed by 200 million people in 141 nations. Clean Air Act amended to increase regulation of air pollutants such as sulfur dioxide and nitrogen oxides and allow trading of air pollution credits. National Environmental Education Act authorizes funding of environmental education programs at elementary and secondary school level.

**1992** Almost 1,700 of the world's senior scientists release a warning about the seriousness of the world's environmental problems. UN environmental summit at Rio de Janeiro, Brazil. International Convention on Biological Diversity.

**1991** Persian Gulf War to protect oil supplies in Middle East. Moratorium on mining in Antarctica for 50 years. National People of Color summit to promote environmental justice.

**1995** Paul Cruzen, Mario Molina, and Sherwood Rowland win Nobel Prize for their work on ozone depletion by chlorofluorocarbons (CFCs).

**1994** UN Conference on Population and Development held in Cairo, Egypt. California Desert Protection Act adds to the National Park System and wilderness system.

**1993** Paul Hawken publishes the *Ecology of Commerce* discussing relationships between ecology and business.

**2000** President Bill Clinton protects large areas in national forests from roads and logging and protects various parcels of public land as national monuments. International Treaty on Persistent Organic Pollutants (POPS) requires phaseout of twelve harmful chemicals.

**1997** Meeting of 161 nations in Kyoto, Japan, to negotiate a treaty to help slow global warming. Evaluation shows little progress in meeting goals of 1992 Earth Summit meeting.

**1996** Theo Coburn publishes *Our Stolen Future* warning of dangers from hormone-disrupting chemicals.

**2001** President George W. Bush attempts to weaken environmental laws, curtails U.S. participation in global climate change treaty, reduces spending on energy conservation and renewable energy, and increases extraction of resources from public lands. UN International Panel on Climate Change (IPCC) cites "new and stonger evidence that most of the observed warming during the past 50 years is attributable to human activities."

**Figure 2-11** Some important environmental events, 1990–2002.

increased federal research spending for fossil fuels and nuclear power.

- Cut funding for the Environmental Protection Agency.

- Opposed increasing automobile gas mileage standards as a way to save energy and reduce dependence on oil imports.

- Supported the relaxing of various federal air and water quality pollution standards.

- Opposed U.S. participation in the international Kyoto treaty designed to reduce carbon dioxide emissions that can promote global warming.

- Repealed or tried to weaken most of the pro-environmental measures established by President Clinton.

Environmentalists and many citizens strongly opposed these measures.

**What Are the Major Components of the Environmental Agenda for the 21st Century?** Environmental leaders believe the five most important environmental issues to be faced in the 21st century are as follows:

- The threat of climate change and ecosystem and economic disruption from enhanced global warming

- Growing water shortages and political conflicts over water supplies in many local and regional areas

- Continuing population growth

- Continuing biodiversity loss

- Continuing poverty

Major goals of U.S. environmental organizations for the early part of the 21st century are to

- Focus on the five major problems just listed.

- Protect an additional 40 million hectares (100 million acres) of land in the United States.

- End commercial logging in U.S. national forests and use these forests primarily for recreation and conservation.

- Slow urban sprawl and build more livable and sustainable cities.

- Build enough public support for these and other environmental issues to counter opposition by the anti-environmental movement.

- Build a pro-environmental coalition in Congress by electing pro-environmental Democrats and Republicans to the U.S. Congress.

- Use the political and economic system to improve environmental quality by **(1)** phasing out environmentally harmful government subsidies, **(2)** replacing taxes on wealth and income with taxes on environmental pollution, and **(3)** having the market prices of all goods and services include their harmful environmental costs.

## 2-5 CASE STUDY: ALDO LEOPOLD AND HIS LAND ETHIC

**Who Was Aldo Leopold?** *Aldo Leopold* (Figure 2-12) is best known as a strong proponent of *land ethics*, a philosophy in which humans as part of nature have an ethical responsibility to preserve wild nature.

After earning a master's degree in forestry from Yale University, he joined the U.S. Forest Service. He became alarmed by overgrazing and land deterioration on public lands where he worked and convinced the United States was losing too much of its mostly untouched wilderness lands.

In 1933, Leopold became a professor at the University of Wisconsin and founded the profession of game management. In 1935, he was one of the founders of the Wilderness Society.

As years passed, he developed a deep understanding and appreciation for wildlife and urged us to include nature in our ethical concerns. Through his writings and teachings he became one of the founders of the *conservation* and *environmental movements* of the 20th century.

Leopold died in 1948 while fighting a brush fire at a neighbor's farm in central Wisconsin. His weekends of planting, hiking, and observing nature at his farm in Wisconsin provided material he used to write his most famous book, *A Sand County Almanac,* published posthumously in 1949. Since then more than 2 million copies of this important book have been sold.

**What Is Leopold's Concept of Land Ethics?** The following quotes from his writings reflect Leopold's land ethic and form the basis of many of the beliefs of the modern *environmental wisdom worldview* (p. 15)

*All ethics so far evolved rest upon a single premise: that the individual is a member of a community of interdependent parts.*

*That land is a community is the basic concept of ecology, but that land is to be loved and respected is an extension of ethics.*

**Figure 2-12** Aldo Leopold (1887–1948) was a forester, writer, and conservationist. His book, *A Sand County Almanac* (published after his death), is considered an environmental classic that inspired the modern environmental movement. His *land ethic* expanded the role of humans as protectors of nature

*The land ethic changes the role of* Homo sapiens *from conqueror of the land-community to plain member and citizen of it.*

*We abuse land because we regard it as a commodity belonging to us. When we see land as a community to which we belong, we may begin to use it with love and respect.*

*Anything is right when it tends to preserve the integrity, stability, and beauty of the biotic community. It is wrong when it tends otherwise.*

*Thank God, they cannot cut down the clouds!*

HENRY DAVID THOREAU

# REVIEW QUESTIONS

**1.** What were the key factors in the near extinction of the American bison from the Great Plains of the United States?

**2.** What are *hunter–gatherers,* and what were their major environmental impacts?

**3.** What is the *agricultural revolution?* What are its major benefits and environmental drawbacks?

**4.** What are *slash-and-burn cultivation* and *shifting cultivation?* Under what conditions can these practices be a sustainable form of agriculture?

**5.** What is the *industrial revolution?* What are its major benefits and environmental drawbacks?

**6.** What is the *information and globalization revolution?* What are its potential major benefits and environmental drawbacks?

**7.** What are the four major eras of environmental history in the United States?

**8.** What major events happened during the *tribal era* of environmental history in North America?

**9.** What major events happened during the *frontier era* of environmental history in the United States? What is the *frontier environmental worldview?* How did it contrast with the environmental worldview of some Native American cultures?

**10.** Summarize the contributions of *early conservationists* **(a)** Henry David Thoreau and **(b)** George Perkins Marsh.

**11.** What major environmental events happened during the *conservation era* of the environmental history of the United States between **(a)** 1870 and 1930 and **(b)** 1930 and 1960?

**12.** Summarize the major contributions of the following people during the *conservation era* of the environmental history of the United States: **(a)** John Muir, **(b)** Theodore Roosevelt, **(c)** Gifford Pinchot, **(d)** Alice Hamilton, and **(e)** Franklin D. Roosevelt.

**13.** Distinguish between *preservationists* and *conservationists.* Describe the ongoing controversy between these two groups in the environmental community.

**14.** What is the *environmental movement* in the United States? What major environmental events happened during the *environmental era* of the environmental history of the United States during the **(a)** 1960s, **(b)** 1970s, **(c)** 1980s, and **(d)** 1990s through 2002?

**15.** Summarize the major contributions of the following people during the *environmental era* of the environmental history of the United States: **(a)** Rachel Carson, **(b)** Jimmy Carter, and **(c)** Bill Clinton.

**16.** What is the *spaceship-earth environmental worldview?* What is the *sagebrush rebellion?* Describe what Ronald Reagan did during his presidency to further this movement and weaken environmental laws.

**17.** Describe why the 1990s through 2002 were largely disappointing for the environmental movement and encouraging for the anti-environmental movement in the United States.

**18.** What do environmental leaders believe are the five most important environmental issues we face during the 21st century?

**19.** What are seven major goals of the U.S. environmental movement during the early 21st century?

**20.** What major contributions did *Aldo Leopold* make to the environmental history of the United States? What is his *land ethic?*

# CRITICAL THINKING

**1.** List the benefits and drawbacks of the *frontier environmental worldview.* List three major ways in which U.S. history might have been different without this worldview. Is this environmental worldview still useful today? Explain.

**2.** On balance do you believe the potential environmental benefits of the current *information and globalization revolution* will outweigh its potentially harmful environmental effects? Explain.

**3.** Summarize the major contributions of the following people to the conservation and environmental movements in the United States: **(a)** John Muir, **(b)** Theodore Roosevelt, **(c)** Franklin D. Roosevelt, **(d)** Rachel Carson, **(e)** Aldo Leopold, and **(f)** Jimmy Carter.

**4.** What one person do you believe has made the greatest and longest lasting contribution to the conservation and environmental movements in the United States? Explain.

**5.** Public forests, grasslands, wildlife reserves, parks, and wilderness areas are owned by all citizens and managed for them by federal and state governments in the United States. In terms of the management policies for most of these lands, would you classify yourself as a **(a)** preservationist, **(b)** conservationist, or **(c)** advocate of transferring most public lands to private enterprise? Explain.

**6.** Do you favor or oppose efforts to greatly weaken or repeal most U.S. environmental laws? Explain.

**7.** Explain why you agree or disagree with the seven major goals of U.S. environmental organizations during the early 21st century listed on p. 36.

**8.** Some analysts believe the world's remaining hunter–gatherer societies should be given title to the land on which they and their ancestors have lived for centuries and should be left alone by modern civilization. They contend that we have created protected reserves for endangered wild species, so why not create reserves for these endangered human cultures? What do you think? Explain.

## PROJECTS

**1.** Use the library or Internet to analyze speeches and writings that indicate continuation of the frontier environmental worldview in American culture.

**2.** What major changes (such as a change from agricultural to industrial, from rural to urban, or changes in population size, pollution, and environmental degradation) have taken place in your locale during the past 50 years? On balance, have these changes improved or decreased **(a)** the quality of your life and **(b)** the quality of life for members of your community as a whole?

**3.** Use the library or Internet to summarize the major goals and accomplishments of the anti-environmental movement in the United States between 1980 and 2003.

**4.** Use the library or Internet to find bibliographic information about *Ernest Hemingway* and *Henry David Thoreau*, whose quotes appear at the beginning and end of this chapter.

**5.** Make a concept map of this chapter's major ideas using the section heads and subheads and the key terms (in boldface type). Look on the website for this book for information about making concept maps.

## INTERNET STUDY RESOURCES AND RESOURCES FOR FURTHER READING AND RESEARCH

The website for this book contains helpful study aids and many ideas for further reading and research. Log on to

www.info.brookscole.com/miller13

and click on the Chapter-by-Chapter area. Choose Chapter 2 and select a resource:

- Flash Cards allows you to test your mastery of the Terms and Concepts to Remember for this chapter.

- Tutorial Quizzes provides a multiple-choice practice quiz.

- Student Guide to InfoTrac will lead you to Critical Thinking Projects that use InfoTrac College Edition as a research tool.

- References lists the major books and articles consulted in writing this chapter.

- Hypercontents takes you to an extensive list of sites with news, research, and images related to individual sections of the chapter.

## INFOTRAC COLLEGE EDITION

Improve your skills with InfoTrac College Edition, a searchable online database of articles from more than 700 periodicals. Log on to

http://www.infotrac-college.com

or access InfoTrac through the website for this book. Try to find the following articles:

**1.** Grove, R. 2002. Climatic fears: Colonialism and the history of environmentalism. *Harvard International Review* 23: 50. *Keywords:* "history" and "environmentalism." Human-caused environmental problems are not new. The history of human exploration shows us that we have not learned the lessons of the past. However, today's problems are becoming more threatening.

**2.** Bond, M. 2001. A new environment for Greenpeace. *Foreign Policy* (November–December): 66. *Keywords:* "history" and "Greenpeace." The group Greenpeace is synonymous with environmental activism. This article gives a brief history of the organization, from its founding in 1971 as a nonviolent grassroots protest group to a leading international NGO (nongovernment organization) with millions of members.

# PART II

## SCIENTIFIC PRINCIPLES AND CONCEPTS

*Animal and vegetable life is too complicated a problem for human intelligence to solve, and we can never know how wide a circle of disturbance we produce in the harmonies of nature when we throw the smallest pebble into the ocean of organic life.*

GEORGE PERKINS MARSH

# 3 SCIENCE, SYSTEMS, MATTER, AND ENERGY

## Two Islands: Can We Treat This One Better?

Easter Island (Rapa Nui) is a small, isolated island in the great expanse of the South Pacific. It was first colonized by Polynesians about 2,500 years ago.

The civilization they developed was based on the island's towering palm trees, which were used for shelter, tools, fishing boats, fuel, food, rope, and clothing. Using these resources, they developed an impressive civilization and a technology capable of making and moving large stone structures, including their famous statues (Figure 3-1).

The people flourished, with the population peaking at about 10,000 (with estimates ranging from 7,000 to 20,000) by 1400. However, they used up the island's precious trees faster than they were regenerated—an example of the tragedy of the commons (p. 11). Each person who cut a tree reaped immediate personal benefits while helping doom the civilization in the long run.

Once the trees were gone, the islanders could not build canoes for hunting porpoises and catching fish. Without the forest to absorb and slowly release water, springs and streams dried up, exposed soils eroded, crop yields plummeted, and famine struck.

The starving people turned to warfare and possibly cannibalism. Both the population and the civilization collapsed. When Dutch explorers first reached the island on Easter Day, 1722, they found only about 2,000 inhabitants, struggling under primitive conditions on a mostly barren island.

Like Easter Island at its peak, the earth is an isolated island (in the vastness of space) with no other suitable planet to migrate to. As on Easter Island, our population and resource consumption are growing.

Will the humans on Earth Island recreate the tragedy of Easter Island on a grander scale, or will we learn how to live sustainably on this planet that is our only home? Some analysts believe that we (1) will not run out of resources and (2) are not living unsustainably. Other analysts disagree and warn that we (1) are already depleting or degrading some of the earth's natural resources in parts of the world and (2) need to learn how to live more sustainably over the next few decades.

Scientific knowledge is a key in evaluating these conflicting claims and learning how to live more sustainably. Thus we need to (1) know what science is, (2) understand the behavior of complex systems studied by scientists, and (3) have a basic knowledge of the nature of the matter and energy that make up the earth's living and nonliving resources.

**Figure 3-1** These massive stone figures on Easter Island are the remains of the technology created by an ancient civilization of Polynesians. This civilization collapsed because the people used up the trees (especially large palm trees) that were the basis of their livelihood. More than 200 of these stone statues once stood on huge stone platforms lining the coast. At least 700 additional statues were abandoned in rock quarries or on ancient roads between the quarries and the coast. No one knows how the early islanders (with no wheels, no draft animals, and no sources of energy except their own muscles) transported these gigantic structures for miles before erecting them. We presume they accomplished it by felling large trees and using them to roll and erect the statues.

*Science is an adventure of the human spirit. It is essentially an artistic enterprise, stimulated largely by curiosity, served largely by disciplined imagination, and based largely on faith in the reasonableness, order, and beauty of the universe.*

WARREN WEAVER

This chapter addresses the following questions:

- What is science, and what do scientists do? What is critical thinking?

- What are major components and behaviors of complex systems?

- What are the basic forms of matter? What is matter made of? What makes matter useful to us as a resource?

- What are the major forms of energy? What makes energy useful to us as a resource?

- What are physical and chemical changes? What scientific law governs changes of matter from one physical or chemical form to another?

- What three main types of nuclear changes can matter undergo?

- What are two scientific laws governing changes of energy from one form to another?

- How are the scientific laws governing changes of matter and energy from one form to another related to resource use and environmental disruption?

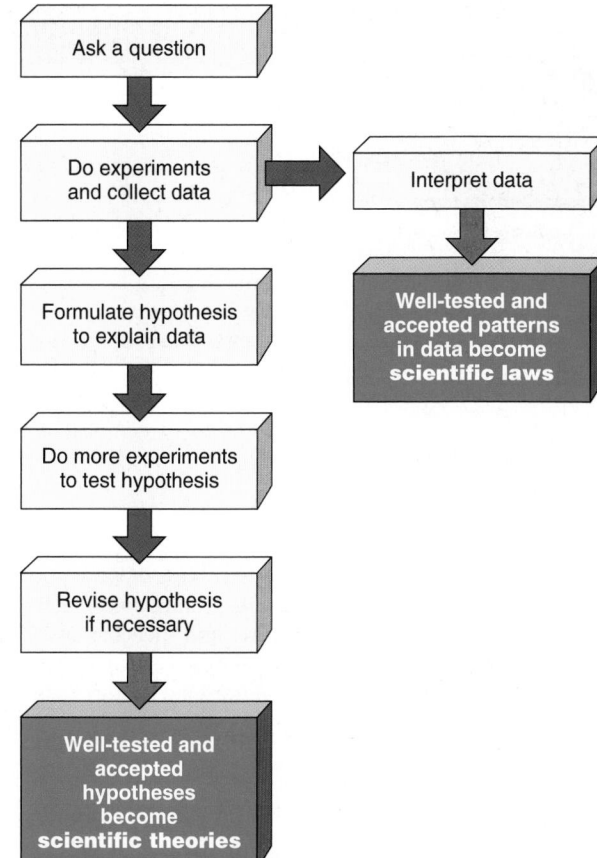

**Figure 3-2** What scientists do.

## 3-1 SCIENCE AND CRITICAL THINKING

**What Is Science and What Do Scientists Do?**
**Science** is an attempt to discover order in nature and use that knowledge to make predictions about what is likely to happen in nature. Figure 3-2 and the Guest Essay on p. 42 summarize the systematic version of the critical thinking process that scientists use.

The first thing scientists do is ask a question or identify a problem to be investigated. Then scientists working on this problem collect **scientific data,** or facts, by making observations and measurements. Repeated observations and measurements must confirm the resulting scientific data or facts, ideally by several different investigators.

The primary goal of science is not facts themselves but a new idea, principle, or model that **(1)** connects and explains certain scientific data and **(2)** leads to useful predictions about what is likely to happen in nature. Scientists working on a particular problem try to come up with a variety of possible or tentative explanations, or **scientific hypotheses,** of what they (or other scientists) observe in nature.

To be accepted, a scientific hypothesis must **(1)** explain scientific data and phenomena and **(2)** make pre-

dictions that can be tested by further experiments. One method scientists use to test a hypothesis is to develop a **model,** an approximate representation or simulation of a system being studied.

If repeated experiments or tests using models support a particular hypothesis or a group of related hypotheses, it becomes a **scientific theory.** In other words, a *scientific theory* is a verified, highly reliable, and widely accepted scientific hypothesis or a related group of scientific hypotheses.

To scientists, scientific theories are not to be taken lightly. They are not guesses, speculations, or suggestions. Instead, scientific theories are useful explanations of processes or natural phenomena that have a high degree of certainty because they are supported by extensive evidence.

A scientific theory is the closest thing to the "truth" or "absolute" proof that science can provide. New evidence or a better explanation may modify, or in rare cases overturn, a particular scientific theory. But unless or until this happens a scientific theory is the best and most reliable knowledge we have about how nature works.

Nonscientists often use the word *theory* incorrectly when they mean to refer to a *scientific hypothesis,*

GUEST ESSAY

Jane Heinze-Fry

Jane Heinze-Fry has a Ph.D. in environmental education and teaches environmental science and biology at Emerson College in Boston, Massachusetts. She is author of
Critical Thinking and Environmental Studies: A Beginner's Guide *(with G. Tyler Miller as coauthor). Previously, she taught and directed environmental studies at Sweet Briar College in Virginia. She also taught biology to students at the junior high, high school, and college levels. Her interdisciplinary orientation is reflected in her concept maps, including the one inside the back cover and those on the website for this textbook.*

Learning how to think critically is essential in helping you evaluate the validity and usefulness of what you **(1)** read in newspapers, magazines, and books (such as this textbook), **(2)** hear in lectures and speeches, and **(3)** see and hear on the news and in advertisements.

Learners engaged in critical thinking try to

- Connect new knowledge to prior knowledge and experience.

- Evaluate the validity of claims made by people.

- Relate what they have learned to their own life experiences.

- Understand and evaluate their environmental worldviews.

- Take and defend positions on issues.

- Develop and implement strategies for dealing with problems.

Whenever we are faced with new information, we need to evaluate it by using critical thinking. Do we believe the information or not, and why? Do the claims seem reasonable or exaggerated? Here are some rules for evaluating scientific evidence and claims:

**1.** Gather all the information you can.

**2.** Understand the definitions of all key terms and concepts.

**3.** Question how the information (data) was obtained.

- Were the studies well designed and carried out?

- Was there an experimental group and a control group? Were the control and experimental groups treated identically except for the variable changed in the experimental group?

- Did the investigators repeat their experiments several times and get essentially the same results?

- Did one or more other investigators verify the results?

**4.** Question the conclusions derived from the data.

- Do the data support the claims, conclusions, and predictions?

---

a tentative explanation that needs further evaluation. The statement, "Oh, that's just a theory," made in everyday conversation, implies a lack of knowledge and careful testing—the opposite of the scientific meaning of the word.

Another important result of science is a **scientific, or natural, law:** a description of what we find happening in nature over and over in the same way. For example, after making thousands of observations and measurements over many decades, scientists discovered the *second law of thermodynamics*. Simply stated, this law says that heat always flows spontaneously from hot to cold—something you learned the first time you touched a hot object. *Scientific laws* describe what we find happening in nature in the same way, whereas *scientific theories* are widely accepted explanations of data and laws.

A scientific law is no better than the accuracy of the observations or measurements upon which it is based. New or more accurate data may result in a scientific law being modified, or in rare cases overturned. However, scientific laws are highly reliable and well-tested descriptions of what we find occurring in nature.

**How Do Scientists Learn About Nature?** We often hear about *the* scientific method. In reality, many **scientific methods** exist: they are ways scientists gather data and formulate and test scientific hypotheses, models, theories, and laws (Figure 3-2, p. 41).

Here is an example of applying the scientific method to an everyday situation.

*Observation:* You walk into your bedroom at night and flick on the light switch. The light does not come on.

*Question:* Why did the light not come on?

*Hypothesis:* Maybe the power for the house is out.

*Test the hypothesis:* If the power is out, the lights in other rooms should also be out.

*Experiment:* To check this prediction, go to other rooms and click light switches.

*Results:* Lights in other rooms come on when their switches are clicked.

*Conclusion:* Power to whole house is not out.

- Are there other more reasonable interpretations?

- Do experts in the field involved base the conclusions on the results of original research, or are they drawn by reporters or scientists in other fields?

- Are the conclusions based on stories or reports of isolated events (*anecdotal information*) or on careful analysis of a large number of related observations?

**5.** Try to determine the assumptions and biases of the investigators and then question them.

- Do the investigators have a monetary or political advantage in the outcome of the investigation or issue involved?

- Would investigators with different basic assumptions or worldviews take the same data and come to different conclusions?

**6.** Are the data, claims, and conclusions based on the tentative results of *frontier science* or the more reliable and widely accepted results of *consensus science?*

**7.** Based on these steps, take a position by either rejecting or conditionally accepting the claims.

Other ways to improve your critical thinking skills involve using

- *Thinking strategies* such as constructing models, brainstorming, creating alternative solutions, and visualizing future possibilities.

- *Attitude and value strategies* such as reflecting on the effects of your lifestyle on the environment and understanding and evaluating your environmental worldview.

- *Action strategies* such as evaluating alternative solutions, creating plans of action, and developing strategies for implementing action plans.

In the environmental course you are taking, you will have many opportunities to develop your critical thinking skills. Your textbook offers Critical Thinking questions at the ends of chapters and in most boxes. If your course uses the supplement *Critical Thinking and Environmental Studies: A Beginner's Guide*, you will learn the critical thinking strategies mentioned here.

**Critical Thinking**

**1.** Can you come up with an example in which critical thinking has helped you make a major change in one or more of your beliefs or helped you make an important personal decision? Can you think of a decision that may have come out better if you had used critical thinking skills such as those discussed in this essay?

**2.** Rote learning often involves the "memorize and spit back" strategy. Meaningful learning (including critical thinking) goes far beyond memorization and requires us to evaluate the validity of what we learn. Currently, about what percentage of your learning involves rote learning and what percentage involves critical thinking as discussed in this essay?

*New hypothesis:* Maybe the light bulb is burned out.

*Experiment:* Replace bulb with a new bulb.

*Results:* Light comes on when switch is flicked.

*Conclusion:* Second hypothesis is verified.

Situations in nature are usually much more complicated than this. A number of *variables* or *factors* influence most processes or parts of nature that scientists seek to understand. Ideally, scientists conduct a *controlled experiment* to isolate and study the effect of a single variable. This *single-variable analysis* is done by setting up two groups: **(1)** an *experimental group,* in which the chosen variable is changed in a known way, and **(2)** a *control group,* in which the chosen variable is not changed. If the experiment is designed properly, any difference between the two groups should result from a variable that was changed in the experimental group (Connections, p. 44).

A basic problem is that many of the problems environmental scientists investigate involve a huge number of interacting variables. This limitation is overcome in some cases by using *multivariable analysis*. This involves using mathematical models run on high-speed computers to analyze the interactions of many variables without having to carry out traditional controlled experiments.

**What Types of Reasoning Do Scientists Use?**
Scientists arrive at certain conclusions with varying degrees of certainty by using inductive and deductive reasoning. **Inductive reasoning** involves using specific observations and measurements to arrive at a general conclusion or hypothesis. In other words, it is a form of *"bottom-up" reasoning* that involves going from the specific to the general. For example, suppose we observe that a variety of different objects fall to the ground when we drop them from various heights. We might then use inductive reasoning to conclude that *all objects fall to the earth's surface when dropped.* Depending on the number of observations made there may be a high degree of certainty in this conclusion. However, what we are really saying is that "All of the objects that we or other observers have dropped from various heights fall to the earth's surface." Although it is extremely

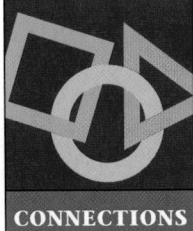

## What Is Harming the Robins?

**CONNECTIONS**

Suppose a scientist observes an abnormality in the growth of robin embryos in a certain area. She knows the area has been sprayed with a pesticide and suspects the chemical may be causing the abnormalities she has observed.

To test this hypothesis, the scientist carries out a *controlled experiment.* She maintains two groups of robin embryos of the same age in the laboratory. Each group is exposed to exactly the same conditions of light, temperature, food supply, and so on, except the embryos in the experimental group are exposed to a known amount of the pesticide in question.

The embryos in both groups are then examined over an identical period of time for the abnormality. If she finds a significantly larger number of the abnormalities in the experimental group than in the control group, the results support the idea that the pesticide is the culprit.

To be sure no errors occur during the procedure, the original researcher should repeat the experiment several times. Ideally one or more other scientists should repeat the experiment on an independent basis.

### Critical Thinking

Can you find flaws in this experiment that might lead you to question the scientist's conclusions? (*Hint:* What other factors in nature—not the laboratory—and in the embryos themselves could possibly explain the results?)

unlikely, we cannot be absolutely sure someone will drop an object that does not fall to the earth's surface. When scientists say that something has been proved or established by inductive reasoning, they do not mean it is absolutely true but that a very high probability or degree of certainty exists that it is true.

**Deductive reasoning** involves using logic to arrive at a specific conclusion based on a generalization or premise. In other words, it is a form of *"top-down"* reasoning that goes from the general to the specific. For example,

*Generalization or premise:* All birds have feathers.

*Example:* Eagles are birds.

*Deductive conclusion:* All eagles have feathers.

This conclusion of this *syllogism* (a series of logically connected statements) is valid as long as **(1)** the premise is correct, and **(2)** we do not use faulty logic to arrive at the conclusion.

Deductive and inductive reasoning are important scientific tools. But scientists also try to come up with new or creative ideas to explain some of the things we observe in nature. Often such ideas defy conventional logic and current scientific knowledge. According to physicist Albert Einstein, "There is no completely logical way to a new scientific idea." Intuition, imagination, and creativity are as important in science as they are in poetry, art, music, and other great adventures of the human spirit.

**How Valid Are the Results of Science?** Scientists can do two major things: **(1)** disprove things, and **(2)** establish that a particular model, theory, or law has a very high probability or degree of certainty of being true. However, like scholars in any field, scientists cannot prove their theories, models, and laws are *absolutely* true.

When people say something has or has not been "scientifically proven," they can mislead us by falsely implying that science yields absolute proof or certainty. Although it may be extremely low, some degree of uncertainty is always involved in any scientific theory, model, or law.

**How Does Frontier Science Differ from Consensus Science?** News reports often focus on **(1)** new so-called scientific breakthroughs and **(2)** disputes between scientists over the validity of preliminary (untested) data, hypotheses, and models. These preliminary results, called **frontier science,** are controversial because they have not been widely tested and accepted. At the preliminary frontier stage, it is normal and healthy for reputable scientists in a field to disagree about **(1)** the meaning and accuracy of scientific data and **(2)** the validity of various hypotheses.

By contrast, **consensus science** consists of data, theories, and laws that scientists who are considered experts in the field involved widely accept. This aspect of science is very reliable but is rarely considered newsworthy. One way to find out what scientists generally agree on is to seek out reports by scientific bodies such as the U.S. National Academy of Sciences and the British Royal Society that attempt to summarize consensus among experts in key areas of science.

## 3-2 MODELS AND BEHAVIOR OF SYSTEMS

**What Is a System, and What Are Its Major Components?** A **system** is a set of components that **(1)** function and interact in some regular and theoretically predictable manner and **(2)** can be isolated for the purposes of observation and study. The environment consists of a vast number of interacting systems involving living and nonliving things.

Most *systems* have the following key components:

- **Inputs** of things such as matter, energy, or information into the system.

- **Flows,** or **throughputs,** of matter, energy, or information within the system at certain rates.

- **Stores,** or **storage areas,** within a system where energy, matter, or information can accumulate for various lengths of time before being released. For example, your body stores various chemicals with different residence times, and water vapor typically remains in the lower atmosphere for about 10 days before it is replaced.

- **Outputs** of certain forms of matter, energy, or information that flow out of the system into *sinks* in the environment (such as the atmosphere, bodies of water, underground water, soil, and land surfaces).

**Why Are Models of Complex Systems Useful?**
Over time, people have learned the value of using models as approximate representations or simulations of real systems to **(1)** find out how systems work and **(2)** evaluate which ideas or hypotheses work.

Some of the most powerful and useful technologies invented by humans are mathematical models, which are used to supplement our mental models. *Mathematical models* consist of one or more equations used to **(1)** describe the behavior of a system and **(2)** make predictions about the behavior of a system.

Making a mathematical model usually requires going many times through three steps: **(1)** Make a guess and write down some equations, **(2)** compute the predictions implied by the equations, and **(3)** compare the predictions with observations, the predictions of mental models, existing experimental data, and scientific hypotheses, laws, and theories.

Mathematical models are important because they can give us improved perceptions and predictions, especially in situations where our mental models are weak. Research has shown that mental models tend to be especially unreliable when **(1)** there are many interacting variables, **(2)** consequences follow actions only after long delays, **(3)** consequences of actions lead to other consequences, **(4)** responses vary from one time to the next, and **(5)** controlled experiments (Connections, p. 44) are impossible, too slow, or too expensive to conduct.

After building and testing a mathematical model, scientists use it to predict what is *likely* to happen under a variety of conditions. In effect, they use mathematical models to answer *if–then* questions: "*If* we do such and such, *then* what is likely to happen now and in the future?"

Despite its usefulness, a mathematical model is nothing more than a set of hypotheses or assumptions about how we think a certain system works. Such models (like all other models) are no better than **(1)** the assumptions built into them and **(2)** the data fed into them to make projections about the behavior of complex systems.

**How Do Feedback Loops Affect Systems?** Systems undergo change as a result of feedback loops. A **feedback loop** occurs when an output of matter, energy, or information is fed back into the system as an input that changes the system.

There are two types of feedback loops:

- A **positive feedback loop** in which a change in a certain direction provides information that causes a system to change further in the same direction. An example involves depositing money in a bank at compound interest and leaving it there. In this case, the interest increases the balance, which through a positive feedback loop leads to more interest and an even higher balance.

- A **negative feedback loop** in which one change leads to a lessening of that change. For example, recycling aluminum cans involves melting aluminum and feeding it back into an economic system to make new aluminum products. This negative feedback loop of matter reduces the **(1)** need to find, extract, and process virgin aluminum ore and **(2)** flow of waste matter (discarded aluminum cans) into the environment.

Most systems contain one or a series of *coupled positive and negative feedback loops*. For example, the temperature-regulating system of your body involves coupled negative and positive feedback loops (Figure 3-3, p. 46). Normally a negative feedback regulates your body temperature. However, if your body temperature exceeds 42°C (108°F), your built-in negative feedback temperature control system breaks down as your body produces more heat than your sweat-dampened skin can get rid of. Then a positive feedback loop caused by overloading the system (Figure 3-3, p. 46) overwhelms the negative or corrective feedback loop. These conditions produce a net gain in body heat, which produces even more body heat, and so on, until you die from heatstroke.

The tragedy on Easter Island discussed earlier (p. 40) also involved the coupling of positive and negative feedback loops. As the abundance of trees turned to a shortage of trees, the positive feedback loop (more births than deaths) became weaker as death rates rose, and the negative feedback loop (more deaths than births) eventually dominated and caused a dieback of the human population.

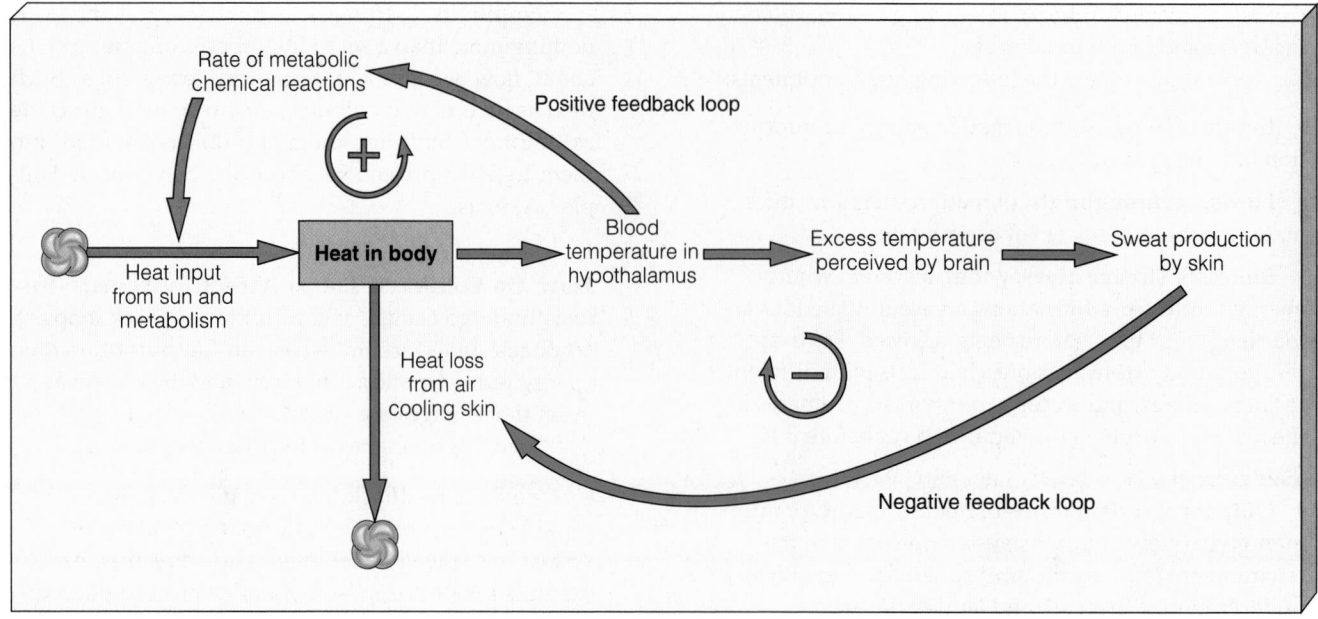

**Figure 3-3** Coupled negative and positive feedback loops involved in temperature control of the human body.

### How Do Time Delays Affect Complex Systems?
Complex systems often show **time delays** between the input of a stimulus and the response to it. A long time delay can mean that corrective action comes too late. For example, a smoker exposed to cancer-causing chemicals in cigarette smoke may not get lung cancer for 20–30 years.

Time delays allow a problem to build up slowly until it reaches a *threshold level* and causes a fundamental shift in the behavior of a system. Examples in which prolonged delays dampen the negative feedback mechanisms that might slow, prevent, or halt environmental problems are (1) population growth, (2) leaks from toxic waste dumps, and (3) degradation of forests from prolonged exposure to air pollutants.

### What Is Synergy, and How Can It Affect Complex Systems?
In arithmetic, 1 plus 1 always equals 2. However, in some of the complex systems found in nature, 1 plus 1 may add up to more than 2 because of synergistic interactions. A **synergistic interaction** occurs when two or more processes interact so the combined effect is greater than the sum of their separate effects.

**Synergy** can result when two people work together to accomplish a task. For example, suppose you and I need to move a 140-kilogram (300-pound) tree that has fallen across the road. By ourselves, each of us can lift only, say, 45 kilograms (100 pounds). If we cooperate and use our muscles properly, however, together we can move the tree out of the way. That is using synergy to solve a problem. Research in the social sciences suggests that most political changes or changes in cultural beliefs are brought about by only

about 5% (and rarely more than 10%) of a population working together (synergizing) and expanding their efforts to influence other people.

### What Is the Law of Conservation of Problems?
Biologist Eric Davidson has proposed a law of techno-dynamics that he calls the *law of conservation of problems.* According to this law, the technological solution of one problem usually creates one or more new unanticipated problems. The reason is that nature's natural systems are connected, so solving a problem by changing one part of a system can affect other parts or other connected systems in unpredictable and sometimes undesirable ways.

For example, modern technology provides cheap chemical fertilizers that can increase crop productivity and replace some of the plant nutrients lost by erosion and poor farming practices. However, the widespread use of such fertilizers creates the new problem of pollution of streams, lakes, and underground water supplies with excess inputs of plant nutrients. In addition, the new water pollution problem is not a local problem confined to a farmer's field. Instead, it becomes a regional problem that affects people who live downstream or who extract and drink polluted groundwater.

The question we face in introducing new technologies and chemicals is: Do the projected or actual *beneficial* effects outweigh the projected or actual *harmful* effects? As we shall see in this book, this is not an easy question to answer because of (1) a lack of data, (2) imperfect models, and (3) different assumptions or beliefs by people about what is considered harmful or beneficial.

**How Can We Anticipate Environmental Surprises?** One of the basic principles of environmental science is that *we can never do one thing.* Any action in a complex system has multiple and often unpredictable effects.

In recent years, we have experienced unforeseen *environmental surprises.* Two examples are **(1)** sudden dying of large areas of forest after years of exposure to air and soil pollutants and **(2)** a rapid decline in the health of coral reefs.

Environmental surprises are the result of

- *Discontinuities,* or abrupt shifts in a previously stable system when some *environmental threshold* is crossed. By analogy, you may be able to lean back in a chair and balance yourself on two of its legs for a long time with only minor adjustments. But if you pass a certain threshold of movement, your balanced system suffers a discontinuity or sudden shift and you may find yourself on the floor.

- *Synergistic interactions,* in which two or more factors interact to produce effects greater than the sum of their effects acting separately.

- *Unpredictable or chaotic events* such as **(1)** hurricanes, **(2)** earthquakes, **(3)** invasions of ecosystems by nonnative species, or **(4)** slowly building but so far unknown environmental problems (such as gradual buildup of some potentially harmful chemicals in human fatty tissue).

Strategies to help deal with and reduce such surprises include the following:

- Greatly increasing research on environmental thresholds and synergistic interactions

- Developing better models to understand the behavior of complex living systems and our economic and political systems

- Formulating scenarios of possible environmental surprises and developing a range of strategies for dealing with them (as defense departments and emergency management agencies do)

- Acting to prevent or lessen the effects of possible surprises through **(1)** pollution prevention, **(2)** more efficient and environmentally benign use of resources, and **(3)** reduced population growth

## 3-3 MATTER: FORMS, STRUCTURE, AND QUALITY

**What Are Nature's Building Blocks?** Matter is anything that has mass (the amount of material in an object) and takes up space. Matter is found in two *chemical forms:*

- **Elements:** the distinctive building blocks of matter that make up every material substance

- **Compounds:** two or more different elements held together in fixed proportions by attractive forces called *chemical bonds*

Various elements, compounds, or both can be found together in **mixtures.**

All matter is built from the 115 known chemical elements (92 of them occur naturally and the other 23 have been synthesized in laboratories). To simplify things, chemists represent each element by a one- or two-letter symbol. Examples used in this book are hydrogen (H), carbon (C), oxygen (O), nitrogen (N), phosphorus (P), sulfur (S), chlorine (Cl), fluorine (F), bromine (Br), sodium (Na), calcium (Ca), lead (Pb), mercury (Hg), arsenic (As), and uranium (U). Chemists have developed a way to classify elements in terms of their chemical behavior by arranging them in a *periodic table of elements,* as discussed in Appendix 2.

If you had a supermicroscope capable of looking at individual elements and compounds, you could see they are made up of three types of building blocks:

- **Atoms:** the smallest units of matter that are unique to a particular element

- **Ions:** electrically charged atoms or combinations of atoms

- **Molecules:** combinations of two or more atoms of the same or different elements held together by chemical bonds

Some elements are found in nature as molecules. Examples are nitrogen and oxygen, which together make up about 99% of the volume of air you breathe. Two atoms of nitrogen (N) combine to form a gaseous molecule, with the shorthand formula $N_2$ (read as "N-two"). The subscript after the element's symbol indicates the number of atoms of that element in a molecule. Similarly, most of the oxygen gas in the atmosphere exists as $O_2$ (read as "O-two") molecules. A small amount of oxygen, found mostly in the second layer of the atmosphere (stratosphere), exists as $O_3$ (read as "O-three") molecules, a gaseous form of oxygen called *ozone.*

**What Are Atoms Made Of?** If you increased the magnification of your supermicroscope, you would find that each different type of atom contains a certain number of *subatomic particles.* The main building blocks of an atom are **(1)** positively charged **protons** (p), **(2)** uncharged **neutrons** (n), and **(3)** negatively charged **electrons** (e).

Each atom consists of **(1)** an extremely small center, or **nucleus,** containing protons and neutrons, and **(2)** one or more electrons in rapid motion somewhere outside the nucleus. Atoms are incredibly small. For example, more than 3 million hydrogen atoms could sit side by side on the period at the end of this sentence.

Each atom has an equal number of positively charged protons (inside its nucleus) and negatively charged electrons (outside its nucleus). Because these electrical charges cancel one another, *the atom as a whole has no net electrical charge.*

Each element has its own specific **atomic number,** equal to the number of protons in the nucleus of each of its atoms. The simplest element, hydrogen (H), has only 1 proton in its nucleus, so its atomic number is 1. Carbon (C), with 6 protons, has an atomic number of 6, whereas uranium (U), a much larger atom, has 92 protons and an atomic number of 92.

Because atoms are electrically neutral, the atomic number of an atom tells us the number of positively charged protons in its nucleus and the equal number of negatively charged electrons outside its nucleus. For example, an atom of uranium with an atomic number of 92 has 92 protons in its nucleus and 92 electrons outside, and thus no net electrical charge.

Because electrons have so little mass compared with the mass of a proton or a neutron, *most of an atom's mass is concentrated in its nucleus.* The mass of an atom is described in terms of its **mass number:** the total number of neutrons and protons in its nucleus. For example, **(1)** a hydrogen atom with 1 proton and no neutrons in its nucleus has a mass number of 1, and **(2)** an atom of uranium with 92 protons and 143 neutrons in its nucleus has a mass number of 235 (92 + 143 = 235).

All atoms of an element have the same number of protons in their nuclei. However, they may have different numbers of uncharged neutrons in their nuclei, and thus may have different mass numbers. Various forms of an element having the same atomic number but a different mass number are called **isotopes** of that element. Isotopes are identified by attaching their mass numbers to the name or symbol of the element. For example, hydrogen has three isotopes: hydrogen-1 (H-1), hydrogen-2 (H-2, common name *deuterium,*) and hydrogen-3 (H-3, common name *tritium.*) A natural sample of an element contains a mixture of its isotopes in a fixed proportion or percentage abundance by weight (Figure 3-4).

**What Are Ions?** Atoms of some elements can lose or gain one or more electrons to form *ions:* atoms or groups of atoms with one or more net positive (+) or negative (−) electrical charges. For example, an atom of sodium (Na, atomic number 11) with 11 positively charged protons and 11 negatively charged electrons can lose one of its electrons. It then becomes a sodium ion with a positive charge of 1 ($Na^+$) because it

Hydrogen (H)

Mass number = 0 + 1 = 1
Hydrogen-1
(99.98%)

Mass number = 1 + 1 = 2
Hydrogen-2
or deuterium (D)
(0.015%)

Mass number = 2 + 1 = 3
Hydrogen-3
or tritium (T)
(trace)

Uranium (U)

Mass number = 143 + 92 = 235
Uranium-235
(0.7%)

Mass number = 146 + 92 = 238
Uranium-238
(99.3%)

**Figure 3-4** Isotopes of hydrogen and uranium. All isotopes of hydrogen have an atomic number of 1 because each has one proton in its nucleus; similarly, all uranium isotopes have an atomic number of 92. However, each isotope of these elements has a different mass number because its nucleus contains a different number of neutrons. Figures in parentheses indicate the percentage abundance by weight of each isotope in a natural sample of the element.

now has 11 positive charges (protons) but only 10 negative charges (electrons). An atom of chlorine (Cl, with an atomic number of 17) can gain an electron and become a chlorine ion with a negative charge of 1 ($Cl^-$) because it then has 17 positively charged protons and 18 negatively charged electrons.

The number of positive or negative charges on an ion is shown as a superscript after the symbol for an atom or a group of atoms. Examples of other ions encountered in this book are **(1)** positive hydrogen ions ($H^+$), calcium ions ($Ca^{2+}$), and ammonium ions ($NH_4^+$), and **(2)** negative nitrate ions ($NO_3^-$), sulfate ions ($SO_4^{2-}$), and phosphate ions ($PO_4^{3-}$).

The amount of a substance in a unit volume of air, water, or other medium is called its **concentration.** The concentration of hydrogen ions ($H^+$) in a water solution is a measure of its acidity or alkalinity. **pH** is a measure of the concentration of $H^+$ in a water solution. On a *pH scale* of 0 to 14, *acids* have a pH less than 7, *bases* have a pH greater than 7, and a *neutral solution* has a pH of 7 (Figure 3-5).

**What Holds the Atoms and Ions in Compounds Together?** Most matter exists as *compounds.* Chemists use a shorthand **chemical formula** to show the number of atoms (or ions) of each type in a compound. The formula **(1)** contains the symbols for each of the elements present and **(2)** uses subscripts to represent the number of atoms or ions of each element in the compound's basic structural unit. Compounds made up of oppositely charged ions are called *ionic compounds.*

**Figure 3-5** The pH scale, used to measure acidity and alkalinity of water solutions. Values shown are approximate. A solution with a pH less than 7 is *acidic*, a *neutral solution* has a pH of 7, and one with a pH greater than 7 is *basic*. Each whole-number drop in pH represents a 10-fold increase in acidity. A pH value is a measure of the concentration of hydrogen ions (H⁺) in a water solution. (From Cecie Starr, *Biology: Concepts and Applications*, 4th ed., Brooks/Cole [Wadsworth], © 2000)

Those made up of molecules of uncharged atoms are called *covalent* or *molecular compounds.*

Sodium chloride (table salt), an *ionic compound,* is represented by NaCl. It consists of a three-dimensional array of oppositely charged *ions* ($Na^+$ and $Cl^-$). The forces of attraction between these oppositely charged ions are called *ionic bonds,* as discussed in more detail in Appendix 2.

Water, a *covalent* or *molecular compound,* consists of molecules made up of uncharged atoms of hydrogen (H) and oxygen (O). Each water molecule consists of two hydrogen atoms chemically bonded to an oxygen atom, yielding $H_2O$ (read as "H-two-O") molecules. The bonds between the atoms in such molecules are called *covalent bonds,* as discussed in Appendix 2. There are also weaker forces of attraction, called *hydrogen bonds,* between the molecules of covalent compounds (such as water), as discussed in Appendix 2.

**What Are Organic and Inorganic Compounds?** Table sugar, vitamins, plastics, aspirin, penicillin, and many other important materials have one thing in common: They are **organic compounds,** containing carbon atoms combined with each other and with atoms of one or more other elements such as hydrogen, oxygen, nitrogen, sulfur, phosphorus, chlorine, and fluorine. Almost all organic compounds are molecular compounds held together by covalent bonds. Organic compounds can be either *natural* or *synthetic* (such as plastics and many drugs made by humans).

The millions of known organic (carbon-based) compounds include the following:

- *Hydrocarbons:* compounds of carbon and hydrogen atoms. An example is methane ($CH_4$), the main component of natural gas.

- *Chlorinated hydrocarbons:* compounds of carbon, hydrogen, and chlorine atoms. Examples are **(1)** the insecticide DDT ($C_{14}H_9Cl_5$) and **(2)** toxic polychlorinated biphenyls, or PCBs (such as $C_{12}H_5Cl_5$), oily compounds used as insulating materials in electric transformers.

- *Chlorofluorocarbons* (CFCs): compounds of carbon, chlorine, and fluorine atoms. An example is Freon-12 ($CCl_2F_2$), until recently widely used as **(1)** a coolant in refrigerators and air conditioners, **(2)** an aerosol propellant, and **(3)** a foaming agent for making some plastics.

- *Simple carbohydrates* (simple sugars): certain types of compounds of carbon, hydrogen, and oxygen atoms. An example is glucose ($C_6H_{12}O_6$), which most plants and animals break down in their cells to obtain energy.

Larger and more complex organic compounds, called *polymers,* consist of a number of basic structural or molecular units (*monomers*) linked by chemical bonds, somewhat like cars linked in a freight train. The three major types of organic polymers are **(1)** *complex carbohydrates* consisting of two or more monomers of simple sugars (such as glucose) linked together, **(2)** *proteins* formed by linking together monomers of amino acids, and **(3)** *nucleic acids,* such as DNA and RNA, made by linked sequences of monomers called nucleotides, as discussed in Appendix 2.

**Genes** consist of specific sequences of nucleotides in a DNA molecule. Each gene carries codes (each consisting of three nucleotides) needed to make various proteins. These coded units of genetic information about specific traits are passed on from parents to offspring during reproduction.

**Chromosomes** are combinations of genes that make up a single DNA molecule, together with a number of proteins. Each chromosome typically contains thousands of genes. Genetic information coded in your chromosomal DNA is what makes you different from an oak leaf, an alligator, or a flea and from your parents. The relationships of genetic material to cells are depicted in Figure 3-6.

All other compounds are called **inorganic compounds.** Such compounds do not have carbon–carbon or carbon–hydrogen covalent bonds. Some of the inorganic compounds discussed in this book are sodium chloride (NaCl), water ($H_2O$), nitrous oxide ($N_2O$), nitric oxide (NO), carbon monoxide (CO), carbon dioxide ($CO_2$), nitrogen dioxide ($NO_2$), sulfur dioxide ($SO_2$), ammonia ($NH_3$), hydrogen sulfide ($H_2S$), sulfuric acid ($H_2SO_4$), and nitric acid ($HNO_3$).

**What Are Four States of Matter?** The atoms, ions, and molecules that make up matter are found in three *physical states:* solid, liquid, and gas. For example, water exists as ice, liquid water, or water vapor depending on its temperature and pressure. The three physical states of matter differ in the spacing and

**Figure 3-7** Comparison of the solid, liquid, and gaseous physical states of matter.

orderliness of its atoms, ions, or molecules, with solids having the most compact and orderly arrangement and gases the least compact and orderly arrangement (Figure 3-7).

A fourth state of matter is called **plasma:** a high energy mixture of roughly equal numbers of positively charged ions and negatively charged electrons. A plasma is formed when enough energy is applied to strip electrons away from the nuclei of atoms.

Plasma is the most abundant form of matter in the universe. The sun and all stars consist mostly of plasma. However, there is little natural plasma on the earth, with most of it found in lightning bolts and flames.

However, artificial plasmas are **(1)** produced in fluorescent lights, arc lamps, neon signs, gas discharge lasers, and in TV and computer screens, by running a high voltage electric current through a gas **(2)** used in arc torches to weld, cut, and process many

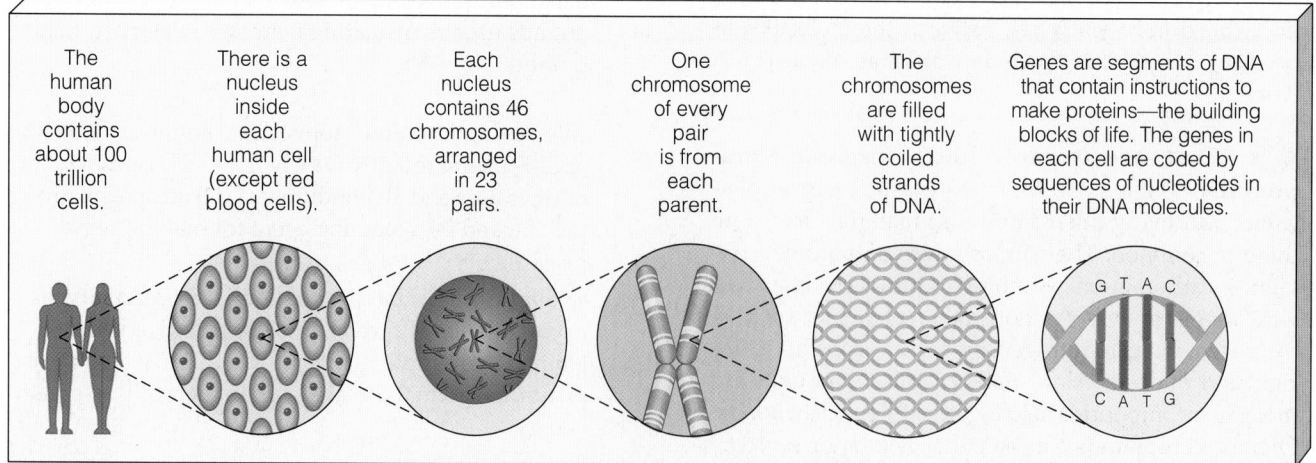

**Figure 3-6** Relationships among cells, nuclei, chromosomes, DNA, and genes.

materials, and **(3)** used to make integrated circuits, solar cells, artificial diamonds, and high temperature superconductors.

Scientists hope to be able to develop affordable plasma torches that can **(1)** destroy toxic wastes, **(2)** sterilize and clean water, **(3)** remove soot from exhaust gases, and **(4)** produce clean burning hydrogen gas from diesel fuel, gasoline, or methane for use in fuel cells.

**What Are Matter Quality and Material Efficiency?** **Matter quality** is a measure of how useful a form of matter is to us as a resource, based on its availability and concentration. **High-quality matter (1)** is concentrated, **(2)** usually is found near the earth's surface, and **(3)** has great potential for use as a matter resource. **Low-quality matter (1)** is dilute, **(2)** often is deep underground or dispersed in the ocean or the atmosphere, and **(3)** usually has little potential for use as a matter resource (Figure 3-8).

High Quality | Low Quality
Solid | Gas
Salt | Solution of salt in water
Coal | Coal-fired power plant emissions
Gasoline | Automobile emissions
Aluminum can | Aluminum ore

**Figure 3-8** Examples of differences in matter quality. High-quality matter (left-hand column) is fairly easy to extract and concentrated; low-quality matter (right-hand column) is more difficult to extract and more dispersed than high-quality matter.

An aluminum can is a more concentrated, higher-quality form of aluminum than aluminum ore containing the same amount of aluminum. That is why it takes less energy, water, and money to recycle an aluminum can than to make a new can from aluminum ore.

**Material efficiency,** or **resource productivity,** is the total amount of material needed to produce each unit of goods or services. Although resource productivity has been improving, only about 2–6% of the matter resources flowing through the economies of developed countries ends up providing useful goods and services. Because of such waste, business expert Paul Hawken (Guest Essay, p. 16) and physicist Amory Lovins contend that resource productivity in developed countries could be improved by 75–90% within two decades using existing technologies.

## 3-4 ENERGY: FORMS AND QUALITY

**What Is Energy and How Is It Transmitted?** **Energy** is the capacity to do work and transfer heat. Work is performed when an object—be it a grain of sand, this book, or a giant boulder—is moved over some distance. Work, or matter movement, also is needed to **(1)** boil water or **(2)** burn natural gas to heat a house or cook food. Energy is also the heat that flows automatically from a hot object to a cold object when they come in contact. **Radiation** is the transmission of energy through space as particles or waves.

**What Is the Difference Between Kinetic Energy and Potential Energy?** Two major types of energy are

- **Kinetic energy,** which matter has because of its mass and its speed or velocity. Examples of this energy in motion are **(1)** wind (a moving mass of air), **(2)** flowing streams, **(3)** heat flowing from a body at a high temperature to one at a lower temperature, and **(4)** electricity (flowing electrons).

- **Potential energy,** which is stored and potentially available for use. Examples of this stored energy are **(1)** a rock held in your hand, **(2)** an unlit stick of dynamite, **(3)** still water behind a dam, **(4)** the chemical energy stored in gasoline molecules, and **(5)** the nuclear energy stored in the nuclei of atoms.

Potential energy can be changed to kinetic energy. When you drop a rock, its potential energy changes into kinetic energy. When you burn gasoline in a car engine, the potential energy stored in the chemical bonds of its molecules changes into heat, light, and mechanical (kinetic) energy that propels the car.

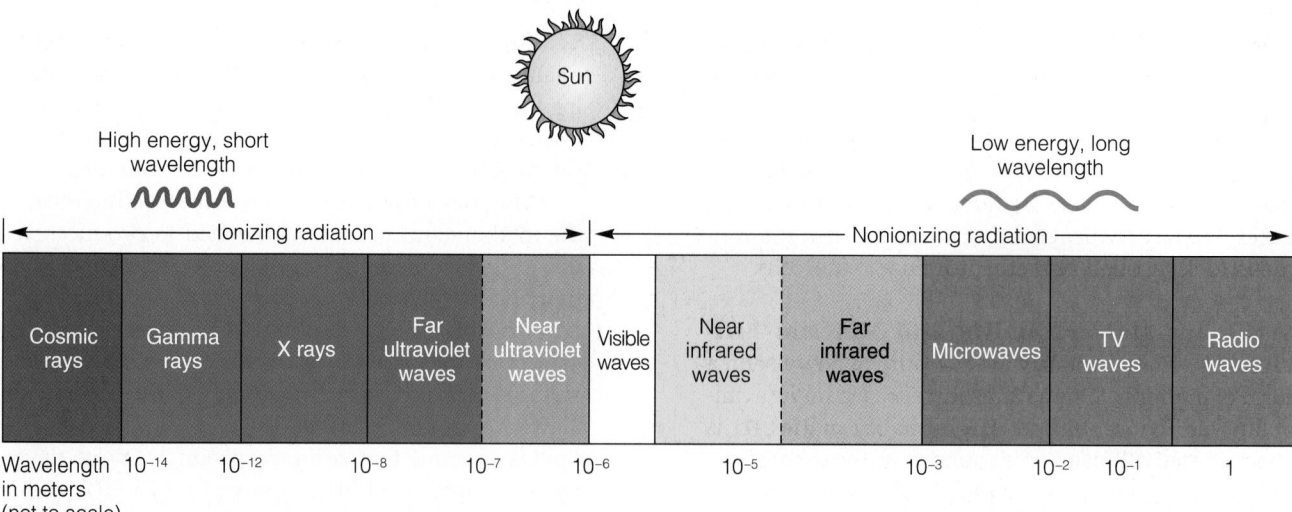

Wavelength in meters (not to scale): $10^{-14}$    $10^{-12}$    $10^{-8}$    $10^{-7}$    $10^{-6}$    $10^{-5}$    $10^{-3}$    $10^{-2}$    $10^{-1}$    $1$

**Figure 3-9** The *electromagnetic spectrum:* the range of electromagnetic waves, which differ in wavelength (distance between successive peaks or troughs) and energy content.

**What Is Electromagnetic Radiation?** Another type of energy is **electromagnetic radiation:** energy radiated in the form of a *wave* as a result of the changing electric and magnetic fields. There are many different forms of electromagnetic radiation, each with a different *wavelength* (distance between successive peaks or troughs in the wave) and *energy content* (Figure 3-9). Such radiation travels through space at the speed of light, which is about 300,000 kilometers per second (186,000 miles per second).

Cosmic rays, gamma rays, X rays, and ultraviolet radiation (Figure 3-9, left side) are called **ionizing radiation** because they have enough energy to knock electrons from atoms and change them to positively charged ions. The resulting highly reactive electrons and ions can **(1)** disrupt living cells, **(2)** interfere with body processes, and **(3)** cause many types of sickness, including various cancers. The other forms of electromagnetic radiation (Figure 3-9, right side) do not contain enough energy to form ions and are called **nonionizing radiation.**

The visible light that we can detect with our eyes is a form of nonionizing radiation that occupies only a small portion of the full range or spectrum of different types of electromagnetic radiation (Figure 3-9). Figure 3-10 shows that visible light makes up most of the spectrum of electromagnetic radiation emitted by the sun (Figure 3-10).

**What Is Heat and How Is It Transferred?** Heat is the total kinetic energy of all the moving atoms, ions, or molecules within a given substance, excluding the overall motion of the whole object. **Temperature** is the average speed of motion of the atoms, ions, or molecules in a sample of matter at a given moment.

Heat can be transferred from one place to another by three different methods (Figure 3-11):

- **Convection:** the transfer of heat by the movement of heated material. For example, heat can be transferred by convection **(1)** through the atmosphere by the movement of heated air and **(2)** through a pot of boiling water (Figure 3-11, left) or the ocean by movement of heated water.

- **Conduction:** the transfer of heat by collisions of atoms or molecules (Figure 3-11, middle). For example, metals are good conductors of heat and air and most plastics are poor heat conductors.

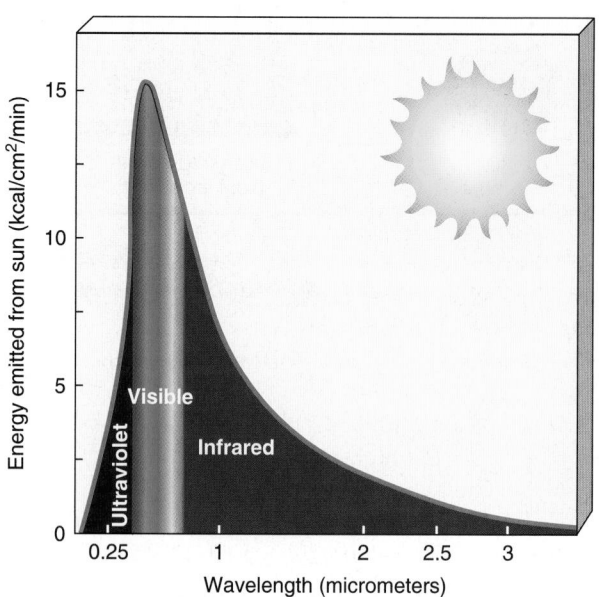

**Figure 3-10** The spectrum of electromagnetic radiation released by the sun consists mostly of visible light.

**Convection**

Heating water in the bottom of a pan causes some of the water to vaporize into bubbles. Because they are lighter than the surrounding water, they rise. Water then sinks from the top to replace the rising bubbles. This up and down movement (convection) eventually heats all of the water.

**Conduction**

Heat from a stove burner causes atoms or molecules in the pan's bottom to vibrate faster. The vibrating atoms or molecules then collide with nearby atoms or molecules, causing them to vibrate faster. Eventually, molecules or atoms in the pan's handle are vibrating so fast it becomes too hot to touch.

**Radiation**

As the water boils, heat from the hot stove burner and pan radiate into the surrounding air, even though air conducts very little heat.

**Figure 3-11** Three ways in which heat can be transferred from one place to another.

- **Radiation:** the transfer of heat by wave motion (Figure 3-11, right).

**What Is Energy Quality?** **Energy quality** is a measure of an energy source's ability to do useful work (Figure 3-12). **High-quality energy** is concentrated and can perform much useful work. Examples are (1) electricity, (2) the chemical energy stored in coal and gasoline, (3) concentrated sunlight, and (4) nuclei of uranium-235 used as fuel in nuclear power plants.

By contrast, **low-quality energy** is dispersed and has little ability to do useful work. An example is heat dispersed in the moving molecules of a large amount of matter (such as the atmosphere or a large body of water) so that its temperature is low. For example, the total amount of heat stored in the Atlantic Ocean is greater than the amount of high-quality chemical energy stored in all the oil deposits of Saudi Arabia. Yet the ocean's heat is so widely dispersed, it cannot be used to move things or to heat things to high temperatures. It makes sense to match the quality of an

Source of Energy

**Electricity**
**Very high temperature heat (greater than 2,500°C)**
**Nuclear fission (uranium)**
**Nuclear fusion (deuterium)**
**Concentrated sunlight**
**High-velocity wind**

**High-temperature heat (1,000–2,500°C)**
**Hydrogen gas**
**Natural gas**
**Gasoline**
**Coal**
**Food**

**Normal sunlight**
**Moderate-velocity wind**
**High-velocity water flow**
**Concentrated geothermal energy**
**Moderate-temperature heat (100–1,000°C)**
**Wood and crop wastes**

**Dispersed geothermal energy**
**Low-temperature heat (100°C or lower)**

Relative Energy Quality (usefulness)

Very high

High

Moderate

Low

Energy Tasks

**Very high-temperature heat (greater than 2,500°C) for industrial processes and producing electricity to run electrical devices (lights, motors)**

**Mechanical motion (to move vehicles and other things)**
**High-temperature heat (1,000–2,500°C) for industrial processes and producing electricity**

**Moderate-temperature heat (100–1,000°C) for industrial processes, cooking, producing steam, electricity, and hot water**

**Low-temperature heat (100°C or less) for space heating**

**Figure 3-12** Categories of the quality of different sources of energy. *High-quality energy* is concentrated and has great ability to perform useful work. *Low-quality energy* is dispersed and has little ability to do useful work. To avoid unnecessary energy waste, it is best to match the quality of an energy source with the quality of energy needed to perform a task.

## Keeping Track of Atoms

In keeping with the law of conservation of matter, each side of a chemical equation must have the same number of atoms of each element involved. When this is the case, the equation is said to be *balanced*. The equation for the burning of carbon ($C + O_2 \longrightarrow CO_2$) is balanced because one atom of carbon and two atoms of oxygen are on both sides of the equation.

Consider the following chemical reaction: When electricity is passed through water ($H_2O$), the latter can be broken down into hydrogen ($H_2$) and oxygen ($O_2$), as represented by the following equation:

$$H_2O \longrightarrow H_2 + O_2$$
2 H atoms     2 H atoms   2 O atoms
1 O atom

This equation is unbalanced because one atom of oxygen is on the left but two atoms are on the right.

We cannot change the subscripts of any of the formulas to balance this equation because then we would be changing the arrangements of the atoms involved. Instead, we could use different numbers of the *molecules* involved to balance the equation. For example, we could use two water molecules:

$$2 H_2O \longrightarrow H_2 + O_2$$
4 H atoms     2 H atoms   2 O atoms
2 O atoms

This equation is still unbalanced because even though the numbers of oxygen atoms on both sides are now equal, the numbers of hydrogen atoms are not.

We can correct this by having the reaction produce two hydrogen molecules:

$$2 H_2O \longrightarrow 2 H_2 + O_2$$
4 H atoms     4 H atoms   2 O atoms
2 O atoms

Now the equation is balanced, and the law of conservation of matter has not been violated. We see that for every two molecules of water through which we pass electricity, two hydrogen molecules and one oxygen molecule are produced.

Try to balance the chemical equation for the reaction of nitrogen gas ($N_2$) with hydrogen gas ($H_2$) to form ammonia gas ($NH_3$).

### Critical Thinking

**1.** Balancing equations is based on the law of conservation of matter. Do you believe this is an ironclad law of nature or one that through new scientific discoveries could be overthrown? Explain.

**2.** Imagine you have the power to revoke the law of conservation of matter. List the three major ways this would affect your life.

energy source with the quality of energy needed to perform a particular task (Figure 3-12, p. 53) because doing so saves energy and usually money (unless government subsidies or taxes have distorted the energy marketplace).

## 3-5 PHYSICAL AND CHEMICAL CHANGES AND THE LAW OF CONSERVATION OF MATTER

**What Is the Difference Between a Physical and a Chemical Change?** A **physical change** involves no change in chemical composition. Cutting a piece of aluminum foil into small pieces is one example. Changing a substance from one physical state to another is a second example. When solid water (ice) is melted or liquid water is boiled, none of the $H_2O$ molecules involved are altered; instead, the molecules are organized in different spatial (physical) patterns (Figure 3-7, p. 50).

In a **chemical change,** or **chemical reaction,** the chemical compositions of the elements or compounds are altered. Chemists use shorthand chemical equations to represent what happens in a chemical reaction. For example, when coal burns completely, the solid carbon (C) it contains combines with oxygen gas ($O_2$) from the atmosphere to form the gaseous compound carbon dioxide ($CO_2$):

Energy is given off in this reaction, making coal a useful fuel. The reaction also shows how the complete burning of coal (or any of the carbon-containing compounds in wood, natural gas, oil, and gasoline) gives off carbon dioxide gas, which is a key gas that can lead to warming of the lower atmosphere (troposphere).

**The Law of Conservation of Matter: Why Is There No "Away"?** *We may change various elements and compounds from one physical or chemical form to another, but in no physical and chemical change can we create or destroy any of the atoms involved.* All we can do is rearrange them into different spatial patterns (physical changes) or different combinations (chemical changes). The italicized statement, based on many thousands of measurements, is known as the **law of conservation of matter.** In describing chemical reactions, chemists use a shorthand system to make sure atoms are neither created nor destroyed, as required by the law of conservation of matter (Spotlight, left).

The law of conservation of matter means there is no "away" in "to throw away." *Everything we think we have thrown away is still here with us in one form or another.* We can collect dust and soot from the smokestacks of industrial plants, but these solid wastes must then be put somewhere. We can remove substances from polluted water at a sewage treatment plant, but we must **(1)** burn them (producing some air pollution), **(2)** bury them (possibly contaminating underground water supplies), or **(3)** clean them up and apply the gooey sludge to the land as fertilizer (dangerous if the sludge contains nondegradable toxic metals such as lead and mercury). Banning use of the pesticide DDT in the United States but still selling it abroad means it can return to the United States as **(1)** DDT residues in imported coffee, fruit, and other foods, or **(2)** fallout from air masses moved long distances by winds.

**How Harmful Are Pollutants?** We can make the environment cleaner and convert some potentially harmful chemicals into less harmful physical or chemical forms. However, *the law of conservation of matter means we will always face the problem of what to do with some quantity of wastes and pollutants.*

Thus, regardless of what we do, we will always have certain pollutants that can cause harm to humans or other forms of life. Three factors determining the severity of a pollutant's harmful effects are its

- *Chemical nature.*

- *Concentration,* which is sometimes expressed in *parts per million (ppm),* with 1 ppm corresponding to 1 part pollutant per 1 million parts of the gas, liquid, or solid mixture in which the pollutant is found. Smaller concentration units are parts per billion (ppb) and parts per trillion (ppt) (Table 3-1). The concentration of a pollutant can be reduced by dumping it into the air or a large volume of water, but there are limits to the effectiveness of this dilution approach.

- **Persistence,** or how long it stays in the air, water, soil, or body.

Pollutants can be classified into three categories based on their persistence as

- **Degradable,** or **nonpersistent, pollutants** that are broken down completely or reduced to acceptable levels by natural physical, chemical, and biological processes. Complex chemical pollutants that living organisms (usually specialized bacteria) break down (metabolize) into simpler chemicals are called **biodegradable pollutants.** Human sewage in a river, for example, is biodegraded fairly quickly by bacteria if the sewage is not added faster than it can be broken down.

- **Slowly degradable,** or **persistent, pollutants** that take decades or longer to degrade. Examples include the insecticide DDT and most plastics.

- **Nondegradable pollutants** that cannot be broken down by natural processes. Examples include the toxic elements lead, mercury, and arsenic.

## 3-6 NUCLEAR CHANGES

**What Is Natural Radioactivity?** In addition to physical and chemical changes, matter can undergo a third type of change known as a **nuclear change.** This occurs when nuclei of certain isotopes

| Table 3-1 Equivalents of Some Trace Concentration Units | | | |
|---|---|---|---|
| Unit | 1 part per million | 1 part per billion | 1 part per trillion |
| Time | 1 minute in two years | 1 second in 32 years | 1 second in 32,000 years |
| Money | 1¢ in $10,000 | 1¢ in $10,000,000 | 1¢ in $10,000,000,000 |
| Weight | 1 pinch of salt in 10 kilograms (22 lbs.) of potato chips | 1 pinch of salt in 10 tons of potato chips | 1 pinch of salt in 10,000 tons of potato chips |
| Volume | 1 drop in 1,000 liters (265 gallons) of water | 1 drop in 1,000,000 liters (265,000 gallons) of water | 1 drop in 1,000,000,000 liters (265,000,000 gallons) of water |

spontaneously change or are made to change into one or more different isotopes. Three types of nuclear change are **(1)** natural radioactive decay, **(2)** nuclear fission, and **(3)** nuclear fusion.

**Natural radioactive decay** is a nuclear change in which unstable isotopes spontaneously emit fast-moving chunks of matter (called particles), high-energy radiation, or both at a fixed rate. The unstable isotopes are called **radioactive isotopes** or **radioisotopes.** Radioactive decay into various isotopes continues until the original isotope is changed into a stable isotope that is not radioactive.

Radiation emitted by radioisotopes is damaging ionizing radiation. The most common form of ionizing energy released from radioisotopes is **gamma rays,** a form of high-energy electromagnetic radiation (Figure 3-9, p. 52). High-speed ionizing particles emitted from the nuclei of radioactive isotopes are most commonly of two types: **(1) alpha particles** (fast-moving, positively charged chunks of matter that consist of two protons and two neutrons) and **(2) beta particles** (high-speed electrons). Figure 3-13 depicts the relative penetrating power of alpha, beta, and gamma ionizing radiation. All of us are exposed to small amounts of harmful ionizing radiation from both natural and human sources.

Each type of radioisotope spontaneously decays at a characteristic rate into a different isotope. This rate of decay can be expressed in terms of **half-life:** the time needed for *one-half* of the nuclei in a radioisotope to decay and emit their radiation to form a different isotope (Figure 3-14). The decay continues, often producing a series of different radioisotopes, until a nonradioactive isotope is formed. Each radioisotope has a characteristic half-life, which may range from a few millionths of a second to several billion years (Table 3-2).

An isotope's half-life cannot be changed by temperature, pressure, chemical reactions, or any other known factor. Half-life can be used to estimate how long a sample of a radioisotope must be stored in a safe container before it decays to what is considered a safe level. A general rule is that such decay takes about

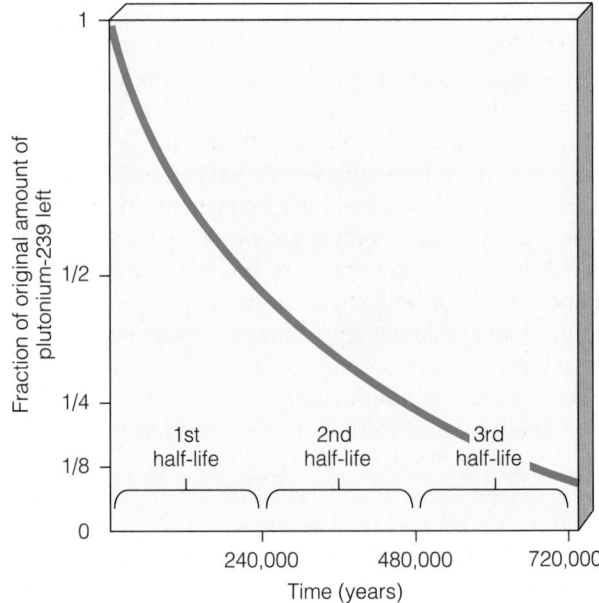

**Figure 3-14** The radioactive decay of plutonium-239, which is produced in nuclear reactors and used as the explosive in some nuclear weapons, has a half-life of 240,000 years. The amount of radioactivity emitted by a radioactive isotope decreases by one-half for each half-life that passes. Thus, after three half-lives, amounting to 720,000 years, one-eighth of a sample of plutonium-239 would still be radioactive.

10 half-lives. Thus people must be protected from radioactive waste containing iodine-131 (which concentrates in the thyroid gland and has a half-life of 8 days) for 80 days (10 × 8 days). Plutonium-239, which has a half-life of 24,000 years and is produced in nuclear reactors and used as the explosive in some nuclear weapons, can cause lung cancer when its particles are inhaled in minute amounts. Thus it must be stored safely for 240,000 years (10 × 24,000 years)—

**Figure 3-13** The three principal types of ionizing radiation emitted by radioactive isotopes differ greatly in their penetrating power.

| Table 3-2 Half-Lives of Selected Radioisotopes | | |
|---|---|---|
| **Isotope** | **Radiation Half-Life** | **Emitted** |
| Potassium-42 | 12.4 hours | Alpha, beta |
| Iodine-131 | 8 days | Beta, gamma |
| Cobalt-60 | 5.27 years | Beta, gamma |
| Hydrogen-3 (tritium) | 12.5 years | Beta |
| Strontium-90 | 28 years | Beta |
| Carbon-14 | 5,370 years | Beta |
| Plutonium-239 | 24,000 years | Alpha, gamma |
| Uranium-235 | 710 million years | Alpha, gamma |
| Uranium-238 | 4.5 billion years | Alpha, gamma |

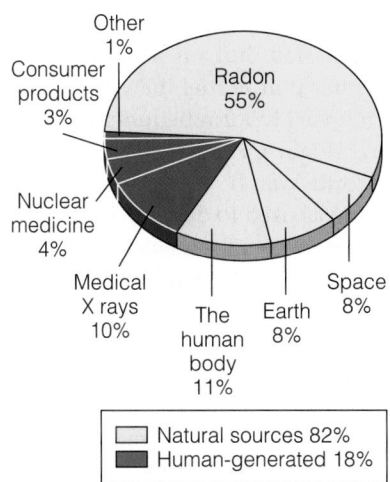

Figure 3-15 Natural and human sources of the average annual dosage of ionizing radiation received by people in the United States. Most studies indicate there is no safe dosage of ionizing radiation. (Data from National Council on Radiation Protection and Measurements)

about four times longer than the latest version of our species has existed.

**How Much Ionizing Radiation Are We Exposed To?** Each year people are exposed to some ionizing radiation (Figure 3-9, left, p. 52) from natural or background sources and from human activities (Figure 3-15). Sources of natural ionizing radiation include cosmic rays from outer space, soil, rocks, air, water, and food.

Nuclear power plants provide very low exposure to ionizing radiation (in the form of gamma rays, alpha particles, or beta particles) if they are operating properly. However, a serious nuclear accident, such as the one that occurred in 1986 at the Chernobyl nuclear power plant in Ukraine, can release large quantities of radioactive materials that can kill and harm people and make large areas uninhabitable. Most human-caused exposure to ionizing radiation comes from medical X rays and from diagnostic tests and treatments using radioactive isotopes. The federal government estimates that one-third of the X rays taken each year in the United States are unnecessary.

**What Are the Effects of Ionizing Radiation?** Ionizing radiation can cause harm by **(1)** penetrating a human cell, **(2)** knocking loose (ionizing) one or more electrons from a cellular chemical, and **(3)** thus altering molecules needed for normal cellular functioning. Exposure to ionizing radiation can damage cells in two ways:

- *Genetic damage* from mutations or changes in DNA molecules that alter genes and chromosomes (Figure 3-6, p. 50). If the mutation is harmful, it can lead to

genetic defects in the next generation of offspring or several generations later.

- *Somatic damage* to tissues, which causes harm during the victim's lifetime. Examples include burns, miscarriages, eye cataracts, and certain cancers.

The effects of ionizing radiation vary with **(1)** the type, **(2)** penetrating power (Figure 3-13), **(3)** source (outside or inside the body), and **(4)** half–life of the radioisotope (Figure 3-14 and Table 3-2). Alpha particles lack the penetrating power of beta particles but have more energy; thus, alpha-emitting isotopes are particularly dangerous when breathed in or ingested with food or water. Alpha particles outside the body can cause skin cancer but cannot penetrate the skin and reach vital organs.

Because beta particles can penetrate the skin, a beta emitter outside the body can damage internal organs. In general, radioisotopes with intermediate half-lives pose the greatest threat to human health; they stay around long enough to reach and enter the human body but decay fast enough to cause considerable damage while they are around.

According to the U.S. National Academy of Sciences, exposure over an average lifetime to average levels of ionizing radiation from natural and human sources (Figure 3-15) causes about 1% of all fatal cancers and 5–6% of all normally encountered genetic defects in the U.S. population. No scientific consensus exists on whether nonionizing forms of electromagnetic radiation (Figure 3-9, right, p. 52) given off when an electric current passes through a wire or a motor is harmful to humans.

**What Is Nuclear Fission? Splitting Nuclei Nuclear fission** is a nuclear change in which nuclei of certain isotopes with large mass numbers (such as uranium-235) are split apart into lighter nuclei when struck by neutrons; each fission releases two or three more neutrons and energy (Figure 3-16). Each of these neutrons, in turn, can cause an additional fission. For these multiple fissions to take place, enough fissionable nuclei must be present to provide the **critical mass** needed for efficient capture of these neutrons.

Figure 3-16 Fission of a uranium-235 nucleus by a neutron (*n*).

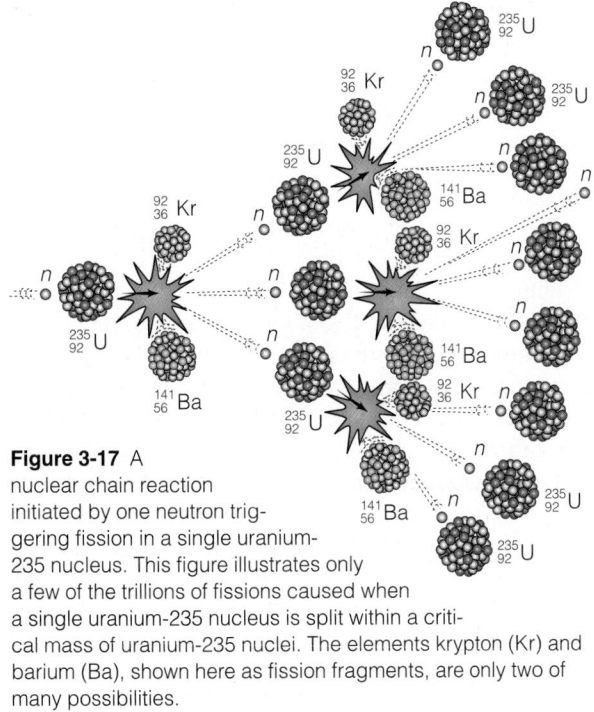

**Figure 3-17** A nuclear chain reaction initiated by one neutron triggering fission in a single uranium-235 nucleus. This figure illustrates only a few of the trillions of fissions caused when a single uranium-235 nucleus is split within a critical mass of uranium-235 nuclei. The elements krypton (Kr) and barium (Ba), shown here as fission fragments, are only two of many possibilities.

Multiple fissions within a critical mass form a **chain reaction,** which releases an enormous amount of energy (Figure 3-17). Living cells can be damaged by the ionizing radiation released by the radioactive lighter nuclei and by high-speed neutrons produced by nuclear fission.

In an atomic bomb, an enormous amount of energy is released in a fraction of a second in an uncontrolled nuclear fission chain reaction. This reaction is initiated by an explosive charge, which **(1)** suddenly pushes two masses of fissionable fuel together and **(2)** causes the fuel to reach the critical mass needed for a chain reaction.

In the reactor of a nuclear power plant, the rate at which the nuclear fission chain reaction takes place is controlled so that under normal operation only one of every two or three neutrons released is used to split another nucleus. In conventional nuclear fission reactors, the splitting of uranium-235 nuclei releases heat, which produces high-pressure steam to spin turbines and thus generate electricity.

**What Is Nuclear Fusion? Forcing Nuclei to Combine** Nuclear fusion is a nuclear change in which two isotopes of light elements, such as hydrogen, are forced together at extremely high temperatures until they fuse to form a heavier nucleus, releasing energy in the process. Temperatures of at least 100 million °C are needed to force the positively charged nuclei (which strongly repel one another) to fuse.

Nuclear fusion is much more difficult to initiate than nuclear fission, but once started it releases far more energy per unit of fuel than does fission. Fusion of hydrogen nuclei to form helium nuclei is the source of energy in the sun and other stars.

After World War II, the principle of *uncontrolled nuclear fusion* was used to develop extremely powerful hydrogen, or thermonuclear, weapons. These weapons use the D–T fusion reaction, in which a hydrogen-2, or deuterium (D) nucleus and a hydrogen-3 (tritium, T) nucleus are fused to form a larger, helium-4 nucleus, a neutron, and energy (Figure 3-18).

Scientists have also tried to develop *controlled nuclear fusion,* in which the D–T reaction is used to produce heat that can be converted into electricity. Despite more than 50 years of research, this process is still in the laboratory stage. Even if it becomes technologically and economically feasible, many energy experts do not expect it to be a practical source of energy until 2030, if then.

**Figure 3-18** The deuterium–tritium (D–T) and deuterium–deuterium (D–D) nuclear fusion reactions, which take place at extremely high temperatures.

## 3-7 TWO LAWS GOVERNING ENERGY CHANGES

**What Is the First Law of Thermodynamics? You Cannot Get Something for Nothing** Scientists have observed energy being changed from one form to another in millions of physical and chemical changes, but they have never been able to detect the creation or destruction of any energy (except in nuclear changes). The results of their experiments have been summarized in the **law of conservation of energy,** also known as the **first law of thermodynamics:** *In all physical and chemical changes, energy is neither created nor destroyed, but it may be converted from one form to another.*

This scientific law tells us that when one form of energy is converted to another form in any physical or chemical change, *energy input always equals energy output.* No matter how hard we try or how clever we are, we cannot get more energy out of a system than we put in; in other words, *we cannot get something for nothing in terms of energy quantity.*

**What Is the Second Law of Thermodynamics? You Cannot Even Break Even** Because the first law of thermodynamics states that energy can be neither created nor destroyed, we may be tempted to think we will always have enough energy. Yet if we fill a car's tank with gasoline and drive around or use a flashlight battery until it is dead, something has been lost. If it is not energy, what is it? The answer is *energy quality* (Figure 3-12, p. 53), the amount of energy available that can perform useful work.

Countless experiments have shown that when energy is changed from one form to another, a decrease in energy quality always occurs. The results of these experiments have been summarized in what is called the **second law of thermodynamics:** *When energy is changed from one form to another, some of the useful energy is always degraded to lower quality, more dispersed, less useful energy.* This degraded energy usually takes the form of heat given off at a low temperature to the surroundings (environment). There it is dispersed by the random motion of air or water molecules and becomes even more disorderly and less useful.

Basically, this law says that in any energy conversion, we always end up with *less* usable energy than we started with. So not only can we not get something for nothing in terms of energy quantity, *we cannot even break even in terms of energy quality because energy always goes from a more useful to a less useful form when energy is changed from one form to another.* No one has ever found a violation of this fundamental scientific law (see quote at the end of this chapter).

Here are three examples of the second law of thermodynamics in action:

- When a car is driven, only about 10% of the high-quality chemical energy available in its gasoline fuel is converted into mechanical energy (to propel the vehicle) and electrical energy (to run its electrical systems). The remaining 90% is degraded to low-quality heat that is released into the environment and eventually lost into space.

- When electrical energy flows through filament wires in an incandescent light bulb, it is changed into about 5% useful light and 95% low-quality heat that flows into the environment. In other words, this so-called *light bulb* is really a *heat bulb.*

- In living systems, solar energy is converted into chemical energy (food molecules) and then into mechanical energy (moving, thinking, and living). During each of these conversions, high-quality energy is degraded and flows into the environment as low-quality heat (Figure 3-19, p. 60).

The second law of thermodynamics also means that *we can never recycle or reuse high-quality energy to perform useful work.* Once the concentrated energy in a serving of food, a liter of gasoline, a lump of coal, or a chunk of uranium is released, it is degraded to low-quality heat that is dispersed into the environment. We can heat air or water at a low temperature and upgrade it to high-quality energy, but the second law of thermodynamics tells us that it will take more high-quality energy to do this than we get in return.

**Energy efficiency,** or **energy productivity,** is a measure of how much useful work is accomplished by a particular input of energy into a system. As with material efficiency (p. 51), there is plenty of room for improvement. For example, scientists estimate that only about 16% of the energy used in the United States ends up performing useful work. The remaining 84% is either unavoidably wasted because of the second law of thermodynamics (41%) or unnecessarily wasted (43%).

**Connections: How Does the Second Law of Thermodynamics Affect Life?** To form and maintain the highly ordered arrangement of molecules and the organized biochemical processes in your body, you must continually get and use high-quality matter and energy resources from your surroundings. As you use these resources, you add low-quality heat and low-quality waste matter to your surroundings. Your body continuously gives off heat roughly equal to that of a 100-watt incandescent light bulb, which is why a closed room full of people gets warm. You also continuously break down solid large molecules (such as glucose) into smaller molecules of carbon dioxide gas and water vapor, which are dispersed in the atmosphere.

Planting, growing, processing, and cooking food all use high-quality energy and matter resources that

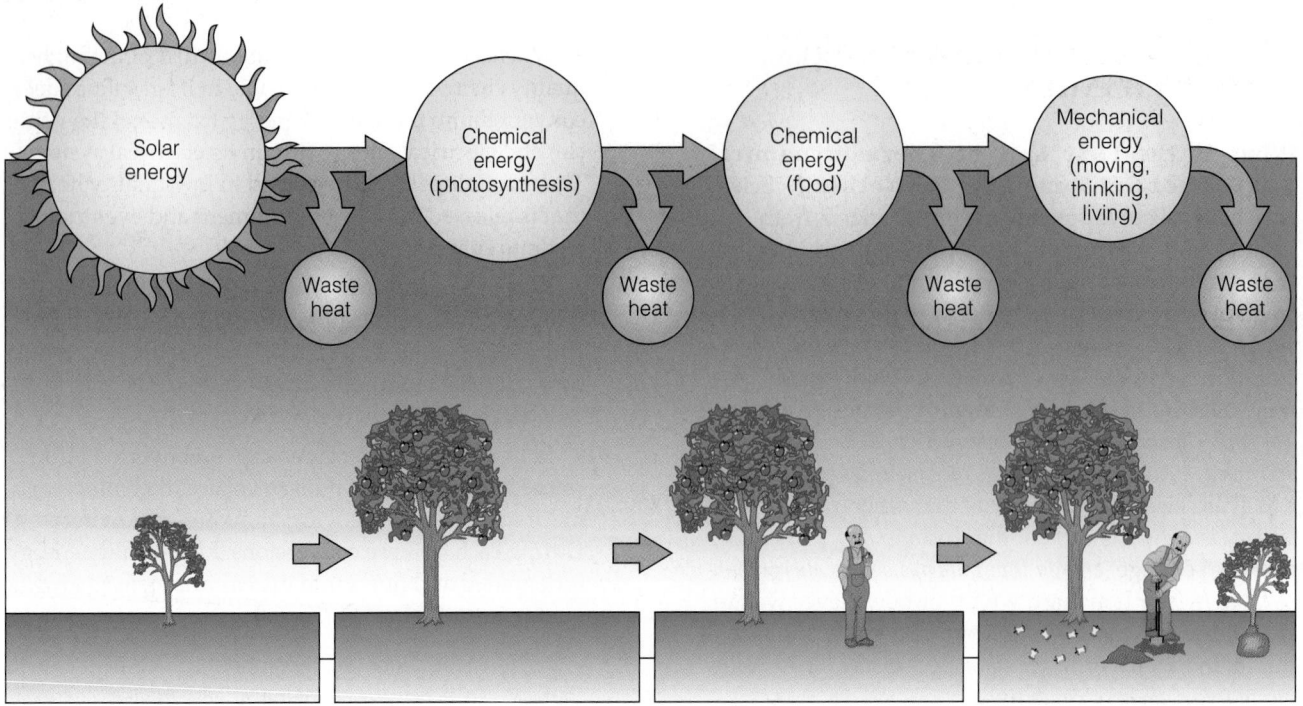

Figure 3-19 The second law of thermodynamics in action in living systems. Each time energy is changed from one form to another, some of the initial input of high-quality energy is degraded, usually to low-quality heat that disperses into the environment.

add low-quality heat and waste materials to the environment. In addition, enormous amounts of low-quality heat and waste matter are added to the environment when concentrated deposits of minerals and fuels are extracted from the earth's crust, processed, and used.

## 3-8 CONNECTIONS: MATTER AND ENERGY CHANGE LAWS AND ENVIRONMENTAL PROBLEMS

**What Is a High-Throughput Economy?** As a result of the law of conservation of matter and the second law of thermodynamics, individual resource use automatically adds some waste heat and waste matter to the environment. Most of today's advanced industrialized countries have **high-throughput (high-waste) economies** that attempt to sustain ever-increasing economic growth by increasing the flow of matter and energy resources through their economic systems (Figure 3-20). These resources flow through their economies into planetary *sinks* (air, water, soil, organisms), where pollutants and wastes end up and can accumulate to harmful levels.

What happens if more and more people continue to use and waste more and more energy and matter resources at an increasing rate? The law of conservation of matter and the two laws of thermodynamics

discussed in this chapter tell us that eventually this will exceed the capacity of the environment to (1) dilute and degrade waste matter and (2) absorb waste heat. However, they do not tell us how close we are to reaching such limits.

**What Is a Matter-Recycling Economy?** A stop-gap solution to this problem is to convert a high-throughput economy to a **matter-recycling economy.** The goal of such a conversion is to allow economic

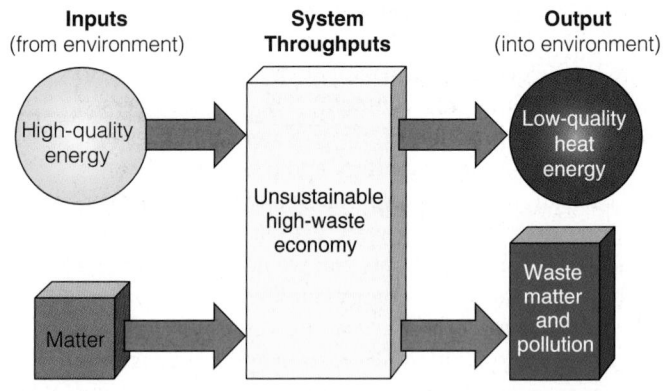

Figure 3-20 The *high-throughput economies* of most developed countries are based on maximizing the rates of energy and matter flow. This process rapidly converts high-quality matter and energy resources into waste, pollution, and low-quality heat.

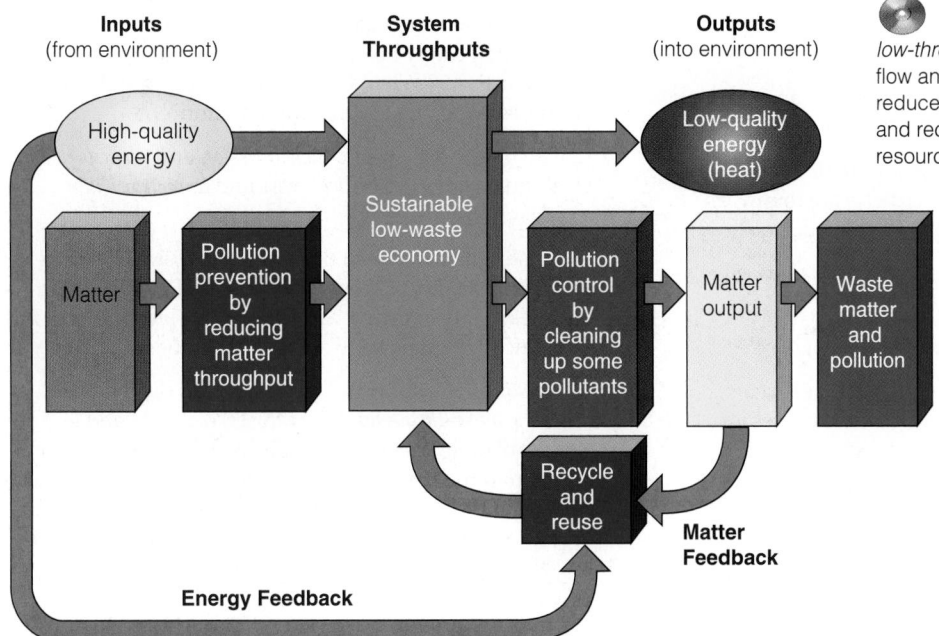

**Inputs** (from environment)      **System Throughputs**      **Outputs** (into environment)

High-quality energy

Matter

Pollution prevention by reducing matter throughput

Sustainable low-waste economy

Pollution control by cleaning up some pollutants

Matter output

Low-quality energy (heat)

Waste matter and pollution

Recycle and reuse

**Matter Feedback**

**Energy Feedback**

**Figure 3-21** Lessons from nature. A *low-throughput economy,* based on energy flow and matter recycling, works with nature to reduce throughput. This is done by **(1)** reusing and recycling most nonrenewable matter resources, **(2)** using renewable resources no faster than they are replenished, **(3)** using matter and energy resources efficiently, **(4)** reducing unnecessary consumption, **(5)** emphasizing pollution prevention and waste reduction, and **(6)** controlling population growth.

growth to continue without depleting matter resources or producing excessive pollution and environmental degradation.

Even though recycling matter saves energy, the two laws of thermodynamics tell us that *recycling matter resources always* **(1)** *requires using high-quality energy (which cannot be recycled) and* **(2)** *adds waste heat to the environment.*

Changing to a matter-recycling economy is an important way to buy some time. However, it does not allow more and more people to use more and more resources indefinitely, even if all of them were somehow perfectly recycled.

**What Is a Low-Throughput Economy? Learning from Nature** The three scientific laws governing matter and energy changes suggest that the best long-term solution to our environmental and resource problems is to shift from an economy based on maximizing matter and energy flow (throughput) to a more sustainable **low-throughput (low-waste) economy,** as summarized in Figure 3-21.

The next five chapters **(1)** apply the three basic scientific laws of matter and thermodynamics to living systems and **(2)** look at some *biological principles* that can teach us how to live more sustainably by working with nature.

*The second law of thermodynamics holds, I think, the supreme position among laws of nature. . . . If your theory is found to be against the second law of thermodynamics, I can give you no hope.*

ARTHUR S. EDDINGTON

## REVIEW QUESTIONS

**1.** Define the boldfaced terms in this chapter.

**2.** Describe what happened to the people on Easter Island and how it may relate to the current situation on the earth.

**3.** Define *science* and explain how it works. Distinguish among *scientific data, scientific hypothesis, scientific model, scientific theory,*and *scientific law.* Explain why we should take a scientific theory seriously.

**4.** What is a *controlled experiment?* What is *multivariable analysis?*

**5.** Distinguish between *inductive reasoning* and *deductive reasoning,* and give an example of each.

**6.** What does "scientifically proven" mean? If scientists cannot establish absolute proof, what do they establish?

**7.** Distinguish between *frontier science* and *consensus science.*

**8.** What is a *mathematical model,* and how is such a model made? Why are mathematical models important?

**9.** What is a *system?* Distinguish among the *inputs, flows* or *throughputs, stores,* and *outputs* of a system.

**10.** What is a *feedback loop?* Distinguish between a *positive feedback loop* and a *negative feedback loop,* and give an example of each.

**11.** Define and give an example of a *time delay* in a system.

**12.** Define *synergy,* and give an example of how it can change a system. List two environmental surprises that we have encountered and three causes of environmental surprises.

**13.** Distinguish among *matter, elements, compounds,* and *mixtures.*

**14.** Distinguish among *atoms, ions,* and *molecules,* and give an example of each. What are four states of matter?

**15.** What three major types of subatomic particles are found in atoms? Which two of these particles are found in the nucleus, and which is found outside the nucleus?

**16.** Distinguish between *atomic number* and *mass number.* What is an *isotope* of an atom?

**17.** What is the *concentration* of a chemical? What is *pH?*

**18.** What is a *chemical formula?* Distinguish between *ionic compounds* and *covalent compounds,* and give the names and chemical formulas for an example of each of these types of compounds.

**19.** Distinguish between *organic compounds* and *inorganic compounds,* and give an example of each type. Distinguish among *hydrocarbons, chlorinated hydrocarbons, chlorofluorocarbons, simple carbohydrates, polymers, complex carbohydrates, proteins, nucleic acids,* and *nucleotides.*

**20.** Distinguish between *genes* and *chromosomes.*

**21.** Distinguish between *high-quality matter* and *low-quality matter,* and give an example of each. What is *material efficiency?*

**22.** What is *energy?* What is *radiation?*

**23.** Distinguish between *kinetic energy* and *potential energy,* and give an example of each.

**24.** What is *electromagnetic radiation?* List three types of electromagnetic radiation.

**25.** Distinguish between *ionizing radiation* and *nonionizing radiation,* and give an example of each.

**26.** Distinguish between *heat* and *temperature.* Explain how heat can be transmitted by *convection, conduction,* and *radiation.*

**27.** Distinguish between *high-quality energy* and *low-quality energy,* and give an example of each. What is *energy efficiency?*

**28.** Distinguish between a *physical change* and a *chemical change,* and give an example of each.

**29.** What is the *law of conservation of matter?* Explain why there is no "away" as a repository for pollution. What is a *balanced chemical equation,* and how is it related to the law of conservation of matter?

**30.** What three factors determine the harm that a pollutant causes? Distinguish among concentrations of *parts per million, parts per billion,* and *parts per trillion.* What is the *persistence* of a pollutant? Distinguish among *degradable (nonpersistent), biodegradable, slowly degradable (persistent),* and *nondegradable pollutants,* and give an example of each type.

**31.** What is a *nuclear change?* Distinguish among *natural radioactive decay, radioisotopes, gamma rays, alpha particles,* and *beta particles.* What is the *half-life* of a radioactive iso-

tope? For how many half-lives should radioactive material be stored safely before it decays to an acceptable level of radioactivity? What are the major sources and effects of human exposure to ionizing radiation?

**32.** Distinguish between *nuclear fission* and *nuclear fusion.* Distinguish between *critical mass* and a *nuclear chain reaction.*

**33.** Distinguish between the *first law of thermodynamics* and the *second law of thermodynamics,* and give an example of each law in action. Use the second law of thermodynamics to explain why energy cannot be recycled.

**34.** Distinguish among a *high-throughput (high-waste) economy,* a *low-throughput (low-waste) economy,* and a *matter-recycling economy.* Use the law of conservation of matter and the first and second laws of thermodynamics to explain the need to shift from a high-throughput economy to a matter-recycling economy and eventually to a low-throughput economy.

## CRITICAL THINKING

**1.** Respond to the following statements:
 **a.** Scientists have not absolutely proven that anyone has ever died from smoking cigarettes.
 **b.** The greenhouse theory—that certain gases (such as water vapor and carbon dioxide) warm the atmosphere—is not a reliable idea because it is only a scientific theory.

**2.** See whether you can find an advertisement or an article describing some aspect of science in which **(a)** the concept of scientific proof is misused, **(b)** the term *theory* is used when it should have been *hypothesis,* and **(c)** a consensus scientific finding is dismissed or downplayed because it is "only a theory."

**3.** How does a scientific law (such as the law of conservation of matter) differ from a societal law (such as one imposing maximum speed limits for vehicles)? Can each be broken?

**4.** Explain why we do not really consume anything and why we can never really throw matter away.

**5.** A tree grows and increases its mass. Explain why this is not a violation of the law of conservation of matter.

**6.** If there is no "away," why isn't the world filled with waste matter?

**7.** Methane ($CH_4$) gas is the major component of natural gas. Write and balance the chemical equation for the burning of methane when it combines with oxygen gas in the atmosphere to form carbon dioxide and water. Use this equation to explain why burning natural gas can contribute to projected warming of the atmosphere (global warming).

**8.** Suppose you have 100 grams of radioactive plutonium-239 with a half-life of 24,000 years. How many grams of plutonium-239 will remain after **(a)** 12,000 years, **(b)** 24,000 years, and **(c)** 96,000 years?

**9.** Someone wants you to invest money in an automobile engine that will produce more energy than the energy in the fuel (such as gasoline or electricity) you use to run the motor. What is your response? Explain.

**10.** Use the second law of thermodynamics to explain why a barrel of oil can be used only once as a fuel.

**11. (a)** Imagine you have the power to violate the law of conservation of energy (the first law of thermodynamics) for 1 day. What are the three most important things you would do with this power? **(b)** Repeat this process, imagining you have the power to violate the second law of thermodynamics for 1 day.

## PROJECTS

**1. (a)** List two examples of negative feedback loops not discussed in this chapter, one that is beneficial and one that is detrimental. Compare your examples with those of other members of your class. **(b)** Give two examples of positive feedback loops not discussed in this chapter. Include one that is beneficial and one that is detrimental. Compare your examples with those of other members of your class.

**2.** If you have the use of a sensitive balance, try to demonstrate the law of conservation of mass in a physical change. Weigh a container with a lid (a glass jar will do), add an ice cube and weigh it again, and then allow the ice to melt and weigh it again.

**3.** Use the library or Internet to find examples of various perpetual motion machines and inventions that allegedly violate the two laws of thermodynamics by producing more high-quality energy than the high-quality energy needed to make them run. What has happened to these schemes and machines (many of them developed by scam artists to attract money from investors)?

**4.** Use the library or the Internet to find bibliographic information about *George Perkins Marsh, Warren Weaver,* and *Arthur S. Eddington,* whose quotes appear at the beginning and end of this chapter.

**5.** Make a concept map of this chapter's major ideas using the section heads and subheads and the key terms (in boldface). Look on the website for this book for information about making concept maps.

## INTERNET STUDY RESOURCES AND RESOURCES FOR FURTHER READING AND RESEARCH

The website for this book contains helpful study aids and many ideas for further reading and research. Log on to

www.info.brookscole.com/miller13

and click on the Chapter-by-Chapter area. Choose Chapter 3 and select a resource:

- Flash Cards allows you to test your mastery of the Terms and Concepts to Remember for this chapter.

- Tutorial Quizzes provides a multiple-choice practice quiz.

- Student Guide to InfoTrac will lead you to Critical Thinking Projects that use InfoTrac College Edition as a research tool.

- References lists the major books and articles consulted in writing this chapter.

- Hypercontents takes you to an extensive list of sites with news, research, and images related to individual sections of the chapter.

## INFOTRAC COLLEGE EDITION

Improve your skills with InfoTrac College Edition, a searchable online database of articles from more than 700 periodicals. Log on to

http://www.infotrac-college.com

or access InfoTrac through the website for this book. Try to find the following articles:

**1.** Scully, M. 2001. Quantum mechanics boosts engine efficiency. (Brief article) *Inside R&D* (February 1) *Keywords:* "quantum mechanics" and "efficiency." This article explores issues in frontier science by examining the theory of coupling the energy of atomic structure with the energy of atomic motion in the internal combustion engine. This type of system could increase the efficiency of current energy use.

**2.** Beals, G. 2001. Pining for a breakthrough: Despite years of ostracism, a small and dwindling army of cold-fusion faithful are ever hopeful. (Brief article) *Newsweek International* (October 15): 57. *Keywords:* "cold fusion" and "breakthrough." Twelve years after the first announcement of "cold fusion," and the subsequent lack of repeatability, people are still searching for this elusive "unlimited energy source." However, life on the frontier of cold fusion is starting to get lonelier.

# 4 ECOSYSTEMS: COMPONENTS, ENERGY FLOW, AND MATTER CYCLING

## Have You Thanked the Insects Today?

Insects have a bad reputation. We classify many insect species as *pests* because they **(1)** compete with us for food, **(2)** spread human diseases (such as malaria), and **(3)** invade our lawns, gardens, and houses. Some people have "bugitis," fear all insects, and think the only good bug is a dead bug. However, this view fails to recognize the vital roles insects play in helping sustain life on earth.

A large proportion of the earth's plant species (including many trees) depend on insects to pollinate their flowers (Figure 4-1, left). In turn, we and other land-dwelling animals depend on plants for food, either by eating them or by consuming animals that eat them. Without pollinating insects, very few fruits and vegetables would be available for us and plant-eating animals to eat.

Insects such as the praying mantis (Figure 4-1, right), which eat other insects, help control the populations of at least half the species of insects we call pests. This free pest control service is an important part of nature's services that help sustain us.

Suppose all insects disappeared today. Within a year most of the earth's animals would become extinct because of the disappearance of so much plant life. The earth would be covered with rotting vegetation and animal carcasses being decomposed by unimaginably huge hordes of bacteria and fungi.

Fortunately, this is not a realistic scenario because insects, which have been around for at least 400 million years, are phenomenally successful forms of life. They were the first animals to invade the land and, later, the air. Today they are by far the planet's most diverse, abundant, and successful animals.

Insects can **(1)** rapidly evolve new genetic traits, such as resistance to pesticides, **(2)** have an exceptional ability to evolve into new species when faced with new environmental conditions, and **(3)** are extremely resistant to extinction.

This is another example of the law of conservation of problems (p. 46). Application of chemical pesticides to protect crops from pests can help grow more food. However, the pesticides can also **(1)** contaminate the air and water far from where they are applied, **(2)** harm beneficial insects that help protect crops from other insects, **(3)** threaten the health of wildlife and people, and **(4)** accelerate the natural ability of rapidly reproducing insect pests to develop genetic resistance (immunity) to such pesticides. Thus, in the long run, pesticide technology can backfire and become less effective in solving the problem of crop losses from insect pests.

The environmental lesson is that although insects can thrive without newcomers such as us, we and most other land organisms would perish quickly without them. Learning about the roles insects play in nature requires us to understand how insects and other organisms living in a biological *community* (such as a forest or pond) interact with one another and with the nonliving environment. *Ecology* is the science that studies such relationships and interactions in nature, as I discuss in this chapter and the six chapters that follow.

**Figure 4-1** Insects play important roles in helping sustain life on earth. The bright green caterpillar moth feeding on pollen in a crocus (left) and other insects pollinate flowering plants that serve as food for many plant eaters. The praying mantis eating a monarch butterfly (right) and many other insect species help control the populations of at least half of the insect species we classify as pests.

*The earth's thin film of living matter is sustained by grand-scale cycles of energy and chemical elements.*

G. Evelyn Hutchinson

This chapter addresses the following questions:

- What is ecology?
- What basic processes keep us and other organisms alive?
- What are the major components of an ecosystem?
- What happens to energy in an ecosystem?
- What happens to matter in an ecosystem?
- How do scientists study ecosystems?
- What are ecosystem services, and how do they affect the sustainability of the earth's life-support systems?

 **4-1 THE NATURE OF ECOLOGY**

**What Is Ecology?** Ecology (from the Greek words *oikos*, "house" or "place to live," and *logos*, "study of") is the study of how organisms interact with one another and with their nonliving environment. In effect, it is a study of *connections in nature*.

**What Are Organisms?** Ecologists focus on trying to understand the interactions among organisms, populations, communities, ecosystems, and the biosphere (Figure 4-2, p. 66).

An **organism** is any form of life. The **cell** is the basic unit of life in organisms. Organisms may consist of a single cell (bacteria, for instance) or many cells.

On the basis of their cell structure, organisms can be classified as either *eukaryotic* or *prokaryotic*. Each cell of a **eukaryotic** organism (1) is surrounded by a membrane, (2) has a distinct *nucleus* (a membrane-bounded structure containing genetic material in the form of DNA), and (3) has several other internal parts called *organelles* (Figure 4-3a, p. 67). All organisms except bacteria are eukaryotic.

A membrane surrounds the cell of a **prokaryotic** organism, but inside the cell no distinct nucleus or other internal parts are enclosed by membranes (Figure 4-3b, p. 67). All bacteria are single-celled prokaryotic organisms. Although most familiar organisms are eukaryotic, they could not exist without hordes of prokaryotic organisms (bacteria; Connections, below). These bacteria are examples of *microorganisms,* so small they can be seen only with the aid of a microscope.

## Microbes: The Invisible Rulers of the Earth

**CONNECTIONS**

They are everywhere and there are trillions of them. Billions are found inside your body, on your body, in a handful of soil, and in a cup of river water.

These mostly invisible rulers of the earth are *microbes*, a catchall term for many thousands of species of bacteria, protozoa, fungi, and yeasts, most of which are too small for us to see with the naked eye.

Most microbes do not get the respect they deserve. Most of us think of them as threats to our health in the form of (1) infectious bacteria or "germs," (2) fungi that cause athlete's foot and other skin diseases, and (3) protozoa that cause killer diseases such as malaria. However, these potentially harmful microbes are in the minority.

Most of the earth's hordes of microbes not only are harmless but also make the rest of life possible.

Some of them play a vital role in producing foods such as bread, cheese, yogurt, vinegar, tofu, soy sauce, beer, and wine. Others provide us with food by converting nitrogen gas in the atmosphere into forms that plants can take up from the soil as nutrients.

Bacteria and fungi in the soil decompose organic wastes into nutrients that can be taken up by plants. Bacteria in your intestinal tract break down the food you eat. Some microbes in your nose prevent harmful bacteria from reaching your lungs. Other microbes have been the source of disease-fighting antibiotics, including penicillin, erythromycin, and streptomycin.

Another vital ecological service that some microbes provide is controlling some plant diseases and populations of insect species that attack food crops. Enlisting some of these microbes for pest control can reduce the use of potentially harmful chemical pesticides.

In addition, genetic engineers are developing microbes that can (1) extract metals from ores, (2) break down various pollutants, and (3) help clean up toxic waste sites.

Harvard biologist Edward O. Wilson, who has developed many important ecological theories and is one of the world's experts on ants, says that if he were starting over he would study microbes.

### Critical Thinking

**1.** A bumper sticker reads, "Have You Thanked Microbes Today?" Give reasons for doing so, and explain why microbes are the real rulers of the earth.

**2.** What are some potentially harmful effects of (a) using genetic engineering to design microbes to break down oil and toxic chemicals and (b) overusing antibacterial soaps, sprays, and antibiotics?

Figure 4-2 Levels of organization of matter in nature. Note the five levels that ecology focuses on.

**What Are Species?** Organisms can be classified into **species,** or groups of organisms that resemble one another in appearance, behavior, chemistry, and genetic makeup. Species differ in how they produce offspring. **Asexual reproduction** is common in species such as bacteria with only one cell, which divides to produce two identical cells that are clones or replicas of the original cell.

**Sexual reproduction** occurs in organisms that produce offspring by combining sex cells or gametes (such as ovum and sperm) from both parents. This produces offspring that have combinations of genetic traits from each parent. Sexual reproduction usually gives the species a greater chance of survival under changing environmental conditions than the genetic clones produced by asexual reproduction.

Organisms that reproduce sexually are classified as members of the same species if, under natural conditions, they can **(1)** actually or potentially breed with one another and **(2)** produce live, fertile offspring. Scientists use a special system to name each species (see Appendix 3).

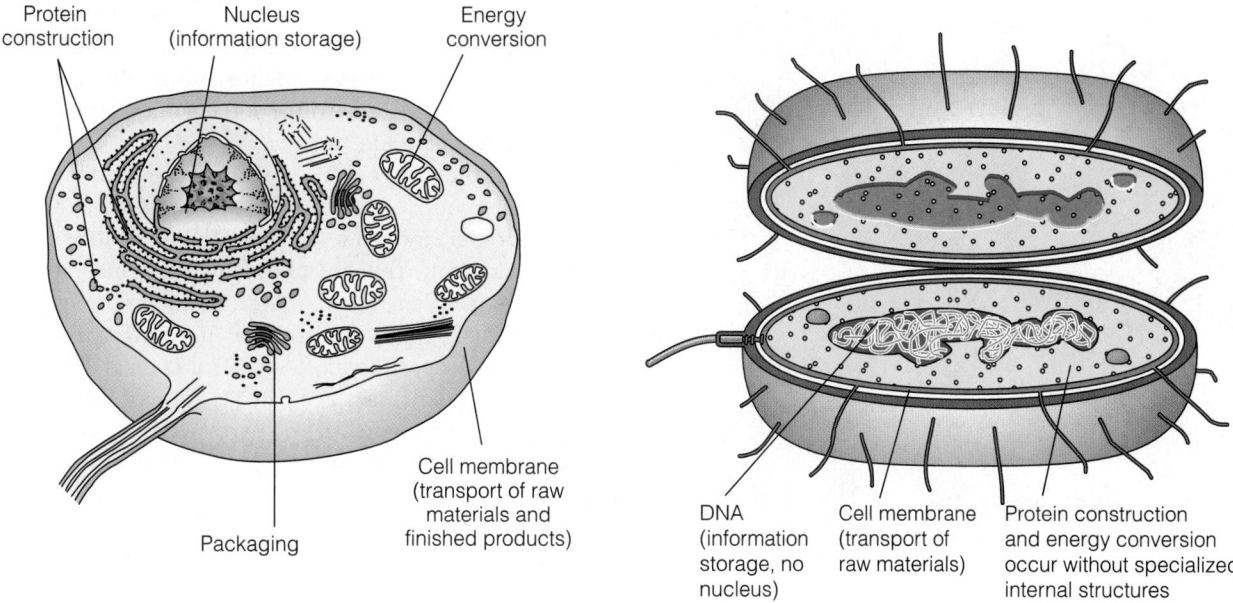

Protein construction | Nucleus (information storage) | Energy conversion

Cell membrane (transport of raw materials and finished products)

Packaging

**(a) Eukaryotic Cell**

DNA (information storage, no nucleus) | Cell membrane (transport of raw materials) | Protein construction and energy conversion occur without specialized internal structures

**(b) Prokaryotic Cell**

**Figure 4-3** **(a)** Generalized structure of a eukaryotic cell. The parts and internal structure of cells in various types of organisms such as plants and animals differ somewhat from this generalized model. **(b)** Generalized structure of a prokaryotic cell. Note that prokaryotic cells lack a distinct nucleus. (Adapted from Cecie Starr and Ralph Taggart, *Biology: The Unity and Diversity of Life*, 8th ed., Wadsworth, © 1998)

We do not know how many species exist on the earth. Estimates range from 3.6 million to 100 million. Most are insects (p. 64) and microorganisms too small to be seen with the naked eye (Connections, p. 65). Excluding hordes of bacterial species, a best guess of the number of species is about 10–14 million.

So far biologists have identified and named about 1.5–1.8 million species, not including bacteria. Biologists know a fair amount about roughly one-third of the known species but understand the detailed roles and interactions of only a few. Each year researchers identify only about 10,000 new species, so we have a long way to go to identify even a fraction of the estimated species.

**What Is a Population?** A **population** consists of a group of interacting individuals of the same species that occupy a specific area at the same time (Figure 4-4). Examples are all **(1)** sunfish in a pond, **(2)** white oak trees in a forest, and **(3)** people in a country. In most natural populations, individuals vary slightly in their genetic makeup, which is why they do not all look or behave exactly alike—a phenomenon called **genetic diversity** (Figure 4-5, p. 68). In response to changes in environmental conditions, populations change in **(1)** *size,* **(2)** *age distribution* (number of individuals in each age group), **(3)** *density* (number of individuals per unit of space), and **(4)** *genetic composition.*

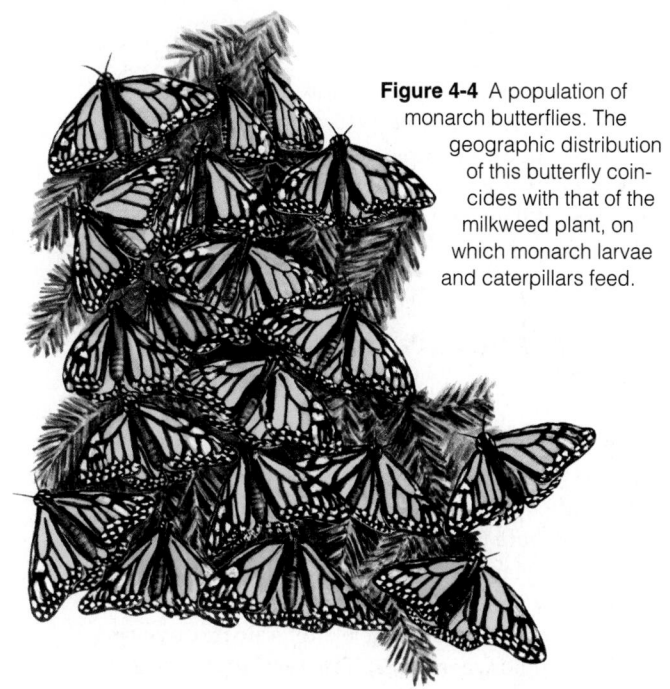

**Figure 4-4** A population of monarch butterflies. The geographic distribution of this butterfly coincides with that of the milkweed plant, on which monarch larvae and caterpillars feed.

The place where a population (or an individual organism) normally lives is its **habitat.** It may be as large as an ocean or prairie or as small as the underside of a rotting log or the intestine of a termite.

**What Are Communities, Ecosystems, and the Biosphere?** Populations of the different species occupying a particular place make up a **community,** or

**Figure 4-5** The genetic diversity among individuals of one species of Caribbean snail is reflected in the variations in shell color and banding patterns.

**biological community.** It is a complex interacting network of plants, animals, and microorganisms.

An **ecosystem** is a community of different species interacting with one another and with their nonliving environment of matter and energy. Ecosystems can range in size from a puddle of water to a stream, a patch of woods, an entire forest, or a desert. Ecosystems can be natural or artificial (human created). Examples of human-created ecosystems are cropfields, farm ponds, and reservoirs. All of the earth's ecosystems together make up what we call the *biosphere.*

## 4-2 THE EARTH'S LIFE-SUPPORT SYSTEMS

**What Are the Major Parts of the Earth's Life-Support Systems?** We can think of the earth as being made up of several spherical layers (Figure 4-6). The **atmosphere** is a thin envelope or membrane of air around the planet. Its inner layer, the **troposphere,** extends only about 17 kilometers (11 miles) above sea level but contains most of the planet's air, mostly nitrogen (78%) and oxygen (21%). The next layer, stretching 17–48 kilometers (11–30 miles) above the earth's surface, is the **stratosphere.** Its lower portion contains enough ozone ($O_3$) to filter out most of the sun's harmful ultraviolet radiation, thus allowing life to exist on land and in the surface layers of bodies of water.

The **hydrosphere** consists of the earth's **(1)** liquid water (both surface and underground), **(2)** ice (polar ice, icebergs, and ice in frozen soil layers, or perma-

frost), and **(3)** water vapor in the atmosphere. The **lithosphere** is the earth's crust and upper mantle; the crust contains nonrenewable fossil fuels and minerals we use as well as renewable soil chemicals (nutrients) needed for plant life.

The **biosphere** is the portion of the earth in which living (biotic) organisms exist and interact with one another and with their nonliving (abiotic) environment. The biosphere includes most of the hydrosphere and parts of the lower atmosphere and upper lithosphere. It reaches from the deepest ocean floor, 20 kilometers (12 miles) below sea level, to the tops of the highest mountains. If the earth were an apple, the biosphere would be no thicker than the apple's skin. *The goal of ecology is to understand the interactions in this thin, life-supporting global skin or membrane of air, water, soil, and organisms.*

**What Sustains Life on Earth?** Life on the earth depends on three interconnected factors (Figure 4-7):

- The *one-way flow of high-quality energy* (Figure 3-12, p. 53) from the sun, **(1)** through materials and living

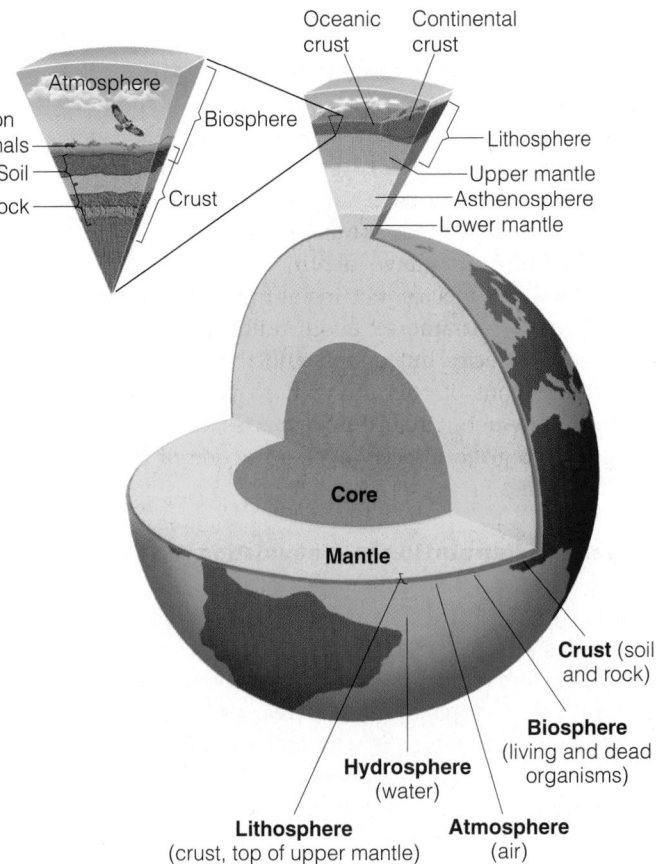

**Figure 4-6** The general structure of the earth.

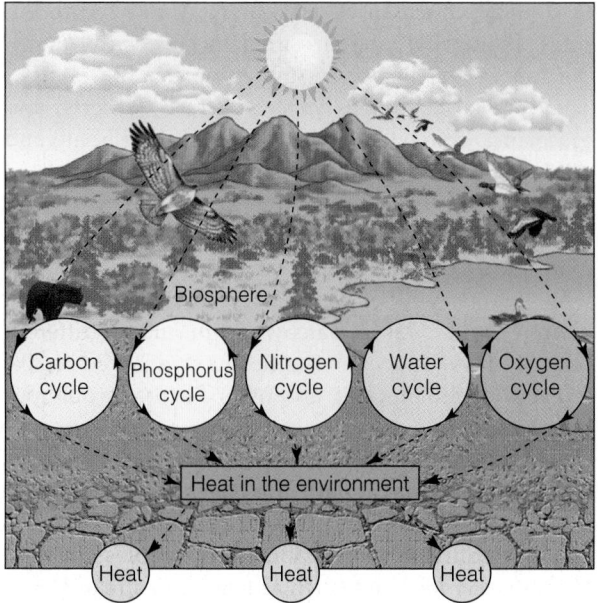

Figure 4-7 Life on the earth depends on (1) the *one-way flow of energy* (dashed lines) from the sun through the biosphere, (2) the *cycling of crucial elements* (solid lines around circles), and (3) *gravity*, which keeps atmospheric gases from escaping into space and draws chemicals downward in the matter cycles. This simplified model depicts only a few of the many cycling elements.

things in their feeding interactions, (2) into the environment as low-quality energy (mostly heat dispersed into air or water molecules at a low temperature), and (3) eventually back into space as heat.

■ The *cycling of matter* (the atoms, ions, or molecules needed for survival by living organisms) through parts of the biosphere. The earth is closed to significant inputs of matter from space. Thus essentially all the nutrients used by organisms are already present on earth and must be recycled again and again for life to continue.

■ *Gravity*, which (1) allows the planet to hold on to its atmosphere and (2) causes the downward movement of chemicals in the matter cycles.

**How Does the Sun Help Sustain Life on Earth?** The sun is a middle-aged star whose energy

■ Lights and warms the planet.

■ Supports *photosynthesis,* the process used by green plants and some bacteria to make compounds such as carbohydrates that keep them alive and feed most other organisms.

■ Powers the cycling of matter.

■ Drives the climate and weather systems that distribute heat and fresh water over the earth's surface.

The sun is a gigantic fireball of hydrogen (72%) and helium (28%) gases. Temperatures and pressures in its inner core are so high that hydrogen nuclei fuse to form helium nuclei (Figure 3-18, p. 58), releasing enormous amounts of energy.

Thus the sun is a gigantic nuclear fusion (thermonuclear) reactor running on hydrogen fuel. This enormous reactor radiates energy in all directions as electromagnetic radiation (Figure 3-10, p. 52). Moving at the speed of light, this radiation makes the 150-million-kilometer (93-million-mile) trip between the sun and the earth in slightly more than 8 minutes.

**What Happens to Solar Energy Reaching the Earth?** Because the earth is a tiny sphere in the vastness of space, it receives only about one-billionth of the sun's output of energy. Much of this energy is either reflected away or absorbed by chemicals in its atmosphere (Figure 4-8).

Most of what reaches the atmosphere is (1) visible light (Figure 3-10, p. 52), (2) infrared radiation (heat), and (3) the small amount of ultraviolet radiation that is not absorbed by ozone in the stratosphere (Figure 4-8). This incoming energy (1) warms the troposphere and land, (2) evaporates water and cycles it through the biosphere, and (3) generates winds. A tiny fraction is

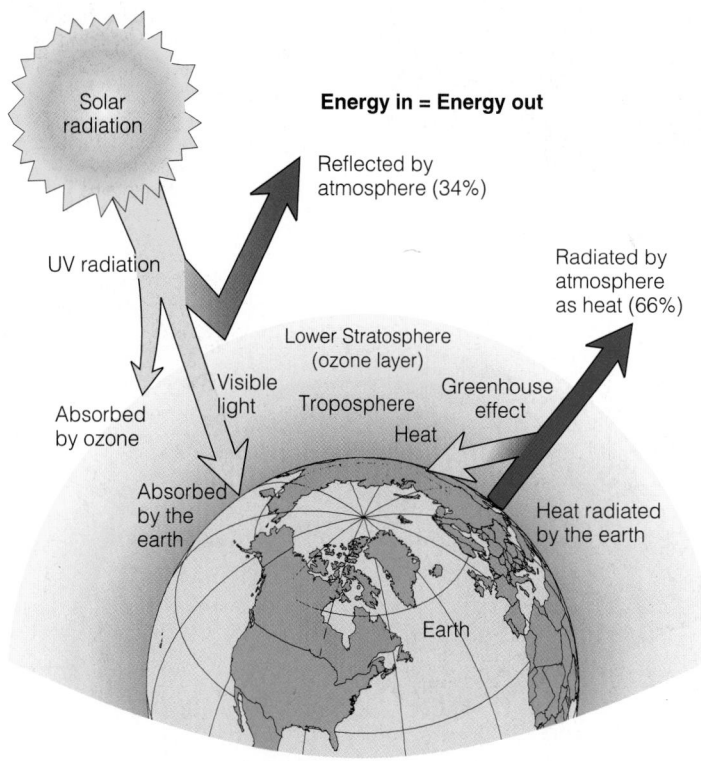

Figure 4-8 The flow of energy to and from the earth.

captured by green plants, algae, and bacteria to fuel photosynthesis and make the organic compounds that most forms of life need to survive.

Most unreflected solar radiation is degraded into infrared radiation (which we experience as heat) as it interacts with the earth. Greenhouse gases (such as water vapor, carbon dioxide, methane, nitrous oxide, and ozone) in the atmosphere reduce this flow of heat back into space. This helps warm the earth by acting somewhat like the glass in a greenhouse or the windows in a closed car, which allow a buildup of heat. Without this **natural greenhouse effect,** the earth would be too cold for life as we know it to exist.

## 4-3 ECOSYSTEM CONCEPTS AND COMPONENTS

### What Are Biomes and Aquatic Life Systems?
Viewed from outer space, the earth resembles an enormous jigsaw puzzle consisting of large masses of land and vast expanses of ocean (p. 1 and Figure 1-1, p. 2). Biologists have classified the terrestrial (land) portion of the biosphere into **biomes** ("BY-ohms"). They are large regions such as forests, deserts, and grasslands characterized by **(1)** a distinct climate and **(2)** specific life-forms (especially vegetation) adapted to it (Figure 4-9).

**Climate**—long-term patterns of weather—is the main factor determining what type of life, especially what plants, will thrive in a given land area. Each biome consists of a patchwork of many different ecosystems whose communities have adapted to differences in climate, soil, and other factors throughout the biome.

Marine and freshwater portions of the biosphere can be divided into **aquatic life zones,** each containing numerous ecosystems. Aquatic life zones are the aquatic equivalent of biomes. Examples include **(1)** *freshwater life zones* (such as lakes and streams) and **(2)** *ocean or marine life zones* (such as estuaries, coastlines, coral reefs, and the deep ocean).

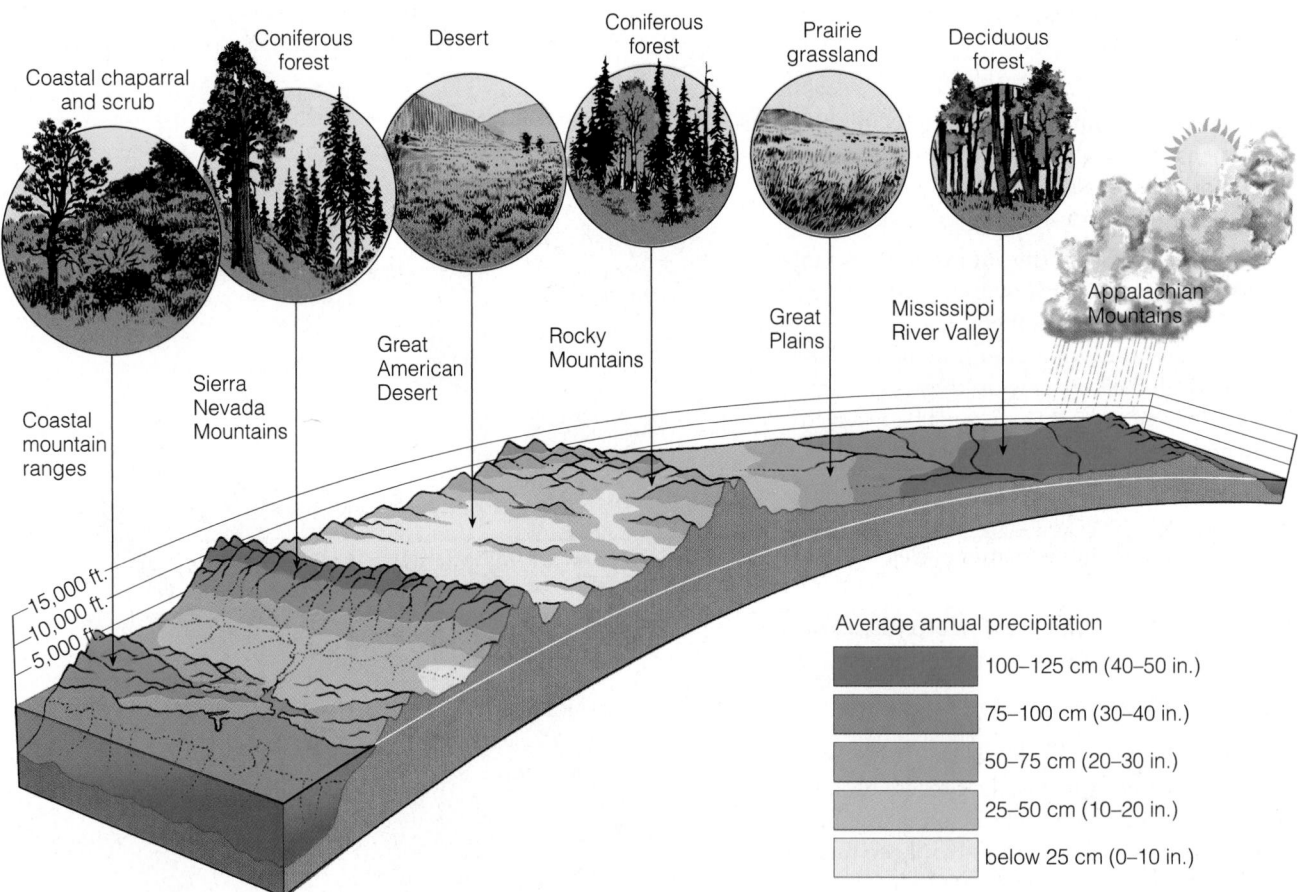

**Figure 4-9** Major biomes found along the 39th parallel across the United States. The differences reflect changes in climate, mainly differences in average annual precipitation and temperature (not shown).

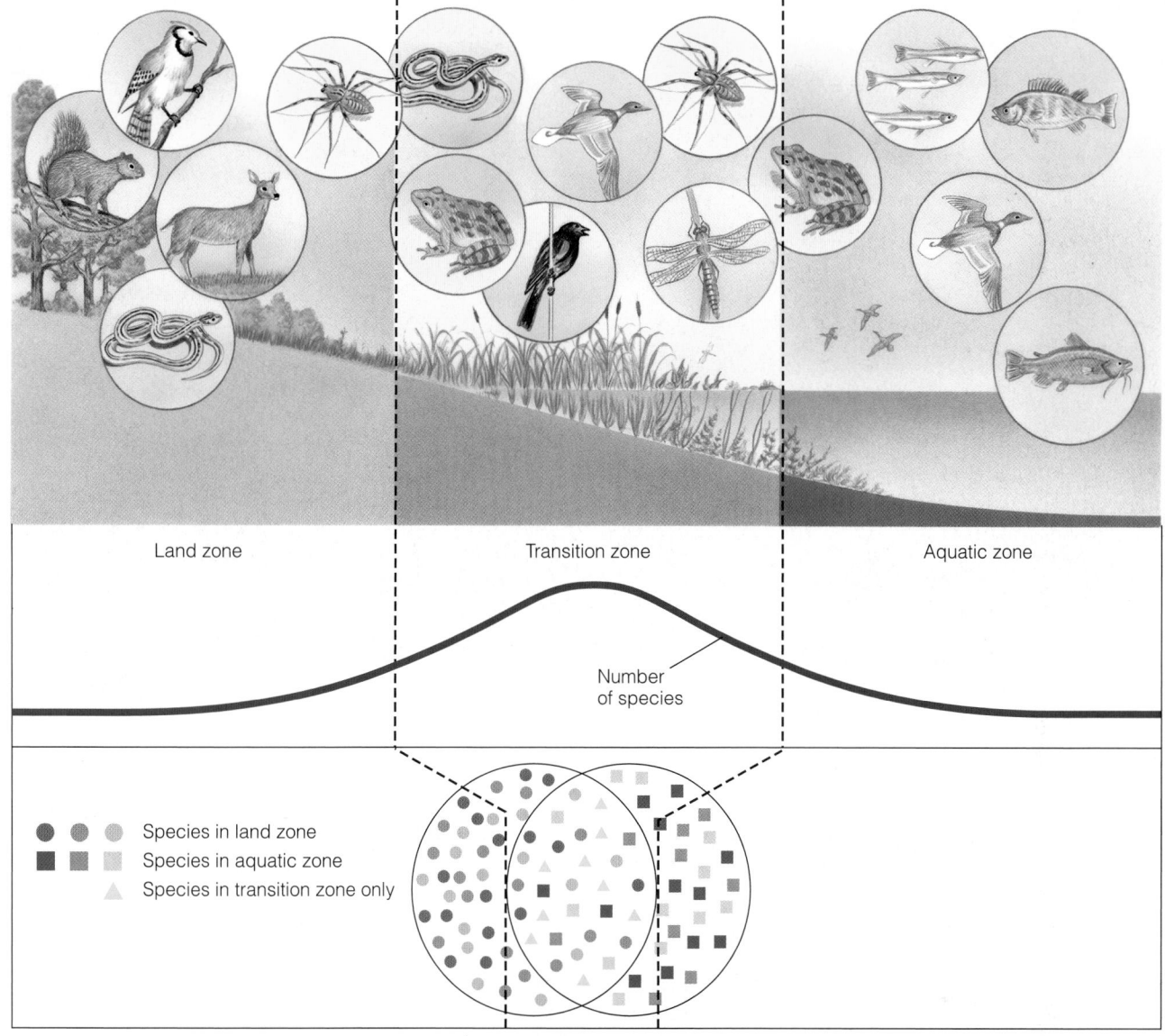

**Figure 4-10** Ecosystems rarely have sharp boundaries. Two adjacent ecosystems such as dry land and an open lake often contain a marsh—an ecotone or transitional zone—between them. This zone contains a mixture of species found in each ecosystem and contains some species not found in either ecosystem.

In the figure:

Land zone

Transition zone

Aquatic zone

Number of species

- Species in land zone
- Species in aquatic zone
- Species in transition zone only

**Do Ecosystems Have Distinct Boundaries?** For convenience, scientists usually consider an ecosystem under study as an isolated unit. However, natural ecosystems **(1)** rarely have distinct boundaries and **(2)** are not truly self-contained, self-sustaining systems.

Instead, one ecosystem tends to merge with the next in a transitional zone called an **ecotone,** a region containing a mixture of species from adjacent ecosystems and often species not found in either of the bordering ecosystems. For example, a marsh or wetland found between dry land and the open water of a lake or ocean is an ecotone (Figure 4-10). Another example

is the zone of grasses, small shrubs, and scattered small trees found between a grassland and a forest.

**What Are the Major Components of Ecosystems?** The biosphere and its ecosystems can be separated into two parts: **(1) abiotic,** or nonliving, components (water, air, nutrients, and solar energy) and **(2) biotic,** or living, components (plants, animals, and microorganisms, sometimes called *biota*). Figures 4-11 and 4-12 (p. 72) are greatly simplified diagrams of some of the biotic and abiotic components in a freshwater aquatic ecosystem and a terrestrial ecosystem.

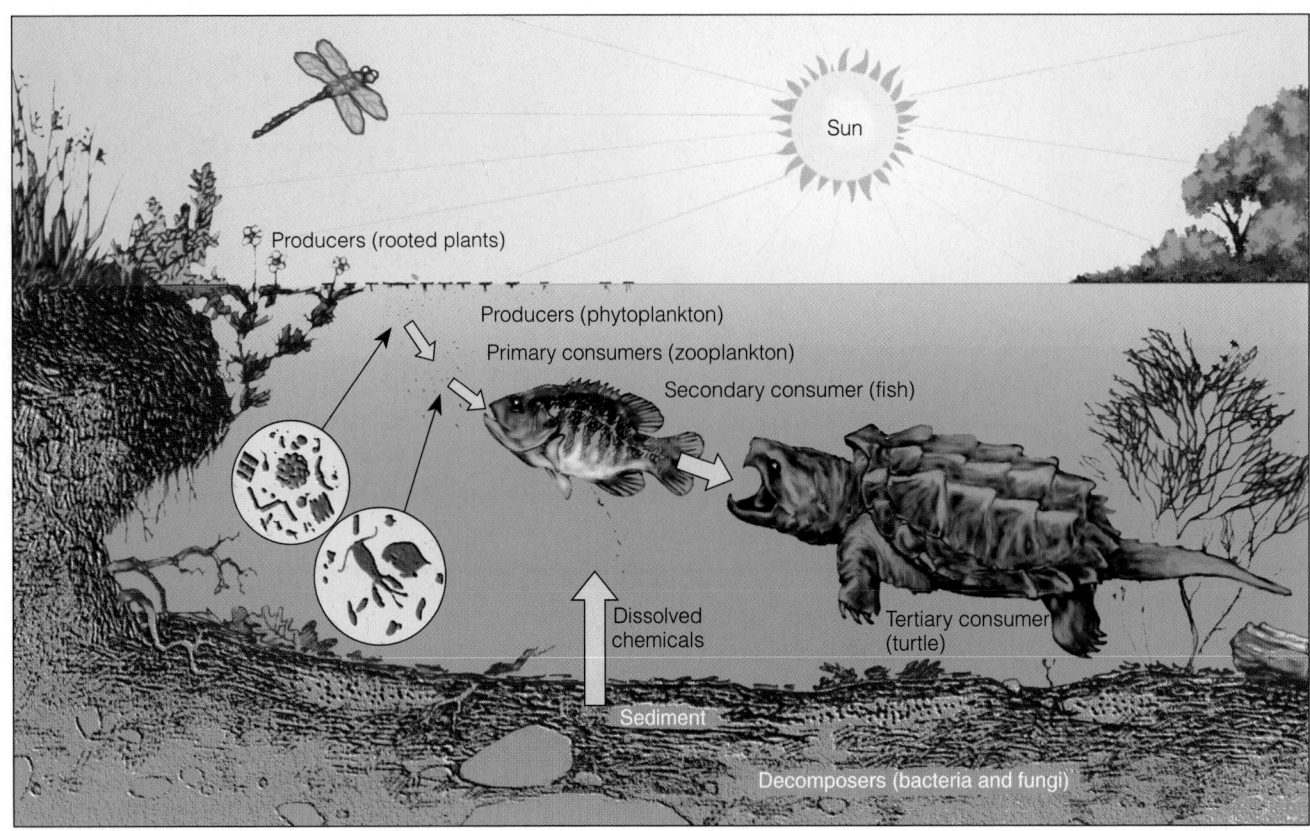

**Figure 4-11** Major components of a freshwater ecosystem.

**Figure 4-12** Major components of an ecosystem in a field.

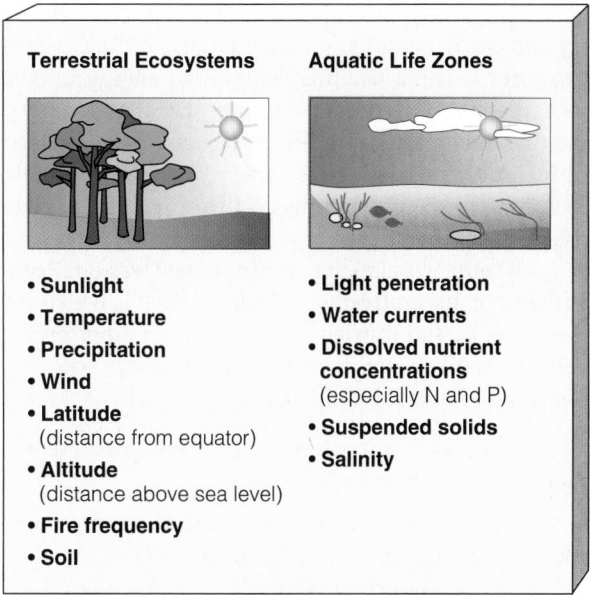

| Terrestrial Ecosystems | Aquatic Life Zones |
|---|---|
| • Sunlight | • Light penetration |
| • Temperature | • Water currents |
| • Precipitation | • Dissolved nutrient concentrations (especially N and P) |
| • Wind | |
| • Latitude (distance from equator) | • Suspended solids |
| • Altitude (distance above sea level) | • Salinity |
| • Fire frequency | |
| • Soil | |

**Figure 4-13** Key physical and chemical or abiotic factors affecting terrestrial ecosystems (left) and aquatic life zones (right).

**What Are the Major Nonliving Components of Ecosystems?** The nonliving, or abiotic, components of an ecosystem are the physical and chemical factors that influence living organisms in land (terrestrial) ecosystems and aquatic life zones (Figure 4-13).

Different species thrive under different physical conditions. Some need bright sunlight, and others thrive better in shade. Some need a hot environment and others a cool or cold one. Some do best under wet conditions and others under dry conditions.

Each population in an ecosystem has a **range of tolerance** to variations in its physical and chemical environment (Figure 4-14). Individuals within a population may also have slightly different tolerance ranges for temperature or other factors because of small differences in genetic makeup, health, and age. Thus, although a trout population may do best within a narrow band of temperatures (*optimum level* or *range*), a few individuals can survive above and below that band. As Figure 4-14 shows, tolerance has its limits, beyond which none of the trout can survive.

These observations are summarized in the **law of tolerance:** *The existence, abundance, and distribution of a species in an ecosystem are determined by whether the levels of one or more physical or chemical factors fall within the range tolerated by that species.* A species may have a wide range of tolerance to some factors and a narrow range of tolerance to others. Most organisms are least tolerant during juvenile or reproductive stages of their life cycles. *Highly tolerant species can live in a variety of habitats with widely different conditions.*

A variety of factors can affect the number of organisms in a population. However, sometimes one factor, known as a **limiting factor,** is more important

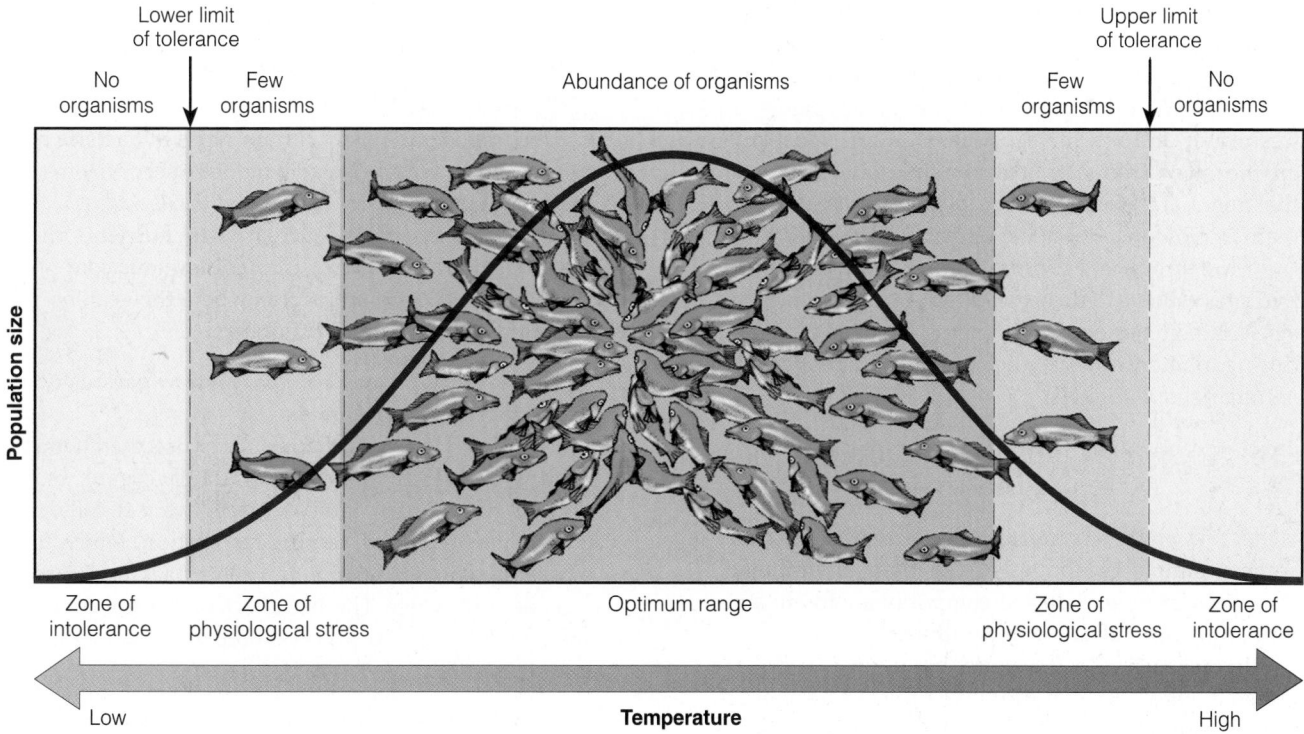

**Figure 4-14** Range of tolerance for a population of organisms to an abiotic environmental factor—in this case, temperature.

in regulating population growth than other factors. This ecological principle, related to the law of tolerance, is called the **limiting factor principle:** *Too much or too little of any abiotic factor can limit or prevent growth of a population, even if all other factors are at or near the optimum range of tolerance.*

On land, precipitation often is the limiting factor. Lack of water in a desert limits plant growth. Soil nutrients also can act as a limiting factor on land. Suppose a farmer plants corn in phosphorus-poor soil. Even if water, nitrogen, potassium, and other nutrients are at optimum levels, the corn will stop growing when it uses up the available phosphorus.

Too much of an abiotic factor can also be limiting. For example, too much water or too much fertilizer can kill plants, a common mistake of many beginning gardeners.

Important limiting factors for aquatic ecosystems include **(1)** temperature, **(2)** sunlight, **(3) dissolved oxygen (DO) content** (the amount of oxygen gas dissolved in a given volume of water at a particular temperature and pressure), and **(4)** nutrient availability. Another limiting factor in aquatic ecosystems is **salinity** (the amounts of various inorganic minerals or salts dissolved in a given volume of water).

**What Are the Major Living Components of Ecosystems?** Living organisms in ecosystems usually are classified as either *producers* or *consumers,* based on how they get food. **Producers,** sometimes called **autotrophs** (self-feeders), make their own food from compounds obtained from their environment. All other organisms are *consumers,* which depend directly or indirectly on food provided by producers.

On land, most producers are green plants. In freshwater and marine ecosystems, algae and plants are the major producers near shorelines. In open water, the dominant producers are *phytoplankton* (most of them microscopic) that float or drift in the water.

Most producers capture sunlight to make carbohydrates (such as glucose, $C_6H_{12}O_6$) by **photosynthesis.** Although hundreds of chemical changes take place during photosynthesis, the overall reaction can be summarized as follows:

carbon dioxide + water + **solar energy** ⟶ glucose + oxygen

$$6\,CO_2 + 6\,H_2O + \textbf{solar energy} \longrightarrow C_6H_{12}O_6 + 6\,O_2$$

A few producers, mostly specialized bacteria, can convert simple compounds from their environment into more complex nutrient compounds without sunlight, a process called **chemosynthesis.**

In one such case, the source of energy is heat generated by the decay of radioactive elements deep in the earth's core. This heat is released at hot-water (hydrothermal) vents in the ocean's depths, where new crust is being formed and reformed. In the pitch darkness around such vents, large populations of specialized producer bacteria use this geothermal energy to convert dissolved hydrogen sulfide ($H_2S$) and carbon dioxide into organic nutrient molecules. These bacteria in turn become food for a variety of aquatic animals, including huge tube worms and various clams, crabs, mussels, and barnacles.

All other organisms in an ecosystem are **consumers,** or **heterotrophs** ("other feeders"), which get their energy and nutrients by feeding on other organisms or their remains. Based on their primary source of food, consumers are classified as

- **Herbivores** (plant eaters), or **primary consumers,** which feed directly on producers.

- **Carnivores** (meat eaters), which feed on other consumers. Those feeding only on primary consumers are called **secondary consumers;** those feeding on other carnivores are called **tertiary (higher-level) consumers.**

- **Omnivores** (such as pigs, rats, foxes, bears, cockroaches, and humans), which eat plants and animals.

- **Scavengers** (such as vultures, flies, hyenas, and some species of sharks and ants), which feed on dead organisms.

- **Detritivores** (detritus feeders and decomposers), which feed on **detritus** ("di-TRI-tus"), or parts of dead organisms and cast-off fragments and wastes of living organisms (Figure 4-15).

- **Detritus feeders** (such as crabs, carpenter ants, termites, and earthworms), which extract nutrients from partly decomposed organic matter in leaf litter, plant debris, and animal dung.

- **Decomposers** (mostly certain types of bacteria and fungi), which recycle organic matter in ecosystems. They do this by **(1)** breaking down (*biodegrading*) dead organic material (detritus) to get nutrients and **(2)** releasing the resulting simpler inorganic compounds into the soil and water, where they can be taken up as nutrients by producers.

Figures 4-11 (p. 72) and 4-12 (p. 72) show various types of producers and consumers.

Both producers and consumers use the chemical energy stored in glucose and other organic compounds to fuel their life processes. In most cells, this energy is released by **aerobic respiration,** which uses oxygen to convert organic nutrients back into carbon dioxide and water. The net effect of the hundreds of steps in this complex process is represented by the following reaction:

glucose + oxygen ⟶ carbon dioxide + water + **energy**

$$C_6H_{12}O_6 + 6\,O_2 \longrightarrow 6\,CO_2 + 6\,H_2O + \textbf{energy}$$

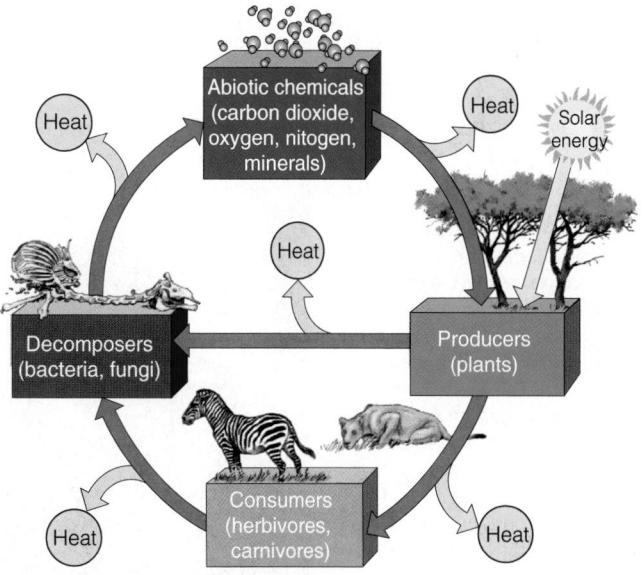

**Figure 4-15** Some detritivores, called *detritus feeders,* directly consume tiny fragments of this log. Other detritivores, called *decomposers* (mostly fungi and bacteria), digest complex organic chemicals in fragments of the log into simpler inorganic nutrients. These nutrients can be used again by producers if they are not washed away or otherwise removed from the system.

Although the detailed steps differ, the net chemical change for aerobic respiration is the opposite of that for photosynthesis.

Some decomposers get the energy they need by breaking down glucose (or other organic compounds) in the absence of oxygen. This form of cellular respiration is called **anaerobic respiration,** or **fermentation.** Instead of carbon dioxide and water, the end products of this process are compounds such as **(1)** methane gas ($CH_4$, the main component of natural gas), **(2)** ethyl alcohol ($C_2H_6O$), **(3)** acetic acid ($C_2H_4O_2$, the key component of vinegar), and **(4)** hydrogen sulfide ($H_2S$, when sulfur compounds are broken down).

The survival of any individual organism depends on the *flow of matter and energy* through its body. However, an ecosystem as a whole survives primarily through a combination of *matter recycling* (rather than one-way flow) and *one-way energy flow* (Figure 4-16).

Decomposers complete the cycle of matter by breaking down detritus into inorganic nutrients that are used by producers. Without decomposers, **(1)** the entire world would be knee-deep in plant litter, dead animal

**Figure 4-16** The main structural components (energy, chemicals, and organisms) of an ecosystem are linked by matter recycling and the flow of energy from the sun, through organisms, and then into the environment as low-quality heat.

bodies, animal wastes, and garbage, and **(2)** most life as we know it would no longer exist.

## What Is Biodiversity and Why Is It Important?

One important renewable resource is **biological diversity,** or **biodiversity:** the different life-forms and life-sustaining processes that can best survive the variety of conditions currently found on the earth. Kinds of biodiversity include the following:

- **Genetic diversity** (variety in the genetic makeup among individuals within a species; Figure 4-5, p. 68)

- **Species diversity** (variety among the species or distinct types of living organisms found in different habitats of the planet; Figure 4-17)

- **Ecological diversity** (variety of forests, deserts, grasslands, streams, lakes, oceans, coral reefs, wetlands, and other biological communities; Figure 4-9, p. 70)

- **Functional diversity** (biological and chemical processes or functions such as energy flow and matter cycling needed for the survival of species and biological communities; Figure 4-16, p. 75)

This rich variety of genes, species, biological communities, and life-sustaining biological and chemical processes

- Gives us food, wood, fibers, energy, raw materials, industrial chemicals, and medicines, all of which pour hundreds of billions of dollars into the world economy each year.

- Provides us with free recycling, purification, and natural pest control services.

Every species here today **(1)** contains genetic information that represents thousands to millions of years of adaptation to the earth's changing environmental conditions and **(2)** is the raw material for future adaptations. Loss of biodiversity **(1)** reduces the availability of ecosystem services and **(2)** decreases the ability of species, communities, and ecosystems to adapt to changing environmental conditions. Biodiversity is nature's insurance policy against disasters.

Some people also include *human cultural diversity* as part of the earth's biodiversity. The variety of human cultures represents numerous social and technological solutions to changing environmental conditions.

## 4-4 CONNECTIONS: FOOD WEBS AND ENERGY FLOW IN ECOSYSTEMS

**What Are Food Chains and Food Webs?** All organisms, whether dead or alive, are potential sources of food for other organisms. A caterpillar eats a leaf, a robin eats the caterpillar, and a hawk eats the robin. Decomposers consume the leaf, caterpillar, robin, and hawk after they die. As a result, *there is little matter waste in natural ecosystems.*

The sequence of organisms, each of which is a source of food for the next, is called a **food chain.** It determines how energy and nutrients move from one organism to another through an ecosystem (Figure 4-18).

Ecologists assign each organism in an ecosystem to a *feeding level,* or **trophic level** (from the Greek word *trophos,* "nourishment"), depending on whether it is a producer or a consumer and on what it eats or decomposes. Producers belong to the first trophic level, primary consumers to the second trophic level, secondary consumers to the third, and so on. Detriti-

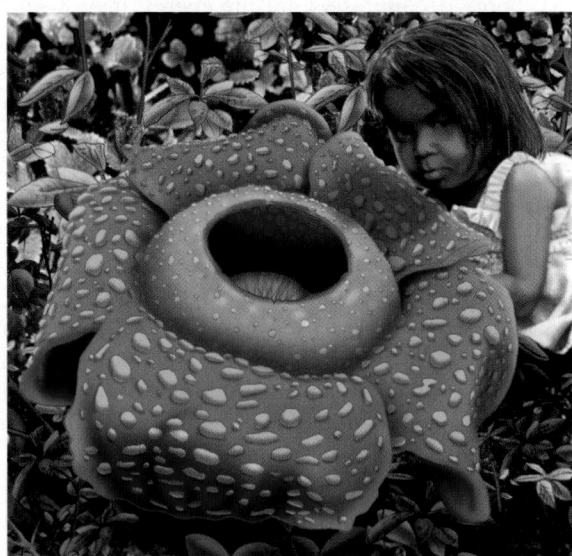

**Figure 4-17** Two species found in tropical forests are part of the earth's biodiversity. On the right is the world's largest flower, the flesh flower (*Rafflesia arnoldi*), growing in a tropical rain forest in Sumatra. The flower of this leafless plant can be as large as 1 meter (4.3 feet) in diameter and weigh 7 kilograms (15 pounds). The plant gives off a smell like rotting meat, presumably to attract flies and beetles that pollinate its flower. After blossoming once a year for a few weeks, the flower dissolves into a slimy black mass. On the left is a cotton top tamarin.

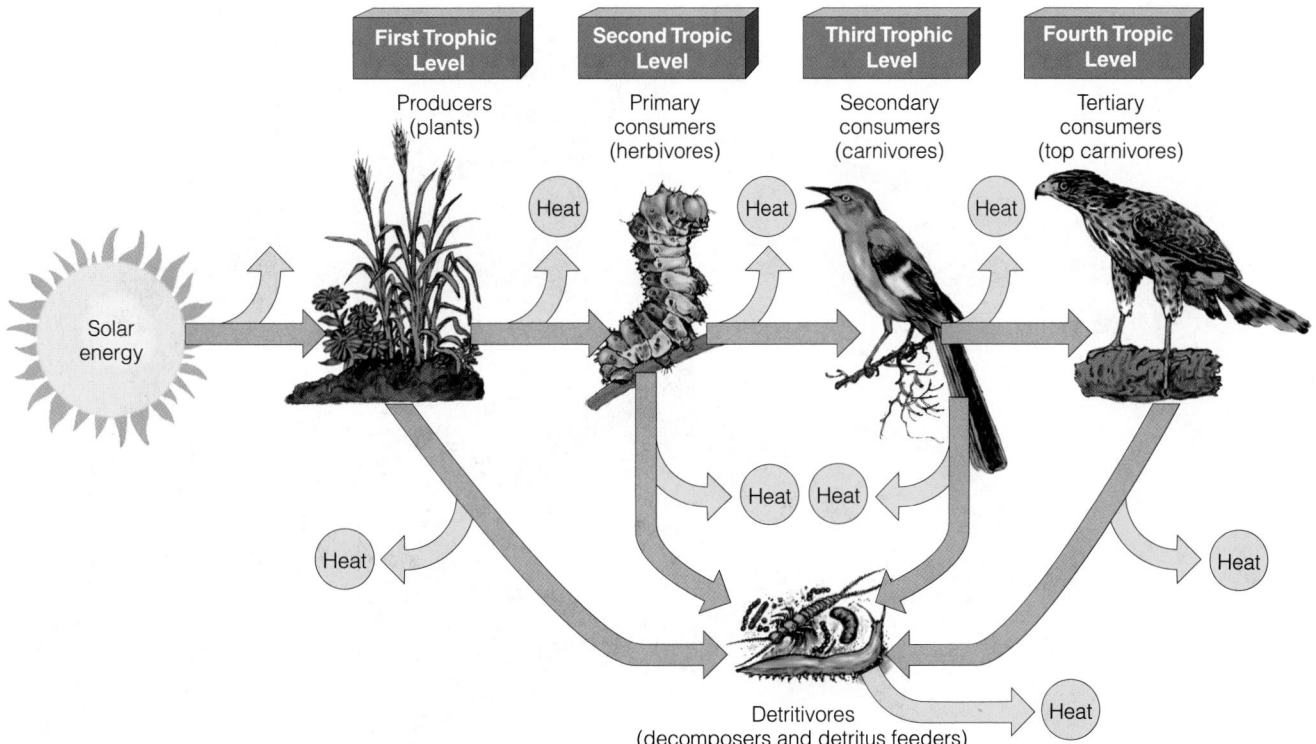

**Figure 4-18** Model of a *food chain*. The arrows show how chemical energy in food flows through various *trophic levels*, or energy transfers; most of the energy is degraded to heat, in accordance with the second law of thermodynamics. Food chains rarely have more than four trophic levels.

vores and decomposers process detritus from all trophic levels.

Real ecosystems are more complex than this. Most consumers feed on more than one type of organism, and most organisms are eaten by more than one type of consumer. Because most species participate in several different food chains, the organisms in most ecosystems form a complex network of interconnected food chains called a **food web** (Figure 4-19, p. 78). Trophic levels can be assigned in food webs just as in food chains.

**How Can We Represent the Energy Flow in an Ecosystem? Pyramids of Energy Flow**
Each trophic level in a food chain or web contains a certain amount of **biomass,** the dry weight of all organic matter contained in its organisms. In a food chain or web, chemical energy stored in biomass is transferred from one trophic level to another.

With each transfer some usable energy is degraded and lost to the environment as low-quality heat. Thus **(1)** only a small portion of what is eaten and digested is actually converted into an organism's bodily material or biomass, and **(2)** the amount of usable energy available to each successive trophic level declines.

The percentage of usable energy transferred as biomass from one trophic level to the next is called **ecological efficiency.** It ranges from 5% to 20% (that is, a loss of 80–95%) depending on the types of species and the ecosystem involved, but 10% is typical.

Assuming 10% ecological efficiency (90% loss) at each trophic transfer, if green plants in an area manage to capture 10,000 units of energy from the sun, then only about 1,000 units of energy will be available to support herbivores and only about 100 units to support carnivores.

The more trophic levels or steps in a food chain or web, the greater the cumulative loss of usable energy as energy flows through the various trophic levels. The **pyramid of energy flow** in Figure 4-20 (p. 79) illustrates this energy loss for a simple food chain, assuming a 90% energy loss with each transfer. Figure 4-21 (p. 79) shows the pyramid of energy flow during 1 year for an aquatic ecosystem in Silver Springs, Florida.* Pyramids of energy flow *always* have an

---

*Because such pyramids represent energy flows, not energy storage, they should not be called pyramids of energy (a common error in some biology and environmental science textbooks).

**Figure 4-19** Greatly simplified food web in the Antarctic. Many more participants in the web, including an array of decomposer organisms, are not depicted here.

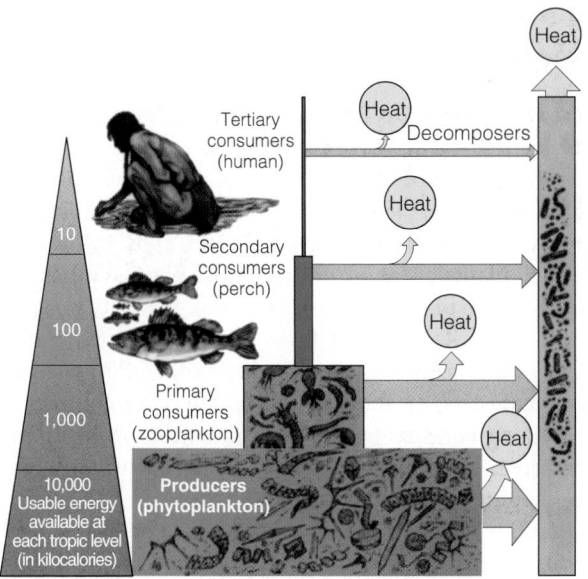

**Figure 4-20** Generalized *pyramid of energy flow* showing the decrease in usable energy available at each succeeding trophic level in a food chain or web. In nature, ecological efficiency varies from 5% to 20%, with 10% efficiency being common. This model assumes a 10% ecological efficiency (90% loss in usable energy to the environment, in the form of low-quality heat) with each transfer from one trophic level to another.

upright pyramidal shape because of the automatic degradation of energy quality required by the second law of thermodynamics.

Energy flow pyramids explain why the earth can support more people if they eat at lower trophic levels by consuming grains, vegetables, and fruits directly (for example, grain ⟶ human) rather than passing such crops through another trophic level and eating grain eaters (grain ⟶ steer ⟶ human).

The large loss in energy between successive trophic levels also explains why food chains and webs rarely have more than four or five trophic levels. In most cases, too little energy is left after four or five transfers to support organisms feeding at these high trophic levels. This explains why **(1)** there are so few top carnivores such as eagles, hawks, tigers, and white sharks, **(2)** such species usually are the first to suffer when the ecosystems that support them are disrupted, and **(3)** these species are so vulnerable to extinction.

**How Can We Represent Biomass Storage in an Ecosystem? Pyramids of Biomass and Numbers** Ecologists use a **pyramid of biomass** (Figure 4-22, p. 80) to represent the storage of biomass at various trophic levels in an ecosystem. They estimate biomass by harvesting organisms from random patches or narrow strips in an ecosystem. The sample

**Figure 4-21** Annual pyramid of energy flow (in kilocalories per square meter per year) for an aquatic ecosystem in Silver Springs, Florida. The pyramid is constructed by using the data on energy flow through this ecosystem shown in the bottom drawing. (From Cecie Starr, *Biology: Concepts and Applications*, 4th ed., Brooks/Cole, [Wadsworth] © 2000)

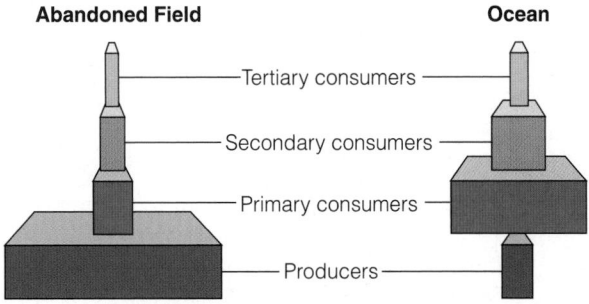

**Abandoned Field**        **Ocean**

Tertiary consumers

Secondary consumers

Primary consumers

Producers

**Figure 4-22** Generalized graphs of *biomass of organisms* in the various trophic levels for two ecosystems. The size of each tier in this conceptual model represents the dry weight per square meter of all organisms at that trophic level.

organisms are then sorted according to trophic levels, dried, and weighed. These data are used to plot a pyramid of biomass.

For most land ecosystems, the total biomass at each successive trophic level decreases. This yields a pyramid of biomass with a large base of producers, topped by a series of increasingly smaller biomasses at higher trophic levels (Figure 4-22, left). In the open waters of aquatic ecosystems, however, the biomass of primary consumers (zooplankton) can exceed that of producers. The reason is that the producers are microscopic phytoplankton that grow and reproduce rapidly, not large plants that grow and reproduce slowly. The graph is not an upright pyramid (Figure 4-22, right) because the zooplankton eat the phytoplankton almost as fast as they are produced so the producer population is never very large.

By estimating the number of organisms at each trophic level, ecologists can also create a **pyramid of numbers** for an ecosystem (Figure 4-23). Numbers of organisms for grasslands and many other ecosystems taper off from the producer level to the higher trophic levels, forming an upright pyramid (Figure 4-23, left).

For other ecosystems the graph can take a different shape. For example, a temperate forest (Figure 4-23, right) has a few large producers (the trees) that support a much larger number of small primary consumers (insects) that feed on the trees.

**Grassland**
(summer)

**Temperate Forest**
(summer)

Tertiary consumers

Secondary consumers

Primary consumers

Producers

**Figure 4-23** Generalized graphs of *numbers of organisms* in the various trophic levels for two ecosystems.

## 4-5 PRIMARY PRODUCTIVITY OF ECOSYSTEMS

**How Rapidly Do Producers in Different Ecosystems Produce Biomass?** The *rate* at which an ecosystem's producers convert solar energy into chemical energy as biomass is the ecosystem's **gross primary productivity (GPP).** In effect, it is the rate at which plants or other producers use photosynthesis to make more plant material (biomass).

Figure 4-24 shows how this productivity varies across the earth. This figure shows that GPP generally is greatest **(1)** in the shallow waters near continents, **(2)** along coral reefs where abundant light, heat, and nutrients stimulate the growth of algae, and **(3)** where upwelling currents bring nitrogen and phosphorus from the ocean bottom to the surface. The lowest GPP is in **(1)** deserts and other arid regions because of their low precipitation and high temperatures and **(2)** the open ocean because of a lack of nutrients and sunlight except near the surface.

To stay alive, grow, and reproduce, an ecosystem's producers must use some of the total biomass they produce for their own respiration. Only what is left, called **net primary productivity (NPP),** is available for use as food by other organisms (consumers) in an ecosystem:

| **Net primary productivity** | = | Rate at which producers store chemical energy as biomass (produced by photosynthesis) | − | Rate at which producers use chemical energy stored as biomass (through aerobic respiration) |
|---|---|---|---|---|

NPP is the *rate* at which energy for use by consumers is stored in new biomass (cells, leaves, roots, and stems). It is measured in units of the energy or biomass available to consumers in a specified area over a given time. Various ecosystems and life zones differ in their NPP (Figure 4-25). The most productive are **(1)** estuaries, **(2)** swamps and marshes, and **(3)** tropical rain forests. The least productive are **(1)** open ocean, **(2)** tundra (arctic and alpine grasslands), and **(3)** desert. Despite its low net primary productivity, there is so much open ocean that it produces more of the earth's NPP per year than any of the other ecosystems and life zones shown in Figure 4-25.

Agricultural land is a highly modified and managed ecosystem. The goal is to increase the NPP and biomass of selected crop plants by adding water (irrigation) and nutrients (fertilizers). Nitrogen as nitrate ($NO_3^-$)

**Figure 4-24**
Three years of
satellite data on the
earth's gross primary productivity. Rain forests and other
highly productive areas appear as dark
green and deserts as yellow. The concentration of
phytoplankton, a primary indicator of ocean productivity, ranges from red (highest) to orange, yellow, green,
and blue (lowest). (Gene Carl Feldman, Compton J. Tucker—NASA/Goddard Space Flight Center)

and phosphorus as phosphate ($PO_4^{3-}$) are the most common nutrients in fertilizers because they are most often the nutrients limiting crop growth. Despite such inputs, the NPP of agricultural land is not particularly high compared with that of other ecosystems (Figure 4-25).

**How Does the World's Net Rate of Biomass Production Limit the Populations of Consumer Species?** As we have seen, producers are the source of all food in an ecosystem. Thus the planet's NPP ultimately limits the number of consumers (including humans) that can survive on the earth. It is tempting to

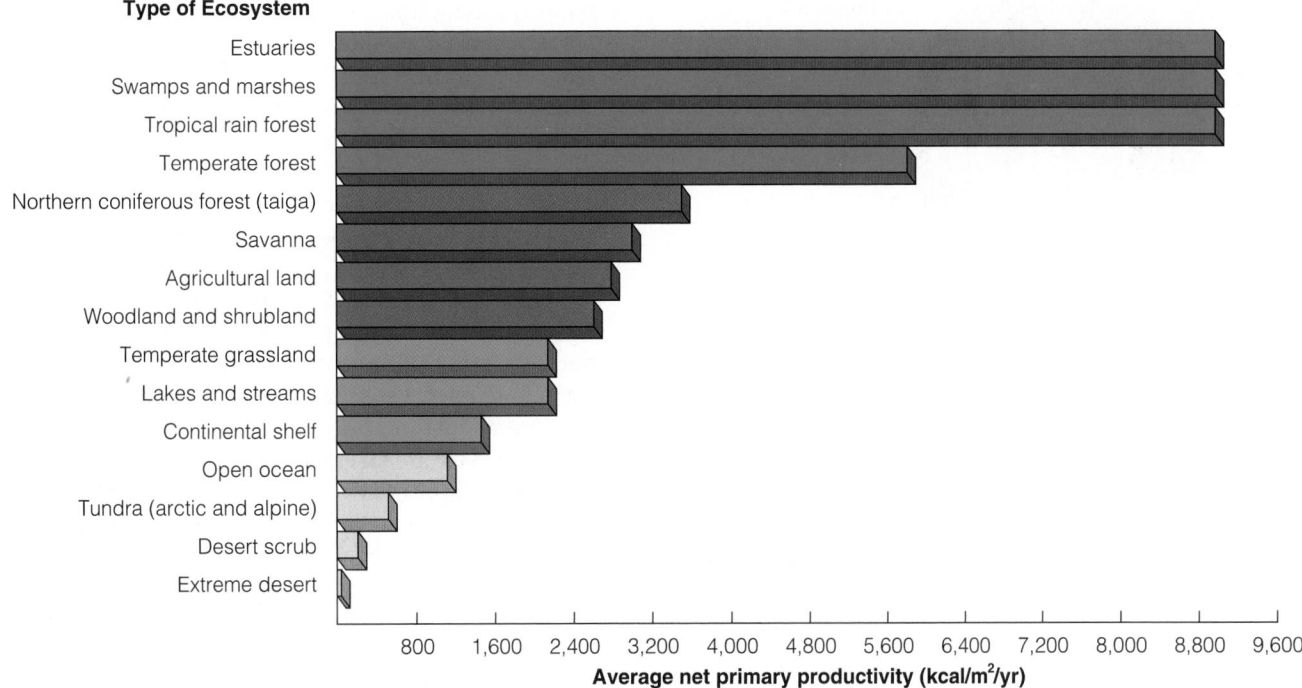

**Figure 4-25** Estimated annual average *net primary productivity* (NPP) per unit of area in major life zones and ecosystems, expressed as kilocalories of energy produced per square meter per year (kcal/m²/yr). (Data from *Communities and Ecosystems*, 2nd ed., by R. H. Whittaker, 1975. New York: Macmillan)

conclude from Figure 4-25 that a good way to feed the world's hungry millions would be to harvest plants in estuaries, swamps, and marshes. But ecologists point out that **(1)** most plants in these areas cannot be eaten by people, and **(2)** these plants are vital food sources (and spawning areas) for fish, shrimp, and other aquatic life-forms that provide us and other consumers with protein.

We might also conclude from Figure 4-25 that we could grow more food for human consumption by clearing tropical forests and planting food crops. According to most ecologists, this is also a bad idea. In tropical forests most of the nutrients needed to grow food crops are stored in the vegetation rather than in the soil. When the trees are removed, the nutrient-poor soils are rapidly depleted by frequent rains and growing crops. Crops can be grown only for a short time without massive and expensive applications of commercial fertilizers.

Because the earth's vast open oceans provide the largest percentage of the earth's net primary productivity, why not harvest its primary producers (floating and drifting phytoplankton) to help feed the rapidly growing human population? The problem is that harvesting the widely dispersed, tiny floating producers in the open ocean would **(1)** take much more fossil fuel and other types of energy than the food energy we would get and **(2)** disrupt the food webs of the open

ocean (Figure 4-19) that provide us and other consumer organisms with important sources of energy and protein from fish and shellfish.

**How Much of the World's Net Rate of Biomass Production Do We Use?** Peter Vitousek and other ecologists estimate that humans now use, waste, or destroy about **(1)** 27% of the earth's total potential NPP and **(2)** 40% of the NPP of the planet's terrestrial ecosystems (Figure 4-26).

This is the main reason why we are crowding out or eliminating the habitats and food supplies of a growing number of other species. What might happen to us and to other consumer species if **(1)** the human population doubles over the next 40–50 years and **(2)** per capita consumption of resources such as food, timber, and grassland rises sharply?

## 4-6 CONNECTIONS: MATTER CYCLING IN ECOSYSTEMS

**What Are Biogeochemical Cycles?** The nutrient atoms, ions, and molecules that organisms need to live, grow, and reproduce are continuously cycled from the nonliving environment (air, water, soil, and rock) to living organisms (biota) and then back again in what are called **nutrient cycles,** or **biogeochemical cycles** (literally, life–earth–chemical cycles). These cycles, driven directly or indirectly by incoming solar energy and gravity, include the carbon, oxygen, nitrogen, phosphorus, and hydrologic (water) cycles (Figure 4-7).

The earth's chemical cycles also connect past, present, and future forms of life. Some of the carbon atoms in your skin may once have been part of a leaf, a dinosaur's skin, or a layer of limestone rock. Your grandmother, Plato, or a hunter–gatherer who lived 25,000 years ago may have inhaled some of the oxygen molecules you just inhaled.

**How Is Water Cycled in the Biosphere?** The **hydrologic cycle,** or **water cycle,** which collects, purifies, and distributes the earth's fixed supply of water, is shown in simplified form in Figure 4-27.

The main processes in this water recycling and purifying cycle are **(1)** *evaporation* (conversion of water into water vapor), **(2)** *transpiration* (evaporation from leaves of water extracted from soil by roots and transported throughout the plant), **(3)** *condensation* (conversion of water vapor into droplets of liquid water), **(4)** *precipitation* (rain, sleet, hail, and snow), **(5)** *infiltration* (movement of water into soil), **(6)** *percolation* (downward flow of water through soil and permeable rock formations to groundwater storage areas called

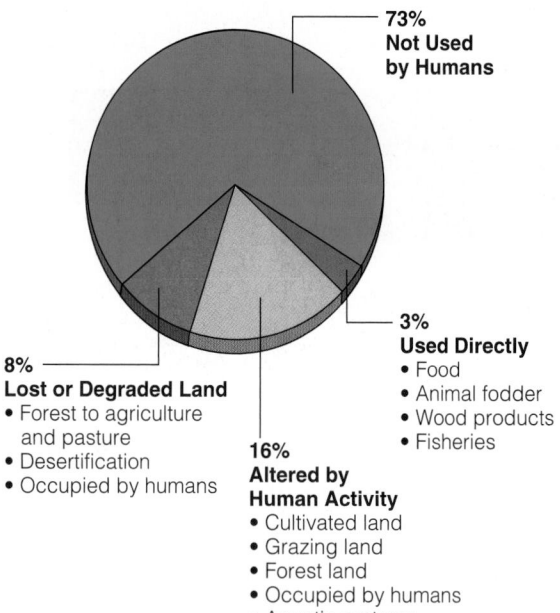

**73%**
**Not Used**
**by Humans**

**3%**
**Used Directly**
• Food
• Animal fodder
• Wood products
• Fisheries

**16%**
**Altered by**
**Human Activity**
• Cultivated land
• Grazing land
• Forest land
• Occupied by humans
• Aquatic systems

**8%**
**Lost or Degraded Land**
• Forest to agriculture and pasture
• Desertification
• Occupied by humans

**Figure 4-26** Human use of the biomass produced by photosynthesis. Humans destroy, alter, and directly use about **(1)** 27% of the earth's total net primary productivity and **(2)** 40% of the net primary productivity of the earth's terrestrial ecosystems. (Data from Peter Vitousek)

aquifers), and **(7)** *runoff* (downslope surface movement back to the sea to resume the cycle).

The water cycle is powered by energy from the sun and by gravity. Incoming solar energy evaporates water from oceans, streams, lakes, soil, and vegetation. About 84% of water vapor in the atmosphere comes from the oceans, and the rest comes from land.

The amount of water vapor air can hold depends on its temperature, with warm air holding more water vapor than cold air. **Absolute humidity** is the amount of water vapor found in a certain mass of air and is usually expressed as grams of water per kilogram of air. **Relative humidity** is the amount of water vapor in a certain mass of air, expressed as a percentage of the maximum amount it could hold at that temperature. For example, a relative humidity of 60% at 27°C (80°F) means that each kilogram (or other unit of mass) of air contains 60% of the maximum amount of water vapor it could hold at that temperature.

Winds and air masses transport water vapor over various parts of the earth's surface, often over long distances. Falling temperatures cause the water vapor to condense into tiny droplets that form clouds or fog. For precipitation to occur, air must contain **condensation nuclei:** tiny particles on which droplets of water vapor can collect. Sources of such particles include **(1)** vol-canic ash, **(2)** soil dust, **(3)** smoke, **(4)** sea salts, and **(5)** particulate matter emitted by factories, coal-burning power plants, and motor vehicles. The temperature at which condensation occurs is called the **dew point.**

Some of the fresh water returning to the earth's surface as precipitation becomes locked in glaciers. Most of the precipitation falling on terrestrial ecosystems becomes *surface runoff* flowing into streams and lakes, which eventually carry water back to the oceans, where it can be evaporated to cycle again.

Besides replenishing streams and lakes, surface runoff also causes soil erosion, which moves soil and weathered rock fragments from one place to another. Water is thus the primary sculptor of the earth's landscape. Because water dissolves many nutrient compounds, it is a major medium for transporting nutrients within and between ecosystems.

Throughout the hydrologic cycle, many natural processes act to purify water. Evaporation and subsequent precipitation act as a natural distillation process that removes impurities dissolved in water. Water flowing above ground through streams and lakes and below ground in aquifers is naturally filtered and purified by chemical and biological processes. Thus the hydrologic cycle also can be viewed as a cycle of natural renewal of water quality.

 **Figure 4-27** Simplified model of the hydrologic cycle.

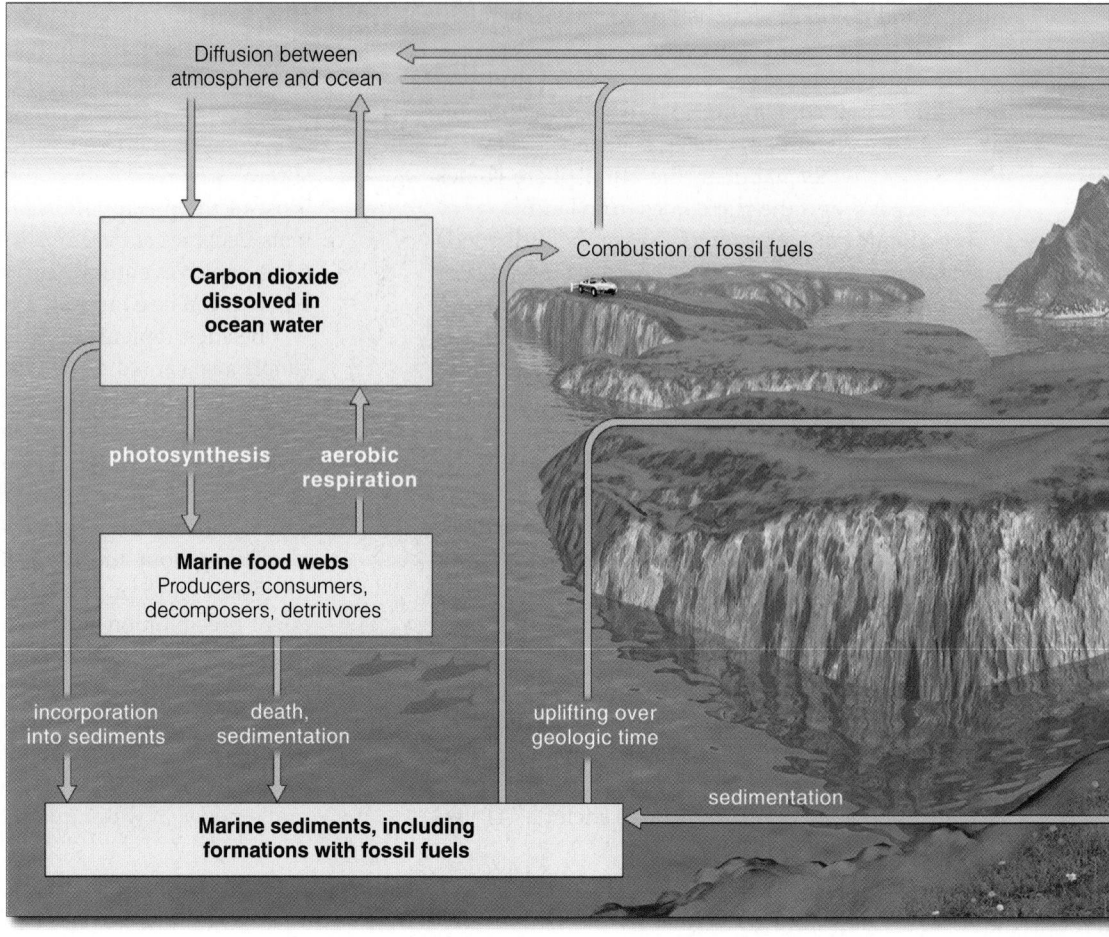

**Figure 4-28** Simplified model of the global carbon cycle. The left portion shows the movement of carbon through marine systems, and the right portion shows its movement through terrestrial ecosystems. Carbon reservoirs are shown as boxes; processes that change one form of carbon to another are shown in unboxed print. (From Cecie Starr, *Biology: Concepts and Applications,* 4th ed., Brooks/Cole, [Wadsworth] © 2000)

**How Are Human Activities Affecting the Water Cycle?** During the past 100 years, we have been intervening in the earth's current water cycle in several ways:

▪ Withdrawing large quantities of fresh water from streams, lakes, and underground sources. In some heavily populated or heavily irrigated areas, withdrawals have led to groundwater depletion or intrusion of ocean salt water into underground water supplies.

▪ Clearing vegetation from land for agriculture, mining, road and building construction, and other activities. This **(1)** increases runoff, **(2)** reduces infiltration that recharges groundwater supplies, **(3)** increases the risk of flooding, and **(4)** accelerates soil erosion and landslides.

▪ Modifying water quality by **(1)** adding nutrients (such as phosphates and nitrates found in fertilizers)

and other pollutants and **(2)** changing ecological processes that purify water naturally.

**How Is Carbon Cycled in the Biosphere?** Carbon is essential to life as we know it. It is the basic building block of the carbohydrates, fats, proteins, DNA, and other organic compounds necessary for life.

The **carbon cycle** (Figure 4-28) is based on carbon dioxide gas, which makes up 0.036% of the volume of the troposphere and is also dissolved in water. Carbon dioxide is a key component of nature's thermostat. If the carbon cycle removes too much $CO_2$ from the atmosphere, the atmosphere will cool; if the cycle generates too much, the atmosphere will get warmer. Thus even slight changes in the carbon cycle can affect climate and ultimately the types of life that can exist on various parts of the planet.

Terrestrial producers remove $CO_2$ from the atmosphere, and aquatic producers remove it from the

The diagram shows carbon cycle components:

**Atmosphere** (mainly carbon dioxide)

volcanic action

Combustion of fossil fuels

combustion of wood (for clearing land; or for fuel)

photosynthesis

aerobic respiration

**Terrestrial rocks**

deforestation

weathering

**Land food webs** Producers, consumers, decomposers, detritivores

**Soil water** (dissolved carbon)

death, burial, compaction over geologic time

**Peat, fossil fuels**

leaching, runoff

water. They then use photosynthesis to convert $CO_2$ into simple carbohydrates such as glucose ($C_6H_{12}O_6$).

The cells in oxygen-consuming producers, consumers, and decomposers then carry out aerobic respiration. This breaks down glucose and other complex organic compounds and converts the carbon back to $CO_2$ in the atmosphere or water for reuse by producers. This linkage between *photosynthesis* in producers and *aerobic respiration* in producers, consumers, and decomposers circulates carbon in the biosphere and is a major part of the global carbon cycle. Oxygen and hydrogen, the other elements in carbohydrates, cycle almost in step with carbon.

Over millions of years, buried deposits of dead plant matter and bacteria are compressed between layers of sediment, where they form carbon-containing *fossil fuels* such as coal and oil (Figure 4-28, above). This carbon is not released to the atmosphere as $CO_2$ for recycling until **(1)** these fuels are extracted and burned, or **(2)** long-term geological processes expose these deposits to air. In only a few hundred years, we

have extracted and burned fossil fuels that took millions of years to form. This is why fossil fuels are nonrenewable resources on a human time scale.

The oceans are a major carbon-storage reservoir in the carbon cycle. Oceans also play a major role in regulating the level of carbon dioxide in the atmosphere. Some carbon dioxide gas, which is readily soluble in water, **(1)** stays dissolved in the sea, **(2)** some is removed by photosynthesizing producers, and **(3)** some reacts with seawater to form carbonate ions ($CO_3^{2-}$) and bicarbonate ions ($HCO_3^-$). As water warms, more dissolved $CO_2$ returns to the atmosphere, just as more carbon dioxide fizzes out of a carbonated beverage when it warms.

In marine ecosystems, some organisms take up dissolved $CO_2$ molecules, carbonate ions, or bicarbonate ions from ocean water. These ions can then react with calcium ions ($Ca^{2+}$) in seawater to form slightly soluble carbonate compounds such as calcium carbonate ($CaCO_3$) to build the shells and skeletons of marine organisms. When these organisms die, tiny particles of

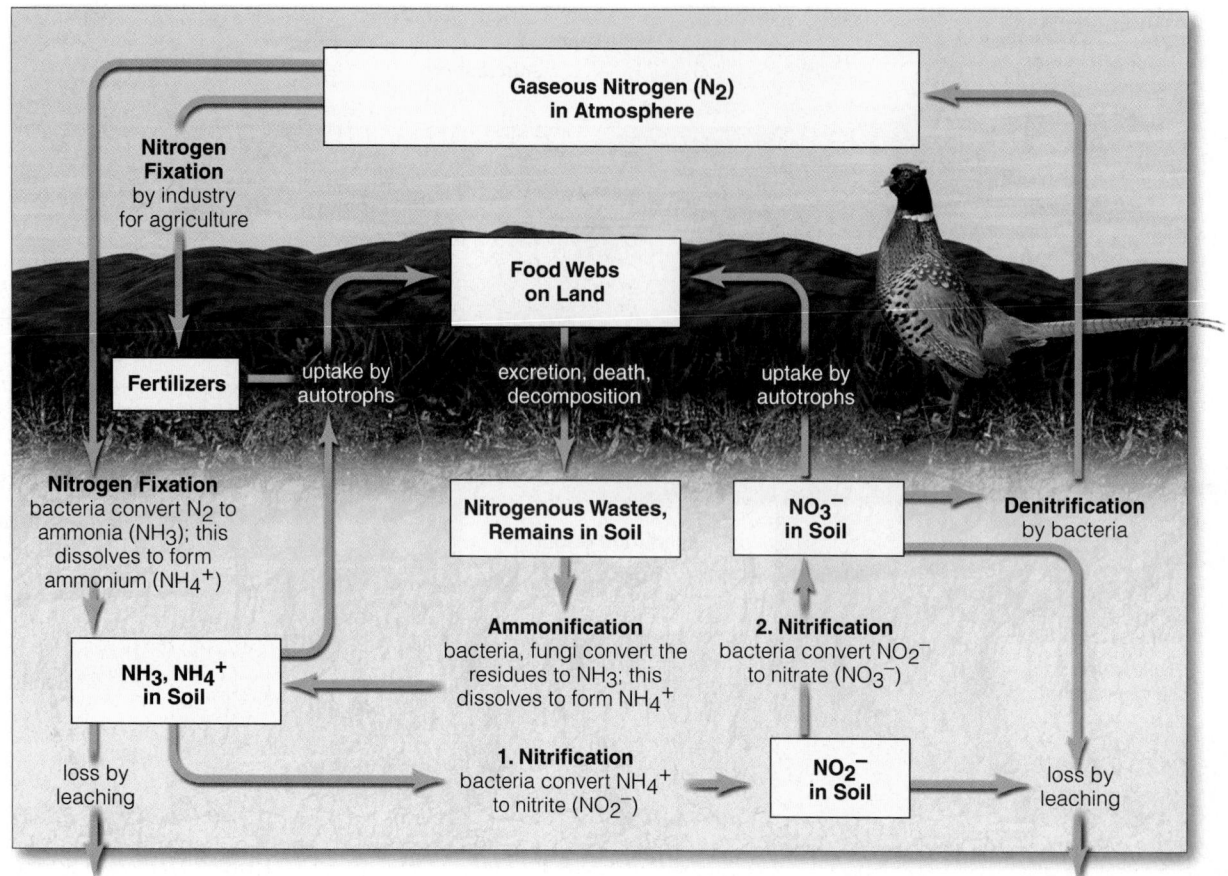

**Figure 4-29** Greatly simplified model of the nitrogen cycle in a terrestrial ecosystem. Nitrogen reservoirs are shown as boxes; processes changing one form of nitrogen to another are shown in unboxed print. (Adapted from Cecie Starr and Ralph Taggart, *Biology: The Unity and Diversity of Life,* 9th ed. Starr & Taggart. Wadsworth © 2001)

their shells and bone drift slowly to the ocean depths. There they are buried for eons (as long as 400 million years) in deep bottom sediments (Figure 4-28, left), where under immense pressure they are converted into limestone rock.

**How Are Human Activities Affecting the Carbon Cycle?** Since 1800 and especially since 1950, we have been intervening in the earth's carbon cycle in two ways that add carbon dioxide to the atmosphere:

- Clearing trees and other plants that absorb $CO_2$ through photosynthesis

- Adding large amounts of $CO_2$ by burning fossil fuels and wood

Computer models of the earth's climate systems suggest that increased concentrations of atmospheric $CO_2$ and other gases we are adding to the atmosphere could enhance the planet's *natural greenhouse effect* that

helps warm the lower atmosphere (troposphere) and the earth's surface (Figure 4-8). The resulting *global warming* could **(1)** disrupt global food production and wildlife habitats and **(2)** raise the average sea level in various parts of the world.

**How Is Nitrogen Cycled in the Biosphere? Bacteria in Action** Nitrogen is the atmosphere's most abundant element, with chemically unreactive nitrogen gas ($N_2$) making up 78% of the volume of the troposphere. However, $N_2$ cannot be absorbed and used (metabolized) directly as a nutrient by multicellular plants or animals.

Fortunately, **(1)** atmospheric electrical discharges in the form of lightning (that causes nitrogen and oxygen in the atmosphere to react and produce oxides of nitrogen, such as $N_2 + O_2 \longrightarrow 2NO$) and **(2)** certain bacteria in the soil and aquatic systems convert nitrogen gas into compounds that can enter food webs as part of the **nitrogen cycle** (Figure 4-29).

The nitrogen cycle consists of several major steps:

- *Nitrogen fixation,* in which specialized bacteria convert gaseous nitrogen ($N_2$) to ammonia ($NH_3$) that can be used by plants by the reaction $N_2 + 3H_2 \longrightarrow 2NH_3$. This is done mostly by **(1)** cyanobacteria in soil and water and **(2)** *Rhizobium* bacteria living in small nodules (swellings) on the root systems of a wide variety of plant species, including soybeans and alfalfa.

- *Nitrification,* a two-step process in which most of the ammonia in soil is converted by specialized aerobic bacteria to **(1)** nitrite ions ($NO_2^-$), which are toxic to plants and **(2)** nitrate ions ($NO_3^-$), which are easily taken up by plants as a nutrient.

- *Assimilation,* in which plant roots absorb inorganic ammonia, ammonium ions, and nitrate ions formed by nitrogen fixation and nitrification in soil water. They use these ions to make nitrogen-containing organic molecules such as DNA, amino acids, and proteins. Animals in turn get their nitrogen by eating plants or plant-eating animals.

- *Ammonification,* in which vast armies of specialized decomposer bacteria convert the nitrogen-rich organic compounds, wastes, cast-off particles, and dead bodies of organisms into **(1)** simpler nitrogen-containing inorganic compounds such as ammonia ($NH_3$) and **(2)** water-soluble salts containing ammonium ions ($NH_4^+$).

- *Denitrification,* in which other specialized bacteria (mostly anaerobic bacteria in waterlogged soil or in the bottom sediments of lakes, oceans, swamps, and bogs) convert $NH_3$ and $NH_4^+$ back into nitrite ($NO_2^-$) and nitrate ($NO_3^-$) ions and then into nitrogen gas ($N_2$) and nitrous oxide gas ($N_2O$). These are then released to the atmosphere to begin the cycle again.

**How Are Human Activities Affecting the Nitrogen Cycle?** Major human interventions in the earth's current nitrogen cycle over the past 100 years include

- Adding large amounts of nitric oxide (NO) into the atmosphere when we burn any fuel ($N_2 + O_2 \longrightarrow 2NO$). In the atmosphere, this nitric oxide combines with oxygen to form nitrogen dioxide gas ($NO_2$), which can react with water vapor to form nitric acid ($HNO_3$). Droplets of $HNO_3$ dissolved in rain or snow are components of *acid deposition,* commonly called *acid rain.* Nitric acid, along with other air pollutants, can **(1)** damage and weaken trees, **(2)** upset aquatic ecosystems, **(3)** corrode metals, and **(4)** damage marble, stone, and other building materials.

- Adding nitrous oxide ($N_2O$) to the atmosphere through the action of anaerobic bacteria on livestock wastes and commercial inorganic fertilizers applied to the soil. When $N_2O$ reaches the stratosphere, it can **(1)** help warm the atmosphere by enhancing the natural greenhouse effect and **(2)** contribute to depletion of the earth's ozone shield, which filters out harmful ultraviolet radiation from the sun.

- Removing nitrogen from topsoil when we **(1)** harvest nitrogen-rich crops, **(2)** irrigate crops, and **(3)** burn or clear grasslands and forests before planting crops (Case Study, p. 90).

- Adding nitrogen compounds to aquatic ecosystems in agricultural runoff and discharge of municipal sewage. This excess of plant nutrients stimulates rapid growth of photosynthesizing algae and other aquatic plants. The subsequent breakdown of dead algae by aerobic decomposers can **(1)** deplete the water of dissolved oxygen and **(2)** disrupt aquatic ecosystems by killing some types of fish and other oxygen-using (aerobic) organisms.

- Accelerating the deposition of acidic nitrogen compounds (such as $NO_2$ and $HNO_3$) from the atmosphere onto terrestrial ecosystems. This excessive input of nitrogen can stimulate the growth of weedy plant species, which can outgrow and perhaps eliminate other plant species that cannot take up nitrogen as efficiently.

**How Is Phosphorus Cycled in the Biosphere?** Phosphorus circulates through water, the earth's crust, and living organisms in the **phosphorus cycle** (Figure 4-30, p. 88). Bacteria are less important here than in the nitrogen cycle. Very little phosphorus circulates in the atmosphere because at the earth's normal temperatures and pressures, phosphorus and its compounds are not gases. Phosphorus is found in the atmosphere only as small particles of dust. In contrast to the carbon cycle, the phosphorus cycle is slow, and on a short human time scale much phosphorus flows one way from the land to the oceans.

Phosphorous typically is found as phosphate salts containing phosphate ions ($PO_4^{3-}$) in terrestrial rock formations and ocean bottom sediments. Because most soils contain little phosphate, it is often the *limiting factor* for plant growth on land unless phosphorus (as phosphate salts mined from the earth) is applied to the soil as a fertilizer.

Phosphorus also limits the growth of producer populations in many freshwater streams and lakes because phosphate salts are only slightly soluble in water. This explains why adding phosphate compounds to lakes greatly increases their biological productivity.

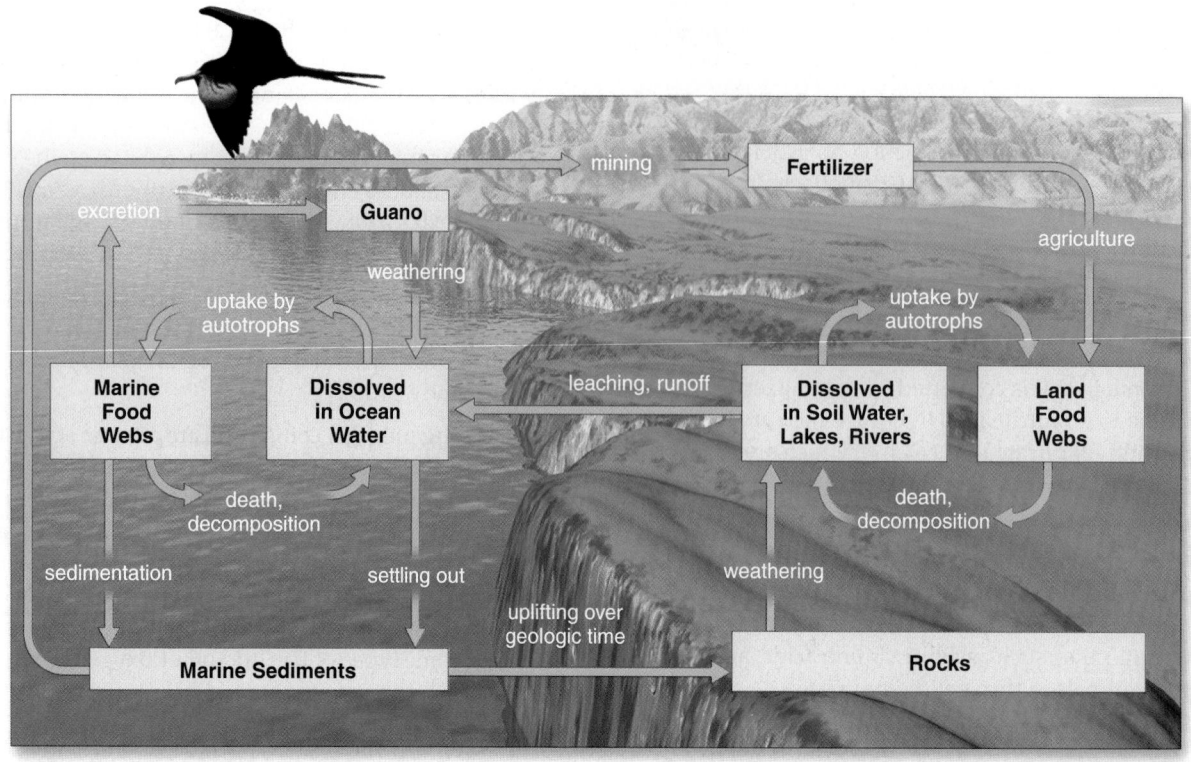

**Figure 4-30** Simplified model of the phosphorus cycle. Phosphorus reservoirs are shown as boxes; processes that change one form of phosphorus to another are shown in unboxed print. (From Cecie Starr and Ralph Taggart, *The Unity and Diversity of Life*, 9th ed., Starr & Taggart. Wadsworth © 2001)

**How Are Human Activities Affecting the Phosphorus Cycle?** We intervene in the earth's phosphorus cycle by

■ Mining large quantities of phosphate rock for use in commercial inorganic fertilizers and detergents.

■ Reducing the available phosphate in tropical forests by removing trees. When such forests are cut and burned, most remaining phosphorus and other soil nutrients are washed away by heavy rains, and the land becomes unproductive.

■ Adding excess phosphate to aquatic ecosystems in **(1)** runoff of animal wastes from livestock feedlots, **(2)** runoff of commercial phosphate fertilizers from cropland, and **(3)** discharge of municipal sewage. Too much of this nutrient causes explosive growth of cyanobacteria, algae, and aquatic plants. When these plants die and are decomposed, they use up dissolved oxygen and disrupt aquatic ecosystems.

**How Is Sulfur Cycled in the Biosphere?** Sulfur circulates through the biosphere in the **sulfur cycle** (Figure 4-31). Much of the earth's sulfur is stored underground in rocks and minerals, including sulfate ($SO_4^{2-}$) salts buried deep under ocean sediments.

Sulfur also enters the atmosphere from several natural sources. Hydrogen sulfide ($H_2S$) is a colorless,

highly poisonous gas with a rotten-egg smell. It is released from active volcanoes and by the breakdown of organic matter in swamps, bogs, and tidal flats caused by decomposers that do not use oxygen (anaerobic decomposers). Sulfur dioxide ($SO_2$), a colorless, suffocating gas, also comes from volcanoes. Particles of sulfate ($SO_4^{2-}$) salts, such as ammonium sulfate, enter the atmosphere from sea spray.

Certain marine algae produce large amounts of volatile dimethyl sulfide, or DMS ($CH_3SCH_3$). Tiny droplets of DMS serve as nuclei for the condensation of water into droplets found in clouds. Thus changes in DMS emissions can affect cloud cover and climate.

In the atmosphere, sulfur dioxide reacts with oxygen to produce sulfur trioxide gas ($SO_3$). Some of the sulfur trioxide then reacts with water droplets in the atmosphere to produce tiny droplets of sulfuric acid ($H_2SO_4$). Sulfur dioxide also reacts with other chemicals in the atmosphere such as ammonia to produce tiny particles of sulfate salts. These droplets and particles fall to the earth as components of *acid deposition*, which along with other air pollutants can harm trees and aquatic life.

**How Are Human Activities Affecting the Sulfur Cycle?** We intervene in the atmospheric phase of the earth's sulfur cycle by

**Figure 4-31** Simplified model of the sulfur cycle. Green shows the movement of sulfur compounds in living organisms, blue in aquatic systems, and orange in the atmosphere.

*Sulfur cycle diagram labels:*

Hydrogen sulfide ($H_2S$)

+ Oxygen ($O_2$)

Atmosphere

Sulfur dioxide ($SO_2$) and Sulfur trioxide ($SO_3$)

+ Water ($H_2O$)

Dimethyl sulfide (DMS)

Industries

Volcanoes and hot springs

Sulfuric acid ($H_2SO_4$)

Oceans

+ Ammonia ($NH_3$)

Ammonium sulfate [$(NH_4)_2SO_4$]

Fog and precipitation (rain, snow)

Animals

Plants

Sulfate salts ($SO_4^{2-}$)

Aerobic conditions in soil and water

Decaying organisms

Sulfur (S)

Anaerobic conditions in soil and water

Hydrogen sulfide ($H_2S$)

- Burning sulfur-containing coal and oil to produce electric power, producing about two-thirds of the human inputs of sulfur dioxide.

- Refining sulfur-containing petroleum to make gasoline, heating oil, and other useful products.

- Using smelting to convert sulfur compounds of metallic minerals into free metals such as copper, lead, and zinc.

## 4-7 HOW DO ECOLOGISTS LEARN ABOUT ECOSYSTEMS?

**What Is Field Research?** *Field research*, sometimes called muddy-boots biology, involves going into nature and observing and measuring the structure of ecosystems and what happens in them. Most of what we know about the structure and functioning of ecosystems described in this chapter has come from such research.

## Effects of Deforestation on Nutrient Cycling

In the 1960s, F. H. Bormann of Yale University, Gene Likens of Cornell University, and their colleagues began carrying out a controlled experiment to compare the loss of water and nutrients from an uncut forest ecosystem (the *control system*) with one that was stripped of its trees (the *experimental system*).

To do this, V-shaped concrete catchment dams were built across the creeks at the bottom of several valleys in the Hubbard-Brook Experimental Forest in New Hampshire. The dams were anchored on impenetrable bedrock so all surface water leaving each forested valley ecosystem had to flow across the dams, where scientists could measure its volume and dissolved nutrient content.

The first project measured the amounts of water that entered and left an undisturbed (control) forest and the amount of dissolved nutrients in this inflow and outflow. These baseline data showed that an undisturbed mature forest ecosystem is very efficient at retaining chemical nutrients (blue area in figure).

The next experiment disturbed the system and observed any changes that occurred. One winter the investigators (1) cut down all trees and shrubs in one valley, (2) left them where they fell, and

(3) sprayed with herbicides to prevent regrowth. They then compared the inflow and outflow of water and nutrients in this modified experimental valley with those in the control valley for 3 years.

With no plants to absorb and transpire water from the soil, water runoff in the deforested valley increased by 30–40%. As this excess water ran rapidly over the surface of the ground, it eroded soil and carried nutrients out of the ecosystem. Overall, the loss of minerals from the cut forest was six to eight times that in a nearby undisturbed forest.

For example, chemical analysis of the water flowing through the dams showed a 60-fold rise in the

concentration of nitrate ions ($NO_3^-$) (purple area in figure below). So much nitrogen as nitrate ($NO_3^-$) was lost from the experimental valley that (1) the water flowing out of it was unsafe to drink, and (2) the overfertilized stream below this valley became covered with populations of cyanobacteria and algae. After a few years, however, vegetation grew back, and nitrate levels returned to normal.

### Critical Thinking

What do you think would be the effect on phosphate levels in runoff water from a Hubbard-Brook valley whose trees were destroyed by a major forest fire?

Loss of nitrate ions ($NO_3^-$) from a deforested watershed in the Hubbard-Brook Experimental Forest in New Hampshire. The concentration of nitrate ions in runoff from the deforested experimental watershed was many times greater than in a nearby unlogged watershed used as a control. (Data from F. H. Bormann and Gene Likens)

Increasingly, ecologists are using new technologies to collect field data. These include (1) *remote sensing* from aircraft and satellites and (2) *geographic information systems (GISs)*, in which information gathered from broad geographic regions is stored in spatial databases (Figure 4-32). Then computers and GIS software can analyze and manipulate the data and combine them with ground and other data to produce computerized maps of (1) forest cover and health, (2) water resources, (3) air pollution emissions, (4) coastal changes, (5) relationships between cancer and other health effects and sources of pollution, and (6) changes in global sea temperatures.

Most satellite sensors use either reflected light or reflected infrared radiation to gather data. However, some new satellites have radar sensors that measure the reflection of microwave energy from the earth. These microwaves can "see" in the dark and penetrate smoke, clouds, haze, and water. This method is also being used to map the topography of the ocean floor and provide information about ocean currents and upward flows of nutrients from the ocean bottom (upwellings) that sustain fisheries.

**What Is Laboratory Research?** In the past 50 years, ecologists have increasingly supplemented field

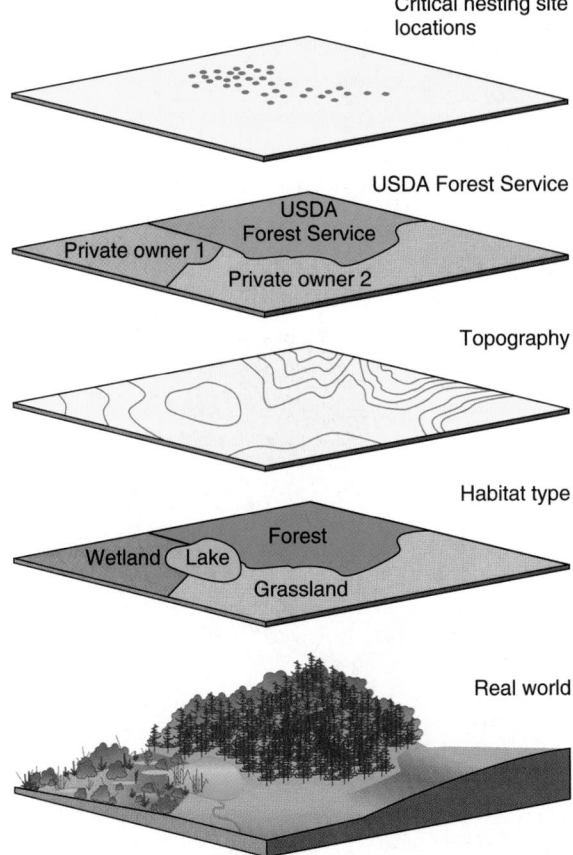

Critical nesting site locations

USDA Forest Service

USDA Forest Service

Private owner 1

Private owner 2

Topography

Habitat type

Forest

Wetland   Lake

Grassland

Real world

**Figure 4-32** Geographic information systems (GISs) provide the computer technology for organizing, storing, and analyzing complex data collected over broad geographic areas. GISs enable scientists to overlay many layers of data (such as soils, topography, distribution of endangered populations, and land protection status).

**What Is Systems Analysis?** Since the late 1960s, ecologists have made increasing use of *systems analysis* to develop mathematical and other models that simulate ecosystems. Computer simulation of such models can help us understand large and very complex systems (such as rivers, oceans, forests, grasslands, cities, and climate) that cannot be adequately studied and modeled in field and laboratory research. Figure 4-33 outlines the major stages of systems analysis.

Researchers can change values of the variables in their computer models to **(1)** project possible changes in environmental conditions, **(2)** help anticipate environmental surprises, and **(3)** analyze the effects of various alternative solutions to environmental problems.

However, simulations and predictions made using ecosystem models are no better than the data and assumptions used to develop the models. Thus careful

research by using *laboratory research* to set up, observe, and make measurements of model ecosystems and populations under laboratory conditions. Such simplified systems have been set up in containers such as **(1)** culture tubes, **(2)** bottles, **(3)** aquarium tanks, and **(4)** greenhouses and in indoor and outdoor chambers where temperature, light, $CO_2$, humidity, and other variables can be controlled carefully.

In such systems, it is easier for scientists to carry out controlled experiments. In addition, such laboratory experiments often are quicker and cheaper than similar experiments in the field.

But we must consider whether what scientists observe and measure in a simplified, controlled system under laboratory conditions takes place in the same way in the more complex and dynamic conditions found in nature. Thus the results of laboratory research must be coupled with and supported by field research.

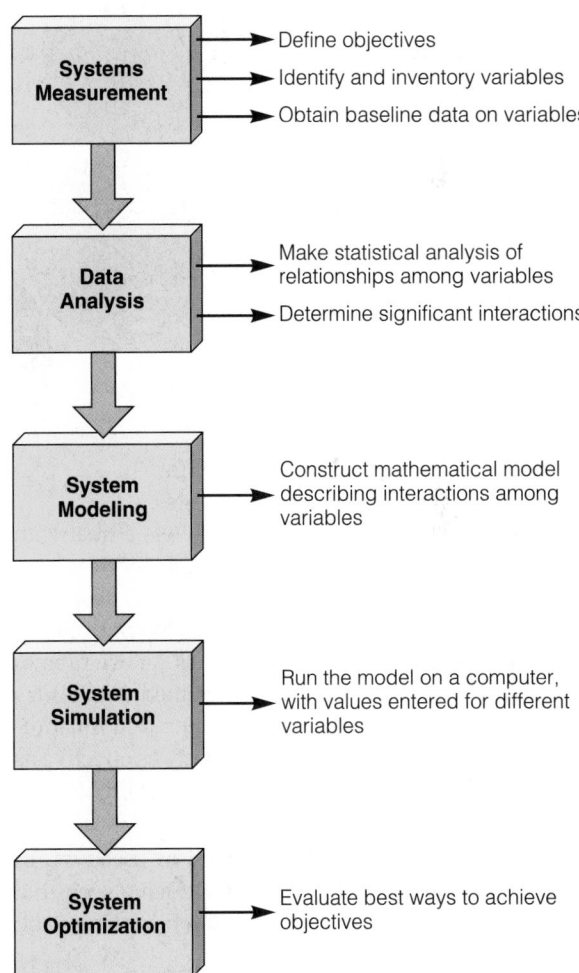

Systems Measurement

Define objectives

Identify and inventory variables

Obtain baseline data on variables

Data Analysis

Make statistical analysis of relationships among variables

Determine significant interactions

System Modeling

Construct mathematical model describing interactions among variables

System Simulation

Run the model on a computer, with values entered for different variables

System Optimization

Evaluate best ways to achieve objectives

**Figure 4-33** Major stages of systems analysis. (Modified data from Charles Southwick)

**Figure 4-34** *Ecosystem services.* Energy from the sun (solar capital) and natural resources (natural capital) provide ecological services that support and sustain the earth's life and economies.

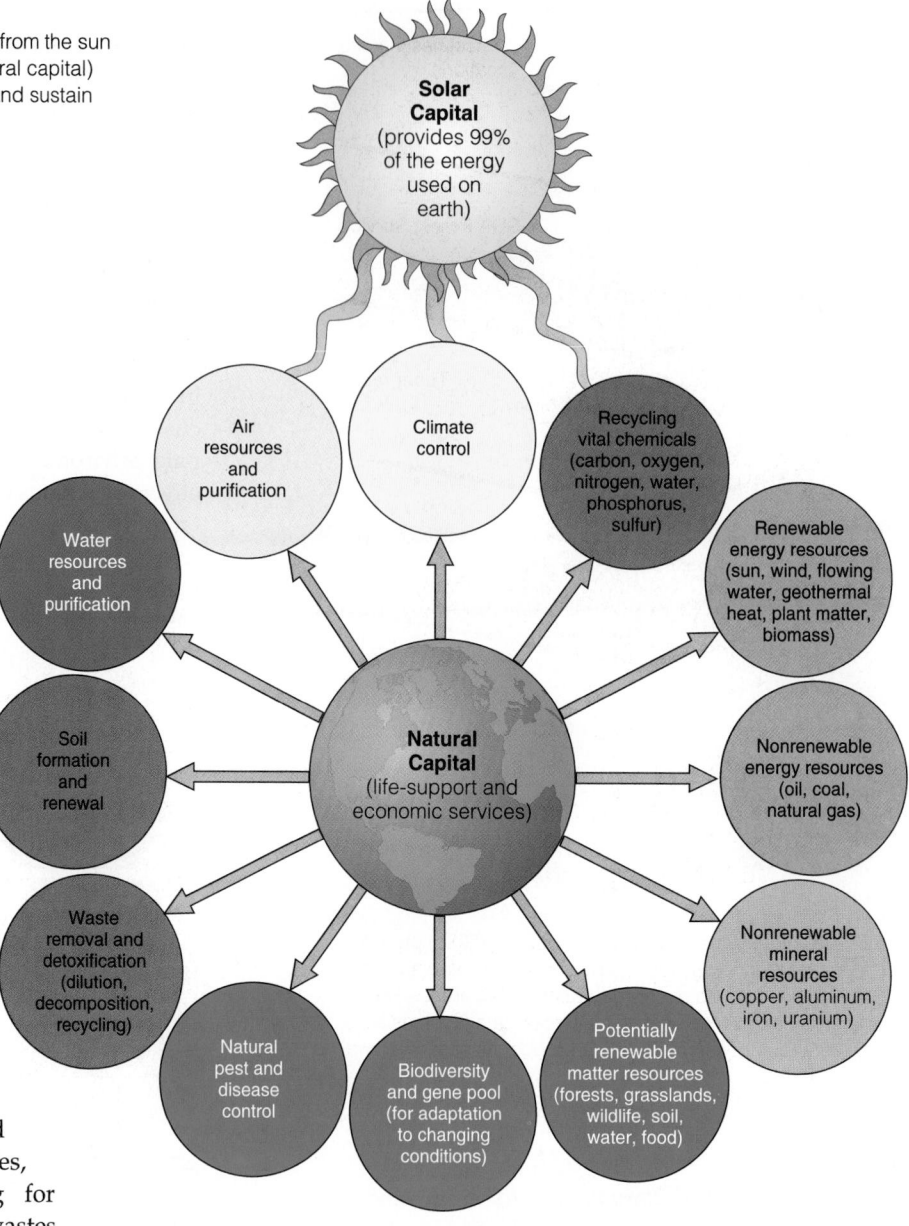

field and laboratory ecological research must be used to provide the baseline data and determine the causal relationships between key variables needed to develop and test ecosystem models.

## 4-8 ECOSYSTEM SERVICES AND SUSTAINABILITY

**What Are Ecosystem Services?** We depend on nature for food, air, water, and almost everything else we use. Ecosystems provide us and other species with a number of **ecosystem services** (Figure 4-34). Without these services performed by diverse communities of species, we would be starving, gasping for breath, and drowning in our own wastes.

It is very expensive to **(1)** build sewage treatment plants to replace free water purification services provided by wetlands, **(2)** rely mostly on pesticides rather than natural biological controls to control crop and forest pests, **(3)** try to save species whose premature extinction could have been prevented, and **(4)** try to restore ecosystems that we have degraded. In addition, these costly replacements are rarely as effective as the free ecological services that nature provides.

**What Are Two Basic Principles of Ecosystem Sustainability?** In this chapter we have seen that almost all natural ecosystems and the biosphere itself achieve *sustainability* by

- Using renewable solar energy as their energy source.

- Recycling the chemical nutrients its organisms need for survival, growth, and reproduction.

These two principles for sustainability arise from the **(1)** structure and function of natural ecosystems (Figures 4-7 and 4-16), **(2)** law of conservation of matter (p. 55), and **(3)** the two laws of thermodynamics (p. 59). Thus the results of basic research in both the physical and biological sciences provide us with the same guidelines or lessons from nature on how we can live more sustainably on the earth, as summarized in Figure 3-21, p. 61.

In this chapter we have learned about **(1)** how the earth's life-support systems work, **(2)** the living and nonliving components of ecosystems, **(3)** how energy flows through ecosystems, **(4)** how rapidly biomass is produced in different ecosystems, **(5)** how matter cycles in ecosystems, **(6)** how ecologists learn about ecosystems, and **(7)** how ecosystem services sustain life.

*All things come from earth, and to earth they all return.*
MENANDER (342–290 B.C.)

## REVIEW QUESTIONS

**1.** Define the boldfaced terms in this chapter.

**2.** Why are insects important for many forms of life and for you and your lifestyle?

**3.** What is *ecology*? What five levels of the organization of matter are the main focus of ecology?

**4.** Distinguish among *organism, eukaryotic organism, prokaryotic organism, species, population, genetic diversity, habitat, community, ecosystem,* and *biosphere.*

**5.** Explain why microbes (microorganisms) are so important.

**6.** Distinguish among the *atmosphere, troposphere, stratosphere, hydrosphere, lithosphere,* and *biosphere.*

**7.** What three processes sustain life on earth?

**8.** How does the sun help sustain life on the earth? How is this related to the earth's natural greenhouse effect?

**9.** What are *biomes,* and how are they related to climate? What are *aquatic life zones*? What is an *ecotone*?

**10.** Distinguish between the *abiotic* and *biotic* components of ecosystems, and give three examples of each.

**11.** Distinguish among *range of tolerance* for a population in an ecosystem, the *law of tolerance,* and *tolerance limits.* How does each of these factors affect the composition (structure) of ecosystems? What is a *limiting factor,* and how do such factors affect the composition of ecosystems? What are two important limiting factors for terrestrial ecosystems and for aquatic ecosystems?

**12.** Distinguish between *producers* and *consumers* in ecosystems, and give three examples of each type. What is *photosynthesis,* and why is it important to both producers and consumers? What is *chemosynthesis*?

**13.** Distinguish among *primary consumers (herbivores), secondary consumers (carnivores), tertiary consumers, omnivores, scavengers, detritivores, detritus feeders,* and *decomposers.* Why are decomposers important, and what would happen without them?

**14.** Distinguish between *aerobic respiration* and *anaerobic respiration.*

**15.** What are the four components of biodiversity? Why is biodiversity important to **(a)** the earth's life-support systems and **(b)** the economy?

**16.** Distinguish between a *food chain* and a *food web.*

**17.** What is *biomass*? What is the *pyramid of energy flow* for an ecosystem? What is the effect of the second law of thermodynamics on **(a)** the flow of energy through an ecosystem and **(b)** the amount of food energy available to top carnivores and humans?

**18.** Distinguish between the *pyramid of biomass* and the *pyramid of numbers.*

**19.** Distinguish between *gross primary productivity* and *net primary productivity.* Explain how net primary productivity affects the number of consumers in an ecosystem and on the earth. List two of the most productive ecosystems or aquatic life zones and two of the least productive ecosystems or aquatic life zones. Use the concept of net primary productivity to explain why harvesting plants from estuaries, clearing tropical forests to grow crops, and harvesting the primary producers in oceans to feed the human population are not good ideas.

**20.** About what percentages of total potential net primary productivity of **(a)** the entire earth and **(b)** the earth's terrestrial ecosystems are used, wasted, or destroyed by humans?

**21.** What is a *biogeochemical cycle*? How do such cycles connect past, present, and future forms of life?

**22.** Describe the *water cycle.* Distinguish between *absolute humidity* and *relative humidity* and between *condensation nuclei* and *dew point.* What is *groundwater*? What is an *aquifer*?

**23.** List three human activities that alter the water cycle.

**24.** Describe the *carbon cycle,* and list two human activities that alter this cycle.

**25.** Describe the *nitrogen cycle.* Distinguish among *nitrogen fixation, nitrification, assimilation, ammonification,* and *denitrification.* Explain why the level of nitrogen in soil often limits plant growth. List five ways in which humans alter this cycle.

**26.** Describe the controlled ecological experiment carried out at the Hubbard-Brook Experimental Forest in New Hampshire and summarize the results.

**27.** Describe the *phosphorus cycle.* Explain why the level of phosphorus in soil often limits plant growth on land and why phosphorus also limits the growth of producers in many freshwater streams and lakes. List three ways in which humans alter this cycle.

**28.** Describe the *sulfur cycle,* and list three ways in which humans alter this cycle.

**29.** Distinguish among *field research, laboratory research,* and *systems analysis* as methods for learning about ecosystems. What are *geographic information systems,* and how are they used to learn about ecosystems?

**30.** Define *ecosystem services,* and list nine examples of such services.

**31.** What are two basic principles of ecosystem sustainability?

## CRITICAL THINKING

**1. (a)** A bumper sticker asks, "Have you thanked a green plant today?" Give two reasons for appreciating a green plant. **(b)** Trace the sources of the materials that make up the bumper sticker, and decide whether the sticker itself is a sound application of the slogan. **(c)** Explain how decomposers help keep you alive.

**2. (a)** How would you set up a self-sustaining aquarium for tropical fish? **(b)** Suppose you have a balanced aquarium sealed with a clear glass top. Can life continue in the aquarium indefinitely as long as the sun shines regularly on it? (c) A friend cleans out your aquarium and removes all the soil and plants, leaving only the fish and water. What will happen?

3. Using the second law of thermodynamics, explain why there is such a sharp decrease in usable energy as energy flows through a food chain or web. Doesn't an energy loss at each step violate the first law of thermodynamics? Explain.

4. Using the second law of thermodynamics, explain why many poor people in developing countries live on a mostly vegetarian diet.

5. Why do farmers not need to apply carbon to grow their crops but often need to add fertilizer containing nitrogen and phosphorus?

6. Carbon dioxide ($CO_2$) in the atmosphere fluctuates significantly on a daily and seasonal basis. Why are $CO_2$ levels higher during the day than at night?

7. Why could the total amount of animal flesh on the earth never exceed the total amount of plant flesh, even if all animals were vegetarians?

8. Which causes a larger loss of energy from an ecosystem: a herbivore eating a plant or a carnivore eating an animal? Explain.

9. Why are there more mice than lions in an African ecosystem supporting both types of animals?

10. What would happen to an ecosystem if (a) all its decomposers and detritus feeders were eliminated or (b) all its producers were eliminated?

## PROJECTS

1. Visit several types of nearby aquatic life zones and terrestrial ecosystems. For each site, try to determine (a) the major producers, consumers, detritivores, and decomposers and (b) the shapes of the pyramids of energy flow, biomass, and numbers.

2. Write a brief scenario describing the sequence of consequences to us and to other forms of life if each of the following nutrient cycles stopped functioning: (a) carbon, (b) nitrogen, (c) phosphorus, and (d) water.

3. Use the library or the Internet to find out bibliographic information about *G. Evelyn Hutchinson* and *Menander,* whose quotes are found at the beginning and end of this chapter.

4. Make a concept map of this chapter's major ideas using the section heads and subheads and the key terms (in boldface). Look on the website for this book for information about making concept maps.

## INTERNET STUDY RESOURCES AND RESOURCES FOR FURTHER READING AND RESEARCH

The website for this book contains helpful study aids and many ideas for further reading and research. Log on to

www.info.brookscole.com/miller13

and click on the Chapter-by-Chapter area. Choose Chapter 4 and select a resource:

■ Flash Cards allows you to test your mastery of the Terms and Concepts to Remember for this chapter.

■ Tutorial Quizzes provides a multiple-choice practice quiz.

■ Student Guide to InfoTrac will lead you to Critical Thinking Projects that use InfoTrac College Edition as a research tool.

■ References lists the major books and articles consulted in writing this chapter.

■ Hypercontents takes you to an extensive list of sites with news, research, and images related to individual sections of the chapter.

## INFOTRAC COLLEGE EDITION

Improve your skills with InfoTrac College Edition, a searchable online database of articles from more than 700 periodicals. Log on to

www.infotrac-college.com

or access InfoTrac through the website for this book. Try to find the following articles:

1. Pauly, D., V. Christensen, R. Froese, and M. L. Palomares. 2000. Fishing down aquatic food webs. *American Scientist* 88: 46. *Keywords:* "fishing" and "aquatic food webs." As pressure on fishing becomes more intense, humans are catching and keeping ever smaller fish. This has implications for the entire aquatic food web, including the recovery of higher-trophic-level species. This work presents a new way of looking at fisheries science using basic ecological principles.

2. Lockaby, B. G., and W. H. Conner. 1999. N:P balance in wetland forests: Productivity across a biogeochemical continuum. *The Botanical Review* 65: 171. *Keywords:* "wetland forests" and "productivity." This paper integrates the concepts of biogeochemical cycling, limiting factors, and productivity by looking at differences among wetland forests.

# 5 EVOLUTION AND BIODIVERSITY: ORIGINS, NICHES, AND ADAPTATION

## Earth: The Just-Right, Resilient Planet

Life on the earth as we know it (Figure 5-1) needs a certain temperature range: Venus is much too hot and Mars is much too cold, but the earth is *just right.* (Otherwise, you would not be reading these words.)

Life as we know it depends on the liquid water that dominates the earth's surface. Again, temperature is crucial; life on the earth needs average temperatures between the freezing and boiling points of water, between 0°C and 100°C (32°F and 212°F) at the earth's range of atmospheric pressures.

The earth's orbit is the right distance from the sun to provide these conditions. If the earth were much closer, it would be too hot—like Venus—for water vapor to condense to form rain. If it were much farther away, its surface would be so cold—like Mars—that its water would exist only as ice. The earth also spins; if it did not, the side facing the sun would be too hot and the other side too cold for water-based life to exist.

The earth is also the right size; that is, it has enough gravitational mass to keep its iron and nickel core molten and to keep the gaseous molecules in its atmosphere from flying off into space. (A much smaller earth would be unable to hold on to an atmosphere consisting of such light molecules as $N_2$, $O_2$, $CO_2$, and $H_2O$.)

The slow transfer of its internal heat (geothermal energy) to the surface also helps keep the planet at the right temperature for life. And thanks to the development of photosynthesizing bacteria more than 2 billion years ago, an ozone sunscreen protects us and many other forms of life from an overdose of ultraviolet radiation.

On a time scale of millions of years, the earth is enormously resilient and adaptive. During the 3.7 billion years since life arose, the average surface temperature of the earth has remained within the narrow range of 10–20°C (50–68°F), even with a 30–40% increase in the sun's energy output. In short, the earth is just right for life as we know it.

We can summarize the 3.7-billion-year biological history of the earth in one sentence: *Organisms convert solar energy to food, chemicals cycle, and a variety of species with different biological roles (niches) has evolved in response to changing environmental conditions.*

Each species here today represents a long chain of evolution, and each of these species plays a unique ecological role in the earth's communities and ecosystems. These species, communities, and ecosystems also are essential for future evolution as the earth continues its long history of environmental change.

This chapter discusses how the earth's species evolved and the nature of their niches or biological roles. This information is important for helping us **(1)** understand the effects of human actions on wild species and **(2)** protect species—including the human species—from premature extinction.

**Figure 5-1** The earth is a blue and white planet in the black void of space. Currently, it has the right physical and chemical conditions to allow the development of life as we know it today.

NASA

*There is a grandeur to this view of life . . . that, whilst this planet has gone cycling on . . . endless forms most beautiful and most wonderful have been, and are being, evolved.*

CHARLES DARWIN

This chapter addresses the following questions:

- How do scientists account for the emergence of life on the earth?

- What is evolution, and how has it led to the current diversity of organisms on the earth?

- How does evolution affect the way organisms fit into their environment?

- What is an ecological niche, and how does it relate to adaptation to changing environmental conditions?

- How do extinction of species and formation of new species affect biodiversity?

 **5-1   ORIGINS OF LIFE**

**How Did Life Emerge on the Earth?**   How did a barren planet become a living jewel in the vastness of space (Figure 5-1)? How did life on the earth evolve to its present incredible diversity of species, living in an interlocking network of matter cycles, energy flows, and species interactions? We do not know the full answer to these questions, but a growing body of evidence suggests what might have happened.

Evidence about the earth's early history comes from chemical analysis and measurements of radioactive elements in primitive rocks and fossils. Chemists have also conducted laboratory experiments showing how simple inorganic compounds in the earth's early atmosphere might have reacted to produce amino acids, simple sugars, and other organic molecules used as building blocks for the protein, complex carbo-

hydrate, RNA, and DNA molecules needed for life (Figure 3-6, p. 50).

From this diverse evidence scientists have hypothesized that life on the earth developed in two phases over the past 4.7–4.8 billion years (Figure 5-2):

- *Chemical evolution* of the organic molecules, biopolymers, and systems of chemical reactions needed to form the first protocells (taking about 1 billion years)

- *Biological evolution* from single-celled prokaryotic bacteria (Figure 4-3b, p. 67), to single-celled eukaryotic creatures (Figure 4-3a, p. 67), and then to multicellular organisms (taking about 3.7–3.8 billion years)

 **How Did Chemical Evolution Take Place?**
Here is an overview of how scientists believe chemical evolution occurred. Some 4.6–4.7 billion years ago, a cloud of cosmic dust condensed into the earth, which soon turned molten from (1) meteorite impacts and (2) the heat produced by the radioactive decay of chemical elements in its interior. About 3.7 billion years ago, the outermost portion of the molten sphere had cooled enough to form a thin, solid crust of rock, devoid of atmosphere and oceans.

Comets hitting the lifeless earth pierced its thin crust, and energy from the earth's highly radioactive contents released water vapor, carbon dioxide, and other gases from the molten interior. Eventually the crust cooled enough for the water vapor to condense and fall to the surface as rain. This rain eroded minerals from rocks, and solutions of these minerals collected in depressions to form the early oceans that covered most of the globe.

As gases were released from the earth's interior, they formed the planet's first atmosphere. The exact composition of this primitive atmosphere is unknown.

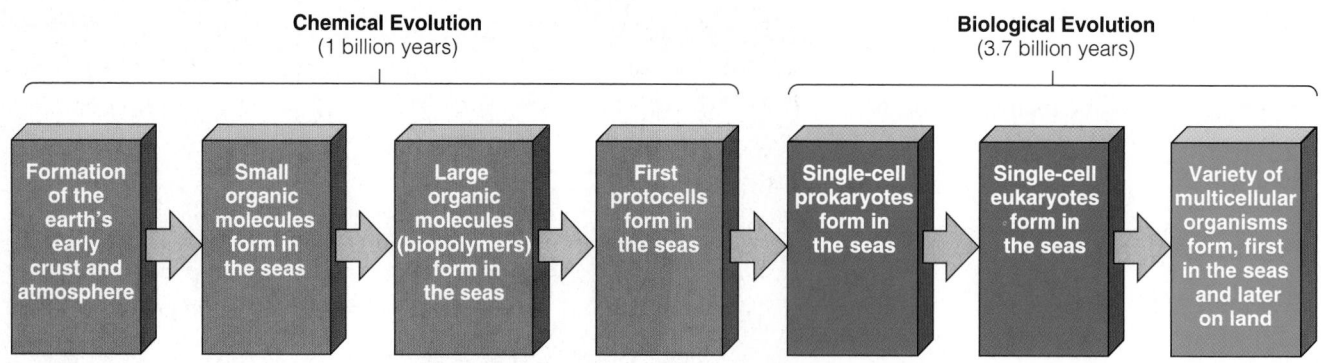

**Figure 5-2** Summary of the hypothesized chemical and biological evolution of the earth. This drawing is not to scale. Note that the time span for biological evolution is almost four times longer than that for chemical evolution.

However, atmospheric scientists believe it was dominated by carbon dioxide ($CO_2$), nitrogen ($N_2$), and water vapor ($H_2O$) and trace amounts of several other gases such as methane ($CH_4$), ammonia ($NH_3$), hydrogen sulfide ($H_2S$), and hydrogen chloride ($HCl$).

Whatever its composition, scientists agree that this primitive atmosphere had no oxygen gas ($O_2$) because this element is so chemically reactive that it would have combined into compounds. The only reason today's atmosphere has so much $O_2$ is that plants and some aerobic bacteria produce it in vast quantities through photosynthesis. But we are getting ahead of the story.

Scientists have come up with several explanations of how the (1) amino acids (the building-block molecules of proteins), (2) simple carbohydrates, (3) nucleic acids (the building-block molecules of DNA and RNA; Appendix 2), and (4) other small organic compounds necessary for life may have formed.

The most widely believed hypothesis is that the building-block *organic* molecules needed for life formed from the *inorganic* chemicals found in the earth's primitive atmosphere under the influence of readily available (1) energy from electrical discharges (lightning), (2) heat from volcanoes, (3) intense ultraviolet (UV) light, and (4) other forms of solar radiation.

In a number of experiments conducted since 1953, scientists placed various mixtures of gases believed to have been in the earth's early atmosphere in closed, sterilized glass containers. Then they subjected the gases in the containers to spark discharges to simulate lightning and heat (Figure 5-3). In these experiments, the building-block molecules necessary for life formed from the inorganic gaseous molecules.

Other possibilities are that the building-block organic molecules necessary for life

- Formed on dust particles in space and reached the earth on meteorites or comets (or on countless interplanetary dust particles floating around in space when the earth was formed). In 1997, researchers found amino acids on a meteorite that struck Australia in 1969.

- Formed deep within the earth.

- Formed around mineral-rich and very hot *hydrothermal vents*, which sit atop cracks in the ocean floor leading to subterranean chambers of molten rock.

However these building-block organic molecules formed, scientists hypothesize that they accumulated and underwent countless chemical reactions for sev-

eral hundred million years. This led to the formation of conglomerates of proteins, RNA, and other biopolymers that may have then combined to form membrane-bound *protocells:* small globules that could take up materials from their environment and grow and divide (much like living cells).

These reactions could have occurred (1) in the earth's warm shallow waters, (2) deep within the earth, or (3) around thermal hydrothermal vents on the ocean bottom. With these forerunners of living cells, the stage was set for the drama of biological evolution (Figure 5-4, p. 98, and Spotlight, p. 99).

**How Do We Know What Organisms Lived in the Past?** Most of what we know of the earth's life history comes from **fossils:** mineralized or petrified replicas of skeletons, bones, teeth, shells, leaves, and seeds, or impressions of such items. Such fossils

**Figure 5-3** Synthesis of organic compounds necessary for life from the gases believed to be in the earth's primitive atmosphere. Stanley Miller and Harold Urey used a similar apparatus to show that under the influence of electrical sparks simulating lightning, simple inorganic compounds believed to be in the earth's primitive atmosphere could be converted into amino acids (the building blocks of proteins) and a variety of other simple organic chemicals necessary for life.

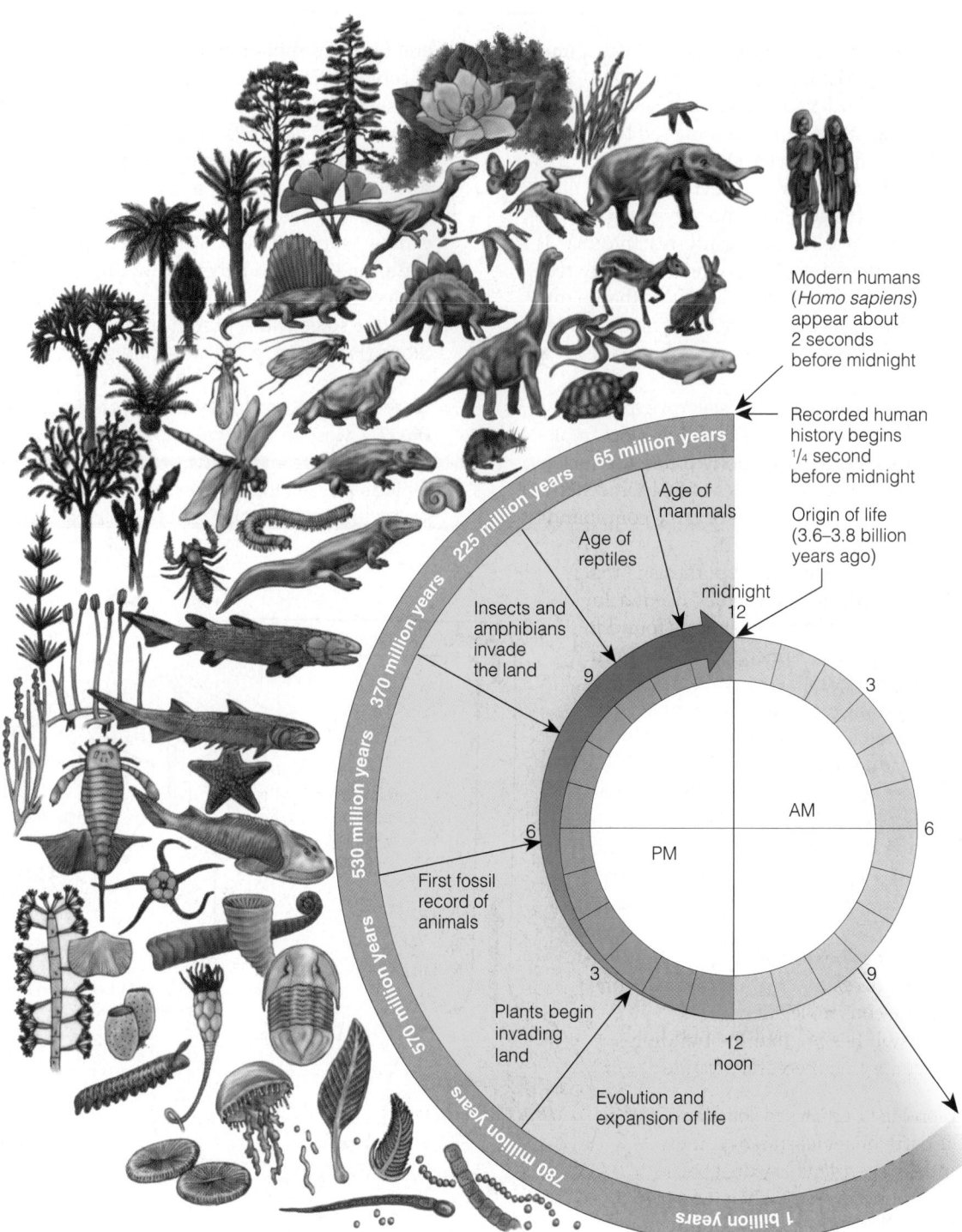

**Figure 5-4** Greatly simplified overview of the biological evolution of life on the earth, which was preceded by about 1 billion years of chemical evolution. Evidence indicates that the early span of biological evolution on the earth, between about 3.7 billion and 1 billion years ago, was dominated by microorganisms (mostly bacteria and, later, protists) that lived in water. Plants and animals evolved first in the seas. Fossil and recent DNA evidence suggests that plants began moving onto land about 780 million years ago, and animals began invading the land about 370 million years ago. Humans arrived on the scene only a very short time ago. If we compress the earth's roughly 3.7-billion-year history of biological evolution to a 24-hour time scale, the first human species (*Homo habilis*) appeared about 47–94 seconds before midnight, and our species (*Homo sapiens sapiens*) appeared about 2 seconds before midnight. Agriculture began only 0.25 second before midnight, and the industrial revolution has been around for only 0.007 second. (Adapted from George Gaylord Simpson and William S. Beck, *Life: An Introduction to Biology*, 2nd ed. New York: Harcourt, Brace, Jovanovich, 1965)

## How Did Life First Evolve?

About 3.2 billion years ago, the earth was a very hostile environment for life. Hot lava spewed from its surface and beneath the sea, much of the land was dotted with boiling hot springs, and the atmosphere was thick with steam and carbon dioxide.

Over time, it is believed that early protocells evolved into single-celled, bacterialike prokaryotes (Figure 4-3b, p. 67) having the properties we describe as life. However, scientists hotly debate the details of how this might have happened.

These anaerobic cells probably evolved (1) in the muddy sediments of tidal flats, (2) at least 10 meters (30 feet) below the ocean's surface, or (3) in the deep ocean near hydrothermal vents. All these environments would have protected these single-celled forms of life from the intense UV radiation that bathed the earth at that time.

The early single-celled organisms probably obtained their energy directly by absorbing hydrogen sulfide molecules. Soon thereafter, they developed the process of *fermentation*, or anaerobic respiration, to (1) break down sugars and other organic compounds, (2) release energy for their use, and (3) store some of this energy in adenosine triphosphate (ATP) molecules.

Scientists believe these single-celled anaerobic bacteria multiplied and underwent genetic changes (mutated) for about a billion years in the earth's warm, shallow seas or in the deep ocean. The result was a variety of new types of prokaryotic cells that began forming about 2.8–3.5 billion years ago.

Eventually the population of these fermenter bacteria expanded to the point at which they exceeded their food supplies. This created the world's first *population crisis*.

This crisis was relieved when different types of bacteria evolved that produced their food through *photosynthesis* (p. 74). About 2.3–2.7 billion years ago, the evolution of these photosynthetic prokaryotes, called *cyanobacteria*, in the ocean drastically changed the earth. These cells could (1) remove carbon dioxide from the water and (2) use sunlight to combine it with water to make the carbohydrates they needed, and (3) release oxygen ($O_2$) into the ocean and the atmosphere.

As these photosynthesizers multiplied for almost 2 billion years in the water and mud, they created large amounts of dissolved oxygen and oxygen that escaped into the atmosphere. This oxygen reacted with the food molecules used by both fermenting and photosynthesizing bacteria. This resulted in the world's first *pollution crisis*, which caused a huge dieback of both types of bacteria.

This spurred a new round of biological innovation. Fermenters survived by living in deep water and mud flats to avoid contact with the oxygen-rich air. However, the most significant event was the development of bacteria that used *aerobic respiration*, in which oxygen molecules are used to break up food molecules to obtain energy (p. 74). At this point, the earth's single-celled organisms had developed three ways to feed themselves: *fermentation*, *photosynthesis*, and *aerobic respiration*.

Over the next half a billion years, the oxygen released by photosynthesizers built up in the atmosphere.

The resulting *oxygen revolution* opened the way for the evolution of a great variety of oxygen-using (aerobic) bacteria. Complex organisms came later, first in the seas and then increasingly on land (after a protective ozone layer formed in the stratosphere).

Fossil evidence indicates that at least 1.2 billion years ago, the first *eukaryotic cells* (with nuclei, Figure 4-3a, p. 67) emerged in earth's shallow seas. Because eukaryotes could reproduce sexually, they produced a variety of offspring with different genetic characteristics. These first eukaryotes were the building blocks for the more complex multicelled life-forms that followed (Figure 5-4).

As oxygen accumulated in the atmosphere, some was converted by incoming solar energy into ozone ($O_3$), which began forming in the lower stratosphere. This shield protected life-forms from the sun's deadly UV radiation, allowing green plants to live closer to the ocean's surface.

Fossil evidence and recent DNA evidence suggests that about 780 million years ago, UV levels were low enough for the first plants (probably waxy-coated algae) to emerge from the underwater world and exist on the land. Over the next several hundred million years, a variety of land plants and animals arose, followed by mammals and eventually the first humans (Figure 5-4).

### Critical Thinking

If photosynthesizing bacteria had not developed, what kinds of life would you expect to find on the earth today? Where would most of it be found?

---

(1) give us physical evidence of organisms that lived long ago and (2) show us what their internal structures looked like.

Despite its importance, the fossil record is uneven and incomplete. Some life-forms left no fossils, some fossils have decomposed, and others are yet to be found.

So far we have found fossils representing only about 1% of the species believed to have ever lived.

Other sources of information include (1) chemical and radioactive dating of fossils, (2) nearby ancient rocks, (3) material in cores drilled out of buried ice, and (4) the DNA of organisms alive today.

## 5-2 EVOLUTION AND ADAPTATION

**What Is Evolution?** According to scientific evidence, the major driving force of adaptation to changes in environmental conditions is **biological evolution,** or **evolution:** the change in a population's genetic makeup (gene pool) through successive generations. Note that *populations, not individuals, evolve by becoming genetically different.*

According to the **theory of evolution,** all species descended from earlier, ancestral species. This widely accepted scientific theory explains how life has changed over the past 3.7 billion years (Figure 5-4) and why life is so diverse today.

Biologists use the term **microevolution** to describe the small genetic changes that occur in a population. The term **macroevolution** is used to describe long-term, large-scale evolutionary changes through which **(1)** new species are formed from ancestral species and **(2)** other species are lost through extinction.

**How Does Microevolution Work?** The first step in evolution is the development of *genetic variability* in a population. Recall that **(1)** genetic information in *chromosomes* is contained in various sequences of chemical units (called *nucleotides*) in DNA molecules (Appendix 2), and **(2)** genes found in chromosomes are segments of DNA coded for certain traits that can be passed on to offspring (Figure 3-6, p. 50).

A population's **gene pool** is the set of all genes in the individuals of the population of a species. *Microevolution* is a change in a population's gene pool over time.

Although members of a population generally have the same number and kinds of genes, a particular gene may have two or more different molecular forms, called **alleles.** Sexual reproduction leads to a random shuffling or recombination of alleles. As a result, each individual in a population has a different combination of alleles.

Genetic variability in a population originates through **mutations:** random changes in the structure or number of DNA molecules in a cell. Mutations can occur in two ways:

- Exposure of DNA to external agents such as radioactivity, X rays, and natural and human-made chemicals (called *mutagens*)

- Random mistakes that sometimes occur in coded genetic instructions when DNA molecules are copied each time a cell divides and whenever an organism reproduces

Mutations can occur in any cells, but only those in reproductive cells are passed on to offspring.

Some mutations are harmless, but most are harmful and alter traits so that an individual cannot survive (lethal mutations). Every so often, a mutation is beneficial. The result is new genetic traits that give their bearer and its offspring better chances for survival and reproduction, **(1)** under existing environmental conditions or **(2)** when such conditions change.

Mutations are **(1)** random and unpredictable, **(2)** the only source of totally new genetic raw material (alleles), and **(3)** rare events. Once created by mutation, new alleles can be shuffled together or recombined *randomly* to create new combinations of genes in populations of sexually reproducing species.

**SPOTLIGHT**

## What Is Artificial Selection?

**Artificial selection** is the process by which humans **(1)** select one or more desirable genetic traits in the population of a plant or animal and **(2)** use *selective breeding* to end up with populations of the species containing large numbers of individuals with the desired traits. This process has been used to develop essentially all of the domesticated breeds of plants and animals from wild populations.

Artificial selection involves several steps:

**1.** Choose the genetic traits desired in a particular species. Examples might be **(1)** wheat that grows short so it will not topple over, **(2)** cattle that need less water, or **(3)** dogs with short legs.

**2.** Examine existing populations of species (such as wheat, cattle, or dogs) to identify individuals that exhibit more of the desired genetic trait than other members of the population.

**3.** Select offspring that exhibit more of the desired trait than their parents to be breeders for the next generation, and prevent other offspring from breeding.

When this process of selection and breeding is carried out over many generations, more and more of the offspring have the selected or desired traits.

Artificial selection results in many different domesticated breeds or hybrids of the same species, all originally developed from a particular wild species. For example, despite their widely different genetic traits, all of the hundreds of different breeds of dogs are members of the same species because they can potentially interbreed and produce fertile offspring.

**Critical Thinking**

How does artificial selection differ from natural selection (p. 101)?

**What Role Does Natural Selection Play in Microevolution?** The process of **natural selection** occurs when some individuals of a population have genetically based traits that increase their chances of survival and their ability to produce offspring. Three conditions are necessary for evolution of a population by natural selection to occur:

- There must be natural *variability* for a trait in a population.

- The trait must be *heritable,* meaning it must have a genetic basis such that it can be passed from one generation to another.

- The trait must somehow lead to **differential reproduction,** meaning it must enable individuals with the trait to leave more offspring than other members of the population.

Natural selection causes **(1)** any allele or set of alleles that result in a beneficial trait to become more common in succeeding generations and **(2)** other alleles to become less common. A heritable trait that enables organisms to better survive and reproduce under a given set of environmental conditions is called an **adaptation,** or **adaptive trait.**

When faced with a change in environmental conditions, a population of a species can **(1)** adapt to the new conditions through natural selection, **(2)** migrate (if possible) to an area with more favorable conditions, or **(3)** become extinct.

The process of microevolution can be summarized as follows: *Genes mutate, individuals are selected, and populations evolve.* The genetic characteristics of populations of a species also can be changed through *artificial selection* (Spotlight, left).

**What Is an Example of Microevolution by Natural Selection?** One of the best-documented examples of microevolution by natural selection involves camouflage coloration in the peppered moth, which is found in England (Figure 5-5).

Natural selection occurred because **(1)** there were two color forms (*variability*), **(2)** color form was genetically based (*heritability*), and **(3)** there was greater survival and reproduction by one of the color forms (*differential reproduction*). First an environmental change in the form of soot caused a change in the background color of tree trunks. This environmental change then allowed bird predators to find and eat the moths with the coloration that no longer blended in with the background (Figure 5-5).

**What Are Three Types of Natural Selection?** Biologists recognize three types of natural selection (Figure 5-6, p. 102):

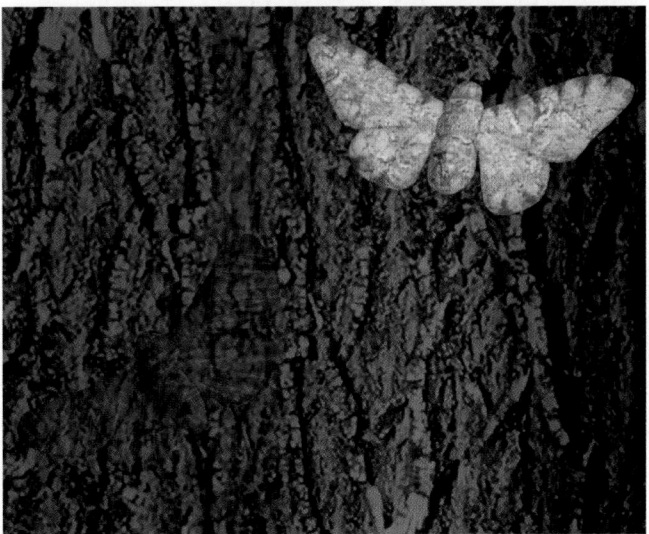

**Figure 5-5** Two varieties of peppered moths found in England illustrate one kind of adaptation: camouflage. Before the industrial revolution in the mid-1800s, the speckled light-gray form of this moth was prevalent. When these night-flying moths rested on light-gray lichens on tree trunks during the day, their color camouflaged them from their predators (top). A dark-gray form also existed but was quite rare. During the industrial revolution, soot and other pollutants from factory smokestacks began killing lichens and darkening tree trunks. As a result, the dark form of moth became the common one, especially near industrial cities. In this new environment, the dark form of moth blended in with the blackened trees, whereas the light form of moth was highly visible to predators (bottom). Through natural selection, the dark form began to survive and reproduce at a greater rate than its light-colored kin. (Both varieties appear in each diagram. Can you spot them?)

- *Directional natural selection* (Figure 5-6, left), in which changing environmental conditions cause allele frequencies to shift so individuals with traits at one end of the normal range become more common than midrange forms. Examples of this "it pays to be different" type of natural selection are **(1)** the changes in the

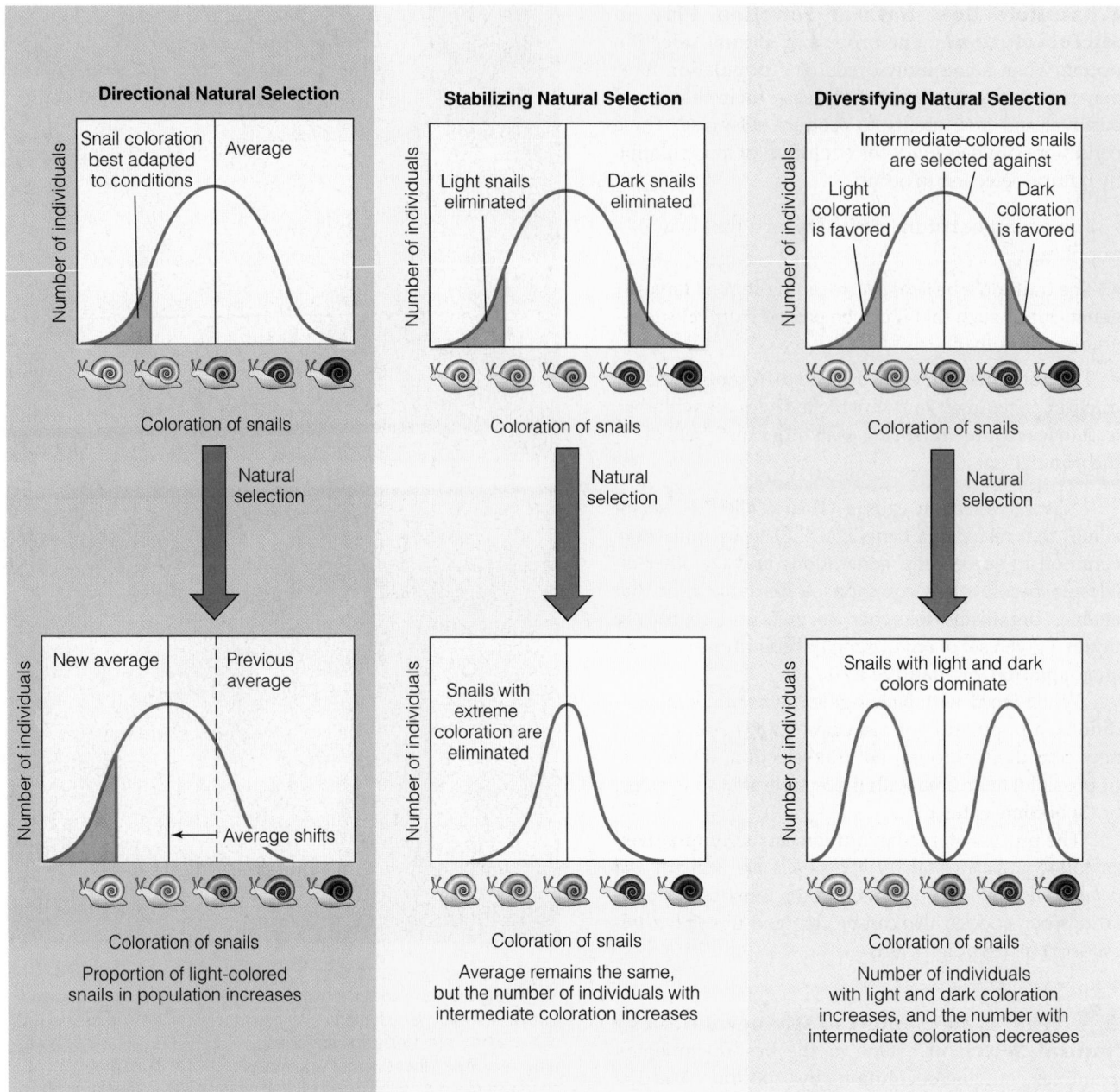

**Directional Natural Selection**

Snail coloration best adapted to conditions

Average

Number of individuals

Coloration of snails

Natural selection

New average

Previous average

Average shifts

Number of individuals

Coloration of snails

Proportion of light-colored snails in population increases

**Stabilizing Natural Selection**

Light snails eliminated

Dark snails eliminated

Number of individuals

Coloration of snails

Natural selection

Snails with extreme coloration are eliminated

Number of individuals

Coloration of snails

Average remains the same, but the number of individuals with intermediate coloration increases

**Diversifying Natural Selection**

Intermediate-colored snails are selected against

Light coloration is favored

Dark coloration is favored

Number of individuals

Coloration of snails

Natural selection

Snails with light and dark colors dominate

Number of individuals

Coloration of snails

Number of individuals with light and dark coloration increases, and the number with intermediate coloration decreases

**Figure 5-6** Three ways in which natural selection can occur, using the trait of coloration in a population of snails. In *directional natural selection*, changing environmental conditions select organisms with alleles that deviate from the norm so their offspring (lighter-colored snails) make up a larger proportion of the population. In *stabilizing selection*, environmental factors eliminate fringe individuals (light- and dark-colored snails) and increase the number of individuals with average genetic makeup (intermediate-colored snails). In *diversifying natural selection*, environmental factors favor individuals with uncommon traits (light- and dark-colored snails) and greatly reduce those with average traits (intermediate-colored snails).

varieties of peppered moths (Figure 5-5) and **(2)** the evolution of genetic resistance to pesticides among insects and to antibiotics among disease-carrying bacteria. This type of natural selection is most common during periods of environmental change or when members of a population migrate to a new habitat with different environmental conditions.

■ *Stabilizing natural selection,* which tends to eliminate individuals on both ends of the genetic spectrum and favor individuals with an average genetic makeup (Figure 5-6, center). This "it pays to be average" type of natural selection occurs when **(1)** an environment changes little, and **(2)** most members of the population are well adapted to that environment.

■ *Diversifying natural selection,* which occurs when environmental conditions favor individuals at both extremes of the genetic spectrum and eliminate or sharply reduce numbers of individuals with normal or intermediate genetic traits (Figure 5-6, right). In this "it does not pay to be normal" type of natural selection, a population is split into two groups.

**What Is Coevolution?** Some biologists have proposed that *interactions between species* also can result in microevolution in each of their populations. According to this hypothesis, when populations of two different species interact over a long time, changes in the gene pool of one species can lead to changes in the gene pool of the other species. This process is called **coevolution.**

Suppose that certain individuals in a population of carnivores (such as owls) become better at hunting prey (such as mice). Because of genetic variation, certain individuals of the prey have traits that allow them to escape or hide from their predators, and they pass these adaptive traits on to some of their offspring. However, a few individuals in the predator population also may have traits (such as better eyesight or quicker reflexes) that allow them to hunt the better-adapted prey successfully. They would then pass these traits on to some of their offspring.

Similarly, individual plants in a population may evolve defenses, such as camouflage, thorns, or poisons, against efficient herbivores. In turn, some herbivores in the population may have genetic characteristics that enable them to overcome these defenses and produce more offspring than those without such traits.

In coevolution, adaptation follows adaptation in something like an ongoing, long-term arms race between individuals in interacting populations of different species.

## 5-3 ECOLOGICAL NICHES AND ADAPTATION

**What Is an Ecological Niche?** If asked what role a certain species such as an alligator plays in an ecosystem, an ecologist would describe its **ecological niche,** or simply **niche** (pronounced "nitch"), the species' way of life or functional role in an ecosystem. A species' niche involves everything that affects its survival and reproduction. This includes **(1)** its range of tolerance for various physical and chemical conditions, such as temperature or water availability (Figure 4-14, p. 73), **(2)** the types and amounts of resources it uses, such as food or nutrients and space, **(3)** how it interacts with other living and nonliving components of the ecosystems in which it is found, and **(4)** the role it plays in the energy flow and matter cycling in an ecosystem (Figure 4-16, p. 75).

The ecological niche of a species is different from its **habitat,** or physical location, where it lives. Ecologists often say that a niche is like a species' occupation, whereas habitat is like its address.

A species' ecological niche represents the *adaptations* or *adaptive traits* that its members have acquired through evolution. These traits enable its members to survive and reproduce more effectively under a given set of environmental conditions.

Understanding a species' niche is important because it can help us **(1)** prevent it from becoming prematurely extinct and **(2)** assess the environmental changes we make in terrestrial and aquatic systems. For example, how will the niches of various species be changed by clearing a forest, plowing up a grassland, filling in a wetland, or dumping pollutants into a lake or stream?

**What Is the Difference Between a Species' Fundamental Niche and Its Realized Niche?** A species' **fundamental niche** is the full potential range of physical, chemical, and biological conditions and resources it could theoretically use if there were no direct competition from other species. But in a particular ecosystem, species often compete with one another for one or more of the same resources. This means the niches of competing species overlap.

To survive and avoid competition for the same resources, a species usually occupies only part of its fundamental niche in a particular community or ecosystem—what ecologists call its **realized niche.** By analogy, you may be capable of being president of a particular company (your *fundamental professional niche*), but competition from others may mean you may become only a vice president (your *realized professional niche*).

**Is It Better to Be a Generalist or a Specialist Species? Broad and Narrow Niches** The niches of species can be used to broadly classify them as *generalists* or *specialists*. **Generalist species** have broad niches (Figure 5-7, right curve, p. 104). They can **(1)** live in many different places, **(2)** eat a variety of foods, and **(3)** tolerate a wide range of environmental conditions. Flies, cockroaches (Spotlight, p. 105), mice, rats, white-tailed deer, raccoons, coyotes, copperheads, channel catfish, and humans are generalist species.

**Specialist species** have narrow niches (Figure 5-7, left curve, p. 104). They may be able to **(1)** live in only one type of habitat, **(2)** use only one or a few types of food, or **(3)** tolerate only a narrow range of climatic and other environmental conditions. This makes them more prone to extinction when environmental conditions change. Examples of specialists are **(1)** *tiger salamanders,* which can breed only in fishless ponds so their larvae will not be eaten, **(2)** *red-cockaded woodpeckers,* which carve nest holes almost exclusively in old (at least 75 years) longleaf pines, **(3)** *spotted owls,* which

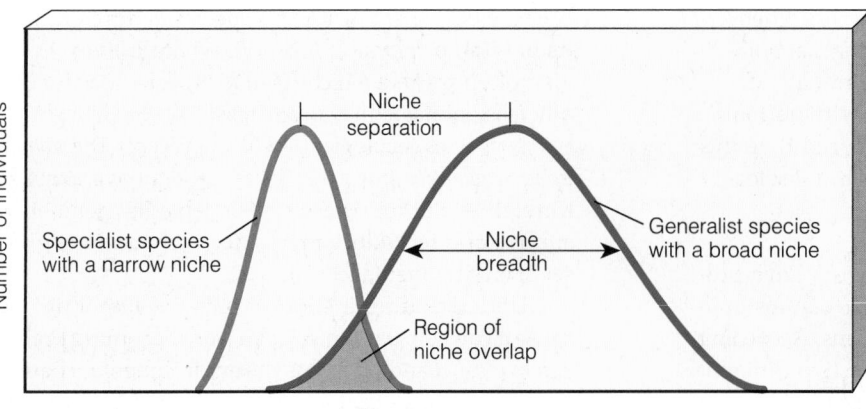

**Figure 5-7** Overlap of the niches of two different species: a specialist and a generalist. In the overlap area the two species compete for one or more of the same resources. As a result, each species can occupy only a part of its fundamental niche and thus occupy its realized niche. Generalist species have a broad niche (right), and specialist species have a narrow niche (left).

need old-growth forests in the Pacific Northwest for food and shelter, and **(4)** China's highly endangered *giant pandas,* which feed almost exclusively on various types of bamboo.

Is it better to be a generalist than a specialist? It depends. When environmental conditions are fairly constant, as in a tropical rain forest, specialists have an advantage because they have fewer competitors. But under rapidly changing environmental conditions, the generalist usually is better off than the specialist.

**What Limits Adaptation?** Shouldn't evolution lead to perfectly adapted organisms? Shouldn't adaptations to new environmental conditions allow **(1)** our skin to become more resistant to the harmful effects of ultraviolet radiation, **(2)** our lungs to cope with air pollutants, and **(3)** our livers to become better at detoxifying pollutants? The answer to these questions is *no* because of the following limits to adaptations in nature:

▪ *A change in environmental conditions can lead to adaptation only for traits already present in the gene pool of a population.*

▪ *Even if a beneficial heritable trait is present in a population, that population's ability to adapt can be limited by its reproductive capacity.* Populations of genetically diverse species that reproduce quickly—such as weeds, mosquitoes, rats, bacteria, or cockroaches—often can adapt to a change in environmental conditions in a short time. In contrast, populations of species such as elephants, tigers, sharks, and humans, which cannot produce large numbers of offspring rapidly, take a long time (typically thousands or even millions of years) to adapt through natural selection.

▪ *Even if a favorable genetic trait is present in a population, most of the population would have to die or become sterile so individuals with the trait could predominate and pass the trait on.* This is hardly a desirable solution to the environmental problems the human species faces.

**What Are Two Common Misconceptions About Evolution?** Two common misconceptions about evolution are as follows:

▪ "Survival of the fittest" means "survival of the strongest." To biologists, *fitness* is a measure of reproductive success not strength. Thus the fittest individuals are those that leave the most descendants.

▪ Evolution involves some grand plan of nature in which species become progressively more perfect. From a scientific standpoint, no plan or goal of perfection exists in the evolutionary process. However, some people (creationists) believe there is a conflict between the scientific theory of evolution and their religious beliefs about how life was created on the earth.

### 5-4 SPECIATION, EXTINCTION, AND BIODIVERSITY

**How Do New Species Evolve?** Under certain circumstances, natural selection can lead to an entirely new species. In this process, called **speciation,** two species arise from one.

The most common mechanism of speciation (especially among animals) takes place in two phases: geographic isolation and reproductive isolation. **Geographic isolation** occurs when groups of the same population of a species become physically separated for long periods. For example, part of a population may migrate in search of food and then begin living in another area with different environmental conditions (Figure 5-8). Populations also may become separated **(1)** by a physical barrier (such as a mountain range, stream, lake, or road), **(2)** by a change such as a volcanic eruption or earthquake, or **(3)** when a few individuals are carried to a new area by wind or water.

The second phase of speciation is **reproductive isolation.** It occurs when mutation and natural selection operate independently in two geographically isolated populations and change the allele frequencies in different ways. If this process, called *divergence,* continues long enough, members of the geographically and reproductively isolated populations may become so different in genetic makeup that **(1)** they cannot interbreed, or **(2)** if they do, they cannot produce live, fer-

## SPOTLIGHT

## Cockroaches: Nature's Ultimate Survivors

Cockroaches, the bugs many people love to hate, have **(1)** been around for about 350 million years and **(2)** are one of the great success stories of evolution. They are so successful because they are *generalists*.

The earth's 4,000 cockroach species can **(1)** eat almost anything (including algae, dead insects, fingernail clippings, salts in tennis shoes, electrical cords, glue, paper, and soap) and **(2)** live and breed almost anywhere except in polar regions.

Some species can go for months without food, survive for a month on a drop of water from a dishrag, and withstand massive doses of radiation. One species can survive being frozen for 48 hours.

They usually can evade their predators and a human foot in hot pursuit because **(1)** the antennae of most cockroach species can detect minute movements of air, **(2)** they have vibration sensors in their knee joints, and **(3)** their rapid response times (faster than you can blink). Some even have wings.

They also have high reproductive rates. In only a year, a single Asian cockroach (especially prevalent in Florida) and its young can add about 10 million new cockroaches to the world. Their high reproductive rate also helps them quickly develop genetic resistance to almost any poison we throw at them.

Most cockroaches also sample food before it enters their mouths and learn to shun foul-tasting poisons. They also clean up after themselves by eating their own dead and, if food is scarce enough, their living.

Only about 25 species of cockroach live in homes. However, such species can **(1)** carry viruses and bacteria that cause diseases such as hepatitis, polio, typhoid fever, plague, and salmonella and **(2)** cause people to have allergic reactions ranging from watery eyes to severe wheezing. Indeed, about 60% of the 12 million Americans suffering from asthma are allergic to dead or live cockroaches.

### Critical Thinking

If you could, would you exterminate all cockroach species? What might be some ecological consequences of doing this?

---

tile offspring. Then one species has become two, and *speciation* has occurred through *divergent evolution*.

For some rapidly reproducing organisms, this type of speciation may occur within hundreds of years. However, for most species such speciation takes from tens of thousands to millions of years. Given this time scale, it is difficult to observe and document the appearance of a new species. As a result, there are many controversial hypotheses about the details of speciation.

**How Do Species Become Extinct?** After speciation, the second process affecting the number and types of species on the earth is **extinction.** When environmental conditions change, a species must **(1)** evolve (become better adapted), **(2)** move to a more favorable area (if possible), or **(3)** cease to exist (become extinct).

The earth's long-term patterns of speciation and extinction have been affected by several major factors: **(1)** large-scale movements of the continents (continental drift) over millions of years (Figure 5-9, p. 106),

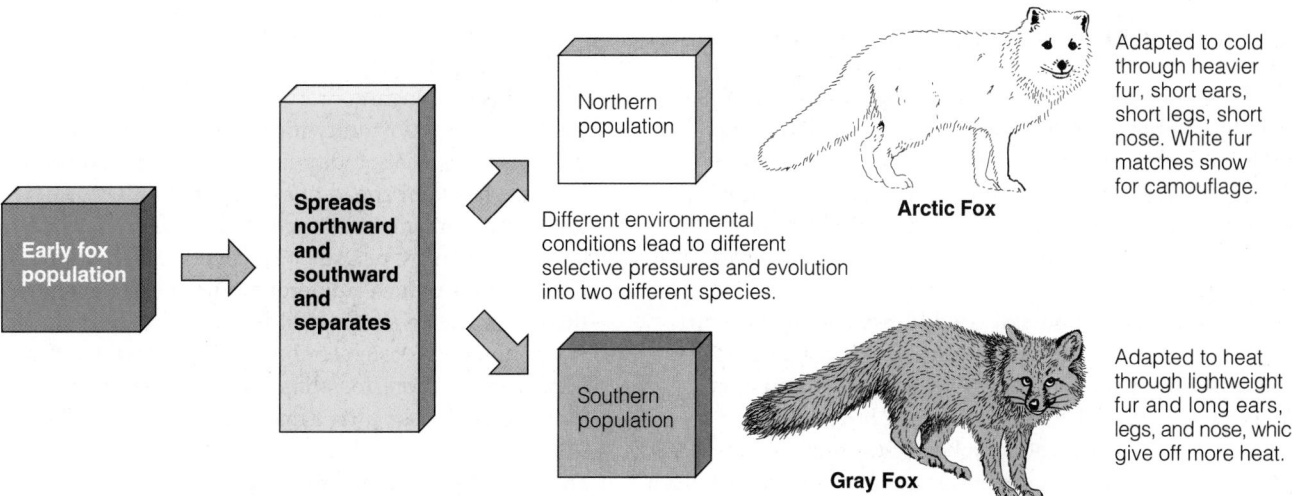

**Figure 5-8** How geographic isolation can lead to reproductive isolation, divergence, and speciation.

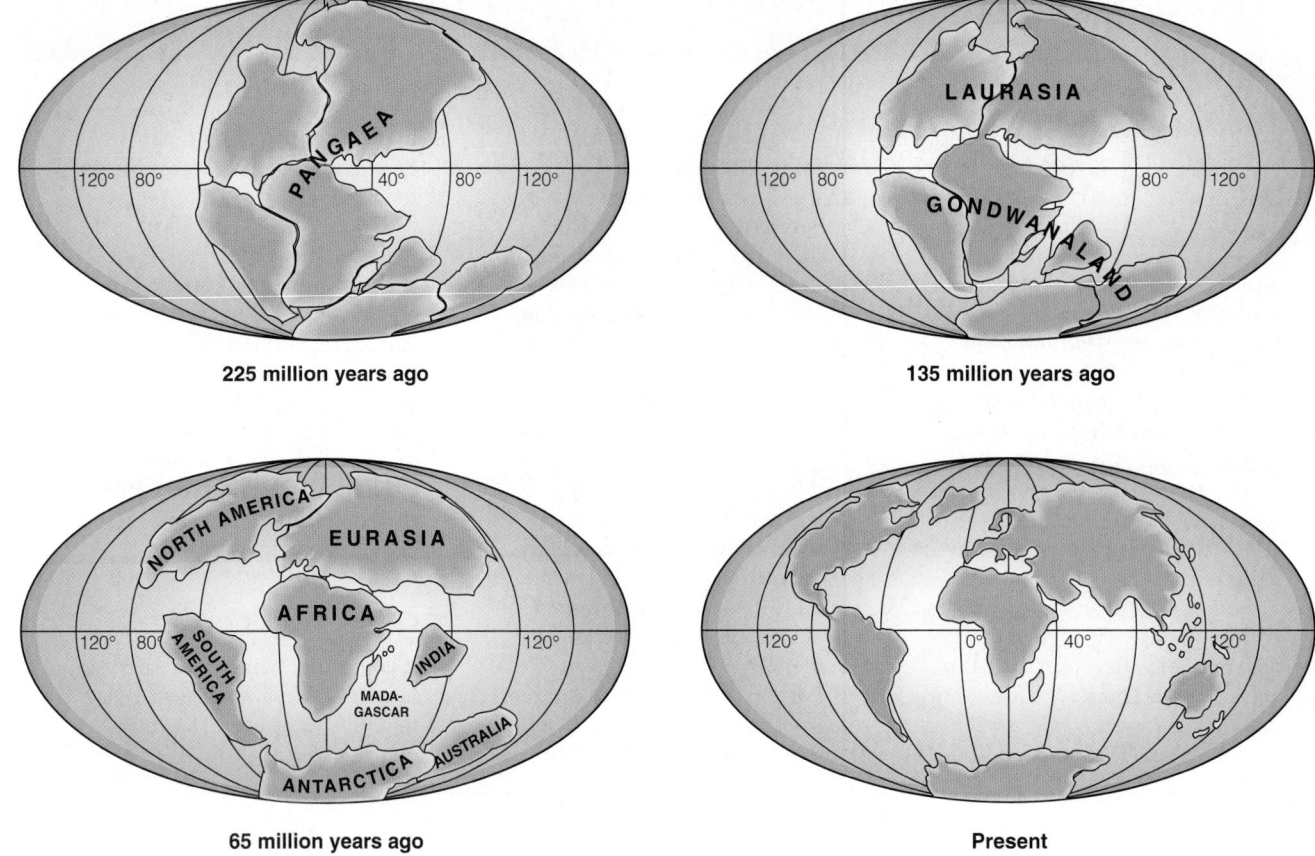

**Figure 5-9** *Continental drift*, the extremely slow movement of continents over millions of years on several gigantic plates. This process plays a role in the extinction of species and the rise of new species. Populations are geographically and eventually reproductively isolated as land masses float apart and new coastal regions are created. Rock and fossil evidence indicates that about 200–250 million years ago all of the earth's present-day continents were locked together in a supercontinent called Pangaea (top left). About 180 million years ago, Pangaea began splitting apart as the earth's huge plates separated and eventually resulted in today's locations of the continents (bottom right).

**(2)** gradual climate changes caused by continental drift and slight shifts in the earth's orbit around the sun, and **(3)** rapid climate change caused by catastrophic events (such as large volcanic eruptions, huge meteorites and asteroids crashing into the earth, and release of large amounts of methane trapped beneath the ocean floor). Some of these events create dust clouds that shut down or sharply reduce photosynthesis long enough to eliminate huge numbers of producers and, soon thereafter, the consumers that fed on them.

Extinction is the ultimate fate of all species, just as death is for all individual organisms. Biologists estimate that 99.9% of all the species that have ever existed are now extinct.

As local environmental conditions change, a certain number of species disappear at a low rate, called **background extinction.** In contrast, **mass extinction** is a significant rise in extinction rates above the background level. It is a catastrophic, widespread (often global) event in which large groups of existing species (perhaps 25–70%) are wiped out. Scientists have also identified periods of **mass depletion** in which extinc-

tion rates are higher than normal but not high enough to classify as a mass extinction. Recent fossil and geological evidence casts doubt on the hypothesis that there have been five mass extinctions over the past 500 million years. The new evidence suggests that there have been two mass extinctions and three mass depletions during this period.

A mass extinction or mass depletion crisis for one species is an opportunity for another. The existence of millions of species today means that speciation, on average, has kept ahead of extinction. Evidence shows that the earth's mass extinctions and depletions have been followed by periods of recovery called **adaptive radiations** in which numerous new species evolve to fill new or vacated ecological roles or niches in changed environments. Fossil records suggest that it takes 5 million years or more for adaptive radiations to rebuild biological diversity after a mass extinction or depletion.

**How Do Speciation and Extinction Affect Biodiversity?** Speciation minus extinction equals *biodiversity*, the planet's genetic raw material for future evolution in response to changing environmental conditions. In this long-term give-and-take between extinction and speciation, mass extinctions and mass depletions temporarily reduce biodiversity. However, they also create evolutionary opportunities for surviving species to undergo adaptive radiations to fill unoccupied and new biological roles or niches.

Although extinction is a natural process, much evidence indicates that humans have become a major force in the premature extinction of species. Biologist Stuart Primm estimates that during the 20th century, extinction rates increased by 100–1,000 times the natural background rate. As human population and resource consumption increase over the next 50–100 years, we are expected to take over more of the earth's surface (Figure 1-5, p. 7) and net primary productivity (Figure 4-25, p. 81, and Figure 4-26, p. 82). During this century, this may cause the premature extinction of up to a quarter of the earth's current species. This could constitute a new *mass depletion* and possibly a new *mass extinction* (Guest Essay, p. 108).

On our short time scale, such major losses cannot be recouped by formation of new species; it took millions of years after each of the earth's past mass extinctions and depletions for life to recover to the previous level of biodiversity. Genetic engineering cannot stop this loss of biodiversity because genetic engineers do not create new genes. Rather, they transfer existing genes or gene fragments from one organism to another and thus rely on natural biodiversity for their raw material.

*Nothing in biology makes sense except in the light of evolution.*

THEODOSIUS DOBZHANSKY

## REVIEW QUESTIONS

**1.** Define the boldfaced terms in this chapter.

**2.** Describe the conditions that make life on the earth just right for life as we know it.

**3.** Distinguish between *chemical evolution* and *biological evolution*.

**4.** Summarize how scientists think chemical evolution took place on the earth.

**5.** Summarize how scientists think biological evolution took place on the earth. What was the *oxygen revolution*, and what is its importance to life as we know it?

**6.** What are *fossils*, and how do they help us formulate ideas about how life developed on the earth?

**7.** Distinguish among *biological evolution, the theory of evolution, microevolution,* and *macroevolution*.

**8.** Distinguish among *genes, gene pool, alleles, mutations, natural selection,* and *differential reproduction,* and explain their roles in microevolution.

**9.** Give an example of microevolution by natural selection. Describe three types of natural selection.

**10.** What is *coevolution,* and what is its importance?

**11.** What is the *ecological niche* of a species, and why is it important to understand the niches of species? What is the difference between a species' *habitat* and its *niche*? What is the difference between a species' *fundamental niche* and its *realized niche*?

**12.** Distinguish between the niches of specialist and generalist species. Explain why cockroaches have been such a successful species.

**13.** List three factors that limit adaptation.

**14.** What are two common misconceptions about evolution?

**15.** What is *speciation*? Distinguish between *geographic isolation* and *reproductive isolation,* and explain how they can lead to speciation through divergent evolution.

**16.** What is *extinction*? List three factors that have affected the earth's long-term patterns of speciation and extinction.

**17.** Distinguish among *background extinction, mass extinction,* and *mass depletion*.

**18.** What is an *adaptive radiation*? How can such a radiation lead to recovery after a mass extinction or depletion?

**19.** What evidence suggests that human activities may be bringing about a new mass depletion or extinction?

**20.** Explain how speciation and extinction result in the planet's biodiversity.

## CRITICAL THINKING

**1.** How would you respond to someone who tells you **(a)** that he or she does not believe in biological evolution because it is "just a theory," and **(b)** we should not worry about air pollution because through natural selection the human species will develop lungs that can detoxify pollutants?

**2.** What would happen if extinction had never occurred during evolutionary history? Do you think we would have more species than we do now? Why?

**3.** How would you respond to someone who says that because extinction is a natural process, we should not worry about the loss of biodiversity?

**4.** Why is it important for somebody studying environmental science to understand the basics of evolution?

**5.** Why is the realized niche of a species narrower, or more specialized, than its fundamental niche?

**6.** As well as you can, describe the major differences between the ecological niches of humans and cockroaches. Are these two species in competition? If so, how do they manage to coexist?

**7.** In what ways do humans occupy generalist niches and in what ways do they occupy specialist niches?

**8.** By analogy, use the concepts of generalist and specialist to evaluate the roles of humans in today's societies. In general, the role of college and graduate education is to create specialists in a particular field or a narrow portion of a field. What are the pros and cons of relying mainly on this approach? Is there a need for

## The Future of Evolution

*Norman Myers*

GUEST ESSAY

*Norman Myers is a tropical ecologist and international consultant in environment and development, with emphasis on conservation of wildlife species and tropical forests. He is one of the world's leading environmental experts. His research and consulting have taken him to 80 countries. Myers has served as a consultant for many development agencies and research organizations, including the U.S. National Academy of Sciences, the World Bank, the Organization for Economic Cooperation and Development, various UN agencies, and the World Resources Institute. Among his many publications (see Further Readings on the website for this book) are* The Primary Source: Tropical Forests and Our Future *(1992),* The Gaia Atlas of Planet Management *(1993),* Scarcity or Abundance: A Debate on Environment *(1994),* Ultimate Security: The Environmental Basis of Political Security *(1996), and* Perverse Subsidies *(2001).*

Human activities have brought the earth to a biotic crisis. Many biologists have commented that this crisis will result in the loss of large numbers of species, possibly 25–50%, within the lifetimes of students reading this book. However, surprisingly few biologists have recognized that in the longer term these extinctions will impoverish evolution's course for several million years.

So the future of evolution should be regarded as one of the most challenging issues humankind has ever encountered because currently we are the world's greatest evolutionary force. After all, we are effectively conducting a planet-scale experiment, with little clue as to how it might turn out, except that it will prove irreversible and will severely reduce human well-being. We could get by without half of all mammals and other vertebrates, but if we lost half of all insects with their pollinating functions [p. 64], let alone their many other services, we would be in trouble in the first crop-growing season.

In addition, the mass extinction or depletion under way is the biggest of our environmental problems in terms of the duration of its impact and the numbers of people to be affected. All our other problems are potentially reversible. If we wanted to clean up acid deposition, we could do it within a few decades. We could push back the deserts, restore topsoil, and allow the ozone layer to be repaired within a century or so. We could probably restore climate stability in the wake of global warming within a thousand years. But once a species is gone, it is gone for good.

Of course, in the long run evolution will generate replacement species with numbers and variety to match today's. But that is likely to take millions of years. We are witnessing the gross reduction if not the elimination of entire sectors of biomes, notably tropical forests, coral reefs, and wetlands, all of which may have served as powerhouses of evolution—centers of new speciation—in the prehistoric past.

Suppose, as has happened after the mass extinctions and depletions of the prehistoric past, that the bounce-back period lasts at least 5 million years. This would be 20 times longer than humans have been a species. Suppose that the average number of people on the earth during that period is 2.5 billion people, as opposed to the 6.2 billion today. Then the total number of people affected

For scientific details, see Norman Myers, "The Biodiversity Crisis and the Future of Evolution," *The Environmentalist* 16 (1996): 37–47.

more generalists? Or are they people who may know a lot about many things (and about connections between things) but not enough about anything in particular? Can they serve a useful role and make a satisfactory living in today's increasingly specialized societies? Explain your answers.

## PROJECTS

**1.** An important adaptation of humans is a strong opposable thumb, which allows us to grip and manipulate things with our hands. As a demonstration of the importance of this trait, fold each of your thumbs into the palm of its hand and then tape them securely in that position for an entire day. After the demonstration, make a list of the things you could not do without the use of your thumbs.

**2.** Visit a local forest, pond, or lake, choose a particular organism, and then use the library or the Internet to describe as much as you can about its niche, including what species it depends on and what species help support its survival. Predict what might happen if your selected species disappeared from the local environment.

**3.** Use the library or the Internet to find out bibliographic information about *Charles Darwin* and *Theodosius Dobzhansky*, whose quotes appear at the beginning and end of this chapter.

**4.** Make a concept map of this chapter's major ideas, using the section heads and subheads and the key terms (in boldface). Look on the website for this book for information about making concept maps.

### INTERNET STUDY RESOURCES AND RESOURCES FOR FURTHER READING AND RESEARCH

The website for this book contains helpful study aids and many ideas for further reading and research. Log on to

www.info.brookscole.com/miller13

and click on the Chapter-by-Chapter area. Choose Chapter 5 and select a resource:

by what we do (or don't do) to protect the biosphere during the next few decades will be about 500 trillion, in contrast with the 50 billion people who have ever existed. Even 1 trillion is a big number: Figure out how long a period of time in years is made up of 1 trillion seconds.

In short, we are engaged in by far the biggest decision ever made by one human community on behalf of future human communities. Yet the issue is almost entirely disregarded, whether scientifically, ethically, or otherwise. How often do you hear leading scientists even mention the issue?

Despite our gross ignorance of what lies ahead, we can venture a few hypotheses:

- *A temporary outburst of speciation.* As large numbers of niches are vacated, there could be an outburst of speciation, although not nearly enough to match the extinction spasm.

- *A proliferation of opportunistic species* such as cockroaches [Spotlight, p. 105], rats, flies, and others that prosper when new niches open up. This proliferation will be enhanced by the likely elimination of species that naturally control opportunistic species.

- *An end to large vertebrates.*

- *An end to speciation of large vertebrates.* Even if larger vertebrates were to survive the extinction spasm ahead, our largest protected areas will prove far too small for further speciation of elephants, rhinoceroses, apes, bears, and the bigger cats, among other large vertebrates.

What does all this imply for our conservation efforts? By far the predominant strategy of conservationists is to save as many species as possible. But we now need to safeguard evolutionary processes as well. A prime goal is to look out especially for endemic species (found only in a particular place) or species confined to small habitats. Examples include the California condor, the black-footed ferret, the giant panda, and the gorilla.

However, the fossil record shows that endemic species often turn out to be evolutionary dead ends: Generally they do not throw off new species. So should we shift our conservation priority from endemic species to broader-ranging species in the hope that they have more genetic variability and thus more of a diversified resource stock on which natural selection can work its creative impact?

Similarly, should we devote more attention to protecting the evolutionary powerhouses such as the forests, coral reefs, and wetlands of the tropics? All these are in dire trouble and may be all but eliminated within just a few decades. Do they deserve preferential treatment ahead of, say, temperate-zone woodlands and grasslands and boreal forests with their lack of species, ecological complexity, and evolutionary potential?

If within your lifetime we allow the current biotic crisis to proceed unchecked (which is what the recent record suggests), it is possible that your children will ask you a key question: "When the evolutionary debacle was becoming all too plain at the start of the new millennium, what did you do to help ward off this disaster?" I hope you will engage yourself in dealing with this crucial issue.

### Critical Thinking

**1.** Do you agree or disagree with the thesis of this essay? Explain.

**2.** If you agree, list three things you could do to help prevent the outcomes described in this essay.

---

- Flash Cards allows you to test your mastery of the Terms and Concepts to Remember for this chapter.

- Tutorial Quizzes provides a multiple-choice practice quiz.

- Student Guide to InfoTrac will lead you to Critical Thinking Projects that use InfoTrac College Edition as a research tool.

- References lists the major books and articles consulted in writing this chapter.

- Hypercontents takes you to an extensive list of sites with news, research, and images related to individual sections of the chapter.

## INFOTRAC COLLEGE EDITION

Improve your skills with InfoTrac College Edition, a searchable online database of articles from more than 700 periodicals. Log on to

http://www.infotrac-college.com

or access InfoTrac through the website for this book. Try to find the following articles:

**1.** Becker, L. 2002. Repeated blows: Did extraterrestrial collisions capable of causing widespread extinctions pound the earth not once, but twice—or even several times? *Scientific American* 286: 76. *Keywords:* "collisions" and "extinction." Mounting evidence suggests that collisions with space debris have occurred many times, and new techniques are demonstrating close links between such collisions and mass extinctions.

**2.** Peterson, A. T., and D. A. Vieglais. 2001. Predicting species invasions using ecological niche modeling: New approaches from bioinformatics attack a pressing problem. *BioScience* 51: 363. *Keywords:* "invasive species" and "niche." Invasive exotic species are rapidly becoming one of the greatest threats to biodiversity. This paper shows how invasiveness of a species can be predicted based upon studies of its ecological niche.

# 6 BIOGEOGRAPHY: CLIMATE, BIOMES, AND TERRESTRIAL BIODIVERSITY

## Connections:
## Blowing in the Wind

*Wind*, a vital part of the planet's circulatory system, connects most life on the earth. Without wind, the tropics would be unbearably hot and most of the rest of the planet would freeze.

Winds also transport nutrients from one place to another. Dust rich in phosphates blows across the Atlantic from the Sahara Desert in Africa (Figure 6-1). This helps replenish rain forest soils in Brazil and build up agricultural soils in the Bahamas. Iron-rich dust blowing from China's Gobi Desert falls into the Pacific Ocean between Hawaii and Alaska. This input of iron stimulates the growth of phytoplankton, the minute producers that support ocean food webs. This is the *good news*.

The *bad news* is that wind also transports harmful viruses, bacteria, fungi, and particles of long-lived pesticides and toxic metals. Particles of reddish-brown soil and pesticides banned in the United States are blown from Africa's deserts and eroding farmlands into the sky over Florida. This **(1)** makes it difficult for the state to meet federal air pollution standards during summer months, and **(2)** fungi in this dust is a suspected factor in degrading or killing coral reefs in the Florida Keys and the Caribbean.

Particles of iron-rich dust from Africa that enhance the productivity of algae have been linked to outbreaks of toxic algal blooms—referred to as *red tides*—in Florida's coastal waters. People who eat shellfish contaminated by a toxin produced in red tides can become paralyzed or even die. Europe and the Middle East also receive African dust.

Pollution and dust from rapidly industrializing China and central Asia blow across the Pacific Ocean and degrade air quality over the western United States. In 2001, climate scientists reported that a huge dust storm of soil particles blown from northern China had blanketed areas from Canada to Arizona with a layer of dust. Studies show that Asian pollution contributes as much as 10% to West Coast smog, a threat expected to increase as China industrializes.

We have *mixed news* as well. Particles from volcanic eruptions ride the winds, circle the globe, and change the earth's climate for a while. Emissions from the 1991 eruption of Mount Pinatubo in the Philippines cooled the earth slightly for 3 years, temporarily masking signs of global warming. On the other hand, volcanic ash, like the blowing desert dust, adds valuable trace minerals to the soil where it settles.

The lesson, once again, is that there is *no away*. Wind acts as part of the planet's circulatory system for heat, moisture, plant nutrients, and long-lived pollutants we put into the air. Movement of soil particles from one place to another by wind and water is a natural phenomenon, but when we disturb the soil and leave it unprotected we hasten the process.

Wind is also an important factor in climate through its influence on global air circulation patterns. Climate, in turn, is crucial for determining what kinds of plant and animal life are found in the major biomes of the biosphere, as we shall see in this chapter.

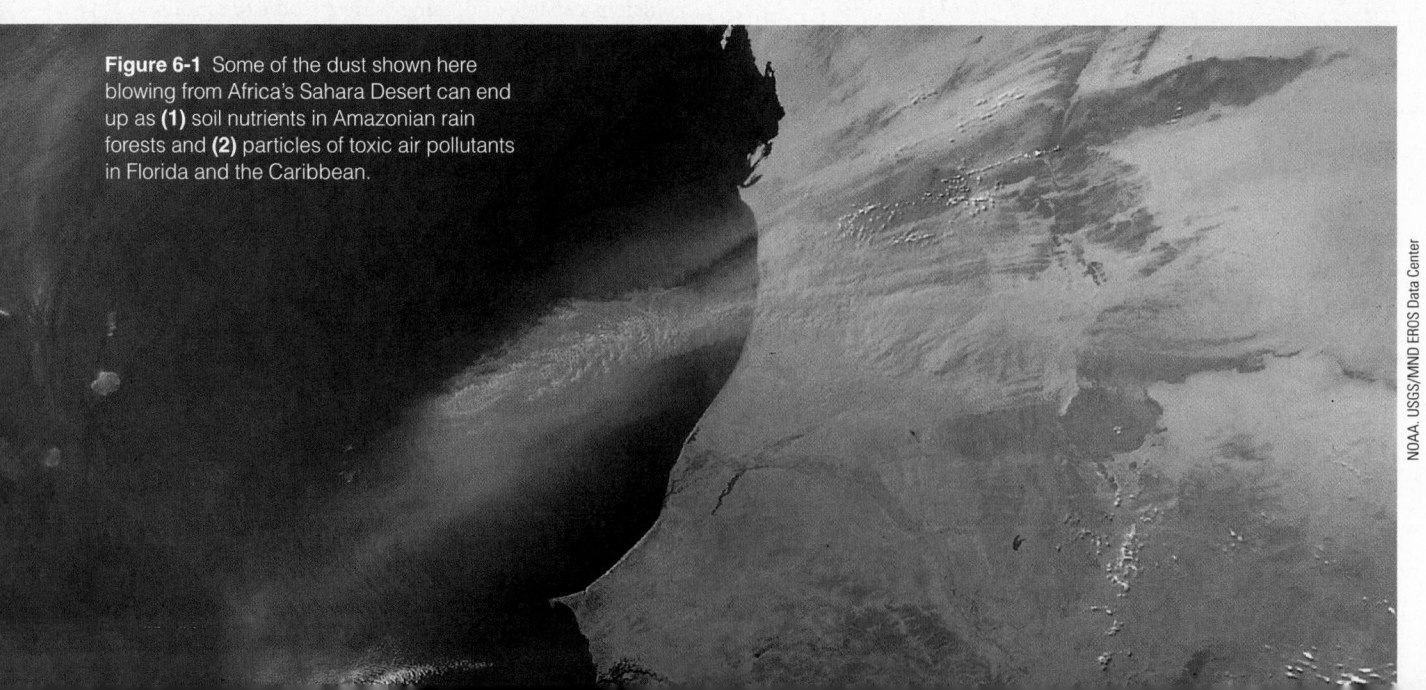

**Figure 6-1** Some of the dust shown here blowing from Africa's Sahara Desert can end up as **(1)** soil nutrients in Amazonian rain forests and **(2)** particles of toxic air pollutants in Florida and the Caribbean.

*To do science is to search for repeated patterns, not simply to accumulate facts, and to do the science of geographical ecology is to search for patterns of plant and animal life that can be put on a map.*

ROBERT H. MACARTHUR

This chapter addresses the following broad questions about geographic patterns of ecology:

- What key factors determine the earth's weather?

- What key factors determine the earth's climate?

- How does climate determine where the earth's major biomes are found?

- What are the major types of desert biomes, and how do human activities affect them?

- What are the major types of grassland biomes and how do human activities affect them?

- What are the major types of forest biomes, and how do human activities affect them?

- Why are mountain and arctic biomes important, and how do human activities affect them?

- What lessons can we learn from a geographic perspective of ecology?

## 6-1 WEATHER: A BRIEF INTRODUCTION

**What Is Weather?** At every moment at any spot on the earth, the *troposphere* (the inner layer of the atmosphere containing most of the earth's air) has a particular set of physical properties. Examples are **(1)** temperature, **(2)** pressure, **(3)** humidity, **(4)** precipitation, **(5)** sunshine, **(6)** cloud cover, and **(7)** wind direction and speed. These short-term properties of the troposphere at a particular place and time are **weather.**

Meteorologists use weather balloons, aircraft, ships, radar, satellites, and other devices to obtain data on variables such as **(1)** atmospheric pressures, **(2)** precipitation, **(3)** temperatures, **(4)** wind speeds, and **(5)** locations of air masses and fronts.

These data are fed into computer models to draw weather maps for each of seven levels of the troposphere, ranging from the ground to 19 kilometers (12 miles) up. Computer models use the map data to forecast the weather in each box of the seven-layer grid for the next 12 hours. Other computer models project the weather for the next several days by calculating the probabilities that air masses, winds, and other factors will move and change in certain ways.

**What Are Warm Fronts and Cold Fronts?** Masses of air that are warm or cold, wet or dry, and contain air at high or low pressure constantly move across the land and sea. Weather changes as one air mass replaces or meets another.

The most dramatic changes in weather occur along a **front,** the boundary between two air masses with different temperatures and densities. A **warm front** is the boundary between an advancing warm air mass and the cooler one it is replacing (Figure 6-2, top). Because warm air is less dense (weighs less per unit of volume) than cool air, an advancing warm front will rise up over a mass of cool air.

As the warm front rises, its moisture begins condensing into droplets to form layers of clouds at different altitudes. High, wispy clouds are the first signs of an advancing warm front. Gradually the clouds thicken, descend to a lower altitude, and often release their moisture as rainfall. A moist warm front can bring days of cloudy skies and drizzle.

A **cold front** (Figure 6-2, bottom) is the leading edge of an advancing mass of cold air. Because cold air

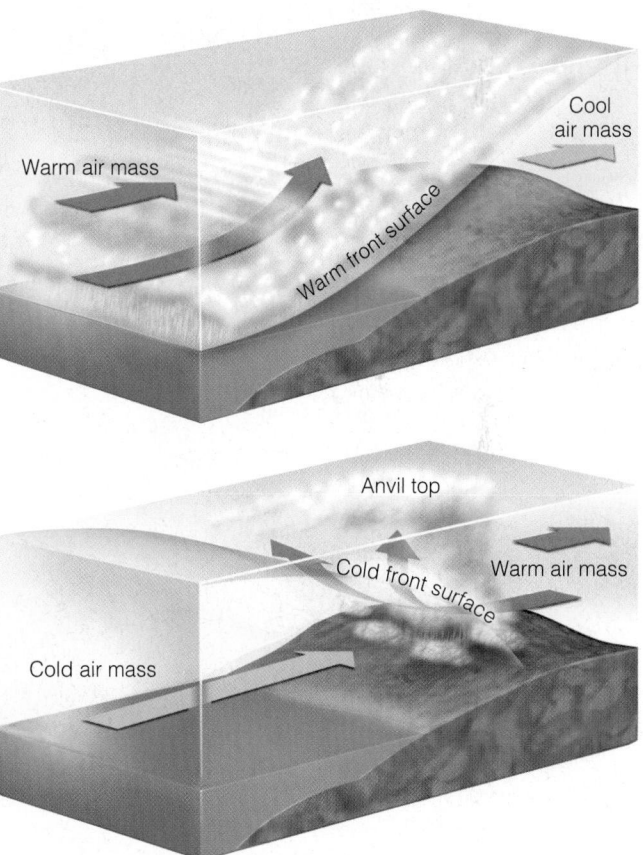

**Figure 6-2** A *warm front* (top) occurs when an advancing mass of warm air meets and rises up over a retreating mass of more dense cool air. A *cold front* (bottom) is the boundary formed when a mass of cold air wedges beneath a retreating mass of less dense warm air.

is denser than warm air, an advancing cold front stays close to the ground and wedges underneath less dense warmer air. An approaching cold front produces rapidly moving, towering clouds called *thunderheads*.

As the overlying mass of warm air is pushed upward, it cools and its water vapor condenses to form large and heavy droplets that fall to the earth's surface as precipitation. As a cold front passes through, we often experience high surface winds and thunderstorms. After the front passes through, we usually have cooler temperatures and a clear sky.

**What Are Highs and Lows?** Weather is also affected by changes in atmospheric pressure. Air pressure results from the zillions of tiny molecules of the gases (mostly nitrogen and oxygen) in the atmosphere zipping around at incredible speeds and hitting and bouncing off of anything they encounter.

Gravity affects atmospheric pressure. Pressure is greater near the earth's surface because the molecules in the atmosphere are squeezed together under the weight of the air above.

An air mass with high pressure, called a **high,** contains cool, dense air that descends toward the earth's surface and becomes warmer. Fair weather follows as long as the high-pressure air mass remains over an area.

In contrast, a low-pressure air mass, called a **low,** produces cloudy and sometimes stormy weather. This happens because less dense warm air spirals inward toward the center of a low-pressure air mass. Because of its low pressure and low density, the center of the low rises, and its warm air expands and cools. When

**Figure 6-3** Formation of a *tornado* or *twister.* Although twisters can form any time of the year, the most active tornado season in the United States is usually March through August. Each year more than 800 tornadoes strike the United States. Meteorologists cannot predict with great accuracy when and where most tornadoes will form.

the temperature drops below the dew point, the moisture in the air condenses and forms clouds. If the droplets in the clouds coalesce into large and heavy drops, precipitation occurs.

**What Causes Tornadoes and Tropical Cyclones?**
In addition to normal weather, we sometimes experience *weather extremes.* Two examples are violent storms called **(1)** *tornadoes* (which form over land) and **(2)** *tropical cyclones* (which form over warm ocean waters and sometimes pass over coastal land).

Figure 6-3 shows how the vortex of a *tornado* (or twister) forms. Strong tornadoes often have two or more smaller vortexes or funnel-shaped clouds that move around the center of a larger vortex. These funnel-shaped clouds often are black or red because of the dust and dirt sucked up from the ground. The United States is the world's most tornado-prone country, followed by Australia.

Figure 6-4 shows the formation and structure of a *tropical cyclone.* Tropical cyclones that form in the Atlantic Ocean are called *hurricanes;* those forming in the Pacific Ocean are called *typhoons.* Tropical cyclones take a long time to form and gain strength. As a result, meteorologists can **(1)** track their path and wind speeds and **(2)** warn people in areas likely to be hit by these violent storms. Figure 6-5 (p. 114) shows the areas of North America most susceptible to tropical cyclones (hurricanes on the East Coast and typhoons on the West Coast).

Hurricanes and typhoons can kill and injure people and damage property and agricultural production. In some cases, however, a tropical cyclone can have long-term ecological and economic benefits that can exceed its short-term negative effects.

For example, in parts of Texas along the Gulf of Mexico, coastal bays and marshes normally are closed off from freshwater and saltwater inflows. In August

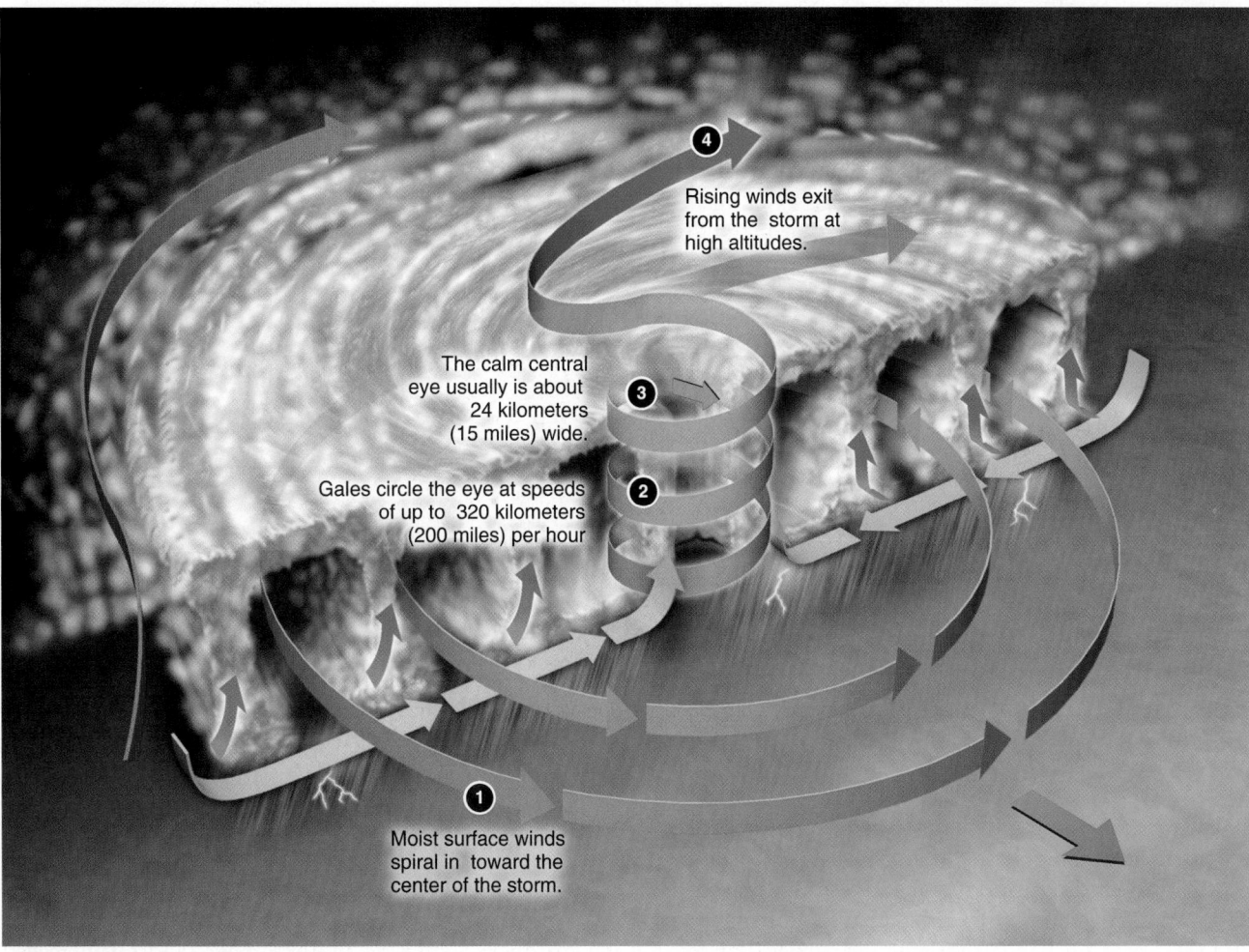

**Figure 6-4** Formation of a *tropical cyclone.* Those forming in the Atlantic Ocean are called *hurricanes;* those forming in the Pacific Ocean are called *typhoons.*

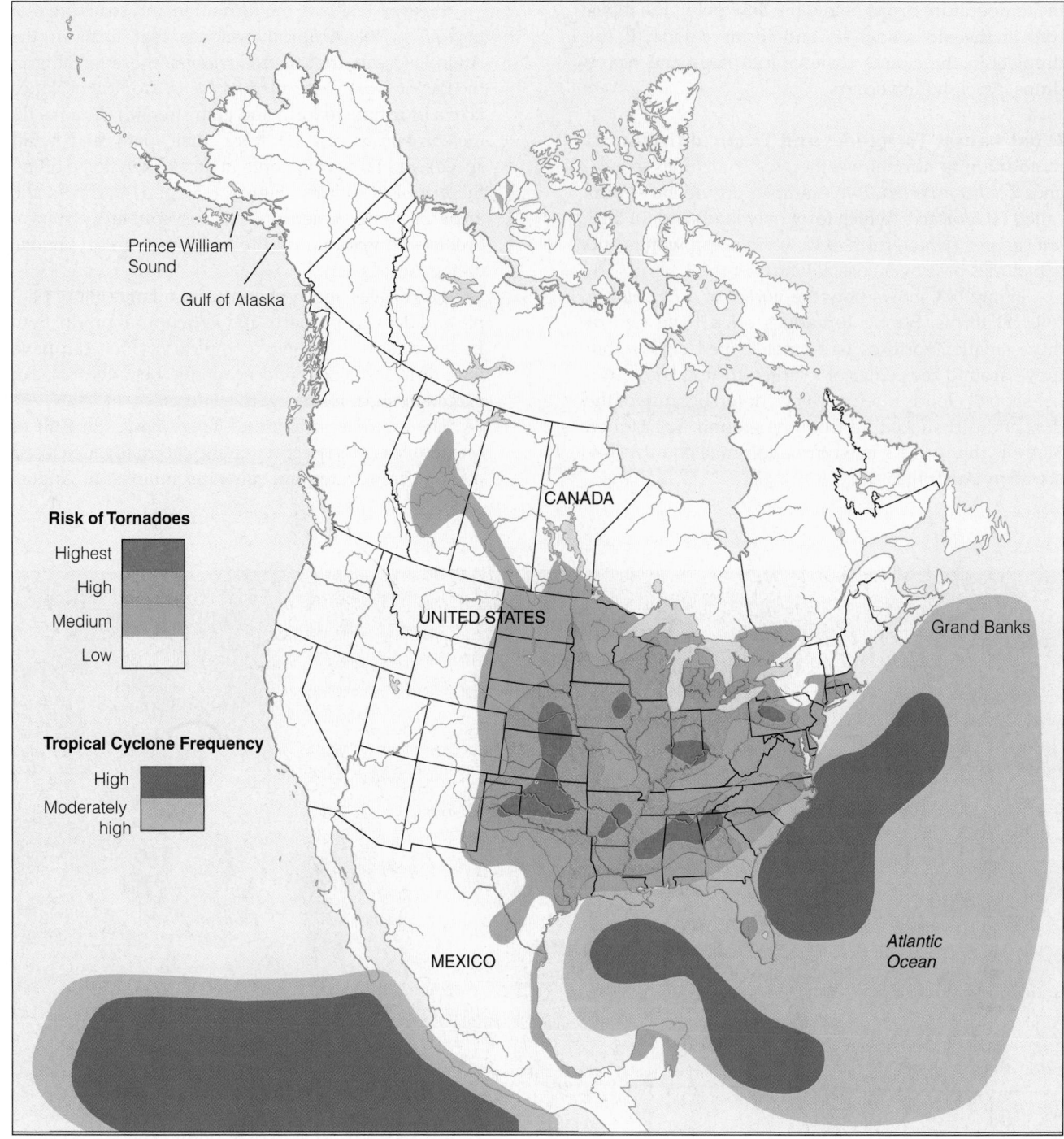

**Figure 6-5** Areas of North America most susceptible to tornadoes and tropical cyclones (hurricanes and typhoons). (Data from NOAA and U.S. Geological Survey)

1999, Hurricane Brett struck this coastal area. According to marine biologists, this hurricane (1) flushed excess nutrients from land runoff and dead sea grasses and rotting vegetation from coastal bays and marshes and (2) carved 12 channels through the barrier islands along the coast that allowed huge quantities of fresh seawater to flood the bays and marshes. This flushing out (1) reduced brown tides, consisting of explosive growth of algae feeding on excess nutrients, (2) increased growth of sea grasses, which serve as nurseries for shrimp, crabs, and fish and food for millions of ducks wintering in Texas bays, and (3) increased production of commercially important species of shellfish and fish.

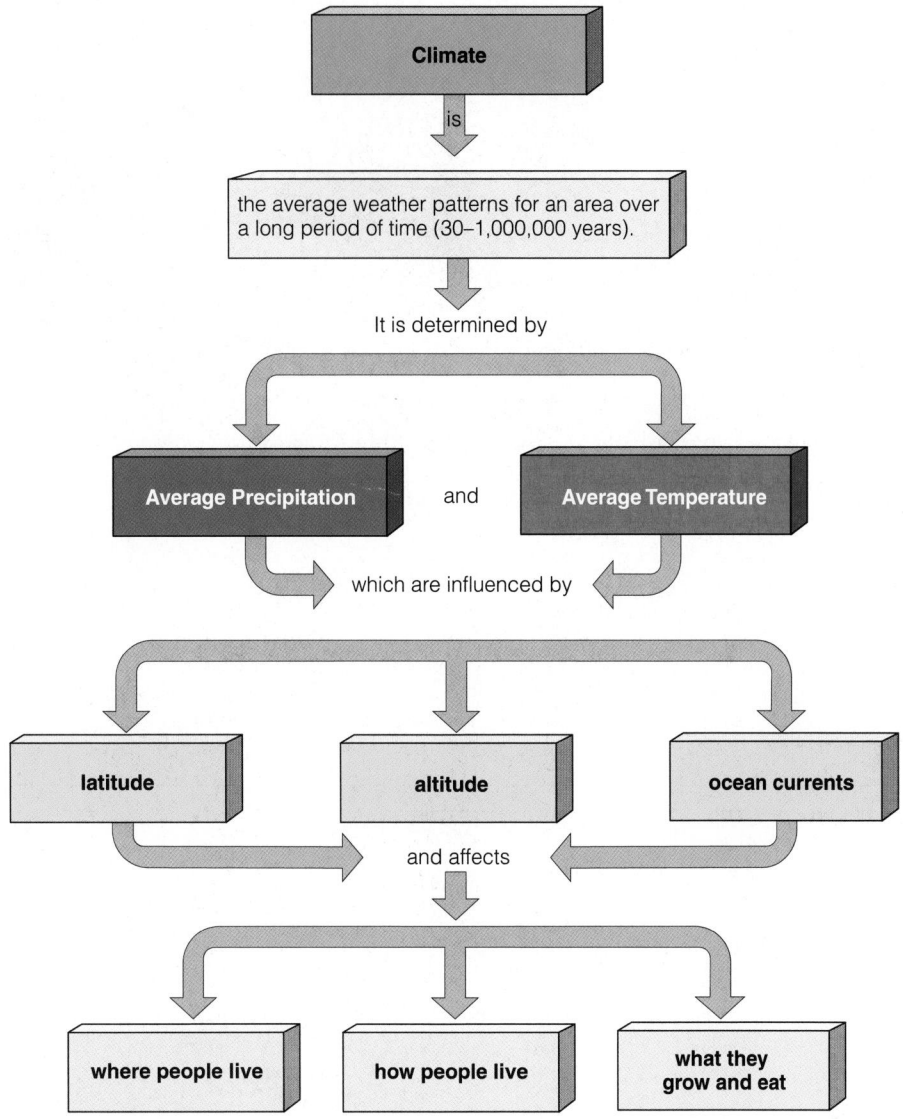

**Figure 6-6** Climate and its effects. (Data from National Oceanic and Atmospheric Administration)

## 6-2 CLIMATE: A BRIEF INTRODUCTION

**What Is Climate?** **Climate** is a region's general pattern of atmospheric or weather conditions over a long period. *Average temperature* and *average precipitation* are the two main factors determining a region's climate and its effects on people (Figure 6-6). Figure 6-7 (p. 116) is a generalized map of the earth's major climate zones.

**How Does Global Air Circulation Affect Regional Climates?** The temperature and precipitation patterns that lead to different climates (Figure 6-7) are caused primarily by the way air circulates over the earth's surface. The following factors determine global air circulation patterns:

- *Uneven heating of the earth's surface* because air is heated much more at the equator (where the sun's rays strike directly throughout the year) than at the poles (where sunlight strikes at an angle and thus is spread out over a much greater area). These differences in incoming solar energy help explain why **(1)** tropical regions near the equator are hot, **(2)** polar regions are cold, and **(3)** temperate regions in between generally have intermediate average temperatures (Figure 6-7).

- *Seasonal changes in temperature and precipitation* because the earth's axis (an imaginary line connecting the north and south poles) is tilted. As a result, various regions are tipped toward or away from the sun as the earth makes its yearlong revolution around the sun

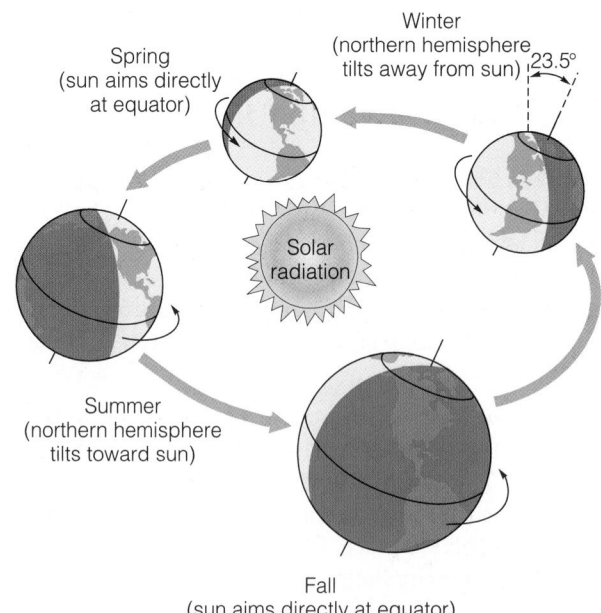

Figure 6-7 Generalized map of global climate zones, showing the major contributing ocean currents and drifts.

**Legend:**

- Polar (ice)
- Subarctic (snow)
- Cool temperate
- Warm temperate
- Dry
- Tropical
- Highland
- Major upwelling zones
- Warm ocean current
- Cold ocean current
- River

(Figure 6-8). This creates opposite seasons in the northern and southern hemispheres.

- *Rotation of the earth on its axis,* which prevents air currents from moving due north and south from the equator. Forces in the atmosphere created by this rotation deflect winds (moving air masses) to the right in the northern hemisphere and to the left in the southern hemisphere. This results in the formation of six huge convection cells of swirling air masses (three north and three south of the equator) that transfer heat and water from one area to another (Figure 6-9, right).

Figure 6-8 The effects of the earth's tilted axis on climate. As the planet makes its annual revolution around the sun on an axis tilted about 23.5°, various regions are tipped toward or away from the sun. The resulting variations in the amount of solar energy reaching the earth create the seasons.

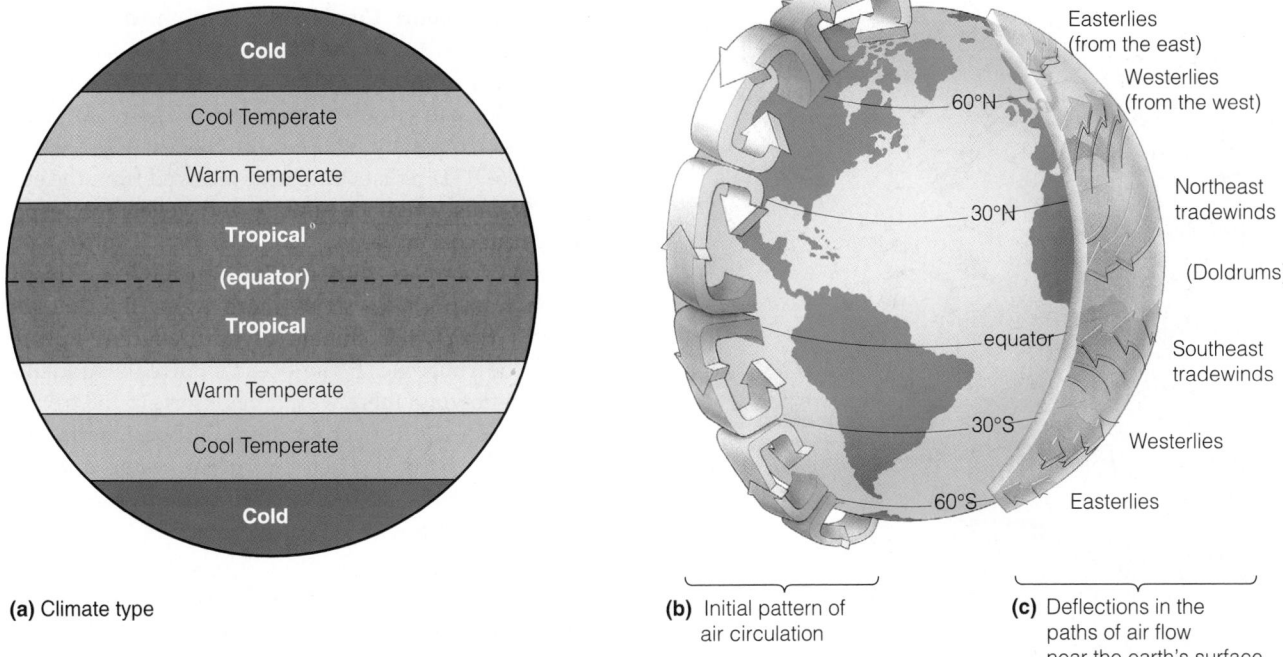

**(a)** Climate type

**(b)** Initial pattern of air circulation

**(c)** Deflections in the paths of air flow near the earth's surface

**Figure 6-9** Formation of prevailing surface winds, which disrupt the general flow of air from the equator to the poles and back to the equator **(b)**. As the earth rotates, its surface turns faster beneath air masses at the equator and slower beneath those at the poles. This deflects air masses moving north and south to the west or east, creating six huge convection cells in which air swirls upward and then descends toward the earth's surface at different latitudes. The direction of air movement in these cells sets up belts of prevailing winds **(c)** that distribute air and moisture over the earth's surface. These winds affect the general types of climate found in different areas **(a)** and drive the circulation of ocean currents. (From Cecie Starr, *Biology: Concepts and Applications,* 4th ed., Brooks/Cole [Wadsworth] © 2000)

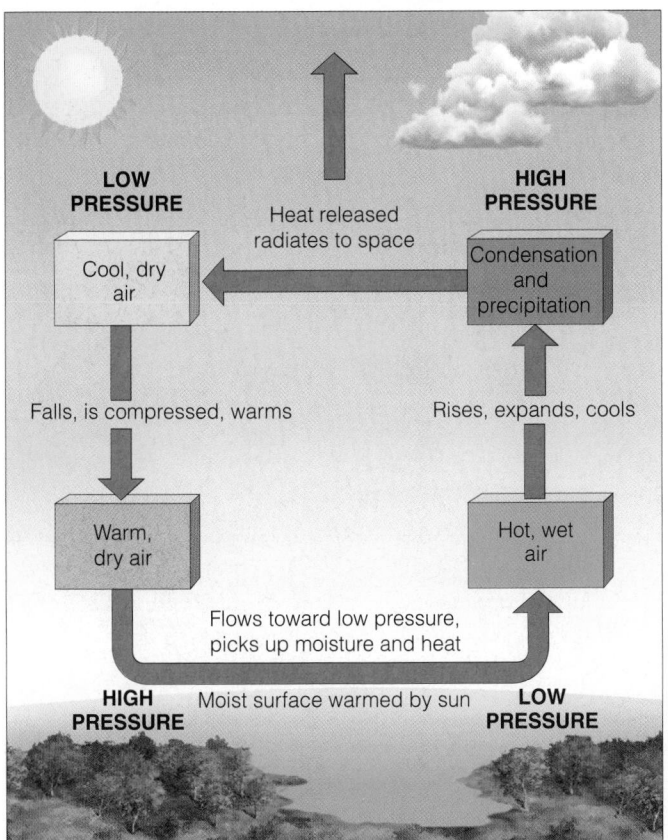

- *Long-term variations in the amount of solar energy striking the earth.* These are caused by occasional changes in solar output and slight planetary shifts in which the earth's axis wobbles (22,000-year cycle) and tilts (44,000-year cycle) as it revolves around the sun.

- *Properties of air and water.* Heat from the sun evaporates ocean water and transfers heat from the oceans to the atmosphere, especially near the hot equator. This creates cyclical convection cells that transport heat and water from one area to another (Figure 6-10). The resulting convection cells circulate air, heat, and moisture both vertically and from place to place in the troposphere. This leads to different climates and patterns of vegetation (Figure 6-11, p. 118).

**Figure 6-10** Transfer of energy by convection in the atmosphere. *Convection* occurs when a matter warms, becomes less dense, and rises within its surroundings. This efficient means of heat transfer occurs in the planet's interior, oceans, and atmosphere (as shown here). Distribution of heat and water occurs in the atmosphere because vertical convection currents stir up air in the troposphere and transport heat and water from one area to another in circular convection cells. The relative humidity increases as the air rises (right side) and decreases as it falls (left side).

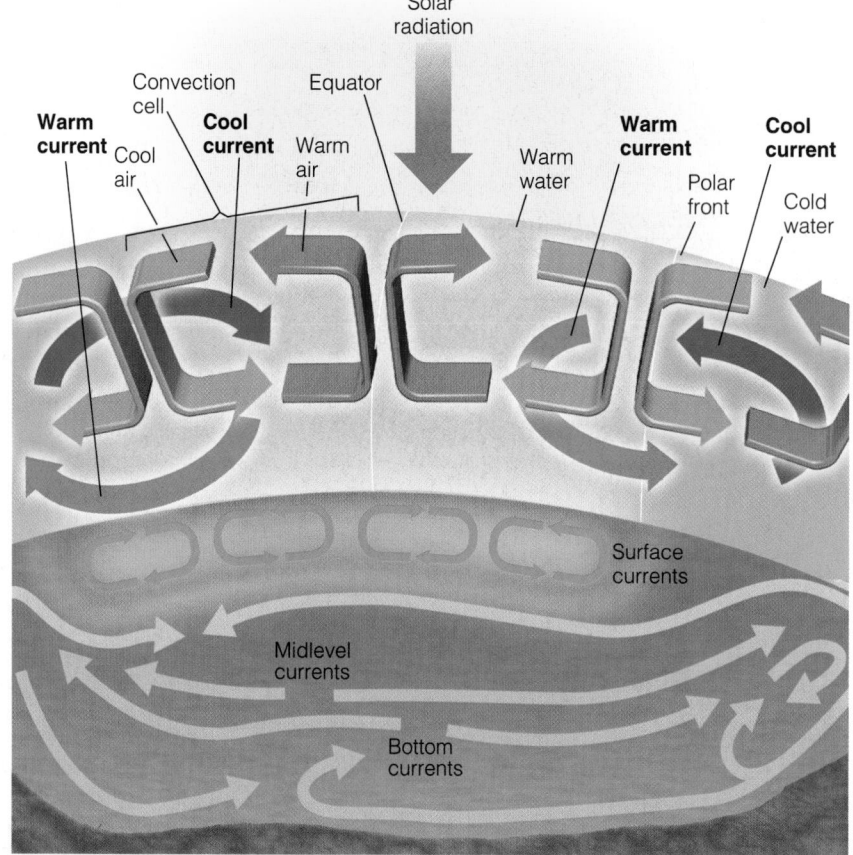

**How Do Ocean Currents Form, and How Do They Affect Regional Climates?** The factors just listed, plus differences in water density, create warm and cold ocean currents (Figures 6-7 and 6-12) These currents, driven by winds and the earth's rotation (Figure 6-9) **(1)** redistribute heat received from the sun and **(2)** thus influence climate and vegetation, especially near coastal areas.

For example, without the warm Gulf Stream, which transports 25 times more water than all the world's rivers, the climate of northwestern Europe would be subarctic. If the ocean's currents suddenly stopped flowing, there would be deserts in the tropics and thick ice sheets over northern Europe, Siberia, and Canada. Currents also help mix ocean waters and distribute nutrients and dissolved oxygen needed by aquatic organisms.

**What Are Upwellings?** The winds blowing along some steep western coasts of continents towards the equator create an effect (called the Ekman spiral) that pushes surface water at right angles from the wind flow away from the land. This outgoing surface water is replaced by an **upwelling** of cold, nutrient-

**Figure 6-11** Model of global air circulation and biomes. Heat and moisture are distributed over the earth's surface by vertical currents that form six large convection cells (called Hadley cells) at different latitudes. The direction of air flow and the ascent and descent of air masses in these convection cells determine the earth's general climatic zones. The resulting uneven distribution of heat and moisture over the planet's surface leads to the forests, grasslands, and deserts that make up the earth's biomes.

**Figure 6-12** Formation of warm and cool *ocean currents.* Energy from the sun drives convection cells, which produce prevailing winds and ocean currents. Figure 6-7 (p. 116) shows the locations and flow directions of some of the earth's major warm and cool currents.

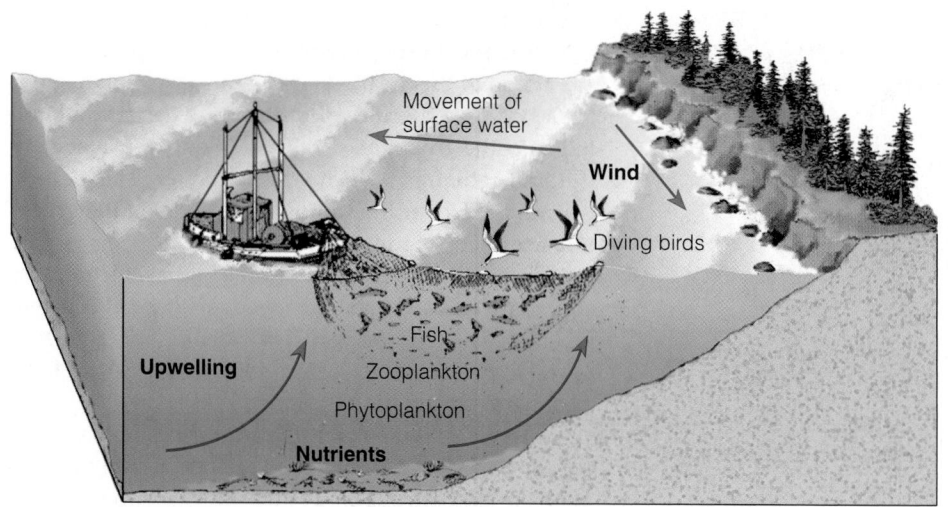

**Figure 6-13** A *shore upwelling* (shown here) occurs when deep, cool, nutrient-rich waters are drawn up to replace surface water moved away from a steep coast by wind flowing along the coast toward the equator. Such areas support large populations of phytoplankton, zooplankton, fish, and fish-eating birds. *Equatorial upwellings* occur in the open sea near the equator when northward and southward currents interact to push deep waters and their nutrients to the surface, thus greatly increasing primary productivity in such areas.

rich bottom water (Figure 6-13). Upwellings, whether far from shore or near shore (Figure 6-7), **(1)** bring plant nutrients from the deeper parts of the ocean to the surface and **(2)** support large populations of phytoplankton, zooplankton, fish, and fish-eating seabirds.

### What Is the El Niño–Southern Oscillation?

Every few years in the Pacific Ocean, normal shore upwellings (Figure 6-14, left) are affected by changes in climate patterns called the *El Niño–Southern Oscillation,* or *ENSO* (Figure 6-14, right). In an ENSO, often called *El Niño,* **(1)** the prevailing westerly winds weaken or cease, **(2)** surface water along the South and North American coasts becomes warmer, and **(3)** the normal upwellings of cold, nutrient-rich water are suppressed, which reduces primary productivity and causes a sharp decline in the populations of some fish species.

A strong ENSO can trigger extreme weather changes over at least two-thirds of the globe, especially in lands along the Pacific and Indian Oceans

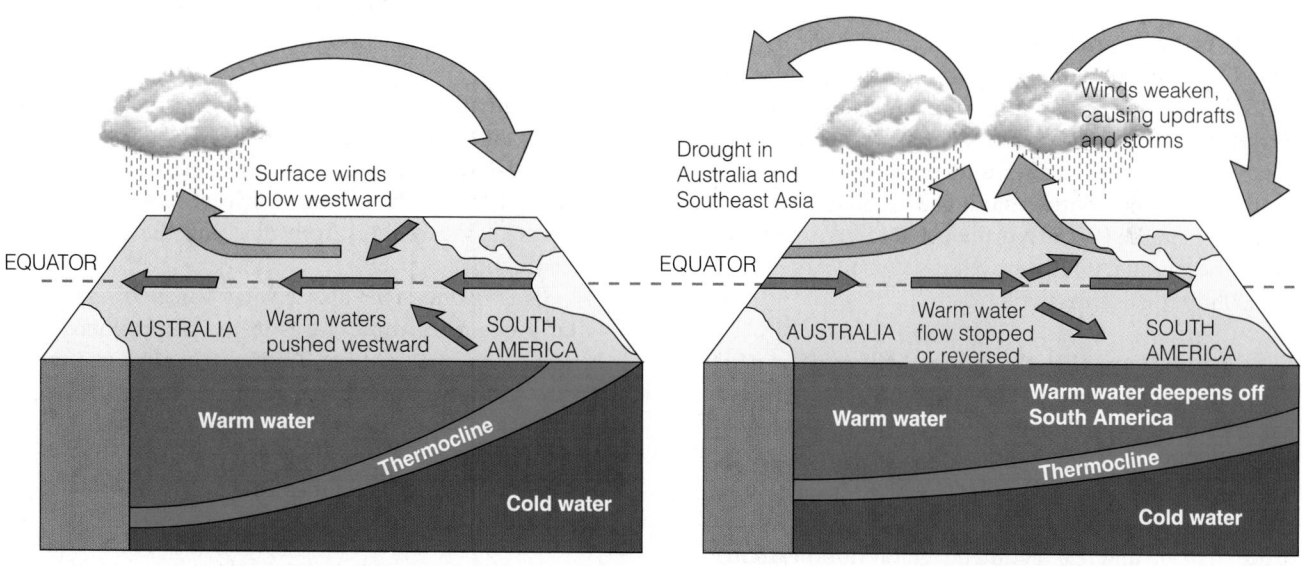

**Figure 6-14** Normal surface winds blowing westward cause shore upwellings of cold, nutrient-rich bottom water in the tropical Pacific Ocean near the coast of Peru (left). A zone of gradual temperature change called the *thermocline* separates the warm and cold water. Every few years a climate shift known as the El Niño–Southern Oscillation (ENSO) disrupts this pattern. Westward surface winds weaken, which depresses the coastal upwellings and warms the surface waters off South America (right). When an ENSO lasts 12 months or longer, it severely disrupts populations of plankton, fish, and seabirds in upwelling areas and can trigger extreme weather changes over much of the globe (Figure 6-15, p. 120).

Drought

Unusually high rainfall

Unusually warm periods

**Figure 6-15** Typical global climatic effects of an El Niño–Southern Oscillation. During the 1996–98 ENSO, huge waves battered the California coast, and torrential rains caused widespread flooding and mudslides. In Peru, floods and mudslides killed hundreds of people, left about 250,000 people homeless, and ruined harvests. Drought in Brazil, Indonesia, and Australia led to massive wildfires in tinder-dry forests. India and parts of Africa also experienced severe drought. A catastrophic ice storm hit Canada and the northeastern United States, but the southeastern United States had fewer hurricanes. (Data from United Nations Food and Agriculture Organization)

(Figure 6-15). Figure 6-16 shows the occurrence of ENSOs (red) between 1950 and 1999.

**What Is La Niña?** Sometimes an El Niño is followed by its cooling counterpart, *La Niña* (Figure 6-16, yellow). Typically a La Niña means **(1)** more Atlantic Ocean hurricanes, **(2)** colder winters in Canada and the Northeast, **(3)** warmer and drier winters in the southeastern and southwestern United States, **(4)** wetter winters in the Pacific Northwest, **(5)** torrential rains in Southeast Asia, **(6)** lower wheat yields in Argentina, and **(7)** more wildfires in Florida.

**How Does the Chemical Makeup of the Atmosphere Lead to the Greenhouse Effect?** Small amounts of certain gases play a key role in determining the earth's average temperatures and thus its climates. These gases include **(1)** water vapor ($H_2O$), **(2)** carbon dioxide ($CO_2$), **(3)** methane ($CH_4$), **(4)** nitrous oxide ($N_2O$), and **(5)** synthetic chlorofluorocarbons (CFCs).

Together, these gases, known as **greenhouse gases,** act somewhat like the glass panes of a greenhouse: They allow mostly visible light and some infrared radiation and ultraviolet (UV) radiation from the sun (Figure 3-10, p. 52) to pass through the troposphere. The earth's surface absorbs much of this solar energy. This transforms

it to longer wavelength infrared radiation (heat), which then rises into the troposphere (Figure 4-8, p. 69).

Some of this heat escapes into space, and some is absorbed by molecules of greenhouse gases and emitted into the troposphere as even longer wavelength infrared radiation, which warms the air. This natural warming effect of the troposphere is called the **greenhouse effect*** (Figure 6-17, p. 121) .

The basic principle behind the natural greenhouse effect is well established. Indeed, without its current greenhouse gases (especially water vapor, which is found in the largest concentration), the earth would be a cold and mostly lifeless planet.

Human activities such as burning fossil fuels, clearing forests, and growing crops release carbon dioxide, methane, and nitrous oxide into the atmosphere. There is concern that large inputs of these greenhouse gases into the troposphere can enhance the earth's natural greenhouse effect and lead to *global warming*. If correct, this could **(1)** alter precipitation patterns, **(2)** shift areas where we can grow crops, **(3)** raise average sea levels, and **(4)** shift areas where some types of plants and animals can live.

**How Does the Chemical Makeup of the Atmosphere Create the Ozone Layer?** In a band of the stratosphere 16–26 kilometers (11–16 miles) above the earth's surface, oxygen ($O_2$) is continuously converted to ozone ($O_3$) and back to oxygen by a sequence of reactions initiated by UV radiation from the sun ($3O_2$ + UV $\rightleftharpoons$ $2O_3$). The result is a thin veil of protective ozone at very low concentrations (up to 12 parts per million).

Normally, the average levels of ozone in this lifesaving layer do not change much because the rate of ozone destruction is equal to its rate of formation. This stratospheric ozone prevents at least 95% of the sun's harmful UV radiation from reaching the earth's surface (Figure 4-8, p. 69).

This ozone layer also creates warm layers of air that prevent churning gases in the troposphere from entering the stratosphere. This *thermal cap* is important in determining the average temperature of the troposphere and thus the earth's current climates. Much evidence indicates that chemicals added to the atmosphere by human activities are decreasing levels of protective ozone in the stratosphere.

---

*To say the earth's atmosphere *traps* heat or *reradiates* heat it has absorbed back toward the earth's surface is scientifically incorrect. Molecules of greenhouse gases absorb various wavelengths of infrared radiation and transform them into infrared radiation with different (longer) wavelengths. Because the originally absorbed wavelengths of infrared radiation no longer exist, it is incorrect to say they have been trapped or reradiated.

**Figure 6-16** El Niño and La Niña conditions between 1950 and 1999. (Data from U.S. National Weather Service)

**(a)** Rays of sunlight penetrate the lower atmosphere and warm the earth's surface.

**(b)** The earth's surface absorbs much of the incoming solar radiation and degrades it to longer-wavelength infrared radiation (heat), which rises into the lower atmosphere. Some of this heat escapes into space and some is absorbed by molecules of greenhouse gases and emitted as infrared radiation, which warms the lower atmosphere.

**(c)** As concentrations of greenhouse gases rise, their molecules absorb and emit more infrared radiation, which adds more heat to the lower atmosphere.

**Figure 6-17** The *greenhouse effect*. Without the atmospheric warming provided by this natural effect, the earth would be a cold and mostly lifeless planet. According to the widely accepted greenhouse theory, when concentrations of greenhouse gases in the atmosphere rise, the average temperature of the troposphere rises. (Modified by permission from Cecie Starr, *Biology: Concepts and Principles*, 4th ed., Pacific Grove, Calif.: Brooks/Cole, 2000)

**How Do Topography and Other Features of the Earth's Surface Create Microclimates?** Various topographic features of the earth's surface create local climatic conditions, or **microclimates,** that differ from the general climate of a region. For example, mountains interrupt the flow of prevailing surface winds and the movement of storms. When moist air blowing inland from an ocean reaches a mountain range, it cools as it is forced to rise and expand. This causes the air to lose most of its moisture as rain and snow on the windward

(wind-facing) slopes. As the drier air mass flows down the leeward (away from the wind) slopes, it draws moisture out of the plants and soil over which it passes. The lower precipitation and the resulting semiarid or arid conditions on the leeward side of high mountains are called the **rain shadow effect** (Figure 6-18, p. 122).

Cities also create distinct microclimates. Bricks, concrete, asphalt, and other building materials absorb and hold heat, and buildings block wind flow. Motor vehicles and the climate control systems of buildings

**Figure 6-18** The *rain shadow effect* is a reduction of rainfall on the side of high mountains facing away from prevailing surface winds. It occurs when warm, moist air in prevailing onshore winds loses most of its moisture as rain and snow on the windward (wind-facing) slopes of a mountain range. This leads to semiarid and arid conditions on the leeward side of the mountain range and the land beyond. The Mojave Desert, east of the Sierra Nevada in California, is produced by this effect.

**Figure 6-19** *Sea and land breezes.* Land heated by the sun during the day heats ground-level air, which rises and is replaced by cooler air drawn from the ocean. As a result, surface wind blows from the ocean to the land, creating a *sea breeze* (top). At night the land loses its heat quickly through radiation while the ocean water remains at about the same temperature. As the land surface cools below the sea surface temperature, warmer air rises over the ocean and is replaced by air from the land. Thus surface wind blows from the land to the ocean, creating a *land breeze* (bottom). (Used by permission from Cecie Starr, *Biology: Concepts and Principles,* 4th ed., Pacific Grove, Calif.: Brooks/Cole, 2000)

release large quantities of heat and pollutants. As a result, cities tend to have more haze and smog, higher temperatures, and lower wind speeds than the surrounding countryside.

Land–ocean interactions affect the local climates of coastal areas by creating **(1)** ocean-to-land breezes (called *sea breezes*) during the day (Figure 6-19, top) and **(2)** land-to-ocean breezes (called *land breezes*) at night (Figure 6-19, bottom).

## 6-3 BIOMES: CLIMATE AND LIFE ON LAND

**Why Do Different Organisms Live in Different Places?** Why is one area of the earth's land surface a desert, another a grassland, and another a forest? Why do different types of deserts, grasslands, and forests exist?

The general answer to these questions is differences in *climate* (Figure 6-7), caused mostly by differences in average temperature and precipitation caused by global air circulation (Figures 6-9 and 6-11). Different climates promote different communities of organisms.

Figure 6-20 and the photo on p. 1 show global distributions of *biomes:* terrestrial regions with characteristic types of natural, undisturbed ecological communities adapted to the climate of the region. By comparing Figure 6-20 with Figure 6-7, you can see how the world's major biomes vary with climate. Figure 4-9 (p. 70) shows major biomes in the United States as one moves through different climates along the 39th parallel. Taken

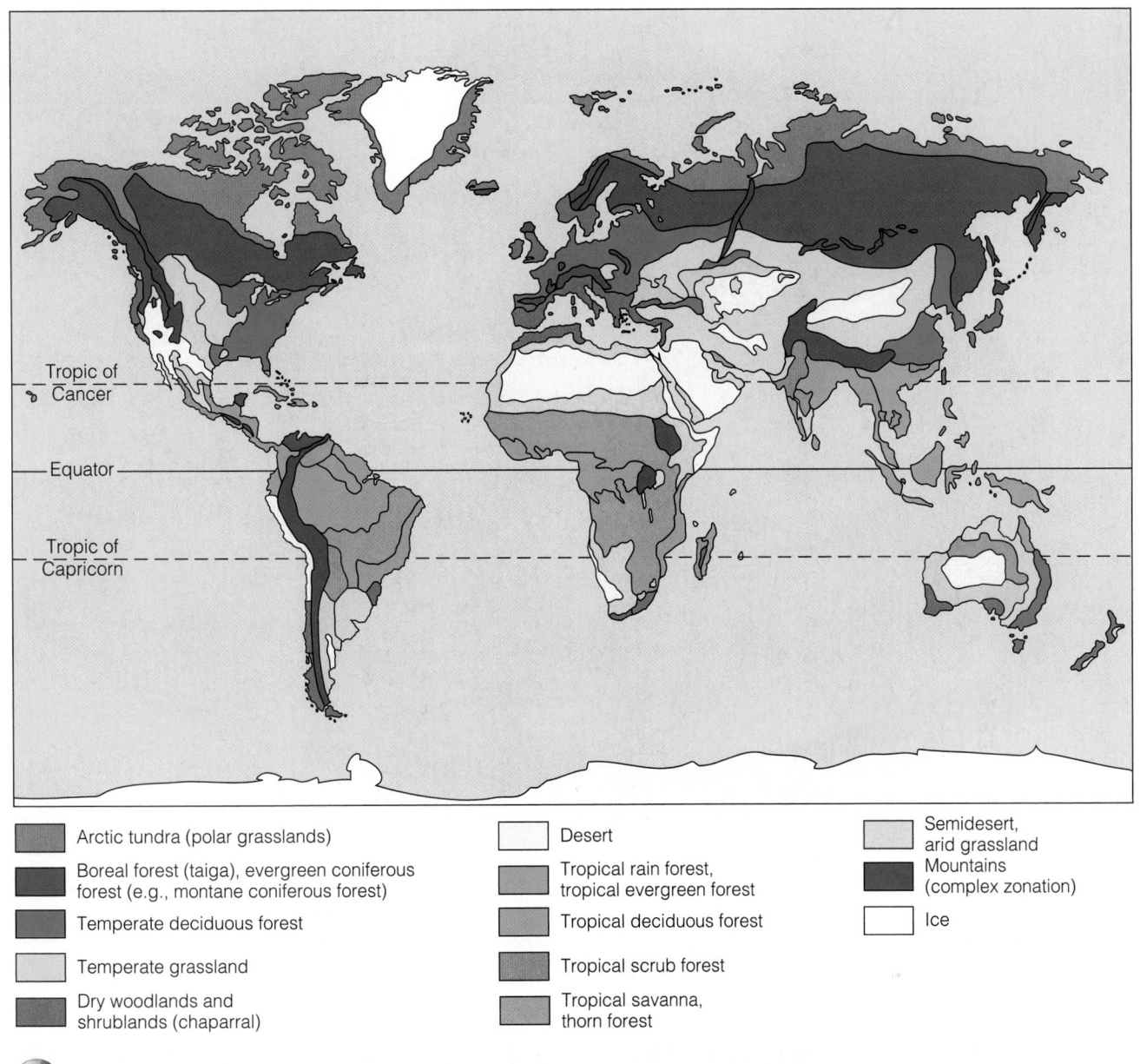

| | | |
|---|---|---|
| ■ Arctic tundra (polar grasslands) | ☐ Desert | ■ Semidesert, arid grassland |
| ■ Boreal forest (taiga), evergreen coniferous forest (e.g., montane coniferous forest) | ■ Tropical rain forest, tropical evergreen forest | ■ Mountains (complex zonation) |
| ■ Temperate deciduous forest | ■ Tropical deciduous forest | ☐ Ice |
| ☐ Temperate grassland | ■ Tropical scrub forest | |
| ■ Dry woodlands and shrublands (chaparral) | ■ Tropical savanna, thorn forest | |

**Figure 6-20** The earth's major *biomes*—the main types of natural vegetation in different undisturbed land areas—result primarily from differences in climate (Figure 6-7). Each biome contains many ecosystems whose communities have adapted to differences in climate, soil, and other environmental factors. In reality, people have removed or altered much of this natural vegetation in some areas for farming, livestock grazing, lumber and fuelwood, mining, and construction, thereby altering the biomes (Figure 1-5, p. 7).

together, average annual precipitation and temperature (along with soil type) are the most important factors in producing tropical, temperate, or polar deserts, grasslands, and forests (Figure 6-21, p. 124).

On maps such as the one in Figure 6-20, biomes are presented as **(1)** having sharp boundaries and **(2)** being covered with the same general type of vegetation. In reality, most biomes do not have sharp boundaries and blend into one another in transitional zones, or *ecotones* (Figure 4-10, p. 71). Also, the types and numbers of plants in a biome vary from one loca-

tion to another because of variations in **(1)** local climate (microclimates), **(2)** soil types, and **(3)** natural and human-caused disturbances (Figure 1-5, p. 7). As a result, *biomes are not uniform*. They consist of a *mosaic of patches*, all with somewhat different biological communities but with similarities unique to the biome.

Figure 6-22 (p. 124) shows how climate and vegetation vary with **latitude** (distance from the equator) and **altitude** (elevation above sea level). If you travel from the equator toward either pole, you will generally encounter colder climates and zones of vegetation

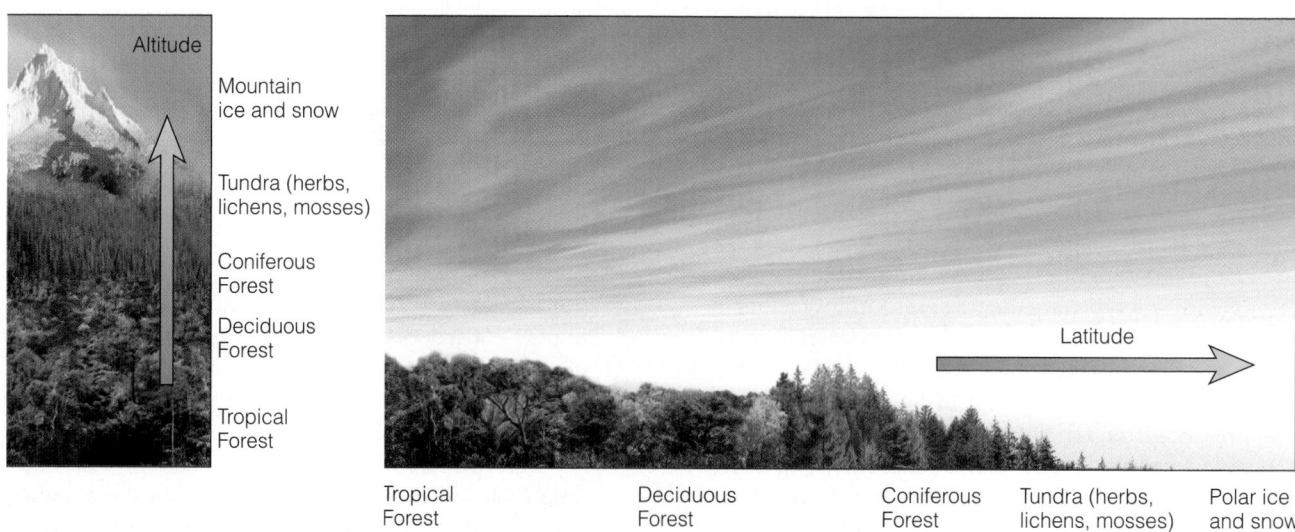

**Figure 6-21** Average precipitation and average temperature, acting together as limiting factors over a period of 30 or more years, determine the type of desert, grassland, or forest biome in a particular area. Although the actual situation is much more complex, this simplified diagram explains how climate determines the types and amounts of natural vegetation found in an area left undisturbed by human activities. (Used by permission of Macmillan Publishing Company, from Derek Elsom, *The Earth,* New York: Macmillan, 1992. Copyright © 1992 by Marshall Editions Developments Limited)

**Figure 6-22** Generalized effects of altitude (left) and latitude (right) on climate and biomes. Parallel changes in vegetation type occur when we travel from the equator to the poles or from lowlands to mountaintops.

adapted to those climates (Figure 6-22, right). Similarly, as elevation above sea level increases, climate becomes colder (Figure 6-22, left). Thus, if you climb a tall mountain from its base to its summit, you can observe changes in plant life similar to those you would encounter in traveling from the equator to the earth's poles (Figure 6-22).

**Why Do Plant Sizes, Shapes, and Survival Strategies Differ?**   Arctic soils are wet and nutrient rich. So why are there no trees in the Arctic, and why are the plants there so close to the ground? Why are there no leaves on desert plants such as cacti? Why do trees in most forests found in both the warm tropics and in cold areas such as Canada and Sweden keep their leaves year round, whereas most trees in temperate forests lose their leaves in winter?

The answers to these questions involve evolutionary responses of plants to different climates.

■ Plants exposed to cold air year round or during winter have traits that keep them from losing too much heat and water. For example, trees or tall plants cannot survive in the cold, windy arctic grasslands (tundra) because they would lose too much of their heat.

■ Desert plants exposed to the sun all day long must **(1)** be able to lose enough heat so they do not overheat and die and **(2)** conserve enough water for survival. **Succulent** (fleshy) **plants,** such as the saguaro ("sah-WAH-row") cactus, survive in dry climates by **(1)** having no leaves, **(2)** storing water and synthesizing food in their expandable, fleshy tissue, and **(3)** reducing water loss by opening their pores (stomata) to take up carbon dioxide ($CO_2$) only at night.

■ Trees of wet tropical rain forests tend to be **broadleaf evergreen plants,** which keep most of their broad leaves year round. The large surface area of the leaves allows them to **(1)** collect ample sunlight for photosynthesis and **(2)** radiate heat during hot weather.

■ In a climate with a cold (and sometimes dry) winter, keeping such leaves would cause plants to lose too much heat and water for survival. In such climates, **broadleaf deciduous plants,** such as oak and maple trees, survive drought and cold by shedding their leaves and becoming dormant during such periods.

■ If we move further north to areas such as Canada and Sweden, where summers are cool and short, this strategy is less successful. Instead evolution has favored **coniferous** (cone-bearing) **evergreen plants** (such as spruces, pines, and firs). These plants keep some of their narrow-pointed leaves (needles) all year. The waxy coating, shape, and clustering of conifer needles slow down heat loss and evaporation during the long, cold winter. Additionally, by keeping their leaves all winter, such trees are ready to take advantage of the brief summer without having to take time to grow new needles.

## 6-4   DESERT BIOMES

**What Are the Major Types of Deserts?**   A desert is an area where evaporation exceeds precipitation. Precipitation typically is **(1)** less than 25 centimeters (10 inches) a year and **(2)** often scattered unevenly throughout the year. Deserts have sparse, widely spaced, mostly low vegetation.

Deserts cover about 30% of the earth's land and are situated mainly between tropical and subtropical regions north and south of the equator, at about 30° north and 30° south latitude (Figure 6-23, p. 126). The largest deserts are in the interiors of continents, far from moist sea air and moisture-bearing winds. Other, more local deserts form on the downwind sides of mountain ranges because of the rain shadow effect (Figure 6-18).

The baking sun warms the ground in the desert during the day. At night, however, most of the heat stored in the ground radiates quickly into the atmosphere because desert soils have little vegetation and moisture to help store the heat and the skies usually are clear. This explains why in a desert you may roast during the day but shiver at night.

A combination of low rainfall and different average temperatures creates tropical, temperate, and cold deserts (Figures 6-21 and 6-24, p. 126).

■ In *tropical deserts,* such as the southern Sahara in Africa, **(1)** temperatures usually are high year round and **(2)** there is little rain, which typically falls during only 1 or 2 months of the year (Figure 6-24, left, p. 126). These driest places on earth typically have few plants and a hard, windblown surface strewn with rocks and some sand.

■ In *temperate deserts,* such as the Mojave in southern California, **(1)** daytime temperatures are high in summer and low in winter and **(2)** there is more precipitation than in tropical deserts (Figure 6-24, center). The vegetation is sparse, consisting mostly of widely dispersed, drought-resistant shrubs and cacti or other succulents, and animals are adapted to the lack of water and temperature variations (Figure 6-25, p. 127).

■ In *cold deserts,* such as the Gobi Desert in China, **(1)** winters are cold, **(2)** summers are warm or hot, and **(3)** precipitation is low (Figure 6-24, right).

In the semiarid zones between deserts and grasslands, we find *semidesert.* This biome is dominated by thorn trees and shrubs adapted to a long dry spells followed by brief, sometimes heavy rains.

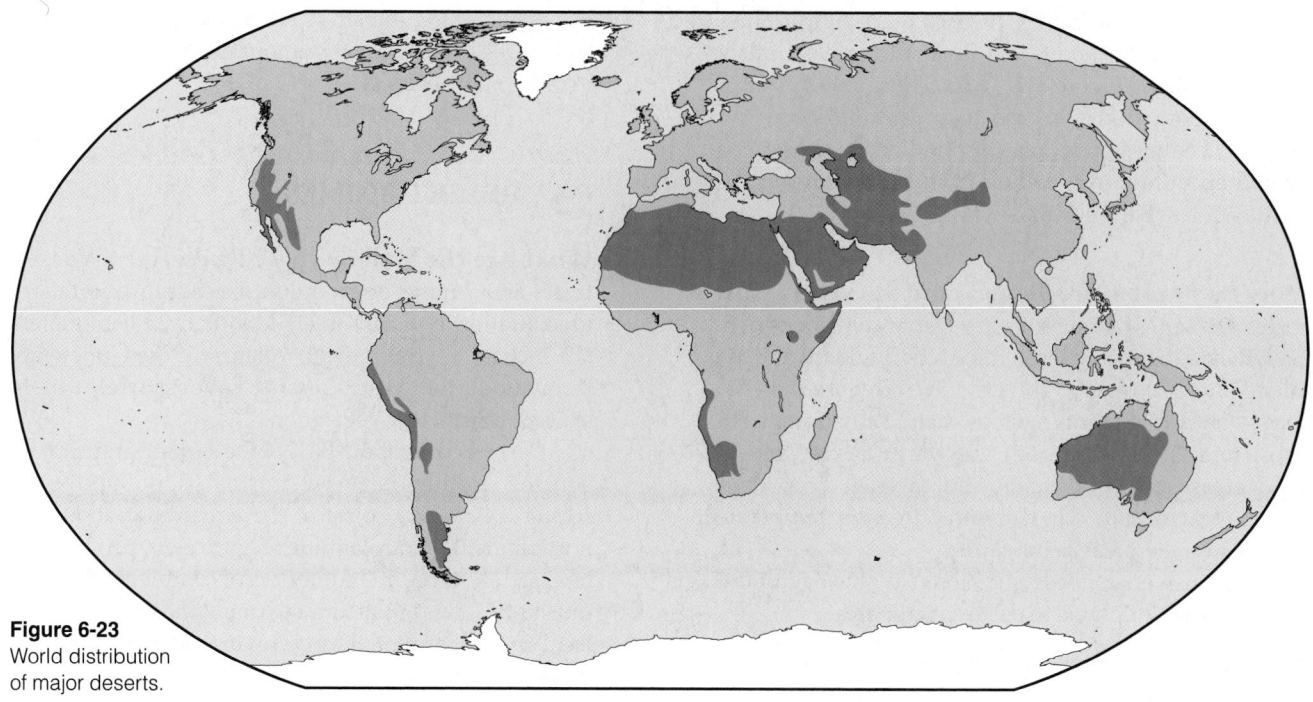

**Figure 6-23**
World distribution of major deserts.

### How Do Desert Plants and Animals Survive?

Adaptations for survival in the desert have two themes: *Beat the heat* and *Every drop of water counts*. These adaptations include:

- Having wax-coated leaves that minimize transpiration (evergreens such as the creosote bush)

- Using deep roots to tap into groundwater

- Using widely spread, shallow roots to collect water after brief showers and store it in their spongy tissue (prickly pear, Figure 6-25, and saguaro cacti)

- Dropping their leaves to survive in a dormant state during long drying spells (mesquite and creosote plants)

- Becoming dormant during dry periods (mosses and lichens)

- Storing much of their biomass in seeds during dry periods and remaining inactive (sometimes for years) until they receive enough water to germinate (annual wildflowers and grasses). Shortly after a rain the seeds **(1)** germinate, **(2)** grow, **(3)** carpet such deserts

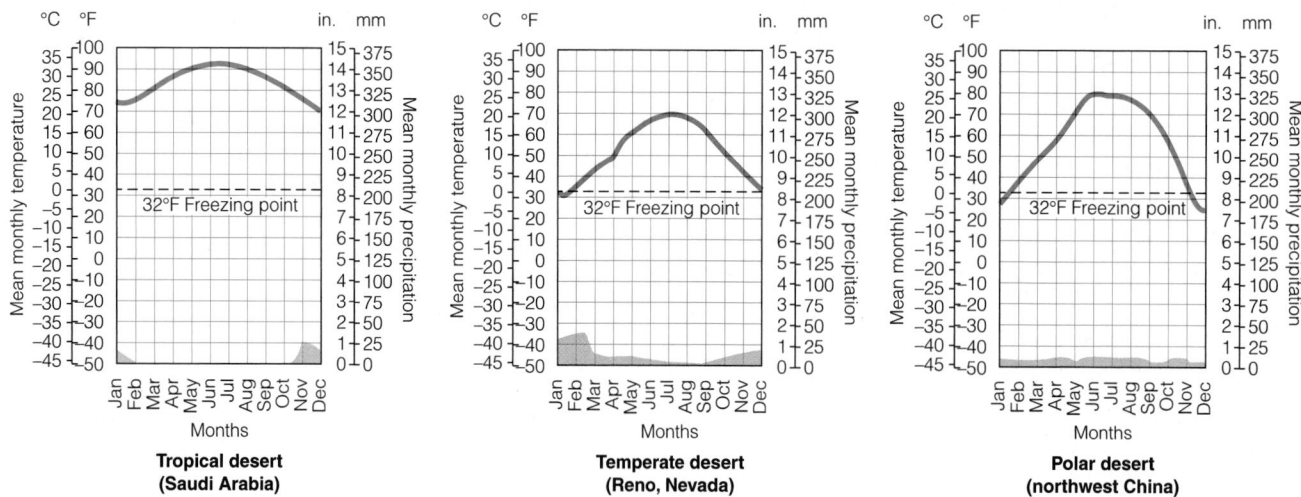

**Figure 6-24** Climate graphs showing typical variations in annual temperature and precipitation in tropical, temperate, and polar (cold) deserts.

| | Producer to primary consumer | | Primary to secondary consumer | | Secondary to higher-level consumer | | All producers and consumers to decomposers |

**Figure 6-25** Some components and interactions in a *temperate desert ecosystem.* When these organisms die, decomposers break down their organic matter into minerals that plants use. Colored arrows indicate transfers of matter and energy between producers, primary consumers (herbivores), secondary (or higher-level) consumers (carnivores), and decomposers. Organisms are not drawn to scale.

- Large desert cities

- Soil destruction by vehicles and urban development

- Soil salinization from irrigation

- Depletion of underground water supplies

- Land disturbance and pollution from mineral extraction

- Storage of toxic and radioactive wastes

- Large arrays of solar cells and solar collectors used to produce electricity

**Figure 6-26** Major human impacts on the world's deserts.

with a dazzling array of colorful flowers, **(4)** produce new seed, and **(5)** die, all in only a few weeks.

Most desert animals are small and beat the heat and reduce water loss by evaporative cooling by

- Hiding in cool burrows or rocky crevices by day and coming out at night or in the early morning.

- Having physical adaptations for conserving water. Insects and reptiles **(1)** have thick outer coverings to minimize water loss through evaporation and **(2)** reduce water loss by having dry feces and excreting a dried concentrate of urine.

- Getting their water from dew or from the food they eat (many spiders and insects). Arabian oryxes survive by licking the dew that accumulates at night on rocks and on one another's hair.

- Becoming dormant during periods of extreme heat or drought.

Figure 6-26 shows major human impacts on deserts. Deserts take a long time to recover from disturbances because of their **(1)** slow plant growth, **(2)** low species diversity, **(3)** slow nutrient cycling (because of little bacterial activity in their soils), and **(4)** water shortages. Desert vegetation destroyed by livestock overgrazing and off-road vehicles may take decades to grow back.

## 6-5 GRASSLAND, TUNDRA, AND CHAPARRAL BIOMES

### What Are the Major Types of Grasslands?

**Grasslands** are regions with enough average annual precipitation to allow grass (and in some areas, a few trees) to prosper but with precipitation so erratic that

drought and fire prevent large stands of trees from growing. Most grasslands are found in the interiors of continents (Figure 6-27).

Grasslands persist because of a combination of **(1)** seasonal drought, **(2)** grazing by large herbivores, and **(3)** occasional fires, all of which keep large numbers of shrubs and trees from invading and becoming established. If not overgrazed by large herbivores, grasses in these biomes are renewable resources because these plants grow out from the bottom. This allows their stems to grow again after being nibbled off by grazing animals.

The three main types of grasslands—tropical, temperate, and polar (tundra)—result from combinations of low average precipitation and various average temperatures (Figures 6-21 and 6-28).

### What Are Tropical Grasslands and Savannas?

*Tropical grasslands* are found in areas with **(1)** high average temperatures, **(2)** low to moderate precipitation, and **(3)** a prolonged dry season. They occur in a wide belt on either side of the equator beyond the borders of tropical rain forests (Figure 6-27).

One type of tropical grassland, called a *savanna*, usually has **(1)** warm temperatures year round, **(2)** two prolonged dry seasons, and **(3)** abundant rain the rest of the year (Figure 6-28, left). The largest savannas are in central and southern Africa, but they are also found in central South America, Australia, and Southeast Asia (Figure 6-27).

African tropical savannas contain enormous herds of **(1)** *grazing* (grass- and herb-eating) and **(2)** *browsing* (twig- and leaf-nibbling) hoofed animals, including wildebeests, gazelles, zebras, giraffes, and antelopes (Figure 6-29, p. 130). These and other large herbivores have evolved specialized eating habits that minimize competition between species for vegetation. For example, **(1)** giraffes eat leaves and shoots from the tops of trees, **(2)** elephants eat leaves and branches further down, **(3)** Thompson's gazelles and wildebeests prefer short grass, and **(4)** zebras graze on longer grass and stems.

During the dry season, wildebeest and other large grazing animals migrate to find enough water and high-quality grasses, and smaller animals become dormant or survive by eating plant seeds. Predators such as cheetahs, lions, hyenas, eagles, and hawks prey on the large grazing animals (and many small ones). Many large savanna animal species are killed for their economically valuable coats and parts (tigers), tusks (rhinoceroses), and ivory tusks (elephants).

### What Are Temperate Grasslands? *Temperate grasslands* cover vast expanses of plains and gently rolling hills in the interiors of North and South America, Europe, and Asia (Figure 6-27). In these grass-

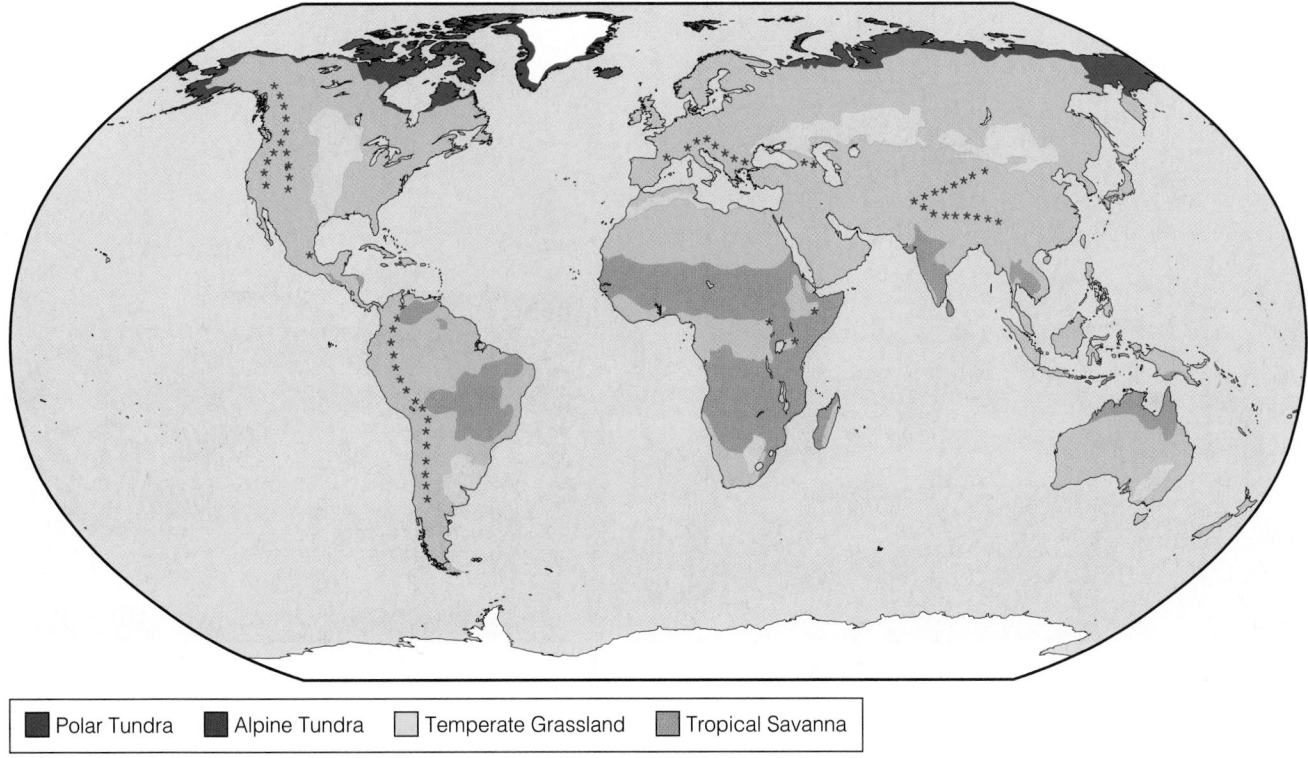

| Polar Tundra | Alpine Tundra | Temperate Grassland | Tropical Savanna |

**Figure 6-27** World distribution of major grasslands.

lands, **(1)** winters are bitterly cold, **(2)** summers are hot and dry, and **(3)** annual precipitation is fairly sparse and falls unevenly through the year (Figure 6-28, center).

Because the aboveground parts of most of the grasses die and decompose each year, organic matter accumulates to produce a deep, fertile soil. This soil is held in place by a thick network of intertwined roots of drought-tolerant grasses unless the topsoil is plowed up and allowed to blow away by prolonged exposure to high winds found in these biomes.

Types of temperate grasslands are the **(1)** *tall-grass prairies* (Figure 6-30, p. 131) and *short-grass prairies* of the midwestern and western United States and Canada,

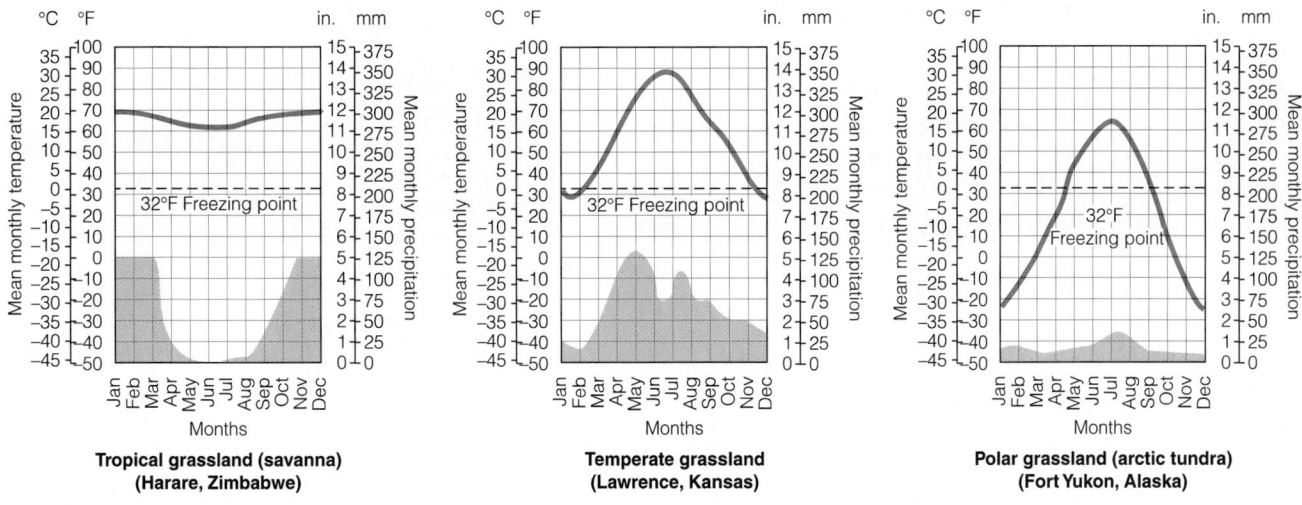

| Tropical grassland (savanna) (Harare, Zimbabwe) | Temperate grassland (Lawrence, Kansas) | Polar grassland (arctic tundra) (Fort Yukon, Alaska) |

**Figure 6-28** Climate graphs showing typical variations in annual temperature and precipitation in tropical, temperate, and polar (arctic tundra) grasslands.

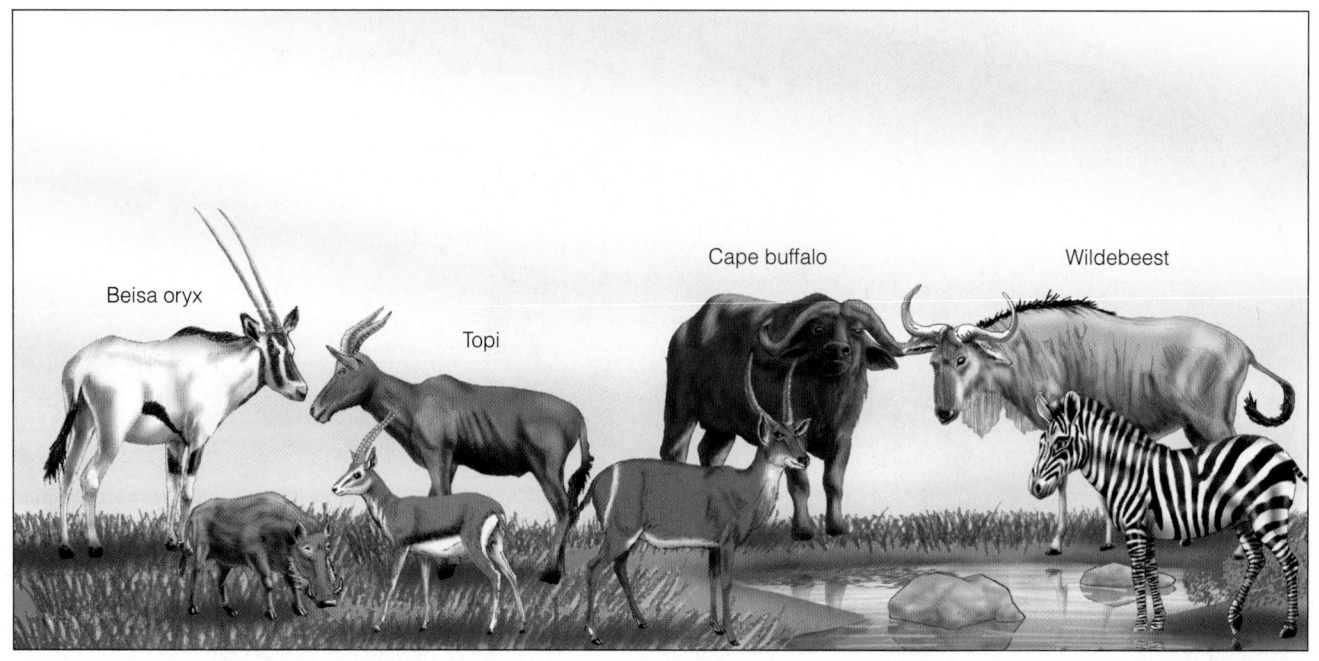

Beisa oryx

Topi

Cape buffalo

Wildebeest

Warthog

Thompson's gazelle

Waterbuck

Grant's zebra

**Dry Grassland**

**Moist Grassland**

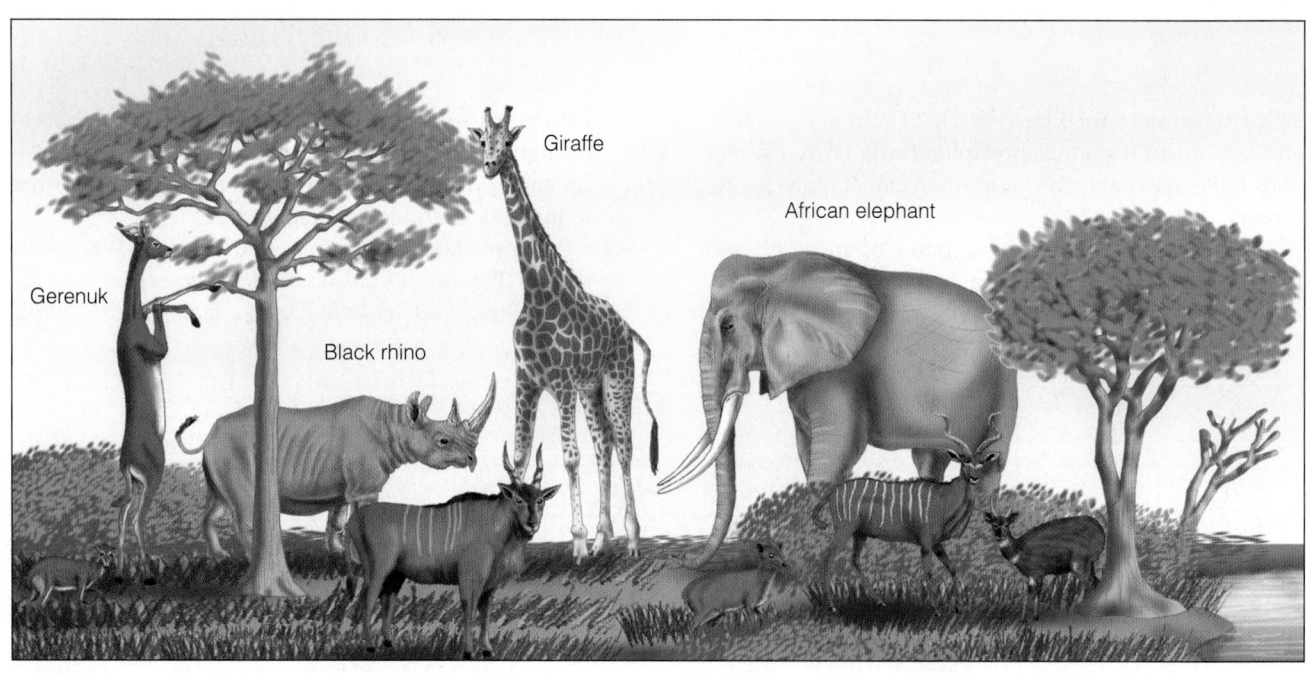

Gerenuk

Giraffe

African elephant

Black rhino

Dik-dik

East African eland

Blue duiker

Greater kudu

Bushbuck

**Dry Thorn Scrub**

**Riverine Forest**

**Figure 6-29** Some of the grazing animals found in different parts of the African savanna. These species share vegetation resources by having different feeding niches.

| | Producer to primary consumer | | Primary to secondary consumer | | Secondary to higher-level consumer | | All producers and consumers to decomposers |

**Figure 6-30** Some components and interactions in *a temperate tall-grass prairie ecosystem* in North America. When these organisms die, decomposers break down their organic matter into minerals that plants use. Colored arrows indicate transfers of matter and energy between producers, primary consumers (herbivores), secondary (or higher-level) consumers (carnivores), and decomposers. Organisms are not drawn to scale.

**Figure 6-31** Replacement of a temperate grassland with a monoculture crop in California. When the tangled root network of natural grasses is removed, the fertile topsoil is subject to severe wind erosion unless it is covered with some type of vegetation.

National Archives/EPA

**(2)** South American *pampas,* **(3)** African *veldt,* and **(4)** *steppes* of central Europe and Asia. Here winds blow almost continuously, and evaporation is rapid, often leading to fires in the summer and fall.

Because of their thick and fertile soils, temperate grasslands are plowed up and widely used to grow crops (Figure 6-31). However, plowing breaks up the soil and leaves it vulnerable to erosion by wind and water.

**What Are Polar Grasslands?** *Polar grasslands,* or *arctic tundra,* occur just south of the arctic polar ice cap (Figure 6-27). During most of the year these treeless plains are **(1)** bitterly cold, **(2)** swept by frigid winds, and **(3)** covered with ice and snow (Figure 6-28, right). Winters are long and dark, and the scant precipitation falls mostly as snow.

This biome is carpeted with a thick, spongy mat of low-growing plants, primarily grasses, mosses, and dwarf woody shrubs (Figure 6-32). Most of the annual growth of these plants occurs during the 6- to 8-week summer, when sunlight shines almost around the clock.

To retain water and survive the winter cold, most tundra plants grow close to the ground, and some have leathery evergreen leaves coated by waxes that reduce heat loss. Other plants survive the long, cold winter underground as roots, stems, bulbs, and tubers; some, such as lichens, dehydrate during winter to avoid frost damage.

One effect of the extreme cold is **permafrost,** a perennially frozen layer of the soil that forms when the water there freezes. In summer, water near the surface thaws, but the permafrost soil layer below stays frozen and prevents liquid water at the surface from seeping into the ground. Thus, during the brief summer, the soil above the permafrost layer remains waterlogged, forming a large number of shallow lakes, marshes, bogs, ponds, and other seasonal wetlands. Hordes of mosquitoes, blackflies, and other insects thrive in these shallow surface pools. They feed large colonies of migratory birds (especially waterfowl) that return from the south to nest and breed in the bogs and ponds.

In North American arctic tundra, caribou herds arrive to feed on the summer vegetation, bringing with them their wolf predators. In arctic tundra in Europe and Asia, reindeer occupy the grazing niche of caribou.

The arctic tundra's permanent animal residents are mostly small herbivores such as lemmings, hares, voles, and ground squirrels that burrow underground to escape the cold. Predators such as the lynx, weasel, snowy owl, and arctic fox (Figure 5-8, p. 105) eat them. Most tundra animals do not hibernate because the summer is too short for them to accumulate adequate fat reserves. Animals in this biome survive the intense winter cold through adaptations such as **(1)** thick coats of fur (arctic wolf, arctic fox, and musk oxen), **(2)** feathers (snowy owl), **(3)** compact bodies to expose as little

Long-tailed jaeger

Grizzly bear

Caribou

Mosquito

Snowy owl

Horned lark

Arctic fox

Willow ptarmigan

Dwarf willow

Lemming

Mountain cranberry

Moss campion

| Producer to primary consumer | Primary to secondary consumer | Secondary to higher-level consumer | All consumers and producers to decomposers |

**Figure 6-32** Some components and interactions in an *arctic tundra (polar grassland) ecosystem*. When these organisms die, decomposers break down their organic matter into minerals that plants use. Colored arrows indicate transfers of matter and energy between producers, primary consumers (herbivores), secondary (or higher-level) consumers (carnivores), and decomposers. Organisms are not drawn to scale.

**Figure 6-33** Major human impacts on the world's grasslands.

The box lists:
- Conversion of savanna and temperate grassland to cropland
- Release of CO₂ to atmosphere from burning and conversion of grassland to cropland
- Overgrazing of tropical and temperate grasslands by livestock
- Damage to fragile arctic tundra by oil production, air and water pollution, and vehicles

surface as possible to the air, and **(4)** living underground (arctic lemming).

Because of the cold, decomposition is slow. Because of low decomposer populations, the soil is poor in organic matter and in nitrates, phosphates, and other minerals.

**What Is Alpine Tundra?**   Another type of tundra, called *alpine tundra,* occurs above the limit of tree growth but below the permanent snow line on high mountains (Figures 6-22, left, and 6-27). The vegetation there is similar to that found in arctic tundra, but it gets more sunlight than arctic vegetation and has no permafrost layer.

Figure 6-33 lists major human impacts on grasslands.

**What Is Chaparral?**   Some temperate areas have a biome known as *temperate shrubland* or *chaparral.* This biome occurs along coastal areas with what is called a *Mediterranean climate:* winters are mild and moderately rainy, and summers are long, hot, and dry. It is found mainly along **(1)** parts of the Pacific coast of North America, **(2)** in southern Texas and northeastern Mexico, and **(3)** in the coastal hills of Chile, the Mediterranean, southwestern Africa, and southwestern Australia (Figure 6-20).

This biome usually is dominated by a dense growth of low-growing evergreen shrubs with leathery leaves that resist water loss and have large underground root systems. Some areas also have a sprinkling of small drought-resistant trees such as pines and scrub oak.

During the long, hot dry season, chaparral vegetation is dormant and becomes very dry and brittle. In the fall, fires started by lightning or human activities spread with incredible swiftness through the dry brush and litter of leaves and fallen branches.

Research reveals that chaparral is adapted to and maintained by periodic fires. Many of the shrubs **(1)** store food reserves in their fire-resistant roots and **(2)** have seeds that sprout only after a hot fire. With the first rain, annual grasses and wildflowers spring up and use nutrients released by the fire. New shrubs grow quickly and crowd out the grasses.

People like living in this biome because of its favorable climate. However, those living in chaparral assume the high risk of losing their homes (and possibly their lives) to the frequent fires associated with it. After fires often comes the hazard of flooding; when heavy rains come, great torrents of water pour off the unprotected burned hillsides to flood lowland areas.

## 6-6   FOREST BIOMES

**What Are the Major Types of Forests?**   Undisturbed areas with moderate to high average annual precipitation tend to be covered with **forest,** which contains various species of trees and smaller forms of vegetation. The three main types of forest—*tropical, temperate,* and *boreal* (polar)—result from combinations of this precipitation level and various average temperatures (Figures 6-21 and 6-36, p. 136).

**What Are Tropical Rain Forests?**   *Tropical rain forests* are a type of broadleaf evergreen forest (Figure 6-34) found near the equator (Figure 6-35, p. 136), where hot, moisture-laden air rises and dumps its moisture (Figure 6-11). These forests have **(1)** a warm annual mean temperature (which varies little, daily or seasonally), **(2)** high humidity, and **(3)** heavy rainfall almost daily (Figure 6-36, left, p. 136).

Tropical rain forests have incredible biological diversity. These diverse forms of life occupy a variety of specialized niches in distinct layers, based mostly on their need for sunlight (Figure 6-37, p. 137). Much of the animal life, particularly insects, bats, and birds, lives in the sunny *canopy* layer, with its abundant shelter and supplies of leaves, flowers, and fruits (Figure 6-37). To study life in the canopy, ecologists climb trees and build platforms and boardwalks in the upper canopy.

The stratification of specialized plant and animal niches in various layers of a tropical rain forest enables coexistence of a great variety of species (biodiversity). Although tropical rain forests cover only about 2% of the earth's land surface, they are habitats for 50–80% of the earth's terrestrial species.

| | | | | | | |
|---|---|---|---|---|---|---|
| ➡ | Producer to primary consumer | ➡ | Primary to secondary consumer | ➡ | Secondary to higher-level consumer | ➡ | All producers and consumers to decomposers |

**Figure 6-34** Some components and interactions in a *tropical rain forest ecosystem*. When these organisms die, decomposers break down their organic matter into minerals that plants use. Colored arrows indicate transfers of matter and energy between producers, primary consumers (herbivores), secondary (or higher-level) consumers (carnivores), and decomposers. Organisms are not drawn to scale.

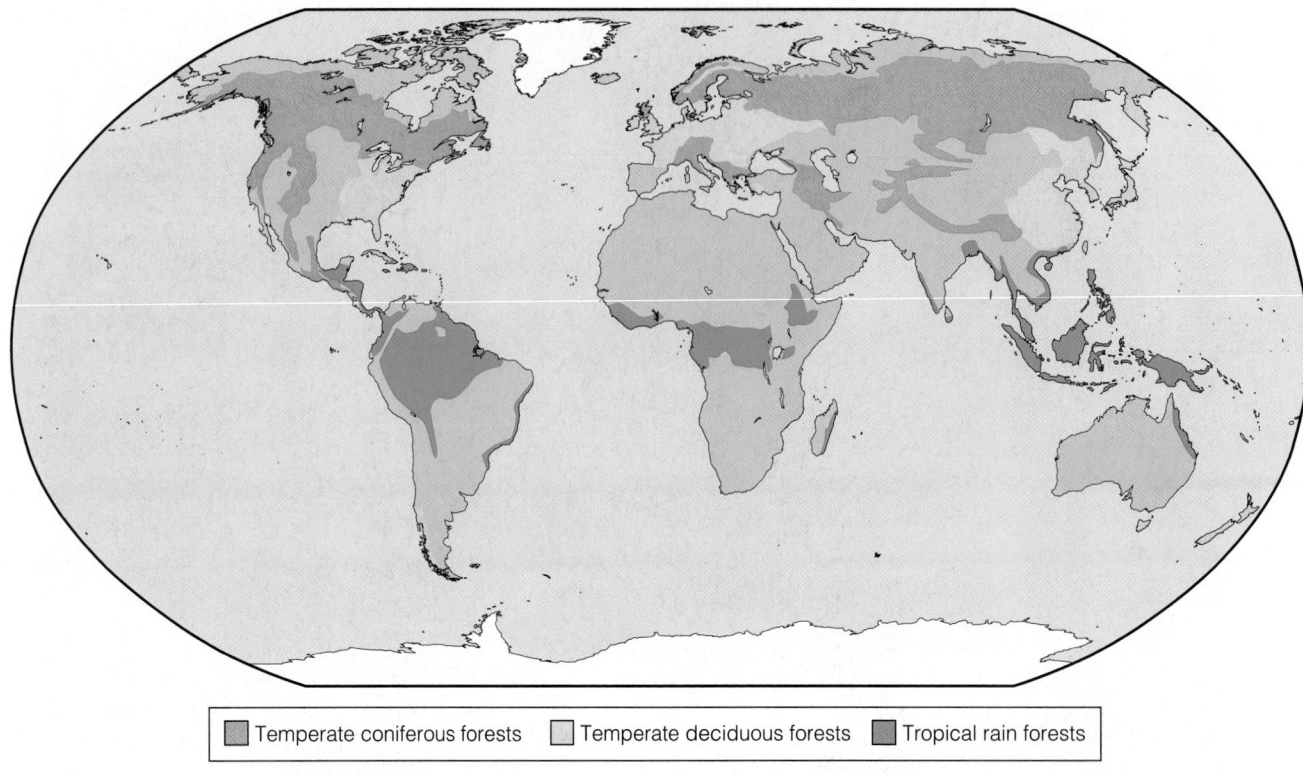

Figure 6-35 World distribution of major forests.

Dropped leaves, fallen trees, and dead animals decompose quickly because of the warm, moist conditions and hordes of decomposers. This rapid recycling of scarce soil nutrients is why little litter is found on the ground. Instead of being stored in the soil, most minerals released by decomposition are taken up quickly by plants. Thus most of a tropical rain forest's nutrients are stored in the biomass of its living organisms.

Because of the dense vegetation, little wind blows in tropical rain forests, eliminating the possibility of wind pollination. Many of the plants have evolved

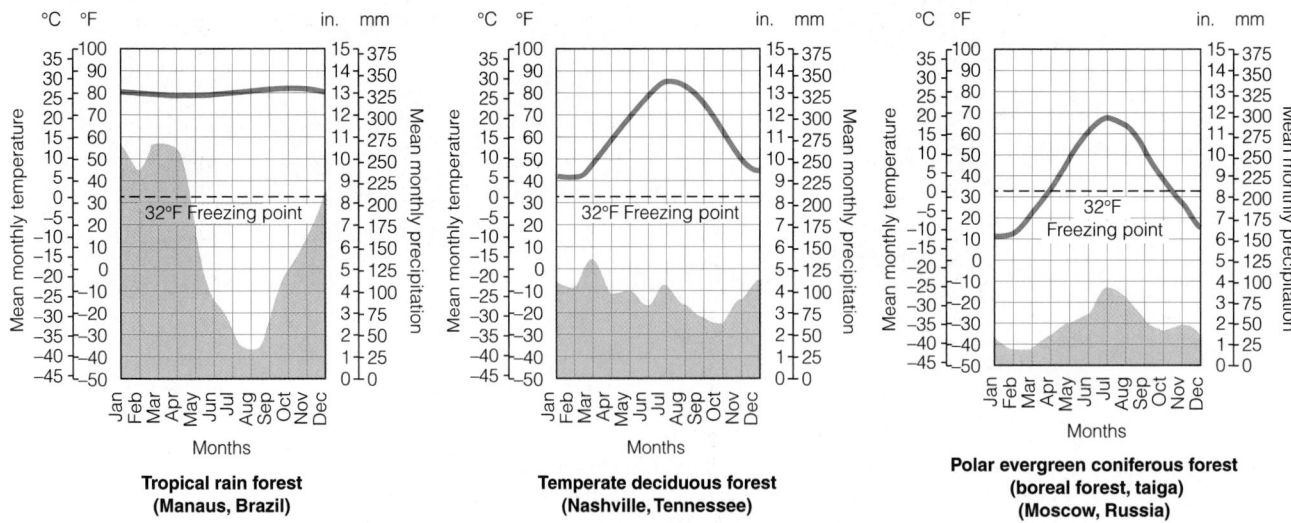

Figure 6-36 Climate graphs showing typical variations in annual temperature and precipitation in tropical, temperate, and polar forests.

**Figure 6-37** Stratification of specialized plant and animal niches in various layers of a *tropical rain forest*. The presence of these specialized niches enables species to avoid or minimize competition for resources and results in the coexistence of a great variety of species (biodiversity).

elaborate flowers (Figure 4-17, right, p. 76) that attract particular insects, birds, or bats as pollinators.

**What Are Tropical Deciduous Forests?** Moving a little farther from the equator (Figure 6-20), we find *tropical deciduous forests* (sometimes called *tropical monsoon forests* or *tropical seasonal forests*). These forests are **(1)** warm year round and **(2)** get most of their plentiful rainfall during a wet (monsoon) season that is followed by a long dry season.

Tropical deciduous forests have a lower canopy than tropical rain forests. They contain a mixture of **(1)** deciduous trees (which lose their leaves to survive the dry season) and **(2)** drought-tolerant evergreen trees (which retain most of their leaves year round). Where the dry season is especially long, we find *tropi-*

*cal scrub forests* (Figure 6-20) containing mostly small deciduous trees and shrubs.

**What Are Temperate Deciduous Forests?** *Temperate deciduous forests* (Figures 6-35 and 6-38, p. 138) grow in areas with moderate average temperatures that change significantly with the season (Figure 6-36, center). These areas have **(1)** long, warm summers, **(2)** cold but not too severe winters, and **(3)** abundant precipitation, often spread fairly evenly throughout the year.

This biome is dominated by a few species of broadleaf deciduous trees such as oak, hickory, maple, poplar, and sycamore. They survive cold winters by dropping their leaves in the fall and becoming dormant. Each spring they grow new leaves that change in the fall into an array of reds and golds before dropping.

| Label | |
|---|---|
| Broad-winged hawk | Hairy woodpecker |
| Gray squirrel | |
| White oak | |
| White-tailed deer | White-footed mouse |
| Shagbark hickory | Metallic wood-boring beetle and larvae |
| | Mountain winterberry |
| Long-tailed weasel | May beetle |
| Fungi | Racer |
| Bacteria | Wood frog |

Producer to primary consumer

Primary to secondary consumer

Secondary to higher-level consumer

All producers and consumers to decomposers

**Figure 6-38** Some components and interactions in a *temperate deciduous forest ecosystem*. When these organisms die, decomposers break down their organic matter into minerals that plants use. Colored arrows indicate transfers of matter and energy between producers, primary consumers (herbivores), secondary (or higher-level) consumers (carnivores), and decomposers. Organisms are not drawn to scale.

Compared with tropical rain forests, temperate deciduous forests have a simpler structure and contain fewer tree species. However, the penetration of more sunlight supports a richer diversity of plant life at ground level. Because of the fairly low rate of decomposition, these forests accumulate a thick layer of slowly decaying leaf litter that is a storehouse of nutrients.

The temperate deciduous forests of the eastern United States were once home for such large predators as bears, wolves, foxes, wildcats, and mountain lions (pumas). Today most of the predators have been killed or displaced, and the dominant mammal species often is the white-tailed deer, along with smaller mammals such as squirrels, rabbits, opossums, raccoons, and mice. Some of these diverse forests have been cleared and replaced with *tree plantations* consisting of a single tree species (Figure 6-39).

Warblers, robins, and other bird species migrate to these forests during the summer to feed and breed. Many of these species are declining in numbers because of loss or fragmentation of their summer and winter habitats, which also makes them more vulnerable to predators and parasitic cowbirds. Small mammals and birds are preyed on by owls, hawks, and, in remote areas, bobcats and foxes.

**What Are Evergreen Coniferous Forests?** *Evergreen coniferous forests*, also called *boreal forests* and *taigas* (pronounced TIE-guhs), are found just south of the arctic tundra in northern regions across North America, Asia, and Europe (Figures 6-20 and 6-35). In this subarctic climate, winters are long, dry, and extremely cold; in the northernmost taiga, sunlight is available only 6–8 hours a day. Summers are short, with mild to warm temperatures (Figure 6-36, right), and the sun typically shines 19 hours a day.

Most boreal forests are dominated by a few species of coniferous (cone-bearing) evergreen trees such as spruce, fir, cedar, hemlock, and pine that keep some of their narrow-pointed leaves (needles) all year long. The small, needle-shaped, waxy-coated leaves of these trees **(1)** can withstand the intense cold and drought of winter when snow blankets the ground and **(2)** are ready to take advantage of the brief summers in these areas without having to take time to grow new needles. Plant diversity is low in these forests because few species can survive the winters when soil moisture is frozen.

Beneath the stands of trees is a deep layer of partially decomposed conifer needles and leaf litter. Decomposition is slow because of the **(1)** low temperatures, **(2)** waxy coating of conifer needles, and **(3)** high soil acidity. As the conifer needles decompose, they make the thin, nutrient-poor soil acidic and prevent

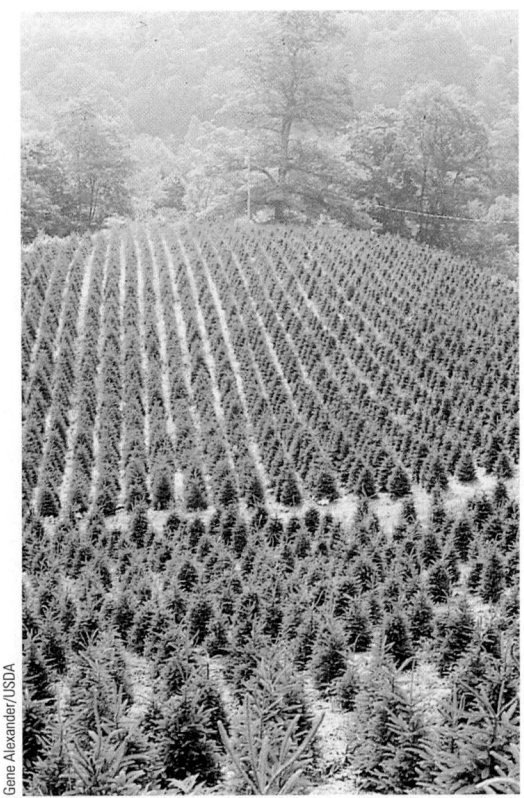

**Figure 6-39** *Tree plantation* in North Carolina. Some diverse virgin (old-growth) and second-growth forests are cleared and replanted with a single tree species (monoculture), often for harvest as Christmas trees, timber, or wood converted to pulp to make paper.

most other plants (except certain shrubs) from growing on the forest floor.

These biomes contain a variety of wildlife (Figure 6-40, p. 140). During the brief summer the soil becomes waterlogged, forming acidic bogs, or *muskegs*, in low-lying areas of these forests. Warblers and other insect-eating birds feed on hordes of flies, mosquitoes, and caterpillars.

**What Are Temperate Rain Forests?** *Coastal coniferous forests* or *temperate rain forests* are found in scattered coastal temperate areas with ample rainfall or moisture from dense ocean fogs. Dense stands of large conifers such as Sitka spruce, Douglas fir, and redwoods dominate undisturbed areas of biomes along the coast of North America, from Canada to northern California.

The ocean moderates the temperature so winters are mild and summers are cool. The trees in these moist forests depend on frequent rains and moisture from summer fog that rolls in off the Pacific.

Figure 6-41 (p. 141) lists major human impacts on the world's forests.

| Producer to primary consumer | Primary to secondary consumer | Secondary to higher-level consumer | All producers and consumers to decomposers |

**Figure 6-40** Some components and interactions in an *evergreen coniferous (boreal or taiga) forest ecosystem.* When these organisms die, decomposers break down their organic matter into minerals that plants use. Colored arrows indicate transfers of matter and energy between producers, primary consumers (herbivores), secondary (or higher-level) consumers (carnivores), and decomposers. Organisms are not drawn to scale.

Clearing and degradation of tropical
forests for agriculture, livestock grazing,
and timber harvesting

Clearing of temperate deciduous
forests in Europe, Asia, and
North America for timber, agriculture,
and urban development

Clearing of evergreen coniferous
forests in North America, Finland,
Sweden, Canada, Siberia,
and Russia

Conversion of diverse forests to less
biodiverse tree plantations

**Figure 6-41** Major human impacts on the world's forests.

## 6-7 MOUNTAIN BIOMES

**Why Are Mountains Ecologically Important?**
Some of the world's most spectacular and important
environments are mountains, which make up about
20% of the earth's land surface. Mountains are places
where dramatic changes in altitude, climate, soil, and
vegetation take place over a very short distance (Figure 6-22, left). Above a certain altitude, known as the
*snow line,* temperatures are so cold that the mountain
is almost permanently covered by snow and ice
(except in places too steep for snow to stick).

Because of the steep slopes, mountain soils are
especially prone to erosion when the vegetation hold-

ing them in place is removed by **(1)** natural disturbances (such as landslides and avalanches) or **(2)** human activities (such as timber cutting and agriculture).

Many freestanding mountains are *islands of biodiversity* surrounded by a sea of lower elevation landscapes transformed by human activities. Mountains
play a number of important ecological roles by:

■ Containing the majority of the world's forests,
which are habitats for much of the world's terrestrial
biodiversity.

■ Often containing endemic species found nowhere
else on earth.

■ Serving as sanctuaries for animal species driven
from lowland areas.

■ Helping regulate the earth's climate when mountaintops covered with ice and snow reflect solar radiation back into space.

■ Affecting sea levels as a result of decreases or
increases in glacial ice, most of which is locked up in
Antarctica, the most mountainous of all continents.

■ Playing a critical role in the hydrologic cycle (Figure 4-27, p. 83) by gradually releasing melting ice,
snow, and water stored in the soils and vegetation of
mountainsides to small streams.

Despite their ecological, economic, and cultural
importance, the fate of mountain ecosystems has not
been a high priority of governments or many environmental organizations. Mountain ecosystems are coming under increasing pressure from several human
activities (Figure 6-42).

## 6-8 LESSONS FROM GEOGRAPHIC ECOLOGY

In this chapter we examined the connections among
weather, climate, and the distribution of the earth's
biomes. Three general ecological lessons emerge from
this study:

■ Different climates occur as a result of currents of air
and water flowing over an unevenly heated planet
spinning on a tilted axis.

■ Different climates result in different communities
of organisms, or biomes.

■ Everything is connected.

Several more particular lessons are as follows:

■ A general climate map for the earth (Figure 6-7) can
be drawn based on broad patterns of temperature and
precipitation.

Landless poor migrating uphill
to survive

Timber extraction

Mineral resource extraction

Hydroelectric dams and reservoirs

Increasing tourism
(such as hiking and skiing)

Air pollution from industrial and
urban centers

Increased ultraviolet radiation from
ozone depletion

**Figure 6-42** Major human impacts on the world's mountains.

- A general biome map for the earth (Figure 6-20) can be drawn that largely follows the general climate map (Figure 6-7).

- Understanding the general characteristics of each biome leads to a general understanding of **(1)** the range of biodiversity on the earth, **(2)** how this biodiversity is distributed, and **(3)** how all biomes are connected through global climate patterns, energy flow, and chemical cycling (Figure 4-7, p. 69, and Figure 4-16, p. 75).

Scientists have made a good start in understanding important aspects of geographic ecology. However, to further our understanding of ecological connections in time and space we need more studies and accurate maps of **(1)** species distributions, **(2)** changes in climate, **(3)** changes in species distribution, and **(4)** how and where human activities are affecting climate, biomes, and species distribution. Obtaining and analyzing such information is vital in helping us learn how to live more sustainably.

*When we try to pick out anything by itself, we find it hitched to everything else in the universe.*
JOHN MUIR

## REVIEW QUESTIONS

1. Define the boldfaced terms in this chapter.

2. How does wind affect climate, global distribution of nutrients, and pollution?

3. What is *weather?*

4. Distinguish between **(a)** a *warm front* and a *cold front,* **(b)** a *high-pressure* and a *low-pressure* air mass, **(c)** a *tornado* and a *tropical cyclone,* and **(d)** a *hurricane* and a *typhoon.*

5. What is *climate?* What two main factors determine a region's climate?

6. What five factors affect global air circulation? How does each factor affect global air circulation? What causes opposite seasons in the northern and southern hemispheres?

7. How do warm and cool ocean currents form? How do oceans affect regional climates? What would happen to the climate of northwestern Europe if the Gulf Stream did not exist? What is an *upwelling,* and why are upwellings important to life?

8. What is *the El Niño–Southern Oscillation (ENSO)?* How does it affect ocean life and weather in various parts of the world? What is *La Niña,* and how does it affect weather in various parts of the world?

9. What are *greenhouse gases?* List four greenhouse gases. What is the *greenhouse effect,* and how does it affect the earth's climate?

10. What is the *ozone layer?* How does it **(a)** help protect life on the earth and **(b)** affect the earth's climate?

11. What are *microclimates?* What is the *rain shadow effect,* and how can it affect the microclimate on each side of high mountains? Why do urban areas have different microclimates than surrounding areas, and how do these microclimates differ from those of surrounding areas? How do *land breezes* and *sea breezes* affect the microclimates of coastal areas?

12. What is a *biome?* What two factors determine whether an area of the earth's surface is a tropical, temperate, or polar desert, grassland, or forest? How do climate and vegetation vary with latitude and altitude?

13. What are the following types of plants, where is each found, and how does each survive: **(a)** *broadleaf evergreen plants,* **(b)** *broadleaf deciduous plants,* and **(c)** *coniferous evergreen plants.*

14. What is a *desert?* What are the three major types of desert, and how do they differ in climate and biological makeup? How do desert plants and animals survive heat and a lack of water? Why are desert ecosystems vulnerable to disruption. List seven types of human activities that have harmful impacts on deserts.

15. What is *grassland?* What are the three major types of grassland, and how do they differ in climate and biological makeup? Distinguish between *arctic tundra* and *alpine tundra.* Why are grasslands vulnerable to disruption? List four types of human activities that have harmful impacts on grasslands. What is *chaparral,* and what is the importance of fire in this biome?

16. What is a *forest?* What are the three major types of forest, and how do they differ in climate and biological makeup? Distinguish among *tropical rain forests, tropical deciduous forests,* and *temperate rain forests.* List four types of human activities that have harmful impacts on forests.

17. Why are *mountains* ecologically important, and what factors make them vulnerable to ecological disruption? List seven types of human activities that have harmful impacts on mountains.

18. List three general lessons and three specific lessons we can learn from geographic ecology.

## CRITICAL THINKING

1. Why might **(a)** the microclimate of a north-facing slope differ from that of a south-facing slope, **(b)** a ridge top differ from that of a valley bottom, and **(c)** an isolated mountaintop differ from a mountaintop surrounded by other mountains?

2. List a limiting factor for each of the following ecosystems: **(a)** a desert, **(b)** arctic tundra, **(c)** alpine tundra, **(d)** the floor of a tropical rain forest, and **(e)** a temperate deciduous forest.

3. Why do deserts and arctic tundra support a much smaller biomass of animals than do tropical forests?

**4.** Well drilling for water in desert areas has allowed many traditional nomadic tribes to raise more livestock by not having to migrate to find water. Is this desirable or undesirable from **(a)** an ecological standpoint, **(b)** an economic standpoint, and **(c)** a cultural standpoint? Explain.

**5.** Why do you think no amphibians and reptiles live in arctic tundra?

**6.** Some biologists have suggested restoring large herds of bison on public lands in the North American plains as a way of restoring remaining tracts of tall-grass prairie. Ranchers with permits to graze cattle and sheep on federally managed lands have strongly opposed this idea. What do you think about the idea of restoring large numbers of bison to the plains of North America? Explain.

**7.** Why do most animals in a tropical rain forest live in its trees?

**8.** What factors in your lifestyle contribute to the destruction and degradation of some tropical forests?

**9.** What biomes are best suited for **(a)** raising crops and **(b)** grazing livestock?

**10.** How might technologies such as remote sensing and geographic information systems (GIS; Figure 4-32, p. 91) help our understanding of ecology and the environment? Do you think it is worth investing in such expensive technologies to help solve environmental problems, or can we find better ways to spend our money? Explain.

## PROJECTS

**1.** How has the climate changed in the area where you live during the past 50 years? Investigate the beneficial and harmful effects of these changes. How have these changes benefited or harmed you personally?

**2.** What type of biome do you live in? What have been the major effects of human activities over the past 50 years on the characteristic vegetation and animal life normally found in the biome you live in? How is your own lifestyle affecting this biome?

**3.** Use the library or the Internet to find bibliographic information about *Robert H. MacArthur* and *John Muir,* whose quotes appear at the beginning and end of this chapter.

**4.** Make a concept map of this chapter's major ideas, using the section heads and subheads and the key terms (in boldface). Look on the website for this book for information about making concept maps.

## INTERNET STUDY RESOURCES AND RESOURCES FOR FURTHER READING AND RESEARCH

The website for this book contains helpful study aids and many ideas for further reading and research. Log on to

www.info.brookscole.com/miller13

and click on the Chapter-by-Chapter area. Choose Chapter 6 and select a resource:

- Flash Cards allows you to test your mastery of the Terms and Concepts to Remember for this chapter.

- Tutorial Quizzes provides a multiple-choice practice quiz.

- Student Guide to InfoTrac will lead you to Critical Thinking Projects that use InfoTrac College Edition as a research tool.

- References lists the major books and articles consulted in writing this chapter.

- Hypercontents takes you to an extensive list of sites with news, research, and images related to individual sections of the chapter.

## INFOTRAC COLLEGE EDITION

Improve your skills with InfoTrac College Edition, a searchable online database of articles from more than 700 periodicals. Log on to

http://www.infotrac-college.com

or access InfoTrac through the website for this book. Try to find the following articles:

**1.** del Tredici, P. 2001. Sprouting in temperate trees: A morphological and ecological review. *The Botanical Review* 67: 121. *Keywords:* "temperate trees" and "ecology." Sprouting in trees is an adaptation to several stressful conditions. These conditions can include competition, limiting factors, natural disturbance, and human disturbance. This article looks at ways in which trees in temperate forests resprout in response to various types of disturbance.

**2.** Petit, C. W. 2002. Perilous waters: Influx of fresh water in North Atlantic Ocean could disrupt world climate patterns. *U.S. News & World Report* (April 1): 64. *Keywords:* "North Atlantic Ocean" and "climate." Climate change is a major environmental issue in the beginning of the 21st century, but it may not all be due to humans and greenhouse gas emissions. This article looks at the effects of water density on a major ocean current system, and the potential effects on climate of changes in this system.

# 7 AQUATIC ECOLOGY: BIODIVERSITY IN AQUATIC SYSTEMS

## *Why Should We Care About Coral Reefs?*

In the shallow coastal zones of warm tropical and sub-tropical oceans we often find **coral reefs** (Figure 7-1, left). These beautiful natural wonders are among the world's oldest, most diverse, and most productive ecosystems.

Coral reefs are formed by massive colonies of tiny animals called *polyps* that are close relatives of jellyfish. They slowly build reefs by secreting a protective crust of limestone (calcium carbonate) around their soft bodies.

When the corals die, their empty crusts or outer skeletons remain as a platform for more reef growth. The result is an elaborate network of crevices, ledges, and holes that serve as calcium carbonate "condominiums" for a variety of marine animals.

Coral reefs involve a mutually beneficial relationship between the polyps and tiny single-celled algae called *zooxanthellae* ("zoh-ZAN-thel-ee") that live in the tissues of the polyps. The algae provide the polyps with color, food, and oxygen through photosynthesis. The polyps in turn provide a well-protected home for the algae.

Coral reefs provide a number of important ecological and economic services valued conservatively at $375 billion a year. These services include the following:

- Removing some of the carbon dioxide from the atmosphere as part of the carbon cycle (when coral polyps form limestone shells)
- Acting as natural barriers that **(a)** help protect 15% of the world's coastlines from erosion by battering waves and storms and **(b)** allow the ocean to replenish nearby beaches with sand
- Supporting at least one-fourth of all identified marine species and 65% of marine fish species even though such reefs occupy less than 1% of the ocean floor
- Producing roughly 10% of the global fish catch and 25% of the catch in developing countries
- Providing fish and shellfish, jobs, and building materials for some of the world's poorest countries
- Supporting fishing and tourism industries worth billions of dollars each year
- Giving us an underwater world to study and enjoy

More than one-fourth of the world's coral reefs have been lost to coastal development, pollution, overfishing, warmer ocean temperatures, and other stresses that are increasing. One problem is *coral bleaching* (Figure 7-1, right), which occurs when a coral becomes stressed and expels most of its colorful algae. This occurs because of stresses such as increased water temperature and runoff of silt that covers the coral and prevents photosynthesis.

This loss of algae exposes the colorless coral animals and the underlying ghostly white skeleton of calcium carbonate. Unable to grow or repair themselves, the corals eventually die unless the stress is removed and algae recolonize them.

Coral reefs sometimes are called the aquatic equivalent of tropical rain forests because they harbor such a high species biodiversity with myriad ecological interrelationships. The decline and degradation of these colorful oceanic sentinels should serve as a warning about the health of their habitats.

**Figure 7-1** A healthy coral reef covered by colorful algae (left) and a bleached coral reef that has lost most of its algae (right) because of changes in the environment (such as cloudy water or too warm temperatures). With the algae gone, the white limestone of the coral skeleton becomes visible. If the environmental stress is not removed and no other alga species fill the abandoned niche, the corals die. These diverse and productive ecosystems are being damaged and destroyed at an alarming rate.

*If there is magic on this planet, it is contained in water.*

LOREN EISLEY

This chapter addresses the following questions:

- What are the basic types of aquatic life zones, and what factors influence the kinds of life they contain?

- What are the major types of saltwater life zones, and how do human activities affect them?

- What are the major types of freshwater life zones, and how do human activities affect them?

- How can we help sustain aquatic life zones?


## 7-1 AQUATIC ENVIRONMENTS: TYPES AND CHARACTERISTICS

**What Are the Two Major Types of Aquatic Life Zones?** The aquatic equivalents of biomes are called *aquatic life zones.* The major types of organisms found in aquatic environments are determined by the water's *salinity* (the amounts of various salts such as sodium chloride [NaCl] dissolved in a given volume of water). As a result, aquatic life zones are divided into two major types: **(1)** *saltwater* or *marine* (particularly estuaries, coastlines, coral reefs, coastal marshes, mangrove swamps, and oceans) and **(2)** *freshwater* (particularly lakes and ponds, streams and rivers, and inland wetlands). Figure 7-2 shows the distribution of the world's major oceans, lakes, rivers, coral reefs, and mangroves.

**What Are the Main Kinds of Organisms in Aquatic Life Zones?** Saltwater and freshwater life zones contain several major types of organisms:

- **Phytoplankton** ("FIE-toe-plank-ton"), or *plant plankton:* free-floating microscopic cyanobacteria and many types of algae that are the producers supporting most aquatic food chains and food webs (Figure 4-19, p. 78).

- **Zooplankton** ("ZOE-oh-plank-ton"), or *animal plankton:* a mixture of **(1)** nonphotosynthetic primary consumers (herbivores) that feed on phytoplankton and **(2)** secondary consumers that feed on other zooplankton. They range from single-celled protozoa to large invertebrates such as jellyfish.

- **Nekton:** strongly swimming consumers such as fish, turtles, and whales.

- **Benthos:** bottom-dwellers such as **(1)** barnacles and oysters that anchor themselves to one spot, **(2)** worms that burrow into the sand or mud, and **(3)** lobsters and crabs that walk about on the bottom. Some of these species get food by filtering it from water (Spotlight, p. 149).

- **Decomposers:** mostly bacteria that break down the organic compounds in the dead bodies and wastes of aquatic organisms into simple nutrient compounds for use by producers.

**What Are Key Characteristics of Aquatic Organisms and Systems?** Living in an aquatic environment has advantages and disadvantages (Figure 7-3, p. 146). Aquatic systems also

- Have less pronounced and fixed physical boundaries than terrestrial ecosystems. This makes it difficult to count and manage populations of aquatic organisms.

- Have more complex and longer food chains and food webs (Figure 4-19, p. 78) than most terrestrial food chains and webs. One reason is that the fluid medium of water systems and the variety of bottom

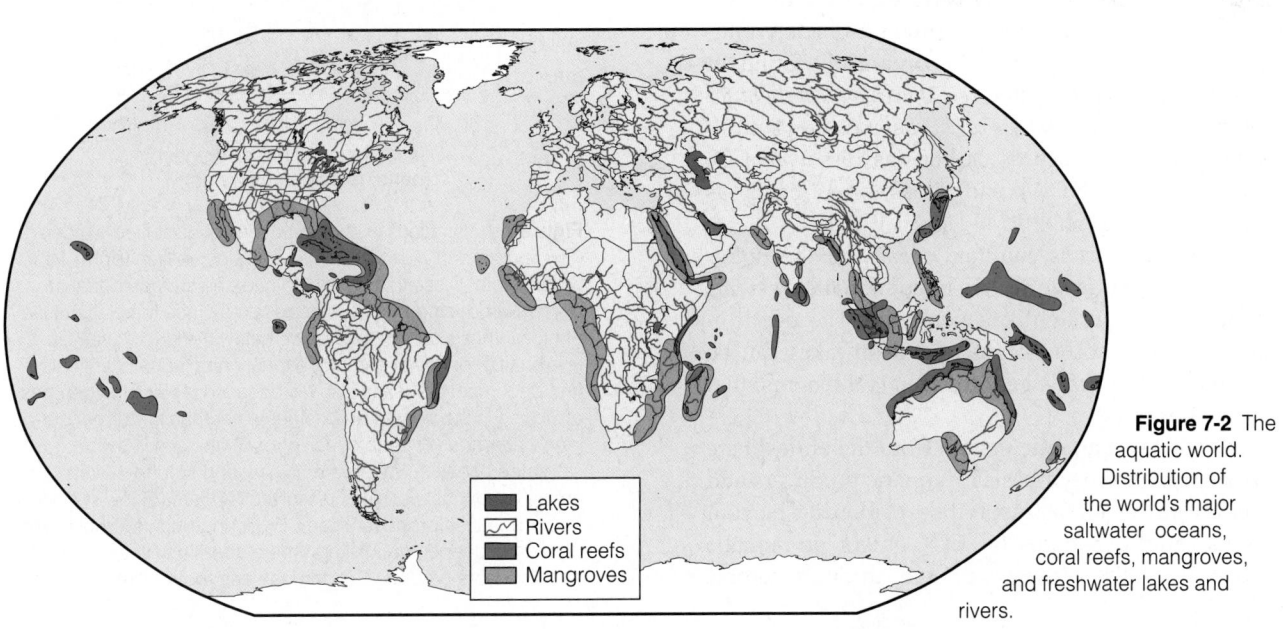

**Figure 7-2** The aquatic world. Distribution of the world's major saltwater oceans, coral reefs, mangroves, and freshwater lakes and rivers.

Lakes
Rivers
Coral reefs
Mangroves

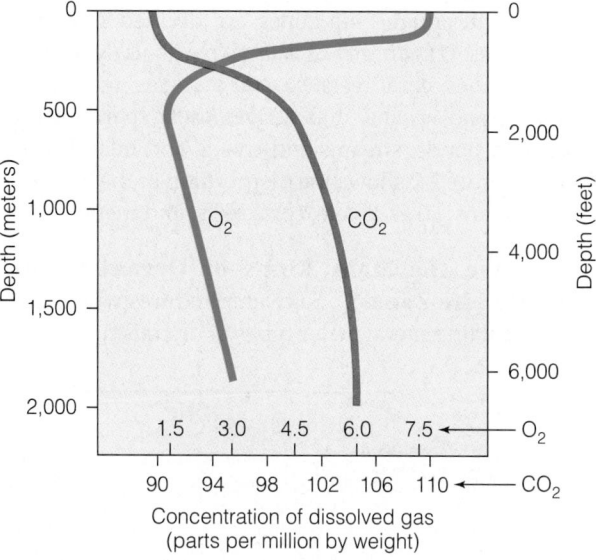

Figure 7-3 Advantages and disadvantages of living in water.

| Advantages | Disadvantages |
| --- | --- |
| Physical support from water bouyancy | Can tolerate a narrow range of temperatures |
| Fairly constant temperature | Exposure to dissolved pollutants |
| Nourishment from dissolved nutrients | Fluctuating population size for many species |
| Water availability | Dispersion separates many aquatic offspring from parents |
| Easy dispersement of organisms, larvae, and eggs | |
| Less exposure to harmful UV radiation | |
| Dilution and dispersion of pollutants | |

habitats open up ways of getting food that are not available on land.

■ Are more difficult to monitor and study (especially marine systems) because of their size and because they are largely hidden from view.

**What Factors Limit Life at Different Depths in Aquatic Life Zones?** Most aquatic life zones can be divided into three layers: **(1)** surface, **(2)** middle, and **(3)** bottom. Important environmental factors determining the types and numbers of organisms found in these layers are **(1)** *temperature,* **(2)** *access to sunlight for photosynthesis,* **(3)** *dissolved oxygen content,* and **(4)** *availability of nutrients* such as carbon (as dissolved $CO_2$ gas), nitrogen (as $NO_3^-$), and phosphorus (mostly as $PO_4^{3-}$) for producers.

Photosynthesis is confined mostly to the upper layer, or **euphotic zone,** of deep aquatic systems through which sunlight can penetrate. The depth of the euphotic zone in oceans and deep lakes can be reduced by excessive algal growth (algal blooms) that make water cloudy.

$O_2$ enters an aquatic system from the atmosphere and through photosynthesis by aquatic producers and is removed by aerobic respiration of producers, consumers, and decomposers. $CO_2$ enters an aquatic system from the atmosphere and through aerobic

respiration by producers, consumers, and decomposers and is removed by photosynthesizing producers. This removal of some of the greenhouse gas $CO_2$ in the atmosphere by aquatic producers helps keep the earth's average atmospheric temperature from rising as a result of the natural greenhouse effect (Figure 6-17, p. 121).

Some dissolved $CO_2$ forms carbonate ions ($CO_3^{2-}$). They are stored mostly as calcium carbonate ($CaCO_3$) for long periods in sediments, minerals, and the shells and skeletons of living aquatic animals as part of the carbon cycle (Figure 4-28, p. 84). The concentration of oxygen in the atmosphere varies little. However, the amount of oxygen dissolved in water can vary widely, depending on factors such as **(1)** temperature, **(2)** number of producers (which add $O_2$), **(3)** number of consumers and aerobic decomposers (which remove $O_2$), and **(4)** deep ocean circulation (which can cause oxygen-saturated surface water in some areas to sink and spread).

Many aquatic organisms, especially fish, die when dissolved oxygen levels fall below 5 ppm. The concentrations of dissolved $O_2$ and $CO_2$ in water vary in different ways with depth (Figure 7-4).

Figure 7-4 Variations in concentrations of dissolved oxygen ($O_2$) and carbon dioxide ($CO_2$) in parts per million (ppm) with water depth. Dissolved $O_2$ is high near the surface because oxygen-producing photosynthesis takes place there. Because photosynthesis cannot take place below the sunlit layer, $O_2$ levels fall because of aerobic respiration by aquatic animals and decomposers. They also fall because **(1)** less oxygen gas dissolves in the deeper and colder water than in warmer surface water and **(2)** deep ocean circulation causes oxygen-saturated ocean surface water to sink and spread in some areas. In contrast, levels of dissolved $CO_2$ are **(1)** low in surface layers because producers use $CO_2$ during photosynthesis and **(2)** high in deeper, dark layers where aquatic animals and decomposers produce $CO_2$ through aerobic respiration.

In shallow waters in streams, ponds, and oceans, ample supplies of nutrients for primary producers are usually available. By contrast, in the open ocean, nitrates, phosphates, iron, and other nutrients often are in short supply and limit net primary productivity (NPP) (Figure 4-25, p. 81). However, NPP is much higher in parts of the open ocean where upwellings (Figure 6-7, p. 116, and Figure 6-13, p. 119) bring such nutrients from the ocean bottom to the surface for use by producers.

Most creatures living on the bottoms of the deep ocean and deep lakes depend on animal and plant plankton that die and fall into deep waters. Because this food is limited, deep-dwelling species tend to reproduce slowly. Thus they are especially vulnerable to depletion from overfishing.

## 7-2 SALTWATER LIFE ZONES

**Why Are the Oceans Important?**  A more accurate name for Earth would be *Ocean* because saltwater oceans cover about 71% of the planet's surface (Figure 7-5). The world's oceans (1) make up 99.5% of the world's habitable volume, (2) contain about 250,000 known species of marine plants and animals, and (3) provide many important ecological and economic services (Figure 7-6).

Despite its ecological and economic importance less than 5% of the earth's global ocean has been explored and mapped with the same level of detail as the surface of the moon and Mars. According to aquatic scientists, the scientific investigation of poorly understood marine and freshwater aquatic systems is a greatly underfunded *research frontier* whose study could result in immense ecological and economic benefits.

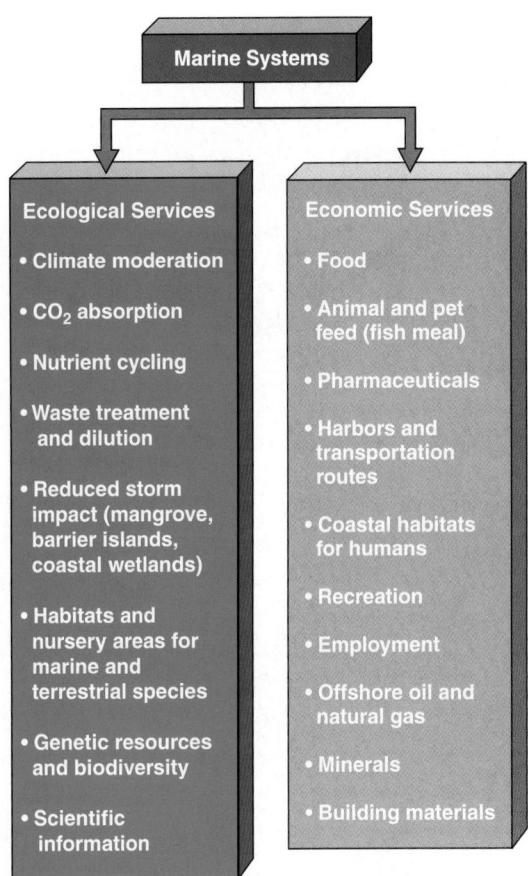

Figure 7-6 Major ecological and economic services provided by marine systems.

**What Is the Coastal Zone?**  Oceans have two major life zones: the *coastal zone* and the *open sea* (Figure 7-7, p. 148). The **coastal zone** is the warm, nutrient-rich, shallow water that extends from the high-tide mark on land to the gently sloping, shallow edge of the *continental shelf* (the submerged part of the continents). This zone has numerous interactions with the land and thus human activities easily affect it.

Although it makes up less than 10% of the world's ocean area, the coastal zone contains 90% of all marine species and is the site of most large commercial marine fisheries. Most ecosystems found in the coastal zone have a very high net primary productivity per unit of area (Figure 4-25, p. 81). This occurs because of the zone's ample supplies of (1) sunlight and (2) plant nutrients (flowing from land and distributed by wind and ocean currents).

**What Are Estuaries and Coastal Wetlands?**  One highly productive area in the coastal zone is an **estuary,** a partially enclosed area of coastal water where seawater mixes with fresh water and nutrients from rivers, streams, and runoff from land (Figure 7-8, p. 148). It is an ecotone (Figure 4-10, p. 71) between

Ocean hemisphere          Land–ocean hemisphere

Figure 7-5 The ocean planet. The salty oceans cover about 71% of the earth's surface. About 97% of the earth's water is in the interconnected oceans, which cover 90% of the planet's mostly ocean southern hemisphere (left) and 50% of its land–ocean northern hemisphere (right).

**Figure 7-7** Major life zones in an ocean (not drawn to scale). Actual depths of zones may vary.

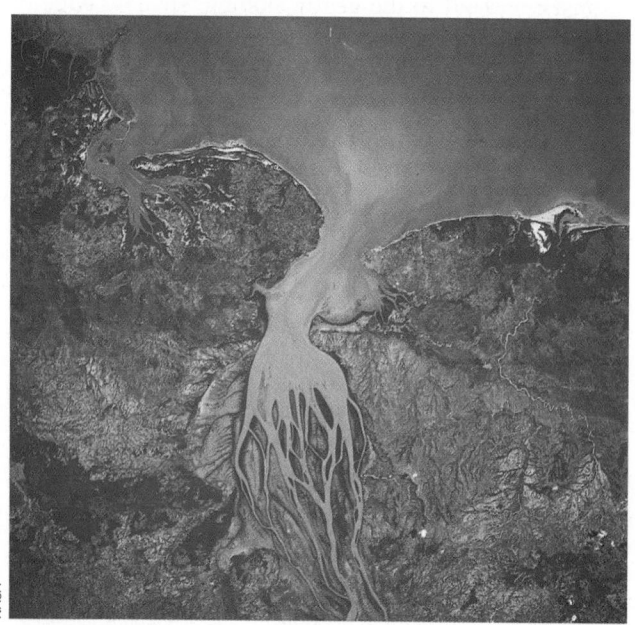

the marine environment and the land where large volumes of fresh water from land and salty ocean water mix.

Estuaries and their associated **coastal wetlands** (land areas covered with water all or part of the year) include **(1)** river mouths, **(2)** inlets, **(3)** bays, **(4)** sounds, **(5)** mangrove forest swamps in tropical waters (Figures 7-2 and 7-9), and **(6)** salt marshes in temperate zones (Figure 7-10 and Figure 7-11, p. 150).

Temperature and salinity levels vary widely in estuaries and coastal wetlands because of **(1)** the daily

**Figure 7-8** View of an *estuary* taken from space. The photo shows the sediment plume at the mouth of Madagascar's Betsiboka River as it flows through the estuary and into the Mozambique Channel. Because of its topography, heavy rainfall, and the clearing of forests for agriculture, Madagascar is the world's most eroded country.

**Figure 7-9** *Mangroves* (Figure 7-2) are important coastal systems that **(1)** protect coastlines and coral reefs (Figure 7-1) and **(2)** provide important habitats for aquatic species. At least 35% of the world's mangroves have been cleared since 1980, mostly for growing crops and raising shrimp in aquaculture ponds.

rhythms of the tides, **(2)** seasonal variations in the flow of fresh water into the estuary, and **(3)** unpredictable flows of fresh water from coastal land and rivers after heavy rains and of salt water from the ocean as a result of storms, hurricanes, and typhoons.

The constant water movement stirs up the nutrient-rich silt, making it available to producers. This explains why estuaries and their associated coastal wetlands are **(1)** some of the earth's most productive ecosystems (Figure 4-25, p. 81) and **(2)** provide other important ecological and economic services (Figure 7-6).

**What Are Rocky and Sandy Shores?** The area of shoreline between low and high tides is called the **intertidal zone**. Organisms living in this stressful zone must be able to avoid being **(1)** swept away or crushed by waves, **(2)** immersed during high tides, and **(3)** left high and dry (and much hotter) at low tides. They must also cope with changing levels of salinity when heavy rains dilute salt water. To deal with such stresses, most intertidal organisms hold on to something, dig in, or hide in protective shells.

The fluctuating tides expose different parts of the intertidal zone to different levels of water, sunlight, and air. This leads to a variety of ecological niches

## Biofiltration

**SPOTLIGHT**

Some aquatic organisms get food by filtering it out of water. Examples of such *filter feeders* are barnacles, clams, oysters, sponges, and baleen whales.

Some species do this by passively sieving the water and others by actively pumping it through their bodies. One of the most efficient biofilter species is the sponge, which is capable of **(1)** pumping an amount of water equal to its own body volume every 10–20 seconds and **(2)** filtering out 99% of the particulate matter.

While feeding themselves, sponges also play an important role in keeping water over coral reefs (Figure 7-1) clean and clear. Most of the water overlying a coral reef could be filtered through its existing sponges in 2–3 days!

Some shellfish such as clams use their muscular foot to burrow down into the sand or mud and then extend input and output tubes, called siphons, up into the water. Water is **(1)** "inhaled" through an incoming siphon, **(2)** filtered for food particles and dissolved oxygen, and **(3)** then "exhaled" through an outgoing siphon.

As huge baleen whales (such as the blue whale) move through the water, tons of speck-sized zooplankton (such as krill) are trapped in large comblike filters, called *baleen*, found in their mouths (Figure 4-19, p. 78). The whales then use their tongues to slurp down the trapped zooplankton.

No equivalent types of filter-feeding organisms exist in terrestrial ecosystems. However, humans have copied nature by developing fishnets to strain food from the water.

### Critical Thinking

Why do some health scientists warn us not to eat raw shellfish such as clams and oysters?

found in fairly clear zones or different-colored bands reflecting the colors of dominant species.

Some coasts have steep *rocky shores* pounded by waves. The numerous pools and other niches in the

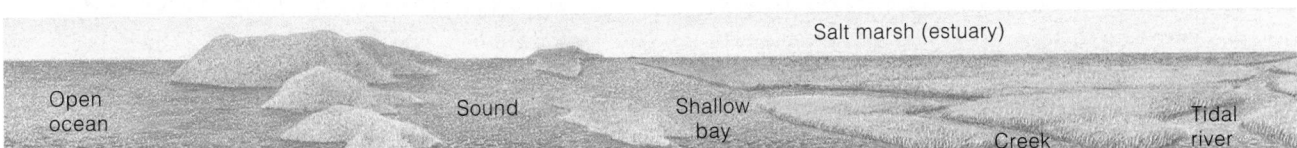

**Figure 7-10** *Salt marsh* of an estuary in a temperate area consists of several connected coastal life zones. (From Cecie Starr, *Biology: Concepts and Applications*, 4th ed., Brooks/Cole [Wadsworth] © 2000)

rocks in the intertidal zone of rocky shores contain a great variety of species (Figure 7-12, top).

Other coasts have gently sloping *barrier beaches,* or *sandy shores,* with niches for different marine organisms, including crabs, lugworms, clams, ghost shrimp, sand dollars, and flounder (Figure 7-12, bottom). Most of them are hidden from view and survive by burrowing, digging, and tunneling in the sand. These sandy beaches and their adjoining coastal wetlands are also home to a variety of shorebirds that

| | | | |
|---|---|---|---|
| Producer to primary consumer | Primary to secondary consumer | Secondary to higher-level consumer | All producers and consumers to decomposers |

**Figure 7-11** Some components and interactions in a *salt marsh ecosystem* in a temperate area such as the United States. When these organisms die, decomposers break down their organic matter into minerals used by plants. Colored arrows indicate transfers of matter and energy between consumers (herbivores), secondary (or higher-level) consumers (carnivores), and decomposers. Organisms are not drawn to scale.

feed in specialized niches on crustaceans, insects, and other organisms (Figure 7-13, p. 152).

One or more rows of natural sand dunes on undisturbed barrier beaches (with the sand held in place by the roots of grasses) serve as the first line of defense against the ravages of the sea (Figure 7-14, p. 152). But when coastal developers remove the protective dunes or build behind the first set of dunes, storms can flood and even sweep away seaside buildings and severely erode the sandy beaches.

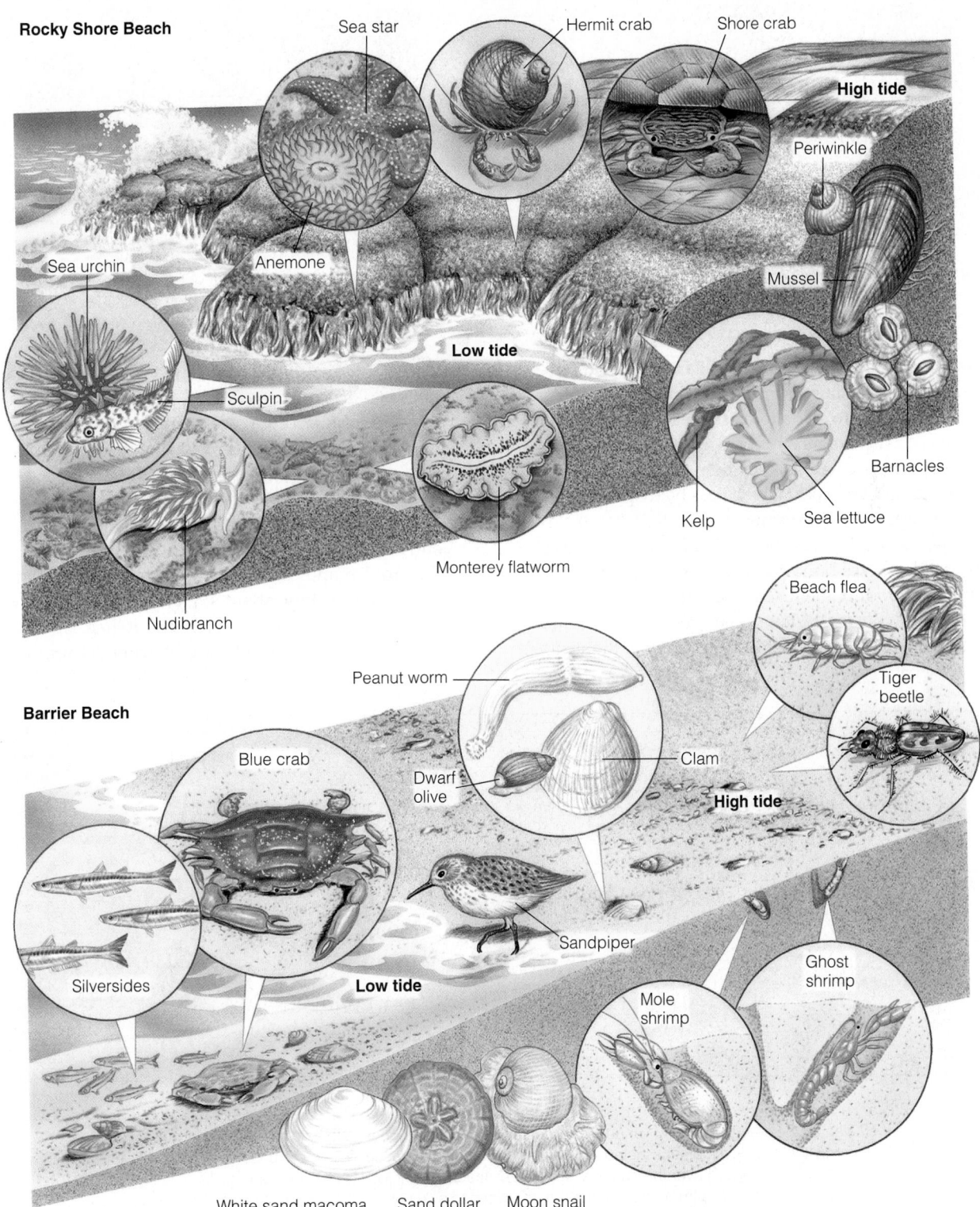

**Figure 7-12** Living between the tides. Some organisms with specialized niches found in various zones on rocky shore beaches (top) and barrier or sandy beaches (bottom). Organisms are not drawn to scale.

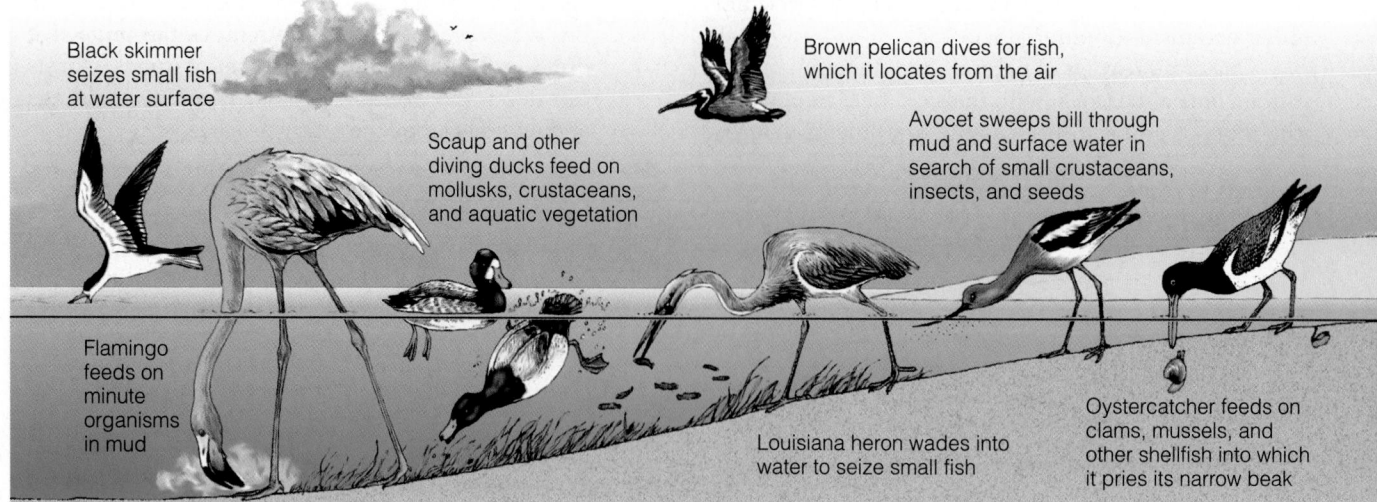

Figure 7-13 Specialized feeding niches of various bird species in a coastal wetland. Such resource partitioning reduces competition and allows sharing of limited resources.

## What Are Barrier Islands?

**Barrier islands** are long, thin, low offshore islands of sediment that generally run parallel to the shore. They are found along some coasts such as most of North America's Atlantic and Gulf coasts. These islands help protect the mainland, estuaries, and coastal wetlands by dispersing the energy of approaching storm waves.

Their low-lying beaches are constantly shifting, with gentle waves building them up and storms flattening and eroding them. Currents running parallel to the beaches constantly take sand from one area and deposit it in another. Sooner or later, many of the structures humans build on low-lying barrier islands (Figure 7-15), such as Atlantic City, New Jersey, and Miami Beach, Florida, are damaged or destroyed by flooding, severe beach erosion, or major storms (including hurricanes).

## What Are Coral Reefs?

Coral reefs (Figures 7-1 and 7-16, p. 154) form in clear, warm coastal waters of the tropics and subtropics (Figure 7-2). Collectively, they occupy only about 0.1% of the world's ocean area—amounting to an area about half the size of France. These beautiful natural wonders are among

Figure 7-14 Primary and secondary dunes on gently sloping sandy beaches play an important role in protecting the land from erosion by the sea. The roots of various grasses that colonize the dunes help hold the sand in place. Ideally, **(1)** construction and development should be allowed only behind the second strip of dunes, and **(2)** walkways to the beach should be built over the dunes to keep them intact. This helps **(1)** preserve barrier beaches and **(2)** protect human structures from being damaged and washed away by wind, high tides, beach erosion, and flooding from storm surges. This type of protection is rare, however, because the short-term economic value of oceanfront land is considered much higher than its long-term ecological and economic values.

Dowitcher probes deeply into mud in search of snails, marine worms, and small crustaceans

Herring gull is a tireless scavenger

Ruddy turnstone searches under shells and pebbles for small invertebrates

Knot (a sandpiper) picks up worms and small crustaceans left by receding tide

Piping plover feeds on insects and tiny crustaceans on sandy beaches

(Birds shown here are not drawn to scale)

the world's oldest, most diverse, and productive ecosystems, and they are homes for about one-fourth of all marine species.

Coral reefs are also ecologically complex in terms of the many interactions among the diverse organisms that live there (Figure 7-16, p. 154). These organisms fall into three main groups: **(1)** attached organisms (such as corals, algae, and sponges) that give the reef its structure, **(2)** fishes, and **(3)** small organisms that bore into, attach to, or hide within a reef's many nooks and crannies.

Coral reefs are vulnerable to damage because they **(1)** grow slowly, **(2)** are disrupted easily, and **(3)** thrive only in clear, warm, and fairly shallow water of constant high salinity. Corals can live only in water with a temperature of 18–30°C (64–86°F), and coral bleaching (Figure 7-1, right) can be triggered by an increase of just 1°C (1.8°F) above the maximum.

**Figure 7-15** A developed barrier island.

Thus the health and survival of coral reefs are closely connected to projected global warming caused by increases in atmospheric concentrations of gases such as $CO_2$. Rising temperatures in tropical oceans also can reduce the levels of calcium needed for reef growth.

The biodiversity of coral reefs can be reduced by natural disturbances such as severe storms, freshwater floods, and invasions of predatory fish. However, throughout their very long geologic history, coral reefs have been able to adapt to such natural environmental changes. Today the biggest threats to the biodiversity of many of the world's coral reefs come from human activities (Figure 7-17, p. 155). Scientists are concerned that these threats are occurring so rapidly (over decades) and over such a wide area that many of the world's coral systems may not have enough time to adapt.

Some 300 coral reefs in 65 countries are protected as reserves or parks, and another 600 have been recommended for protection. The *good news* is that protected coral reefs often can recover (Connections, p. 155). However, protecting reefs is difficult and expensive, and only half of the countries with coral reefs have set aside reserves that receive some protection from human activities.

**What Biological Zones Are Found in the Open Sea?** The sharp increase in water depth at the edge of the continental shelf separates the coastal zone from the vast volume of the ocean called the **open sea.** Based primarily on the penetration of sunlight, it is divided into three vertical zones (Figure 7-7):

- *Euphotic zone:* the lighted upper zone where **(1)** photosynthesis occurs mostly by phytoplankton, **(2)** nutrient levels are low (except around upwellings, Figure 6-13, p. 119), and **(3)** levels of dissolved oxygen are high (Figure 7-4). Large, fast-swimming predatory fish such as swordfish, sharks, and bluefin tuna populate this zone.

- *Bathyal zone:* dimly lit middle zone that does not contain photosynthesizing producers because of a lack of sunlight. Various types of zooplankton and smaller fish, many of which migrate to feed on the surface at night, populate this zone.

- *Abyssal zone:* dark lower zone that is **(1)** very cold, **(2)** has little dissolved oxygen (Figure 7-4), and **(3)** has enough nutrients on the ocean floor to support about 98% of the 250,000 identified species living in the ocean.

Dead and decaying organisms fall to the ocean floor to feed microscopic decomposers and scavengers such as crabs and sea urchins. Some of these organisms (such as many worms) are *deposit feeders,* which take mud into their guts and extract nutrients from it.

Others (such as oysters and mussels) are *filter feeders*, which pass water through or over their bodies and extract nutrients from it (Spotlight, p. 149). On portions of the dark, deep ocean floor near hydrothermal vents, scientists have recently found communities of organisms where specialized bacteria use chemosynthesis to produce their own food and food for other organisms feeding on them.

Average primary productivity and NPP per unit of area are quite low in the open sea (Figure 4-25, p. 81)

| Gray reef shark |
| Green sea turtle |
| Sea nettle |
| Fairy basslet |
| Parrot fish |
| Blue tangs |
| Sergeant major |
| Hard corals |
| Algae |
| Brittle star |
| Banded coral shrimp |
| Phytoplankton |
| Symbiotic algae |
| Coney |
| Zooplankton |
| Blackcap basslet |
| Sponges |
| Bacteria |
| Moray eel |

| Producer to primary consumer | Primary to secondary consumer | Secondary to higher-level consumer | All consumer and producers to decomposers |

**Figure 7-16** Some components and interactions in a *coral reef ecosystem*. When these organisms die, decomposers break down their organic matter into minerals used by plants. Colored arrows indicate transfers of matter and energy between producers, primary consumers (herbivores), secondary (or higher-level) consumers (carnivores), and decomposers. Organisms are not drawn to scale.

Ocean warming

Soil erosion

Algae growth from fertilizer runoff

Mangrove destruction

Coral reef bleaching

Rising sea levels

Increased UV exposure from ozone depletion

Using cyanide and dynamite to harvest coral reef fish

Coral removal for building material, aquariums, and jewelery

Damage from anchors, ships, and tourist divers

**Figure 7-17** Major threats to coral reefs.

except at an occasional equatorial upwelling, where currents bring up nutrients from the ocean bottom. However, because the open sea covers so much of the earth's surface (Figure 7-5), it makes the largest contribution to the earth's overall NPP.

**What Impacts Do Human Activities Have on Marine Systems?** In their desire to live near the coast, people are destroying or degrading the resources that make coastal areas so enjoyable and economically and ecologically valuable. Currently, about 40% of the world's population live along coasts or within 100 kilometers (62 miles) of a coast. Some 13 of the world's 19 megacities with populations of 10 million or more people are in coastal zones. By 2030, at least 6.3 billion people—more than the current global population—are expected to live in or near coastal areas.

Here are some major impacts of human activities on marine systems:

- Salt marshes, mangrove forests, and sea-grass meadows—the sea's three great marine nurseries—are being lost and degraded at a high rate to make way for real estate developments, marinas, golf courses, and shrimp farms.

- Scientists estimate that half the world's original coastal wetlands and 53% of those in the lower 48 U.S. states (91% in California) have disappeared since 1800, mostly by being filled in for agriculture and coastal development. According to scientists, by 2080 half of the world's remaining coastal wetlands is likely to be lost to **(1)** agriculture, **(2)** urban development, and **(3)** rising sea levels from climate change.

- At least 35% of the world's original mangrove forests (Figures 7-2 and 7-9) have disappeared since 1980, mostly because of clearing for **(1)** coastal

---

## Coral Partners May Enhance Reef Survival

**CONNECTIONS**

All of the news about coral reefs is not bad. In 1998, researchers found that in some cases coral bleaching (Figure 7-1, right)—in which coral reefs turn ghostly white—may not be as fatal to reefs as once thought.

Researchers have been puzzled because corals in shallow water in some areas might be healthy, whereas at a slightly greater depth they find extensive bleaching. Marine biologist Rob Rowan studied DNA extracted from coral at different depths and locations and identified up to three different algae species (which he labeled A, B, and C) in the same coral.

He also noticed a pattern in the distribution of these algae species. Two species, which he called A and B, preferred areas on coral with lots of light, and species C was adapted to lower light at greater depths. He hypothesized that coral with species A and B in shallow water may have some resistance to bleaching. In deeper and darker water, species C can grow on top of the corals.

Recent research also suggests that bleaching may allow some types of coral to switch to new algae species more adapted to the changed water conditions.

Additional research indicates that some types of coral which appear dead from bleaching may have a hidden reserve of algae that may

eventually allow the coral to come back to life. But these researchers caution that we still have much to learn about the complex interactions between various types of algae and coral.

More *good news* is the growing evidence that coral reefs can recover when given a chance. When localities or nations have imposed restrictions on reef fishing or reduced inputs of nutrients and other pollutants, reefs have rebounded.

**Critical Thinking**

Does the research described here mean that we do not need to worry so much about protecting coral reefs? Explain.

development, **(2)** rice fields, and **(3)** aquaculture shrimp farms. The percentage of mangrove forest loss exceeds those for tropical rain forests and coral reefs. Much of the remaining mangroves are threatened. The clearing of mangroves also causes erosion that kills coral reefs by smothering the corals in plumes of soil.

■ According to a World Wildlife Fund study, almost 70% of the world's beaches are eroding rapidly because of coastal developments and a rising sea level (caused mostly by global warming).

■ Ocean bottom habitats are being degraded and destroyed by dredging operations and trawler boats, which drag huge nets weighted down with chains over ocean bottoms to harvest bottom fish and shell-fish (Figure 7-18).

■ According to a 2000 report from the Global Coral Reef Monitoring Network, **(1)** about 27% of the world's coral reefs have been severely damaged (up from 10% in 1992), **(2)** 11% have been destroyed, and **(3)** another 70% could be gone by 2050. In addition to the biodiversity losses, such a collapse would **(1)** sharply reduce fish harvests and **(2)** greatly increase storm damage on the coasts of tropical and warm temperate areas.

## 7-3 FRESHWATER LIFE ZONES

**What Are Freshwater Life Zones?** **Freshwater life zones** occur where water with a dissolved salt concentration of less than 1% by volume accumulates on or flows through the surfaces of terrestrial biomes. Examples are **(1)** *standing* (lentic) bodies of fresh water such as lakes, ponds, and inland wetlands and **(2)** *flowing* (lotic) systems such as streams and rivers. Although freshwater systems cover less than 1% of the earth's surface (Figure 7-2), they provide a number of important ecological and economic services (Figure 7-19).

Runoff from nearby land provides freshwater life zones with an almost constant input of organic material, inorganic nutrients, and pollutants. Thus these life zones are closely connected to nearby terrestrial biomes.

**What Life Zones Are Found in Freshwater Lakes?** **Lakes** are large natural bodies of standing fresh water formed when precipitation, runoff, or groundwater seepage fills depressions in the earth's surface. Causes of such depressions include **(1)** glaciation (the Great Lakes of North America), **(2)** crustal displacement (Lake Nyasa in East Africa), and **(3)** volcanic activity (Crater Lake in Oregon; see photo on p. iii). Rainfall, melting snow, and streams that drain the surrounding watershed feed lakes.

Because ponds (Figure 4-11, p. 72) are shallow, sunlight often penetrates to the bottom so ponds usually have only one zone. In contrast, lakes normally consist of four distinct zones that are defined by their depth and distance from shore (Figure 7-20, p. 158):

■ *Littoral zone* ("LIT-tore-el"): consists of the shallow sunlit waters near the shore to the depth at which rooted plants stop growing. It has a high biological diversity.

■ *Limnetic zone* ("limb-NET-ic"): the open, sunlit water surface layer away from the shore that extends to the depth penetrated by sunlight. As the main photosynthetic body of the lake, it produces the food and oxygen that support most of the lake's consumers.

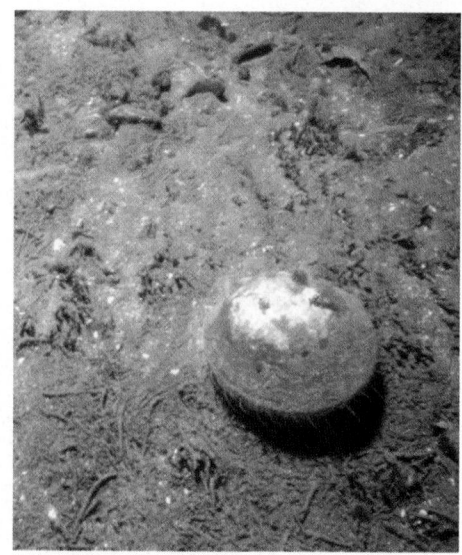

**Figure 7-18** Area of ocean bottom before (left) and after (right) a trawler net scraped it like a gigantic plow. These ocean floor communities can take decades or centuries to recover. According to marine scientist Elliot Norse, "Bottom trawling is probably the largest human-caused disturbance to the biosphere." Trawler fishers disagree and claim that ocean bottom life recovers after trawling. (Peter J. Auster, National Undersea Research Center)

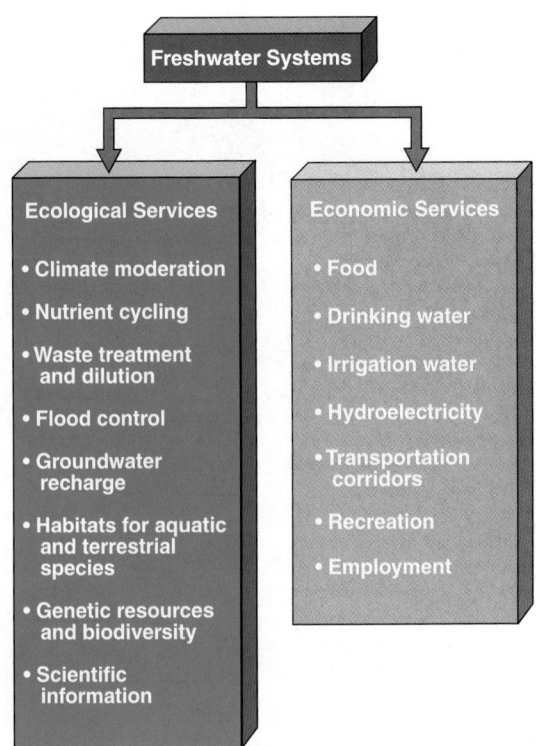

**Figure 7-19** Major ecological and economic services provided by freshwater systems.

■ *Profundal zone* ("pro-FUN-dahl"): the deep, open water where it is too dark for photosynthesis. Without sunlight and plants, oxygen levels are low. Fish adapted to its cooler and darker water are found in this zone.

■ *Benthic zone* ("BEN-thick"): at the bottom of the lake. It is inhabited mostly by organisms that tolerate cool temperatures and low oxygen levels.

**How Do Plant Nutrients Affect Lakes?** Ecologists classify lakes according to their nutrient content and primary productivity. A newly formed lake generally has a small supply of plant nutrients and is called an **oligotrophic** (poorly nourished) **lake** (Figure 7-21, left, p. 158). This type of lake is often deep, with steep banks. Because of its low NPP, such a lake usually has **(1)** crystal-clear blue or green water and **(2)** small populations of phytoplankton and fish (such as smallmouth bass and trout).

Over time, sediment washes into an oligotrophic lake, and plants grow and decompose to form bottom sediments. A lake with a large or excessive supply of nutrients (mostly nitrates and phosphates) needed by producers is called a **eutrophic** (well-nourished) **lake** (Figure 7-21, right, p. 158). Such lakes typically are shallow and have murky brown or green water with very poor visibility. Because of their high levels of nutrients, these lakes have a high NPP.

In warm months the bottom layer of a eutrophic lake often is depleted of dissolved oxygen. Human inputs of nutrients from the atmosphere and from nearby urban and agricultural areas can accelerate the eutrophication of lakes, a process called *cultural eutrophication.* Many lakes fall somewhere between the two extremes of nutrient enrichment and are called **mesotrophic lakes.**

**What Seasonal Changes Occur in Temperate Lakes?** Most substances become denser as they go from gaseous to liquid to solid physical states. Water does not follow this typical behavior; it is densest as a liquid at 4°C (39°F). In other words, solid ice at 0°C (32°F) is less dense than liquid water at 4°C (39°F), which is why ice floats on water.

This unusual property of water causes *thermal stratification* of deep lakes in temperate areas (Figure 7-22, p. 159). During the summer these lakes have the following three distinct layers characterized by different temperatures:

■ *Epilimnion* ("ep-eh-LIM-knee-on"): an upper layer of warm water with high levels of dissolved oxygen.

■ *Thermocline* ("THUR-moe-cline"): where the water temperature changes rapidly with depth and with moderate levels of dissolved oxygen.

■ *Hypolimnion* ("high-poe-LIM-knee-on"): a lower layer of colder, denser water, usually with a lower concentration of dissolved oxygen because it is not exposed to the atmosphere. During the summer the thermocline acts as a barrier preventing the transfer of nutrients and dissolved oxygen between the epilimnion and hypolimnion.

In the fall, the surface water gradually cools, becomes denser, and sinks to the bottom when it cools to 4°C (39°F), and the thermocline disappears (Figure 7-22, top right). This mixing, or *fall overturn,* **(1)** brings nutrients from bottom sediments to the surface, **(2)** brings dissolved oxygen from the surface to the bottom, and **(3)** allows fish to live at various depths.

During the winter the colder temperatures cause the lake to separate into layers of different density (Figure 7-22, bottom left). In the spring, the lake's surface water reaches maximum density when it warms to 4°C (39°F) and sinks through and below the cooler, less dense water. Winds blowing across the lake's surface cause strong vertical currents that mix the surface and bottom water. This brings dissolved oxygen from the surface to the bottom and nutrients from the bottom to the surface. During this brief *spring overturn,* the temperature of the lake and dissolved oxygen levels are roughly the same at all depths (Figure 7-22, bottom right).

**Figure 7-20** The distinct zones of life in a fairly deep temperate zone lake.

**Figure 7-21** An *oligotrophic,* or nutrient-poor, lake (left) and a *eutrophic,* or nutrient-rich, lake (right). Mesotrophic lakes fall between these two extremes of nutrient enrichment. Nutrient inputs from human activities can accelerate eutrophication.

**What Are the Major Characteristics of Freshwater Streams and Rivers?** Precipitation that does not sink into the ground or evaporate is **surface water**. It becomes **runoff** when it flows into streams. The land area that delivers runoff, sediment, and dissolved substances to a stream is called a **watershed,** or **drainage basin.** Small streams join to form rivers, and rivers flow downhill to the ocean (Figures 7-2 and 7-23, p. 160) as part of the hydrologic cycle (Figure 4-27, p. 83).

In many areas, streams begin in mountainous or hilly areas that collect and release water falling to the earth's surface as rain or snow. The downward flow of surface water and groundwater from mountain highlands to the sea takes place in three different aquatic life zones with different environmental conditions: the **(1)** *source zone*, **(2)** *transition zone*, and **(3)** *floodplain zone* (Figure 7-23, p. 160).

In the first, narrow *source zone* (Figure 7-23, top), headwater or mountain highland streams of cold, clear water rush over waterfalls and rapids. As this turbulent water flows and tumbles downward, it dissolves large amounts of oxygen from the air so photosynthesis is a less important source of oxygen than it is in ponds and lakes. Here plants such as algae and mosses are attached to rocks and the zone is populated by cold-water fish (such as trout in some areas), which need lots of dissolved oxygen. Many fish and other animals in headwater streams have compact and flattened bodies that allow them to live under stones.

In the *transition zone* (Figure 7-23, middle), the headwater streams merge to form wider, deeper streams that flow down gentler slopes with fewer obstacles. The warmer water and other conditions in this zone support more producers (phytoplankton) and a variety of cool-water and warm-water fish species (such as black bass) with slightly lower oxygen requirements. Figure 7-24 (p. 161) shows some species and interactions in the transition zone of a river in a tropical forest.

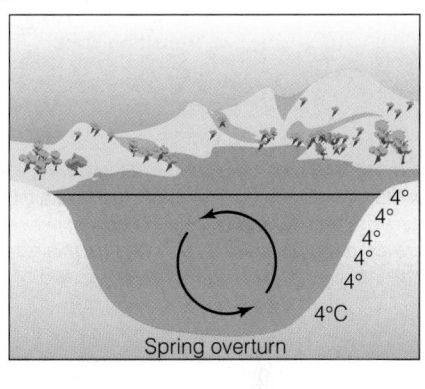

Dissolved O$_2$ concentration ▮ High ▮ Medium ☐ Low

**Figure 7-22** During the summer and winter, the water in deep temperate zone lakes becomes stratified into different temperature layers, which do not mix. Twice a year, in the fall and spring, the waters at all layers of these lakes mix in overturns that equalize the temperature at all depths. These overturns bring **(1)** oxygen from the surface water to the lake bottom and **(2)** nutrients from the lake bottom to the surface waters.

In the *floodplain zone* (Figure 7-23, bottom), streams join into wider and deeper rivers that meander across broad, flat valleys. Water in this zone usually has higher temperatures and less dissolved oxygen than water in the first two zones. These slow-moving rivers sometimes support fairly large populations of producers such as algae and cyanobacteria and rooted aquatic plants along the shores. Because of increased erosion and runoff over a larger area, water in this zone often is muddy and contains high concentrations of suspended particulate matter (silt). The main channels of these slow-moving, wide, and murky rivers support distinctive varieties of fish (carp and catfish), whereas their backwaters support species similar to those present in lakes. At its mouth, a river may divide into many channels as it flows through coastal wetlands and estuaries, where the river water mixes with ocean water (Figure 7-8).

As streams flow downhill, they become powerful shapers of land. Over millions of years the friction of

**Figure 7-23** The three zones in the downhill flow of water: **(1)** *source zone* containing mountain (headwater) streams, **(2)** *transition zone* containing wider, lower-elevation streams, and **(3)** *floodplain zone* containing rivers, which empty into the ocean.

Labels in figure: Rain and snow, Lake, Glacier, Rapids, Waterfall, Tributary, Flood plain, Oxbow lake, Salt marsh, Delta, Deposited sediment, Ocean, Water, Sediment, **Source Zone**, **Transition Zone**, **Floodplain Zone**

moving water levels mountains and cuts deep canyons, and the rock and soil the water removes are deposited as sediment in low-lying areas.

Streams are fairly open ecosystems that receive many of their nutrients from bordering land ecosystems. Such nutrient inputs come from falling leaves, animal feces, insects, and other forms of biomass washed into streams during heavy rainstorms or by melting snow. To protect a stream or river system from excessive inputs of nutrients and pollutants, we must protect its watershed, the land around it.

**What Are Freshwater Inland Wetlands?** Inland wetlands are lands covered with fresh water all or part of the time (excluding lakes, reservoirs, and streams) and located away from coastal areas (Figure 7-25, p. 162). They include **(1)** *marshes* with few trees (Figure 7-25, bottom), **(2)** *swamps* dominated by trees and shrubs (Figure 7-25, middle), **(3)** *prairie potholes,* which are depressions carved out by glaciers (Figure 7-25, top), **(4)** *floodplains,* which receive excess water during heavy rains and floods (Figure 7-23, bottom), **(5)** *bogs* and *fens* that have waterlogged soils, which tend to accumulate peat, and may or may not have trees, and **(6)** *wet arctic tundra* in summer.

Some of these wetlands are covered with water year round. Others, called *seasonal wetlands,* usually are underwater or soggy for only a short time each year. They include prairie potholes (Figure 7-25, top), flood-

plain wetlands, and bottomland hardwood swamps. Some stay dry for years before being covered with water again. In such cases, scientists must use the composition of the soil or the presence of certain plants (such as cattails, bulrushes, or red maples) to determine that a particular area is really a wetland.

Inland wetlands need to be protected because of the important ecological and economic roles they play (Figure 7-19). For example, according to conservative estimates by the Audubon Society, inland wetlands in the United States provide **(1)** water quality protection worth at least $1.6 billion per year and **(2)** flood control worth $7.7–31 billion per year.

**What Are the Impacts of Human Activities on Freshwater Systems?** Here are some major impacts of human activities on freshwater systems:

■ According to a 2000 study by the World Resources Institute, almost 60% of the world's 237 large rivers are strongly or moderately fragmented by dams, diversions, or canals. This alters and destroys wildlife habitats along rivers and in coastal deltas and estuaries by reducing water flow.

■ Flood control levees and dikes built along rivers **(1)** alter and destroy aquatic habitats, **(2)** disconnect rivers from their floodplains, and **(3)** eliminate wetlands and backwaters that are important spawning grounds for fish.

| | Producer to primary consumer | | Producer to secondary consumer | | Secondary to higher-level consumer | | All producers and consumers to decomposers |
|---|---|---|---|---|---|---|---|

**Figure 7-24** Some components and interactions in a river in a tropical forest. When these organisms die, decomposers break down their organic matter into minerals used by plants. Colored arrows indicate transfers of matter and energy between producers, primary consumers (herbivores), secondary (or higher-level) consumers, and decomposers. Organisms are not drawn to scale.

■ In the United States, 53% of the inland wetlands estimated to have existed in the lower 48 states during the 1600s have been drained or filled to grow crops (about 80% of wetland loss) or have been covered up with concrete, asphalt, and buildings. This has been an important factor in increased flood and drought damage in the United States. Many other countries have suffered similar losses.

## 7-4 SUSTAINABILITY OF AQUATIC LIFE ZONES

**How Sustainable Are Aquatic Ecosystems?** The *bad news* in terms of human impacts is that each stream, river, and lake reflects the sum of all that occurs in their watersheds. Also, many of the nutrients, wastes, and pollutants produced by human activities end up in the

Prairie Pothole

Cypress swamp

Freshwater marsh

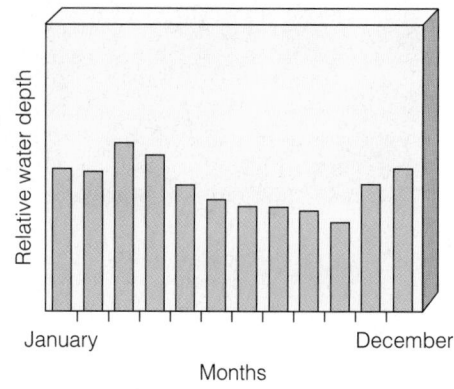

**Figure 7-25** Inland wetlands are not always wet. The graphs show the fluctuating water levels of three types of inland wetlands. (Data from Jon A. Kusler, William J. Mitsch, and Joseph S. Larson, 1994)

ocean. Recent research also shows that many of the chemicals reaching aquatic systems come from the atmosphere.

The *good news* is that aquatic life zones are constantly renewed because **(1)** water is purified by natural hydrologic processes (Figure 4-27, p. 83), **(2)** nutrients cycle in and out, and **(3)** populations of biological organisms can be replenished, given sufficient opportunity and time. However, these life-sustaining processes work only if they are not **(1)** overloaded with pollutants and excessive nutrients and **(2)** overfished.

Scientists have made a start in understanding important aspects of the ecology of the aquatic systems discussed in this chapter and of terrestrial systems (see Chapter 6). One of the main lessons from such research is that in nature *everything is connected.* Most aquatic life zones are connected by flows of water and nutrients from one type to another. In addition, nutrients and pollutants flowing from the land and deposited from the atmosphere affect the ecological processes of aquatic systems.

According to scientists, we urgently need more research on how the world's terrestrial and aquatic systems work. With such information we will have a clearer picture of **(1)** the impacts of our activities on the earth's biodiversity and **(2)** what we can do to live more sustainably.

*All at last returns to the sea—to Oceanus, the ocean river, like the ever-flowing stream of time, the beginning and the end.*

RACHEL CARSON

## REVIEW QUESTIONS

**1.** Define the boldfaced terms in this chapter.

**2.** What are *coral reefs* and *coral polyps?* How are coral reefs formed? List seven ecological and economic services that coral reefs provide. What is *coral bleaching,* and what are its main causes?

**3.** What are the two major types of aquatic life zones?

**4.** Distinguish among *phytoplankton, zooplankton, nekton, benthos,* and *decomposers* found in saltwater and freshwater life zones.

**5.** Describe major advantages and disadvantages of living in an aquatic environment.

**6.** List four major factors determining the types and numbers of organisms found in the surface, middle, and bottom layers of aquatic systems. How do the concentrations of carbon dioxide and dissolved oxygen vary in these three layers? What is the *euphotic zone?*

**7.** List the major ecological and economic services provided by the world's marine systems.

**8.** What is the *coastal zone?* Distinguish among *estuaries, coastal wetlands,* and *mangroves.* List three reasons why

temperature and salinity vary widely in estuaries and coastal wetlands, and explain why they have such a high NPP.

**9.** What is the *intertidal zone?* Distinguish between *rocky shores* and *sandy beaches,* and describe the major types of aquatic life found in each. Why is it important to preserve the dunes on barrier beaches?

**10.** What are *barrier islands?* Why are they so attractive for human development, and why are human structures built there so vulnerable to destruction?

**11.** What are the three main groups of organisms found in coral reefs? List three reasons why coral reefs are vulnerable to damage. List 10 harmful impacts of human activities on coral reefs. Describe recent frontier research indicating that coral bleaching may not be as fatal to reefs as we once thought.

**12.** What is the *open sea,* and what are its three major zones? Why is the NPP per unit of area so low in the open sea?

**13.** List six major harmful human impacts on coastal zones.

**14.** What is a *freshwater life zone,* and what are the two major types of such zones?

**15.** List the major ecological and economic services provided by freshwater systems.

**16.** What is a *lake?* Distinguish among the *littoral, limnetic, profundal,* and *benthic zones* of a lake.

**17.** What are the three types of lakes, based on their nutrient content and primary productivity?

**18.** Describe the seasonal changes that can take place in deep lakes in northern temperate areas. What three layers are found in such lakes during the summer? What happens to these layers and to levels of dissolved oxygen and nutrients in such lakes during the fall, winter, and spring?

**19.** Distinguish among *surface water, runoff,* and a *watershed.* Describe the properties and general forms of life found in the three zones of a river as it flows from mountain highlands to the sea.

**20.** What are *inland wetlands?* List six examples of such wetlands. What are *seasonal inland wetlands?*

**21.** List three major harmful human impacts on freshwater systems.

**22.** Summarize *bad* and *good* news about the sustainability of aquatic systems.

**23.** Explain why a study of terrestrial and aquatic systems reinforces the basic ecological principle that *everything is connected.*

## CRITICAL THINKING

**1.** List a limiting factor for each of the following: **(a)** the surface layer of a tropical lake, **(b)** the surface layer of the open sea, **(c)** an alpine stream, **(d)** a large, muddy river, **(e)** the bottom of a deep lake.

2. Why do terrestrial organisms evolve tolerances to broader temperature ranges than aquatic organisms? Why do aquatic plants tend to be very small (e.g., phytoplankton), whereas most terrestrial plants tend to be larger (e.g., trees) and have more specialized structures for growth (e.g., stems and leaves)? Why are some aquatic animals (especially marine mammals) extremely large compared with terrestrial animals?

3. How would you respond to someone who proposes that we use the deep portions of the world's oceans to deposit our radioactive and other hazardous wastes because the deep oceans are vast and are located far away from human habitats? Give reasons for your response.

4. What factors in your lifestyle contribute to the destruction and degradation of coastal and inland wetlands?

5. Someone tries to sell you several brightly colored pieces of dry coral. Explain in biological terms why this transaction is probably fraudulent.

6. Developers want to drain a large area of inland wetlands in your community and build a large housing development. List **(a)** the main arguments the developers would use to support this project and **(b)** the main arguments ecologists would use in opposing this project. If you were an elected city official, would you vote for or against this project? Can you come up with a compromise plan?

7. You are a defense attorney arguing in court for sparing an undeveloped old-growth tropical rain forest and a coral reef from severe degradation or destruction by development. Write your closing statement for the defense of each of these ecosystems. If the judge decides you can save only one of the ecosystems, which one would you choose, and why?

## PROJECTS

1. Search for information about mangrove trees, using the Internet and library. Are the different species of mangrove trees closely related? What characteristics do they have in common? What characteristics do they have that make them a good place for fish to breed?

2. If possible, visit a nearby lake, pond, or reservoir. Would you classify it as oligotrophic, mesotrophic, or eutrophic? What are the primary factors contributing to its nutrient enrichment? Which of these factors are related to human activities?

3. Examine a topographic map for the area around a stream or lake near where you live to define the watershed for the stream. What human activities occur in the watershed? What influence, if any, do you expect these activities to have on the ecology of the stream or lake?

4. Use the library or the Internet to find bibliographic information about *Loren Eisley* and *Rachel Carson,* whose quotes appear at the beginning and end of this chapter.

5. Make a concept map of this chapter's major ideas, using the section heads and subheads and the key terms

(in boldface). Look on the website for this book for information about making concept maps.

## INTERNET STUDY RESOURCES AND RESOURCES FOR FURTHER READING AND RESEARCH

The website for this book contains helpful study aids and many ideas for further reading and research. Log on to

http://www.info.brookscole.com/miller13

and click on the Chapter-by-Chapter area. Choose Chapter 7 and select a resource:

- Flash Cards allows you to test your mastery of the Terms and Concepts to Remember for this chapter.

- Tutorial Quizzes provides a multiple-choice practice quiz.

- Student Guide to InfoTrac will lead you to Critical Thinking Projects that use InfoTrac College Edition as a research tool.

- References lists the major books and articles consulted in writing this chapter.

- Hypercontents takes you to an extensive list of sites with news, research, and images related to individual sections of the chapter.

## INFOTRAC COLLEGE EDITION

Improve your skills with InfoTrac College Edition, a searchable online database of articles from more than 700 periodicals. Log on to

http://www.infotrac-college.com

or access InfoTrac through the website for this book. Try to find the following articles:

1. Taylor, P. 2001. Phantoms of the deep—What are stingrays doing in a freshwater Florida spring? The answer is found in these ocean creatures' unusual adaptations. *National Wildlife* (August–September). *Keywords:* "freshwater stingrays." In Florida's St. Johns River, there is a large population of what is usually considered a saltwater species: the Atlantic stingray. This article looks at the ways in which these fish make the transition from a saltwater to a freshwater environment.

2. Valiela, I, J. L. Bowen, and J. K. York. 2001. Mangrove forests: One of the world's threatened major tropical environments. *BioScience* 51: 807. *Keywords:* "mangrove" and "deforestation." The loss of mangrove forests has not received the type of media attention that has characterized human activities in other ecosystems. However, the coastal mangrove forests of tropical and subtropical areas support a wide array of important ecological functions.

# 8 COMMUNITY ECOLOGY: STRUCTURE, SPECIES INTERACTIONS, SUCCESSION, AND SUSTAINABILITY

## Flying Foxes: Keystone Species in Tropical Forests

The durian (Figure 8-1, top right) is one of the most prized fruits growing in Southeast Asian tropical forests. The odor of this football-sized fruit is so strong, it is illegal to have them on trains and in many hotel rooms in Southeast Asia. However, its custard-like flesh has been described as "exquisite," "sensual," "intoxicating," and "the world's finest fruit."

Durian fruits come from a wild tree that grows in the tropical rain forest. The tree depends on nectar- and pollen-feeding various species of bats called flying foxes (Figure 8-1, left and bottom right) to pollinate the flowers that hang high in the durian trees. Pollination by flying foxes is an example of *mutualism:* an interaction between two species in which both species benefit. Hundreds of tropical plant species depend entirely on various flying fox species for pollination and seed dispersal.

Many species of flying foxes are listed as *endangered,* and most populations are much smaller than historic numbers. One reason for these population declines is *deforestation.* Another is *hunting* of these bat species for their meat, which is sold in China and other parts of Asia. The bats also are viewed as pests and are killed to keep them from eating commercially grown fruits (even though these fruits are picked green). Flying foxes are easy to hunt because they tend to congregate in large numbers when they feed or sleep.

According to ecologists, flying foxes are *keystone species* in tropical forest ecosystems. They are important for **(1)** the plant species they pollinate, **(2)** the plant seeds they disperse in their droppings (which help maintain forest biodiversity and regenerate deforested areas), and **(3)** the many other species that depend on them.

Rain forest ecologists are concerned that the decline of flying fox populations could lead to a cascade of linked extinctions. Their decline also has important economic effects. Studies have shown that flying foxes are economically important for many products including **(1)** fruits (such as the durian and wild bananas), **(2)** other foods, **(3)** medicine, **(4)** timber (such as ebony and mahogany), **(5)** fibers, **(6)** dyes, **(7)** medicines, **(8)** animal fodder, and **(9)** fuel.

The story of flying foxes and durians illustrates **(1)** the unique role (niche) of each species in a community or ecosystem and **(2)** how interactions between species can affect ecosystem structure and function. This chapter discusses these topics and the subjects of *community structure, ecological succession,* and *ecosystem sustainability.*

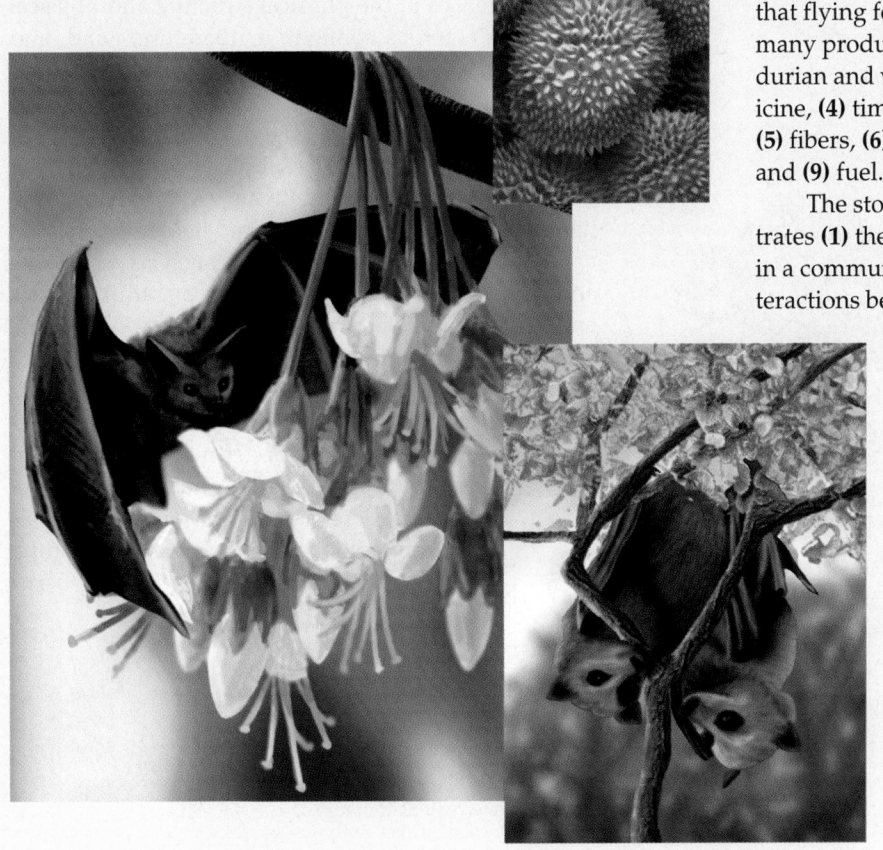

**Figure 8-1** Flying foxes (left and bottom right) are bats that play key ecological roles in tropical rain forests in Southeast Asia by pollinating (left) and spreading the seeds of durian trees that produce durians, a highly prized tropical fruit (top right).

*What is this balance of nature that ecologists talk about?*
STUART L. PIMM

This chapter addresses the following questions:

- What determines the number of species in a community?

- How can we classify species according to their roles?

- How do species interact with one another?

- How do communities and ecosystems change as environmental conditions change?

- Does high species diversity increase the stability of ecosystems?

## 8-1 COMMUNITY STRUCTURE: APPEARANCE AND SPECIES DIVERSITY

**What Is Community Structure?** One property of a community or ecosystem is the *structure* or *spatial distribution* of its individuals and populations. Ecologists usually describe the structure of a community or ecosystem in terms of four characteristics:

- *Physical appearance:* relative sizes, stratification, and distribution of its populations and species

- *Species diversity or richness:* the number of different species

- *Species abundance:* the number of individuals of each species

- *Niche structure:* the number of ecological niches (Section 5-3, p. 103), how they resemble or differ from each other, and how they interact (species interactions)

**How Do Communities Differ in Physical Appearance and Population Distribution?** The types, relative sizes, and stratification of plants and animals vary in different terrestrial communities and biomes (Figure 8-2). Marked differences are also apparent in the physical structures of different types of aquatic life zones such as (1) oceans (Figure 7-7, p. 148), (2) rocky shores and sandy beaches (Figure 7-12, p. 151), (3) lakes (Figure 7-20, p. 158), (4) river systems (Figure 7-23, p. 160), and (5) inland wetlands (Figure 7-25, p. 162).

The physical structure within a particular type of community or ecosystem also can vary. A close look at most large terrestrial communities, ecosystems, and biomes reveals that they usually consist of a mosaic of *vegetation patches* of differing size. This leads to a combination of (1) fairly sharp edges or boundaries such as that between a forest and an open field and (2) wider and more diffuse *ecotones*, or transition zones, between one patch or community and another (Figure 4-10, p. 71).

Differences in the physical structure and physical properties (such as sunlight, temperature, wind, and humidity) at boundaries and in transition zones between two ecosystems (*ecotones*) are called **edge effects.** For example, the edge area between a forest and an open field may (1) be sunnier, warmer, and drier than the forest interior and (2) have a different combination of species than the forest and field interiors.

Popular wild game animals, such as pheasants and white-tailed deer, often are more plentiful in edges and ecotones between forests and fields. Wild game managers sometimes create patches and edges to increase populations of such species for sport hunters.

However, increased edge area from habitat fragmentation (1) makes many species more vulnerable to stresses such as predators and fire and (2) creates barriers that can prevent some species from colonizing new areas and finding food and mates.

**Figure 8-2** Generalized types, relative sizes, and stratification of plant species in various terrestrial communities or ecosystems.

**Where Is Most of the World's Biodiversity Found?** Studies indicate that the most species-rich environments are **(1)** tropical rain forests (Figure 6-35, p. 136), **(2)** coral reefs (Figure 7-1, p. 144, and Figure 7-16, p. 154), **(3)** the deep sea, and **(4)** large tropical lakes.

Communities such as a tropical rain forest or a coral reef with a large number of different species (high species diversity) generally have only a few members of each species (low species abundance).

During field investigations, ecologists have found that three major factors affect species diversity:

- *Latitude* (distance from the equator) in terrestrial communities. Research shows that for most groups of plants and animals, species diversity on continents decreases steadily with distance from the equator toward either pole (Figure 8-3 and Figure 6-22, right, p. 124). This *latitudinal species diversity gradient* leads to

**(1)** the highest species diversity in tropical areas such as tropical rain forests (Figure 6-35, p. 136) and **(2)** the lowest in polar areas such as arctic tundra (Figure 6-32, p. 133). For example, the typical number of tree species per hectare (2.5 acres) is about 40–100 in a tropical forest, 10–30 in a temperate forest (Figure 6-38, p. 138), and 1–5 in a northern coniferous (taiga) forest (Figure 6-40, p. 140).

- *Depth* in aquatic systems. Research shows that in marine communities, species diversity increases from the surface to a depth of 2,000 meters (6,600 feet) and then begins to decline with depth (Figure 8-4) until the deep sea bottom is reached, where species diversity is very high.

- *Pollution* in aquatic systems. Research shows a decrease in species diversity and species abundance in aquatic systems as pollution increases and kills off or

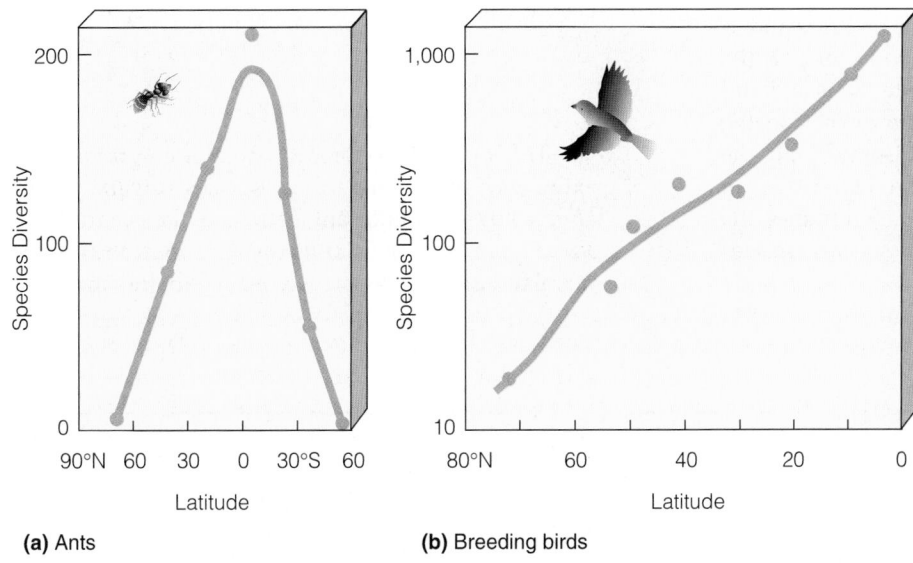

**(a)** Ants  **(b)** Breeding birds

**Figure 8-3** Changes in species diversity at different latitudes (distances from the equator) in terrestrial communities for **(a)** ants and **(b)** breeding birds of North and Central America. As a general rule, species diversity steadily declines as we go away from the equator toward either pole. (Adapted from Cecie Starr, *Biology: Concepts and Applications*, 4th ed. Brooks/Cole [Wadsworth] © 2000)

**(a)**

**(b)**

**Figure 8-4** Changes in species diversity with depth in marine environments for **(a)** snails and **(b)** tube worms. As a general rule, species diversity in the ocean **(1)** increases from the surface to a depth of about 2,000 meters and **(2)** decreases until the sea bottom, where species diversity is usually high.

impairs the reproductivity of various aquatic species (Figure 8-5, p. 168).

In terrestrial communities, species diversity tends to increase with **(1)** increasing solar radiation, **(2)** increasing precipitation, **(3)** decreasing elevation (Figure 6-22, left, p. 124), and **(4)** pronounced seasonal variations.

**What Determines the Number of Species on Islands?** Two factors affecting the species diversity found in an isolated ecosystem such as an island are its *size* and *degree of isolation*. In the 1960s, Robert MacArthur and Edward O. Wilson began studying communities on islands to discover why large islands tend to have more species of a certain category (such as insects, birds, or ferns) than do small islands.

To explain these differences in species diversity with island size, MacArthur and Wilson proposed what is called the **species equilibrium model,** or the **theory of island biogeography.** According to this model, the number of species found on an island is determined by a balance between two factors: **(1)** the rate at which new species immigrate to the island and **(2)** the rate at which species become extinct on the island. The model predicts that at some point the rates of immigration and extinction will reach an equilibrium point (Figure 8-6a) that determines the island's average number of different species (species diversity).

**Figure 8-5** Changes in the species diversity and species abundance of diatom species in an unpolluted stream and a polluted stream. Both species diversity and species abundance decrease with pollution.

The model also predicts that immigration and extinction rates (and thus species diversity) are affected by two important features of the island: **(1)** its *size* (Figure 8-6b) and **(2)** its distance from the nearest mainland (Figure 8-6c). According to the model, a

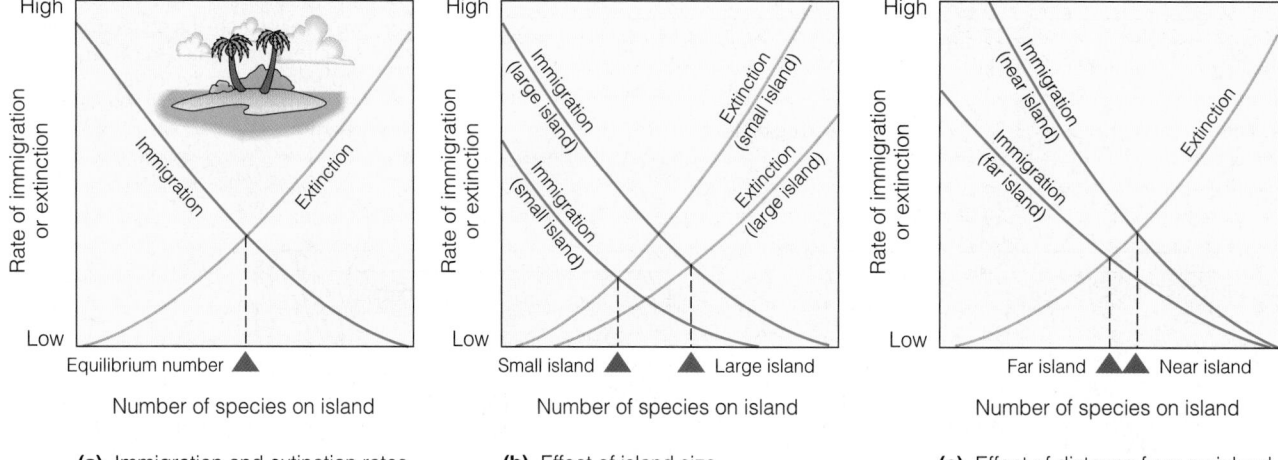

**(a)** Immigration and extinction rates  **(b)** Effect of island size  **(c)** Effect of distance from mainland

**Figure 8-6** The *species equilibrium model* or *theory of island biogeography*, developed by Robert MacArthur and Edward O. Wilson. **(a)** The equilibrium number of species (blue triangle) on an island is determined by a balance between the immigration rate of new species and the extinction rate of species already on the island. **(b)** With time, large islands have a larger equilibrium number of species than smaller islands because of higher immigration rates and lower extinction rates on large islands. **(c)** Assuming equal extinction rates, an island near a mainland will have a larger equilibrium number of species than a more distant island because the immigration rate to a near island is higher than that to a more distant one.

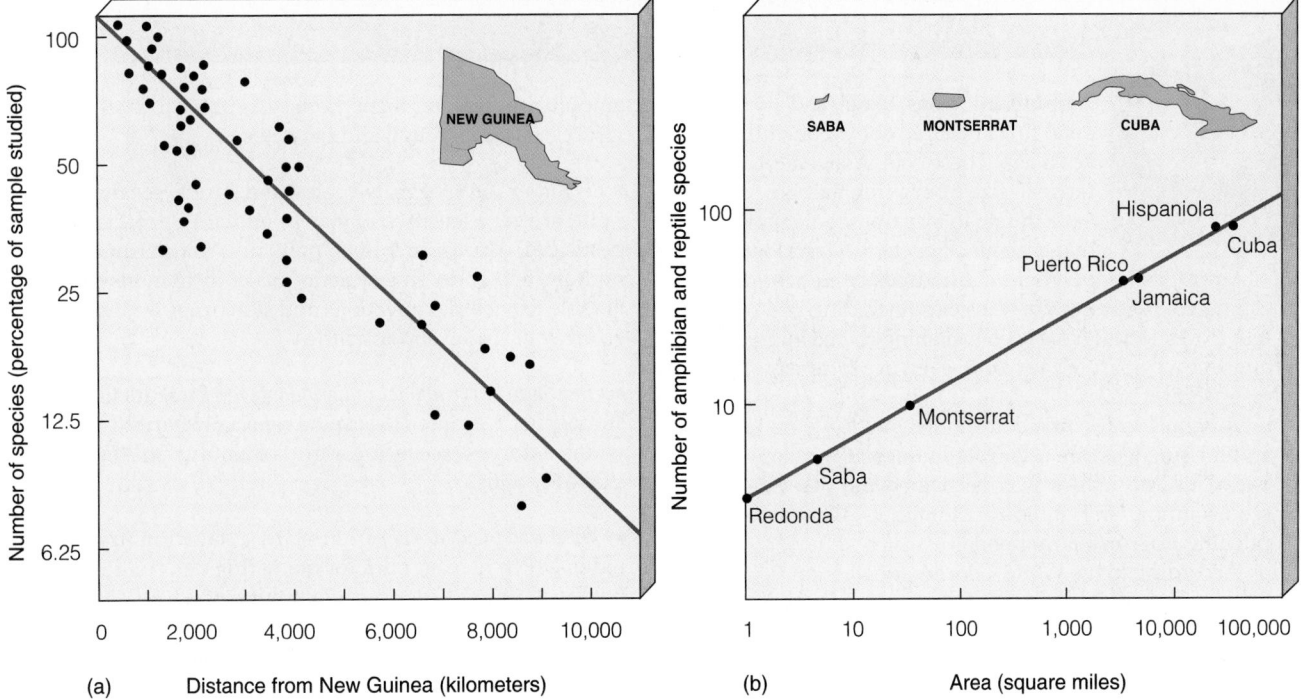

**Figure 8-7** Research data supporting the theory of island biogeography with **(a)** the left graph showing that the species diversity of birds occupying lowland areas of South Pacific islands decreases with distance from New Guinea and **(b)** the right graph showing that species diversity increases with island size. (Used by permission from Cecie Starr, *Biology: Concepts and Applications*, 4th ed. Brooks/Cole [Wadsworth] © 2000)

small island tends to have a lower species diversity than a large one for two reasons: **(1)** a small island generally has a lower immigration rate because it is a smaller target for potential colonizers, and **(2)** a small island should have a higher extinction rate because it generally has fewer resources and less diverse habitats for colonizing species.

The model also predicts that an island's distance from a mainland source of new species is important in determining species diversity. For two islands of about equal size and other factors, the island closest to a mainland source of immigrant species will have the higher immigration rate and thus a higher species diversity (assuming that extinction rates on both islands are about the same).

A series of field experiments have tested and supported MacArthur and Wilson's original model or scientific hypothesis (Figure 8-7). As a result, biologists have elevated it to the status of an important and useful scientific theory, although it may apply to a limited number of cases over short periods of time. In recent years, it has also been applied to conservation efforts to protect wildlife on land in *habitat islands* such as national parks surrounded by a sea of developed and fragmented land.

## 8-2 GENERAL TYPES OF SPECIES

**What Different Roles Do Various Species Play in Ecosystems?**  When examining ecosystems, ecologists often apply particular labels—such as *native, nonnative, indicator,* or *keystone*—to various species to clarify their ecological roles or niches (p. 103). Any given species may function as more than one of these four types in a particular ecosystem.

**How Can Nonnative Species Cause Problems?**  Species that normally live and thrive in a particular ecosystem are known as **native species.** Others that migrate into an ecosystem or are deliberately or accidentally introduced into an ecosystem by humans are called **nonnative species, exotic species,** or **alien species.** Some of these introduced species (such as crops and game species for sport hunting) are beneficial to humans, but some thrive and crowd out native species.

From a human standpoint, introduction of some nonnative species can become a nightmare. In 1957, Brazil imported wild African bees to help increase honey production. Instead, these bees have displaced domestic honeybees and have reduced the honey supply.

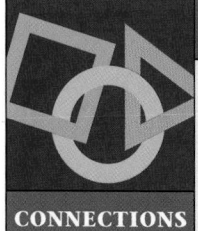

**CONNECTIONS**

## Why Are Amphibians Vanishing?

Amphibians (frogs, toads, and salamanders) first appeared about 350 million years ago. These cold-blooded creatures range in size from a frog that can sit on your thumb to a Japanese salamander that is about 1.5 meters (5 feet) long.

Since 1980, populations of hundreds of the world's estimated 5,280 amphibian species (including 2,700 frog and toad species) have been vanishing or declining in almost every part of the world, even in protected wildlife reserves and parks.

In some locales, frog deformities (such as extra legs and missing legs) are occurring in unusually high numbers. This information was discovered and published by schoolchildren in Henderson, Minnesota, who were catching frogs in a farm pond.

According to the World Conservation Union, 25% of all known amphibian species are extinct, endangered, or vulnerable. The Nature Conservancy estimates that 38% of the amphibian species in the United States are endangered.

Frogs are especially vulnerable to environmental disruption at various points in their life cycle (see figure, right). As tadpoles they live in water and eat plants, and as adults they live mostly on land and eat insects (which can expose them to pesticides). Their eggs have no protective shells to block ultraviolet radiation or pollution. As adults, they take in water and air through their thin, permeable skins that can readily absorb pollutants from water, air, or soil.

Although no single cause has been identified to explain the cause of amphibian declines, scientists have identified a number of contributing factors that can affect amphibians such as frogs at various points in their life cycle (see figure, right). They include the following:

- *Habitat loss and fragmentation,* especially because of **(1)** the draining and filling of inland wetlands, **(2)** deforestation, and **(3)** development.

- *Prolonged drought,* which dries up breeding pools so that few tadpoles survive. Dehydration can also weaken amphibians, making them more susceptible to fatal viruses, bacteria, fungi, and parasites.

- *Pollution.* Frog eggs, tadpoles, and adults (see figure, right) are very sensitive to many pollutants (especially pesticides). Exposure to such pollutants may harm their immune and endocrine systems, make them more vulnerable to bacterial infections and skin fungi, and cause an array of sexual abnormalities.

- *Increases in ultraviolet radiation* caused by reductions in stratospheric ozone. This can be especially harmful to young embryos (see figure, right) of amphibians found in shallow ponds.

- *Increased incidence of parasitism* by a flatworm (trematode), which may account for many frog deformities but not the worldwide decline of amphibians.

- *Overhunting,* especially in Asia and France, where frog legs are a delicacy.

- *Epidemic diseases* such as the chytrid fungus and iridoviruses. Pollution and other factors that weaken the immune systems of amphibians may make them more susceptible to these and other disease organisms.

- *Immigration or introduction of nonnative* **(1)** *predators and competitors* (such as fish) and **(2)** *disease organisms* such as the chytrid (which may have been introduced into Australia by imported tropical fish).

In most cases, the decline or disappearance of amphibian species probably is caused by a combination of such factors. Scientists are concerned about amphibians' decline for three reasons:

- It suggests that the world's environmental health is deteriorating rapidly because amphibians generally are **(1)** tough survivors and **(2)** sensitive biological indicators of changes in environmental conditions such as habitat loss and degradation, pollution, UV exposure, and climate change.

---

Since then, these nonnative bee species, popularly known as "killer bees," have moved northward into Central America. They have become established in Texas, Arizona, New Mexico, Puerto Rico, and California and are heading north at 240 kilometers (150 miles) per year. They should be stopped eventually by cold winters in the central United States unless they can adapt genetically to cold weather.

Although they are not the killer bees portrayed in some horror movies, these bees are aggressive and unpredictable. They have killed thousands of domesticated animals and an estimated 1,000 people in the western hemisphere. Fortunately, most people not allergic to bee stings can run away. Most of the people killed by these honeybees died because they fell down or became trapped and could not flee.

**What Are Indicator Species?** Species that serve as early warnings of damage to a community or an ecosystem are called **indicator species.** Birds are ex-

Adult frog (3 years)

Young frog

Sperm

Sexual reproduction

Eggs

Fertilized egg development

Organ formation

Egg hatches

Tadpole

Tadpole develops into frog

Typical *life cycle of a frog*. Populations of various frog species can decline because of the effects of various harmful factors at different points in their life cycle. Such factors include habitat loss, drought, pollution, increased ultraviolet radiation, parasitism, disease, overhunting for food (frog legs), and nonnative predators and competitors.

■ Adult amphibians play important roles in the world's ecosystems. For example, amphibians eat more insects (including mosquitoes) than do birds. In some habitats, extinction of certain amphibian species could also result in extinction of other species, such as reptiles, birds, aquatic insects, fish, mammals, and other amphibians that feed on them or their larvae.

■ From a human perspective, amphibians represent a genetic storehouse of pharmaceutical products waiting to be discovered. Hundreds of secretions from amphibian skin have been isolated, and some of these compounds are being used as painkillers and antibiotics and in treating burns and heart disease.

As possible indicator species, amphibians may be sending us an important message. They do not need us, but we and other species need them.

**Critical Thinking**

On an evolutionary time scale, all species eventually become extinct. Some people suggest that the widespread disappearance of amphibians is the result of natural responses to changing environmental conditions. Others contend that these losses are **(1)** caused mostly by human activities and **(2)** a warning of possible danger for our own species and other species. What is your position? Why?

cellent biological indicators because they are found almost everywhere and respond quickly to environmental change. Research indicates that a major factor in the current decline of some species of migratory, insect-eating songbirds in North America is habitat loss or fragmentation. The tropical forests of Latin America and the Caribbean that are winter habitats for such birds are disappearing rapidly. Their summer habitats in North America also are disappearing or are being fragmented into patches that make the

birds more vulnerable to attack by predators and parasites.

The presence or absence of trout species in water at temperatures within their range of tolerance (Figure 4-14, p. 73) is an indicator of water quality because trout need clean water with high levels of dissolved oxygen. Some amphibians (frogs, toads, and salamanders), which live part of their lives in water and part on land, are also classified as indicator species (Connections, above).

**What Are Keystone Species?** The roles of some species in an ecosystem are much more important than their abundance or biomass suggests. Ecologists call such species **keystone species,** although this designation is controversial.* Such species play pivotal roles in the structure and function of an ecosystem because **(1)** their strong interactions with other species affect the health and survival of these species, and **(2)** they process material out of proportion to their numbers or biomass.

Critical roles of keystone species include **(1)** pollination of flowering plant species by bees, hummingbirds, bats (Figure 8-1), and other species, **(2)** dispersion of seeds by fruit-eating animals such as bats (Figure 8-1), with the undigested seeds scattered in their feces, **(3)** habitat modification, **(4)** predation by top carnivores that helps control the populations of various species, **(5)** improving the ability of plant species to obtain soil minerals and water, and **(6)** efficient recycling of animal wastes. Some species play more than one of these roles.

Beneficial *habitat modifications* by keystone species include the following:

■ Elephants push over, break, or uproot trees, creating forest openings in the savanna grasslands and woodlands of Africa. This **(1)** promotes the growth of grasses and other forage plants that benefit smaller grazing species such as antelope and **(2)** accelerates nutrient cycling rates.

■ Bats (p. 165) and birds regenerate deforested areas by depositing plant seeds in their droppings.

■ Beaver dams can change a fast-moving stream into a pond or lake. This attracts fish (such as bluegill), muskrats, herons, and ducks that prefer deeper, slower-moving water, as well as woodpeckers that feed on dead trees emerging from the pond. However, by felling trees to build dams, beavers can also destroy large expanses of terrestrial forests.

*Top predator* keystone species exert a stabilizing effect on their ecosystems by feeding on and helping regulate the populations of certain species. Examples are the wolf, leopard, lion, alligator (Connections, p. 173), sea otter, and great white shark.

Have you thanked a *dung beetle* today? You should because these keystone species play a combination of vital roles in the ecosystems where they are found:

■ They rapidly remove, bury, and recycle animal wastes (dung). Without them we would be up to our

eyeballs in such waste, and many plants would be starved for nutrients.

■ They establish new plants because the dung they bury contains seeds that have passed through the digestive tracts of fruit-eating animals.

■ They churn and aerate the soil, making it more suitable for plant life.

■ They reduce populations of microorganisms that spread disease to wild and domesticated animals (including humans) because the beetle larvae feed on parasitic worms and maggots that live in the dung.

The loss of a keystone species can lead to population crashes and extinctions of other species that depend on it for certain services, a ripple or domino effect that spreads throughout an ecosystem. According to biologist Edward O. Wilson, "The loss of a keystone species is like a drill accidentally striking a power line. It causes lights to go out all over."

## 8-3 SPECIES INTERACTIONS: COMPETITION AND PREDATION

**How Do Species Interact? An Overview** When different species in an ecosystem have activities or resource needs in common, they may interact with one another. Members of these species may **(1)** be harmed by, **(2)** benefit from, or **(3)** be unaffected by the interaction. Ecologists identify five basic types of interactions between species: **(1)** *interspecific competition,* **(2)** *predation,* **(3)** *parasitism,* **(4)** *mutualism,* and **(5)** *commensalism.*

**How Do Members of the Same Species Compete for Resources?** Competition between members of the *same* species for the same resources is called **intraspecific competition.** Intraspecific competition can be intense because members of a particular species compete directly for the same resources.

For example, some plants (especially in deserts) gain a competitive advantage by secreting chemicals that inhibit the growth of seedlings of their own and other species. Other plant species, such as dandelions, compete with other members of their species for living space and soil nutrients by dispersing their seeds to other sites by air (wind), water, or animals.

Another way members of the same species compete is through **territoriality,** in which organisms **(1)** patrol or mark an area around their home, nesting, or major feeding site and **(2)** defend it against members of their own species. Robins chase other robins away from their mating and nesting sites, and rhinos and lions use urine or scent to mark their breeding areas.

---

*All species play some role in their ecosystems and thus are important. Whereas some scientists consider all species equally important, others consider certain species to be more important than others in helping maintain the structure and function of ecosystems of which they are a part.

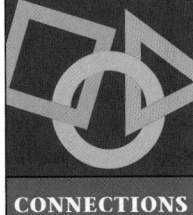

## Why Should We Care About Alligators?

The American alligator, North America's largest reptile, has no natural predators except humans. This species, which has been around for about 200 million years, has been able to adapt to numerous changes in the earth's environmental conditions.

This changed when hunters began killing large numbers of these animals for their exotic meat and their supple belly skin, used to make shoes, belts, and pocketbooks.

Other people considered alligators to be useless and dangerous and hunted them for sport or out of hatred. Between 1950 and 1960, hunters wiped out 90% of the alligators in Louisiana, and by the 1960s, the alligator population in the Florida Everglades also was near extinction.

People who say "So what?" are overlooking the alligator's important ecological role or *niche* in subtropical wetland ecosystems. Alligators dig deep depressions, or gator holes, that **(1)** collect fresh water during dry spells, **(2)** serve as refuges for aquatic life, and **(3)** supply fresh water and food for many animals.

In addition, large alligator nesting mounds provide nesting and feeding sites for herons and egrets. Alligators also eat large numbers of gar (a predatory fish) and thus help maintain populations of game fish such as bass and bream.

As alligators move from gator holes to nesting mounds, they help keep areas of open water free of invading vegetation. Without these ecosystem services, freshwater ponds and shrubs and trees would fill in coastal wetlands in the alligator's habitat, and dozens of species would disappear.

Some ecologists classify the North American alligator as a *keystone species* because of these important ecological roles in helping maintain the structure and function of its natural ecosystems.

In 1967, the U.S. government placed the American alligator on the endangered species list. Protected from hunters, the alligator population made a strong comeback in many areas by 1975—too strong, according to those who find alligators in their backyards and swimming pools, and to duck hunters, whose retriever dogs sometimes are eaten by alligators.

In 1977, the U.S. Fish and Wildlife Service reclassified the American alligator from an *endangered* species to a *threatened* species in Florida, Louisiana, and Texas, where 90% of the animals live. In 1987, this reclassification was extended to seven other states.

Alligators now number perhaps 3 million, most in Florida and Louisiana. It is generally illegal to kill members of a threatened species, but limited kills by licensed hunters are allowed in some areas of Florida, Louisiana, and South Carolina to control the population. To biologists, the comeback of the American alligator from near premature extinction by overhunting is an important success story in wildlife conservation.

The increased demand for alligator meat and hides has created a booming business in alligator farms, especially in Florida. Such success reduces the need for illegal hunting of wild alligators.

### Critical Thinking

Some home owners in Florida believe they should have the right to kill any alligator found on their property. Others argue this should not be allowed because **(1)** alligators are a threatened species, and **(2)** housing developments have invaded the habitats of alligators, not the other way around. What is your opinion on this issue? Explain.

---

A territory is essentially a set of resources a species needs for successful breeding. Factors contributing to a good territory are **(1)** an abundant food supply, **(2)** a good nesting site, **(3)** an absence or low population of predators, and **(4)** an absence of environmental factors that would reduce breeding success.

Territory size varies and is small for robins but large for species such as tigers. Two potential disadvantages of territoriality are **(1)** exclusion of many male members of a population from breeding and **(2)** large energy expenditure in defending the territory.

### How Do Members of Different Species Compete for Resources?

Competition between members of two or more *different* species for food, space, or any other limited resource is called **interspecific competition.**

As long as commonly used resources are abundant, different species can share them. This allows each species to come closer to occupying the *fundamental niche* it would occupy if there were no competition from other species.

However, most species face competition from other species for one or more limited resources (such as food, sunlight, water, soil nutrients, space, nesting sites, and good places to hide). Because of such *interspecific competition*, parts of the fundamental niches of different species overlap (Figure 5-7, p. 104). The more the niches of two species overlap, the more they compete with one another. With significant niche overlap, one of the competing species must **(1)** migrate to another area (if possible), **(2)** shift its feeding habits or behavior through natural selection and evolution (Section 5-2, p. 100), **(3)** suffer a sharp population decline, or **(4)** become extinct in that area.

Species compete with other species by:

- **Interference competition,** in which one species may limit another's access to some resource, regardless of its abundance, using the same types of methods found in intraspecific competition. For example, a territorial hummingbird species may defend patches of spring wildflowers from which it gets nectar by chasing away members of other hummingbird species. In desert and grassland habitats, many plants release chemicals into the soil. These chemicals prevent the growth of competing species or reduce the rates at which their seeds germinate.

- **Exploitation competition,** in which competing species have roughly equal access to a specific resource but differ in how fast or efficiently they exploit it. The species that can use the resource more quickly **(1)** gets more of the resource and **(2)** hampers the growth, reproduction, or survival of the other species.

Humans are in competition with other species for space, food, and other resources. As we convert more and more of the earth's land and aquatic resources and net primary productivity (Figure 4-26, p. 82) to our uses (Figure 1-5, p. 7, and Figure 1-8, p. 10), we deprive many other species of resources they need to survive.

**What Is the Competitive Exclusion Principle?** Sometimes one species eliminates another species in a particular area through competition for limited resources. In 1934, Russian ecologist G. F. Gause demonstrated this effect in a laboratory experiment. Two closely related species of single-celled, bacteria-eating *Paramecium* were grown, first separately and then together in culture tubes (Figure 8-8).

The graph on the left of Figure 8-8 shows what happened when both species were grown under identical conditions in separate containers with ample supplies of food (bacteria). In this case, both species grew rapidly and established stable populations. However, the smaller *Paramecium aurelia* (red curve) grew faster than the larger *Paramecium caudatum* (green curve), indicating that the former used the available food supply more efficiently than the latter. The graph on the right shows that when both species were grown together in a culture tube with a limited amount of bacteria, the smaller *Paramecium aurelia* (red curve) outmultiplied and eliminated the larger *Paramecium caudatum* (green curve).

This research, which has been supported by various laboratory and field experiments using other animal species, showed that two species needing the same resource cannot coexist indefinitely in an ecosystem in which not enough of that resource is available to meet the needs of both species. In other words, the niches of two species cannot overlap completely or significantly for very long. This finding is called the **competitive exclusion principle.**

**How Have Some Species Reduced or Avoided Competition?** Over a time scale long enough for evolution to occur, some species that compete for the same resources evolve adaptations that reduce or avoid competition or an overlap of their fundamental niches (Figure 5-7, p. 104). One way this happens is through **resource partitioning,** the dividing up of scarce resources so that species with similar needs use them **(1)** at different times, **(2)** in different ways, or

**Each species grown alone**

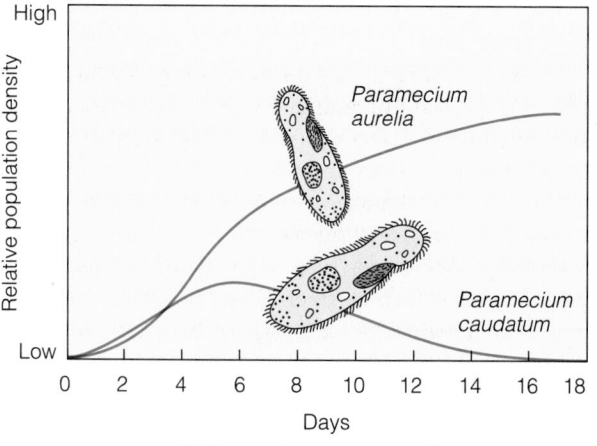

**Both species grown together**

**Figure 8-8** The results of G. F. Gause's classic laboratory experiment with two similar single-celled, bacteria-eating *Paramecium* species (which reproduce asexually). These data support the *competitive exclusion principle* that similar species cannot occupy the same ecological niche indefinitely.

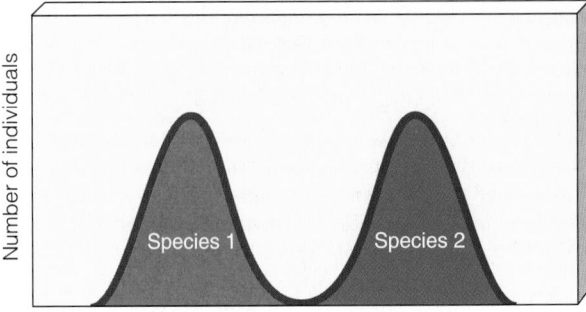

**Figure 8-9** *Resource partitioning* and *niche specialization* as a result of competition between two species. The top diagram shows the overlapping niches of two competing species. The bottom diagram shows that through evolution the niches of the two species become separated and more specialized (narrower) so that they avoid competing for the same resources.

**(3)** in different places (Figure 7-13, p. 152). In effect, they evolve traits that allow them to share the wealth.

Each of the competing species occupies a *realized niche* that makes up only part of its *fundamental niche*. Thus through evolution the fairly broad niches of two competing species (Figure 8-9, top) become more specialized (Figure 8-9, bottom). Resource partitioning through niche specialization also occurs in the different layers of tropical rain forests (Figure 6-37, p. 137) and in coastal wetlands (Figure 7-13, p. 152).

Here are some other examples of resource partitioning. When lions and leopards live in the same area, lions take mostly larger animals as prey, and leopards take smaller ones. Hawks and owls feed on similar prey, but hawks hunt during the day and owls hunt at night. Some bird species feed on the ground, whereas others seek food in trees and shrubs.

Ecologist Robert H. MacArthur studied the feeding habits of five species of warblers (small insect-eating birds) that coexist in the forests of the northeastern United States and in the adjacent area of Canada. Although they appear to be competing for the same food resources, MacArthur found that the bird species reduce competition through resource partitioning by spending at least half their time hunting for insects in different parts of trees (Figure 8-10).

**Figure 8-10** *Resource partitioning* of five species of common insect-eating warblers in the spruce forests of Maine. Each species minimizes competition with the others for food by **(1)** spending at least half its feeding time in a distinct portion (shaded areas) of the spruce trees, and **(2)** consuming somewhat different insect species. (After R. H. MacArthur, "Population Ecology of Some Warblers in Northeastern Coniferous Forests," *Ecology* 36 [1958]: 533–36)

## Why Are Sharks Important Species?

The world's 370 shark species vary widely in size. The smallest is the dwarf dog shark, about the size of a large goldfish. The largest is the whale shark, the world's largest fish, which can grow to 15 meters (50 feet) long and weigh as much as two full-grown African elephants.

Various shark species, feeding at the top of food webs, cull injured and sick animals from the ocean and thus play an important ecological role. Without such shark species, the oceans would be overcrowded with dead and dying fish.

Many people—influenced by movies (such as *Jaws*), popular novels, and widespread media coverage of a fairly small number of shark attacks per year—think of sharks as people-eating monsters. However, the three largest species—the whale shark, basking shark, and megamouth shark—are gentle giants that swim through the water with their mouths open, filtering out and swallowing huge quantities of *plankton* (small free-floating sea creatures).

Every year, members of a few species of shark—mostly great white, bull, tiger, gray reef, lemon, hammerhead, shortfin mako, and blue—typically injure about 100 people worldwide and kill between 5 and 15 people. Most attacks are by great white sharks, which feed on sea lions and other marine mammals and sometimes mistake divers and surfers for their usual prey.

Media coverage of shark attacks greatly distort the danger from

sharks. You are 30 times more likely to be killed by lightning than by a shark. Each year **(1)** dogs inflict serious bites on many thousands more people than the 100 or so persons bitten by sharks, and **(2)** the number of people bitten by other people is more than 10 times the number of people bitten by sharks.

For every shark that injures a person, we kill at least 1 million sharks, for a total of 100 million sharks each year. Sharks are killed mostly for their fins, widely used in Asia as a soup ingredient and as a pharmaceutical cure-all and worth as much as $563 per kilogram ($256 per pound). In Hong Kong, a single bowl of shark fin soup can sell for as much as $100.

According to a 2001 study by Wild Aid, shark fins sold in restaurants throughout Asia and in Chinese communities in cities such as New York, San Francisco, and London contain dangerously high levels of toxic mercury. Consumption of high levels of mercury is especially threatening for pregnant women and their babies.

Sharks are also killed for their **(1)** livers, **(2)** meat (especially mako and thresher), **(3)** hides (a source of exotic, high-quality leather), and **(4)** jaws (especially great whites, whose jaws are worth thousands of dollars to collectors), or **(5)** just because we fear them. Some sharks (especially blue, mako, and oceanic whitetip) die when they are trapped as bycatch in nets or lines deployed to catch swordfish, tuna, shrimp, and other commercially important species.

Sharks also help save human lives. In addition to providing peo-

ple with food, they are helping us learn how to fight cancer (which sharks almost never get), bacteria, and viruses. Their highly effective immune system is being studied because it allows wounds to heal without becoming infected.

Sharks have several natural traits that make them prone to population declines from overfishing. They **(1)** have only a few offspring (between 2 and 10) once every year or two, **(2)** take 10–24 years to reach sexual maturity and begin reproducing, and **(3)** have long gestation (pregnancy) periods, up to 24 months for some species.

Sharks are among the most vulnerable and least protected animals on the earth. Eight of the world's shark species, including great whites, sandtigers, and kitefins, are now considered critically endangered, endangered, or vulnerable to extinction. Of the 125 countries that commercially catch more than 100 million sharks per year, only four—Australia, Canada, New Zealand, and the United States—have implemented management plans for shark fisheries, and these plans are hard to enforce.

With more than 400 million years of evolution behind them, sharks have had a long time to get things right. Preserving their evolutionary genetic development begins with the knowledge that sharks do not need us, but we and other species need them.

### Critical Thinking

After reading this information, has your attitude toward sharks changed? If so, how has it changed?

---

**How Do Predator and Prey Species Interact?**
In **predation,** members of one species (the *predator*) feed directly on all or part of a living organism of another species (the *prey*). However, they do not live on or in the prey, and the prey may or may not die from the interaction.

In this interaction, the predator benefits and the individual prey is clearly harmed. Together, the two kinds of organisms, such as lions (the predator or

hunter) and zebras (the prey or hunted), are said to have a **predator–prey relationship,** as depicted in Figures 4-11 (p. 72), 4-12 (p. 72), 4-18 (p. 77), and 4-19 (p. 78).

At the individual level, members of the prey species are clearly harmed. However, at the population level, predation can benefit the prey species because predators such as tigers and some types of sharks often kill the sick, weak, and aged members (Case Study, above). Reducing the prey population **(1)** gives remaining prey greater access to the available food supply and **(2)** can improve the genetic stock of the prey population, which enhances its chances of reproductive success and long-term survival.

Some people tend to view predators with contempt. When a hawk tries to capture and feed on a rabbit, some tend to root for the rabbit. Yet the hawk (like all predators) is merely trying to get enough food to feed itself and its young; in the process, it is playing an important ecological role in controlling rabbit populations.

**How Do Predators Increase Their Chances of Getting a Meal?** Predators have a variety of methods that help them capture prey. *Herbivores* can simply walk, swim, or fly up to the plants they feed on.

*Carnivores* feeding on mobile prey have two main options: *pursuit* and *ambush.* Some, such as the cheetah, catch prey by being able to run fast; others, such as the American bald eagle, fly and have keen eyesight; still others, such as wolves and African lions, cooperate in capturing their prey by hunting in packs.

Other predators have characteristics or strategies that enable them to hide and ambush their prey. Examples include **(1)** praying mantises (Figure 4-1, right, p. 64) sitting in flowers of a similar color and ambushing visiting insects, **(2)** white ermines (a type of weasel) and snowy owls hunting in snow-covered areas, **(3)** the alligator snapping turtle lying camouflaged on its stream-bottom habitat and dangling its worm-shaped tongue to entice fish into its powerful jaws, and **(4)** people camouflaging themselves to hunt wild game and using traps to ambush wild game.

**How Do Prey Defend Themselves Against or Avoid Predators?** Species have various characteristics that enable them to avoid predators. They include **(1)** the ability to run, swim, or fly fast, **(2)** a highly developed sense of sight or smell that alerts them to the presence of predators, **(3)** protective shells (as on armadillos, which roll themselves up into an armorplated ball, and turtles), **(4)** thick bark (giant sequoia), and **(5)** spines (porcupines) or thorns (cacti and rosebushes). Many lizards have brightly colored tails that break off when they are attacked, often giving them enough time to escape.

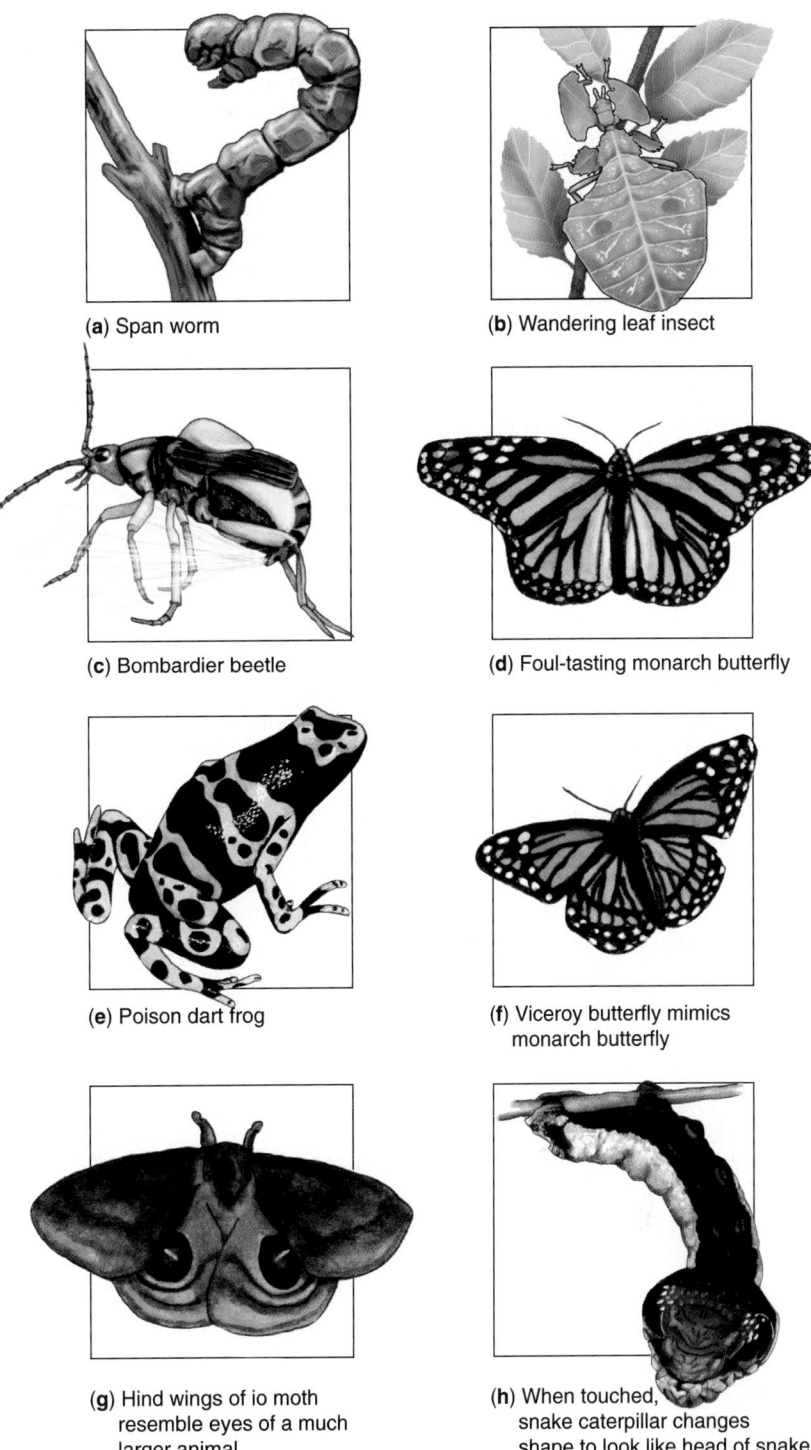

**(a)** Span worm

**(b)** Wandering leaf insect

**(c)** Bombardier beetle

**(d)** Foul-tasting monarch butterfly

**(e)** Poison dart frog

**(f)** Viceroy butterfly mimics monarch butterfly

**(g)** Hind wings of io moth resemble eyes of a much larger animal.

**(h)** When touched, snake caterpillar changes shape to look like head of snake.

**Figure 8-11** Some ways in which prey species avoid their predators by **(1)** *camouflage* (a and b), **(2)** *chemical warfare* (c and e), **(3)** *warning coloration* (d and e), **(4)** *mimicry* (f), **(5)** *deceptive looks* (g), and **(6)** *deceptive behavior* (h).

Other prey species use *camouflage* by having certain shapes or colors (Figure 8-11a) or the ability to change color (chameleons and cuttlefish). A leaf insect may be almost invisible against its background (Figure 8-11b), and an arctic hare in its white winter fur blends into the snow. Some insect species have evolved shapes that look like twigs (Figure 8-11a) or bird droppings on leaves.

*Chemical warfare* is another common strategy. Some prey species discourage predators with chemicals that are (1) poisonous (oleander plants), (2) irritating (bombardier beetles, Figure 8-11c), (3) foul smelling (skunks, skunk cabbages, and stinkbugs), or (4) bad tasting (buttercups and monarch butterflies, Figure 8-11d). Scientists have identified more than 10,000 defensive chemicals made by plants, including cocaine, caffeine, nicotine, cyanide, opium, strychnine, peyote, and rotenone (used as an insecticide).

Many bad-tasting, bad-smelling, toxic, or stinging prey species have evolved *warning coloration,* brightly colored advertising that enables experienced predators to recognize and avoid them. Examples are (1) brilliantly colored poisonous frogs (Figure 8-11e) and red-, yellow-, and black-striped coral snakes and (2) foul-tasting monarch butterflies (Figure 8-11d) and grasshoppers. Other butterfly species, such as the nonpoisonous viceroy (Figure 8-11f), gain some protection by looking and acting like the poisonous monarch (Figure 8-11d), a protective device known as *mimicry.*

Some prey species use behavioral strategies to avoid predation. Some attempt to scare off predators by (1) puffing up (blowfish), (2) spreading their wings (peacocks), or (3) mimicking a predator (Figure 8-11h). To help fool or frighten would-be predators, some moths have wings that look likes the eyes of much larger animals (Figure 8-11g). Other prey gain some protection by living in large groups (schools of fish, herds of antelope, flocks of birds).

## 8-4 SYMBIOTIC SPECIES INTERACTIONS: PARASITISM, MUTUALISM, AND COMMENSALISM

**What Is Symbiosis?** Symbiosis is a relationship in which species live together in an intimate association. There are three types of symbiosis: *parasitism, mutualism,* and *commensalism.*

**What Are Parasites, and Why Are They Important?** Parasitism occurs when one species (the *parasite*) feeds on part of another organism (the *host*) by living on or in the host. In this symbiotic relationship, the parasite benefits and the host is harmed.

Parasitism can be viewed as a special form of predation. But unlike a conventional predator, a parasite (1) usually is smaller than its host (prey), (2) remains closely associated with, draws nourishment from, and may gradually weaken its host over time, and (3) rarely kills its host.

Tapeworms, disease-causing microorganisms (or pathogens), and other parasites live *inside* their hosts.

Other parasites, such as ticks, fleas, mosquitoes, mistletoe plants, and fungi (that cause diseases such as athlete's foot), attach themselves to the *outside* of their hosts. Some parasites move from one host to another, as fleas and ticks do; others, such as tapeworms, spend their adult lives with a single host.

From the host's point of view, parasites are harmful, but parasites play important ecological roles. Collectively, the complex matrix of parasitic relationships in an ecosystem acts somewhat like glue that helps hold the species in an ecosystem together. Parasites also promote biodiversity by helping prevent some species from becoming too plentiful and eliminating other species through competition.

**How Do Species Interact So That Both Species Benefit?** In mutualism, two species involved in a symbiotic relationship interact in ways that benefit both. Such benefits include (1) having pollen and seeds dispersed for reproduction, (2) being supplied with food, or (3) receiving protection.

The *pollination* relationship between flowering plants and animals such as insects (Figure 4-1, left, p. 64), birds, and bats (p. 165) is one of the most common forms of mutualism. Examples of *nutritional mutualism* include the following:

■ *Lichens,* hardy species that can grow on trees or barren rocks, consist of colorful photosynthetic algae and chlorophyll-lacking fungi living together. The fungi provide a home for the algae, and their bodies collect and hold moisture and mineral nutrients used by both species. The algae, through photosynthesis, provide sugars as food for themselves and the fungi.

■ Plants in the legume family support root nodules, where *Rhizobium* bacteria convert atmospheric nitrogen into a form usable by the plants (Figure 4-29, p. 86), and the plants provide the bacteria with some simple sugars.

■ One-celled algae called *zooxanthellae* that live in the tissues of the tiny animals called *polyps* that make up coral reefs (Figure 7-1, left, p. 144). The algae provide the polyps with color, food, and oxygen through photosynthesis, and the polyps provide a protected home for the algae.

■ Vast armies of bacteria in the digestive systems of animals break down (digest) their food. The bacteria gain a safe home with a steady food supply; the animal gains more efficient access to a large source of energy.

Examples of mutualistic relationships involving *nutrition* and *protection* are as follows.

■ Birds ride on the backs of large animals such as African buffalo, elephants, and rhinoceroses (Figure 8-12a). The birds remove and eat parasites from the animal's body and often make noises warning the animal when predators approach.

- Clownfish species live within sea anemones, whose tentacles sting and paralyze most fish that touch them (Figure 8-12b). The clownfish, which are not harmed by tentacles, gain protection from predators and feed on the detritus left from the meals of the anemones. The sea anemones benefit because the clownfish protect them from some of their predators.

- Minute fungi called mycorrhizae live on the roots of many plants (Figure 8-12c). The fungi get nutrition from a plant's roots and in turn benefit the plant by using their myriad networks of hairlike extensions to improve the plant's ability to extract nutrients and water from the soil.

- Our domesticated plants and animals rely on us for nutrition and protection. In return, we use them as sources of food and companionship and in some cases protection (guard dogs).

It is tempting to think of mutualism as an example of cooperation between species, but actually it involves each species benefiting by exploiting the other.

**How Do Species Interact So That One Benefits But the Other Is Not Harmed?** Commensalism is a symbiotic interaction that benefits one species but neither harms nor helps the other species much, if at all. Examples are as follows:

- A redwood sorrel, a small herb, benefits from growing in the shade of tall redwood trees, with no known negative effects on the redwood trees.

- Plants called *epiphytes* (such as some types of orchids and bromeliads) attach themselves to the trunks or branches of large trees (Figure 8-13, p. 180) in tropical and subtropical forests. These so-called air plants benefit by **(1)** having a solid base on which to grow and **(2)** living in an elevated spot that gives them better access to sunlight, water from the humid air and rain, and nutrients falling from the tree's upper leaves and limbs. This apparently does not harm the tree.

- Raccoons, opossums, and rats obtain food by robbing our garbage. This usually causes us no harm unless we have to pick up trash that scavenging animals have strewn around.

**(a)** Oxpeckers and black rhinoceros

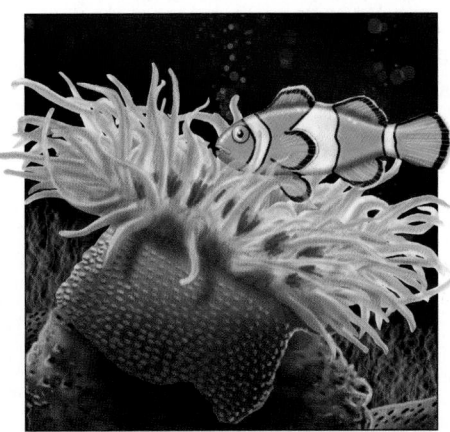

**(b)** Clown fish and sea anemone

**(c)** Mycorrhizae fungi on juniper seedlings in normal soil

**(d)** Lack of mycorrhizae fungi on juniper seedlings in sterilized soil

**Figure 8-12** Examples of *mutualism.* **(a)** Oxpeckers (or tickbirds) feed on and remove parasitic ticks that infest large thick-skinned animals such as a black rhinoceros, **(b)** a clownfish gains protection and food by living among deadly stinging sea anemones and helps protect the anemones from some of their predators, and **(c)** beneficial effects of mycorrhizae fungi attached to roots of juniper seedlings on plant growth **(d)** compared to growth of such seedlings in sterilized soil without mycorrhizae fungi (right).

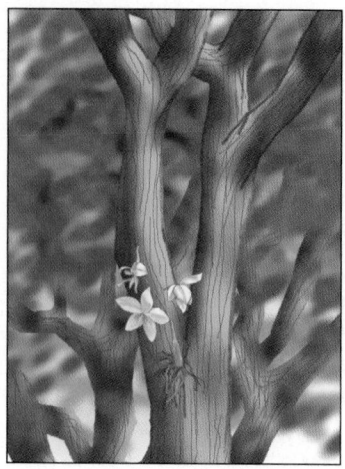

**Figure 8-13** *Commensalism* between a white orchid (an epiphyte or air plant from the tropical forests of Latin America) that roots in the fork of a tree rather than the soil. In this interaction, the epiphytes gain access to water, nutrient debris, and sunlight; the tree apparently remains unharmed unless it contains a large number of epiphytes.

## 8-5 ECOLOGICAL SUCCESSION: COMMUNITIES IN TRANSITION

**How Do Ecosystems Respond to Change?**  One characteristic of all communities and ecosystems is that their structures change constantly in response to changing environmental conditions. The gradual change in species composition of a given area is called **ecological succession.** During succession some species colonize an area and their populations become more numerous, whereas populations of other species decline and even disappear.

Ecologists recognize two types of ecological succession, depending on the conditions present at the beginning of the process:

- **Primary succession** involves the gradual establishment of biotic communities on nearly lifeless ground.

- **Secondary succession,** the more common type, involves the reestablishment of biotic communities in an area where some type of biotic community is already present.

**What Is Primary Succession? Establishing Life on Lifeless Ground**  Primary succession begins with an essentially lifeless area where there is no soil in a terrestrial ecosystem (Figure 8-14) or no bottom sediment in an aquatic ecosystem. Examples include **(1)** bare rock exposed by a retreating glacier or severe soil erosion, **(2)** newly cooled lava, **(3)** an abandoned highway or parking lot, or **(4)** a newly created shallow pond or reservoir.

Before a community of plants (producers), consumers, and decomposers can become established on land, there must be *soil:* a complex mixture of rock particles, decaying organic matter, air, water, and living organisms. Depending mostly on the climate, it takes natural processes several hundred to several thousand years to produce fertile soil.

Soil formation begins when hardy **pioneer species** attach themselves to inhospitable patches of bare rock. Examples are wind-dispersed lichens and mosses, which can withstand the lack

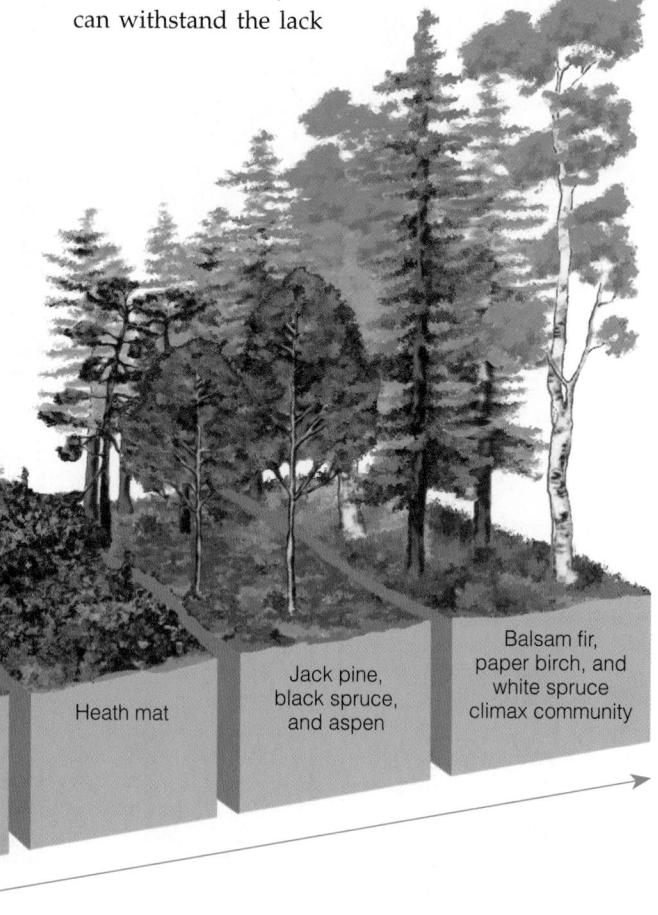

**Figure 8-14** Starting from ground zero. *Primary ecological succession* over several hundred years of plant communities on bare rock exposed by a retreating glacier on Isle Royal in northern Lake Superior.

Exposed rocks

Lichens and mosses

Small herbs and shrubs

Heath mat

Jack pine, black spruce, and aspen

Balsam fir, paper birch, and white spruce climax community

Time

of moisture and soil nutrients and hot and cold temperature extremes found in such habitats.

These species start the soil formation process on patches of bare rock by (1) trapping wind-blown soil particles and tiny pieces of detritus, (2) producing tiny bits of organic matter, and (3) secreting mild acids that slowly fragment and break down the rock. This chemical breakdown (weathering) is hastened by physical weathering such as the fragmentation of rock when water freezes in cracks and expands.

As patches of soil build up and spread, eventually the community of lichens and mosses is replaced by a community of (1) small perennial grasses (plants that live for more than 2 years without having to reseed) and (2) herbs (ferns in tropical areas), whose seeds germinate after being blown in by the wind or carried there in the droppings of birds or on the coats of mammals.

These **early successional plant species (1)** grow close to the ground, (2) can establish large populations quickly under harsh conditions, and (3) have short lives. Some of their roots penetrate the rock and help break it up into more soil particles, and the decay of their wastes and dead bodies adds more nutrients to the soil.

After hundreds of years, the soil may be deep and fertile enough to store enough moisture and nutrients to support the growth of less hardy **midsuccessional plant species** of herbs, grasses, and low shrubs. Trees that need lots of sunlight and are adapted to the area's climate and soil usually replace these species.

As these tree species grow and create shade, they are replaced by **late successional plant species** (mostly trees) that can tolerate shade. Unless fire, flooding, severe erosion, tree cutting, climate change, or other natural or human processes disturb the area, what was once bare rock becomes a complex forest community (Figure 8-14).

**What Is Secondary Succession?** Secondary succession begins in an area where the natural community of organisms has been disturbed, removed, or destroyed but some soil or bottom sediment remains. Candidates for secondary succession include (1) abandoned farmlands, (2) burned or cut forests, (3) heavily polluted streams, and (4) land that has been dammed or flooded. Because some soil or sediment is present, new vegetation usually can begin to germinate within a few weeks. Seeds can be present in soils, or they can be carried from nearby plants by wind or by birds and animals.

In the central (Piedmont) region of North Carolina, European settlers cleared the mature native oak and hickory forests and replanted the land with crops. Later they abandoned some of this farmland because of erosion and loss of soil nutrients. Figure 8-15 shows how such abandoned farmland has undergone secondary succession.

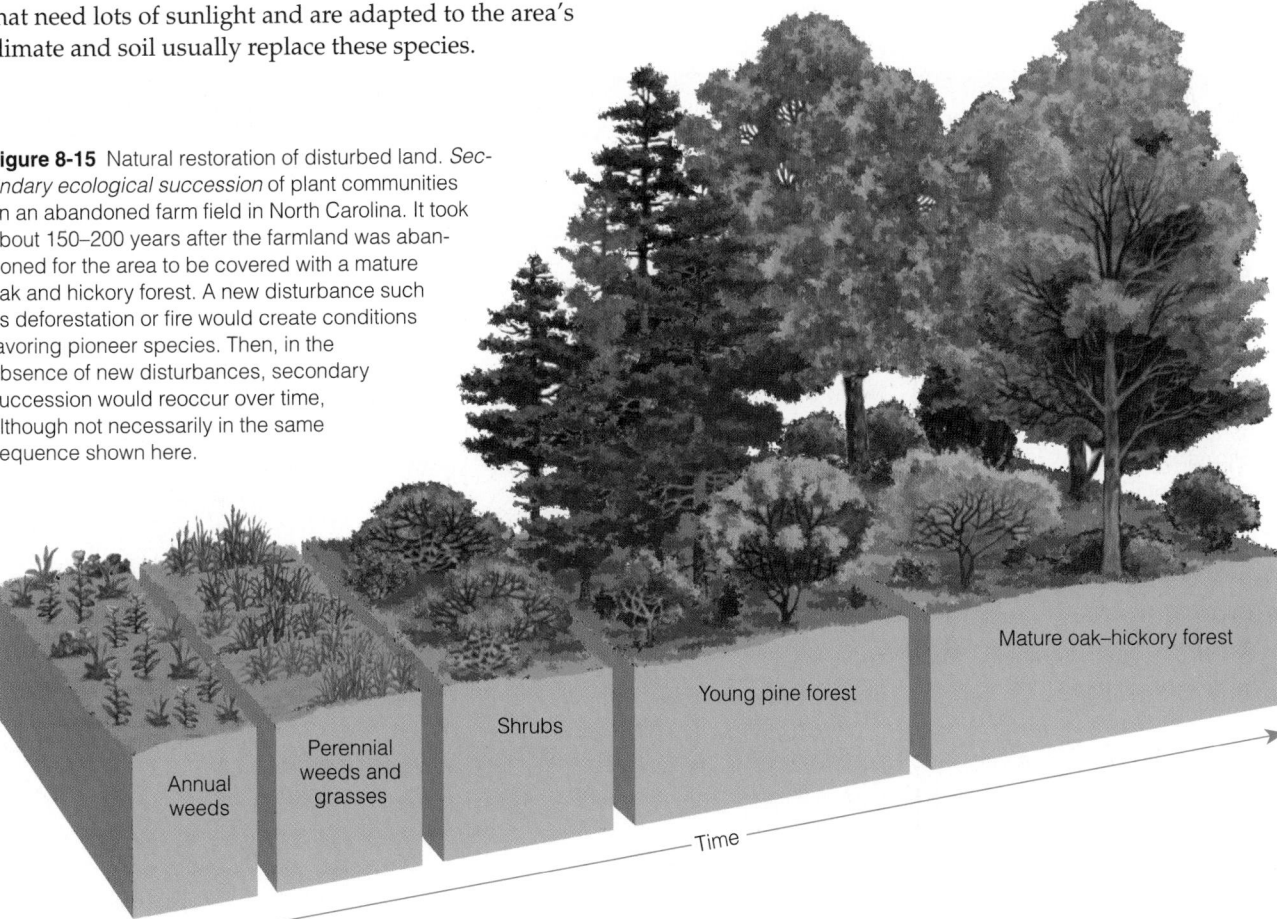

**Figure 8-15** Natural restoration of disturbed land. *Secondary ecological succession* of plant communities on an abandoned farm field in North Carolina. It took about 150–200 years after the farmland was abandoned for the area to be covered with a mature oak and hickory forest. A new disturbance such as deforestation or fire would create conditions favoring pioneer species. Then, in the absence of new disturbances, secondary succession would reoccur over time, although not necessarily in the same sequence shown here.

Annual weeds

Perennial weeds and grasses

Shrubs

Young pine forest

Mature oak–hickory forest

Time

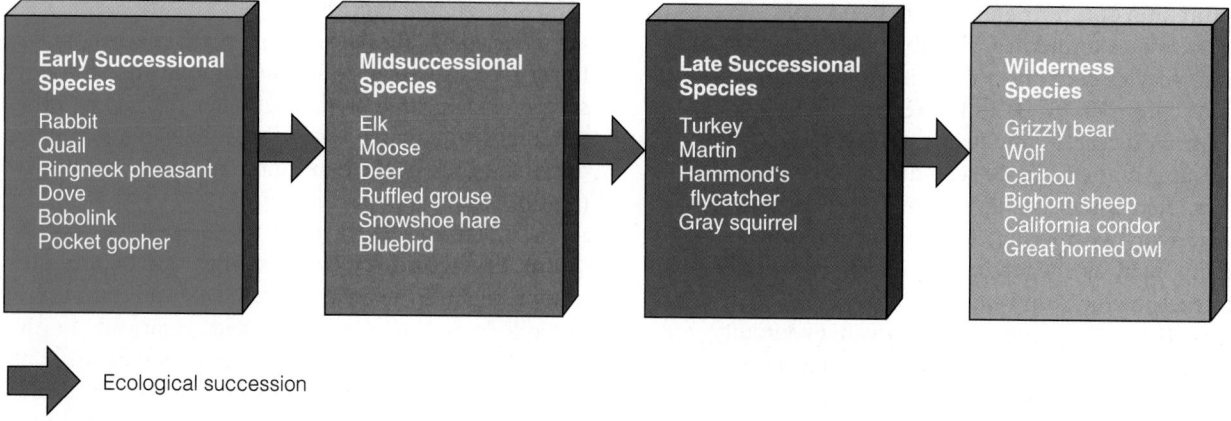

Figure 8-16 Examples of wildlife species typically found at different stages of ecological succession in areas of the United States with a temperate climate.

Descriptions of ecological succession usually focus on changes in vegetation. However, these changes in turn affect food and shelter for various types of animals. Thus, as succession proceeds, the numbers and types of animals and decomposers also change. Figure 8-16 shows some of the wildlife species likely to be found at various stages of secondary ecological succession in areas with a temperate climate.

Because primary and secondary succession involve changes in community structure, the various stages of succession have different patterns of **(1)** species diversity, **(2)** trophic structure, **(3)** niches, **(4)** nutrient cycling, and **(5)** energy flow and efficiency, as shown by the work of ecologists such as Eugene Odum (Table 8-1).

**How Do Species Replace One Another in Ecological Succession?** Ecologists have identified three factors that affect how and at what rate succession occurs.

| Table 8-1 Ecosystem Characteristics at Immature and Mature Stages of Ecological Succession | | |
|---|---|---|
| **Characteristic** | **Immature Ecosystem (Early Successional Stage)** | **Mature Ecosystem (Late Successional Stage)** |
| **Ecosystem Structure** | | |
| Plant size | Small | Large |
| Species diversity | Low | High |
| Trophic structure | Mostly producers, few decomposers | Mixture of producers, consumers, and decomposers |
| Ecological niches | Few, mostly generalized | Many, mostly specialized |
| Community organization (number of interconnecting links) | Low | High |
| **Ecosystem Function** | | |
| Biomass | Low | High |
| Net primary productivity | High | Low |
| Food chains and webs | Simple, mostly plant → herbivore with few decomposers | Complex, dominated by decomposers |
| Efficiency of nutrient recycling | Low | High |
| Efficiency of energy use | Low | High |

- *Facilitation,* in which one set of species makes an area suitable for species with different niche requirements. For example, as lichens and mosses gradually build up soil on a rock in primary succession, herbs and grasses can colonize the site. Similarly, plants such as legumes add nitrogen to the soil, making it more suitable for other plants found at later stages of succession.

- *Inhibition,* in which early species hinder the establishment and growth of other species. Inhibition often occurs when plants release toxic chemicals that reduce competition from other plants (interference competition). Succession then can proceed only when a fire, bulldozer, or other disturbance removes most of the inhibiting species.

- *Tolerance,* in which late successional plants are largely unaffected by plants at earlier stages of succession. Tolerance may explain why late successional plants can thrive in mature communities without eliminating some early successional and midsuccessional plants.

**How Do Disturbances Affect Succession and Species Diversity?** A disturbance is a change in environmental conditions that disrupts an ecosystem or community. Such disturbances can be catastrophic or gradual and caused by natural or human-caused changes (Table 8-2). At any time during primary or secondary succession, disturbances such as those listed in Table 8-2 can convert a particular stage of succession to an earlier stage.

Many people think of all environmental disturbances as harmful processes. Large catastrophic disturbances (Table 8-2) can devastate communities and ecosystems. However, many ecologists contend that in the long run some types of disturbances such as fires can be beneficial for the species diversity of some communities and ecosystems. Such disturbances create new conditions that can discourage or eliminate some species but encourage others by releasing nutrients and creating unfilled niches.

For example, when a large tree falls in a tropical forest, this local disturbance increases sunlight and

**Table 8-2 Changes Affecting Ecosystems**

| Catastrophic* | | Gradual* | |
|---|---|---|---|
| Natural | Drought | Natural | Climate change |
| | Flood | | Immigration |
| | Fire | | Adaption and evolution |
| | Volcanic eruption | | Ecological succession |
| | Earthquake | | Disease |
| | Hurricane or tornado | | |
| | Landslide | | |
| | Change in stream course | | |
| | Disease | | |
| Human-caused | Deforestation | Human-caused | Salinization and waterlogging of soils from irrigation |
| | Overgrazing | | Soil compaction |
| | Plowing | | Groundwater depletion |
| | Erosion | | Water and air pollution |
| | Pesticide application | | Loss and degradation of wildlife habitat |
| | Fire | | "Pests" and predator elimination |
| | Mining | | Introduction of nonnative species |
| | Toxic contamination | | Overhunting and overfishing |
| | Urbanization | | Toxic contamination |
| | Water and air pollution | | Urbanization |
| | Loss and degradation of wildlife habitat | | Excessive tourism |

*Many changes can be either catastrophic or gradual.

nutrients for growth of plants in the understory. When a log hits a rock in an intertidal zone (Figure 7-12, top, p. 151), this **(1)** dislodges or kills many of the organisms that are growing on the rock and **(2)** provides space for colonization of new intertidal organisms.

According to the *intermediate disturbance hypothesis,* communities that experience fairly frequent but moderate disturbances have the greatest species diversity (Figure 8-17). Researchers hypothesize that in such communities, moderate disturbances are large enough to create openings for colonizing species in disturbed areas but mild and infrequent enough to allow the survival of some mature species in undisturbed areas. Some field experiments have supported this hypothesis.

**How Predictable Is Succession, and Is Nature in Balance?** We may be tempted to conclude that ecological succession is an orderly sequence in which each stage leads predictably to the next, more stable stage. According to this classic view, succession proceeds until an area is occupied by a generally predictable and stable type of *climax community* that is **(1)** dominated by a few long-lived plant species and **(2)** in balance with its environment. This equilibrium model of succession is what ecologists meant when they talked about the *balance of nature.*

Over the last several decades, many ecologists have changed their views about balance and equilibrium in nature. When these ecologists look at a community or ecosystem, such as a young forest, they see continuous change, instability, and unpredictability instead of equilibrium, stability, and predictability.

Under the old *balance-of-nature* view, a large terrestrial community undergoing succession was viewed as eventually being covered with a predictable green blanket of climax vegetation. However, a close look at almost any ecosystem or community reveals that it consists of an ever-changing mosaic of vegetation patches at different stages of succession. These patches result from a variety of mostly unpredictable small and medium-sized disturbances (Figure 8-17).

This irregular quilt of vegetation increases the diversity of plant and animal life and provides sites where early successional species can gain a foothold. We can also observe a mosaic of shifting patches of plant and animal species in intertidal communities (Figure 7-12, p. 151) as a result of the random actions of waves.

Such research indicates that **(1)** *we cannot predict the course of a given succession or* **(2)** *view it as preordained progress toward an ideally adapted climax community.* Rather, succession reflects the ongoing struggle by different species for enough light, nutrients, food, and space to survive and gain reproductive advantages

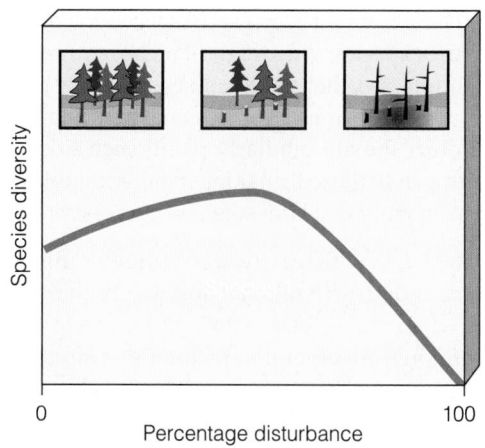

**Figure 8-17** According to the *intermediate disturbance hypothesis,* moderate disturbances in communities promote greater species diversity than small or major disturbances.

over other species by occupying as much of their fundamental niches as possible.

This change in the way we view what is happening in nature explains why a growing number of ecologists prefer terms such as *biotic change* instead of *succession* (which implies an ordered and predictable sequence of changes). Many ecologists have also replaced the term *climax community* with terms such as *mature community* or a mosaic of *vegetation patches* at different stages of succession. Ecologists do not consider nature totally chaotic and unpredictable, but they have lowered their expectations of being able to make accurate predictions about the course of succession.

## 8-6 ECOLOGICAL STABILITY AND SUSTAINABILITY

**What Is Stability?** All living systems, from single-celled organisms to the biosphere, contain complex networks of negative and positive feedback loops (p. 45) that interact to provide some degree of stability or sustainability over each system's expected life span.

*This stability is maintained only by constant dynamic change in response to changing environmental conditions.* For example, in a mature tropical rain forest, some trees die and others take their places. However, unless the forest is cut, burned, or otherwise destroyed, you will still recognize it as a tropical rain forest 50 or 100 years from now.

It is useful to distinguish among three aspects of stability or sustainability in living systems:

- **Inertia,** or **persistence:** the ability of a living system to resist being disturbed or altered

- **Constancy:** the ability of a living system such as a population to keep its numbers within the limits imposed by available resources

- **Resilience:** the ability of a living system to bounce back after an external disturbance that is not too drastic

**Does Species Diversity Increase Ecosystem Stability?** In the 1960s, most ecologists believed the greater the species diversity and the accompanying web of feeding and biotic interactions in an ecosystem, the greater its stability. According to this hypothesis, an ecosystem with a diversity of species and feeding paths has more ways to respond to most environmental stresses because it does not have "all its eggs in one basket." However, recent research has found exceptions to this intuitively appealing idea.

Because no ecosystem can function without some plants and decomposers, there is a minimum threshold of species diversity below which ecosystems cannot function.

Beyond this, it is difficult **(1)** to know whether simple ecosystems are less stable than complex ones or **(2)** to identify the threshold below which complex ecosystems fail. In part because some species play redundant roles (niches) in ecosystems, we do not know how many or which species can be eliminated before the entire ecosystem begins to lose stability or collapse.

Recent research by ecologist David Tilman and others indicates that **(1)** ecosystems with more species tend to have a higher net primary productivity and can be more resilient, but **(2)** the populations of individual species can fluctuate more widely in diverse ecosystems than in simpler ones. In 2002, biologists Margaret Palmer and Bradley Cardinale found that when several species of the caddisfly insect live together in a stream they get more food and are likely to be more productive than when a single caddisfly species lives in the same area.

Such studies support the idea that some level of biodiversity provides insurance against catastrophe, but how much biodiversity is needed in various ecosystems remains uncertain. For example, some recent research suggests that average annual net primary productivity of an ecosystem reaches a peak with 10–40 producer species. Many ecosystems contain more producer species than this, but it is difficult to distinguish among those that are essential and those that are not.

Part of the problem is that ecologists disagree on how to define *stability* and *diversity.* Does an ecosystem need both high inertia and high resilience to be considered stable? Evidence suggests that some ecosystems have one of these properties but not the other. For example, tropical rain forests have high species diversity and high inertia; that is, they are resistant to significant alteration or destruction. However, once a large tract of tropical forest is severely degraded, the ecosystem's resilience sometimes is so low that the forest may not be restored. Nutrients (which are stored primarily in the vegetation, not in the soil) and other factors needed for recovery may no longer be present. Such a large-scale loss of forest cover may so change the local or regional climate that forests can no longer be supported.

By contrast, grasslands **(1)** are much less diverse than most forests and **(2)** have low inertia because they burn easily. However, because most of their plant matter is stored in underground roots, these ecosystems have high resilience and recover quickly. A grassland can be destroyed only if **(1)** its roots are plowed up and something else is planted in its place, or **(2)** it is severely overgrazed by livestock or other herbivores.

Another difficulty is that populations, communities, and ecosystems are rarely, if ever, at equilibrium (balance). Instead, nature is in a continuing state of disturbance, fluctuation, and change.

**Why Should We Bother to Protect Natural Systems? The Precautionary Principle** Some developers argue that if biodiversity does not necessarily lead to increased ecological stability and if nature is mostly unpredictable, there is no point in trying to preserve and manage old-growth forests and other ecosystems. They conclude that we should **(1)** cut down diverse old-growth forests, use the timber resources, and replace the forests with tree plantations (Figure 6-39, p. 139), **(2)** convert the world's grasslands to cropfields (Figure 6-31, p. 132), **(3)** drain and develop inland wetlands, **(4)** dump our toxic and radioactive wastes into the deep ocean, and **(5)** not worry about the premature extinction of species.

Ecologists and conservation biologists point to the overwhelming evidence that human disturbances (Figure 8-18, p. 186) are disrupting some of the ecosystem services (Figure 4-34, p. 92) that support and sustain all life and all economies. They contend that our ignorance about the effects of our actions means we need to use great caution in making potentially harmful changes to ecosystems.

By analogy, we know that eating too much of certain types of foods and not getting enough exercise can greatly increase our chances of heart attacks, diabetes, and other disorders. But the exact connections between chemicals in these foods and between exercise and these health problems are largely unknown. Instead of using this uncertainty and unpredictability

**Figure 8-18** Examples of how some of the earth's natural resources are being depleted and degraded at an accelerating rate as a result of the exponential growth of the human population and resource use by humankind. (Data from the World Conservation Union, World Wildlife Fund, Conservation International, United Nations, Population Reference Bureau, U.S. Fish and Wildlife Service, and Daniel Boivin)

Grizzly bear

NORTH AMERICA

More than 60% of the Pacific Northwest coastal forest has been cut down.

Spotted owl

Eastern cougar

St. Lawrence beluga whale

Humpback whale

Fish catch in the north-west Atlantic has fallen 42% since its peak in 1973.

40% of North America's range and cropland has lost productivity.

Black-footed ferret

Florida panther

Chesapeake Bay is overfished and polluted.

California condor

Kemp's ridley turtle

Manatee

ATLANTIC OCEAN

Much of Everglades National Park has dried out and lost 90% of it's wading birds.

Hawaiian monk seal

Golden toad

Coral reef destruction

Every year 14,000 square kilometers of rain forest is destroyed in the Amazon Basin.

Half of the forest in Honduras and Nicaragua has disappeared.

Colombia has lost one-third of its forest.

Mangroves cleared in Equador for shrimp ponds.

PACIFIC OCEAN

Black lion tamarin

SOUTH AMERICA

Little of Brazil's Atlantic forest remains.

Southern Chile's rain forest is threatened.

Environmental degradation

Vanishing biodiversity

Endangered species

6.0 or more children per woman

as an excuse to continue overeating and not exercising, the wise course is to eat better and exercise more to help *prevent* potentially serious health problems.

This approach is based on the **precautionary principle:** When evidence indicates that an activity can harm human health or the environment, we should take precautionary measures to prevent harm even if some of the cause-and-effect relationships have not been fully established scientifically. It is based on the commonsense idea behind many adages such as "Better safe than sorry," "Look before you leap," "First, do no harm," and "Slow down for speed bumps."

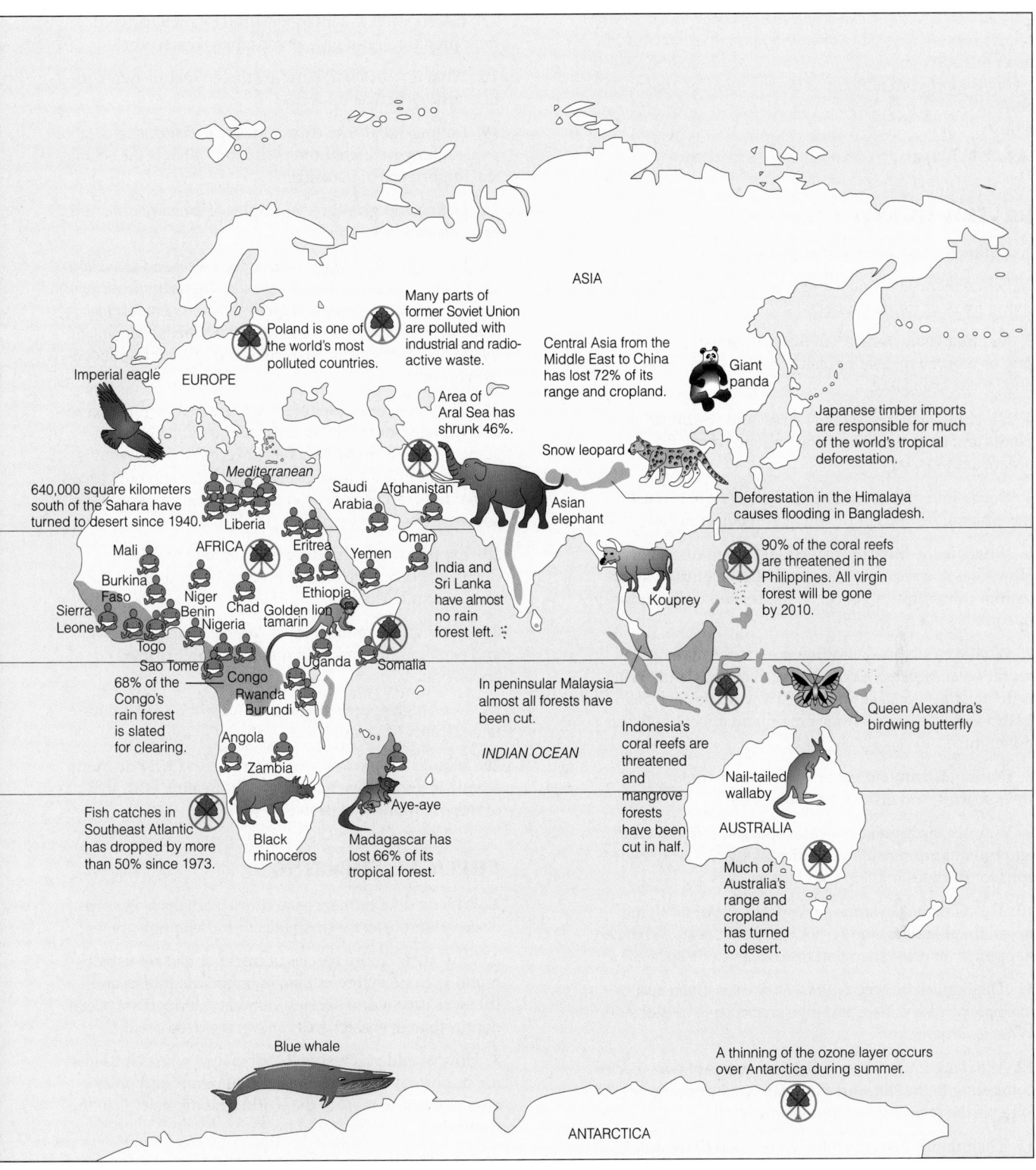

Imperial eagle

EUROPE

Poland is one of the world's most polluted countries.

Many parts of former Soviet Union are polluted with industrial and radioactive waste.

ASIA

Central Asia from the Middle East to China has lost 72% of its range and cropland.

Giant panda

Japanese timber imports are responsible for much of the world's tropical deforestation.

Area of Aral Sea has shrunk 46%.

Snow leopard

Mediterranean

640,000 square kilometers south of the Sahara have turned to desert since 1940.

Liberia

Saudi Arabia

Afghanistan

Asian elephant

Deforestation in the Himalaya causes flooding in Bangladesh.

Mali

AFRICA

Eritrea

Oman

Yemen

90% of the coral reefs are threatened in the Philippines. All virgin forest will be gone by 2010.

Burkina Faso

Niger

Chad

Ethiopia

India and Sri Lanka have almost no rain forest left.

Sierra Leone

Benin

Nigeria

Golden lion tamarin

Kouprey

Togo

Sao Tome

Uganda

Somalia

68% of the Congo's rain forest is slated for clearing.

Congo

Rwanda

Burundi

In peninsular Malaysia almost all forests have been cut.

INDIAN OCEAN

Queen Alexandra's birdwing butterfly

Angola

Zambia

Indonesia's coral reefs are threatened and mangrove forests have been cut in half.

Nail-tailed wallaby

AUSTRALIA

Fish catches in Southeast Atlantic has dropped by more than 50% since 1973.

Black rhinoceros

Aye-aye

Madagascar has lost 66% of its tropical forest.

Much of Australia's range and cropland has turned to desert.

Blue whale

A thinning of the ozone layer occurs over Antarctica during summer.

ANTARCTICA

This commonsense idea has been used for more than 20 years as a formal principle of German law called the *Vorsorgeprinzip* principle ("forecaring" principle). Recently the precautionary principle has formed the basis of several international environmental treaties. One example is the global treaty developed by 122 countries in 2000 to ban or phase out 12 *persistent organic pollutants* (POPs).

In this chapter we have seen that interdependence and connectedness of species, communities, and ecosystems are essential features of life on the earth.

*The old idea of a static landscape, like a single musical chord sounded forever, must be abandoned, for such a landscape never existed except in our imagination. Nature undisturbed by human influence seems more like a symphony whose harmonies arise from variation and change over every interval of time.*

DANIEL B. BOTKIN

## REVIEW QUESTIONS

**1.** Define the boldfaced terms in this chapter.

**2.** Describe the ecological and economic importance of flying foxes in tropical forests.

**3.** List four characteristics of the structure of a community or ecosystem. Distinguish between *species diversity* and *species abundance*.

**4.** Describe the types, relative sizes, and stratification of plants and animals in **(a)** a tropical rain forest, **(b)** an ocean, and **(c)** a lake.

**5.** Define and give an example of an *edge effect*. What are the advantages and disadvantages of edge effects?

**6.** What are the three most species-rich environments? How does species diversity vary with **(a)** latitude in terrestrial communities, **(b)** ocean depth, and **(c)** pollution in aquatic systems?

**7.** What two factors determine the species diversity found on an isolated ecosystem such as an island? What is the *theory of island biodiversity*? How do the size of an island and its distance from a mainland affect its species diversity?

**8.** Distinguish among *native*, *nonnative*, *indicator*, and *keystone* species, and give an example of each.

**9.** Why are birds good indicator species? Explain why amphibians are considered indicator species, and list reasons for declines in their populations.

**10.** Describe the keystone ecological roles of **(a)** flying foxes, **(b)** alligators, and **(c)** some shark species. What can happen in an ecosystem that loses a keystone species?

**11.** Distinguish between *intraspecific competition* and *interspecific competition*, and give an example of each. What is *territoriality*?

**12.** What are four options when the niches of two species competing in the same area overlap to a large degree? What is the *competitive exclusion principle*?

**13.** Distinguish between *interference competition* and *exploitation competition*, and give an example of each.

**14.** Define and give two examples of *resource partitioning*. How does it allow species to avoid overlap of their fundamental niches?

**15.** What is *predation*? Describe the *predator–prey relationship*, and give two examples of this type of species interaction.

**16.** Give two examples of how predators increase their chances of finding prey by **(a)** pursuit and **(b)** ambush.

**17.** List six ways (adaptations) used by prey to avoid their predators, and give an example of each type.

**18.** What is *symbiosis*? What are three types of symbiotic interactions between species?

**19.** Define and give two examples of *parasitism*, and explain how it differs from predation. What is the ecological importance of parasitism?

**20.** Define and give three examples of **(a)** *mutualism* and **(b)** *commensalism*.

**21.** Distinguish between *primary succession* and *secondary succession*. Distinguish among *pioneer* (or *early successional*) *species*, *midsuccessional plant species*, and *late successional plant species*. Distinguish among *facilitation*, *inhibition*, and *tolerance* as factors that affect how and at what rate succession occurs.

**22.** Give three examples of environmental disturbances, and explain how they can affect succession. How can some disturbances be beneficial to ecosystems? What is the *intermediate disturbance hypothesis*? Explain how occasional fires can be beneficial to succession and species in some types of ecosystems.

**23.** Explain why most ecologists contend that **(a)** the details of succession are not predictable and **(b)** no balance of nature exists.

**24.** Distinguish among *inertia*, *constancy*, and *resilience*, and explain how they help maintain stability in an ecosystem.

**25.** Does high species diversity always increase ecosystem stability? Explain.

**26.** What is the *precautionary principle*, and why do many scientists find it a useful strategy for dealing with some of the environmental problems we face?

## CRITICAL THINKING

**1.** Why do deer hunters sometimes plant corn on strips of open land used for firebreaks or for telephone poles?

**2.** Why are **(a)** more species of trees per hectare usually found in tropical forests than in temperate forests and **(b)** more tube worm species found at intermediate ocean depths than in coastal areas and in the deep ocean?

**3.** How would you respond to someone who claims it is not important to protect areas of temperate and polar biomes because most of the world's biodiversity is in the tropics?

**4.** What two factors determine the number of different species found on an island? Why is the species diversity of a large island usually higher than that on a smaller island?

**5.** What would you do if large numbers of cockroaches (Spotlight, p. 105) invaded your home? See whether you can come up with an ecological rather than a chemical (pesticide) approach to this problem.

**6.** How would you determine whether a particular species found in a given area is a keystone species?

**7.** Some butterfly species mimic other butterfly species that taste bad to predators such as birds (Figure 8-12f). Design an experiment to determine whether a particular mimic species of butterfly **(a)** tastes bad like its model (called *Müllerian mimicry* after Fritz Müller, who first recorded this phenomenon in 1878) or **(b)** does not taste bad but gains some protection by looking and acting like its bad-tasting model (called *Batesian mimicry* after Henry W. Bates, who first described this phenomenon in the 1860s).

**8.** Describe how evolution can affect predator–prey relationships.

**9.** How would you reply to someone who argues that **(a)** we should not worry about our effects on natural systems because succession will heal the wounds of human activities and restore the balance of nature, **(b)** if nature is largely unpredictable, why should we bother to preserve any natural systems, and **(c)** because there is no balance in nature and no stability in species diversity we should cut down diverse old-growth forests and replace them with tree plantations (Figure 6-39, p. 139)?

**10.** Suppose a hurricane blows down most of the trees in a forest. Timber company officials offer to salvage the fallen trees and plant a tree plantation to reduce the chances of fire and to improve the area's appearance, with an agreement that they can harvest the trees when they reach maturity and plant another tree plantation. Others argue that the damaged forest should be left alone because hurricanes and other natural events are part of nature, and the dead trees will serve as a source of nutrients for natural recovery through ecological succession. What do you think should be done, and why?

## PROJECTS

**1.** Make field studies, consult research papers, and interview people to identify and evaluate **(a)** the effects of the deliberate introduction of a beneficial nonnative species into the area where you live and **(b)** the effects of the deliberate or accidental introduction of a harmful nonnative species into the area where you live.

**2.** Use the library or Internet to find and describe two species not discussed in this textbook that are engaged in **(a)** a commensalistic interaction, **(b)** a mutualistic interaction, and **(c)** a parasite–host relationship.

**3.** Visit a nearby natural area and identify examples of **(a)** territoriality, **(b)** interference competition, **(c)** exploitation competition, **(d)** mutualism, and **(e)** resource partitioning.

**4.** Use the library or Internet to identify the parasites likely to be found in your body.

**5.** Visit a nearby land area such as a partially cleared or burned forest or grassland or an abandoned cropfield and record signs of secondary ecological succession. Study the area carefully to see whether you can find patches that are at different stages of succession because of various disturbances.

**6.** Use the library or the Internet to find bibliographic information about *Stuart L. Pimm* and *Daniel B. Botkin*, whose quotes appear at the beginning and end of this chapter.

**7.** Make a concept map of this chapter's major ideas, using the section heads and subheads and the key terms (in boldface). Look on the website for this book for information about making concept maps.

## INTERNET STUDY RESOURCES AND RESOURCES FOR FURTHER READING AND RESEARCH

The website for this book contains helpful study aids and many ideas for further reading and research. Log on to

www.info.brookscole.com/miller13

and click on the Chapter-by-Chapter area. Choose Chapter 8 and select a resource:

■ Flash Cards allows you to test your mastery of the Terms and Concepts to Remember for this chapter.

■ Tutorial Quizzes provides a multiple-choice practice quiz.

■ Student Guide to InfoTrac will lead you to Critical Thinking Projects that use InfoTrac College Edition as a research tool.

■ References lists the major books and articles consulted in writing this chapter.

■ Hypercontents takes you to an extensive list of sites with news, research, and images related to individual sections of the chapter.

## INFOTRAC COLLEGE EDITION

Improve your skills with InfoTrac College Edition, a searchable online database of articles from more than 700 periodicals. Log on to

http://www.infotrac-college.com

or access InfoTrac through the website for this book. Try to find the following articles:

**1.** Byers, J. E. 2000. Competition between two estuarine snails: Implications for invasions of exotic species. *Ecology* 81: 1225. *Keywords:* "competition" and "exotic species." The effects of exploitative competition between a native and an exotic species is examined to determine how competition influences the ability of exotic species to drive native species from a habitat.

**2.** Miller, L.A., and A. Surlykke. 2001. How some insects detect and avoid being eaten by bats: Tactics and countertactics of prey and predator. *BioScience* 51: 570. *Keywords:* "bats," "insects," and "tactics." Echolocating bats and their prey insects appear to be in an evolutionary relay race. This article describes in detail how these bats find the insects and how insects can avoid the bats.

# 9 POPULATION DYNAMICS, CARRYING CAPACITY, AND CONSERVATION BIOLOGY

## Sea Otters: Are They Back from the Brink of Extinction?

Southern sea otters (Figure 9-1a) live in kelp forests (Figure 9-1c) in shallow waters along the Pacific coast from Baja Mexico up the California coast. These tool-using animals use stones to **(1)** pry shellfish off rocks underwater and **(2)** break open the shells while swimming on their backs and using their bellies as a table. Each day a sea otter consumes about 25% of its weight in sea urchins (Figure 9-1b), clams, mussels, crabs, abalone, and about 40 other species of bottom-dwelling organisms.

Before European settlers arrived, about 1 million southern sea otters lived along the Pacific coastline of North America. By the early 1900s, this species was almost extinct mostly because of **(1)** overhunting for their warm, beautiful fur and **(2)** removal by abalone fishers.

Biologists have learned that southern sea otters are *keystone species* (p. 172) that help keep sea urchins from depleting kelp forests in offshore waters from Alaska to southern California. Without significant predation by sea otters, sea urchin populations expand and consume much of the kelp, which in turn lowers the diversity of other plants and animals in kelp forest ecosystems.

Preventing the loss of kelp forests has important ecological and economic benefits because they **(1)** provide essential habitats for a variety of species, **(2)** inhibit shore erosion, and **(3)** reduce the impact of storm waves on coastlines.

Since 1938, the population of southern sea otters has increased from about 300 to around 2,100. Wherever southern sea otters have returned or have been reintroduced, formerly deforested kelp areas recover within a few years and fish populations increase. This pleases biologists but upsets commercial fishers, who argue that sea otters consume too many abalone and compete with commercial fishing.

During the past few years, however, the southern sea otter population has been declining for unknown reasons. One possibility is increased pollution of coastal waters. Shellfish tend to concentrate toxins that are released into coastal waters. High levels of toxins may directly kill sea otters, and exposure to lower levels over long periods may reduce their resistance to disease and parasites.

Another possibility is increased predation of the otters by killer whales (orcas). Evidence indicates in some areas that they may consume southern sea otters when there is a decline in their normal prey of Stellar sea lions and harbor seals—whose numbers may have dropped because of overfishing of species they eat.

The dynamics of southern sea otter populations have helped us to better understand the ecological importance of this keystone species. *Population dynamics, conservation biology,* and *human impacts on natural ecosystems* are the subject of this chapter.

(a)

(b)

(c)

**Figure 9-1** **(a)** A southern sea otter. **(b)** A sea urchin. **(c)** A kelp bed.

*In looking at nature . . . never forget that every single organic being around us may be said to be striving to increase its numbers.*

CHARLES DARWIN, 1859

This chapter addresses the following questions:

- How do populations change in size, density, and makeup in response to environmental stress?

- What is the role of predators in controlling population size?

- What different reproductive patterns enhance the survival of different species?

- What is conservation biology?

- What are the major impacts of human activities on populations, communities, and ecosystems?

- How can we live more sustainably?

## 9-1 POPULATION DYNAMICS AND CARRYING CAPACITY

**What Are the Major Characteristics of a Population?** Populations are dynamic and change in response to environmental stress or changes in environmental conditions. They change in **(1)** *size* (number of individuals), **(2)** *density* (number of individuals in a certain space), **(3)** *dispersion* (spatial pattern such as clumping, uniform dispersion, or random dispersion, depending mostly on resource availability, Figure 9-2), and **(4)** *age distribution* (proportion of individuals of each age in a population) These changes, called **population dynamics,** occur in response to **(1)** environmental stress (Table 8-2, p. 183) and **(2)** changes in environmental conditions.

**What Limits Population Growth?** Four variables—*births, deaths, immigration,* and *emigration*—gov-

ern changes in population size. A population gains individuals by birth and immigration and loses them by death and emigration:

Population change = (Births + Immigration) − (Deaths + Emigration)

These variables depend on changes in resource availability or on other environmental changes (Figure 9-3, p. 192).

Populations vary in their capacity for growth, also known as the **biotic potential** of the population. The **intrinsic rate of increase (r)** is the rate at which a population would grow if it had unlimited resources. Generally, individuals in populations with a high intrinsic rate of increase **(1)** *reproduce early in life,* **(2)** *have short generation times* (the time between successive generations), **(3)** *can reproduce many times* (have a long reproductive life), and **(4)** *have many offspring each time they reproduce.*

Some species have an astounding biotic potential. For example, without any controls on its population growth, the ancestors of a single female housefly could total about 5.6 trillion flies within about 13 months, and within a few years there would be enough flies to cover the earth's entire surface.

However, this is not a realistic scenario because *no population can grow indefinitely.* In the real world, a rapidly growing population reaches some size limit imposed by a shortage of one or more limiting factors, such as light, water, space, or nutrients or too many competitors or predators. *There are always limits to population growth in nature.*

**Environmental resistance** consists of all the factors acting jointly to limit the growth of a population. The population size of a species in a given place and time is determined by the interplay between its biotic potential and environmental resistance (Figure 9-3, p. 192).

Together biotic potential and environmental resistance determine the **carrying capacity (K),** the number of individuals of a given species that can be sustained indefinitely in a given space (area or volume).

Clumped (elephants)

Uniform (creosote bush)

Random (dandelions)

**Figure 9-2** Generalized *dispersion patterns* for individuals in a population throughout their habitat. The most common pattern is one in which members of a population exist in *clumps* throughout their habitat (left), mostly because resources usually are found in patches.

POPULATION SIZE

0

| Growth factors (biotic potential) | Decrease factors (environmental resistance) |
|---|---|
| **Abiotic** | **Abiotic** |
| Favorable light | Too much or too little light |
| Favorable temperature | Temperature too high or too low |
| Favorable chemical environment (optimal level of critical nutrients) | Unfavorable chemical environment (too much or too little of critical nutrients) |
| **Biotic** | **Biotic** |
| High reproductive rate | Low reproductive rate |
| Generalized niche | Specialized niche |
| Adequate food supply | Inadequate food supply |
| Suitable habitat | Unsuitable or destroyed habitat |
| Ability to compete for resources | Too many competitors |
| Ability to hide from or defend against predators | Insufficient ability to hide from or defend against predators |
| Ability to resist diseases and parasites | Inability to resist diseases and parasites |
| Ability to migrate and live in other habitats | Inability to migrate and live in other habitats |
| Ability to adapt to environmental change | Inability to adapt to environmental change |

**Figure 9-3** Factors that tend to increase or decrease the size of a population. Whether the size of a population grows, remains stable, or decreases depends on interactions between its growth factors (*biotic potential*) and decrease factors (*environmental resistance*).

The intrinsic rate of increase (r) of many species depends on having a certain minimum population size, called the **minimum viable population (MVP).** If a population declines below the MVP needed to support a breeding population, **(1)** certain individuals may not be able to locate mates, **(2)** genetically related individuals may interbreed and produce weak or malformed offspring, and **(3)** the genetic diversity may be too low to enable adaptation to new environmental conditions. Then the intrinsic rate of increase falls and extinction is likely.

**What Is the Difference Between Exponential and Logistic Population Growth?** A population that has few if any resource limitations grows exponentially. *Exponential growth* starts out slowly and then proceeds faster and faster as the population increases. If number of individuals is plotted

against time, this sequence yields a *J*-shaped exponential growth curve (Figure 9-4a).

**Logistic growth** involves exponential population growth when there is a steady decrease in population growth with time as the population encounters environmental resistance and approaches the carrying capacity of its environment and levels off. After leveling off, a population with this type of growth typically fluctuates slightly above and below the carrying capacity. A plot of the number of individuals against time yields a sigmoid, or *S*-shaped logistic growth curve (Figure 9-4b). A case of such growth involves the sheep population on the island of Tasmania, south of Australia, in the early 19th century (Figure 9-5).

**What Happens If the Population Size Exceeds the Carrying Capacity?** The populations of some species do not make a smooth transition from exponential growth to logistic growth. Instead, such a population uses up its resource base and temporarily *overshoots,* or exceeds, the carrying capacity of its environment. This overshoot occurs because of a *reproductive time lag,* the period needed for the birth rate to fall and the death rate to rise in response to resource overconsumption.

In such cases the population suffers a *dieback,* or *crash,* unless the excess individuals switch to new resources or move to an area with more favorable conditions. Such a crash occurred when reindeer were introduced onto a small island off the southwest coast of Alaska (Figure 9-6).

Carrying capacity is not a simple, fixed quantity and is affected by many factors. Examples are **(1)** competition within and between species, **(2)** immigration and emigration, **(3)** natural and human-caused catastrophic events, and **(4)** seasonal fluctuations in the supply of food, water, hiding places, and nesting sites.

Humans are not exempt from overshoot and dieback, as shown by the tragedy on Easter Island (p. 40). Ireland also experienced a population crash after a fungus destroyed the potato crop in 1845. About 1 million people died, and 3 million people emigrated to other countries.

Technological, social, and other cultural changes (Section, 2-1, p. 22) have extended the earth's carrying

**(a) Exponential Growth**

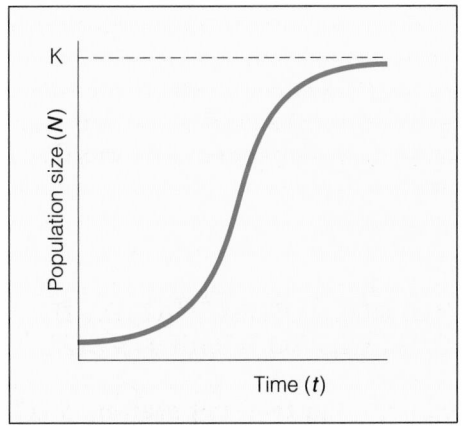

**(b) Logistic Growth**

**Figure 9-4** Theoretical population growth curves. **(a)** *Exponential growth*, in which the population's growth rate increases with time. Exponential growth occurs when resources are not limiting and a population can grow at its *intrinsic rate of increase* (r). Exponential growth of a population cannot continue forever because eventually some factor limits population growth. **(b)** *Logistic growth*, in which the growth rate decreases as the population gets larger. With time, the population size stabilizes at or near the *carrying capacity* (K) of its environment and results in a sigmoid (S-shaped) population growth curve.

capacity for the human species. We have increased food production and used large amounts of energy and matter resources to make normally uninhabitable areas of the earth habitable. However, there is growing concern about how long we will be able to keep doing this on a planet with **(1)** a finite size and resources and **(2)** a human population whose size (Figure 1-1, p. 2) and per capita resource use (Figure 1-11, p. 13) are growing exponentially.

**How Does Population Density Affect Population Growth?** *Density-independent population controls* affect a population's size regardless of its population density. Examples include **(1)** floods, **(2)** fires, **(3)** hurricanes, **(4)** unseasonable weather, **(5)** habitat

**Figure 9-5** *Logistic growth* of a sheep population on the island of Tasmania between 1800 and 1925. After sheep were introduced in 1800, their population grew exponentially because of ample food. By 1855, they overshot the land's carrying capacity. Their numbers then stabilized and fluctuated around a carrying capacity of about 1.6 million sheep.

destruction (such as clearing a forest of its trees or filling in a wetland), and **(6)** pesticide spraying. For example, a severe freeze in late spring can kill many individuals in a plant population, regardless of its density.

Some limiting factors have a greater effect as a population's density increases. Examples of such *density-dependent population controls* are **(1)** competition for resources, **(2)** predation, **(3)** parasitism, and **(4)** disease. As prey populations become denser, their members

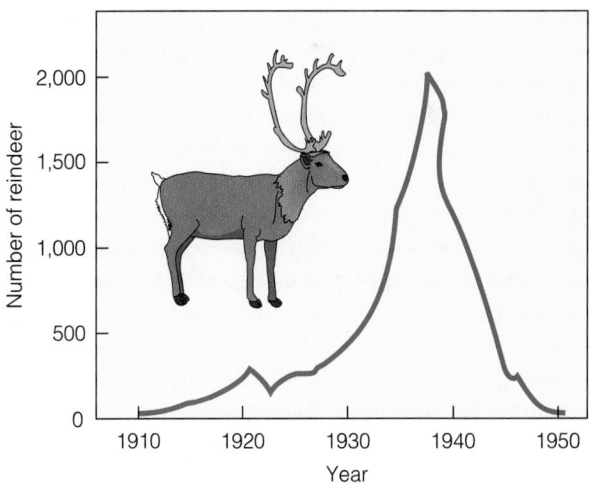

**Figure 9-6** Exponential growth, overshoot, and population crash of reindeer introduced to a small island off the southwest coast of Alaska. When 26 reindeer (24 of them female) were introduced in 1910, lichens, mosses, and other food sources were plentiful. By 1935, the herd's population had soared to 2,000, overshooting the island's carrying capacity. This led to a population crash, with the herd plummeting to only 8 reindeer by 1950.

compete more for limited resources. Individuals in a dense population also are more likely to be infected by parasites or contagious disease organisms.

Infectious disease is a classic example of density-dependent population control. An example is the *bubonic plague,* which swept through Europe during the 14th century. The bacterium that causes this disease normally lives in rodents. It was transferred to humans by fleas that fed on infected rodents and then bit humans. The disease spread like wildfire through crowded cities, where sanitary conditions were poor and rats were abundant. At least 25 million people in European cities died from the disease.

Many health scientists are becoming increasingly alarmed about the possibility of new epidemics of common infectious diseases in crowded urban areas. The primary reason is that many common strains of disease-causing bacteria are becoming genetically resistant to most existing antibiotics through directional natural selection (Figure 5-6, left, p. 102).

**What Kinds of Population Change Curves Do We Find in Nature?** In nature we find four general types of *population fluctuations:* stable, irruptive, irregular, and cyclic (Figure 9-7). A species whose population size fluctuates slightly above and below its carrying capacity is said to have a fairly *stable* population size (Figures 9-5 and 9-7a). Such stability is characteristic of many species found in undisturbed tropical rain forests, where average temperature and rainfall varies little from year to year.

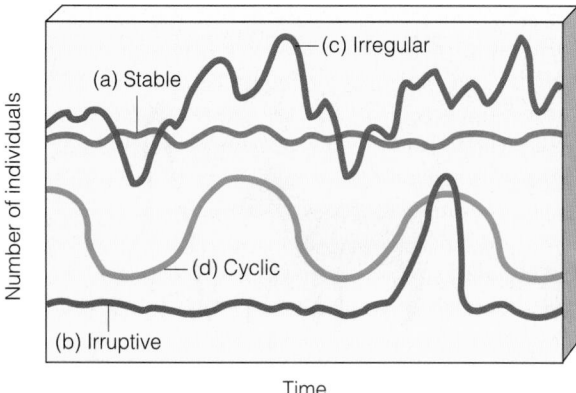

**Figure 9-7** General types of simplified population change curves found in nature. **(a)** The population size of a species with a fairly *stable* population fluctuates slightly above and below its carrying capacity. **(b)** The populations of some species may occasionally explode, or *irrupt,* to a high peak and then crash to a more stable lower level. **(c)** The population sizes of some species change irregularly for mostly unknown reasons. **(d)** Other species undergo sharp increases in their numbers, followed by crashes over fairly regular time intervals. Predators sometimes are blamed, but the actual causes of such boom-and-bust cycles are poorly understood.

Some species, such as the raccoon and feral house mouse, normally have a fairly stable population that may occasionally explode, or *irrupt,* to a high peak and then crash to a more stable lower level or in some cases to a very low level (Figures 9-6 and 9-7b). The population explosion is caused by some factor that temporarily increases carrying capacity for the population, such as **(1)** favorable weather, **(2)** more food, or **(3)** fewer predators.

Some populations exhibit what appears to be irregular *chaotic behavior* in their changes in population size, with no recurring pattern (Figure 9-7c). Some scientists attribute such behavior to chaos in such systems. Other scientists contend that the behavior may be caused by orderly, nonchaotic behavior whose details and interactions are still poorly understood.

The fourth type consists of *cyclic fluctuations* of population size over a regular time period (Figure 9-7d). Examples are **(1)** lemmings, whose populations rise and fall every 3–4 years, and **(2)** grouse, lynx, and snowshoe hare, whose populations generally rise and fall on a 10-year cycle.

## 9-2 THE ROLE OF PREDATION IN CONTROLLING POPULATION SIZE

**Do Predators Control Population Size? The Lynx–Hare Cycle** Some species that interact as predator and prey undergo cyclic changes in their numbers, with sharp increases in their numbers followed by seemingly periodic crashes (Figure 9-8).

For decades, predation has been the explanation for the 10-year population cycles of the snowshoe hare and its predator, the Canadian lynx (Figure 9-8). According to this *top-down control* hypothesis, lynx preying on hares periodically reduce their population. The shortage of hares then reduces the lynx population, which allows the hare population to build up again. At some point the lynx population increases to take advantage of the increased supply of hares, starting the cycle again.

Some research has cast doubt on this appealing hypothesis because snowshoe hare populations have been found to have similar 10-year boom-and-bust cycles on islands where lynx are absent. Researchers now hypothesize that the periodic crashes in the hare population can also be influenced by the food supply of the hares. Large numbers of hares can die when they **(1)** consume food plants faster than they can be replenished (especially during winter) and **(2)** have a decrease in the quantity and quality of their food. Once the hare population crashes, the plants recover, and the hare population begins rising again in a hare–plant cycle. If this *bottom-up control* hypothesis is

**Figure 9-8** Population cycles for the snowshoe hare and Canadian lynx. At one time it was widely believed these curves provided circumstantial evidence that these predator and prey populations regulated one another. More recent research suggests that the periodic swings in the hare population are caused by a combination of **(1)** predation by lynx and other predators (*top-down population control*) and **(2)** changes in the availability of the food supply for hares with the rise and fall of the hare population helping determine the lynx population (*bottom-up population control*). (Data from D. A. MacLulich)

correct, instead of lynx controlling hare populations, the changing hare population size may be causing fluctuations in the lynx population.

These two hypotheses are not mutually exclusive. According to extensive research by Charles J. Krebs, the 10-year population cycle of snowshoe hares in boreal forests is caused by an interaction between predation (by lynx, coyotes, and other predators) and food supplies (especially in winter), with predation being the dominant process.

According to biologists, genuine cases of top-down control systems by predators exist in a number of ecosystems. Examples are **(1)** wolves controlling deer populations and moose populations (Case Study, p. 197), **(2)** large predatory fish controlling other fish populations in lakes, and **(3)** sharks (Case Study, p. 176) and alligators (Connections, p. 173) controlling some fish populations.

## 9-3 REPRODUCTIVE PATTERNS AND SURVIVAL

**How Do Species Reproduce?** Reproductive individuals in populations of all species engage in a struggle for genetic immortality by trying to have as many members of the next generation as possible carry their genes. Genes can be passed on to offspring by the following means:

- **Asexual reproduction,** in which all offspring are exact genetic copies (clones) of a single parent. This type of reproduction is common in single-celled

species such as bacteria, in which the mother cell divides to produce two identical cells that are genetic clones or replicas of the mother cell.

- **Sexual reproduction,** in which organisms produce offspring by combining the gametes or sex cells (such as sperm and ovum) from both parents. This produces offspring that have combinations of traits (chromosomes) from each parent. About 97% of known organisms use sexual reproduction to perpetuate their species.

Sexual reproduction has several ecological costs and risks, which include the following:

- Females have to produce twice as many offspring to maintain the same number of young in the next generation as an asexually reproducing organism because males do not give birth.

- The chances of genetic errors and defects increase during the splitting and recombination of chromosomes.

- Mating entails costs such as **(1)** time-consuming courtship and mating rituals, **(2)** disease transmission, and **(3)** injury inflicted by males during mating.

So if sexual reproduction has so many costs and risks, why do 97% of the earth's organisms use it? Consider these two important advantages of sexual reproduction:

- It provides a greater genetic diversity in the offspring. Thus sexually reproducing organisms with "many different eggs in their genetic basket" have a greater chance of reproducing when environmental conditions change than does a brood of genetically identical clones with "only one type of egg in their genetic basket."

- Males can gather food for the female and the young and may protect and help train the young of some species. This is especially helpful for species such as mammals and birds that produce only a few young.

**What Types of Reproductive Patterns Do Species Have?** In 1967, Robert H. MacArthur and Edward O. Wilson suggested that species could be classified into two fundamental reproductive patterns, *r-selected* and *K-selected species,* on the basis of **(1)** their position on the sigmoid (S-shaped) population growth curve (Figure 9-9, p. 196) and **(2)** the characteristics of their reproductive patterns (Figure 9-10, p. 196).

**What Are Opportunist or r-Selected Species?** Species with a capacity for a high intrinsic rate of

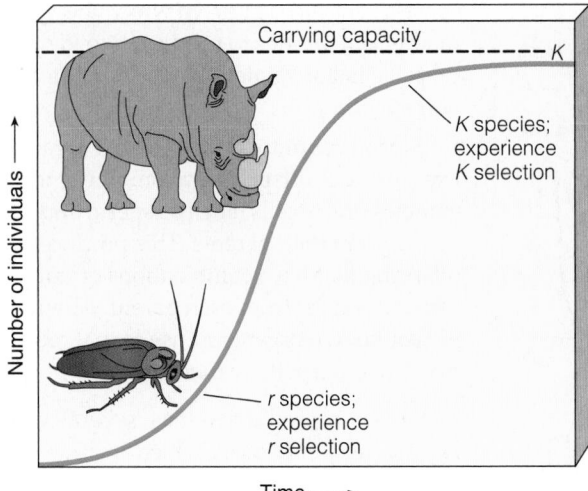

**Figure 9-9** Positions of *r-selected* and *K-selected* species on the sigmoid (S-shaped) population growth curve.

increase (*r*) are called **r-selected species** (Figure 9-9 and Figure 9-10, left). Such species reproduce early and put most of their energy into reproduction. Examples are algae, bacteria, rodents, annual plants (such as dandelions), and most insects (p. 64).

These species **(1)** have many (usually small) offspring each time they reproduce, **(2)** reach reproductive age rapidly, **(3)** have short generation times,

**(4)** give their offspring little or no parental care or protection to help them survive, and **(5)** are short lived (usually with a life span of less than a year). Species with this reproductive pattern overcome the massive loss of their offspring by producing so many unprotected young that a few will survive to reproduce many offspring to begin the cycle again.

Such species tend to be *opportunists*. They reproduce and disperse rapidly when conditions are favorable or when a disturbance (Table 8-2, p. 183) opens up a new habitat or niche for invasion, as in the early stages of ecological succession (Figures 8-14, p. 180, and 8-15, p. 181).

Changed environmental conditions from disturbances can allow opportunist species to gain a foothold. However, once established, their populations may crash because of **(1)** changing or unfavorable environmental conditions or **(2)** invasion by more competitive species. Therefore, most r-selected or opportunist species go through irregular and unstable boom-and-bust cycles in their population size. To survive, opportunists must continually invade new areas to compensate for being displaced by more competitive species.

**What Are Competitor or K-Selected Species?**
At the other extreme are *competitor*, or **K-selected species** (Figure 9-9 and Figure 9-10, right). These

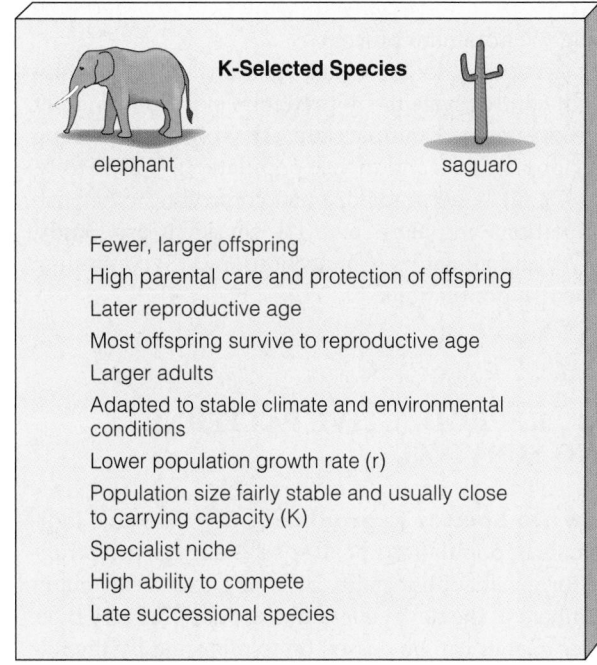

**Figure 9-10** Generalized characteristics of *r-selected* or opportunist species and *K-selected* or competitor species. Many species have characteristics between these two extremes.

## Wolf and Moose Interactions on Isle Royale

For decades, wildlife biologists have been studying the relationship between the moose and wolf populations on Isle Royale, an island in Lake Superior between Minnesota in the United States and Ontario in Canada (see figure).

In the early 1900s, a small herd of moose wandered across the frozen ice of Lake Superior to this island. With an abundance of food, the moose population exploded (see figure). In 1928, a wildlife biologist visiting the island successfully predicted that the large moose population would soon crash because the moose had stripped the island of most of its preferred food plants.

Sometime during the 1940s, timber wolves (probably a single pair) reached Isle Royale by traveling over the ice from the Canadian mainland during winter. They reproduced and slowly grew in numbers.

Since 1958, wildlife biologists have been tracking the populations of the two species (see figure). You might think that the wolves would have completely exterminated the moose, but instead the two species

have been interacting in what appears to be an oscillating predator–prey cycle (see figure). If the wolves could drive the moose to extinction they probably would, but the moose are too formidable for this to happen.

Since 1980, the wolf population has declined from a high of about 50 and fluctuated between 12 and 25 individuals. Possible reasons for this decline are **(1)** a canine virus introduced to wolves by dogs and **(2)** a low reproduction rate because of a lack of genetic variability from inbreeding.

With the decline in wolves, the moose population rose sharply until

1995. Then it crashed from a combination of lack of food, poor reproduction, a severe winter, and a tick infestation. By 1999, the wolf population, with plenty of weakened prey, had grown to 25. If their population continues to grow, they may hold the moose numbers in check and allow damaged vegetation to recover and begin a new cycle of interactions.

### Critical Thinking

What is the primary ecological lesson to be learned from the moose–wolf interaction on Isle Royale?

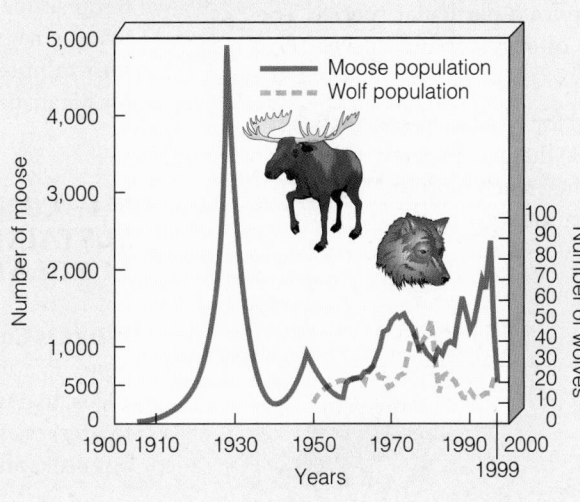

Changes in moose and wolf populations on Isle Royale, 1900–99. (Data from Rolf O. Peterson)

species **(1)** put fairly little energy into reproduction, **(2)** tend to reproduce late in life, **(3)** have few offspring with long generation times, and **(4)** put most of their energy into nurturing and protecting their young until they reach reproductive age.

Typically the offspring of such species **(1)** develop inside their mothers (where they are safe), **(2)** are fairly large, **(3)** mature slowly, and **(4)** are cared for and protected by one or both parents until they reach reproductive age. This reproductive pattern results in a few big and strong individuals that can compete for resources and reproduce a few young to begin the cycle again (Figure 9-10, right).

Such species are called K-selected species because they tend to do well in competitive conditions when their population size is near the carrying capacity (K) of

their environment. Their populations typically follow a logistic growth curve (Figure 9-4b and Figure 9-9). Examples are **(1)** most large mammals (such as elephants, whales, and humans), **(2)** birds of prey, and **(3)** large and long-lived plants (such as the saguaro cactus, oak trees, redwood trees, and most tropical rain forest trees). Many K-selected species, especially those with long generation times and low reproductive rates (such as elephants, rhinoceroses, and sharks, Case Study, p. 176), are prone to extinction.

Most competitor or K-selected species thrive best in ecosystems with fairly constant environmental conditions. In contrast, opportunists thrive in habitats that have experienced disturbances (Table 8-2, p. 183) such as a tree falling, a forest fire, or the clearing of a forest or grassland for raising crops.

Many organisms have reproductive patterns between the extremes of r-selected species and K-selected species, or they change from one extreme to the other under certain environmental conditions. In agriculture we raise both r-selected species (crops) and K-selected species (livestock).

The reproductive pattern of a species may give it a temporary advantage, but *the availability of suitable habitat for individuals of a population in a particular area is what determines its ultimate population size.* Regardless of how fast a species can reproduce, there can be no more dandelions than there is dandelion habitat and no more zebras than there is zebra habitat in a particular area.

**What Are Survivorship Curves?** Individuals of species with different reproductive strategies tend to have different *life expectancies.* One way to represent the age structure of a population is with a **survivorship curve,** which shows the number of survivors of each age group for a particular species. The three generalized types of survivorship curves (Figure 9-11) are

- *Late loss curves,* typical for K-selected species (such as elephants and humans) that produce few young and care for them until they reach reproductive age (thus reducing juvenile mortality).

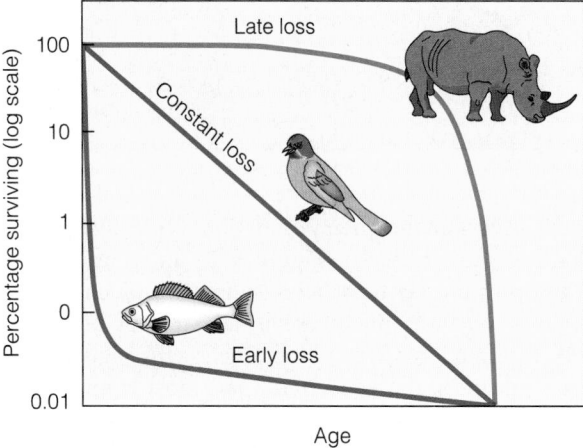

**Figure 9-11** Three general *survivorship curves* for populations of different species, obtained by showing the percentages of the members of a population surviving at different ages. For a *late loss* population (such as elephants, rhinoceroses, and humans), there is typically high survivorship to a certain age, then high mortality. A *constant loss* population (such as many songbirds) shows a fairly constant death rate at all ages. For an *early loss* population (such as annual plants and many bony fish species), survivorship is low early in life. These generalized survivorship curves only approximate the behavior of species.

- *Early loss curves,* typical for r-selected species (such as most annual plants and most bony fish species) that have **(1)** many offspring, **(2)** high juvenile mortality, and **(3)** high survivorship once the surviving young reach a certain age and size.

- *Constant loss curves,* characteristic of species with intermediate reproductive patterns with a fairly constant rate of mortality in all age classes and thus a steadily declining survivorship curve. Examples include many types of songbirds, lizards, and small mammals that face a fairly constant threat from starvation, predation, and disease throughout their lives.

A *life table* shows the numbers of individuals at each age from a survivorship curve. It illustrates the projected life expectancy and probability of death for individuals at each age. Insurance companies use life tables of human populations in various countries or regions to determine policy costs for their customers. Because life tables show that women in the United States survive an average of 7 years longer than men, for example, a 65-year-old man normally pays more for life insurance than a 65-year-old woman.

## 9-4 CONSERVATION BIOLOGY: SUSTAINING WILDLIFE POPULATIONS

**What Is Conservation Biology?** **Conservation biology** is a multidisciplinary science, originated in the 1970s, that uses the best available science to take action to preserve species and ecosystems. Conservation biology seeks answers to three questions:

- *Which species are in danger of extinction?*

- *What is the status of the functioning of ecosystems, and what ecosystem services (Figure 4-34, p. 92) of value to humans and other species are we in danger of losing?*

- *What measures can we take to help sustain ecosystem functions and viable populations of wild species?*

These are challenging questions, and the answers require extensive field research. To understand the status of natural populations, we must **(1)** measure the current population size, **(2)** project how population size is likely to change with time, and **(3)** determine whether existing populations are likely to be sustainable.

Conservation biology rests on three underlying principles:

- Biodiversity is necessary to all life on earth and should not be reduced by human actions.

- Humans should not **(1)** cause or hasten the extinction of wildlife populations and species or **(2)** disrupt vital ecological processes.

- The best way to preserve earth's biodiversity and ecological functions is to protect intact ecosystems that provide sufficient habitat for sustaining natural populations of species.

Conservation biology is based on Aldo Leopold's ethical principle that something is right when it tends to maintain the earth's life-support systems for us and other species and wrong when it does not (Section 2-5, p. 36).

**What Is Bioinformatics?**   Good conservation biology depends on good information. Increasingly, efforts of conservation biologists are focused on building computer databases that store useful information about biodiversity. Recently, a new discipline called *bioinformatics* has developed that **(1)** provides tools for storage and access to key biological information and **(2)** builds databases that contain the needed biological information.

## 9-5   HUMAN IMPACTS ON ECOSYSTEMS: LEARNING FROM NATURE

**How Have Humans Modified Natural Ecosystems?**   To survive and support growing numbers of people, we have greatly increased the number and area of the earth's natural systems that we have modified, cultivated, built on, or degraded (Figure 1-5, p. 7). We have used technology to alter much of the rest of nature in the following ways:

- *Fragmenting and degrading habitat.*
- *Simplifying natural ecosystems.* When we plow grasslands and clear forests, we often replace their thousands of interrelated plant and animal species with one crop (Figure 6-31, p. 132) or one kind of tree (Figure 6-39, p. 139)—called *monocultures*—or with buildings, highways, and parking lots. Then we spend a lot of time, energy, and money trying to protect such monocultures from invasion by **(1)** opportunist species of plants (weeds), **(2)** pests (mostly insects, to which a monoculture crop is like an all-you-can-eat restaurant), and **(3)** pathogens (fungi, viruses, or bacteria that harm the plants we want to grow).
- *Using, wasting, or destroying an increasing percentage of the earth's net primary productivity that supports all consumer species (including humans)* (Figure 4-26, p. 82). This is the main reason we are crowding out or eliminating the habitats and food supplies of a growing number of species.
- *Strengthening some populations of pest species and disease-causing bacteria by* **(1)** *speeding up natural selection and* **(2)** *causing genetic resistance through overuse of pesticides and antibiotics* (Figure 5-6, left, p. 102).

- *Eliminating some predators.* Some ranchers want to eradicate bison or prairie dogs that compete with their sheep or cattle for grass. They also want to eliminate wolves, coyotes, eagles, and other predators that occasionally kill sheep. Big game hunters also push for elimination of predators that prey on game species.
- *Deliberately or accidentally introducing new or nonnative species,* some beneficial (such as most food crops) and some harmful to us and other species.
- *Overharvesting renewable resources.* Ranchers and nomadic herders sometimes allow livestock to overgraze grasslands until erosion converts these ecosystems to less productive semideserts or deserts. Farmers sometimes deplete soil nutrients by excessive crop growing. Fish species are overharvested. Illegal hunting (poaching) endangers wildlife species with economically valuable parts (such as elephant tusks, rhinoceros horns, and tiger skins).
- *Interfering with the normal chemical cycling and energy flows in ecosystems.* Soil nutrients can erode from monoculture crop fields, tree plantations, construction sites, and other simplified ecosystems and can overload and disrupt other ecosystems such as lakes and coastal ecosystems. Chemicals such as chlorofluorocarbons (CFCs) released into the atmosphere can increase the amount of harmful ultraviolet energy reaching the earth by reducing ozone levels in the stratosphere. Emissions of carbon dioxide and other greenhouse gases—from burning fossil fuels and from clearing and burning forests and grasslands—can trigger global climate change by altering energy flow through the atmosphere.

To survive we must exploit and modify parts of nature. But, we are beginning to understand that any human intrusion into nature has multiple effects, most of them unpredictable (p. 46 and Connections, p. 200).

The challenge is to **(1)** maintain a balance between simplified, human-altered ecosystems and the neighboring, more complex natural ecosystems on which we and other life-forms depend and **(2)** slow down the rates at which we are altering nature for our purposes. If we simplify and degrade too much of the planet to meet our needs and wants, what is at risk is not the earth but our own species.

**Solutions: What Can We Learn from Nature About Living More Sustainably?**   Organisms, populations, and ecosystems are remarkably resilient when exposed to stresses (Table 8-2, p. 183) caused by natural or human-induced changes in environmental conditions. However, scientific research indicates that environmental stresses have harmful effects on organisms, populations, and ecosystems that can affect their environmental health and long-term sustainability (Figure 9-12, p. 200).

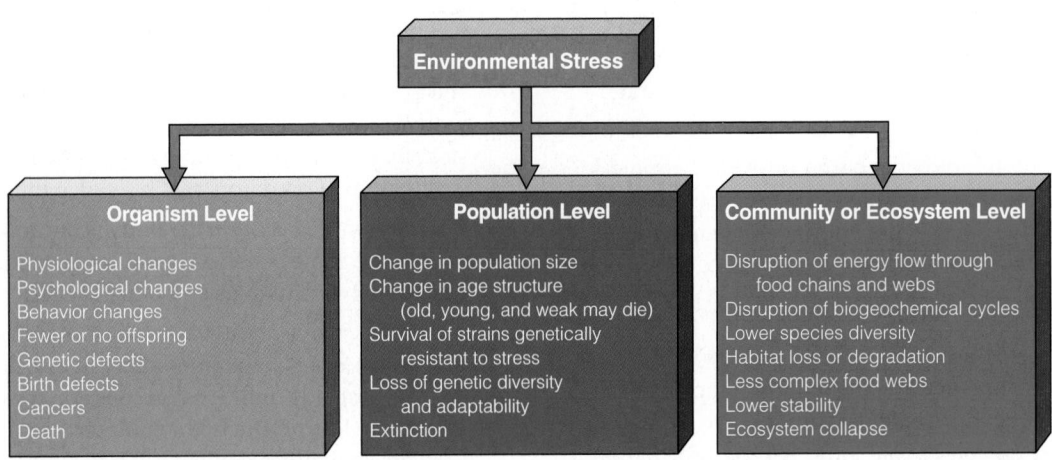

**Figure 9-12** Some effects of environmental stress on organisms, populations, communities, and ecosystems.

Many biologists believe the best way for us to live more sustainably is to **(1)** learn about the processes and adaptations by which nature sustains itself (Solutions, p. 201) and **(2)** mimic these lessons from nature.

Biologists have used these lessons from nature to formulate several principles to guide us in our search for more sustainable lifestyles:

- *Our lives, lifestyles, and economies are totally dependent on the sun and the earth.* We need the earth, but the earth does not need us.

- *Everything is connected to everything else.* The primary goal of ecology is to discover which connections in nature are the strongest, most important, and most vulnerable to disruption.

- *We can never do merely one thing.* Any human intrusion into nature has mostly unpredictable side effects. When we alter nature, we should ask, "And then what?"

- *We should reduce and minimize the damage we do to nature and help heal some of the ecological wounds we have inflicted.*

- *We should use care, restraint, humility, and cooperation with nature as we alter the biosphere to meet our needs and wants.*

Using such guidelines, we can create a more ecologically and economically sustainable society that lives within its ecological means by **(1)** taking no more than we need, **(2)** using renewable resources no faster

## Ecological Surprises

**CONNECTIONS**

Malaria once infected 9 out of 10 people in North Borneo, now known as Sabah. In 1955, the World Health Organization (WHO) began spraying the island with dieldrin (a DDT relative) to kill malaria-carrying mosquitoes. The program was so successful that the dreaded disease was nearly eliminated.

However, unexpected things began to happen. The dieldrin also killed other insects, including flies and cockroaches living in houses. The islanders applauded this turn of events, but then small lizards that also lived in the houses died after gorging themselves on dieldrin-contaminated insects.

Next, cats began dying after feeding on the lizards. Then, in the absence of cats, rats flourished and overran the villages. When the people became threatened by sylvatic plague carried by rat fleas, the WHO parachuted healthy cats onto the island to help control the rats.

Then the villagers' roofs began to fall in. The dieldrin had killed wasps and other insects that fed on a type of caterpillar that either avoided or was not affected by the insecticide. With most of its predators eliminated, the caterpillar population exploded, munching its way through its favorite food: the leaves used in thatched roofs.

Ultimately, this episode ended happily: both malaria and the unexpected effects of the spraying program were brought under control. Nevertheless, the chain of unforeseen events emphasizes the unpredictability of interfering with an ecosystem. It reminds us that when we intervene in nature, we need to ask, "And then what?"

### Critical Thinking

Do you believe the beneficial effects of spraying pesticides on Sabah outweighed the resulting unexpected and harmful effects? Explain.

## Principles of Sustainability: Learning from Nature

**SOLUTIONS**

Here are four basic ecological lessons or principles of sustainability derived from observing how nature works:

■ *Most ecosystems use renewable solar energy as their primary source of energy.* Thus a sustainable society would be powered mostly by current sunlight, not ancient sunlight stored as polluting fossil fuels.

■ *Ecosystems replenish nutrients and dispose of wastes by recycling chemicals.* There is almost no waste in nature because the waste outputs and decomposed remains of one organism are resource inputs for other organisms. Thus a sustainable society would emphasize **(1)** preventing and reducing waste and **(2)** recycling and reusing resources (Figure 3-21, p. 61).

■ *Biodiversity **(1)** helps maintain the sustainability and ecological functioning of ecosystems and **(2)** serves as a source of adaptations to changing environmental conditions.* Thus a sustainable society emphasizes conserving biodiversity by protecting ecosystems and preventing the premature extinction of species.

■ *In nature there are always limits to population growth and resource consumption.* The population size and growth rate of all species are controlled by their interactions with other species and with their nonliving environment, especially resource availability. Thus a sustainable society emphasizes reducing **(1)** births to control population growth and **(2)** resource consumption to prevent environmental overload and depletion of natural resources.

### Critical Thinking

List two ways in which human activities violate each of these four principles of sustainability. In what ways does your lifestyle violate these principles? Would you be willing to change these practices? What beneficial and harmful effects would such changes have on your lifestyle?

than nature replaces them, **(3)** preserving biodiversity and human cultural diversity, and **(4)** not depleting natural capital (Figure 4-34, p. 92).

*We cannot command nature except by obeying her.*
SIR FRANCIS BACON

## REVIEW QUESTIONS

**1.** Define the boldfaced terms in this chapter.

**2.** Explain how the populations of southern sea otters and kelp interact and why the southern sea otter is considered a keystone species.

**3.** What four factors affect population change?

**4.** Write an equation showing how population change is related to births, deaths, immigration, and emigration.

**5.** What is the *biotic potential* of a population? What are four characteristics of a population with a high *intrinsic rate of increase* (r)?

**6.** What are *environmental resistance* and *carrying capacity*? How do biotic potential and environmental resistance interact to determine carrying capacity? List four factors that can alter an area's carrying capacity. What is the *minimum viable population* size of a population?

**7.** Distinguish between *exponential* and *logistic growth* of a population, and give an example of each type.

**8.** How can a population overshoot its carrying capacity, and what are the consequences of doing this?

**9.** Distinguish between *density-dependent* and *density-independent factors* that affect a population's size, and give an example of each.

**10.** Distinguish among *stable, irruptive, irregular,* and *cyclic* forms of population change.

**11.** Distinguish between *top-down control* and *bottom-up control* of a population's size. Use these concepts to describe the effects of the predator–prey interactions between the snowshoe hare and the Canadian lynx on the population of each species.

**12.** Describe the predator–prey interactions between wolf and moose populations on Isle Royale. Is this a *top-down* or *bottom-up* form of population control?

**13.** Distinguish between *asexual reproduction* and *sexual reproduction*. What are the disadvantages and advantages of sexual reproduction?

**14.** List the characteristics of **(a)** *r-selected* or *opportunist species* and **(b)** *K-selected* or *competitor* species, and give two examples of each type. Under what environmental conditions are you most likely to find **(a)** r-selected species and **(b)** K-selected species?

**15.** What is a *survivorship curve*, and how is it used? List three general types of survivorship curves, and give an example of a species with each type.

**16.** What is *conservation biology*? What three questions does conservation biology try to answer? What are the three underlying principles of conservation biology? What is *bioinformatics*, and what is its importance?

**17.** List eight potentially harmful ways in which humans modify natural ecosystems.

**18.** List four *principles of sustainability* derived from observing how natural systems are sustained.

**19.** List five principles we could use to help us live more sustainably.

## CRITICAL THINKING

**1.** Why do **(a)** biotic factors that regulate population growth tend to depend on population density and **(b)** abiotic factors that regulate population tend to be independent of population density?

**2.** What are the advantages and disadvantages of a species undergoing **(a)** exponential growth (Figure 9-4a) and **(b)** logistic growth (Figure 9-4b)?

**3.** Suppose that because of disease or genetic defects from inbreeding, the wolves on Isle Royale (Case Study, p. 197) die off. Should we **(a)** intervene and import new wolves to help control the moose population or **(b)** let the moose population grow until it exceeds its carrying capacity and suffers another population crash? Explain.

**4.** Why are pest species likely to be extreme r-selected species? Why are many endangered species likely to be extreme K-selected species?

**5.** Why is an animal that devotes most of its energy to reproduction likely to be small and weak?

**6.** Given current environmental conditions, if you had a choice would you rather be an r-strategist or a K-strategist? Explain your answer. What implications does your decision have for your current lifestyle?

**7.** Predict the type of survivorship curve you would expect given descriptions of the following organisms:
  **a.** This organism is an annual plant. It lives only 1 year. During that time, it sprouts, reaches maturity, produces many wind-dispersed seeds, and dies.
  **b.** This organism is a mammal. It reaches maturity after 10 years. It bears one young every 2 years. The parents and the rest of the herd protect the young.

**8.** Explain why a simplified ecosystem such as a cornfield usually is much more vulnerable to harm from insects and plant diseases than a more complex, natural ecosystem such as a grassland.

**9.** How has the human population generally been able to avoid environmental resistance factors that affect other populations? Is this likely to continue? Explain.

**10.** Explain why you agree or disagree with the five principles for living more sustainably listed on p. 200.

## PROJECTS

**1.** Use the principles of sustainability derived from the scientific study of how nature sustains itself (Solutions, p. 201) to evaluate the sustainability of the following parts of human systems: **(a)** transportation, **(b)** cities, **(c)** agriculture, **(d)** manufacturing, **(e)** waste disposal, and **(f)** your own lifestyle. Compare your analysis with those made by other members of your class.

**2.** Use the library and Internet to choose one wild plant species and one animal species and analyze the factors that are likely to limit the populations of each species.

**3.** Use the library or the Internet to find bibliographic information about *Charles Darwin* and *Sir Francis Bacon,* whose quotes appear at the beginning and end of this chapter.

**4.** Make a concept map of this chapter's major ideas, using the section heads and subheads and the key terms (in boldface). Look on the website for this book for information about making concept maps.

## INTERNET STUDY RESOURCES AND RESOURCES FOR FURTHER READING AND RESEARCH

The website for this book contains helpful study aids and many ideas for further reading and research. Log on to

**www.info.brookscole.com/miller13**

and click on the Chapter-by-Chapter area. Choose Chapter 9 and select a resource:

- Flash Cards allows you to test your mastery of the Terms and Concepts to Remember for this chapter.

- Tutorial Quizzes provides a multiple-choice practice quiz.

- Student Guide to InfoTrac will lead you to Critical Thinking Projects that use InfoTrac College Edition as a research tool.

- References lists the major books and articles consulted in writing this chapter.

- Hypercontents takes you to an extensive list of sites with news, research, and images related to individual sections of the chapter.

## INFOTRAC COLLEGE EDITION

Improve your skills with InfoTrac College Edition, a searchable online database of articles from more than 700 periodicals. Log on to

http://www.infotrac-college.com

or access InfoTrac through the website for this book. Try to find the following articles:

**1.** Wangersky, R. 2000. Too many moose. *Canadian Geographic* 120: 44. *Keywords:* "Newfoundland," "moose," and "problems." Moose were introduced into Newfoundland where it is now thriving. But even though the introduction of moose has some benefits for humans, it is having significant adverse ecological impact.

**2.** Michigan Technological University. 2002. Longest-running predator-prey study in world links lack of wintry weather to changes in wolf, moose populations on Isle Royale in Lake Superior. *Ascribe Higher Education News Service* (March 12). *Keywords:* "predator-prey" and "Isle Royale." Most population-ecology books refer to the classic case of population regulation of moose and wolves on Isle Royale. This article indicates that other factors may also be affecting the populations of these animals.

# 10 GEOLOGY: PROCESSES, HAZARDS, AND SOILS

## The Mount St. Helens Eruption

For 123 years the volcano at Mount St. Helens (Figure 10-1, top) in the Cascade Range near the Washington–Oregon border, had slumbered. On May 18, 1980, it erupted with an enormous explosive force (Figure 10-1, bottom), causing the worst volcanic disaster in U.S. history.

Devastation occurred in three semicircular zones reaching out about 44 kilometers (27 miles) to the north of the volcano:

- In the *blast zone* or *tree-removal zone*, extending about 13 kilometers (8 miles), everything was obliterated or carried away.

- In the *tree-down zone*, extending 30 kilometers (19 miles) beyond the blast zone, a wave of ash-laden air blew the trees down like matchsticks.

- In the *seared zone*, 1–2 kilometers (0.6–1.2 miles) further out, trees were left standing but were scorched brown.

The explosion also threw ash more than 7 kilometers (4 miles) up into the atmosphere, high enough to be injected into global atmospheric circulation patterns. Several hours after the blast, ash-darkened sky triggered automatic streetlights during the morning in Yakima and Spokane, Washington. Within two weeks the ash cloud had traveled around the globe and eventually circled the planet several times before settling to the ground.

Fifty-seven people died in the eruption, and several hundred cabins and homes were destroyed or severely damaged. Tens of thousands of hectares of forest were obliterated, along with campgrounds and bridges. An estimated 7,000 big game animals (bear, deer, elk, and mountain lions) died, as did millions of smaller animals and birds and some 11 million fish.

Salmon hatcheries were damaged, and crops (including alfalfa, apples, potatoes, and wheat) were lost. Many people living in the area lost their jobs.

On the positive side, trace elements from ash that were added to the soil may eventually benefit agriculture. Increased tourism to the area to view the destruction also brought new jobs and income.

By 1990, biologists were surprised at how fast various forms of life had begun colonizing many of the most devastated areas. This rapid recovery taught biologists important and often surprising lessons about nature's ability to recover from what seems to be devastation.

We live on a dynamic planet. Energy from the sun and from the earth's interior, coupled with the erosive power of flowing water, have created continents, mountains, valleys, plains, and ocean basins in an ongoing process that continues to change the landscape. **Geology** is the science devoted to the study of these dynamic processes. Geologists study and analyze rocks and the features and processes of the earth's interior and surface. Some of these processes lead to geologic hazards such as earthquakes and volcanic eruptions (Figure 10-1), and others produce the renewable soil and nonrenewable mineral resources and energy resources that support life and economies.

U.S. Geological Survey

U.S. Geological Survey

**Figure 10-1** Mount St. Helens, a composite volcano in Washington, near the Oregon border, before (top), and shortly after (bottom), its major eruption in May 1980.

*Civilization exists by geological consent, subject to change without notice.*

WILL DURANT

This chapter addresses the following questions:

- What major geologic processes occur within the earth and on its surface?
- What are rocks, and how are they recycled by the rock cycle?
- What are the hazards from earthquakes and volcanic eruptions?
- What are soils, and how are they formed?
- What is soil erosion, and how can it be reduced?

## 10-1 GEOLOGIC PROCESSES

**What Is the Earth's Structure?**  As the primitive earth cooled over eons, its interior separated into three major concentric zones, which geologists identify as the *core,* the *mantle,* and the *crust* (Figure 4-6, p. 68, and Figure 10-2). What we know about the earth's interior comes mostly from indirect evidence: **(1)** density measurements, **(2)** seismic (earthquake) wave studies, **(3)** measurements of heat flow from the interior, **(4)** lava analyses, and **(5)** research on meteorite composition.

The earth's innermost zone, the **core** (Figure 10-2), is very hot and has a solid inner part, surrounded by a liquid core of molten material. A thick, solid zone called the **mantle** surrounds the earth's core (Figure 10-2). Most of the mantle is solid rock, but under its rigid outermost part is a zone of very hot, partly melted rock that flows like soft plastic. This plastic region of the mantle is called the *asthenosphere.*

The outermost and thinnest zone of the earth is called the **crust** (Figure 10-2). It consists of **(1)** the *continental crust,* which underlies the continents (including the continental shelves extending into the oceans, Figure 10-3 and Figure 7-7, p. 148), and **(2)** the *oceanic crust,* which underlies the ocean basins and covers 71% of the earth's surface (Figure 10-3).

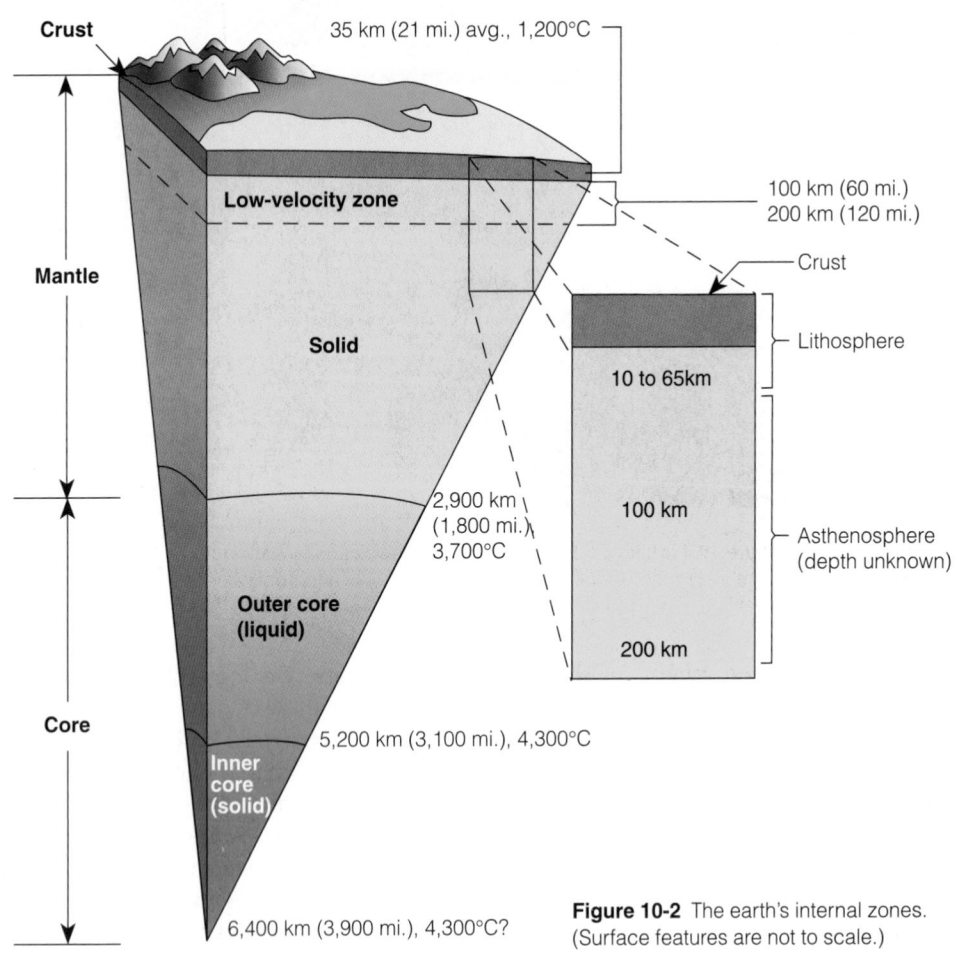

**Figure 10-2** The earth's internal zones. (Surface features are not to scale.)

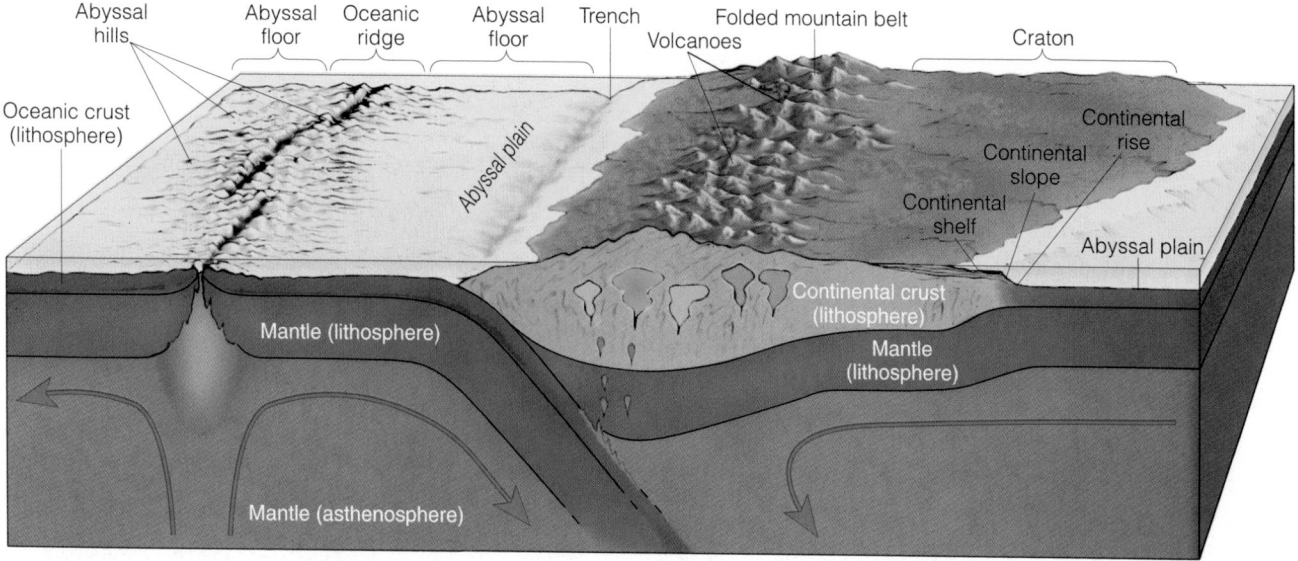

Abyssal hills
Abyssal floor
Oceanic ridge
Abyssal floor
Trench
Volcanoes
Folded mountain belt
Craton
Oceanic crust (lithosphere)
Abyssal plain
Continental rise
Continental slope
Continental shelf
Abyssal plain
Mantle (lithosphere)
Continental crust (lithosphere)
Mantle (lithosphere)
Mantle (asthenosphere)

**Figure 10-3** Major features of the earth's crust and upper mantle. The *lithosphere*, composed of the crust and outermost mantle, is rigid and brittle. The *asthenosphere*, a zone in the mantle, can be deformed by heat and pressure.

## 10-2 INTERNAL AND EXTERNAL EARTH PROCESSES

**What Geologic Processes Occur Within the Earth's Interior?** We tend to think of the earth's crust, mantle, and core as fairly static. However, they are constantly changed by geologic processes taking place within the earth and on the earth's surface, most over thousands to millions of years (Figure 10-4, p. 206).

Geologic changes originating from the earth's interior are called *internal processes*; generally they build up the planet's surface. Heat from the earth's interior provides the energy for these processes (Figure 10-4, p. 206), but gravity also plays a role.

Residual heat from the earth's formation is still being given off as the inner core cools and as the outer core cools and solidifies. Continued decay of radioactive elements in the crust, especially the continental crust, adds to the heat flow from within.

This heat from the earth's core causes much of the mantle to deform and flow slowly like heated plastic (in the same way that a red-hot iron horseshoe behaves plastically). Measurements of heat flow within the earth suggest that two kinds of movement occur in the mantle's asthenosphere:

- *Convection cells*, in which large volumes of heated rock move (Figure 10-4), following a pattern resembling convection in the atmosphere (Figure 6-10, p. 117) or a pot of boiling water (Figure 3-11, left, p. 53)

- *Mantle plumes*, in which mantle rock flows slowly upward in a column (Figure 10-4, p. 206), like smoke from a chimney on a cold, calm morning. When the moving rock reaches the top of the plume, it moves out in a radial pattern, as if it were flowing up an umbrella through the handle and then spreading out in all directions from the tip of the umbrella to the rim.

**What Is Plate Tectonics?** Both convection currents and mantle plumes move upward as the heated material is displaced by denser, cooler material sinking under the influence of gravity (Figure 10-4). These flows of energy and heated material in the mantle convection cells cause movement of rigid plates, called **tectonic plates** (Figure 10-4 and Figure 10-5b, p. 207). These plates are about 100 kilometers (60 miles) thick. They are composed of the continental and oceanic crust and the rigid, outermost part of the mantle (above the asthenosphere), a combination called the **lithosphere** (Figure 10-3).

These plates move constantly, supported by the slowly flowing asthenosphere like large pieces of ice floating on the surface of a lake. Some plates move faster than others do, but a typical speed is about the rate at which fingernails grow.

The theory explaining the movements of the plates and the processes that occur at their boundaries is called **plate tectonics.** The concept, which became widely accepted by geologists in the 1960s, was developed from an earlier idea called *continental drift.* Throughout the earth's history, continents have split

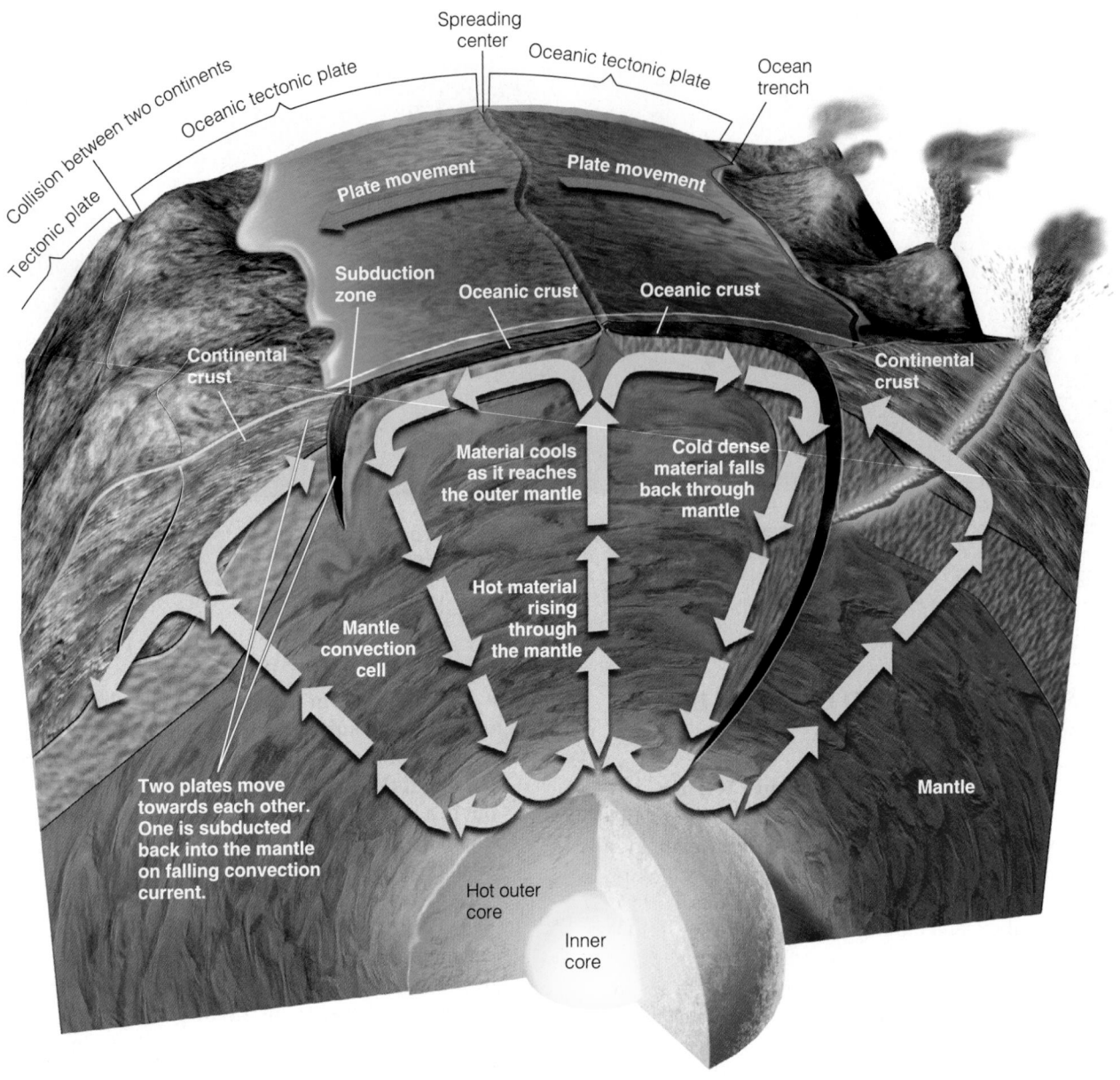

Spreading
center

Collision between two continents

Oceanic tectonic plate

Oceanic tectonic plate

Ocean
trench

Tectonic plate

**Plate movement**

**Plate movement**

**Subduction
zone**

**Oceanic crust**

**Oceanic crust**

**Continental
crust**

**Continental
crust**

**Material cools
as it reaches
the outer mantle**

**Cold dense
material falls
back through
mantle**

**Mantle
convection
cell**

**Hot material
rising
through
the mantle**

**Mantle**

**Two plates move
towards each other.
One is subducted
back into the mantle
on falling convection
current.**

Hot outer
core

Inner
core

**Figure 10-4** The earth's crust is made up of a series of rigid plates, called *tectonic plates*, which move around in response to forces in the mantle.

and joined as plates have drifted thousands of kilometers back and forth across the planet's surface (Figure 5-9, p. 106).

Plate motion produces mountains (including volcanoes), the oceanic ridge system, trenches, and other features of the earth's surface (Figure 10-3). Natural hazards such as volcanoes and earthquakes are likely to be found at plate boundaries (Figure 10-5a), and plate movements and interactions concentrate many of the minerals we extract and use.

The theory of plate tectonics also helps explain how certain patterns of biological evolution occurred. By reconstructing the course of continental drift over

millions of years (Figure 5-9, p. 106), we can trace how life-forms migrated from one area to another when continents that are now far apart were still joined together. As the continents separated, populations became geographically and reproductively isolated, and speciation occurred (Figure 5-8, p. 105).

**Figure 10-5** (facing page) Earthquake and volcano sites are distributed mostly in bands along the planet's surface **(a)**. These bands correspond to the patterns for the types of lithospheric plate boundaries **(b)** shown in Figure 10-6 (p. 208).

(a)  ● Volcanoes  ● Earthquakes

EURASIAN PLATE

JUAN DE
FUCA PLATE

NORTH
AMERICAN
PLATE

Transform
fault

Mid-
Atlantic
Ocean
Ridge

Reykjanes
Ridge

EURASIAN
PLATE

ANATOLIAN PLATE

CHINA
SUBPLATE

PHILIPPINE
PLATE

PACIFIC
PLATE

COCOS
PLATE

CARIBBEAN
PLATE

ARABIAN
PLATE

Mid-
Indian
Ocean
Ridge

Transform
fault

East Pacific
Rise

SOUTH
AMERICAN
PLATE

NAZCA
PLATE

AFRICAN
PLATE

SOMALIAN
SUBPLATE

Carlsberg
Ridge

INDIAN-AUSTRALIAN PLATE

Southeast Indian
Ocean Ridge

Transform
fault

Southwest Indian
Ocean Ridge

ANTARCTIC PLATE

(b)  ▲▲▲ Convergent
plate boundaries

Plate motion
at convergent
plate boundaries

Divergent ( ╱ ) and
transform fault (⇌)
boundaries

Plate motion
at divergent
plate boundaries

**Oceanic ridge at a divergent plate boundary**

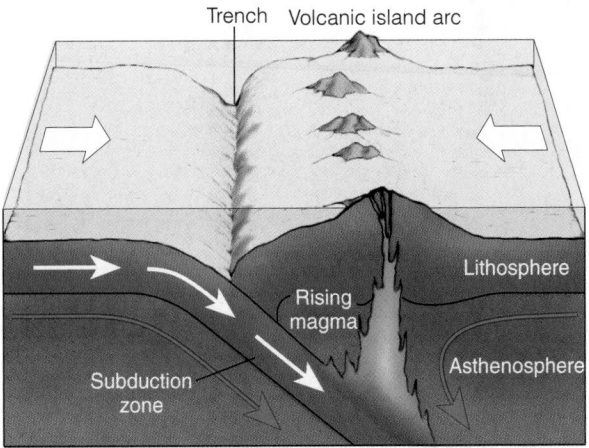

**Trench and volcanic island arc at a convergent plate boundary**

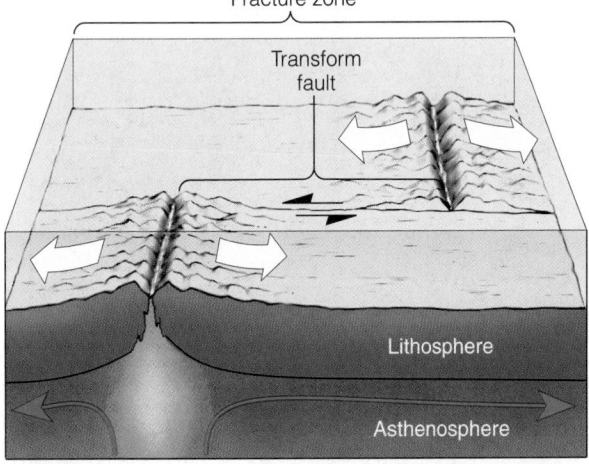

**Transform fault connecting two divergent plate boundaries**

**Figure 10-6** Types of boundaries between the earth's lithospheric plates. All three boundary types occur both in oceans and on continents.

**What Types of Boundaries Occur Between the Earth's Plates?** Lithospheric plates have three types of boundaries (Figure 10-6):

■ **Divergent plate boundaries,** where the plates move apart in opposite directions (Figure 10-4 and Figure 10-6, top)

■ **Convergent plate boundaries,** where the plates are pushed together by internal forces (Figures 10-5b and 10-6, middle). At most convergent plate boundaries, oceanic lithosphere is carried downward (subducted) under the island arc or the continent at a **subduction zone.** A *trench* ordinarily forms at the boundary between the two converging plates (Figure 10-6, middle). Stresses in the plate undergoing subduction cause earthquakes at convergent plate boundaries.

■ **Transform faults,** which occur where plates slide past one another along a fracture (fault) in the lithosphere (Figure 10-6, bottom). Most transform faults are on the ocean floor (Figure 10-5b).

**What Geologic Processes Occur on the Earth's Surface? Erosion and Weathering** Geological changes based directly or indirectly on energy from the sun and on gravity (rather than on heat in the earth's interior) are called *external processes.* Whereas internal processes generally build up the earth's surface, external processes tend to wear it down and produce a variety of landforms and environments formed by the buildup of eroded sediment (Figure 10-7).

A major external process is **erosion:** the process by which material is **(1)** dissolved, loosened, or worn away from one part of the earth's surface and **(2)** deposited in other places. Streams, the most important agent of erosion, operate everywhere on the earth except in the polar regions (Figure 7-2, p. 145). They produce valleys and canyons, and may form deltas where streams flow into lakes and oceans (Figure 7-23, p. 160). Some erosion is caused when wind blows particles of soil from one area to another (Figure 6-1, p. 110). Human activities, particularly those that destroy vegetation, accelerate erosion.

**Weathering** caused by mechanical or chemical processes usually produces loosened material that can be eroded. There are two types of weathering processes:

■ *Mechanical weathering,* in which a large rock mass is broken into smaller fragments of the original material, similar to the results you would get by using a hammer to break a rock into small fragments. The most important agent of mechanical weathering is *frost wedging,* in which water **(1)** collects in pores and cracks of rock, **(2)** expands upon freezing, and **(3)** splits off pieces of the rock.

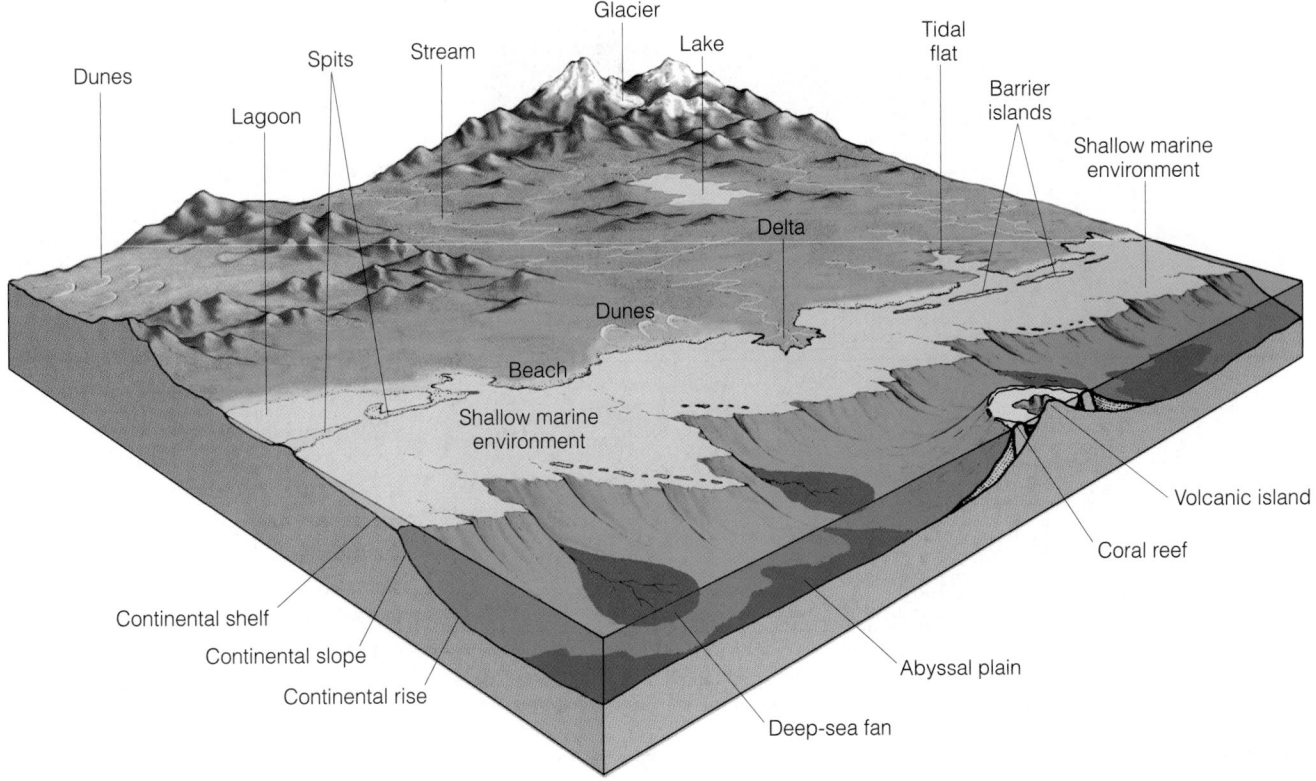

Dunes

Lagoon

Spits

Stream

Glacier

Lake

Tidal flat

Barrier islands

Shallow marine environment

Delta

Dunes

Beach

Shallow marine environment

Volcanic island

Coral reef

Continental shelf

Continental slope

Continental rise

Abyssal plain

Deep-sea fan

**Figure 10-7** The variety of landforms and sedimentary environments depicted here result mainly from *external processes*. They are powered primarily by solar energy (as it drives the hydrologic cycle and wind) and gravity, with some assistance from organisms such as reef-building corals.

■ *Chemical weathering,* in which one or more chemical reactions decompose a mass of rock. Most chemical weathering involves a reaction of rock material with oxygen, carbon dioxide, and moisture in the atmosphere and the ground.

## 10-3 MINERALS, ROCKS, AND THE ROCK CYCLE

**What Are Minerals and Rocks?**    The earth's crust, still forming in various places, is composed of minerals and rocks. It is the source of almost all the nonrenewable resources we use: fossil fuels, metallic minerals, and nonmetallic minerals (Figure 1-6, p. 9). It is also the source of soil and of the elements that make up our bodies and those of other living organisms.

A **mineral** is an element or inorganic compound that occurs naturally and is solid. Some minerals consist of a single element, such as gold, silver, diamond (carbon), and sulfur. However, most of the more than 2,000 identified minerals occur as inorganic compounds formed by various combinations of elements. Examples are salt, mica, and quartz.

**Rock** is any material that makes up a large, natural, continuous part of the earth's crust. Some kinds of rock, such as limestone (calcium carbonate, or $CaCO_3$) and quartzite (silicon dioxide, or $SiO_2$), contain only one mineral, but most rocks consist of two or more minerals.

**What Are the Three Major Rock Types?**    Based on the way it forms, rock is placed in three broad classes:

■ **Igneous rock** formed below or on the earth's surface when molten rock material (magma) **(1)** wells up from the earth's upper mantle or deep crust, **(2)** cools, and **(3)** hardens into rock. Examples are **(1)** granite (formed underground) and **(2)** lava rock (formed above ground when molten lava cools and hardens). Although often covered by sedimentary rocks or soil, igneous rocks form the bulk of the earth's crust. They also are the main source of many nonfuel mineral resources.

■ **Sedimentary rock** formed from sediment when preexisting rocks are **(1)** weathered and eroded into small pieces, **(2)** transported from their sources, and **(3)** deposited in a body of surface water. Examples are **(1)** sandstone and shale formed from pressure created

**Figure 10-8** The *rock cycle*, the slowest of the earth's cyclic processes. The earth's materials are recycled over millions of years by three processes: *melting, erosion,* and *metamorphism,* which produce *igneous, sedimentary,* and *metamorphic* rocks. Rock of any of the three classes can be converted to rock of either of the other two classes (or can even be recycled within its own class).

by deposited layers of sediment, **(2)** dolomite and limestone formed from the compacted shells, skeletons, and other remains of dead organisms, and **(3)** lignite and bituminous coal derived from plant remains.

■ **Metamorphic rock** produced when a preexisting rock is subjected to **(1)** high temperatures (which may cause it to melt partially), **(2)** high pressures, **(3)** chemically active fluids, or **(4)** a combination of these agents. Examples are anthracite (a form of coal), slate, and marble.

**What Is the Rock Cycle?**   Rocks are constantly exposed to various physical and chemical conditions that can change them over time. The interaction of processes that change rocks from one type to another is called the **rock cycle** (Figure 10-8).

The slowest of the earth's cyclic processes, the rock cycle recycles material over millions of years. It concentrates the planet's nonrenewable mineral resources on which we depend.

## 10-4 NATURAL HAZARDS: EARTHQUAKES AND VOLCANIC ERUPTIONS

**What Are Earthquakes?**   Stress in the earth's crust can cause solid rock to deform until it suddenly fractures and shifts along the fracture, producing a *fault*

(Figure 10-6, bottom. The faulting or a later abrupt movement on an existing fault causes an **earthquake.**

An earthquake has certain features and effects (Figure 10-9). When the stressed parts of the earth suddenly fracture or shift, energy is released as shock waves, which move outward from the earthquake's focus like ripples in a pool of water. The *focus* of an earthquake is the point of initial movement, and the *epicenter* is the point on the surface directly above the focus (Figure 10-9).

One way to measure the severity of an earthquake is by its *magnitude* on a modified version of the Richter scale. The magnitude is a measure of the amount of energy released in the earthquake, as indicated by the amplitude (size) of the vibrations when they reach a recording instrument (seismograph). Using this approach, seismologists rate earthquakes as **(1)** *insignificant* (less than 4.0 on the Richter scale), **(2)** *minor* (4.0–4.9), **(3)** *damaging* (5.0–5.9), **(4)** *destructive* (6.0–6.9), **(5)** *major* (7.0–7.9), and **(6)** *great* (over 8.0). Each unit on the Richter scale represents an amplitude that is 10 times greater than the next smaller unit. Thus a magnitude 5.0 earthquake is 10 times greater than a magnitude 4.0, and a magnitude 6.0 quake is 100 times greater than a magnitude 4.0 quake.

Earthquakes often have *aftershocks* that gradually decrease in frequency over a period of up to several

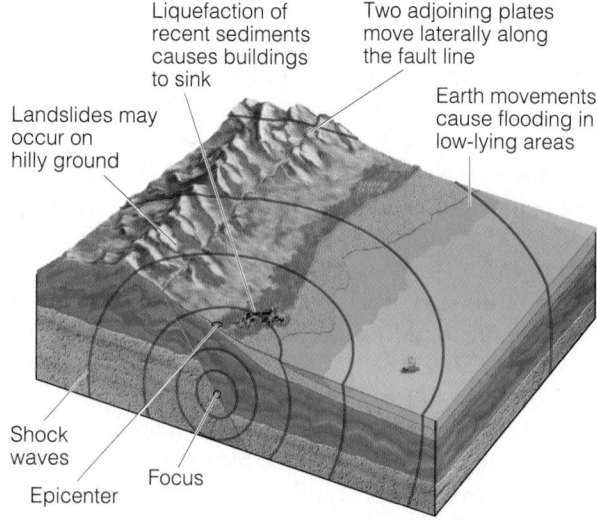

**Figure 10-9** Major features and effects of an *earthquake.*

months, and some have *foreshocks* from seconds to weeks before the main shock.

The *primary effects of earthquakes* include shaking and sometimes a permanent vertical or horizontal displacement of the ground. These effects may have serious consequences for people and for buildings, bridges, freeway overpasses, dams, and pipelines.

*Secondary effects of earthquakes* include rock slides, urban fires, and flooding caused by subsidence (sinking) of land. Coastal areas also can be severely damaged by large earthquake-generated water waves, called *tsunamis* (misnamed "tidal waves," even though they have nothing to do with tides) that travel as fast as 950 kilometers (590 miles) per hour.

**Solutions: How Can We Reduce Earthquake Hazards?** We can reduce loss of life and property from earthquakes by **(1)** examining historical records and making geologic measurements to locate active fault zones, **(2)** making maps showing high-risk areas (Figure 10-10), **(3)** establishing building codes that regulate the placement and design of buildings in areas of high risk, and **(4)** trying to predict when and where earthquakes will occur.

Engineers know how to make homes, large buildings, bridges, and freeways more earthquake resistant. But this can be expensive, especially if existing structures must be reinforced.

**What Are Volcanoes?** An active **volcano** occurs where magma (molten rock) reaches the earth's surface through a central vent or a long crack (fissure; Figure 10-11). Volcanic activity can release **(1)** *ejecta* (debris ranging from large chunks of lava rock to ash that may be glowing hot), **(2)** liquid lava, and **(3)** gases (such as water vapor, carbon dioxide, and sulfur dioxide) into the environment.

Volcanic activity is concentrated for the most part in the same areas as seismic activity (Figure 10-5a). Some volcanoes, such as those at Mount St. Helens in Washington (which erupted in 1980; Figure 10-1) and Mount Pinatubo in the Philippines (which erupted in 1991), have a steep, flaring cone shape. They usually erupt explosively and eject large quantities of gases and particulate matter (soot and mineral ash) high into the troposphere.

Most of the particles of soot and ash soon fall back to the earth's surface. However, gases such as sulfur dioxide remain in the atmosphere and are converted to tiny droplets of sulfuric acid, many of which stay above the clouds and may not be washed out by rain for up to 3 years.

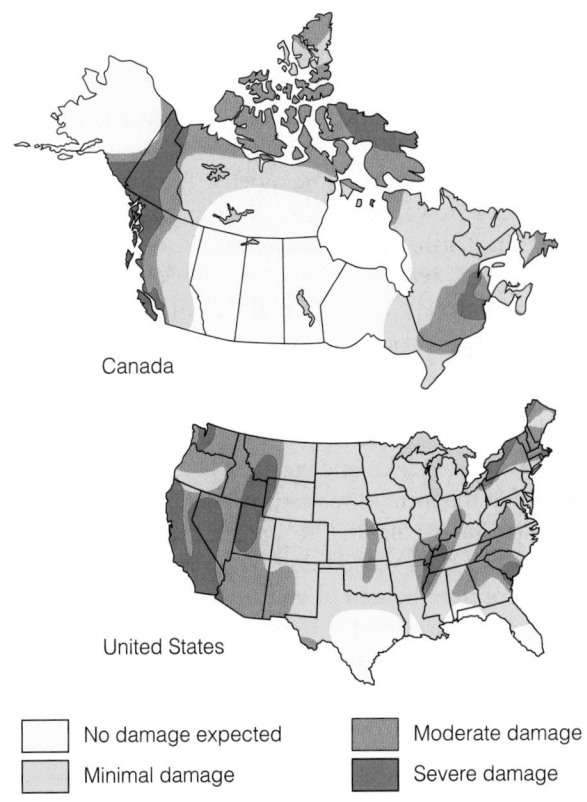

Canada

United States

| | |
|---|---|
| No damage expected | Moderate damage |
| Minimal damage | Severe damage |

**Figure 10-10** Expected damage from earthquakes in Canada and the contiguous United States. This map is based on earthquake records. (Data from U.S. Geological Survey)

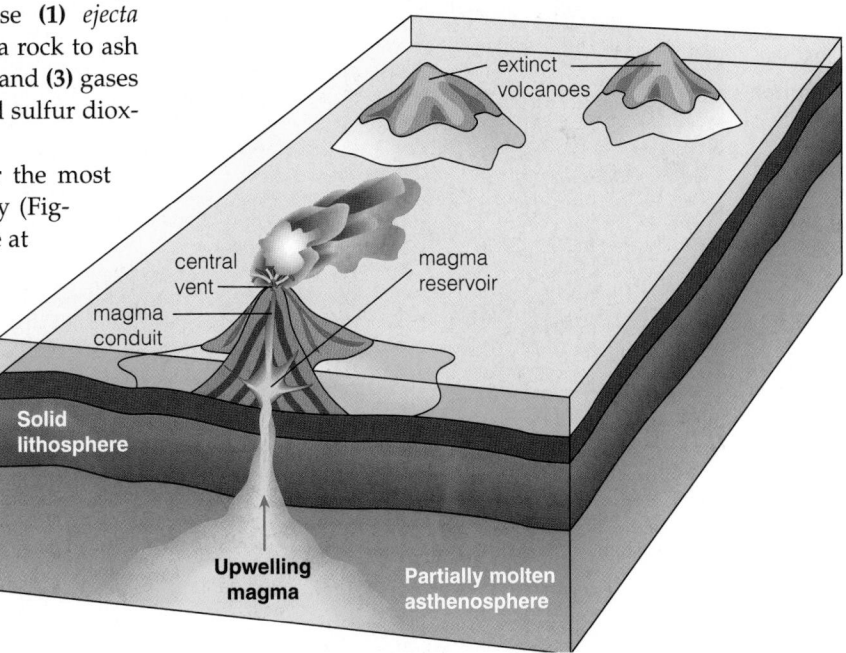

**Figure 10-11** A *volcano* erupts when molten magma in the partially molten asthenosphere rises in a plume through the lithosphere to erupt on the surface as lava that can spill over or be ejected into the atmosphere. Chains of islands can be created by the action of volcanoes that then become inactive.

These tiny droplets reflect some of the sun's energy and can cool the atmosphere by as much as 0.5°C (1°F) for 1–4 years.

Other volcanic eruptions at divergent boundaries (e.g., in Iceland) and ocean islands (e.g., the Hawaiian Islands) usually erupt more quietly. They involve primarily lava flows, which can cover roads and villages and ignite brush, trees, and homes.

Between 1985 and 1999, nearly 561,000 people died prematurely from natural catastrophes such as floods, earthquakes, volcanic eruptions, and windstorms. About 30%, or 169,000, of these deaths resulted from earthquakes and volcanic eruptions.

We tend to think negatively of volcanic activity, but it also provides some benefits. One is outstanding scenery in the form of majestic mountains, some lakes (such as Crater Lake in Oregon; see photo on the title page of this book), and other landforms. Perhaps the most important benefit of volcanism is the highly fertile soils produced by the weathering of lava.

**Solutions: How Can We Reduce Volcano Hazards?** We can reduce the loss of human life and sometimes property from volcanic eruptions by **(1)** land-use planning, **(2)** better prediction of volcanic eruptions, and **(3)** effective evacuation plans. The eruptive history of a volcano or volcanic center can provide some indication of where the risks are.

Scientists are also studying phenomena that precede an eruption such as **(1)** tilting or swelling of the cone, **(2)** changes in magnetic and thermal properties of the volcano, **(3)** changes in gas composition, and **(4)** increased seismic activity.

## 10-5 SOIL RESOURCES: FORMATION AND TYPES

**What Major Layers Are Found in Mature Soils?** Soil is a complex mixture of eroded rock, mineral nutrients, decaying organic matter, water, air,

**Figure 10-12** Soil formation and generalized soil profile. Horizons, or layers, vary in number, composition, and thickness, depending on the type of soil. (From Derek Elsom, *Earth*, 1992. Copyright © 1992 by Marshall Editions Developments Limited. New York: Macmillan. Used by permission)

and billions of living organisms, most of them microscopic decomposers (Figure 10-12). Although soil is a renewable resource, it is produced very slowly by the (1) weathering of rock, (2) deposit of sediments by erosion, and (3) decomposition of organic matter in dead organisms.

Mature soils are arranged in a series of zones called **soil horizons,** each with a distinct texture and composition that varies with different types of soils. A cross-sectional view of the horizons in a soil is called a **soil profile.** Most mature soils have at least three of the possible horizons (Figure 10-12).

The top layer, the *surface litter layer,* or *O horizon,* consists mostly of (1) freshly fallen and partially decomposed leaves, (2) twigs, (3) animal waste, (4) fungi, and (5) other organic materials. Normally, it is brown or black. The *topsoil layer,* or *A horizon,* is a porous mixture of (1) partially decomposed organic matter, called **hu-**

**mus,** and (2) some inorganic mineral particles. It is usually darker and looser than deeper layers. A fertile soil that produces high crop yields has a thick topsoil layer with lots of humus. This helps topsoil hold water and nutrients taken up by plant roots. Thus the thin mantle of productive topsoil found over much of the earth's terrestrial surface is the foundation of civilization.

The roots of most plants and most of a soil's organic matter are concentrated in these two upper layers. As long as vegetation anchors these layers, soil stores water and releases it in a nourishing trickle instead of a devastating flood.

The two top layers of most well-developed soils teem with bacteria, fungi, earthworms, and small insects that interact in complex food webs (Figure 10-13). Bacteria and other decomposer microorganisms found by the billions in every handful of topsoil recycle the nutrients we and other land organisms need

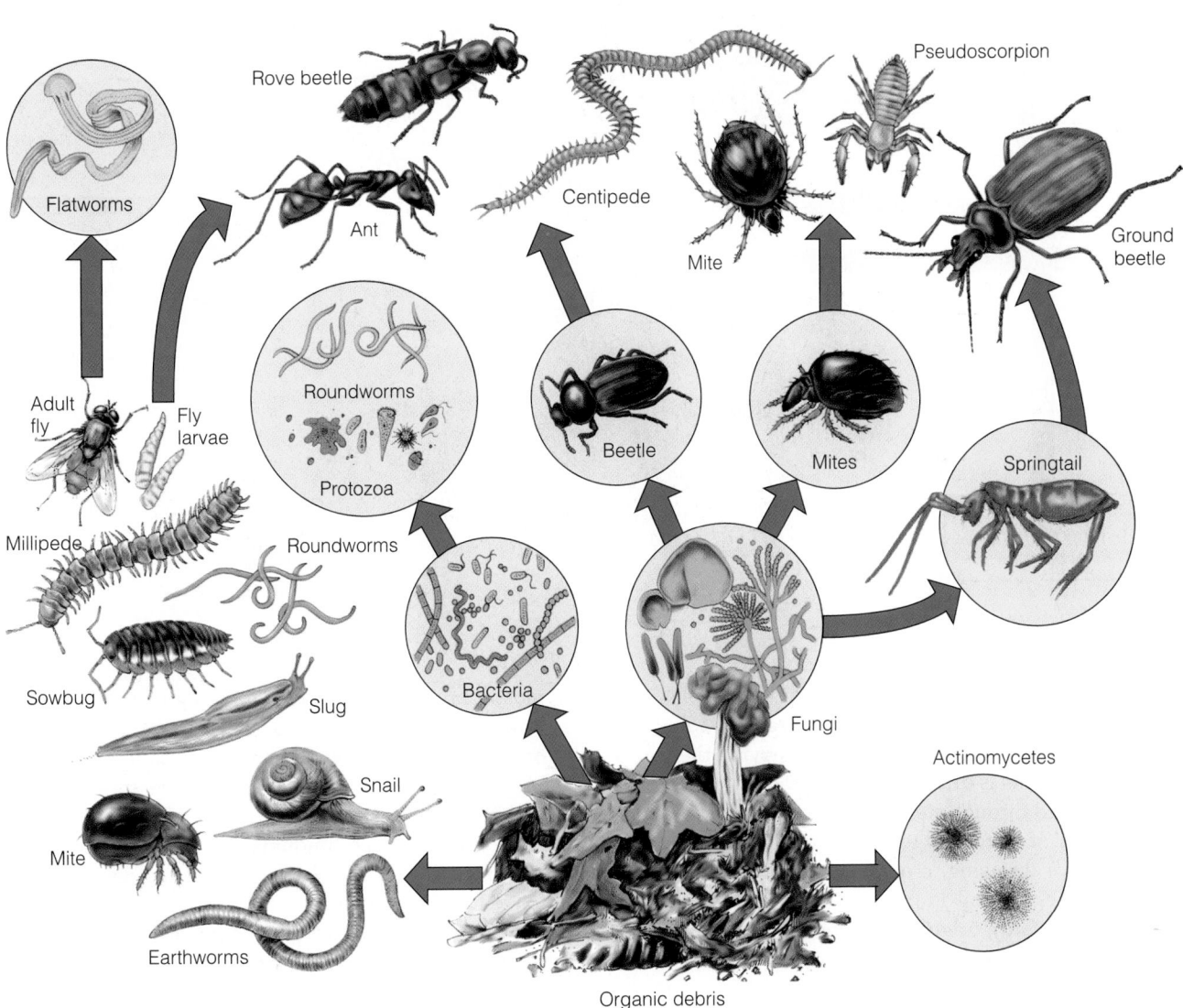

**Figure 10-13** Greatly simplified food web of living organisms found in soil.

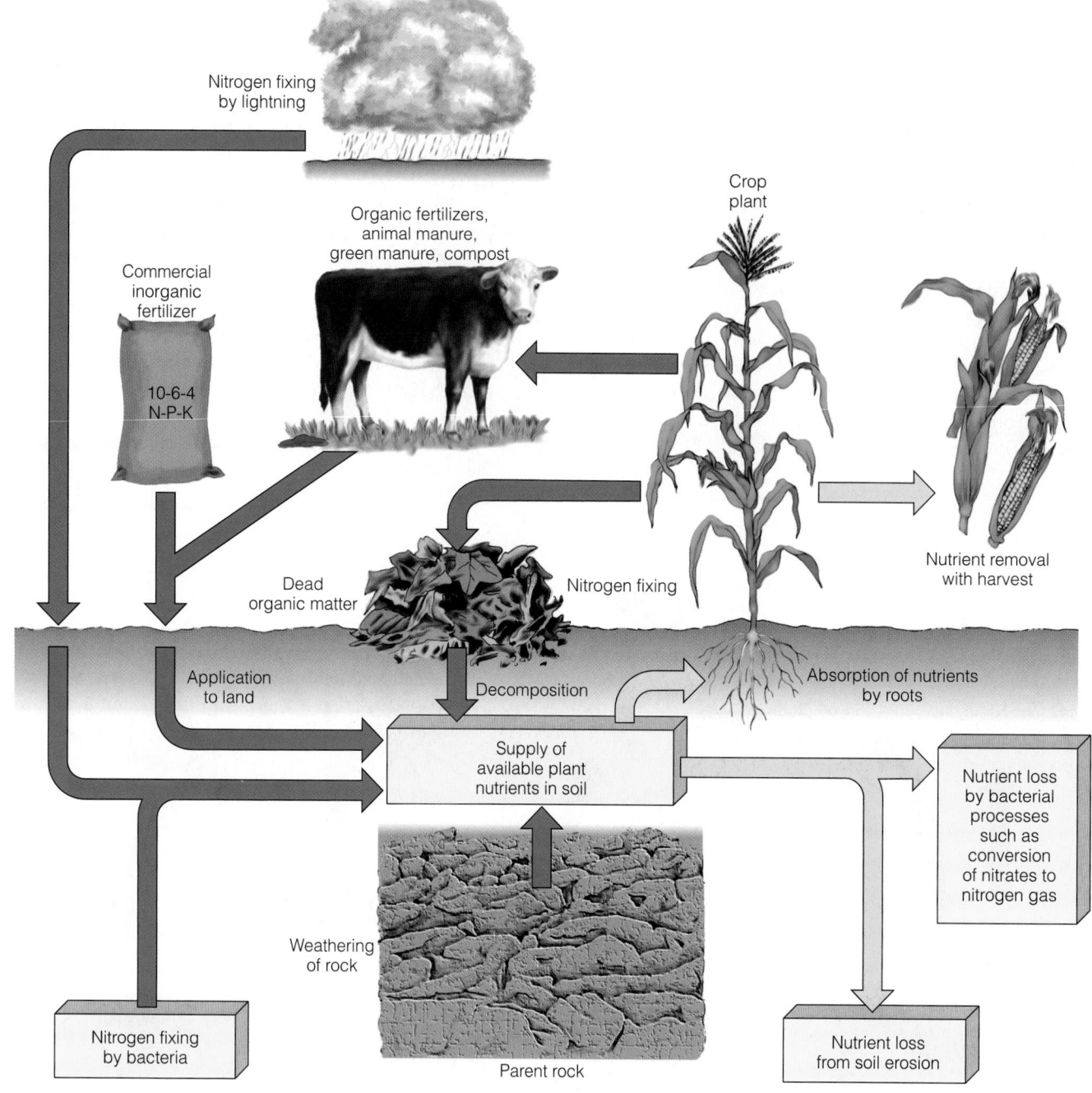

**Figure 10-14** Pathways of plant nutrients in soils.

(Figure 10-14). They break down some complex organic compounds into simpler inorganic compounds soluble in water. Soil moisture carrying these dissolved nutrients is drawn up by the roots of plants and transported through stems and into leaves.

The color of its topsoil tells us a lot about a soil's usefulness for growing crops. For example, dark brown or black topsoil is nitrogen-rich and high in organic matter. Gray, bright yellow, or red topsoils are low in organic matter and need nitrogen enrichment to support most crops.

The *B horizon (subsoil)* and the *C horizon (parent material)* contain most of a soil's inorganic matter,

mostly broken-down rock consisting of varying mixtures of sand, silt, clay, and gravel. The C horizon lies on a base of unweathered parent rock called *bedrock.*

The spaces, or pores, between the solid organic and inorganic particles in the upper and lower soil layers contain varying amounts of air (mostly nitrogen and oxygen gas) and water. Plant roots need oxygen for cellular respiration.

Some of the precipitation that reaches the soil percolates through the soil layers and occupies many of the soil's open spaces or pores. This downward movement of water through soil is called **infiltration.** As the water seeps down, it dissolves various soil compo-

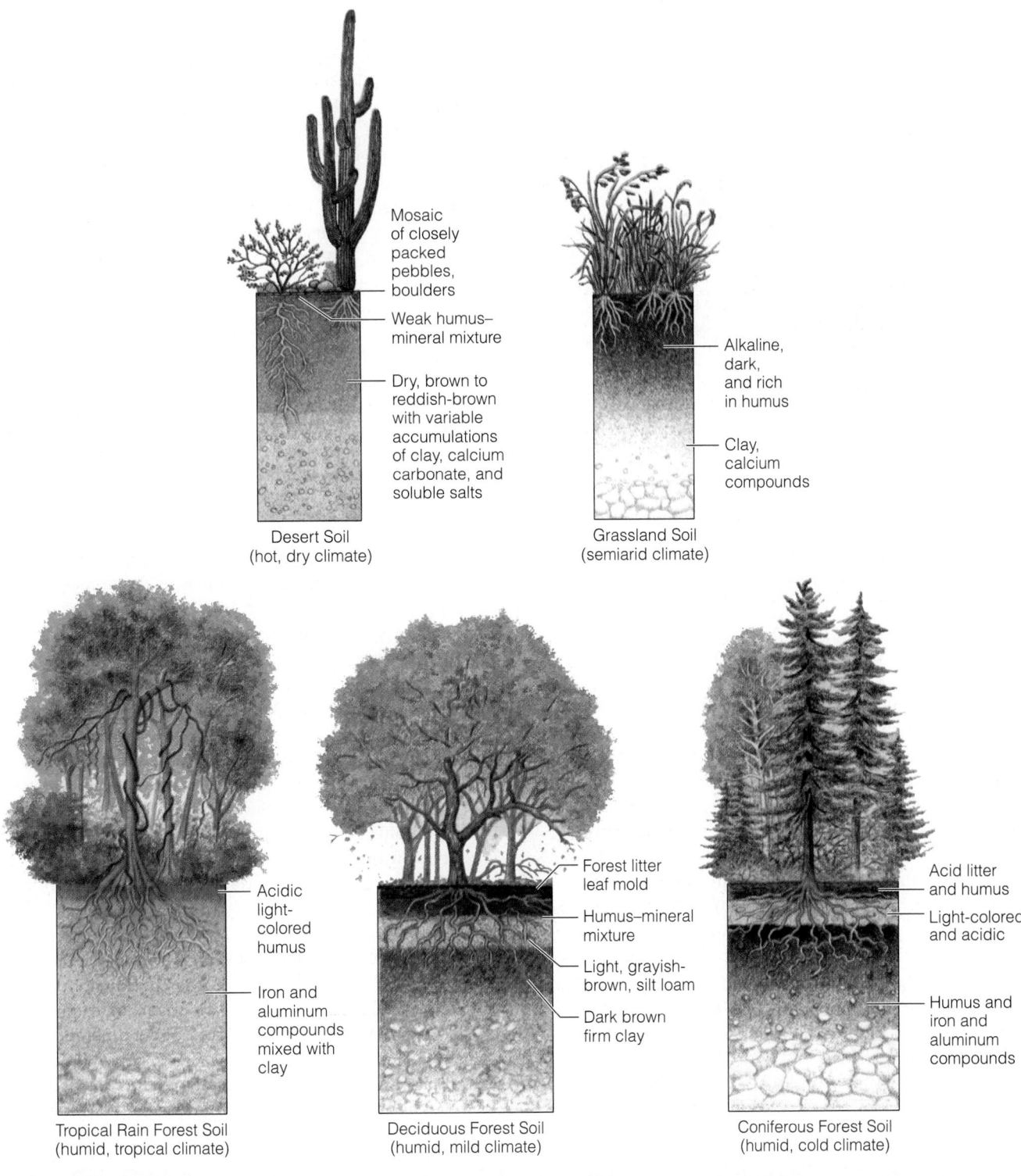

Mosaic
of closely
packed
pebbles,
boulders

Weak humus–
mineral mixture

Dry, brown to
reddish-brown
with variable
accumulations
of clay, calcium
carbonate, and
soluble salts

Desert Soil
(hot, dry climate)

Alkaline,
dark,
and rich
in humus

Clay,
calcium
compounds

Grassland Soil
(semiarid climate)

Acidic
light-
colored
humus

Iron and
aluminum
compounds
mixed with
clay

Tropical Rain Forest Soil
(humid, tropical climate)

Forest litter
leaf mold

Humus–mineral
mixture

Light, grayish-
brown, silt loam

Dark brown
firm clay

Deciduous Forest Soil
(humid, mild climate)

Acid litter
and humus

Light-colored
and acidic

Humus and
iron and
aluminum
compounds

Coniferous Forest Soil
(humid, cold climate)

**Figure 10-15** Soil profiles of the principal soil types typically found in five different biomes.

nents in upper layers and carries them to lower layers in a process called **leaching.**

Five important soil types, each with a distinct profile, are shown in Figure 10-15. Most of the world's crops are grown on soils exposed when grasslands (Figure 6-31, p. 132) and deciduous forests are cleared.

**How Do Soils Differ in Texture, Porosity, and Acidity?** Soils vary in their content of (**1**) *clay* (very fine particles), (**2**) *silt* (fine particles), (**3**) *sand* (medium-size particles), and (**4**) *gravel* (coarse to very coarse particles). The relative amounts of the different sizes and types of mineral particles determine **soil texture,** as depicted in Figure 10-16 (p. 216). Soils with roughly equal mixtures of clay, sand, silt, and humus are called **loams.**

To get an idea of a soil's texture, take a small amount of topsoil, moisten it, and rub it between your

**Figure 10-16** *Soil texture* depends on the proportions of clay, silt, and sand particles in the soil. Soil texture affects *soil porosity*, the average number and spacing of pores in a given volume of soil. Loams—roughly equal mixtures of clay, sand, silt, and humus—are the best soils for growing most crops. (Data from Natural Resources Conservation Service)

particles are organized and clumped together (Figure 10-17). Table 10-1 compares the main physical and chemical properties of sand, clay, silt, and loam soils.

Loams are the best soils for growing most crops because they hold lots of water, but not too tightly for plant roots to absorb. Sandy soils are easy to work, but water flows rapidly through them (Figure 10-17, left). They are useful for growing irrigated crops or those with low water needs, such as peanuts and strawberries.

The particles in clay soils are very small and easily compacted. When these soils get wet, they form large, dense clumps, which is why wet clay can be molded into bricks and pottery. Clay soils are more porous and have a greater water-holding capacity than sandy soils, but the pore spaces are so small that these soils have a low permeability (Figure 10-17, right). Because little water can infiltrate to lower levels, the upper layers can easily become too waterlogged for growing most crops.

The acidity or alkalinity of a soil, as measured by its pH (Figure 3-5, p. 49), influences the uptake of soil nutrients by plants. When soils are too acidic, the acids can be partially neutralized by an alkaline substance such as lime. Because lime speeds up the decomposition of organic matter in the soil, however, manure or another organic fertilizer should be added to maintain soil fertility.

In dry regions such as much of the western and southwestern United States, rain does not leach away calcium and other alkaline compounds, so soils in such areas may be too alkaline (pH above 7.5) for some crops. Adding sulfur, which is gradually converted into sulfuric acid by soil bacteria, reduces soil alkalinity.

## 10-6 SOIL EROSION AND DEGRADATION

**What Causes Soil Erosion?** **Soil erosion** is the movement of soil components, especially surface litter and topsoil (Figure 10-12), from one place to another. It results in the buildup of sediments and sedimentary

fingers and thumb. A gritty feel means it contains a lot of sand. A sticky feel means a high clay content, and you should be able to roll it into a clump. Silt-laden soil feels smooth, like flour. A loam topsoil, best suited for plant growth, has a texture between these extremes—a crumbly, spongy feeling—with many of its particles clumped loosely together.

Soil texture helps determine **soil porosity,** a measure of the volume of pores or spaces per volume of soil and of the average distances between those spaces. Fine particles are needed for water retention and coarse ones for air spaces. A porous soil has many pores and can hold more water and air than a less porous soil. The average size of the spaces or pores in a soil determines **soil permeability:** the rate at which water and air move from upper to lower soil layers. Soil porosity is also influenced by **soil structure:** the ways in which soil

| Table 10-1  Properties of Soils with Different Textures | | | | | |
|---|---|---|---|---|---|
| **Soil Texture** | **Nutrient-Holding Capacity** | **Water Infiltration Capacity** | **Water-Holding Capacity** | **Aeration** | **Workability** |
| Clay | Good | Poor | Good | Poor | Poor |
| Silt | Medium | Medium | Medium | Medium | Medium |
| Sand | Poor | Good | Poor | Good | Good |
| Loam | Medium | Medium | Medium | Medium | Medium |

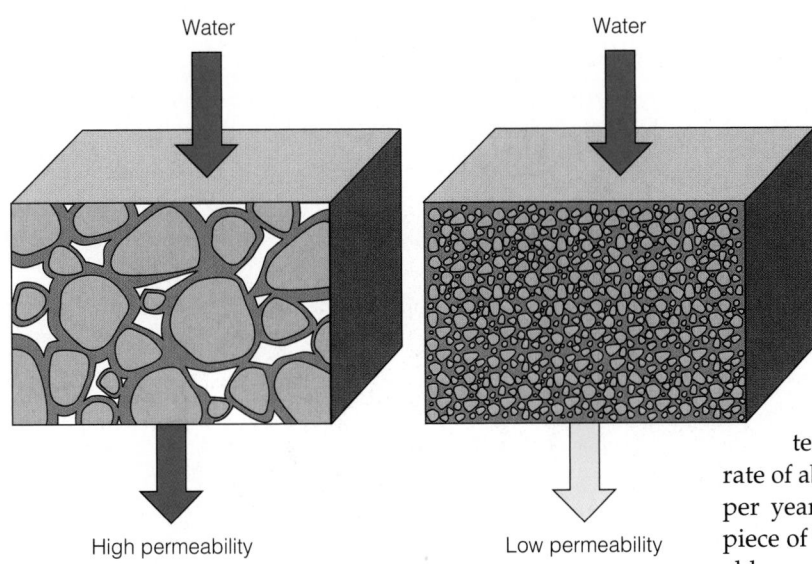

Water    Water

High permeability    Low permeability

**Figure 10-17** The size, shape, and degree of clumping of soil particles determine the number and volume of spaces for air and water within a soil. Soils with more pore spaces (left) contain more air and are more permeable to water flows than soils with fewer pores (right).

ever, in tropical and temperate areas it takes 200–1,000 years (depending on climate and soil type) for 2.54 centimeters (1 inch) of new topsoil to form. In tropical and temperate areas soil is renewed at an average rate of about 1 metric ton of topsoil per hectare of land per year. If topsoil erodes faster than it forms on a piece of land, its soil eventually becomes a nonrenewable resource.

**How Serious Is Global Soil Erosion?** Several studies document the seriousness of soil erosion:

■ A 1992 joint survey by the United Nations (UN) Environment Programme and the World Resources Institute estimated that **(1)** topsoil is eroding faster than it forms on about 38% of the world's cropland (Figure 10-19, p. 218) and **(2)** 17% of the world's land (two-thirds of it in Asia and Africa) was degraded to some extent by soil erosion.

■ In Northwest China, a combination of overplowing and overgrazing is causing massive wind erosion of topsoil. The resulting huge dust plumes of eroded soil **(1)** blot out the sun and reduce visibility in China's northeastern cities and **(2)** reduce visibility and

rock on land and in bodies of water (Figure 10-7). The two main agents of erosion are *flowing water* and *wind.* Some soil erosion is natural, and some is caused by human activities. In undisturbed vegetated ecosystems, the roots of plants help anchor the soil, and usually soil is not lost faster than it forms.

Farming, logging, construction, overgrazing by livestock, off-road vehicles, deliberate burning of vegetation, and other activities that destroy plant cover leave soil vulnerable to erosion. Such human activities can speed up erosion and destroy in a few decades what nature took hundreds to thousands of years to produce.

Moving water causes most soil erosion. Soil scientists distinguish among three types of water erosion:

■ *Sheet erosion* occurs when surface water moves down a slope or across a field in a wide flow and peels off fairly uniform sheets or layers of soil. Because the topsoil disappears evenly, sheet erosion may not be noticeable until much damage has been done.

■ *Rill erosion* (Figure 10-18) occurs when surface water forms fast-flowing rivulets that cut small channels in the soil.

■ *Gully erosion* (Figure 10-18) occurs when rivulets of fast-flowing water join together and with each succeeding rain cut the channels wider and deeper until they become ditches or gullies. Gully erosion usually happens on steep slopes where all or most vegetation has been removed.

The two major harmful effects of soil erosion are **(1)** loss of soil fertility and its ability to hold water and **(2)** runoff of sediment that pollutes water, kills fish and shellfish, and clogs irrigation ditches, boat channels, reservoirs, and lakes.

Soil, especially topsoil, is classified as a renewable resource because natural processes regenerate it. How-

Natural Resources Conservation Service

**Figure 10-18** Rill and gully erosion of vital topsoil from irrigated cropland in Arizona.

**Figure 10-19** Global soil erosion. (Data from UN Environment Programme and the World Resources Institute)

increase air pollution in Japan, the Korea Peninsula, and the northwestern United States (p. 110)

- According to a 2000 study by the Consultative Group on International Agricultural Research, **(1)** nearly 40% of the world's land (75% in Central America) used for agriculture is seriously degraded by erosion, salt buildup (salinization), and waterlogging, and **(2)** soil degradation has reduced food production on about 16% of the world's cropland.

The situation is worsening as many poor farmers in some developing countries plow up marginal (easily erodible) lands to survive. Soil erosion has a number of harmful economic and ecological effects. They include **(1)** loss of soil organic matter and vital plant nutrients, **(2)** reduced ability to store water for use by crops, **(3)** increased use of costly fertilizer to maintain soil fertility, **(4)** increased water runoff on eroded mountain slopes that can flood agricultural land and dwellings in the valleys below, **(5)** increased buildup of soil sediment in navigable waterways and coastal areas that reduces ship navigation, decreases fish production, and harms many other forms of aquatic life, and **(6)** increased input of sediment into reservoirs that shortens their useful life. Any evaluation of the harm

caused by soil erosion should include these effects—not just the effect of topsoil loss on crop productivity.

According to ecologist and agricultural expert David Pimentel,

> *One reason that soil erosion is not a high priority for many governments and farmers is that it usually occurs so slowly that its cumulative effects may take decades to become apparent. For example, the loss of 1 millimeter (0.04 inch) of soil is so small that it goes undetected. But over a 25-year period the loss would be 25 millimeters (1 inch), which would take about 500 years to replace by natural processes.*

There is no doubt that as agriculture has spread over the past 100 years topsoil has been lost faster than it is created in many areas and the total loss of topsoil is increasing. However, some analysts and the FAO contend that

- There is insufficient data on soil erosion to draw firm conclusions about its effect on crop productivity.

- Much of the eroded topsoil does not go far and is deposited further down a slope, valley, or plain. In some places, the loss in crop yields in one area could be offset by increased yields elsewhere.

- Incomplete studies suggest that the annual loss in crop productivity is only about 0.3% per year—much less than the world's 1–2% annual increase in crop productivity. However, some soil scientists point out that this global average **(1)** masks much higher rates of soil erosion in heavily farmed areas and **(2)** does not include the other harmful ecological effects of soil erosion. When such effects are included, some soil scientists and ecologists estimate that soil erosion causes a 15–30% reduction in crop productivity in some areas.

## How Serious Is Soil Erosion in the United States?

According to the National Resources Conservation Service, about one-third of the nation's original prime topsoil has been washed or blown into streams, lakes, and oceans, mostly as a result of overcultivation, overgrazing, and deforestation (Case Study, below).

According to the U.S. Department of Agriculture (USDA), soil on cultivated land in the United States is eroding about 16 times faster than it can form. Erosion rates are even higher in heavily farmed regions. An

**CASE STUDY**

## The Dust Bowl

In the 1930s, Americans learned a harsh environmental lesson when much of the topsoil in several dry and windy midwestern states was lost through a combination of poor cultivation practices and prolonged drought.

Before settlers began grazing livestock and planting crops there in the 1870s, the deep and tangled root systems of native prairie grasses anchored the fertile topsoil firmly in place (Figure 10-15, top right). Plowing the prairie tore up these roots, and the agricultural crops the settlers planted annually in their place had less extensive root systems.

After each harvest, the land was plowed and left bare for several months, exposing it to high winds. Overgrazing also destroyed large expanses of grass, denuding the ground. The stage was set for severe wind erosion and crop failures; all that was needed was a long drought.

Such a drought occurred between 1926 and 1934. In the 1930s, dust clouds created by hot, dry windstorms darkened the sky at midday in some areas; rabbits and birds choked to death on the dust.

During May 1934, a cloud of topsoil blown off the Great Plains traveled some 2,400 kilometers (1,500 miles) and blanketed most of the eastern United States with dust. Journalists gave the Great Plains a new name: the *Dust Bowl* (see figure).

During the "dirty thirties," large areas of cropland were stripped of

topsoil and severely eroded. This triggered one of the largest internal migrations in U.S. history as thousands of displaced farm families from Oklahoma, Texas, Kansas, and Colorado migrated to California or to the industrial cities of the Mid-

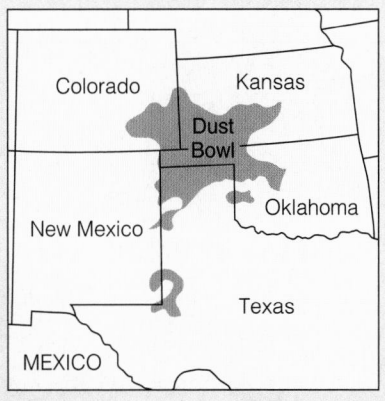

The *Dust Bowl* of the Great Plains, where a combination of extreme drought and poor soil conservation practices led to severe wind erosion of topsoil in the 1930s.

west and East. Most found no jobs because the country was in the midst of the Great Depression.

In May 1934, Hugh Bennett of the U.S. Department of Agriculture (USDA) went before a congressional hearing in Washington to plead for new programs to protect the country's topsoil. Lawmakers took action when Great Plains dust began seeping into the hearing room.

In 1935, the United States passed the Soil Erosion Act, which estab-

lished the Soil Conservation Service (SCS) as part of the USDA. With Bennett as its first head, the SCS (now called the Natural Resources Conservation Service) began promoting sound conservation practices, first in the Great Plains states and later elsewhere. Soil conservation districts were formed throughout the country, and farmers and ranchers were given technical assistance in setting up soil conservation programs.

Climate researchers see signs of a returning Dust Bowl period because of a megadrought that lasts 2 to 4 decades. By examining tree rings, archeological finds, lake sediments, and sand dunes, scientists have found that prolonged megadroughts generally hit twice a century as part of a complex drought cycle. They also found that smaller 2-year droughts strike every 20 years or so. If the earth warms as projected, the region could become even drier, and farming in some areas might have to be abandoned.

### Critical Thinking

**1.** Do you think Americans learned a lesson about protecting soil as a result of the Dust Bowl in the 1930s? Explain.

**2.** Recent scientific studies and news reports indicate that a massive dust bowl is now forming in northern China. What do you believe are the three most important things for Chinese officials to do to help ward off this threat to China's food production?

example is the Great Plains, which has lost one-third or more of its topsoil in the 150 years since it was first plowed. Some of the country's most productive agricultural lands, such as those in Iowa, have lost about half their topsoil.

Because of soil conservation efforts, the USDA estimates that soil erosion in the United States decreased by about 40% between 1985 and 1997. Using these data, USDA researchers estimate that soil erosion cost the United States about $30 billion in 1997, an average loss of $3.4 million per hour.

Critics such as Pierre Crosson say these estimates of soil erosion and damages from such erosion are exaggerated and based on inexact models instead of field measurements of soil loss and sedimentation rates in nearby bodies of water. However, other soil scientists point out that current estimates by models and a few on-site measurements do not include all the ecological effects of soil erosion.

**What Is Desertification, and How Serious Is This Problem?** In **desertification**, the productive potential of arid or semiarid land falls by 10% or more because of a combination of **(1)** natural climate change that causes prolonged drought and **(2)** human activities that reduce or degrade topsoil. The process can be **(1)** *moderate* (with a 10–25% drop in productivity), **(2)** *severe* (with a 25–50% drop), or **(3)** *very severe* (with a drop of 50% or more, usually creating huge gullies and sand dunes). Desertification is a serious and growing problem in many parts of the world (Figure 10-20).

Desertification is a complex process that involves multiple natural and human-related causes and that proceeds at varying rates in different climates. It results mainly from a combination of prolonged drought and unsustainable human activities. Figure 10-21 summarizes the major causes and consequences of desertification.

An estimated 8.1 million square kilometers (3.1 million square miles)—an area the size of Brazil and 12 times the size of Texas—have become desertified in the past 50 years. According to a 1999 UN conference on desertification, **(1)** about 40% of the world's land and

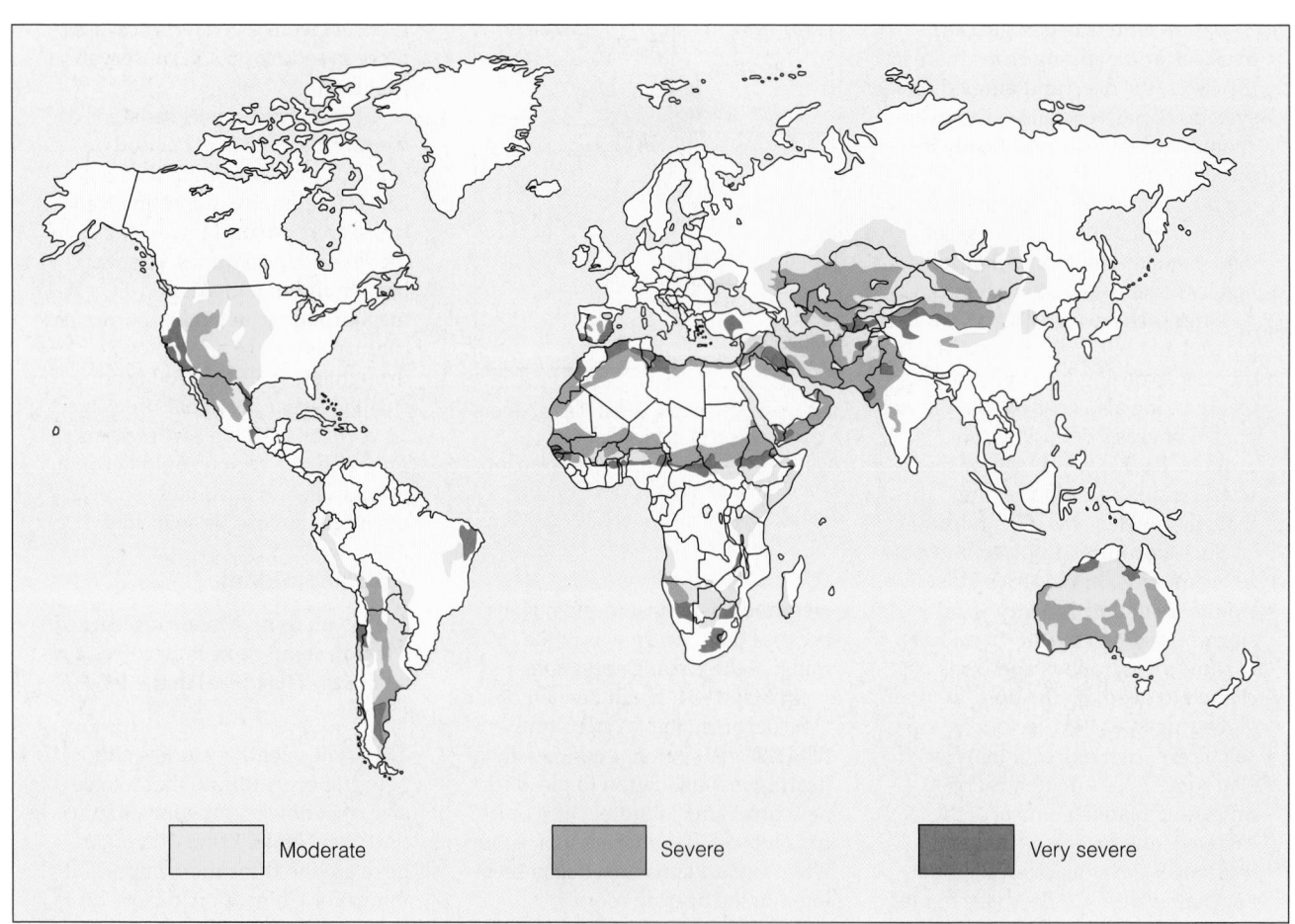

Moderate    Severe    Very severe

**Figure 10-20** *Desertification* of arid and semiarid lands. (Data from UN Environmental Programme and Harold E. Drengue)

| Causes | | Consequences |
|---|---|---|
| Overgrazing | | Worsening drought |
| Deforestation | | Famine |
| Surface mining | | Economic losses |
| Erosion | | Lower living standards |
| Salinization | | Environmental refugees |
| Soil compaction | | |

**Figure 10-21** Causes and consequences of desertification. Natural climate change also plays a role in desertification.

70% of all drylands is suffering from the effects of desertification, and **(2)** each year about 150,000 square kilometers (58,000 square miles)—an area larger than Greece—becomes desertified. This threatens the livelihoods of at least 135 million people in 100 countries and causes economic losses estimated at $42 billion per year.

Desertification can feed on itself through positive feedback. Changes in the reflectivity of the land surface because of widespread desertification can change local climates in ways that increase drought and thus the area of land affected by desertification.

Here are the most effective ways to slow desertification:

- Reduce **(1)** overgrazing, **(2)** deforestation, and **(3)** destructive forms of planting, irrigation, and mining.

- Plant trees and grasses that will **(1)** anchor the soil, **(2)** hold water, and **(3)** help reduce the threat of global warming by increasing uptake of carbon dioxide from the atmosphere.

### How Do Excess Salts and Water Degrade Soils?

Some *good news* is that the approximately 17% of the world's cropland that is irrigated produces almost 40% of the world's food. Irrigated land can produce crop yields two to three times greater than those from rain watering.

But irrigation also has a downside. Most irrigation water is a dilute solution of various salts, picked up as the water flows over or through soil and rocks. Small quantities of these salts are essential nutrients for plants, but they are toxic in large amounts.

Irrigation water not absorbed into the soil evaporates, leaving behind a thin crust of dissolved salts (such as sodium chloride) in the topsoil. This accumulation of salts is called **salinization** (Figure 10-22), which **(1)** stunts crop growth, **(2)** lowers crop yields, and **(3)** eventually kills plants and ruins the land (Figure 10-23, p. 222).

According to a 1995 study, severe salinization has reduced yields on 21% of the world's irrigated cropland, and another 30% has been moderately salinized. The most severe salinization occurs in Asia, especially in China, India, and Pakistan.

In the United States, salinization affects 23% of all irrigated cropland. However, the proportion is much higher in some heavily irrigated western states, including **(1)** 66% of the irrigated land in the lower

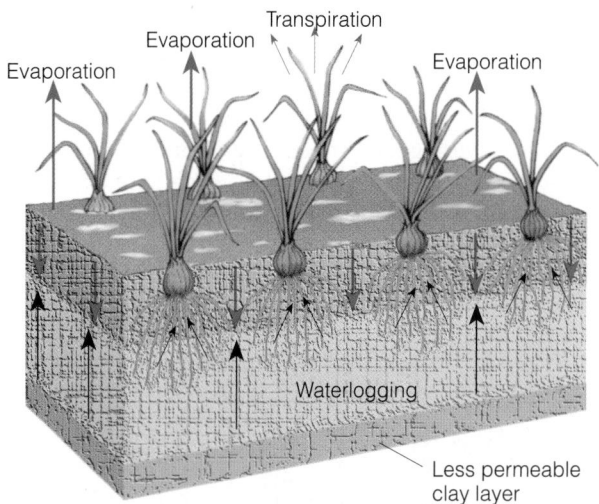

**Salinization**

1. Irrigation water contains small amounts of dissolved salts.

2. Evaporation and transpiration leave salts behind.

3. Salt builds up in soil.

**Waterlogging**

1. Precipitation and irrigation water percolate downward.

2. Water table rises.

**Figure 10-22** *Salinization* and *waterlogging* of soil on irrigated land without adequate drainage lead to decreased crop yields.

Figure 10-23 Severe *salinization*. Because of high evaporation, poor drainage, and severe salinization, white alkaline salts have displaced crops that once grew on this heavily irrigated land in Colorado.

Colorado Basin and **(2)** 35% of such land in California. Figure 10-24 summarizes solutions for preventing and dealing with soil salinization.

Another problem with irrigation is **waterlogging** (Figure 10-22). Farmers often apply large amounts of irrigation water to leach salts deeper into the soil. Without adequate drainage, however, water accumulates underground and gradually raises the water table. Saline water then envelops the deep roots of plants, lowering their productivity and killing them after prolonged exposure. At least one-tenth of all irrigated land worldwide suffers from waterlogging, and the problem is getting worse.

| Prevention | | Cleanup |
|---|---|---|
| Reduce irrigation<br><br>Switch to salt-tolerant crops (such as barley, cotton, sugarbeet) | | Flushing soil (expensive and wastes water)<br><br>Not growing crops for 2–5 years<br><br>Installing underground drainage systems (expensive) |

Figure 10-24 *Solutions:* methods for preventing and cleaning up soil salinization.

# 10-7 SOLUTIONS: SOIL CONSERVATION

**How Can Conservation Tillage Reduce Soil Erosion?** **Soil conservation** involves reducing soil erosion and restoring soil fertility. For hundreds of years, farmers have used various methods to reduce soil erosion, mostly by keeping the soil covered with vegetation.

In **conventional-tillage farming**, farmers plow the land and then break up and smooth the soil to make a planting surface. In areas such as the midwestern United States, harsh winters prevent plowing just before the spring growing season. Thus crop fields often are plowed in the fall. This leaves the soil bare during the winter and early spring and makes it vulnerable to erosion.

To reduce erosion, many U.S. farmers are using **conservation-tillage farming** (either *minimum-tillage* or *no-till farming*). The idea is to disturb the soil as little as possible while planting crops. With *minimum-tillage farming*, special tillers break up and loosen the subsurface soil without turning over the topsoil, previous crop residues, and any cover vegetation. In *no-till farming*, special planting machines inject seeds, fertilizers, and weed killers (herbicides) into slits made in the unplowed soil. Figure 10-25 lists the advantages and disadvantages of conservation tillage.

By 2001, conservation tillage was used on about 45% of U.S. cropland. In Indiana, the Nature Conservancy is giving farmers money to buy no-till equipment in exchange for a promise to use conservation tillage for at least 3 years. The USDA estimates that using conservation tillage on 80% of U.S. cropland would reduce soil erosion by at least half. Conservation tillage is used in Brazil, Argentina, Canada, and Paraguay and beginning to be embraced by more farmers worldwide.

**Solutions: What Other Methods Can Reduce Soil Erosion?** Farmers have developed a number of other ways to reduce soil erosion (Figure 10-26, p. 224). They include the following:

■ **Terracing,** which can reduce soil erosion on steep slopes by converting the land into a series of broad, nearly level terraces that run across the land contour (Figure 10-26a). This **(1)** retains water for crops at each level and **(2)** reduces soil erosion by controlling runoff. Although most poor farmers know the risk of not terracing, many have too little time and too few workers to build terraces; they must plant crops without terracing hillsides or starve.

■ **Contour farming,** which involves plowing and planting crops in rows across the contour of gently sloped land (Figure 10-26b). Each row acts as a small dam to help hold soil and to slow water runoff.

| Advantages | | Disadvantages |
|---|---|---|
| Reduces erosion |  | Can increase herbicide use for some crops |
| Saves fuel | | |
| Cuts costs | | Leaves stalks that can harbor crop pests and fungal diseases and increase pesticide use |
| Holds more soil water | | |
| Reduces soil compaction | | |
| Allows several crops per season | | Requires investment in expensive equipment |
| Does not reduce crop yields | | |
| Reduces $CO_2$ release from soil | | |

**Figure 10-25** Advantages and disadvantages of using *conservation tillage*.

- **Strip cropping,** which involves planting alternating strips of **(1)** a row crop (such as corn) and **(2)** another crop (such as a grass or a grass and legume mixture) that completely covers the soil (Figure 10-26b, p. 224). The cover crop strips **(1)** trap soil that erodes from the row crop, **(2)** catch and reduce water runoff, and **(3)** help prevent the spread of pests and plant diseases. Planting strips of nitrogen-fixing legumes (such as soybeans or alfalfa) helps restore soil fertility.

- **Alley cropping** or **agroforestry,** in which several crops are planted together in strips or alleys between trees and shrubs that can provide fruit or fuelwood (Figure 10-26c, p. 224). The trees or shrubs **(1)** provide shade (which reduces water loss by evaporation), **(2)** help retain and slowly release soil moisture, and **(3)** can provide fruit, fuelwood, and trimmings that can be used as mulch (green manure) for the crops and as fodder for livestock.

## Slowing Soil Erosion in the United States

**CASE STUDY**

Of the world's major food-producing countries, only the United States is sharply reducing some of its soil losses through conservation tillage and government-sponsored soil conservation programs.

The 1985 Farm Act established a strategy for reducing soil erosion in the United States. In the first phase of this program, farmers are given a subsidy for taking highly erodible land out of production and replanting it with soil-saving grass or trees for 10–15 years. By 2001, approximately 15 million hectares (37 million acres), roughly one-tenth of U.S. cropland, were in this Conservation Reserve Program (CRP).

The land in such a *conservation reserve* cannot be farmed, grazed, or cut for hay. Farmers who violate their contracts must pay back all subsidies plus interest.

According to the U.S. Department of Agriculture, since 1985 this program has cut soil losses on cropland in the United States by about 65%—a shining example of *good news*—and could eventually cut such losses as much as 80%. In 1996, Congress reauthorized the CRP until 2002. If lawmakers continue to support this program, it could eventually cut such soil losses as much as 80%.

The second phase of the program required all farmers with highly erodible land to develop government-approved 5-year soil conservation plans for their entire farms by the end of 1990. A third provision of the Farm Act authorizes the government to forgive all or part of farmers' debts to the Farmers Home Administration if they agree not to farm highly erodible cropland or wetlands for 50 years. The farmers must plant trees or grass on this land or restore it to wetland.

The 1985 Farm Act made the United States the first major food-producing country to make soil conservation a national priority. Even though these efforts to slow soil erosion are an important step, effective soil conservation is practiced on only about half of all U.S. agricultural land and on less than half of the country's most erodible cropland.

### Critical Thinking

Do you believe U.S. tax dollars should be used to pay farmers for taking highly erodible land out of production? Explain. What are the alternatives?

**(a)** Terracing

**(b)** Contour planting and strip cropping

**(c)** Alley cropping

**(d)** Windbreaks

**Figure 10-26** In addition to conservation tillage, soil conservation methods include **(a)** terracing, **(b)** contour planting and strip cropping, **(c)** alley cropping, and **(d)** windbreaks.

- Establishing **windbreaks,** or **shelterbelts,** of trees (Figure 10-26d) to **(1)** reduce wind erosion, **(2)** help retain soil moisture, **(3)** supply some wood for fuel, and **(4)** provide habitats for birds, pest-eating and pollinating insects, and other animals.

- **Gully reclamation,** which involves restoring severely eroded bare land by **(1)** planting fast-growing shrubs, vines, and trees to stabilize the soil, **(2)** building small dams at the bottoms of gullies to collect silt and gradually fill in the channels, and **(3)** building channels to divert water from the gully.

- Using *land classification* to identify easily erodible (marginal) land that should be neither planted in crops nor cleared of vegetation. In the United States, the National Resources Conservation Service has set up a classification system to identify types of land that are suitable or unsuitable for cultivation. Such efforts and recent farm legislation have helped reduce soil erosion in the United States (Case Study, p. 223).

**How Can We Maintain and Restore Soil Fertility?** Fertilizers partially restore plant nutrients lost by erosion, crop harvesting, and leaching. Farmers can use **(1)** organic fertilizer from plant and animal materials or **(2)** commercial inorganic fertilizer produced from various minerals.

Types of *organic fertilizer* include the following:

- **Animal manure:** the dung and urine of cattle, horses, poultry, and other farm animals. It improves **(1)** soil structure, **(2)** adds organic nitrogen, and **(3)** stimulates beneficial soil bacteria and fungi. However, its use in the United States has decreased because of **(1)** replacement of most mixed animal-raising and crop-farming operations with separate operations for growing crops and raising animals, **(2)** the high costs of transporting animal manure from feedlots near urban areas to distant rural crop-growing areas, and **(3)** the use of tractors and other motorized farm machinery to replace horses and other draft animals that added manure to the soil. Researchers at the U.S. Department of Agriculture are evaluating the use of phosphorus-rich ash produced from burning poultry wastes to produce electricity as an organic fertilizer.

- **Green manure:** fresh or growing green vegetation plowed into the soil to increase the organic matter and humus available to the next crop.

- **Compost:** a sweet-smelling, dark-brown, humus-like material that is rich in organic matter and soil nutrients. It is produced when microorganisms (mostly fungi and aerobic bacteria) in soil break down organic matter such as leaves, food wastes, paper, and wood in the presence of oxygen. Compost is a rich natural fertilizer and soil conditioner that **(1)** aerates soil, **(2)** improves its ability to retain water

and nutrients, **(3)** helps prevent erosion, and **(4)** prevents nutrients from being wasted by being dumped in landfills.

- **Spores of mushrooms, puffballs, and truffles:** Rapidly growing and spreading mycorrhizae fungi (Figure 8-12c, p. 179) in the spores attach to plant roots and help them **(1)** take in moisture and nutrients from the soil and **(2)** make plants more disease resistant. Unlike typical fertilizers that farmers must apply every few weeks, one application of mushroom fungi lasts all year and costs just pennies per plant.

Crops such as corn, tobacco, and cotton can deplete the topsoil of nutrients (especially nitrogen) if planted on the same land several years in a row (Figure 10-14). One way to reduce such losses is **crop rotation.** Farmers plant areas or strips with nutrient-depleting crops one year. In the next year they plant the same areas with legumes (whose root nodules add nitrogen to the soil). In addition to helping restore soil nutrients, this method **(1)** reduces erosion by keeping the soil covered with vegetation and **(2)** helps reduce crop losses to insects by presenting them with a changing target.

**Can Inorganic Fertilizers Save the Soil?** Today, many farmers (especially in developed countries) rely on *commercial inorganic fertilizers* containing **(1)** nitrogen (as ammonium ions, nitrate ions, or urea), **(2)** phosphorus (as phosphate ions), and **(3)** potassium (as potassium ions). Other plant nutrients may also be present in low or trace amounts.

Inorganic commercial fertilizers are easily transported, stored, and applied. Worldwide, their use increased about nine-fold between 1950 and 1989 but has leveled off since then. The good news is that the additional food these fertilizers help produce feeds one of every three people in the world; without them, world food output would drop an estimated 40%.

Commercial inorganic fertilizers have some disadvantages, however. These include **(1)** not adding humus to the soil, **(2)** reducing the soil's content of organic matter and thus its ability to hold water (unless animal manure and green manure are also added to the soil), **(3)** lowering the oxygen content of soil and keeping fertilizer from being taken up as efficiently, **(4)** typically supplying only 2 or 3 of the 20 or so nutrients needed by plants, **(5)** requiring large amounts of energy for their production, transport, and application, and **(6)** releasing nitrous oxide ($N_2O$), a greenhouse gas that can enhance global warming, from the soil.

The widespread use of commercial inorganic fertilizers, especially on sloped land near streams and lakes, also causes water pollution as nitrate ($NO_3^-$) and phosphate ($PO_4^{3-}$) fertilizer nutrients are washed into nearby bodies of water. The resulting plant nutrient enrichment (cultural eutrophication) causes algae blooms that use up oxygen dissolved in the water, thereby killing fish. Rainwater seeping through the soil can also leach nitrates in commercial fertilizers into groundwater. Drinking water drawn from wells containing high levels of nitrate ions can be toxic, especially for infants, and cause bladder cancer.

According to soil scientists, responsibility for reducing soil erosion should not be limited to farmers. Timber cutting, overgrazing, mining, and urban development that are carried out without proper regard for soil conservation also cause soil erosion. See the website material for this chapter for what you can do to reduce soil erosion.

*The challenge is to arrest the excessive loss of topsoil on all land everywhere, reducing it to below the level of new soil formation. The world cannot afford this loss of natural capital. If we cannot preserve the foundation of civilization, we cannot preserve civilization itself.*

LESTER R. BROWN

## REVIEW QUESTIONS

**1.** Define all boldfaced terms in this chapter.

**2.** Describe the harmful and beneficial effects of the Mount St. Helens volcanic eruption in the United States in 1980.

**3.** What are the main characteristics of the earth's *core, mantle,* and *crust?*

**4.** What are *tectonic plates?* What is the *lithosphere?* What is the *theory of plate tectonics,* and how is it important to physical and biological processes on the earth?

**5.** What are the three different types of boundaries between the earth's lithospheric plates?

**6.** What is *erosion,* and what are its two major causes?

**7.** Distinguish between a *mineral* and a *rock.* Distinguish among *igneous, sedimentary,* and *metamorphic rock,* and give two examples of each type.

**8.** Describe the *rock cycle,* and explain its importance.

**9.** What is an *earthquake,* and what are its major harmful effects? List ways to reduce the hazards from earthquakes.

**10.** What is a *volcanic eruption?* What are some of the hazards and benefits of volcanic eruptions? List ways to reduce the hazards from volcanic eruptions.

**11.** What is *soil?* Distinguish between a *soil horizon* and a *soil profile.*

**12.** What is *humus,* and what is its importance? What does the color of topsoil tell you about its usefulness as a soil for growing crops?

**13.** Distinguish between *soil infiltration* and *leaching.* Distinguish among *soil texture, soil porosity,* and *soil permeability.*

**14.** What are *loams,* and why are they the best soils for growing most crops?

**15.** What is *soil erosion,* and what are its major natural and human-related causes? Describe three types of soil erosion.

**16.** What are the major harmful effects of soil erosion?

**17.** How serious is soil erosion **(a)** globally and **(b)** in the United States?

**18.** Describe the *Dust Bowl* event in the United States. Describe how the U.S. government is reducing soil erosion.

**19.** What is *desertification?* How serious is this problem? What are its major causes and consequences? How can we slow desertification?

**20.** Distinguish between *salinization* and *waterlogging* of soils. How serious are these problems? List five ways to reduce the threat of soil salinization.

**21.** What is *soil conservation?* Distinguish between *conventional-tillage farming* and *conservation-tillage farming.* What are the advantages and disadvantages of conservation-tillage farming?

**22.** Distinguish among *terracing, contour farming, strip cropping, alley cropping, windbreaks, gully reclamation,* and *land classification* as methods for reducing soil erosion.

**23.** Distinguish between *organic fertilizer* and *commercial inorganic fertilizer,* and list the advantages of each approach for maintaining or restoring soil fertility. Discuss using *animal manure, green manure, compost,* and *mushroom spores* as methods for fertilizing soil. What is *crop rotation,* and why is it useful in helping maintain soil fertility?

**24.** List the advantages and disadvantages of using commercial inorganic fertilizers to maintain and restore soil fertility.

## CRITICAL THINKING

**1.** List some ways, positive and negative, in which **(a)** the external earth processes of weathering and erosion and **(b)** plate tectonics are important to you.

**2.** Explain what would happen if **(a)** plate tectonics stopped and **(b)** erosion and weathering stopped. If you could, would you eliminate either group of processes? Explain.

**3.** Imagine you are an igneous rock. Act as a reporter and send in a written report on what you experience as you move through various parts of the rock cycle (Figure 10-8, p. 210). Repeat this experience, assuming in turn you are a sedimentary rock and then a metamorphic rock.

**4.** In the area where you live, are you more likely to experience an earthquake or a volcanic eruption? What can you do to escape or reduce the harm if such a disaster strikes? What actions can you take when it occurs?

**5.** How does your lifestyle directly or indirectly contribute to soil erosion?

**6.** Some analysts contend that average soil erosion rates around the world are low and the soil erosion problem can be solved easily with improved agricultural technology such as no-till cultivation and increased use of commercial inorganic fertilizers. Do you agree or disagree with this position? Explain.

**7.** Why should everyone, not just farmers, be concerned about soil conservation?

**8.** What are the main advantages and disadvantages of using commercial inorganic fertilizers to restore or increase soil fertility? Why should both inorganic and organic fertilizers be used?

**9.** Congratulations! You are in charge of the world. What are the three most important features of your policy to reduce soil erosion?

## PROJECTS

**1.** Write a brief scenario describing the sequence of consequences to us and to other forms of life if the rock cycle stopped functioning.

**2.** Use the library or the Internet to find out where earthquakes and volcanic eruptions have occurred during the past 30 years, and then stick small flags on a map of the world or place dots on Figure 10-5a (p. 207). Compare their locations with the plate boundaries shown in Figure 10-5b.

**3.** Conduct a survey of soil erosion and soil conservation in and around your community on cropland, construction sites, mining sites, grazing land, and deforested land. Use these data to develop a plan for reducing soil erosion in your community.

**4.** Use the library or the Internet to find bibliographic information about *Will Durant* and *Lester R. Brown*, whose quotes appear at the beginning and end of this chapter.

**5.** Make a concept map of this chapter's major ideas using the section heads and subheads and the key terms (in boldface). Look on the website for this book for information about making concept maps.

## INTERNET STUDY RESOURCES AND RESOURCES FOR FURTHER READING AND RESEARCH

The website for this book contains helpful study aids and many ideas for further reading and research. Log on to

www.info.brookscole.com/miller13

and click on the Chapter-by-Chapter area. Choose Chapter 10 and select a resource:

■ Flash Cards allows you to test your mastery of the Terms and Concepts to Remember for this chapter.

■ Tutorial Quizzes provides a multiple-choice practice quiz.

■ Student Guide to InfoTrac will lead you to Critical Thinking Projects that use InfoTrac College Edition as a research tool.

■ References lists the major books and articles consulted in writing this chapter.

■ Hypercontents takes you to an extensive list of sites with news, research, and images related to individual sections of the chapter.

## INFOTRAC COLLEGE EDITION

Improve your skills with InfoTrac College Edition, a searchable online database of articles from more than 700 periodicals. Log on to

http://www.infotrac-college.com

or access InfoTrac through the website for this book. Try to find the following articles:

**1.** Pearce, F. 2002. On shaky ground. *Geographical* 74: 32. *Keywords:* "Peru," "earthquake," and "aftermath." Damaging earthquakes are a way of life in Peru. However, not all the damage is caused by the shaking of the earth. Now developers are displacing people after areas are considered unsafe for habitation.

**2.** Sparks, D. L. 2000. Soil as an endangered ecosystem. (brief article) *BioScience* 50 : 947. *Keywords:* "endangered ecosystem" and "soil." This article explores several issues related to soil erosion and ecosystem damage.

# 11 RISK, TOXICOLOGY, AND HUMAN HEALTH

## The Big Killer

What is roughly the diameter of a 30-caliber bullet, can be bought almost anywhere, is highly addictive, and kills about 11,000 people every day, 460 per hour, or 1 person every 8 seconds? It is a cigarette. *Cigarette smoking is the single most preventable major cause of death and suffering among adults.*

According to the World Health Organization (WHO) between 1950 and 2000, tobacco helped kill 60 million people. WHO estimates that each year tobacco contributes to the premature deaths of at least 4 million people from 25 illnesses including **(1)** heart disease, **(2)** lung cancer, **(3)** other cancers, **(4)** bronchitis, **(5)** emphysema, and **(6)** stroke. The annual death toll from smoking-related diseases is projected to reach 10 million by 2030 (70% of them in developing countries)—an average of about 27,400 preventable deaths per day or 1 death every 3 seconds.

According to a 2002 study by the Centers for Disease Control and Prevention, smoking prematurely kills about 440,000 Americans per year, an average of 1,205 deaths per day (Figure 11-1). This death toll is roughly equivalent to three fully loaded jumbo (400-passenger) jets crashing accidentally every day with no survivors. Smoking causes more deaths each year in the United States than do all illegal drugs, alcohol (the second most harmful legal drug after nicotine), accidents, suicide, and homicide combined (Figure 11-1).

According to a 1998 study, secondhand smoke (inhaled by nonsmokers) causes 30,000–60,000 premature deaths per year in the United States. Each year, parental smoking prematurely kills an estimated 6,000 children and causes 5.4 million serious child ailments in the United States.

The overwhelming consensus in the scientific community is that the nicotine (and probably the acetaldehyde) inhaled in tobacco smoke is highly addictive. Only 1 in 10 people who try to quit smoking succeed, about the same relapse rate as for recovering alcoholics and those addicted to heroin or crack cocaine. A British government study showed that adolescents who smoke more than one cigarette have an 85% chance of becoming smokers. According to a 1999 World Bank study, each day some 80,000–100,000 young people become regular long-term smokers, primarily in developing countries, where 73% of the world's smokers live.

According to a 2002 study by the Centers for Disease Control and Prevention, smoking costs the United States about $158 billion a year for **(1)** medical bills, **(2)** increased insurance costs, **(3)** disability, **(4)** lost earnings and productivity because of illness, and **(5)** property damage from smoking-caused fires. This is an average of $7 per pack of cigarettes sold in the United States.

Many health experts urge that a $3–5 federal tax be added to the price of a pack of cigarettes in the United States. Such a tax would mean that the users of cigarettes (and other tobacco products), not the rest of society, would pay a much greater share of the health, economic, and social costs associated with their smoking: a *user-pays* approach. WHO and the World Bank estimate that a 10% global tax on cigarettes would cause 40 million smokers to quit and would prevent the premature deaths of 10 million people alive today.

Other suggestions for reducing the death toll and health effects of smoking in the United States include **(1)** banning all cigarette advertising, **(2)** prohibiting the sale of cigarettes and other tobacco products to anyone under 21 (with strict penalties for violators), **(3)** banning all cigarette vending machines, **(4)** classifying nicotine as an addictive and dangerous drug (and placing its use in tobacco or other products under the jurisdiction of the Food and Drug Administration), **(5)** eliminating all federal subsidies and tax breaks to U.S. tobacco farmers and tobacco companies, and **(6)** using cigarette tax income to finance an aggressive antitobacco advertising and education program.

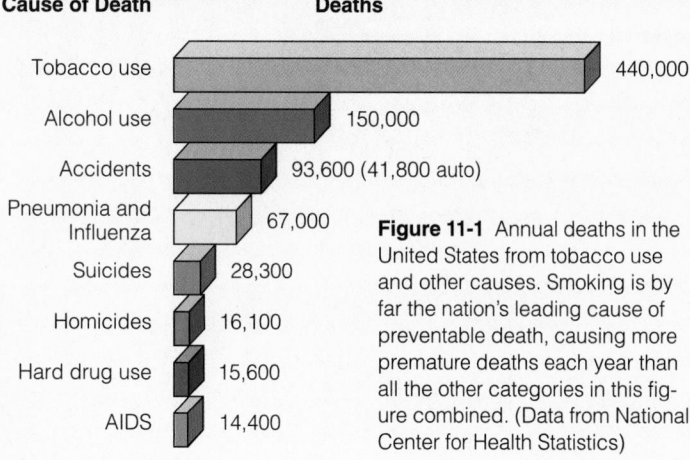

**Cause of Death**      **Deaths**

| Cause of Death | Deaths |
|---|---|
| Tobacco use | 440,000 |
| Alcohol use | 150,000 |
| Accidents | 93,600 (41,800 auto) |
| Pneumonia and Influenza | 67,000 |
| Suicides | 28,300 |
| Homicides | 16,100 |
| Hard drug use | 15,600 |
| AIDS | 14,400 |

**Figure 11-1** Annual deaths in the United States from tobacco use and other causes. Smoking is by far the nation's leading cause of preventable death, causing more premature deaths each year than all the other categories in this figure combined. (Data from National Center for Health Statistics)

*The dose makes the poison.*

PARACELSUS, 1540

This chapter addresses the following questions:

- What types of hazards do people face?
- What is toxicology, and how do scientists measure toxicity?
- What chemical hazards do people face, and how can they be measured?
- What types of disease (biological hazards) threaten people in developing countries and developed countries?
- How can risks be estimated, managed, and reduced?

## 11-1 RISK, PROBABILITY, AND HAZARDS

**What Is Risk?** Risk is the possibility of suffering harm from a hazard that can cause injury, disease, economic loss, or environmental damage. Risk is expressed in terms of **probability:** a mathematical statement about how likely it is that some event or effect will occur. In these terms, *risk* is defined as the probability of exposure times the probability of harm (Risk = Exposure × Harm).

Probability often is stated in terms such as "The lifetime probability of developing cancer from exposure to a certain chemical is 1 in 1 million." This means that 1 of every 1 million people exposed to the chemical at a specified average daily dosage will develop cancer over a typical lifetime (usually considered 70 years).

**How Are Risks Assessed and Managed?** Risk **assessment** involves **(1)** identifying a real or potential hazard ("What is the hazard?"), **(2)** determining the probability of its occurrence ("How likely is the event?"), and **(3)** assessing the severity of its health, environmental, economic, and social impact ("How much damage is it likely to cause?" (Figure 11-2, left).

This is a complex, difficult, and controversial process. For example, assessing the risk of exposure to a toxic chemical involves estimating **(1)** the number of people or other organisms exposed, **(2)** the level and duration of exposure, and **(3)** other possible contributing factors such as age, health, sex, personal habits, and interactions with other chemicals.

After a risk has been assessed, the next step is **risk management,** in which people make decisions about **(1)** how serious it is compared to other risks (*comparative risk analysis*), **(2)** how much (if at all) the risk should be reduced, **(3)** how such risk reduction can be accomplished, and **(4)** how much money should be devoted to reducing the risk to an acceptable level

**Figure 11-2** *Risk assessment* and *risk management.* These are important, difficult, and controversial processes.

(Figure 11-2, right). This is even more difficult and controversial than risk assessment because of **(1)** a lack of information and **(2)** the economic, health, and political implications of such decisions.

**What Are the Major Types of Hazards?** The various kinds of hazards we face can be categorized as follows:

- *Cultural hazards* such as unsafe working conditions, smoking (p. 228), poor diet, drugs, drinking, driving, criminal assault, unsafe sex, and poverty.
- *Chemical hazards* from harmful chemicals in the air, water, soil, and food. The bodies of most human beings contain small amounts of about 500 synthetic organic chemicals—whose health effects are mostly unknown—that did not exist in 1920.
- *Physical hazards* such as ionizing radiation (p. 57), fire, earthquake (p. 210), volcanic eruption (p. 211), flood, tornadoes (p. 113), and hurricanes (p. 113).
- *Biological hazards* from pathogens (bacteria, viruses, and parasites), pollen and other allergens, and animals such as bees and poisonous snakes.

According to a 1998 study by Cornell University scientist David Pimentel, *environmental factors* such as malnutrition, smoking, cooking fires, skin cancer, exposures to pesticides and other hazardous chemicals, and air and water pollution contribute to about 40% of the world's annual deaths.

## 11-2 TOXICOLOGY

**What Determines Whether a Chemical Is Harmful? Dose and Response** Toxicity measures how harmful a substance is. Whether a chemical (or other agent such as ionizing radiation) is harmful depends on several factors. One is the **dose,** the amount of a potentially harmful substance that a person has ingested, inhaled, or absorbed through the skin. Whether a chemical is harmful depends on **(1)** the size of the dose over a certain period of time, **(2)** how often an exposure occurs, **(3)** who is exposed (adult or child, for example), **(4)** how well the body's detoxification systems (liver, lungs, and kidneys) work, and **(5)** genetic makeup that determines an individual's sensitivity to a particular toxin (Figure 11-3).

This genetic variation in individual responses to exposure to various toxins raises a difficult ethical, political, and economic question. When regulating levels of a toxin in the environment, should the allowed level be set to protect **(1)** the most sensitive individuals (at great cost) or **(2)** the average person?

A substance's harm can also be affected by

- *Solubility. Water-soluble toxins* (which are often inorganic compounds) can move throughout the environment and get into water supplies. *Oil- or fat-soluble toxins* (which are usually organic compounds) can accumulate in body tissues and cells.

- *Persistence.* Many chemicals, such as chlorofluorocarbons (CFCs), chlorinated hydrocarbons, and plastics, are used widely because of their persistence or resistance to breakdown. However, this persistence also means they can have long-lasting effects on the health of wildlife and people.

- **Bioaccumulation,** in which some molecules are absorbed and stored in specific organs or tissues at levels higher than normally would be expected.

- **Biomagnification,** in which the levels of some toxins in the environment are magnified as they pass through food chains and webs (Figure 11-4). Examples of chemicals that can be biomagnified include long-lived, fat-soluble organic compounds such as **(1)** the pesticide DDT, **(2)** PCBs (oily chemicals used in electrical transformers), and **(3)** some radioactive isotopes (such as strontium-90; Table 3-2, p. 56). Stored in body fat, such chemicals can be passed along to offspring during gestation or egg laying and as mothers nurse their young.

- *Chemical interactions* that can decrease or multiply the harmful effects of a toxin. An *antagonistic interaction* can reduce the harmful response. For example, vitamins E and A apparently interact to reduce the body's response to some carcinogens. A *synergistic interaction* (p. 46) multiplies harmful effects. For example, workers exposed to asbestos increase their chances of getting lung cancer 20-fold. However, asbestos workers who also smoke have a 400-fold increase in lung cancer rates.

The type and amount of health damage that result from exposure to a chemical or other agent are called the **response.** An *acute effect* is an immediate or rapid harmful reaction to an exposure; it can range from dizziness or a rash to death. A *chronic effect* is a permanent or long-lasting consequence (kidney or liver damage, for example) of exposure to a harmful substance.

**Should We Be Concerned About Trace Levels of Toxic Chemicals in the Environment and in Our Bodies?** The answer is that it depends on the chemical and its concentration. The detection of trace amounts of a chemical in air, water, or food does not necessarily mean it is there at a level harmful to most people or to wildlife.

A basic concept of toxicology is that *any synthetic or natural chemical (even water) can be harmful if ingested in a large enough quantity.* Drinking 100 cups of strong coffee one after another would expose most people to a lethal dosage of caffeine. Similarly, downing 100 tablets of aspirin or 1 liter (1.1 quarts) of pure alcohol (ethanol) would kill most people.

The critical question is how much exposure to a particular toxic chemical causes a harmful response. This is the meaning of the quote by German scientist Paracelsus about the dose making the poison (found at the top of p. 229 in this chapter).

Most chemicals have some safe, or *threshold level*, of exposure below which their harmful effects are insignificant because

- The human body has mechanisms for breaking down (usually by enzymes found in the liver), diluting, or excreting small amounts of most toxins to keep them from reaching harmful levels.

- Individual cells have enzymes that can repair damage to DNA and protein molecules.

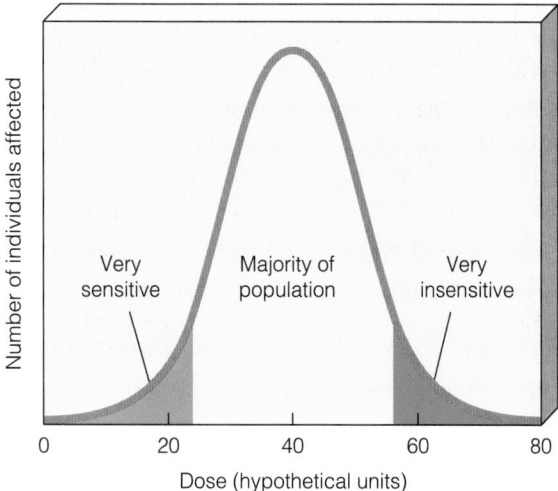

**Figure 11-3** Typical variations in sensitivity to a toxic chemical within a population, mostly because of differences in genetic makeup. Some individuals in a population are very sensitive to small doses of a toxin (left), and others are very insensitive (right). Most people fall between these two extremes (middle).

DDT in fish-eating
birds (ospreys)
25 ppm

DDT in large
fish (needle fish)
2 ppm

DDT in small
fish (minnows)
0.5 ppm

DDT in
zooplankton
0.04 ppm

DDT in water
0.000003 ppm,
or 3 ppt

**Figure 11-4** *Bioaccumulation* and *biomagnification*. DDT is a fat-soluble chemical that can accumulate in the fatty tissues of animals. In a food chain or food web, the accumulated concentrations of DDT can be biologically magnified in the bodies of animals at each higher trophic level. This diagram shows that the concentration of DDT in the fatty tissues of organisms was biomagnified about 10 million times in this food chain in an estuary near Long Island Sound in New York. If each phytoplankton organism in such a food chain takes up from the water and retains one unit of DDT, a small fish eating thousands of zooplankton (which feed on the phytoplankton) will store thousands of units of DDT in its fatty tissue. Then each large fish that eats 10 of the smaller fish will ingest and store tens of thousands of units, and each bird (or human) that eats several large fish will ingest hundreds of thousands of units. Dots represent DDT, and arrows show small losses of DDT through respiration and excretion.

Cells in some parts of the body (such as the skin and linings of the gastrointestinal tract, lungs, and blood vessels) reproduce fast enough to replace damaged cells. However, such high rates of cell reproduction can sometimes be altered by exposure to ionizing radiation and certain chemicals so that cell growth accelerates and creates a nonmalignant or malignant (cancerous) tumor.

Some people have the mistaken idea that all natural chemicals are safe and all synthetic chemicals are harmful. In fact, many synthetic chemicals are quite safe if used as intended, and many natural chemicals are deadly. For example, the average person is far more likely to be killed by aflatoxin in peanut butter than by lightning or a shark. However, the chance of dying from eating several spoonfuls of peanut butter a day is quite small.

In addition, the ability of chemists to detect increasingly small amounts of potentially toxic chemicals in air, water, and food can give the false impression that dangers from toxic chemicals are increasing. In 1980, chemists could routinely detect concentrations of substances in parts per million (ppm) (Table 3-1, p. 55). By 1990, chemists could detect parts per billion (ppb), and today they can detect concentrations of parts per trillion (ppt) and in some cases parts per quadrillion (ppq).

**What Is a Poison?** Legally, a **poison** is a chemical that has an $LD_{50}$ of 50 milligrams or less per kilogram of body weight. The **$LD_{50}$** is the **median lethal dose:** the amount of a chemical received in one dose that kills exactly 50% of the animals (usually rats and mice) in a

test population, within a 14-day period (Figure 11-5). Until recently 50–200 rodents were needed for each $LD_{50}$, but new procedures require only 8–15 rodents per test.

Chemicals vary widely in their toxicity (Table 11-1, p. 232). Some poisons can cause serious harm or death after a single acute exposure at very low dosages. Others cause such harm only at such huge dosages that it is nearly impossible to get enough into the body. Most chemicals fall between these two extremes.

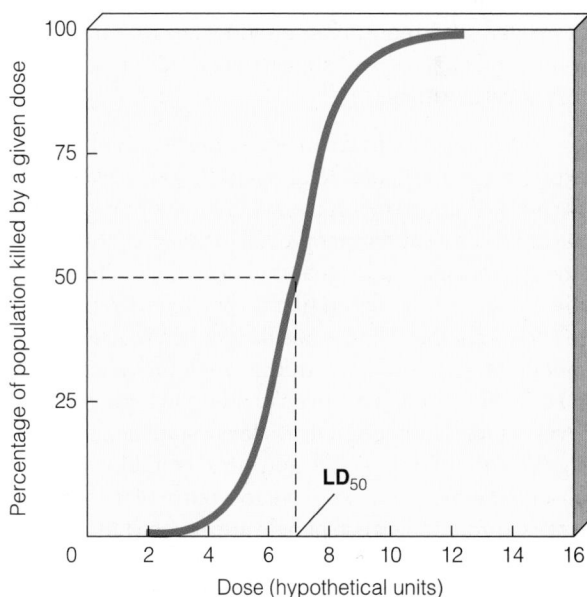

**Figure 11-5** Hypothetical *dose-response curve* showing determination of the $LD_{50}$, the dosage of a specific chemical that kills 50% of the animals in a test group.

| Table 11-1 Toxicity Ratings and Average Lethal Doses for Humans | | | |
|---|---|---|---|
| **Toxicity Rating** | **LD$_{50}$ (milligrams per kilogram of body weight)*** | **Average Lethal Dose†** | **Examples** |
| Supertoxic | Less than 0.01 | Less than 1 drop | Nerve gases, botulism toxin, mushroom toxins, dioxin (TCDD) |
| Extremely toxic | Less than 5 | Less than 7 drops | Potassium cyanide, heroin, atropine, parathion, nicotine |
| Very toxic | 5–50 | 7 drops to 1 teaspoon | Mercury salts, morphine, codeine |
| Toxic | 50–500 | 1 teaspoon to 1 ounce | Lead salts, DDT, sodium hydroxide, sodium fluoride, sulfuric acid, caffeine, carbon tetrachloride |
| Moderately toxic | 500–5,000 | 1 ounce to 1 pint | Methyl (wood) alcohol, ether, phenobarbital, amphetamines (speed), kerosene, aspirin |
| Slightly toxic | 5,000–15,000 | 1 pint to 1 quart | Ethyl alcohol, Lysol, soaps |
| Essentially nontoxic | 15,000 or greater | More than 1 quart | Water, glycerin, table sugar |

*Dosage that kills 50% of individuals exposed
†Amounts of substances that are liquids at room temperature when given to a 70.4-kilogram (155-pound) human

**How Are Case Reports and Epidemiological Studies Used to Estimate Toxicity?** Two methods scientists use to get information about the harmful effects of chemicals on human health are

- *Case reports* (usually made by physicians) provide information about people suffering some adverse health effect or death after exposure to a chemical. Such information often involves accidental poisonings, drug overdoses, homicides, or suicide attempts. Most case reports are not a reliable source for determining toxicity because the actual dosage and the exposed person's health status often are not known. However, such reports can provide clues about environmental hazards and suggest the need for laboratory investigations.

- *Epidemiological studies* in which the health of people exposed to a particular toxic agent (the *experimental group*) is compared with the health of another group of statistically similar people not exposed to the agent (the *control group*). The goal is to determine whether the statistical association (if any) between a exposure to a toxic chemical and a health problem is strong, moderate, or weak. Such studies are limited because **(1)** too few people have been exposed to high enough levels of many toxic agents to detect statistically significant differences, **(2)** conclusively linking an observed effect with exposure to a particular chemical is very difficult because people are exposed to many different toxic agents throughout their lives, and **(3)** they cannot be used to evaluate hazards from new technologies or chemicals to which people have not been exposed.

**How Are Laboratory Experiments Used to Estimate Toxicity?** The most widely used method for determining acute toxicity and chronic toxicity is to expose a population of live laboratory animals (especially mice and rats) to measured doses of a specific substance under controlled conditions. Animal tests take 2–5 years and cost $200,000 to $2 million per substance tested.

Animal welfare groups want to limit or ban use of test animals or ensure that experimental animals are treated in the most humane manner possible. More humane methods for carrying out toxicity tests include using **(1)** bacteria, **(2)** cell and tissue cultures, and **(3)** chicken egg membranes. In 1999, scientists developed a cheaper and much more sensitive way to determine toxicity by almost continuous measurement of changes in the electrical properties of individual animal cells. The United States, Japan, and most European countries are gradually replacing older LD$_{50}$ methods with these newer procedures.

These alternatives can greatly decrease the use of animals for testing toxicity. However, scientists point out that some animal testing is needed because the alternative methods cannot adequately mimic the complex biochemical interactions of a live animal.

Acute toxicity tests are run to develop a **dose-response curve,** which shows the effects of various dosages of a toxic agent on a group of test organisms (Figure 11-6). Such tests are *controlled experiments* in which the effects of the chemical on a *test group* are compared with the responses of a *control group* of organisms not exposed to the chemical. Care is taken to ensure that organisms in each group are **(1)** as identical

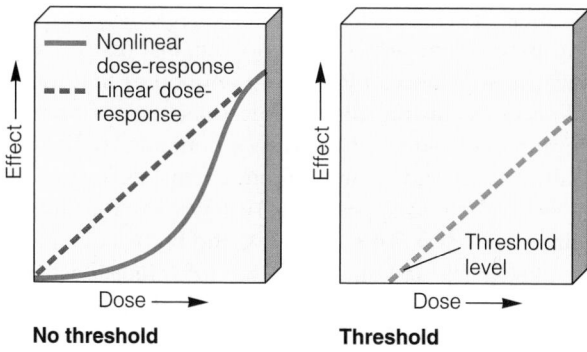

**Figure 11-6** Hypothetical *dose-response curves.* The linear and nonlinear curves in the left graph show that exposure to any dosage of a chemical or ionizing radiation has a harmful effect that increases with the dosage. The curve on the right shows that a harmful effect occurs only when the dosage exceeds a certain *threshold level.* Which of these models applies to various harmful agents is very uncertain because of the difficulty in estimating the response to very low dosages. (Adapted from Chiras, *Environmental Science,* 5th ed., p. 352, fig. 19.12. Copyright © 1998 by Wadsworth)

as possible in age, health status, and genetic makeup and **(2)** exposed to the same environmental conditions.

Fairly high dosages are used to reduce the number of test animals needed, obtain results quickly, and lower costs. Otherwise, tests would have to be run on millions of laboratory animals for many years, and manufacturers could not afford to test most chemicals. For the same reasons, the results of high-dose exposures usually are extrapolated to low-dose levels using mathematical models. Then the low-dose results on the test organisms are extrapolated to humans to estimate $LD_{50}$ values for acute toxicity (Table 11-1).

According to the *nonthreshold dose-response model* (Figure 11-6, left), any dosage of a toxic chemical or ionizing radiation causes harm that increases with the dosage. Many chemicals that cause birth defects or cancers show this kind of response.

With the *threshold dose-response model* (Figure 11-6, right), a threshold dosage must be reached before any detectable harmful effects occur, presumably because the body can repair the damage caused by low dosages of some substances. Establishing which of these models applies at low dosages is extremely difficult. To be on the safe side, the nonthreshold dose-response model often is assumed.

Some scientists challenge the validity of extrapolating data from test animals to humans because human physiology and metabolism often are different from those of the test animals. Also, different species of test animals can react differently to the same toxin because of differences in body size, physiology, metabolism, and toxin sensitivity (Figure 11-3). Other scientists counter that such tests and models work fairly well (especially for revealing cancer risks) when the correct experimental animal is chosen or when a chemical is toxic to several different test animal species.

**How Valid Are Estimates of Toxicity?** As we have seen, all methods for estimating toxicity levels and risks have serious limitations. However, they are all we have. To take this uncertainty into account and minimize harm, standards for allowed exposure to toxic substances and ionizing radiation typically are set at levels 1/100 or even 1/1,000 of the estimated harmful levels.

Despite their many limitations, carefully conducted and evaluated toxicity studies are important sources of information for understanding dose-response effects and estimating and setting exposure standards. However, citizens, lawmakers, and regulatory officials must recognize the huge uncertainties and guesswork involved in all such studies.

## 11-3 CHEMICAL HAZARDS

**What Are Toxic and Hazardous Chemicals?** **Toxic chemicals** generally are defined as substances that are fatal to more than 50% of test animals ($LD_{50}$) at given concentrations. **Hazardous chemicals** cause harm by **(1)** being flammable or explosive, **(2)** irritating or damaging the skin or lungs (strong acidic or alkaline substances such as oven cleaners), **(3)** interfering with or preventing oxygen uptake and distribution (asphyxiants such as carbon monoxide and hydrogen sulfide), or **(4)** inducing allergic reactions of the immune system (allergens).

**What Are Mutagens?** **Mutagens** are agents, such as chemicals and ionizing radiation, that cause random *mutations,* or changes, in the DNA molecules found in cells. Mutations in a sperm or egg cell can be passed on to future generations and cause diseases such as **(1)** bipolar disorder, **(2)** cystic fibrosis, **(3)** hemophilia, **(4)** sickle-cell anemia, **(5)** Down syndrome, and **(6)** some types of cancer. Mutations in other cells are not inherited but may cause harmful effects.

*Most mutations are harmless,* probably because all organisms have biochemical repair mechanisms that can correct mistakes or changes in the DNA code. In addition, some mutations play a vital role in microevolution (p. 100).

**What Are Teratogens?** **Teratogens** are chemicals, radiation, or viruses that cause birth defects while the human embryo is growing and developing during pregnancy, especially during the first 3 months. Chemicals known to cause birth defects in laboratory animals include **(1)** PCBs, **(2)** thalidomide, **(3)** steroid hormones, and **(4)** heavy metals such as arsenic, cadmium, lead, and mercury.

**What Are Carcinogens?** **Carcinogens** are chemicals, radiation, or viruses that cause or promote the growth of a malignant (cancerous) tumor, in which certain cells multiply uncontrollably. Many cancerous tumors spread by **metastasis** when malignant cells break off from tumors and travel in body fluids to other parts of the body. There, they start new tumors, making treatment much more difficult.

According to the WHO, environmental and lifestyle factors play a key role in causing or promoting up to 80% of all cancers. Major sources of carcinogens are **(1)** cigarette smoke (30–40% of cancers), **(2)** diet (20–30%), **(3)** occupational exposure (5–15%), and **(4)** environmental pollutants (1–10%). Inherited genetic factors and certain viruses cause about 10–20% of all cancers.

Typically, 10–40 years may elapse between the initial exposure to a carcinogen and the appearance of detectable symptoms. Partly because of this time lag, many healthy teenagers and young adults have trouble believing that their smoking (p. 228), drinking, eating, and other lifestyle habits today could lead to some form of cancer before they reach age 50.

**How Can Chemicals Harm the Immune, Nervous, and Endocrine Systems?** Since the 1970s, a growing body of research on wildlife and laboratory animals and epidemiological studies of humans has indicated that long-term (often low-level) exposure to various toxic chemicals in the environment can disrupt the body's immune, nervous, and endocrine systems.

The *immune system* consists of specialized cells and tissues that protect the body against disease and harmful substances by forming antibodies that make invading agents harmless. Viruses such as the human immunodeficiency virus (HIV), ionizing radiation, malnutrition, and some synthetic chemicals (including several widely used pesticides) can weaken the human immune system. This can leave the body vulnerable to attacks by **(1)** allergens, **(2)** infectious bacteria, **(3)** viruses, and **(4)** protozoans. Recent studies of laboratory animals and wildlife as well as epidemiological studies of humans (especially in developing countries) have linked immune system suppression to several widely used pesticides.

Synthetic chemicals in the environment threaten the human *nervous system* (brain, spinal cord, and peripheral nerves). Many poisons are *neurotoxins*, which attack nerve cells (neurons). Examples are **(1)** chlorinated hydrocarbons (DDT, PCBs, dioxins), **(2)** organophosphate pesticides, **(3)** formaldehyde, **(4)** various compounds of arsenic, mercury, lead, and cadmium, and **(5)** widely used industrial solvents such as trichloroethylene (TCE), toluene, and xylene.

The *endocrine system* is a complex network of glands that release small amounts of *hormones* into the bloodstream. In humans and other animals, these chemicals control body functions such as **(1)** sexual reproduction, **(2)** growth, **(3)** development, and behavior.

Each type of hormone has a specific molecular shape that allows it to attach only to certain cell receptors (Figure 11-7, left). Once bonded together, the hormone and its receptor molecule move to the cell's

**Normal Hormone Process**

**Hormone Mimic**

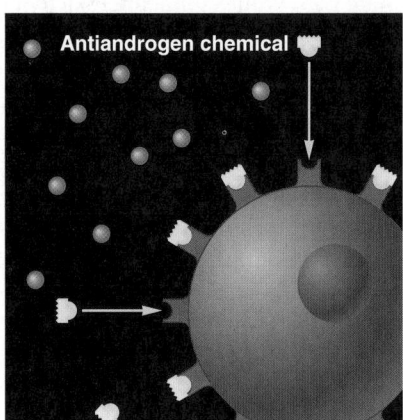
**Hormone Blocker**

**Figure 11-7** Hormones are molecules that act as messengers in the endocrine system to regulate various bodily processes, including reproduction, growth, and development. Each type of hormone has a unique molecular shape that allows it to attach to specially shaped receptors on the surface of or inside cells and transmit its chemical message (left). Molecules of certain pesticides and other synthetic chemicals have shapes similar to those of natural hormones and can affect the endocrine system in people and various other animals. These molecules are called *hormonally active agents* (HAAs). Some HAAs, sometimes called *hormone mimics*, disrupt the endocrine system by attaching to estrogen receptor molecules (center). Other HAAs, sometimes called *hormone blockers*, prevent natural hormones such as androgens (male sex hormones) from attaching to their receptors (right). Some pollutants called *thyroid disrupters* may disrupt hormones released by thyroid glands and cause growth and weight disorders and brain and behavioral disorders.

**CONNECTIONS**

Over the last 25 years, experts from a number of disciplines have been piecing together (1) field studies on wildlife, (2) studies on laboratory animals, and (3) epidemiological studies of human populations. This analysis suggests that a variety of human-made chemicals can act as *hormone* or *endocrine disrupters,* known as *hormonally active agents (HAAs).* So far more than 60 endocrine disrupters have been identified, and the list of HAAs could reach several hundred.

Some, called *hormone mimics,* are estrogenlike chemicals that disrupt the endocrine system by attaching to estrogen receptor molecules (Figure 11-7, center).

Others, called *hormone blockers,* disrupt the endocrine system by preventing natural hormones such as androgens (male sex hormones) from attaching to their receptors (Figure 11-7, right). There is also growing concern about pollutants that can act as *thyroid disrupters* and cause growth, weight, brain, and behavioral disorders.

Most natural hormones are broken down or excreted. However, many synthetic hormone impostors are stable fat-soluble compounds whose concentrations can be biomagnified as they move through food chains and webs (Figure 11-4). Thus they can pose a special threat to humans and other carnivores dining at the top of food webs.

Numerous wildlife and laboratory studies reveal various possible effects of estrogen mimics and hormone blockers (HAAs). Here are a few of many examples:

- Ranch minks that were fed Lake Michigan fish contaminated with endocrine disrupters such as DDT and PCBs failed to reproduce.

- Exposure to PCBs has reduced penis size in some test animals and in 118 boys born to women who were exposed to a PCB spill in Taiwan in 1979.

- Female shell fish (dog whelks) and snails exposed to tributyl tin (TBT) grew male sex organs. TBT has been widely used since the 1960s in marine paints to prevent the growth of barnacles and other crustaceans on the bottoms of ships and boats.

- A 1999 study by Michigan State University zoologists found that female rats exposed to PCBs were reluctant to mate, raising the possibility that such contaminants could cause low sex drives in women.

- In 1973, estrogen mimics called PBBs accidentally got into cattle feed in Michigan, and from there into beef. Pregnant women who ate the beef (and whose breast milk had high levels of PBBs) had sons with undersized penises and malformed testicles.

- The past 50 years have seen dramatic increases in testicular and prostate cancer in humans almost everywhere.

In 1999, the U.S. National Academy of Sciences released a report based on a 4-year review of the scientific literature on hormone disrupters (HAAs). The panel concluded that far too little is known about the effects of such chemicals to come to a definitive conclusion about their effects on humans.

Scientists on this panel called for greatly increased research to (1) verify current frontier science findings and (2) determine whether low levels of most hormone-disrupting chemicals in the environment pose a threat to the human population. However, the report also concluded that at present the 75,000 or more industrial chemicals in commercial use cannot be tested to determine whether they are hormone disrupters because the necessary tests do not exist.

Some health scientists believe we should begin sharply reducing the use of potential hormone disrupters now because they meet the two requirements of the *precautionary principle:* great scientific uncertainty and a reasonable suspicion of harm (p. 236).

Other researchers disagree. They point out that (1) the hormonal effects of synthetic hormone imposters are much weaker than those of naturally occurring hormones and (2) current levels of exposure to such chemicals are not high enough to pose any real danger to humans.

## Critical Thinking

**1.** Do you consider the possible threat from hormone disrupters a problem that could affect you or any child you might have? Explain.

**2.** Do you believe the precautionary approach should be used to deal with this problem while more definitive research is carried out over the next two decades? Explain. What harmful effects could using this approach have on the economy and on your lifestyle? Do these potentially harmful effects outweigh the benefits of continuing to use HAAs? Explain.

nucleus to execute the chemical message carried by the hormone. There is concern that human exposure to low levels of synthetic chemicals, known as *hormonally active agents* (HAAs), can mimic and disrupt the effects of natural hormones (Connections, above).

**Why Do We Know So Little About the Harmful Effects of Chemicals?** According to risk assessment expert Joseph V. Rodricks, "Toxicologists know a great deal about a few chemicals, a little about many, and next to nothing about most." The U.S. National

Academy of Sciences estimates that only about **(1)** 10% of at least 75,000 chemicals in commercial use have been thoroughly screened for toxicity, and **(2)** 2% have been adequately tested to determine whether they are carcinogens, teratogens, or mutagens. Hardly any of the chemicals in commercial use have been screened for damage to the nervous, endocrine, and immune systems.

Each year manufacturers introduce about 1,000 new synthetic chemicals into the marketplace, with little knowledge about their potentially harmful effects. Currently, federal and state governments do not regulate about 99.5% of the commercially used chemicals in the United States. There are three major reasons for this lack of information and regulation:

- Under existing laws, most chemicals are considered innocent until proven guilty.

- Not enough funds, personnel, facilities, and test animals are available to provide such information for more than a small fraction of the many chemicals we encounter in our daily lives.

- Analyzing the combined effects of multiple exposures to various chemicals and the possible interactions of such chemicals is too difficult and expensive. For example, just studying the possible different three-chemical interactions of the 500 most widely used industrial chemicals would take 20.7 million experiments—a physical and financial impossibility.

**What Is the Precautionary Approach?** Because of the difficulty and expense of getting information about the harmful effects of chemicals, an increasing number of scientists and health officials are pushing for much greater emphasis on *pollution prevention.* This strategy greatly reduces **(1)** the need for statistically uncertain and controversial toxicity studies and exposure standards and **(2)** the risk posed by exposure to potentially hazardous chemicals and products and their possible but poorly understood multiple interactions.

This approach is based on the **precautionary principle.** According to this concept, when we are uncertain about potentially serious harm from chemicals or technologies, decision makers should act to prevent harm to humans and the environment. The principle is based on familiar axioms: "Look before you leap," "better safe than sorry," and "an ounce of prevention is worth a pound of cure."

Under this approach, those proposing to introduce a new chemical or technology would bear the burden of establishing its safety. In other words, new chemicals and technologies would be assumed guilty until proven innocent. Manufacturers and businesses contend that doing this would make it too expensive and almost impossible to introduce any new chemical or technology.

## 11-4 BIOLOGICAL HAZARDS: DISEASE IN DEVELOPED AND DEVELOPING COUNTRIES

**What Are Nontransmissible Diseases?** A non-transmissible disease is not caused by living organisms and does not spread from one person to another. Examples are **(1)** cardiovascular (heart and blood vessel) disorders, **(2)** most cancers, **(3)** diabetes, **(4)** asthma, **(5)** emphysema, and **(6)** malnutrition. Such diseases typically have multiple (and often unknown) causes and tend to develop slowly and progressively. The world's population is growing and getting older. Thus, the incidence of and deaths from many nontransmissible diseases (especially cardiovascular disorders and cancers) are expected to increase.

**What Are Transmissible Diseases?** A transmissible disease is caused by a living organism (such as a bacterium, virus, protozoa, or parasite) and can be spread from one person to another (Figure 11-8). These infectious agents, called *pathogens,* are spread by air, water, food, body fluids, some insects, and other nonhuman carriers called *vectors.*

**Figure 11-8** Examples of *pathogens* or agents that can cause transmissible diseases. A micrometer is one-millionth of a meter.

Typically, a *bacterium* is a one-celled microorganism capable of replicating itself by simple cell division. A *virus* is a microscopic, noncellular infectious agent. Its DNA or RNA contains instructions for making more viruses, but it has no apparatus to do so. To replicate, a virus must invade a host cell and take over the cell's DNA to create a factory for producing more viruses (Figure 11-9).

Antibiotics have greatly reduced the incidence of infectious disease caused by bacteria. However, their widespread use and misuse have increased the genetic resistance of many disease-causing bacteria, which can reproduce rapidly (Spotlight, p. 238).

Some *great news* is that since 1900, and especially since 1950, we have greatly reduced the incidence of infectious diseases and the death rates from such diseases. Some *bad news* is that worldwide, infectious diseases cause about one of every four deaths each year—mostly in developing countries.

According to the WHO, the world's seven deadliest infectious diseases are **(1)** *acute respiratory infections,* mostly pneumonia and flu (caused by bacteria and viruses and killing about 3.9 million people per year, about 2.5 million of them children under age 5), **(2)** *acquired immune deficiency syndrome* (AIDS, a viral disease, killing about 3 million people per year, most of them young adults), **(3)** *diarrheal diseases* (caused by bacteria and viruses, killing about 2.1 million per year, 1.9 million of them children under age 5), **(4)** *tuberculosis* (TB, a bacterial disease, with 1.6 million deaths per year; Case Study, p. 241), **(5)** *malaria* (caused by parasitic protozoa, with 1.1 million annual deaths, about 700,000 of them children under age 5), **(6)** *hepatitis B* (a viral disease, killing 1 million people per year) and **(7)** *measles* (a viral disease, which kills about 800,000 people annually, most of them in children under age 5).

As a country industrializes, it usually makes an *epidemiological transition.* The infectious diseases of childhood become less important, and the chronic diseases of adulthood (heart disease and stroke, cancer, and respiratory conditions) become more important in causing mortality. In 1999, for example, infectious and parasitic diseases were responsible for 43% of all deaths in developing countries but only 1% in developed countries.

### How Rapidly Are Viral Diseases Spreading?

Viral diseases include **(1)** *influenza* or *flu* (transmitted by the body fluids or airborne emissions of an infected person), **(2)** *Ebola* (transmitted by the blood or other body fluids of an infected person), **(3)** *West Nile virus* (transmitted by the bite of a common mosquito that became infected by feeding on birds that carry the virus), **(4)** *rabies* (transmitted by dogs, coyotes, raccoons, skunks, and bats), and **(5)** *AIDS* (transmitted by unsafe sex, sharing of needles by

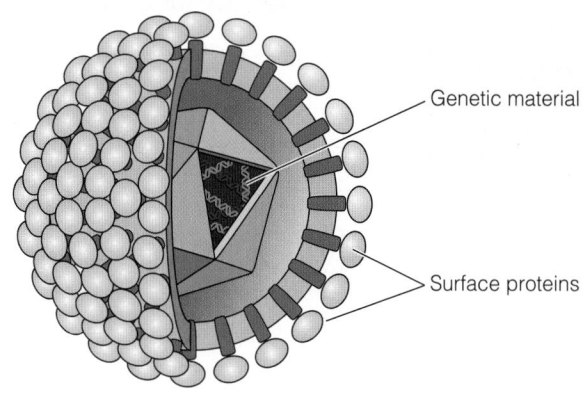

**A typical virus consists of a shell of proteins surrounding genetic material**

Genetic material

Surface proteins

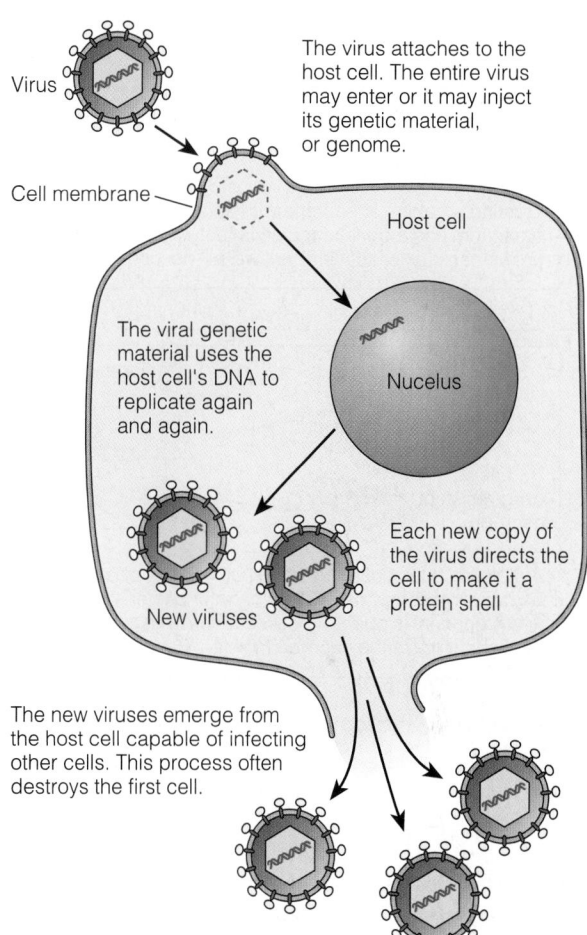

Virus

The virus attaches to the host cell. The entire virus may enter or it may inject its genetic material, or genome.

Cell membrane

Host cell

The viral genetic material uses the host cell's DNA to replicate again and again.

Nucelus

New viruses

Each new copy of the virus directs the cell to make it a protein shell

The new viruses emerge from the host cell capable of infecting other cells. This process often destroys the first cell.

**Figure 11-9** How a virus reproduces. (American Medical Association)

drug users, infected mothers to offspring before or during birth, and exposure to infected blood). Viruses, like bacteria, can genetically adapt rapidly to different conditions.

We are exposed to news reports about the emergence of new viral diseases such those caused by Ebola

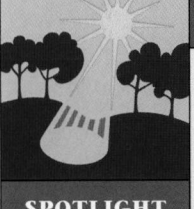

## Are We Losing Ground In Our War Against Infectious Bacteria?

Growing evidence indicates we may be falling behind our war against infectious bacterial diseases because bacteria are among the earth's ultimate survivors. When a colony of bacteria is dosed with an antibiotic such as penicillin, most of the bacteria are killed.

However, a few have mutant genes that make them immune to the drug (see figure, below, top). Through

natural selection (Figure 5-6, left, p. 102), a single mutant can pass such traits on to most of its offspring, which can amount to 16,777,216 in only 24 hours.

Even worse, bacteria can become genetically resistant to antibiotics they have never been exposed to. When a resistant and a nonresistant bacterium touch one another (say, on a hospital bedsheet or in a human stomach), they can exchange a small loop of DNA called a plasmid, thereby transferring genetic resistance

Treating a colony of bacteria with an antibiotic kills most of the microbes. Sometimes, a bacterium has a genetic mutation that makes it resistant to the drug. When the colony grows back, all of its members will be descended from the drug-resistant survivor.

Antibiotics attack harmless and harmful microbes. Drug resistance that develops in harmless bacteria may be transferred to harmful bacteria. One bacterium attaches itself to another, and a channel is opened between them in a process called *conjugation*. A copy of the genes that make the microbe resistant can then be passed from one microbe to the other.

Development of genetic resistance in strains of bacteria exposed to repeated doses of antibiotics.

viruses (Figure 11-8) and the West Nile virus. Heath officials are concerned about such diseases but point out that they cause relatively few deaths.

They also point out that the greatest virus health threat to humans is the emergence of new, very virulent strains of influenza. Flu viruses move through the air and are highly contagious. During 1918 and 1919, a flu epidemic infected more than half the world's population and killed 20–30 million people (including about 500,000 in the United States). Today, flu kills about 1 million people per year (20,000 of them in the United States).

Sex can be dangerous to one's health. According to the U. S. Centers for Disease Control, (1) about 65

million Americans (23% of the population) are walking around with a *sexually transmitted disease* (STD), and (2) each year STDs infect about 15.3 million Americans. According to a 1998 report by the American Social Health Association, at least one in every three sexually active people in the United States will contract an STD by age 24. Some of these diseases can cause infertility in men and women. Others can cause warts and genital cancers or, in the case of HIV, death. Worldwide, about 333 million adults are infected with an STD (excluding HIV) each year.

Globally, the spread of *acquired immune deficiency syndrome (AIDS)*, caused by the human immunodeficiency virus (HIV), is a growing threat. The virus itself from one organism to another (see figure, left, bottom).

The incredible genetic adaptability of bacteria is one reason the world faces a potentially serious rise in the incidence of some infectious bacterial diseases once controlled by antibiotics. Other factors also play a key role, including **(1)** spread of bacteria (some beneficial and some harmful) around the globe by human travel and the trade of goods, **(2)** overuse of antibiotics by doctors, often at the insistence of their patients (with a 2000 study by Richard Wenzel and Michael Edward suggesting that at least half of all antibiotics used to treat humans are prescribed unnecessarily), **(3)** failure of many patients to take all of their prescribed antibiotics, which promotes bacterial resistance, **(4)** availability of antibiotics in many countries without prescriptions, **(5)** overuse of pesticides, which increases populations of pesticide-resistant insects and other carriers of bacterial diseases, and **(6)** widespread use of antibiotics in the livestock and dairy industries to control disease in livestock animals and to promote animal growth.

The result of these factors acting together is that every major disease-causing bacterium now has strains that resist at least one of the roughly 160 antibiotics we use to treat bacterial infections. In 1998, health officials were alarmed to learn of the existence of a strain of bubonic plague in Madagascar that is resistant to multiple antibiotics.

In 2000, officials at the U.S. Centers for Disease Control and Prevention estimated that **(1)** about 2.2 million people (most with a weakened immune system) a year get sick, and **(2)** at least 88,000 die from infectious diseases they pick up in U.S. hospitals, nursing homes, or home health-care settings. Most of these infections are caused by **(1)** contaminated catheters, intravenous lines, and breathing tubes and **(2)** failure of doctors and other health-care personnel to carefully wash their hands

with water or alcohol-based antimicrobial hand rubs and frequently change their latex gloves. Patients and their loved ones can reduce such infections by asking any doctor or health-care worker coming into their room, "Did you wash your hands?" or "Did you change your gloves?"

The widespread use of antibiotics to increase the growth rate of about 80% of the livestock animals raised each year in the United States, mainly cattle, pigs, and poultry, is a controversial issue. According to a 2000 study by Margaret Mellon and other researchers, about 84% of all antibiotics in the United States are used mostly as feed additives to boost livestock production. Resistant strains of infectious diseases that develop in livestock animals can spread to humans through contact with infected animals or water and through food chains.

The European Union, the World Health Organization, the American Public Health Association, and the U.S. Centers for Disease Control and Prevention all favor the immediate phaseout of all antibiotics used to promote growth in livestock animals that are the same as or closely related to antibiotics used in humans. Several European countries have imposed such bans, and since 1986 Sweden has banned all use of antibiotics for growth promotion in livestock.

### Critical Thinking

**1.** What role, if any, have you played in the increase in genetic resistance of bacteria to widely used antibiotics? List three ways to reduce this threat.

**2.** Do you believe the use of the same antibiotics to treat human illness and to fatten livestock should be banned in the United States (or the country where you live)? Explain. Would you favor using small amounts of such antibiotics to treat disease in livestock?

is not deadly, but it kills immune cells and leaves the body defenseless against infectious bacteria and other viruses.

According to the WHO, by the end of 2001 some 40 million people worldwide (two-thirds of them in sub-Saharan Africa were infected with HIV (Figure 11-10, p. 240). During 2001, 5.4 million people (80% of them in Africa and Asia) were newly infected with HIV—an average of almost 15,300 new infections per day. In seven sub-Saharan African countries 20% or more of adults are infected with HIV.

Within about 7–10 years, at least half of those with HIV develop AIDS. This long incubation period means that infected people often spread the virus for several

years without knowing they are infected. So far, no cure for AIDS exists, although drugs may help some infected people live longer (if they can afford the treatment, which can cost up to $15,000 per year).

According to the United Nations, by the end of 2001 about 24.8 million people (420,000 in the United States), had died of AIDS-related diseases. Most of these deaths occurred in developing countries (80% of them in sub-Saharan Africa).

During the last two decades, people in eight African countries have lost more than 10 years in their expected life span. In two African countries, Zimbabwe (where 33% of adults are HIV positive) and Botswana (with 39% of adults infected with HIV),

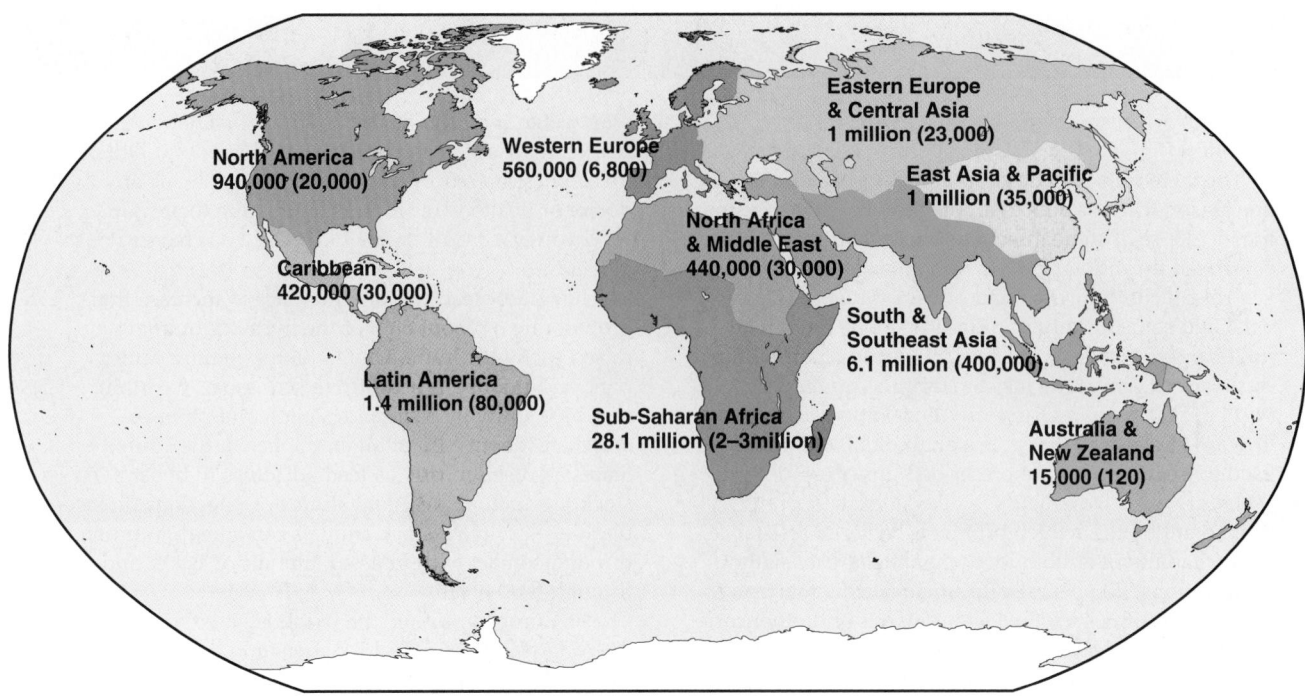

**Figure 11-10** Distribution of the 40 million people infected with HIV in 2001. Numbers in parentheses give the number of deaths from AIDS in 2001. (Data from United Nations)

**Figure 11-11** Synergistic interactions among HIV/AIDS, TB, and hunger/malnutrition. (Data from Daniel W. Fitzgerald and Patrice Joseph)

average life expectancy has dropped by more than 30 years since 1980. Because of AIDS the populations of 35 African countries were projected to have a 10% drop between 2000 and 2015. Between 2001 and 2020, 69 million people are expected to die of AIDS—equivalent to a loss of one-fourth the current U. S. population and more than all people currently living in the United Kingdom.

HIV/AIDS and TB problems among the poor are made worse by synergistic interactions between HIV/AIDS, TB, and hunger/malnutrition (Figure 11-11). According to a 2001 WHO report, up to 50% of the people infected with HIV/AIDS can expect to develop TB. Testing in a number of developing countries shows that up to 70% of TB patients are infected with HIV.

**How Are Viral Diseases Treated?** Once a viral infection starts, it is much harder to fight than infections by bacteria and protozoans. Only a few antiviral drugs exist because most drugs that will kill a virus also harm the cells of its host. Treating viral infections (such as colds, flu, and most mild coughs and sore throats) with antibiotics is useless and increases genetic resistance in disease-causing bacteria (Spotlight, p. 238).

Medicine's only effective weapons against viruses are *vaccines* that stimulate the body's immune system to produce antibodies to ward off viral infections.

# The Global Tuberculosis Epidemic

Since 1990, one of the world's most underreported stories has been the rapid spread of tuberculosis (TB). According to the World Health Organization, this highly infectious bacterial disease kills about 1.6 million people and infects about 8 million people per year (see figure).

The bacterium causing TB infection moves from person to person, mainly in airborne droplets produced by coughing, sneezing, singing, or even talking. About one of every three people in the world is infected with the TB bacillus.

During their lifetime about 5–10% of these people will become sick or infectious with active TB, especially when their immune system is weakened. Left untreated, each person with active TB will infect 10–15 other people. Many infected people do not appear to be sick, and about half of them do not know they are infected. As a result, this serious health problem has been called a *silent global epidemic*.

Major reasons for the recent increase in TB are **(1)** poor TB screening and control programs (especially in developing countries, where about 95% of the new cases occur), **(2)** development of strains of the tuberculosis bacterium that are genetically resistant to almost all effective antibiotics (typically leading to mortality rates of more than 50%), **(3)** population growth and increased urbanization (which increase contacts between people), **(4)** poverty, and **(5)** the spread of AIDS (Figures 11-10 and 11-11), which greatly weakens the immune system and allows TB bacteria to multiply.

Slowing the spread of the disease involves early identification and treatment of people with active TB, usually those with a chronic cough. Treatment with a combination of four inexpensive drugs can cure 90% of those with active TB. However, to be successful the drugs must be taken every day for 6–8 months. Because the symptoms disappear after a few weeks, many patients think they are cured and stop taking the drugs. This allows the disease to recur in a hard-to-treat form. It then spreads to other people, and drug-resistant strains of TB bacteria develop.

According to the World Health Organization, a worldwide campaign to help control TB would cost about $360 million to help save at least 20 million lives during the next decade.

## Critical Thinking

Before you read this report, were you aware of the serious global TB epidemic, primarily in developing countries? Why do you think this important story has gotten so little media attention compared to other diseases that cause many fewer deaths per year?

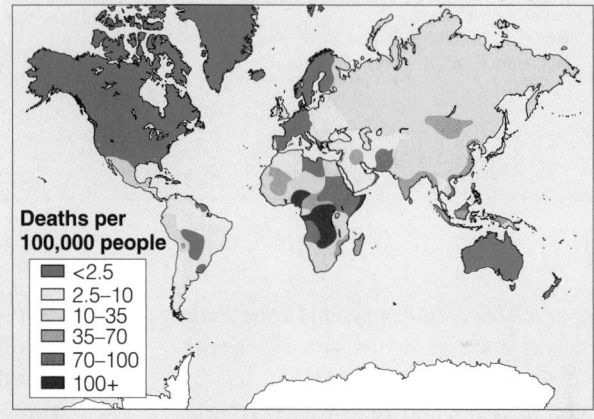

**Deaths per 100,000 people**
- <2.5
- 2.5–10
- 10–35
- 35–70
- 70–100
- 100+

The current global tuberculosis epidemic. This easily transmitted disease is spreading rapidly and now kills about 1.6 million people a year, mostly in developing countries. (Data from World Health Organization)

---

Immunization with vaccines has helped reduce the spread of viral diseases such as **(1)** smallpox, **(2)** polio, **(3)** rabies, **(4)** influenza, **(5)** measles, and **(6)** hepatitis B (Solutions, p. 242).

## Connections: What Factors Can Affect the Spread of Transmissible Diseases?

Outbreaks of infectious diseases often occur because of a change in the physical, social, or biological environment of disease reservoirs, carrier vectors, or exposure to new host populations. Important factors include the following:

- *Increased international air travel.*

- *Migration to urban areas,* which increases the probability of infection from diseases such as TB (Case Study, above), cholera, and STDs.

## Producing an Edible Hepatitis B Vaccine

Worldwide, about 300 million people (most in developing countries, with China having the world's highest infection rate) are infected with liver-damaging hepatitis B. Each year about 1 million people die from this disease and about 1 million new infections occur.

A vaccine for hepatitis B has been developed from bioengineered yeast. But it **(1)** costs about $100 per person, **(2)** requires three shots over a 6-month period, and **(3)** must be refrigerated continuously before use. This makes it impractical to carry out mass immunizations for hepatitis B in developing countries.

Researchers are developing a much cheaper and easily administered vaccine by inserting DNA extracted from the hepatitis B virus into the cells of leaves of plants such as potatoes (see figure). Mice eating raw potatoes from the plant developed immunity to hepatitis B. Researchers hope to introduce the vaccine into bananas, which might cost as little as 5¢ per dose to produce.

### Critical Thinking

What might be some disadvantages of introducing hepatitis B vaccine into the genes of food plants? Do you believe the advantages of using this vaccine in food outweigh its disadvantages? Explain.

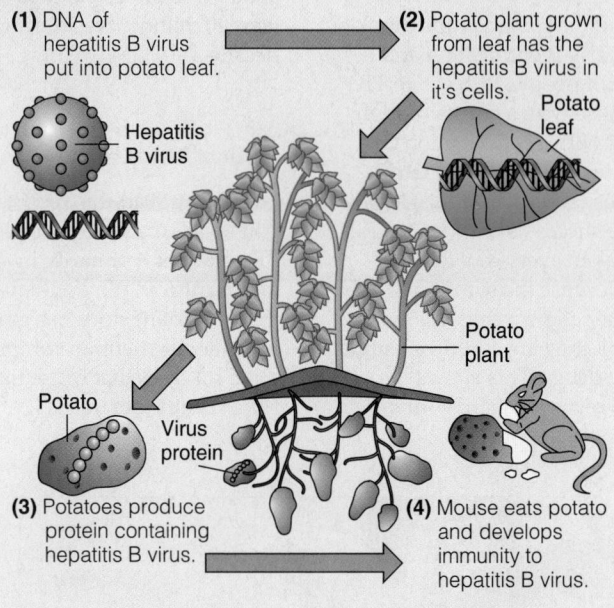

**(1)** DNA of hepatitis B virus put into potato leaf.

Hepatitis B virus

**(2)** Potato plant grown from leaf has the hepatitis B virus in it's cells.

Potato leaf

Potato plant

Potato

Virus protein

**(3)** Potatoes produce protein containing hepatitis B virus.

**(4)** Mouse eats potato and develops immunity to hepatitis B virus.

Using genetic engineering to produce food crops that contain a vaccine for hepatitis B.

---

■ *Migration to uninhabited rural areas and deforestation in tropical developing countries,* which can expose people to new diseases and disease vectors such as malaria, sleeping sickness, and yellow fever.

■ *Migration to suburbs in developed countries.* For example, as more people have moved to wooded suburbs in the eastern United States, they have come into greater contact with ticks infested with bacteria that cause Lyme disease, which causes fever, lethargy, and (sometimes) long-lasting arthritis.

■ *Hunger and malnutrition,* which increase the number of children killed by infectious diseases such as measles and diarrhea.

■ *Increased rice cultivation* in flooded fields and paddies, which creates ideal breeding grounds for mosquitoes and other insects that transmit diseases to humans.

■ *Global warming,* which is leading to the spread of tropical infectious diseases such as malaria, yellow fever, and dengue fever (called "breakbone fever" by those who experience the excruciating pain it causes in joints) to temperate areas.

■ *High winds or hurricanes,* which can transfer infectious organisms and carriers of disease (such as insects) from tropical to temperate areas.

■ *Accidental introduction of insect vectors.* The Asian tiger mosquito is a vector for dengue fever, yellow fever, and other viruses. In 1985, it was brought accidentally to the United States inside used tires shipped from Asia. Since then, this mosquito species has spread from Texas to at least 21 other states.

■ *Deliberate introduction of pathogens as an act of bioterrorism.* This occurred in 2001 when strains of potentially fatal anthrax bacteria were introduced into the United States, mostly through deliberately contaminated letters and packages.

■ *Flooding,* which **(1)** often contaminates water supplies with raw sewage and **(2)** creates areas of stand-

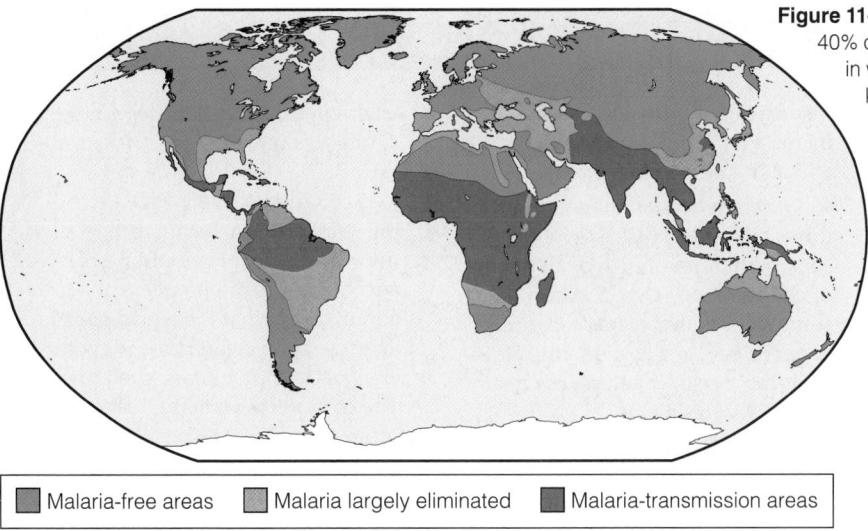

**Figure 11-12** Worldwide distribution of *malaria*. About 40% of the world's current population lives in areas in which malaria is present, with the disease killing at least 1.1 million people a year. In some African countries, 80% of the children are infected with the malaria parasite. (Data from the World Health Organization)

| Malaria-free areas | Malaria largely eliminated | Malaria-transmission areas |

ing water and moist soil that are ideal breeding grounds for mosquitoes and other insects that spread infectious diseases.

### Case Study: Malaria, a Protozoal Disease

About 40% of the world's people live in tropical and subtropical regions where malaria is present (Figure 11-12). Currently, an estimated 300–500 million people are infected with malaria parasites worldwide, and 270–500 million new cases are reported each year.

Malaria's symptoms come and go and include (1) fever and chills, (2) anemia, (3) an enlarged spleen, (4) severe abdominal pain and headaches, (5) extreme weakness, and (6) greater susceptibility to other diseases. The disease kills about 1.1 million people each year, about 700,000 of them children under age 5.

Malaria is caused by four protozoa species of the genus *Plasmodium* (Figure 11.8). Most cases of the disease are transmitted when an uninfected female of any one of 60 *Anopheles* mosquito species (1) bites an infected person, (2) ingests blood that contains the parasite, and (3) later bites an uninfected person (Figure 11-13). When this happens, *Plasmodium* parasites (1) move out of the mosquito and into the human's bloodstream, (2) multiply in the liver, and (3) enter blood cells to continue multiplying. Malaria also can be transmitted by blood transfusions or by sharing needles.

The malaria cycle repeats itself until immunity develops, treatment is given, or the victim dies. *Over the course of human history, malarial protozoa probably have killed more people than all the wars ever fought.*

During the 1950s and 1960s, the spread of malaria was sharply curtailed by (1) draining swamplands and marshes, (2) spraying breeding areas with insecticides,

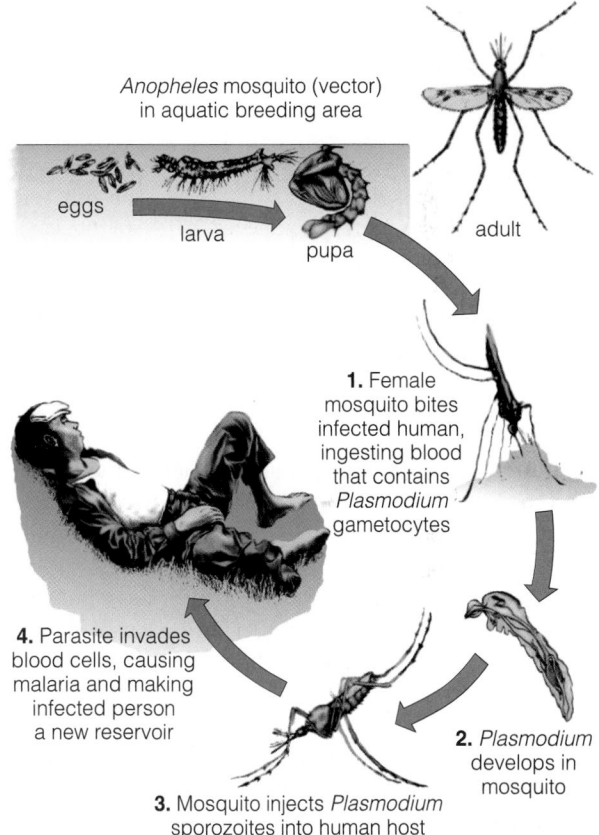

*Anopheles* mosquito (vector) in aquatic breeding area

eggs
larva
pupa
adult

**1.** Female mosquito bites infected human, ingesting blood that contains *Plasmodium* gametocytes

**2.** *Plasmodium* develops in mosquito

**3.** Mosquito injects *Plasmodium* sporozoites into human host

**4.** Parasite invades blood cells, causing malaria and making infected person a new reservoir

**Figure 11-13** The life cycle of malaria. This life cycle of *Plasmodium* circulates from mosquito to human and back to mosquito. Although various mosquito species carry diseases (such as malaria, yellow fever, encephalitis, and dengue fever to humans and heartworm to dogs), mosquitoes also play important ecological roles. Their eggs are a major food source for fish, various insects, and frogs and other amphibians, and adult mosquitoes are an important source of food for bats, spiders, and many insect and bird species.

## Improving Health Care in Developing Countries

With adequate funding, the health of people in developing countries and the poor in developed countries can be improved dramatically, quickly, and cheaply by providing the following forms of mostly preventive health care:

- Better nutrition, prenatal care, and birth assistance for pregnant women.

- Better nutrition for children.

- Greatly improved postnatal care (including promotion of breast-feeding, except for mothers infected with HIV) to reduce infant mortality. Breast-fed babies get natural immunity to many diseases from antibodies in their mothers' milk.

- Immunization against the world's five largest preventable infectious diseases: tetanus, measles, diphtheria, typhoid fever, and polio. Some good news is that since 1971, the percentage of children in developing countries immu-

nized against these diseases has increased from 10% to 84%, saving about 10 million lives a year.

- Oral rehydration therapy for victims of diarrheal diseases, which cause about one-fourth of all deaths of children under age 5. A simple solution of boiled water, salt, and sugar or rice, at a cost of only a few cents per person, can prevent death from dehydration.

- Careful and selective use of antibiotics for infections (Spotlight, p. 238).

- Clean drinking water and sanitation facilities for the one-third of the world's population that lacks them. In 2001, the WHO began promoting a simple, do-it-yourself technique that uses sunlight to disinfect water. The process is simple: **(1)** fill a transparent plastic bottle with contaminated water and **(2)** lay it horizontally on a flat black surface (which absorbs more heat and kills more pathogens). The heat and ultraviolet rays of the sun kill most illness-causing microorganisms in polluted water. This method is especially

useful in tropical countries where sunlight is intense.

According to the WHO, extending such primary health care to all the world's people would cost an additional $10 billion per year, about 4% of what the world spends every year on cigarettes or devotes every 4 days to military spending. The cost of this primary health-care program is about $1 per child. In 2002, Bill and Melinda Gates created a fund of more than $24 billion to help fight diseases that affect the world's poorest people.

### Critical Thinking

**1.** Do you believe developed countries should foot at least half the bill for implementing such proposals? What economic and environmental benefits would this provide for developed countries?

**2.** How many dollars per year of your taxes would you be willing to spend for such a preventive health program in developing countries?

and **(3)** using drugs to kill the parasites in the bloodstream. Since 1970, malaria has come roaring back. Most species of the malaria-carrying *Anopheles* mosquito have become genetically resistant to most insecticides. Worse, the *Plasmodium* parasites have become genetically resistant to common antimalarial drugs. According to the United Nations, since the 1980s, death rates from malaria among African children have tripled, due mostly to the drug-resistant strains of mosquitoes and overly used antimalarial drugs.

Researchers are working to develop new antimalarial drugs (such as artemisinins derived from the Chinese herbal remedy quihaosu), vaccines, and biological controls for *Anopheles* mosquitoes. However, such approaches receive too little funding and have proved more difficult than originally thought. Researchers also are studying the feasibility of altering the genetic makeup of mosquitoes so they cannot carry and transmit the parasite to humans.

According to health experts, prevention is the best approach to slowing the spread of malaria. Methods

include **(1)** increasing water flow in irrigation systems to prevent mosquito larvae from developing (an expensive and wasteful use of water), **(2)** using mosquito nets dipped in a nontoxic insecticide (permethrin) in windows and doors of homes, **(3)** cultivating fish that feed on mosquito larvae (biological control), **(4)** clearing vegetation around houses, **(5)** planting trees that soak up water in low-lying marsh areas where mosquitoes thrive (a method that can degrade or destroy ecologically important wetlands), **(6)** using zinc and vitamin A supplements to boost children's resistance to malaria, and **(7)** greatly increased public education. In 1998, the World Bank, the WHO, and several other organizations launched the Roll Back Malaria program to help reduce the mortality rate from malaria.

**How Can We Reduce the Incidence of Infectious Diseases?** Figure 11-14 lists measures that health scientists and public health officials suggest for preventing or reducing the incidence of infectious dis-

**Figure 11-14** *Solutions:* ways to prevent or reduce the incidence of infectious diseases.

The image panel (left) lists:

Increase research on tropical diseases and vaccines

Reduce poverty

Decrease malnutrition

Improve drinking water quality

Reduce unnecessary use of antibiotics

Educate people to take all of an antibiotic prescription

Reduce antibiotic use to promote livestock growth

Careful hand washing by all medical personnel

Slow global warming to reduce spread of tropical diseases to temperate areas

Increase preventative health care

eases that affect humanity (especially in developing countries). They also call for increased emphasis on preventive health care in developing countries (Solutions, p. 244).

The WHO estimates that only 2% of the world's global research and development funds are devoted to infectious diseases in developing countries, even though more people worldwide suffer and die from these diseases than from all others combined. Indeed, according to a 2000 study by the International Federation of Red Cross, an estimated 150 million people have died from tuberculosis, malaria, and AIDS since 1945, compared to 23 million in wars.

The *good news* is that **(1)** the global death rate from infectious diseases has decreased by about 66% between 1970 and 2000 and is projected to continue dropping and **(2)** the average life expectancy of people in developed and developing countries is more than twice what it was a hundred years ago.

The *bad news* is that death rates from infectious diseases in developing countries are still unacceptably high. This situation could be greatly reduced by devoting **(1)** much more of the world's global research and development funds to infectious diseases in developing countries, and **(2)** more funds and efforts to preventive health care in such countries (Solutions, p. 244)

## 11-5 RISK ANALYSIS

**How Can We Estimate Risks?**   Risk analysis involves **(1)** identifying hazards and evaluating their associated risks (*risk assessment*, Figure 11-2, left), **(2)** ranking risks (*comparative risk analysis*), **(3)** determining options and making decisions about reducing or eliminating risks (*risk management*, Figure 11-2, right), and **(4)** informing decision makers and the public about risks (*risk communication*).

Statistical probabilities based on past experience, animal testing and other tests, and epidemiological studies are used to estimate risks from older technologies and chemicals. To evaluate new technologies and products, risk evaluators use more uncertain statistical probabilities, based on models rather than actual experience and testing.

The left side of Figure 11-15 (p. 246) illustrates *comparative risk analysis,* summarizing the greatest ecological and health risks identified by a panel of scientists acting as advisers to the U.S. Environmental Protection Agency. Note the difference between the comparison of relative risk by scientists (Figure 11-15, left) and the general public (Figure 11-15, right). These differences result largely from failure of professional risk evaluators to educate the public about the nature of risks and their relative importance. Some risk experts contend that much of our risk education is based on often misleading media reports on the latest risk scare (based mainly on frontier science, p. 44) that do not put such risks in perspective.

Once a risk assessment has been completed, decision makers must decide what level of risk is acceptable. Figure 11-16 (p. 247) shows four methods used to determine the acceptability of a risk. The most widely used method is *benefit–cost analysis,* which attempts to determine whether the estimated short- and long-term benefits of using a particular technology or chemical outweigh the estimated short- and long-term risks or costs.

**What Are the Greatest Risks People Face?**   The greatest risks many people face today are rarely dramatic enough to make the daily news. In terms of the number of premature deaths per year (Figure 11-17, p. 247) and reduced life span, *the greatest risk by far is poverty* (Figure 11-18, p. 248).

**Figure 11-15** *Comparative risk analysis* of the most serious ecological and health problems according to scientists acting as advisers to the U.S. Environmental Protection Agency (left column). Risks in each of these categories are not listed in rank order. The right side of this figure represents polls showing how U.S. citizens rank the ecological and health risks they perceive as the most serious. Why do you think there is such a great difference between the ranking by risk experts and by the general public? (Data from Science Advisory Board, *Reducing Risks*, Washington, D.C.: Environmental Protection Agency, 1990)

**Scientists**
(Not in rank order in each category)

**Citizens**
(In rank order in each category)

**High-Risk Health Problems**
- Indoor air pollution
- Outdoor air pollution
- Worker exposure to industrial or farm chemicals
- Pollutants in drinking water
- Pesticide residues on food
- Toxic chemicals in consumer products

**High-Risk Ecological Problems**
- Global climate change
- Stratospheric ozone depletion
- Wildlife habitat alteration and destruction
- Species extinction and loss of biodiversity

**High-Risk Problems**
- Hazardous waste sites
- Industrial water pollution
- Occupational exposure to chemicals
- Oil spills
- Stratospheric ozone depletion
- Nuclear power-plant accidents
- Industrial accidents releasing pollutants
- Radioactive wastes
- Air pollution from factories
- Leaking underground tanks

**Medium-Risk Ecological Problems**
- Acid deposition
- Pesticides
- Airborne toxic chemicals
- Toxic chemicals, nutrients, and sediment in surface waters

**Medium-Risk Problems**
- Coastal water contamination
- Solid waste and litter
- Pesticide risks to farm workers
- Water pollution from sewage plants

**Low-Risk Ecological Problems**
- Oil spills
- Groundwater pollution
- Radioactive isotopes
- Acid runoff to surface waters
- Thermal pollution

**Low-Risk Problems**
- Air pollution from vehicles
- Pesticide residues in foods
- Global climate change
- Drinking water contamination

After the health risks associated with poverty, the greatest risks of premature death are mostly the result of voluntary choices people make about their lifestyles (Figures 11-1 and 11-18, p. 248).

By far the best ways to reduce one's risk of premature death and serious health risks are to (1) not smoke, (2) avoid excess sunlight (which ages skin and causes skin cancer), (3) not drink alcohol or drink only in moderation (no more than two drinks in a single day), (4) reduce consumption of foods containing cholesterol and saturated fats, (5) eat a variety of fruits and vegetables, (6) exercise regularly, (7) lose excess weight, and (8) for those who can afford a car, drive as safely as possible in a vehicle with the best available safety equipment.

However, we have little or no control over some factors that can influence our vulnerability to some risks. For example, we cannot control (1) our gender,

(2) the genes we inherited from our parents, and (3) our social and psychological environment during early childhood.

**How Can We Estimate Risks for Technological Systems?** The more complex a technological system and the more people needed to design and run it, the more difficult it is to estimate the risks. The overall reliability of any technological system (expressed as a percentage) is the product of two factors:

System reliability (%) = Technology reliability × Human reliability

With careful design, quality control, maintenance, and monitoring, a highly complex system such as a nuclear power plant or space shuttle can achieve a high degree of technology reliability. However, human reliability usually is much lower than technology reliability and is almost impossible to predict: To err is human.

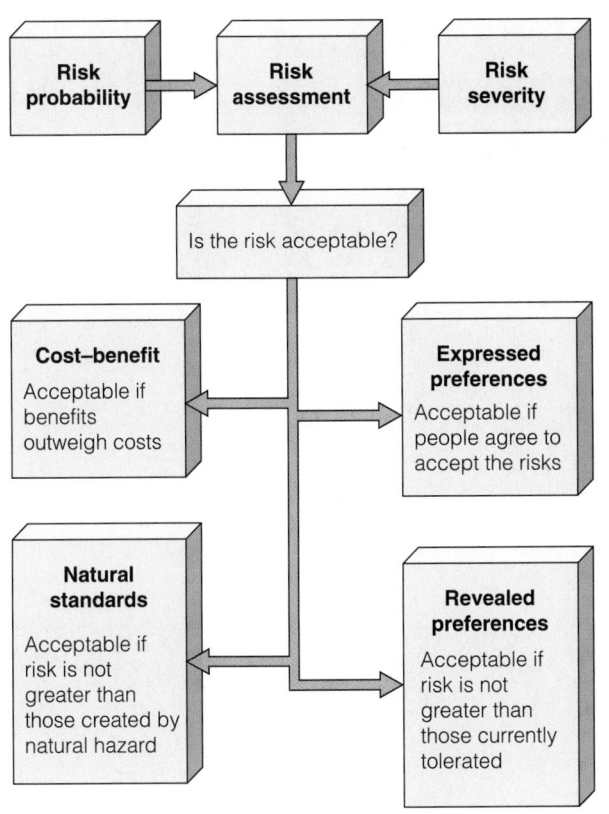

**Figure 11-16** Methods for determining the acceptability of a risk after a risk assessment has been made. Cost–benefit analysis is the most widely used method. (Adapted from Chiras, *Environmental Science*, 5th ed., p. 351. Copyright © 1998 by Wadsworth)

Suppose the technology reliability of a nuclear power plant is 95% (0.95) and human reliability is 75% (0.75). Then the overall system reliability is 71% (0.95 × 0.75 = 0.71 = 71%). Even if we could make the technology 100% reliable (1.0), the overall system reliability would still be only 75% (1.0 × 0.75 = 0.75 = 75%). The crucial dependence of even the most carefully designed systems on unpredictable human reliability helps explain essentially "impossible" tragedies such as the **(1)** Chernobyl nuclear power plant accident and **(2)** explosion of the space shuttle *Challenger*.

One way to make a system more foolproof or failsafe is to move more of the potentially fallible elements from the human side to the technical side. However, **(1)** chance events such as a lightning bolt can knock out an automatic control system, **(2)** no machine or computer program can completely replace human judgment, **(3)** the parts in any automated control system are manufactured, assembled, tested, certified, and maintained by fallible human beings, and **(4)** computer software programs used to monitor and control complex

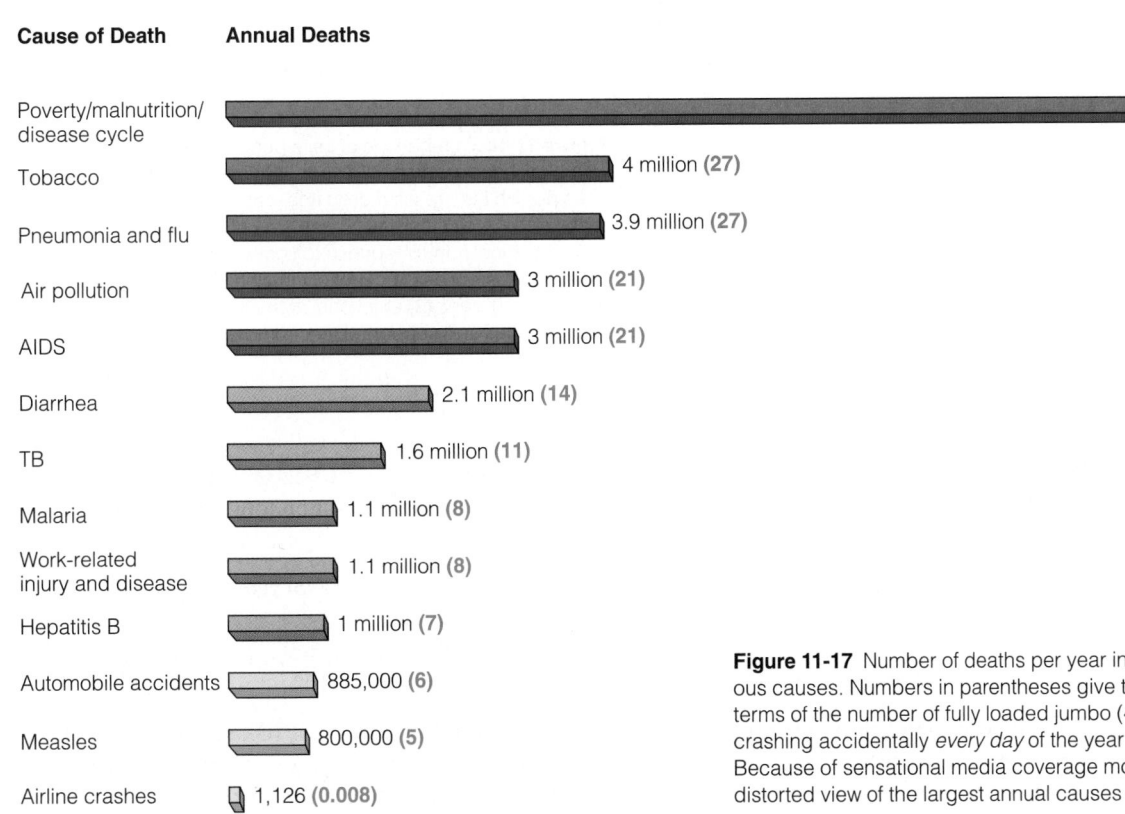

**Figure 11-17** Number of deaths per year in the world from various causes. Numbers in parentheses give these deaths in terms of the number of fully loaded jumbo (400-passenger) jets crashing accidentally *every day* of the year with no survivors. Because of sensational media coverage most people have a distorted view of the largest annual causes of death.

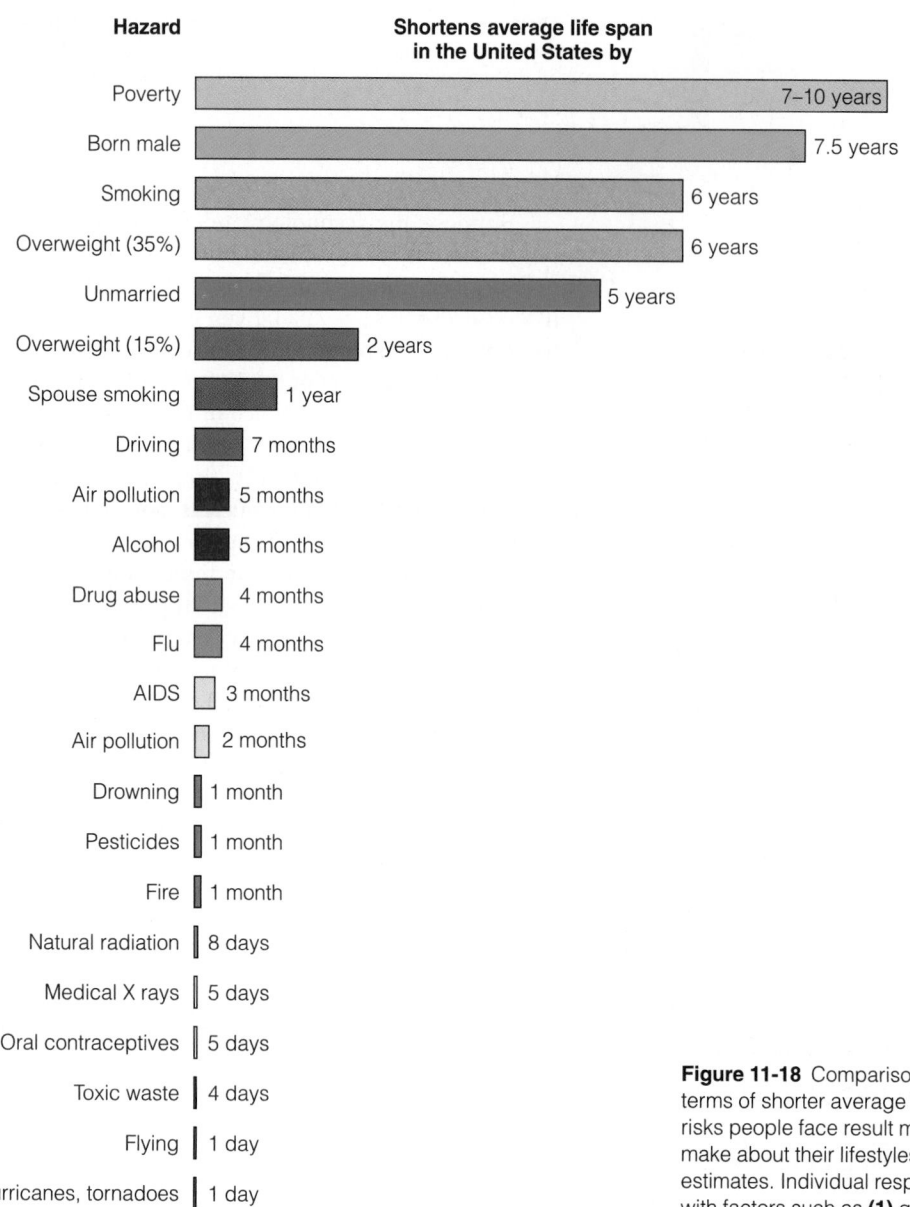

| Hazard | Shortens average life span in the United States by |
|---|---|
| Poverty | 7–10 years |
| Born male | 7.5 years |
| Smoking | 6 years |
| Overweight (35%) | 6 years |
| Unmarried | 5 years |
| Overweight (15%) | 2 years |
| Spouse smoking | 1 year |
| Driving | 7 months |
| Air pollution | 5 months |
| Alcohol | 5 months |
| Drug abuse | 4 months |
| Flu | 4 months |
| AIDS | 3 months |
| Air pollution | 2 months |
| Drowning | 1 month |
| Pesticides | 1 month |
| Fire | 1 month |
| Natural radiation | 8 days |
| Medical X rays | 5 days |
| Oral contraceptives | 5 days |
| Toxic waste | 4 days |
| Flying | 1 day |
| Hurricanes, tornadoes | 1 day |
| Living lifetime near nuclear plant | 10 hours |

**Figure 11-18** Comparison of risks people face, expressed in terms of shorter average life span. After poverty, the greatest risks people face result mostly from voluntary choices they make about their lifestyles. These are only generalized relative estimates. Individual response to some of these risks can vary with factors such as **(1)** genetic variation (Figure 11-3), **(2)** family medical history, **(3)** emotional makeup, **(4)** stress, and **(5)** social ties and support. (Data from Bernard L. Cohen)

systems can also contain human error or can be deliberately modified by computer viruses to malfunction.

**What Are the Limitations of Risk Analysis?** Here are some of the key questions involved in evaluating risk analysis:

- How reliable are risk assessment data and models?

- Who profits from allowing certain levels of harmful chemicals into the environment, and who suffers? Who decides this?

- Should estimates emphasize short-term risks, or should more weight be put on long-term risks? Who should make this decision?

- Should the primary goal of risk analysis be to **(1)** determine how much risk is acceptable (the current approach) or **(2)** figure out how to do the least damage (a prevention approach)?

- Who should do a particular risk analysis, and who should review the results? A government agency? Independent scientists? The public?

- Should cumulative effects of various risks be considered, or should risks be considered separately, as is usually done? Suppose a pesticide is found to have an annual risk of killing 1 person in 1 million from cancer, the current EPA limit. Cumulatively, however, effects from 40 such pesticides might kill 40, or 400, of every 1 million people. Is this acceptable, and to whom is it acceptable?

- How widespread is each risk?

- Should risk levels be higher for workers (as is almost always the case) than for the general public? What say should workers and their families have in this decision? For example, work-related illnesses and injuries kill about 80,000 workers each year in the United States—about twice the country's annual death toll from automobile accidents (Figure 11-1). The situation is much worse in developing countries, with more than 1 million work-related deaths occurring worldwide each year.

- How much risk is acceptable, and to whom is it acceptable? According to the National Academy of Sciences, exposure to toxic chemicals is responsible for 2–4% of the 521,000 cancer deaths in the United States; this amounts to 10,400–20,800 premature cancer deaths per year.

Proponents contend that risk analysis is a useful way to (1) organize and analyze available scientific information, (2) identify significant hazards, (3) focus on areas that need more research, (4) help regulators decide how money for reducing risks should be allocated, and (5) stimulate people to make more informed decisions about health and environmental goals and priorities.

However, critics point out that results of risk analysis are very uncertain. For example, a recent study documented the significant uncertainties involved in even simple risk analysis. Eleven European governments established 11 different teams of their best scientists and engineers (including those from private companies) to assess the hazards and risks from a small plant storing only one hazardous chemical (ammonia). The 11 teams, consisting of world-class experts analyzing this very simple system, disagreed with one another on fundamental points and varied in their assessments of the hazards by a factor of 25,000. Such inherent uncertainty explains why regulators setting human exposure levels for toxic substances usually divide the best results by 100 to 1,000 to provide the public with a margin of safety.

According to critics, the main decision-making tool we should rely on is not to find out how much risk is acceptable, which they contend is mostly a political decision. Instead, it should be to find out the least damaging reasonable alternatives by asking, "Which alternative will bring sufficient benefits and minimize damage to humans and to the earth?" To these critics, the emphasis should be on *alternative assessment*, not *risk assessment*.

**How Should Risks Be Managed?** *Risk management* includes the administrative, political, and economic actions taken to decide whether and how to reduce a particular societal risk to a certain level and at what cost.

Risk management involves answering the following questions:

- How reliable is the risk analysis for each risk?

- Which risks should be given the highest priority?

- How much risk is acceptable (Figure 11-16)?

- How much it will cost to reduce each risk to an acceptable level?

- How should limited funds be spent to provide the greatest benefit?

- How will the risk management plan be monitored, enforced, and communicated to the public?

Each step in this process involves making value judgments and weighing trade-offs to find some reasonable compromise among conflicting political, economic, health, and environmental interests.

**How Well Do We Perceive Risks?** How much risk is acceptable? Studies indicate that if the chance of death from a chemical or activity is less than 1 in 100,000, most people are not likely to be worried enough to change their ways.

However, most of us do poorly in assessing the relative risks from the hazards that surround us (Figures 11-15, 11-17, and 11-18). Also, many people deny or shrug off the high-risk chances of death (or injury) from voluntary activities they enjoy, such as (1) motorcycling (1 death in 50 participants), (2) smoking (1 in 300 participants by age 65 for a pack-a-day smoker), (3) hang gliding (1 in 1,250), and (4) driving (1 in 3,000 without a seatbelt and 1 in 6,000 with a seatbelt).

Yet some of these same people may be terrified about the possibility of dying from a (1) commercial airplane crash (1 in 1 million), (2) being killed by a handgun (1 in 2 million), (3) being struck by lightning (1 in 4 million), (4) a train crash (1 in 20 million), (5) snakebite (1 in 36 million), (6) shark attack (1 in 300 million), or (7) exposure to trichloroethylene (TCE) in drinking water at the trace levels allowed by the EPA (1 in 2 billion).

Being bombarded with news about people killed or harmed by various hazards distorts our sense of risk (Figures 11-17 and 11-18). However, *the most important good news each year is that about 99.1% of the people on the earth did not die.* Despite the greatly increased use of synthetic chemicals in food production and processing, the general health and average life expectancy of people in the United States (and most developed countries) have increased during the past 50 years.

Our perceptions of risk and our responses to perceived risks often have little to do with how risky the experts say something is (Figure 11-15). The public generally sees a technology or a product as being riskier than experts do when the following conditions exist:

- *It is new or complex rather than familiar.* Examples include genetic engineering and genetically modified food or nuclear power, as opposed to large dams or coal-fired power plants.

- *It is perceived as mostly involuntary.* Examples include nuclear power plants or food additives, as opposed to driving or smoking.

- *It is viewed as unnecessary rather than as beneficial or necessary.* Examples might include using chlorofluorocarbons (CFC) propellants in aerosol spray cans or using food additives that increase sales appeal, as opposed to cars or aspirin.

- *Its use involves a large, well-publicized death toll from a single catastrophic accident rather than the same or an even larger death toll spread out over a longer time.* Examples might include a severe nuclear power plant accident, an industrial explosion, or an accidental plane crash, as opposed to coal-burning power plants, automobiles, or smoking (Figure 11-17).

- *Its use involves unfair distribution of the risks.* Citizens are outraged when government officials decide to put a hazardous waste landfill or incinerator in or near their neighborhood, even when the decision is based on risk analysis. This decision is usually seen as politics, not science. Residents will not be satisfied by estimates that the lifetime risks of cancer death from the facility are not greater than, say, 1 in 100,000. Living near the facility means that they, not the vast majority of people living farther away, have a much higher risk of dying from cancer by having this risk involuntarily imposed on them.

- *The people affected are not involved in the decision-making process from start to finish.*

- *Its use does not involve a sincere search for and evaluation of alternatives.* People who believe their lives and the lives of their families are being threatened want to know **(1)** what the alternatives are and **(2)** which alternative causes the least harm to them and the earth.

Better education and communication about the nature of risks will help bring the public's perceptions of various risks closer to those of professional risk evaluators. However, such education will not eliminate the emotional, cultural, and ethical factors that decision makers must take into account in determining the acceptability of a particular risk and evaluating the possible alternatives.

*The burden of proof imposed on individuals, companies, and institutions should be to show that pollution prevention options have been thoroughly examined, evaluated, and used before lesser options are chosen.*
JOEL HIRSCHORN

## REVIEW QUESTIONS

**1.** Define the boldfaced terms in this chapter.

**2.** What voluntary human activity kills the largest number of people each year? List six ways to help reduce the harmful effects of smoking.

**3.** What are *risk* and *probability?* Distinguish between *risk assessment* and *risk management.*

**4.** List two **(a)** cultural hazards, **(b)** chemical hazards, **(c)** physical hazards, and **(d)** biological hazards.

**5.** What is *toxicity?* Distinguish between *dose* and *response* for a potentially harmful substance. List five factors that determine whether a chemical is harmful. Distinguish between *bioaccumulation* and *biomagnification.* List three mechanisms of the human body that can reduce the effects of most harmful chemicals.

**6.** What is a *poison?* What is an $LD_{50}$? List three methods used to determine toxicity, and list the limitations of each method. Describe how laboratory tests are used to determine toxicity. What is a *dose-response curve?* Distinguish between a *linear dose-response curve* and a *threshold dose-response curve.*

**7.** Distinguish between *toxic chemicals* and *hazardous chemicals.* Distinguish among *mutagens, teratogens,* and *carcinogens,* and give one example of each.

**8.** Distinguish among the *immune system, nervous system,* and *endocrine system,* and give an example of something that causes harm to each system. What are *hormone disrupters* and *hormone mimics?* List two examples of such chemicals.

**9.** About what percentage of the 75,000 chemicals in commercial use in the United States have been screened **(a)** to assess toxicity, **(b)** to determine whether they are carcinogens, teratogens, or mutagens, and **(c)** to determine whether they damage the nervous, endocrine, or immune systems?

**10.** List three reasons for the lack of information about the potentially harmful effects of most chemicals in commercial use. Distinguish between the regulation strategy and the pollution prevention strategy for protecting the public from potentially harmful chemicals. What is the *precautionary principle?* Why is it rarely used?

**11.** Distinguish between *nontransmissible* and *transmissible diseases,* and give two examples of each type. What are the seven deadliest infectious diseases in order of the number of deaths they cause each year?

**12.** How do infectious bacteria become resistant to antibiotics?

**13.** What is the best way to treat **(a)** a bacterial disease and **(b)** a viral disease? List two examples of each type of disease.

**14.** What causes tuberculosis, and how is it transmitted? About how many people died of TB during the past year? List five reasons for the increase in TB infections in recent years. How can the spread of this bacterial infectious disease be slowed?

**15.** Distinguish between *HIV* and *AIDS.* List four ways that HIV can be transmitted. About how many people in the world **(a)** are infected with HIV and **(b)** have died of AIDS? List ways to prevent the spread of this viral infectious disease.

**16.** List 11 factors that can affect the spread of infectious diseases.

**17.** What causes *malaria?* About how many people die from malaria each year? List seven ways to help prevent this protozoal infectious disease.

**18.** List 10 ways to prevent or reduce the incidence of infectious diseases throughout the world. List seven major ways to improve health care in developing countries.

**19.** What is *risk analysis?* What are its major limitations?

**20.** List five of the greatest risks people face in terms of **(a)** number of premature deaths per year and **(b)** reduced life span. List eight ways to reduce your risk of premature death and serious health problems. How can we estimate the risks from technological systems?

**21.** What is *risk management?* What six questions do risk managers try to answer? About what percentage of the people on the earth die each year? List seven reasons why people often perceive that certain risks are greater than experts say they are.

## CRITICAL THINKING

**1.** Explain why you agree or disagree with the proposals made by health officials for reducing the death toll and other harmful effects of smoking listed on p. 228.

**2.** Do you think chemicals should be regulated based on their effects on the nervous, immune, and endocrine systems? Explain.

**3.** Should we have zero pollution levels for all hazardous chemicals? Explain.

**4.** Evaluate the following statements:
   **a.** We should not get so worked up about exposure to toxic chemicals because almost any chemical can cause some harm at a large enough dosage.
   **b.** We should not worry so much about exposure to toxic chemicals because through genetic adaptation we can develop immunity to such chemicals.
   **c.** We should not worry so much about exposure to toxic chemicals because we can use genetic engineering to reduce or eliminate such problems.

**5.** Assume you are a government official responsible for regulating chemicals. What information would you require in order to make a decision about the safety of a particular chemical? What level of risk of exposure to the chemical would you consider acceptable for **(a)** society, **(b)** yourself, and **(c)** any child you might have?

**6.** Should pollution levels be set to protect the most sensitive people in a population (Figure 11-3, left) or the average person (Figure 11-3, middle)? Explain.

**7.** What are the five major risks you face from **(a)** your lifestyle, **(b)** where you live, and **(c)** what you do for a living? Which of these risks are voluntary and which are involuntary? List the five most important things you can do to reduce these risks. Which of these things do you actually plan to do?

**8.** How would you answer each of the questions raised about **(a)** risk analysis on pp. 248–249 and **(b)** risk assessment and risk management on p. 249? Explain each of your answers.

## PROJECTS

**1.** Assume that members of your class (or small manageable groups in your class) have been appointed to a technology benefit–risk assessment board. As a group, decide why you would approve or disapprove of widespread use of each of the following: **(a)** drugs to retard aging, **(b)** electrical or chemical devices that would stimulate the brain to eliminate anxiety, fear, unhappiness, and aggression, and **(c)** genetic engineering to produce people with superior intelligence and strength.

**2.** Use the library or the Internet to find recent articles describing the rise of genetic resistance of disease-causing bacteria to commonly used antibiotics. Evaluate the evidence and claims in these articles.

**3.** Pick a specific viral disease and use the library or Internet to find out about **(a)** how it spreads, **(b)** its effects, **(c)** strategies for controlling its spread, and **(d)** possible treatments.

**4.** Use the library or the Internet to find bibliographic information about *Paracelsus* and *Joel Hirschorn*, whose quotes appear at the beginning and end of this chapter.

**5.** Make a concept map of this chapter's major ideas, using the section heads and subheads and the key terms (in boldface). Look on the website for this book for information about making concept maps.

## INTERNET STUDY RESOURCES AND RESOURCES FOR FURTHER READING AND RESEARCH

The website for this book contains helpful study aids and many ideas for further reading and research. Log on to

www.info.brookscole.com/miller13

and click on the Chapter-by-Chapter area. Choose Chapter 11 and select a resource:

- Flash Cards allows you to test your mastery of the Terms and Concepts to Remember for this chapter.

- Tutorial Quizzes provides a multiple-choice practice quiz.

- Student Guide to InfoTrac will lead you to Critical Thinking Projects that use InfoTrac College Edition as a research tool.

- References lists the major books and articles consulted in writing this chapter.

- Hypercontents takes you to an extensive list of sites with news, research, and images related to individual sections of the chapter.

## INFOTRAC COLLEGE EDITION

Improve your skills with InfoTrac College Edition, a searchable online database of articles from more than 700 periodicals. Log on to

http://www.infotrac-college.com

or access InfoTrac through the website for this book. Try to find the following articles:

**1.** Frank, C., A. D. Fix, C. A. Pena, and G. T. Strickland. 2002. Mapping Lyme disease incidence for diagnostic and preventive decisions, Maryland. *Emerging Infectious Diseases* 8: 427. *Keywords:* "lyme disease" and "mapping." GIS mapping technology was used to illustrate the distribution of Lyme disease in Maryland. This information could then be used by doctors and state health departments to assist in diagnosis and distribution of vaccine.

**2.** Thiele, L. P. 2000. Limiting risks: Environmental ethics as a policy primer. *Policy Studies Journal* 20: 540. *Keywords:* "risk" and "environmental ethics." This article explores the ethical aspects of evaluating involuntary human-caused environmental risks in a technologically driven society.

# PART III

## POPULATION, RESOURCES, AND SUSTAINABILITY

*I recognize the right and duty of this generation to develop and use our natural resources, but I do not recognize the right to waste them, or to rob by wasteful use, the generations that come after us.*

THEODORE ROOSEVELT, 1900

# 12 THE HUMAN POPULATION: GROWTH, DEMOGRAPHY, AND CARRYING CAPACITY

## Slowing Population Growth in Thailand

Can a country sharply reduce its population growth in only 15 years? Thailand did.

In 1971, Thailand (Figure 12-7, p. 257) adopted a policy to reduce its population growth. When the program began, the country's population was growing at a rate of 3.2% per year, and the average Thai family had 6.4 children.

Fifteen years later in 1986, the country's population growth rate had been cut in half to 1.6%. By 2002, the rate had fallen to 0.8%, and the average number of children per family was 1.8. Thailand's population is projected to grow from 63 million in 2002 to 72 million by 2025.

Several reasons account for this impressive feat: **(1)** the creativity of the government-supported family planning program, **(2)** a high literacy rate among women (90%), **(3)** an increasing economic role for women and advances in women's rights, **(4)** better health care for mothers and children, **(5)** the openness of the Thai people to new ideas, **(6)** the willingness of the government to encourage and financially support family planning and to work with the private, non-profit Population and Community Development Association (PCDA), and **(7)** support of family planning by the country's religious leaders (95% of Thais are Buddhist).

This transition was catalyzed by the charismatic leadership of Mechai Viravidaiya (Figure 12-1), a public relations genius and former government economist who launched the PCDA in 1974 to help make family planning a national goal. PCDA workers handed out condoms at festivals, movie theaters, and even traffic jams, and they developed ads and witty songs about contraceptive use. Between 1971 and 2002, the percentage of married women using modern birth control rose from 15% to 70%—higher than the 58% usage in developed countries and the 54% usage in developing countries.

Viravidaiya helped establish a German-financed revolving loan plan to enable people participating in family planning programs to install toilets and drinking water systems. Low-rate loans were offered to farmers practicing family planning. The government also offers loans to individuals from a fund that increases as their village's level of contraceptive use rises.

All is not completely rosy. Although Thailand has done well in slowing population growth and raising per capita income, it has been less successful in reducing pollution and improving public health. Its capital, Bangkok, remains one of the world's most polluted and congested cities. It is plagued with notoriously high levels of traffic congestion and air pollution (Figure 12-2). The typical motorist in Bangkok spends 44 days per year sitting in traffic, costing $2.3 billion in lost work time.

**Figure 12-1** Individuals Matter. *Mechai Viravidaiya*, a charismatic leader, played a major role in Thailand's successful efforts to reduce its population growth. In 1974, he established the private, non-profit Population and Community Development Association (PCDA), to help implement family planning as a national goal.

**Figure 12-2** This policeman and schoolchildren in Bangkok, Thailand, are wearing masks to reduce their intake of air polluted mainly by automobiles. Bangkok is one of the world's most car-clogged cities, with car commutes averaging 3 hours per day. Roughly one of every nine of its residents has a respiratory ailment.

*The problems to be faced are vast and complex, but come down to this: 6.2 billion people are breeding exponentially. The process of fulfilling their wants and needs is stripping earth of its biotic capacity to produce life; a climactic burst of consumption by a single species is overwhelming the skies, earth, waters, and fauna.*

PAUL HAWKEN

This chapter addresses the following questions:

- How is population size affected by birth, death, fertility, and migration rates?

- How is population size affected by the percentage of males and females at each age level?

- How can population growth be slowed?

- What success have India and China had in slowing population growth?

- How can global population growth be reduced?

## 12-1 FACTORS AFFECTING HUMAN POPULATION SIZE

**How Is Population Size Affected by Birth Rates and Death Rates?** Populations grow or decline through the interplay of three factors: *births, deaths,* and *migration.* **Population change** is calculated by subtracting the number of people leaving a population (through death and emigration) from the number entering it (through birth and immigration) during a specified period of time (usually a year):

Population change = (Births + Immigration) − (Deaths + Emigration)

When births plus immigration exceed deaths plus emigration, population increases; when the reverse is true, population declines.

Instead of using the total numbers of births and deaths per year, demographers use **(1)** the **birth rate,** or **crude birth rate** (the number of live births per 1,000 people in a population in a given year) and **(2)** the **death rate,** or **crude death rate** (the number of deaths per 1,000 people in a population in a given year). Figure 12-3 shows the crude birth and death rates for various groupings of countries in 2002.

Birth rates and death rates are coming down worldwide, but death rates have fallen more sharply than birth rates. As a result, more births are occurring than deaths; every time your heart beats, 2.3 more babies are added to the world's population. At this rate, we share the earth and its resources with about

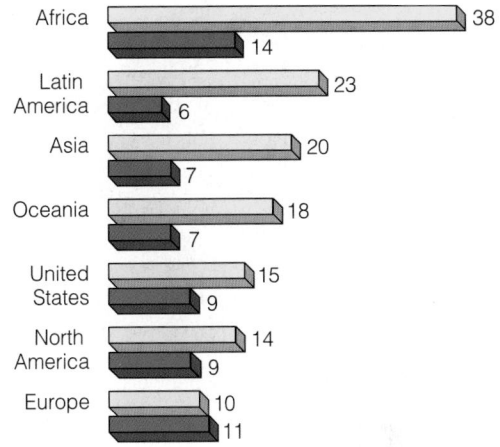

**Figure 12-3** Average crude birth and death rates for various groupings of countries in 2002. (Data from Population Reference Bureau)

216,000 more people each day (95% of them in developing countries). This is equivalent to filling up a jumbo jet with 400 new passengers every 2.7 minutes around the clock.

The rate of the world's annual population change (excluding migration) usually is expressed as a percentage:

$$\text{Annual rate of natural population change (\%)} = \frac{\text{Birth rate} - \text{Death rate}}{1{,}000 \text{ persons}} \times 100$$

$$= \frac{\text{Birth rate} - \text{Death rate}}{10}$$

Exponential population growth has not disappeared but is occurring at a slower rate. The rate of the world's annual population growth (natural increase) dropped 42% between 1963 and 2002, from 2.2% to 1.28%. This is *good news,* but during the same period the population base rose by about 94%, from 3.2 billion to 6.2 billion. The *bad news* is that this drop in the rate of population increase is somewhat like learning that a truck heading straight at you has slowed from 100

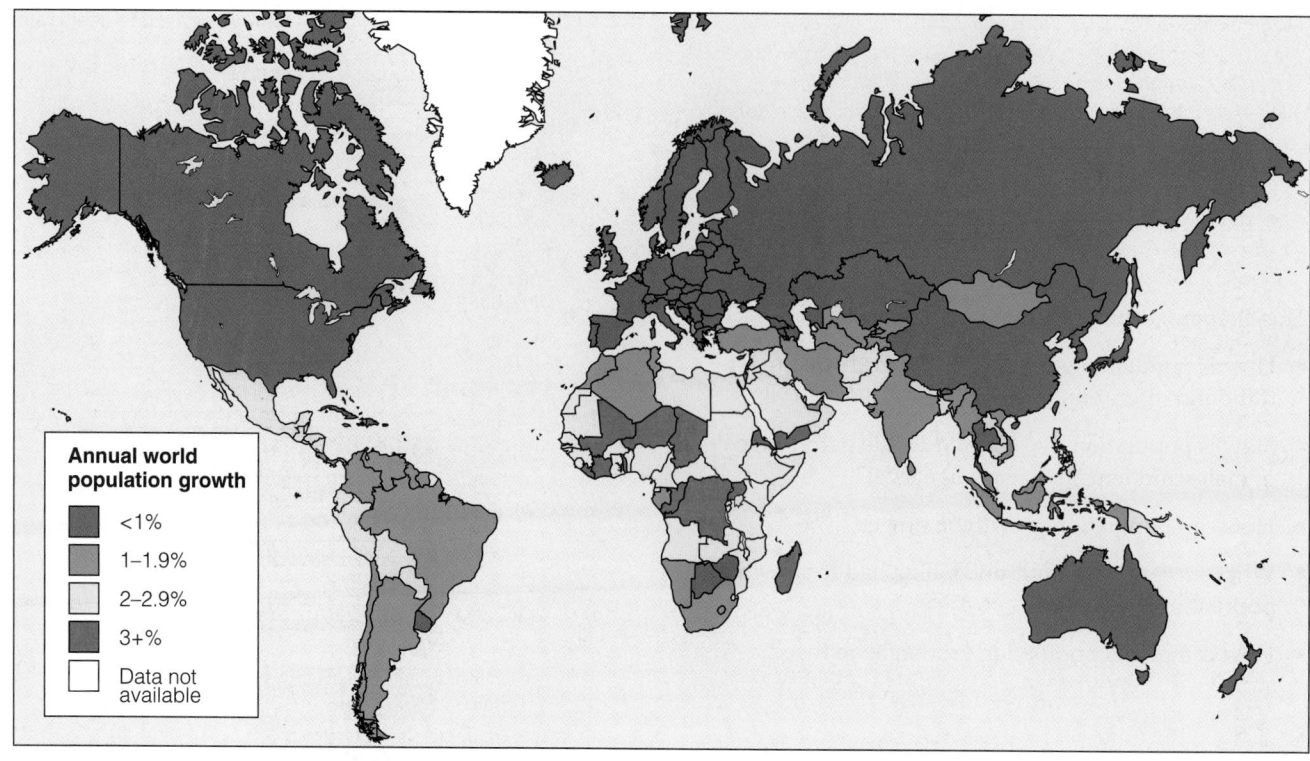

**Figure 12-4** Average annual rate of population change (natural increase) in 2002. (Data from Population Reference Bureau)

kilometers per hour (kph) to 58 kph while its weight has almost doubled.

Figure 12-4 presents the annual rates of population change for major parts of the world in 2002. An exponential growth rate of 1.28% may seem small but it adds about 79 million people per year to the world's population. This is roughly equal to adding **(1)** another New York City every month, **(2)** a Germany every year, and **(3)** a United States every 3.6 years. Despite the drop in the rate of population growth, the larger base of population means that 79 million people were added in 2002, compared to 69 million in 1963, when the world's population growth rate reached its peak. Figure 12-5 shows **(1)** the average annual increase in the world's population and the increase in population size from 1950 to 2002 and **(2)** projected increases to 2050.

In numbers of people, China (with 1.28 billion in 2002, about one of every five people in the world) and India (with 1 billion) dwarf all other countries (Figures 12-6 and 12-7). Together they make up 37% of the

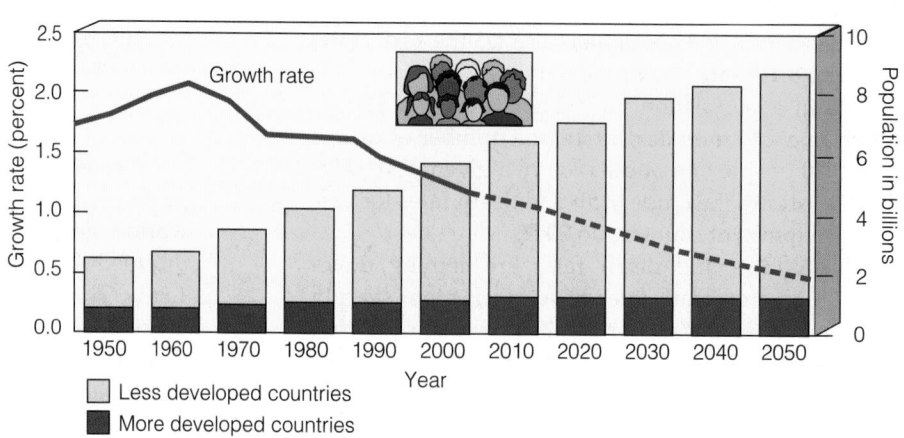

**Figure 12-5** Average annual increase in the world's population, 1950–2002, and projected increase 2002–2050 (dotted line). (Data from United Nations)

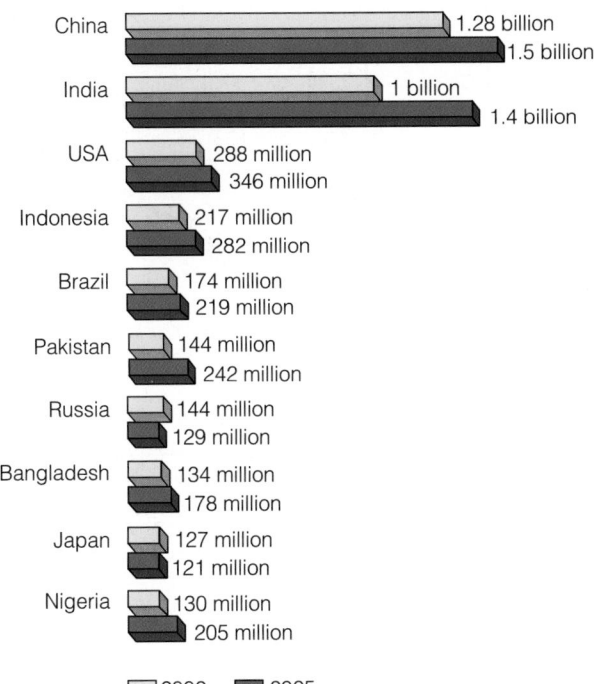

**Figure 12-6** The world's 10 most populous countries in 2002, with projections of their population size in 2025. In 2002, more people lived in China than in all of Europe, Russia, North America, Japan, and Australia combined. (Data from World Bank and Population Reference Bureau)

.**Figure 12-7** Where are Japan, Thailand, Indonesia, India, China, and Bangladesh? Some of the countries highlighted here are discussed in other chapters.

world's population. The United States, with 288 million people in 2002, has the world's third largest population but only 4.6% of the world's people. Figure 12-8 gives projected population growth in various regions between 2002 and 2025.

**How Have Global Fertility Rates Changed?** Two types of fertility rates affect a country's population size and growth rate. The first type, **replacement-level fertility,** is the number of children a couple must bear to replace themselves. It is slightly higher than two children per couple (2.1 in developed countries and as high as 2.5 in some developing countries), mostly because some female children die before reaching their reproductive years.

Does reaching replacement-level fertility mean an immediate halt in population growth? No, because so many future parents are alive. If each of today's couples had an average of 2.1 children and their children also had 2.1 children, the world's population would grow for 50 years or more (assuming death rates do not rise).

The second type of fertility rate is the **total fertility rate (TFR):** an estimate of the average number of children a woman will have during her childbearing years if between ages 15 and 49 she bears children at the same rate as women did this year. TFRs have dropped sharply since 1950 (Figure 12-9, p. 258). In 2002, the average global TFR was 2.8 children per woman. It was 1.6 in developed countries (down from 2.5 in 1950) and 3.1 in developing countries (down from 6.5 in 1950). This drop in the average number of

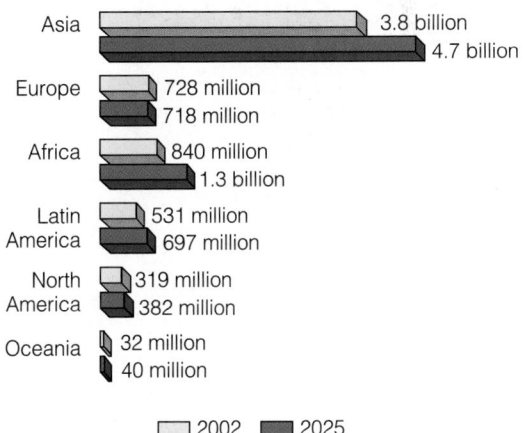

**Figure 12-8** Population projections by region, 2002–2025. About 61% of the world's people live in Asia. (Data from United Nations and Population Reference Bureau)

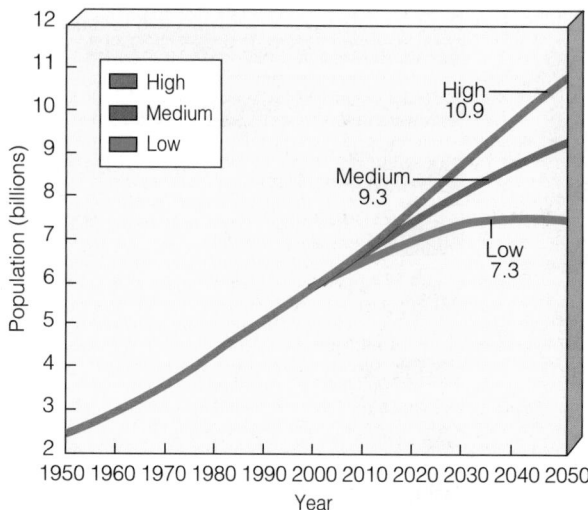

Figure 12-9 Decline in total fertility rates for various groupings of countries, 1950–2002. (Data from United Nations)

Figure 12-11 UN world population projection, assuming that by 2050 the world's total fertility rate is 2.6 (high), 2.1 (medium), or 1.7 (low) children per woman. (Data from United Nations, *World Population Prospects: The 2000 Revision*, 2001)

children born to women in developing countries is impressive, but this level of fertility is still far above the replacement level of 2.1 (Figure 12-10).

UN population projections to 2050 vary depending on the world's projected average TFR (Figure 12–11). More than 95% of this growth is projected

to take place in developing countries (Figure 1-4, p. 6), where acute poverty (living on less than $1 per day) is a way of life for about 1.4 billion people. Between 2002 and 2050, using medium estimates, the population of developing countries is projected to increase from 5 billion to 8 billion. By 2050, the world's population is

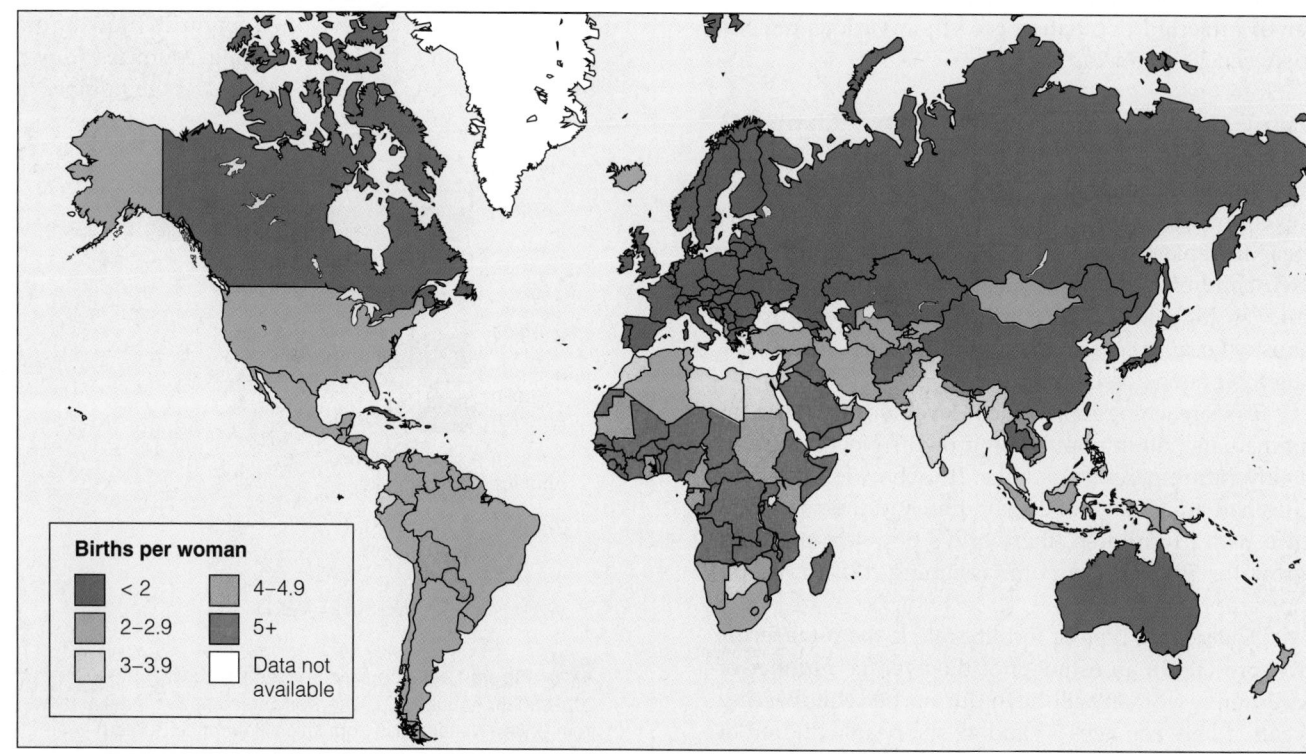

Figure 12-10 Total fertility rates in 2002. (Data from Population Reference Bureau)

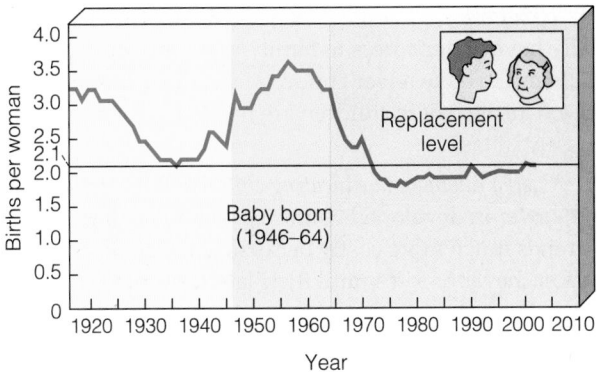

**Figure 12-12** Total fertility rates for the United States between 1917 and 2002. (Data from Population Reference Bureau and U.S. Census Bureau)

projected to be 63% urban, more tropical, and considerably older than today.

**Case Study: How Have Fertility Rates Changed in the United States?** The population of the United States has grown from 76 million in 1900 to 288 million in 2002, even though the country's TFR has oscillated wildly (Figure 12-12). In 1957, the peak of the baby boom after World War II, the TFR reached 3.7 children per woman. Since then it has generally declined, remaining at or below replacement level since 1972.

The drop in the TFR has led to a decline in the rate of population growth in the United States. However, the country's population is still growing faster (1.2% a year, including immigration) than that of any other developed country and is not even close to leveling off. In 2002, this growth added about 2.9 million people: **(1)** 1.7 million more births than deaths (accounting for about 60% of the growth), **(2)** about 900,000 legal immigrants and refugees, and **(3)** an estimated 300,000 illegal immigrants.

Figure 12-13 shows U.S. birth rates between 1910 and 2002. Between 1910 and 1930, birth rates fell sharply as **(1)** the country underwent industrialization and urbanization, and **(2)** more women got an education and began working outside the home. This shift from high birth rates to low birth rates during industrialization is called a *demographic transition.*

Birth rates remained low in the 1930s because of the Great Depression and then began rising in the 1940s during World War II. A sharp rise in the birth rate occurred after World War II. This period of high birth rates between 1946 and 1964 is known as the *baby-boom period* (Figure 12-13), when 79 million people were added to the U.S. population. Between 1956 and 1972, birth rates began to decline as more women began working outside the home and the desired family size dropped from 4 to 2 (or no) children (Figure 12-13).

Between 1977 and 2000, a small *echo boom* in the number of births per year occurred as the large number of people born during the baby boom began having children. Birth rates are projected to rise again between 2002 and 2050. According to U.S. Bureau of Census medium projections, the U.S. population will increase from 288 million to 414 million between 2002 and 2050 and reach 571 million by 2100 (Figure 12-14, p. 260). Because of a high per capita rate of resource use, each addition to the U.S. population has an enormous environmental impact (Figure 1-8, p. 10).

Figure 12-15 (p. 260) lists basic demographic data for the United States and its two neighboring countries, Mexico and Canada.

**What Factors Affect Birth Rates and Fertility Rates?** Key factors affecting a country's average birth rate and TFR are the following:

- *Importance of children as a part of the labor force.* Rates tend to be higher in developing countries (especially in rural areas, where children begin working to help raise crops at an early age).

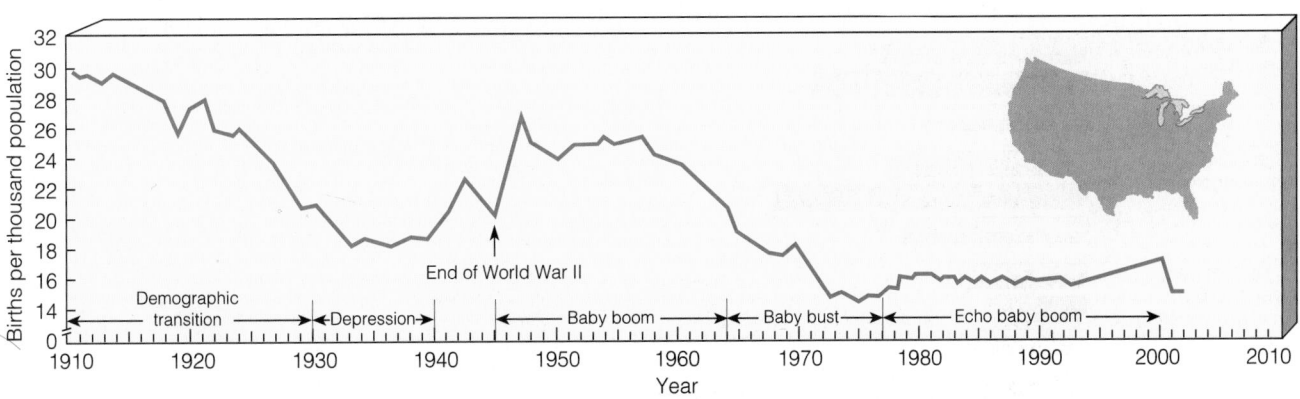

**Figure 12-13** Birth rates in the United States, 1910–2002. (Data from U.S. Bureau of Census and U.S. Commerce Department)

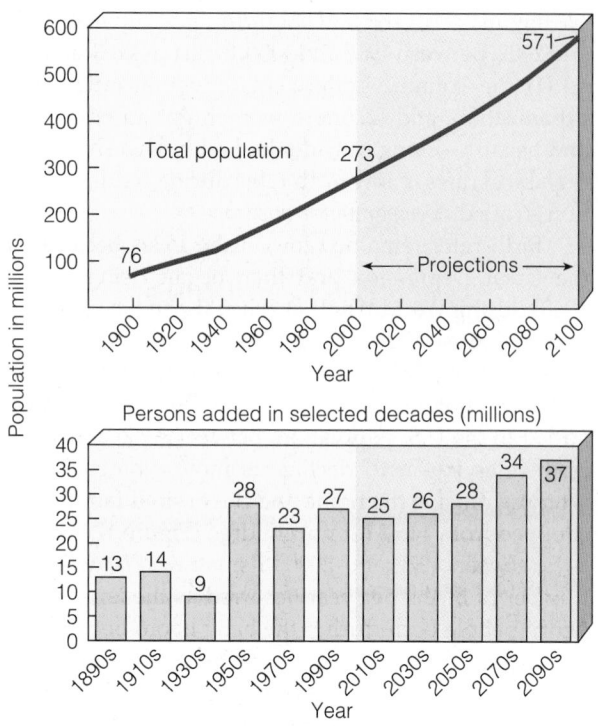

**Figure 12-14** U.S. population growth, 1900–2000, and projections to 2100. (Data from U.S. Census Bureau)

- *Urbanization.* People living in urban areas **(1)** usually have better access to family planning services and **(2)** tend to have fewer children than those living in rural areas, where children are needed to perform essential tasks.

- *Cost of raising and educating children.* Rates tend to be lower in developed countries, where raising children is much more costly because children do not enter the labor force until their late teens or early 20s, or even later.

- *Educational and employment opportunities for women.* TFRs tend to be low when women have access to education and paid employment outside the home. In developing countries, women with no education generally have two more children than women with a secondary school education.

- *Infant mortality rate.* In areas with low infant mortality rates, people tend to have less children because fewer children die at an early age.

- *Average age at marriage* (or, more precisely, the average age at which women have their first child). Women normally have fewer children when their average age at marriage is 25 or older.

| | United States | Mexico | Canada |
|---|---|---|---|

| | United States | Mexico | Canada |
|---|---|---|---|
| Population (2002) | 288 million | 102 million | 31 million |
| Projected population (2025) | 346 million | 132 million | 36 million |
| Infant mortality rate | 6.6 | 25 | 5.3 |
| Life expectancy | 77 years | 75 years | 79 years |
| Total fertility rate (TFR) | 2.1 | 2.9 | 1.5 |
| % population under age 15 | 21% | 33% | 19% |
| % population over age 65 | 13% | 5% | 13% |
| Per capita GNI PPP | $34,110 | $8,790 | $27,170 |

**Figure 12-15** Comparison of basic demographic data for the United States (red), Mexico (blue), and Canada (yellow). (Data from U.S. Census Bureau and Population Reference Bureau)

- *Availability of private and public pension systems.* Pensions eliminate parents' need to have many children to help support them in old age.

- *Availability of legal abortions.* According to the United Nations and the World Bank, an estimated 26 million legal abortions and 20 million illegal (and often unsafe) abortions are performed worldwide each year among the roughly 190 million pregnancies per year.

- *Availability of reliable birth control methods* (Figure 12–16).

- *Religious beliefs, traditions, and cultural norms.* In some countries, these factors favor large families and strongly oppose abortion and some forms of birth control.

**What Factors Affect Death Rates?** The rapid growth of the world's population over the past 100 years is not the result of a rise in the crude birth rate. Instead, it has been caused largely by a decline in crude death rates, especially in developing countries (Figure 12-17, p. 262).

More people started living longer (and fewer infants died) because of **(1)** increased food supplies and distribution, **(2)** better nutrition, **(3)** improvements in medical and public health technology (such as immunizations and antibiotics), **(4)** improved sanitation and personal hygiene, and **(5)** safer water supplies (which has curtailed the spread of many infectious diseases).

Two useful indicators of overall health of people in a country or region are **(1) life expectancy** (the average number of years a newborn infant can expect to live) and **(2)** the **infant mortality rate** (the number of babies out of every 1,000 born who die before their first birthday).

Some *good news* is that global life expectancy at birth **(1)** increased from 48 years to 67 years (76 years in developed countries and 65 years in developing countries) between 1955 and 2002 and **(2)** is projected to reach 73 by 2025. Between 1900 and 2002, life expectancy in the United States increased from 47 to 77 years and is projected to reach 81 years by 2025.

Some *bad news* is that in the world's 49 poorest countries, mainly in Africa, life expectancy is 55 years or less. In many African countries life expectancy is expected to fall further because of increased deaths from AIDS (Figure 11-10, p. 240).

*Because it reflects the general level of nutrition and health care, infant mortality probably is the single most important measure of a society's quality of life.* A high infant mortality rate usually indicates **(1)** insufficient food (undernutrition), **(2)** poor nutrition (malnutrition), and **(3)** a high incidence of infectious disease (usually from contaminated drinking water). Figure 12-18 (p. 262) shows the infant mortality rates in various parts of the world in 2002.

**Extremely Effective**

| | |
|---|---|
| Total abstinence | 100% |
| Sterilization | 99.6% |
| Vaginal ring | 98–99% |
| Hormonal implant (Norplant) | 98% |

**Highly Effective**

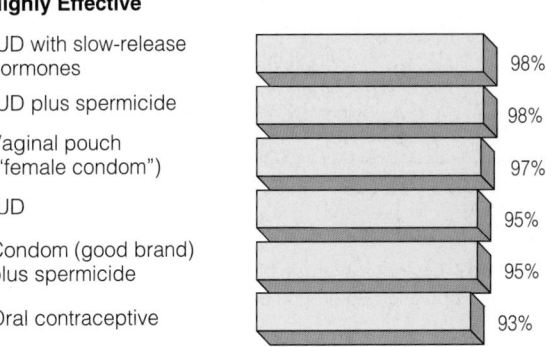

| | |
|---|---|
| IUD with slow-release hormones | 98% |
| IUD plus spermicide | 98% |
| Vaginal pouch ("female condom") | 97% |
| IUD | 95% |
| Condom (good brand) plus spermicide | 95% |
| Oral contraceptive | 93% |

**Effective**

| | |
|---|---|
| Cervical cap | 89% |
| Condom (good brand) | 86% |
| Diaphragm plus spermicide | 84% |
| Rhythm method (Billings, Sympto-Thermal) | 84% |
| Vaginal sponge impregnated with spermicide | 83% |
| Spermicide (foam) | 82% |

**Moderately Effective**

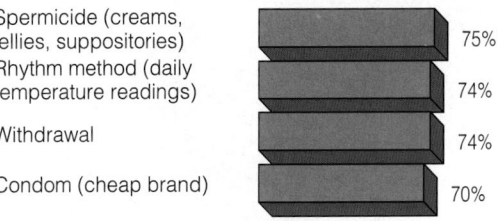

| | |
|---|---|
| Spermicide (creams, jellies, suppositories) | 75% |
| Rhythm method (daily temperature readings) | 74% |
| Withdrawal | 74% |
| Condom (cheap brand) | 70% |

**Unreliable**

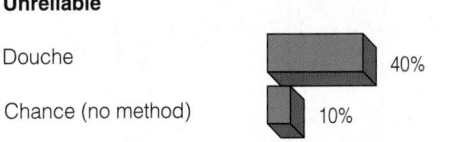

| | |
|---|---|
| Douche | 40% |
| Chance (no method) | 10% |

**Figure 12-16** Typical effectiveness rates of birth control methods in the United States. Percentages are based on the number of undesired pregnancies per 100 couples using a specific method as their sole form of birth control for a year. For example, an effectiveness rating of 93% for oral contraceptives means that for every 100 women using the pill regularly for 1 year, 7 will get pregnant. Effectiveness rates tend to be lower in developing countries, primarily because of lack of education. (Data from Alan Guttmacher Institute)

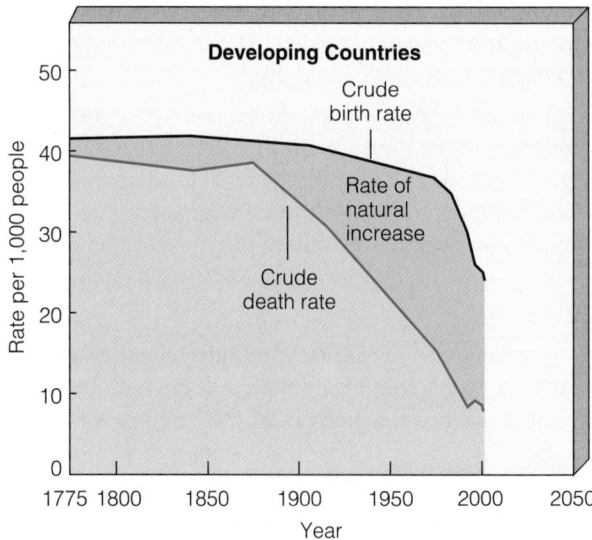

**Figure 12-17** Changes in crude birth and death rates for developed and developing countries, 1775–2002. (Data from Population Reference Bureau and United Nations)

Between 1965 and 2002, the world's infant mortality rate dropped from 20 per 1,000 live births to 7 in developed countries and from 118 to 60 in developing countries. This is an impressive achievement, but it still means that at least 8 million infants (most in developing countries) die of preventable causes during their first year of life—an average of 22,000 mostly unnecessary infant deaths per day. This is equivalent to 55 jumbo jets, each loaded with 400 infants under age 1, crashing accidentally each day with no survivors.

Between 1900 and 2002, the U.S. infant mortality rate declined from 165 to 6.8. This sharp decline in

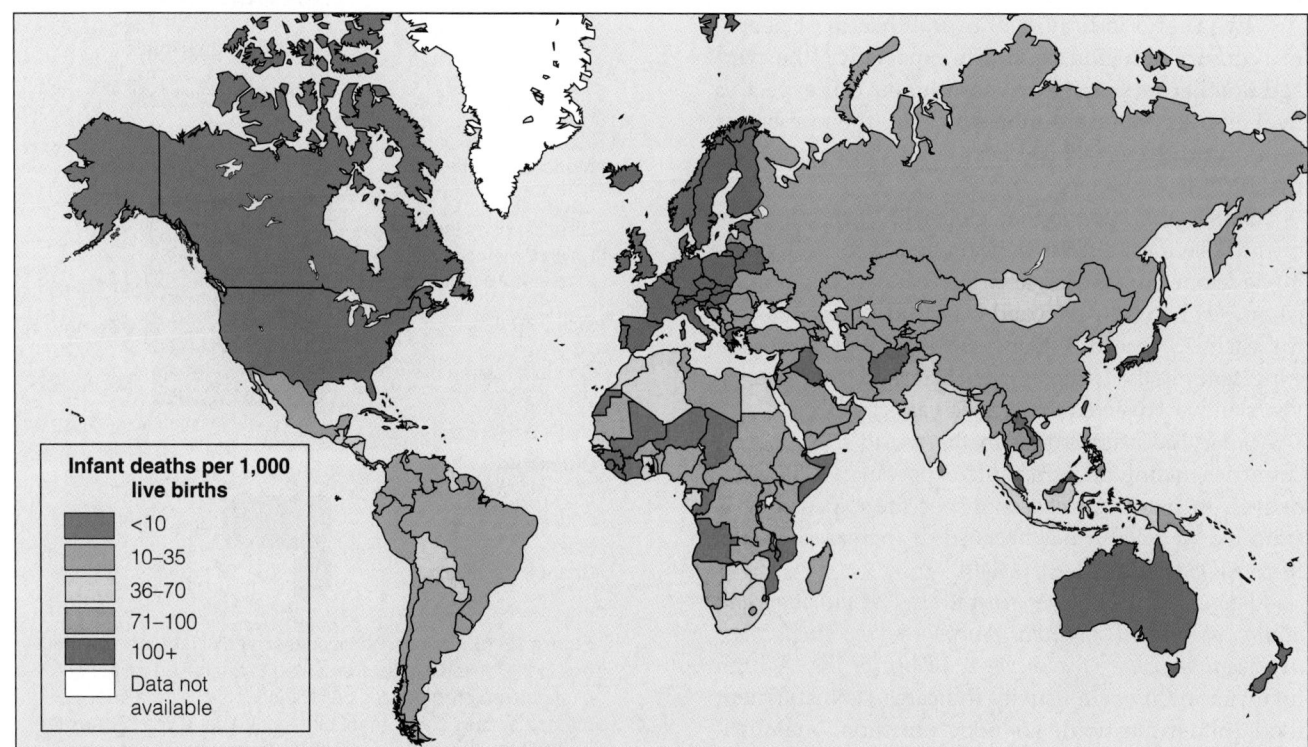

**Figure 12-18** Infant mortality rates in 2002. (Data from Population Reference Bureau)

infant mortality rates was a major factor in the marked increase in U.S. average life expectancy during this period.

Despite this improvement, 37 countries had lower infant mortality rates than the United States in 2002. Three factors keeping the U.S. infant mortality rate higher than it could be are **(1)** inadequate health care (for poor women during pregnancy and for their babies after birth), **(2)** drug addiction among pregnant women, and **(3)** the high birth rate among teenagers.

Some *good news* is that the U.S. birth rate among girls ages 15–19 in 2002 was lower than at any time since 1940. Some *bad news* is that the United States has the highest teenage pregnancy rate of any industrialized country. Each year about 872,000 teenage girls become pregnant in the United States (78% of them unplanned) and about 253,000 of them have abortions. Babies born to teenagers are more likely to have low birth weights, the most important factor in infant deaths.

## 12-2 POPULATION AGE STRUCTURE

**What Are Age Structure Diagrams?** As mentioned earlier, even if the replacement-level fertility rate of 2.1 were magically achieved globally tomorrow, the world's population would keep growing for at least another 50 years. The reason for this is a population's **age structure:** the proportion of the population (or of each sex) at each age level.

Demographers typically construct a population age structure diagram by plotting the percentages or numbers of males and females in the total population in each of three age categories: **(1)** *prereproductive* (ages 0–14), **(2)** *reproductive* (ages 15–44), and **(3)** *postreproductive* (ages 45 and up). Figure 12-19 presents generalized age structure diagrams for countries with rapid, slow, zero, and negative population growth rates.

**How Does Age Structure Affect Population Growth?** Any country with many people below age 15 (represented by a wide base in Figure 12-19, left) has a powerful built-in momentum to increase its population size unless death rates rise sharply. The number of births rises even if women have only one or two children because of the large number of girls who will soon be moving into their reproductive years.

*In 2002, 30% of the people on the planet were under 15 years old.* These 1.9 billion young people are poised to move into their prime reproductive years. In developing countries the number is even higher: 33%, compared with 18% in developed countries. This powerful force for continued population growth, mostly in developing countries, could be slowed by **(1)** an effective program to reduce birth rates or **(2)** a sharp rise in death rates. Suppose that somehow the world's average TFR fell immediately to the replacement level of 2.1 children. According to the UN Population Fund, even then more than 75% of the world's projected population growth (Figure 12-11) would still occur.

Figure 12-20 (p. 264) shows the age structure in developed and developing countries in 2002. We live in a *demographically divided world,* as shown by population data for the United States, Brazil, and Nigeria

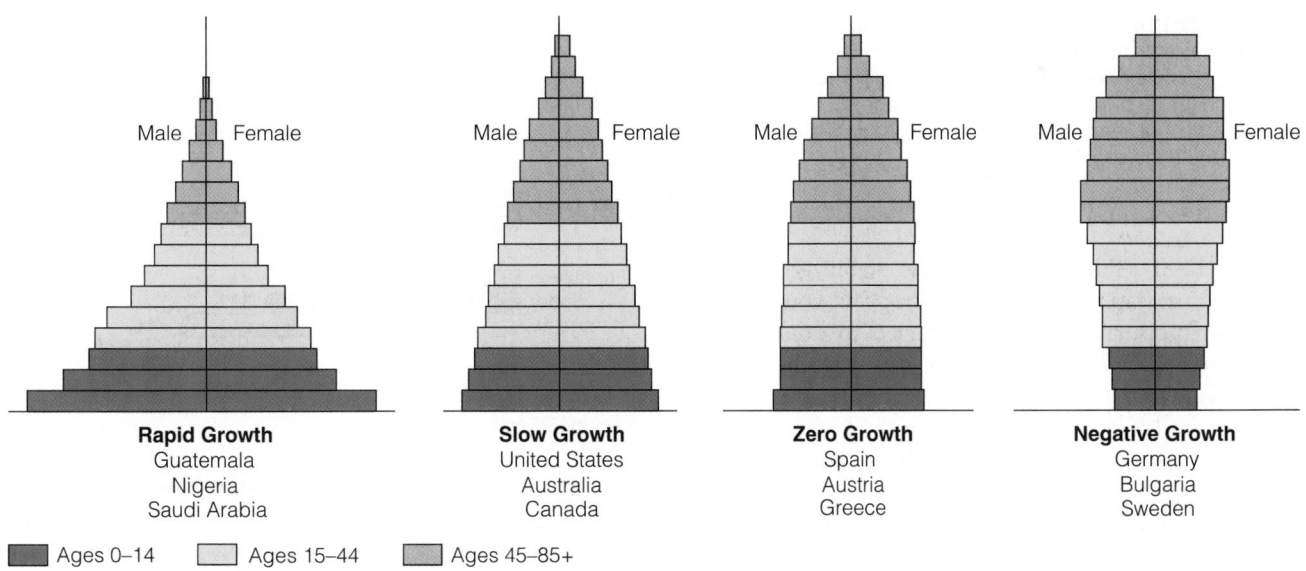

| | | | |
|---|---|---|---|
| **Rapid Growth** | **Slow Growth** | **Zero Growth** | **Negative Growth** |
| Guatemala | United States | Spain | Germany |
| Nigeria | Australia | Austria | Bulgaria |
| Saudi Arabia | Canada | Greece | Sweden |

■ Ages 0–14    ☐ Ages 15–44    ▨ Ages 45–85+

**Figure 12-19** Generalized population age structure diagrams for countries with rapid (1.5–3%), slow (0.3–1.4%), zero (0–0.2%), and negative population growth rates. (Data from Population Reference Bureau)

Developed Countries

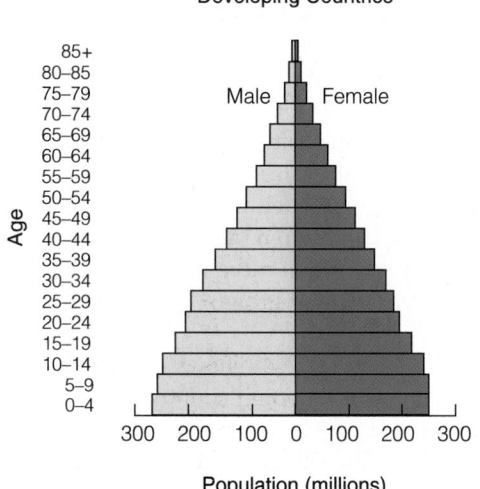

Developing Countries

**Figure 12-20** Population structure by age and sex in developing countries and developed countries, 2002. In 2002, **(1)** 1 billion young people were in their prime reproductive years of 15–24 and **(2)** 1.9 billion people were under age 15, moving into their reproductive years. (Data from United Nations Population Division and Population Reference Bureau)

(Figure 12-21). Population size has stabilized or is declining in Japan and most European countries. However, population size is projected to double or even triple before stabilizing for many developing countries with fairly large populations and large numbers of people under age 15. Examples of such countries are Nigeria, Ethiopia, Mexico, Brazil, Bangladesh, and Pakistan.

For example, 44% of Nigeria's population is under age 15 and its TFR is 5.8 children per woman. As a result, Nigeria's current population of about 130 million is projected to reach about 304 million by 2050. With 44% of its population under age 15 and a TFR of 5.2 children per woman, the population of the continent of Africa is projected to more than double from 840 million to 1.8 billion between 2002 and 2050.

### How Can Age Structure Diagrams Be Used to Make Population and Economic Projections?

The 79-million-person increase that occurred in the U.S. population between 1946 and 1964, known as the *baby boom* (Figures 12-12 and 12-13), will continue to move up through the country's age structure as the members of this group grow older (Figure 12-22).

Baby boomers now make up nearly half of all adult Americans. As a result, they **(1)** dominate the population's demand for goods and services and **(2)** play an increasingly important role in deciding who gets elected and what laws are passed. Baby boomers who created the youth market in their teens and 20s are **(1)** now creating the 50-something market and **(2)** will soon move on to create a 60-something market.

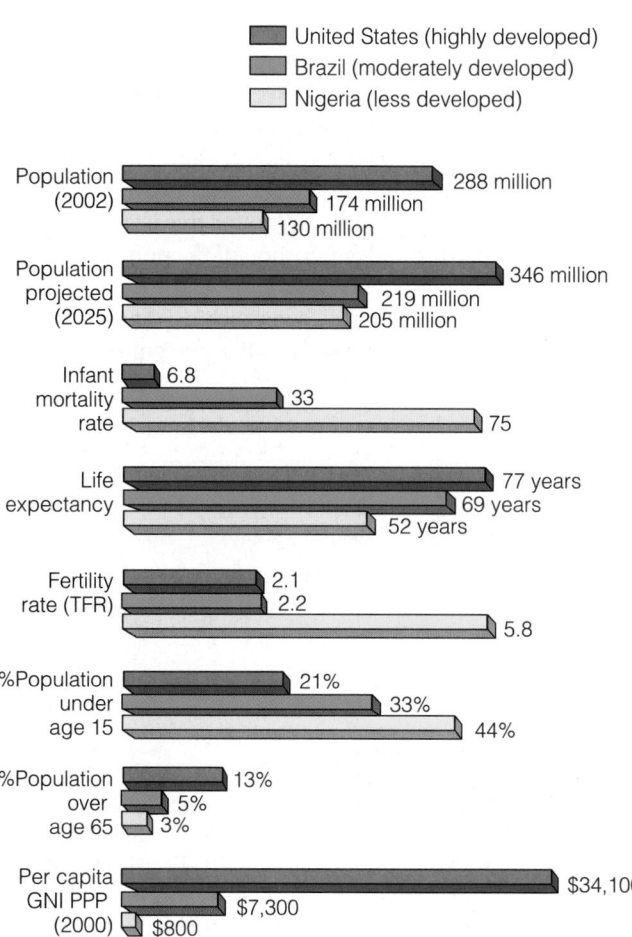

**Figure 12-21** Comparison of key demographic indicators in **(1)** highly developed (United States), **(2)** moderately developed (Brazil), and **(3)** less developed (Nigeria) countries in 2002. (Data from Population Reference Bureau)

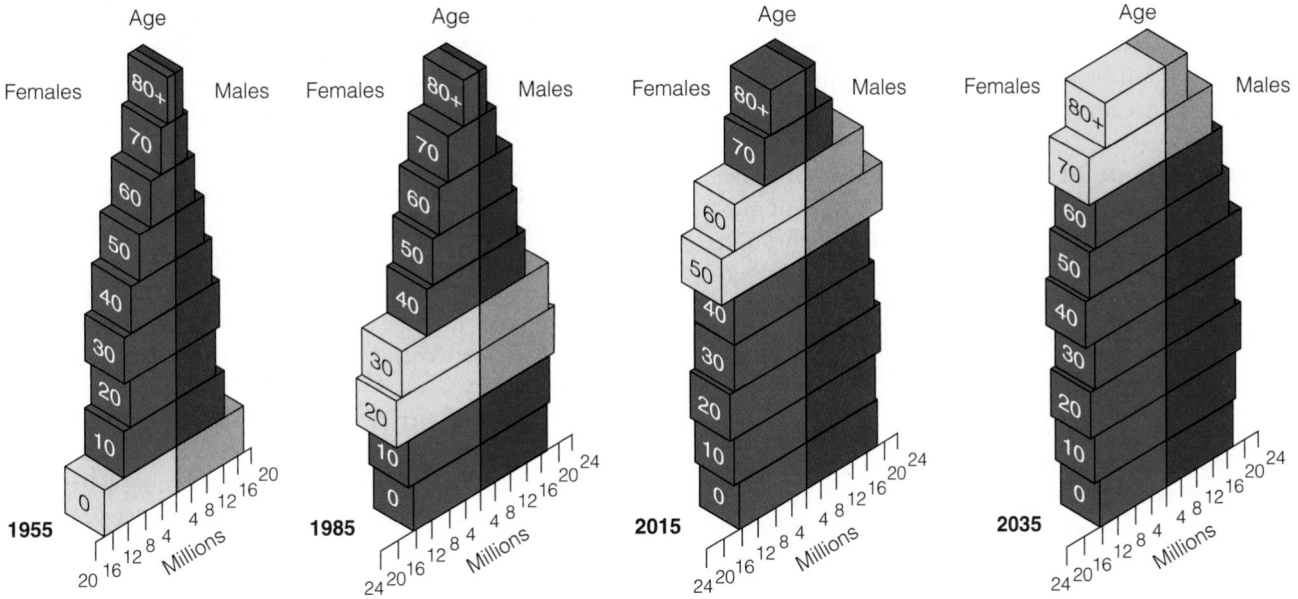

**Figure 12-22** Tracking the baby-boom generation in the United States. (Data from Population Reference Bureau and U.S. Census Bureau)

Many Americans are unaware that Social Security taxes on workers in the current generation are used to pay off current beneficiaries. Thus, as the number of workers supporting each beneficiary declines (Figure 12-23), it will be necessary to **(1)** dramatically increase the Social Security taxes on workers, **(2)** decrease retirement benefits, **(3)** extend the official retirement age, or **(4)** make up the shortfall from other government funds (which could greatly increase income taxes).

Much of the economic burden of helping support a large number of retired baby boomers will fall on the *baby-bust generation* (also called *generation X*): the 44 million people born between 1965 and 1976 (when TFRs fell sharply and have remained below 2.1 since 1970; Figure 12-12). Retired baby boomers are likely to use their political clout to force the smaller number of people in the baby-bust generation to pay higher income, health-care, and Social Security taxes. This could cause resentment and conflicts between the two generations.

In some respects, the baby-bust generation should have an easier time than the baby-boom generation. Fewer people will be competing for educational opportunities, jobs, and services, and labor shortages may drive up their wages, at least for jobs requiring education or technical training beyond high school. But members of the baby-bust group may find it difficult to get job promotions as they reach middle age because members of the much larger baby-boom

group will occupy most upper-level positions. Many baby boomers may delay retirement because of **(1)** improved health, **(2)** the need to accumulate adequate retirement funds, or **(3)** extension of the retirement age needed to begin collecting Social Security.

The baby-bust generation is being followed by the *echo-boom generation* (Figure 12-13) consisting of about 83 million people born from 1977 to 2000. This largest generation ever, also known as *generation Y* and the *millenials*, will soon have more economic power than their baby-boom parents.

**Figure 12-23** Number of workers supporting each beneficiary of the Social Security program in the United States, 1945–2075 (projected).

From these few projections, we can see that any booms or busts in the age structure of a population create social and economic changes that ripple through a society for decades.

**What Are Some Effects of Population Decline from Reduced Fertility?** The populations of most of the world's countries are projected to grow throughout most of the 21st century. By 2002, however, 38 countries (most of them in Europe) with about 815 million people had roughly stable populations (annual growth rates at or below 0.3%) or declining populations. In other words, about 13% of humanity in industrialized Europe plus Japan has achieved a stable population.

As the age structure of the world's population changes and the percentage of people age 60 or older increases (Figure 12-24), more and more countries will begin experiencing population declines. By 2020, an estimated 1 billion people will be age 60 or older. According to a 2001 UN study, by 2050 the populations of 39 countries (including Japan, Germany, Italy, Hungary, and Ukraine) are projected to be smaller than today.

If population decline is gradual, its harmful effects usually can be managed. However, rapid population decline, like rapid population growth, can lead to severe economic and social problems. A country undergoing rapid population decline **(1)** has a sharp rise in the proportion of older people, who consume a large share

of medical care, Social Security, and other costly public services funded by working taxpayers, and **(2)** can face labor shortages unless it relies on greatly increased automation or immigration of foreign workers.

**What Are Some Effects of Population Decline from a Rise in Death Rates?** Demographers and health officials project that the current HIV/AIDS epidemic will claim more lives (mostly in Africa and eventually in India and China) in the early part of this century than World War II did near the middle of the last century.

The HIV/AIDS epidemic ravaging Africa (Figure 11-10, p. 240) kills over 6,000 people each day—equivalent to 15 jumbo jets, each containing 400 people, crashing accidentally each day with no survivors. This number of deaths is expected to double within the next decade.

Hunger and malnutrition kill mostly infants and children, but AIDS kills many young adults. This change in the young adult age structure of a country has a number of harmful effects. They include the following:

- A sharp drop in average life expectancy. In 16 African counties, where 10–36% of the adult population is infected with HIV, life expectancy could drop to 35–40 years.

- A loss of a country's most productive young adult workers and trained personnel such as scientists, farmers, engineers, teachers, and government, business, and health-care workers. This greatly increases the dependency ratio—the number of productive adults available to support the young and elderly (Figure 12-23).

- A sharp rise in the number of orphans whose parents have died from AIDS. In Africa, the AIDS epidemic could easily result in 40 million orphans by 2010.

- A drop in food production because of a decline in the number of adults producing food.

Analysts call for the international community—especially developed countries—to develop a Marshall Plan (used to rebuild Europe after World War II) to help affected countries in Africa and elsewhere to

- Reduce the spread of HIV through a combination of improved education, health care, and family planning. Emphasis would be on delaying first sexual activity, using condoms, early detection of HIV infections, and reducing the number of sexual partners.

- Restore economic progress through **(1)** debt relief, **(2)** incentives to encourage investment, **(3)** financial assistance for education and health care, and **(4)** send-

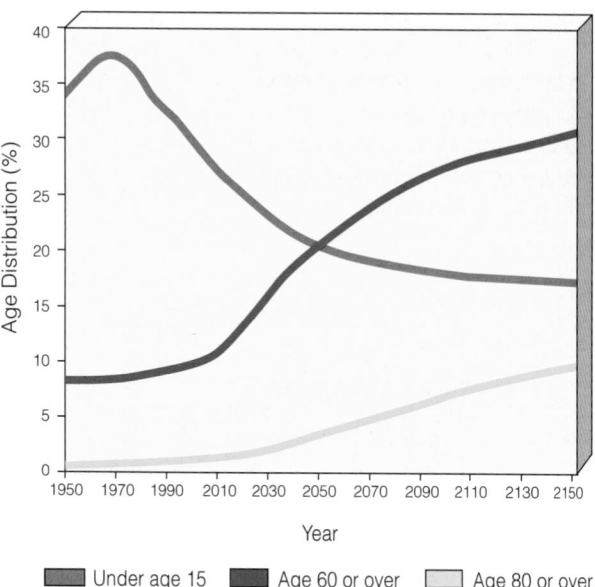

**Figure 12-24** *Global aging.* Projected percentage of world population **(1)** under age 15, **(2)** age 60 or over, and **(3)** age 80 or over, 1950–2150, assuming the medium fertility projection shown in Figure 12-11. Between 1998 and 2050 the number of people over age 80 is projected to increase from 66 million to 370 million. The cost of supporting a much larger elderly population will place enormous strains on the world's economy. (Data from the United Nations)

ing in volunteer teachers and health-care and social workers to help compensate for the missing young adult generation.

## 12-3 SOLUTIONS: INFLUENCING POPULATION SIZE

**How Is Population Size Affected by Migration?**
The population of an area is affected by movement of people into (immigration) and out of (emigration) that area. Most countries influence their rates of population growth to some extent by restricting immigration. Only a few countries—chiefly Canada, Australia, and the United States (Case Study, p. 268)—allow large annual increases in population from immigration.

International migration to developed countries absorbs only about 1% of the annual population growth in developing countries. Thus population change for most countries is determined mainly by the difference between their birth rates and death rates.

Migration within countries, especially from rural to urban areas, plays an important role in the population dynamics of cities, towns, and rural areas.

**What Are the Pros and Cons of Reducing Births?**
The projected increase of the human population from 6.2 to 9.3 billion or more between 2002 and 2050 (Figure 12-11) raises an important question: *Can the world provide an adequate standard of living for 3.1 billion more people without causing widespread environmental damage?*

There is intense controversy over (1) this question, (2) whether the earth is already overpopulated, and (3) what measures, if any, should be taken to slow population growth. To some the planet is already overpopulated, but others disagree. Some analysts, mostly economists, argue that we should encourage population growth to help stimulate economic growth.

Others believe that asking how many people the world can support is the wrong question, equivalent to asking how many cigarettes one can smoke before getting lung cancer. Instead, they say, we should be asking what the *optimum sustainable population* of the earth might be, based on the planet's *cultural carrying capacity* (Guest Essay, p. 272).

Such an optimum level would allow most people to live in reasonable comfort and freedom without impairing the ability of the planet to sustain future generations. No one knows what this optimum population might be. Some consider it a meaningless concept; some put it at 20 billion, others at 8 billion, and others as low as 2 billion.

Those who do not believe the earth is overpopulated point out that the average life span of the world's 6.2 billion people is longer today than at any time in the past. They say that (1) the world can support billions more people, and (2) people are the world's most valuable resource for solving the problems we face and stimulating economic growth by becoming consumers.

Some people view any form of population regulation as a violation of their religious beliefs, whereas others see it as an intrusion into their privacy and personal freedom. They believe all people should be free to have as many children as they want. Some developing countries and some members of minorities in developed countries regard population control as a form of genocide to keep their numbers and power from rising.

Proponents of slowing and eventually stopping population growth point out that we fail to provide the basic necessities for one out of six people on the earth today. If we cannot (or will not) do this now, they ask, how will we be able to do this for the projected 3.1 billion more people by 2050?

Proponents of slowing population growth contend that if we do not sharply lower birth rates, we are deciding by default to (1) raise death rates for humans (already occurring in parts of Africa) and (2) greatly increase environmental harm. In 1992, for example, the U.S. National Academy of Sciences and the Royal Society of London issued the following joint statement: "If current predictions of population growth and patterns of human activity on the planet remain unchanged, science and technology may not be able to prevent either irreversible degradation of the environment or continued poverty for much of the world."

Proponents of this view recognize that population growth is not the only cause of environmental and resource problems. However, they argue that adding several hundred million more people in developed countries and several billion more in developing countries can only intensify existing environmental and social problems.

These analysts believe people should have the freedom to produce as many children as they want. However, such freedom would apply only if it did not reduce the quality of other people's lives now and in the future, either by (1) impairing the earth's ability to sustain life or (2) causing social disruption. They point out that limiting the freedom of individuals to do anything they want to protect the freedom of other individuals is the basis of most laws in modern societies. What is your opinion on this issue?

**How Can Economic Development Help Reduce Birth Rates?** Demographers have examined the birth and death rates of western European countries that industrialized during the 19th century. From these data they developed a hypothesis of

**CASE STUDY**

Between 1820 and 2000, the United States admitted almost twice as many immigrants and refugees as all other countries combined. However, the number of legal immigrants has varied during different periods because of changes in immigration laws and rates of economic growth (see figure).

In 2000, the United States received about 850,000 legal immigrants and refugees and 300,000 illegal immigrants, together accounting for 40% of the country's population growth. The U.S. Census Bureau estimates that 8–11 million illegal immigrants currently live in the United States.

Currently, more than 75% of all legal immigrants live in six states: California, Florida, Illinois, New York, New Jersey, and Texas. If illegal immigrants are included, this figure rises to about 90%.

Immigrants place a tax burden on residents of such states. In California, for example, the average household pays an extra $1,200 in taxes per year because of immigrants. However, according to a 1997 study by the National Academy of Sciences, **(1)** the work and taxes paid by immigrants add $1–10 billion per year to the overall U.S. economy, largely because immigration holds down wages (and thus prices) for some jobs, and **(2)** during their lifetimes immigrants pay an average of $80,000 more per person in taxes than they cost in services.

Between 1820 and 1960, most legal immigrants to the United States came from Europe; since then, most have come from Latin America (53%) and Asia (30%). Between 2002 and 2050, the percentage of Latinos in the U.S. population is projected to double from 13% to 24%.

In 1995, the U.S. Commission on Immigration Reform recommended reducing the number of legal immigrants and refugees to about 700,000 per year for a transition

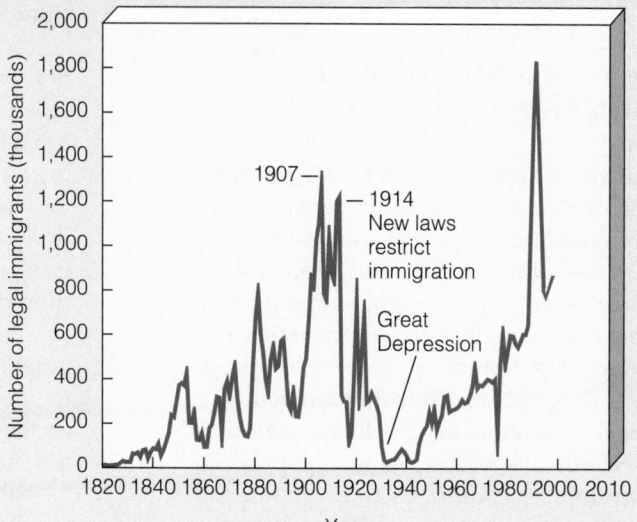

Legal immigration to the United States, 1820–2000. The large increase in immigration since 1989 resulted mostly from the Immigration Reform and Control Act of 1986, which granted legal status to illegal immigrants who could show they had been living in the country for several years. (Data from U.S. Immigration and Naturalization Service)

period and then to 550,000 a year. Some demographers and environmentalists go further and call for **(1)** lowering the annual ceiling for legal immigrants and refugees into the United States to 300,000–450,000 or **(2)** limiting legal immigration to about 20% of annual population growth. They would accept immigrants only if they can support themselves, arguing that providing immigrants with public services turns the United States into a magnet for the world's poor.

Most of these analysts also support efforts to sharply reduce illegal immigration. However, some are concerned that a crackdown on illegal immigrants can also lead to discrimination against legal immigrants.

The public strongly supports reducing U.S. immigration levels. A 1998 *Wall Street Journal*/NBC News poll found that 72% of the people polled were against the country's high immigration rate. A 1993 Hispanic Research Group survey found 89% of Hispanic Americans sup-

ported an immediate moratorium on immigration.

Proponents argue that reducing immigration would allow the United States to stabilize its population sooner and help reduce the country's enormous environmental impact. Others oppose reducing current levels of legal immigration, arguing that **(1)** it would diminish the historical role of the United States as a place of opportunity for the world's poor and oppressed, **(2)** immigrants pay taxes and take many menial, low-paying jobs that other Americans shun, **(3)** few immigrants receive public assistance, **(4)** many immigrants open businesses and create jobs, and **(5)** according to the U.S. Census bureau, after 2020 higher immigration levels will be needed to supply enough workers as baby boomers retire.

### Critical Thinking

Should the United States reduce its current level of legal immigration and crack down on illegal immigration? Explain.

**Figure 12-25** Generalized model of the demographic transition.

population change known as the **demographic transition:** as countries become industrialized, first their death rates and then their birth rates decline.

According to this hypothesis, the transition takes place in four stages (Figure 12-25):

- *Preindustrial stage,* when there is little population growth because harsh living conditions lead to both a high birth rate (to compensate for high infant mortality) and a high death rate.

- *Transitional stage,* when industrialization begins, food production rises, and health care improves. Death rates drop and birth rates remain high, so the population grows rapidly (typically 2.5–3% a year).

- *Industrial stage,* when the birth rate drops and eventually approaches the death rate as industrialization and modernization become widespread. Population growth continues, but at a slower and perhaps fluctuating rate, depending on economic conditions. Most developed countries are now in this third stage (Figure 12-25), and a few developing countries are entering this stage.

- *Postindustrial stage,* when the birth rate declines further, equaling the death rate and thus reaching zero population growth. Then the birth rate falls below the death rate and total population size decreases slowly. Thirty-eight countries (most of them in Europe) containing about 13% of the world's population have entered this stage.

In most developing countries today, death rates have fallen much more than birth rates (Figure 12-17). In other words, these developing countries are still in the transitional stage, halfway up the economic ladder, with high population growth rates. Some economists believe that developing countries will make the demographic transition over the next few decades without increased family planning efforts.

However, despite encouraging declines in fertility (Figure 12-9), some population analysts fear that the still-rapid population growth in many developing countries will outstrip economic growth and overwhelm local life-support systems. This could cause many of these countries to be caught in a *demographic trap* at stage 2, something that is currently happening in a number of developing countries, especially in Africa. Indeed, countries in Africa being ravaged by the HIV/AIDS epidemic are falling back to stage 1 as their death rates rise.

Analysts also point out that some of the conditions that allowed developed countries to develop are not available to many of today's developing countries. Even with large and growing populations, many developing countries **(1)** do not have enough skilled workers to produce the high-tech products needed to compete in the global economy, **(2)** lack the capital and resources needed for rapid economic development, and **(3)** since 1980 have experienced a drop in economic assistance from developed countries and a rise in their debt to such countries. Indeed, since the mid-

1980s, developing countries have paid developed countries $40–50 billion a year (mostly in debt interest) more than they have received from these countries.

**How Can Family Planning Help Reduce Birth and Abortion Rates and Save Lives?** Family **planning** provides educational and clinical services that help couples choose how many children to have and when to have them. Such programs vary from culture to culture, but most provide information on **(1)** birth spacing, **(2)** birth control, and **(3)** health care for pregnant women and infants.

The advantages of family planning include the following:

- Helping increase the proportion of married women in developing countries who use modern forms of contraception from 10% of married women of reproductive age in the 1960s to 54% of these women in 2002 (41% if China is excluded) (Figure 12-26).

- Being responsible for at least 55% of the drop in TFRs in developing countries, from 6 in 1960 to 3.1 in 2002 (3.5 if China is excluded).

- Reducing the number of legal and illegal abortions per year.

- Decreasing the risk of death from pregnancy.

Despite such successes,

- According to John Bongaarts of the Population Council, 42% of all pregnancies in the developing countries are unplanned and 26% end with abortion.

- An estimated 250–350 million women in developing countries want to limit the number and determine the spacing of their children, but they lack access to services. According to the United Nations, extending family planning services to these women and to those who will soon be entering their reproductive years could prevent an estimated 5.8 million births a year and more than 5 million abortions a year.

Other analysts call for

- Expanding existing family planning programs to include teenagers and sexually active unmarried women, who often are excluded.

- Pro-choice and pro-life groups to join forces in greatly reducing unplanned births and abortions, especially among teenagers.

- Programs to educate men about the importance of having fewer children and taking more responsibility for raising them.

- Increased research on developing new, more effective, and more acceptable birth control methods for men.

According to the United Nations, family planning could be provided in developing countries to all couples who want it for about $17 billion a year, the equivalent of about 8 days worth of worldwide military expenditures. If developed countries provided one-third of this $17 billion, each person in the developed countries would spend only $4.80 a year to help reduce the world's population by about 3.1 billion people.

**How Can Empowering Women Help Reduce Birth Rates?** Studies show that women tend to have fewer and healthier children and live longer when they **(1)** have access to education and to paying jobs outside the home and **(2)** live in societies in which their rights are not suppressed.

Women, roughly half of the world's population, **(1)** do almost all of the world's domestic work and child care, **(2)** provide more health care with little or no pay than all the world's organized health services combined, and **(3)** do 60–80% of the work associated with growing food, gathering fuelwood, and hauling water in rural areas of Africa, Latin America, and Asia (Figure 12-27). As one Brazilian woman put it, "For poor women the only holiday is when you are asleep."

Women work two-thirds of all hours worked but **(1)** receive only 10% of the world's income and **(2)** own only 0.01% of the world's property. In most developing countries, women do not have the legal right to own land or to borrow money to increase agricultural productivity.

According to UNESCO, women also make up 70% of the world's poor and two-thirds of the more than 876 million adults who can neither read nor write. In developing countries, the adult literacy rate for men is almost twice as high as that for women.

Most analysts believe that women everywhere should have full legal rights and the opportunity to become educated and earn income outside the home. This would not only slow population growth but also promote human rights and freedom. However, empowering women by seeking gender equality will take some major social changes that will be difficult to achieve in male-dominated societies.

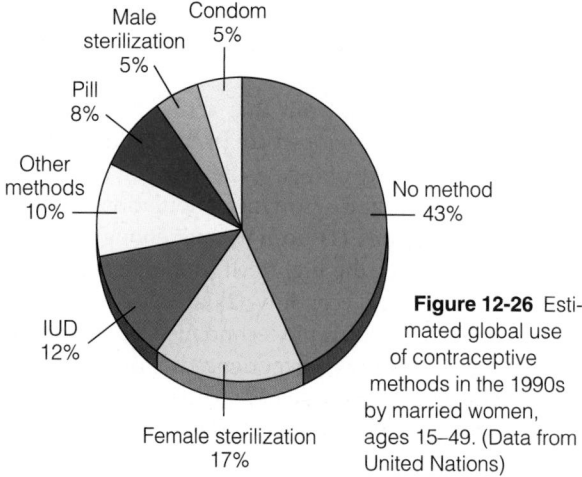

**Figure 12-26** Estimated global use of contraceptive methods in the 1990s by married women, ages 15–49. (Data from United Nations)

Male sterilization 5%
Condom 5%
Pill 8%
Other methods 10%
No method 43%
IUD 12%
Female sterilization 17%

**Figure 12-27** Typical workday for a woman in rural Africa. In addition to their domestic work, rural African women perform about 75% of all agricultural work. (Data from United Nations)

**How Can Economic Rewards and Penalties Be Used to Help Reduce Birth Rates?** Some population experts point out that most couples in developing countries want three or four children. This is well above the replacement-level fertility needed to bring about eventual population stabilization.

These analysts believe we must go beyond family planning and offer economic rewards and penalties to help slow population growth. About 20 countries offer small payments to people who agree to use contraceptives or to be sterilized. However, such payments are most likely to attract people who already have all the children they want.

Some countries, including China, penalize couples who have more than one or two children by **(1)** raising their taxes, **(2)** charging other fees, or **(3)** eliminating income tax deductions for a couple's third child (e.g., in Singapore, Hong Kong, and Ghana). Families who have more children than the prescribed limit may also lose health-care benefits, food allotments, and job options.

Economic rewards and penalties designed to lower birth rates work best if they **(1)** encourage (rather than coerce) people to have fewer children, **(2)** reinforce existing customs and trends toward smaller families, **(3)** do not penalize people who produced large families before the programs were established, and **(4)** increase a poor family's economic status. Once a country's population growth is out of control, it may be forced to use coercive methods to prevent mass starvation and hardship, as has been the case for China.

## 12-4 CASE STUDIES: SLOWING POPULATION GROWTH IN INDIA AND CHINA

**What Success Has India Had in Controlling Its Population Growth?** The world's first national family planning program began in India (Figure 12-7)

in 1952, when its population was nearly 400 million. In 2002, after 50 years of population control efforts, India was the world's second most populous country, with a population of 1 billion.

In 1952, India added 5 million people to its population, and in 2002 it added 18 million. Figure 12-28 compares demographic data for India and China.

India faces the following already serious poverty, malnutrition, and environmental problems that could worsen as its population continues to grow rapidly:

- By global standards, India's people are poor, with an average per capita GNI PPP of about $2,340 a year; for 30% of the population it is less than $800 a year, or $2.19 a day.

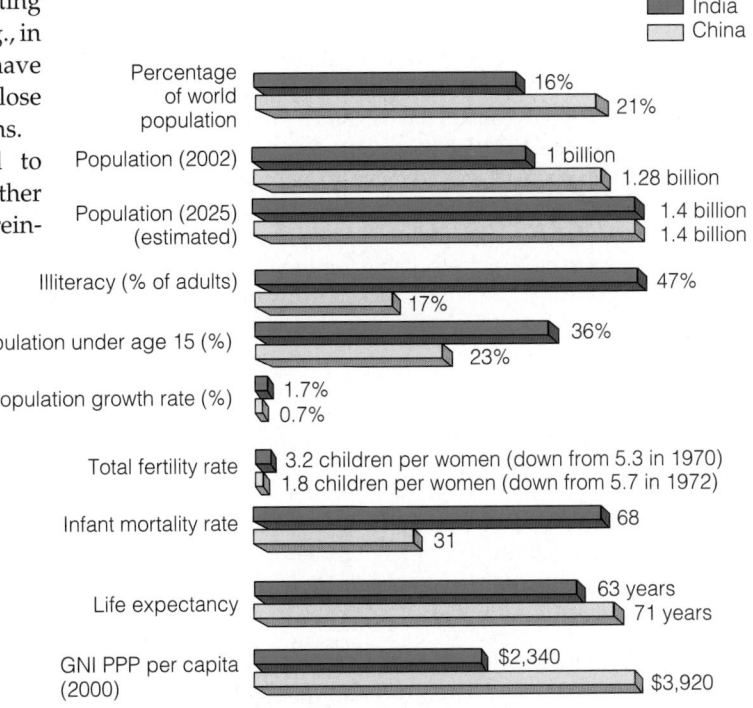

**Figure 12-28** Comparison of basic demographic data for India (green) and China (yellow). (Data from United Nations and Population Reference Bureau).

## Moral Implications of Cultural Carrying Capacity

*Garrett Hardin*

**GUEST ESSAY**

*As a longtime professor of human ecology at the University of California at Santa Barbara, Garrett Hardin made important contributions in relating ethics to biology. He has raised hard ethical questions, sometimes taken unpopular stands, and forced people to think deeply about environmental problems and their possible solutions. He is best known for his 1968 essay "The Tragedy of the Commons," which has had a significant impact on the disciplines of economics and political science and on the management of potentially renewable resources. His 17 books include* Filters Against Folly: How to Survive Despite Economists, Ecologists, and the Merely Eloquent, Living Within Limits, *and* The Ostrich Factor: Our Population Myopia *(see Further Readings for this chapter on the website for this book).*

For many years, Angel Island in San Francisco Bay was plagued with too many deer. A few animals transplanted there in the early 1900s lacked predators and rapidly increased to nearly 300 deer—far beyond the carrying capacity of the island. Scrawny, underfed animals tugged at the heartstrings of Californians, who carried extra food for them from the mainland to the island.

Such well-meaning charity worsened the plight of the deer. Excess animals trampled the soil, stripped the bark from small trees, and destroyed seedlings of all kinds. The net effect was to lower the island's carrying capacity, year by year, as the deer continued to multiply in a deteriorating habitat.

State game managers proposed that the excess deer be shot by skilled hunters. "How cruel!" some people protested. Then the managers proposed that coyotes be introduced onto the island. Though not big enough to kill adult deer, coyotes can kill fawns, thereby reducing the size of the herd. However, the Society for the Prevention of Cruelty to Animals was adamantly opposed to this proposal.

In the end, it was agreed that some deer would be transported to other areas suitable for deer. A total of 203 animals were caught and trucked many miles away.

From the fate of a sample of animals fitted with radio collars, it was estimated that 85% of the transported deer died within a year (most of them within 2 months) from various causes: predation by coyotes, bobcats, and domestic dogs, shooting by poachers and legal hunters, and being run over by cars.

The net cost (in 1982 dollars) for relocating each animal surviving for a year was $2,876. The state refused to continue financing the program, and no volunteers stepped forward to pay future bills.

Angel Island is a microcosm of the planet as a whole. Organisms reproduce exponentially, but the environment does not increase at all. The moral is a simple ecological commandment: *Thou shalt not transgress the carrying capacity.*

Now let's examine the situation for humans. A competent physicist has placed global human carrying capacity at 50 billion, about eight times the current world population. Before you give in to the temptation to urge women to have more babies, consider what Robert Malthus said nearly 200 years ago: "There should be no more people in a country than could enjoy daily a glass of wine and piece of beef for dinner."

A diet of grain or bread and water is symbolic of minimum living standards; wine and beef are symbolic of higher living standards that make greater demands on the environment. When land that could produce plants for direct human consumption is used to grow grapes for wine or corn for cattle, more energy is expended to feed the human population. Because carrying capacity is defined as the *maximum* number of animals (humans) an area can support, using part of the area to support such cultural luxuries as wine and beef reduces the carrying capacity. This reduced capacity is called the *cultural carrying capacity,* and it is always smaller than simple carrying capacity.

Energy is the common coin of the realm for all competing demands on the environment. Energy saved by giving up a luxury can be used to produce more food staples and support more people. We could increase the simple carrying capacity of the earth by giving up any (or all) of the following "luxuries": street lighting, vacations, private cars, air conditioning, and artistic performances

- Nearly half of India's labor force is unemployed or can find only occasional work.

- Although India currently is self-sufficient in food grain production, about 40% of its population and 53% of its children suffer from malnutrition, mostly because of poverty.

- With 16% of the world's people, India has just 2.3% of the world's land resources and 2% of the world's forests.

- About half of India's cropland is degraded as a result of soil erosion, waterlogging, salinization, overgrazing, and deforestation.

- About 70% of India's water is seriously polluted, and sanitation services often are inadequate.

Without its long-standing family planning program, India's population and environmental problems would be growing even faster. Still, to its supporters the results of the program have been disappointing of all sorts. But what we consider luxuries depends on our values as individuals and societies, and values are largely matters of choice. At one extreme, we could maximize the number of human beings living at the lowest possible level of comfort. Or we could try to optimize the quality of life for a much smaller human population.

The carrying capacity of the earth is a scientific question. It may be possible to support 50 billion people at a bread-and-water level. Is that what we choose? The question, "What is the cultural carrying capacity?" requires that we debate questions of value, about which opinions differ.

An even greater difficulty must be faced. So far, we have been treating carrying capacity as a *global* issue, as if there were some global sovereignty capable of enforcing a solution on all people. But there is no global sovereignty ("one world"), nor is there any prospect of one in the foreseeable future. Thus, we must ask how some 200 nations are to coexist in a finite global environment if different sovereignties adopt different standards of living.

Consider a protected redwood forest that produces neither food for humans nor lumber for houses. Because people must travel many kilometers to visit it, the forest is a net loss in the national energy budget. However, for those fortunate enough to wander through the cathedral-like aisles beneath an evergreen vault, a redwood forest does something precious for the human spirit. But then intrudes an appeal from a distant land, where millions are starving because their population has overshot the carrying capacity; we are asked to save lives by sending food. As long as we have surpluses, we may safely indulge in the pleasures of philanthropy. But after we have run out of our surpluses, then what?

A spokesperson for the needy from that land makes a proposal: "If you would only cut down your redwood forests, you could use the lumber to build houses and then grow potatoes on the land, shipping the food to us. Since we are all passengers together on Spaceship Earth, are you not duty bound to do so? Which is more precious, trees or human beings?"

This last question may sound ethically compelling, but let's look at the consequences of assigning a preemp-tive and supreme value to human lives. At least 2 billion people in the world are poorer than the 34 million "legally poor" in America, and their numbers are increasing by about 1 million per year. Unless this increase is halted, sharing food and energy on the basis of need would require the sacrifice of one amenity after another in rich countries. The ultimate result of sharing would be complete poverty everywhere on the earth to maintain the earth's simple carrying capacity. Is that the best humanity can do?

To date, there has been overwhelmingly negative reaction to all proposals to make international philanthropy conditional on the cessation of population growth by overpopulated recipient nations. Foreign aid is governed by two apparently inflexible assumptions:

- The right to produce children is a universal, irrevocable right of every nation, no matter how hard it presses against the carrying capacity of its territory.

- When lives are in danger, the moral obligation of rich countries to save human lives is absolute and undeniable.

Considered separately, each of these two well-meaning doctrines might be defensible; taken together, they constitute a fatal recipe. If humanity gives maximum carrying capacity precedence over problems of cultural carrying capacity, the result will be universal poverty and environmental ruin.

Or do you see an escape from this harsh dilemma?

### Critical Thinking

**1.** What population size would allow the world's people to have a good quality of life? What do you believe is the cultural carrying capacity of the United States? Should the United States have a national policy to establish this population size as soon as possible? Explain.

**2.** Do you support the two principles this essay lists as the basis of foreign aid to needy countries? If not, what changes would you make in the requirements for receiving such aid?

---

because of **(1)** poor planning, **(2)** bureaucratic inefficiency, **(3)** the low status of women (despite constitutional guarantees of equality), **(4)** extreme poverty, and **(5)** a lack of administrative and financial support.

Even though the government has provided information about the advantages of small families for years, Indian women still have an average of 3.2 children because most couples believe they need many children to do work and care for them in old age. Because of the strong cultural preference for male chil-dren, some couples keep having children until they produce one or more boys. These factors in part explain why even though 90% of Indian couples know of at least one modern birth control method, only 43% actually use one.

**What Success Has China Had in Controlling Its Population Growth?** Since 1970, China (Figure 12-7) has made impressive efforts to feed its people and bring its population growth under control.

Between 1972 and 2002, China cut its crude birth rate in half and cut its TFR from 5.7 to 1.8 children per woman (Figure 12-28).

To achieve its sharp drop in fertility, China has established the most extensive, intrusive, and strict population control program in the world. For example,

■ Couples are strongly urged to postpone the age at which they marry and to have no more than one child.

■ Married couples have ready access to free sterilization, contraceptives, and abortion. About 83% of married women in China use modern contraception.

■ Married couples who pledge to have no more than one child receive (1) extra food, (2) larger pensions, (3) better housing, (4) free medical care, (5) salary bonuses, (6) free school tuition for their one child, and (7) preferential treatment in employment when their child enters the job market. Couples who break their pledge lose all the benefits.

Because of the success of its population control program, the United Nations projects that China's population will start declining in 2042. This has stirred some members of China's parliament to propose amending the country's one-child policy so that some urban couples can have a second child. The goal would be to provide more workers to help support China's aging population, which is expected to peak in 2040.

Government officials realized in the 1960s that the only alternative to strict population control was mass starvation. China is a dictatorship, and thus, unlike India, it has been able to impose a consistent population policy throughout its society.

China's large and still growing population has an enormous environmental impact that could reduce its ability to produce enough food and threaten the health of many of its people. China has 21% of the world's population but only 7% of its fresh water and cropland, 4% of its forests, and 2% of its oil. Soil erosion in China is serious and apparently getting worse.

In the 1970s, the Chinese government had a system of health clinics that provided moderate health care for its rural farm population. This system collapsed in the 1980s as China embraced capitalist reforms. According to government estimates, more than 800 million people—90% of rural Chinese—now have no health insurance or social safety net.

Most countries prefer to avoid the coercive elements of China's program. Perhaps the best lesson for other countries is to act to curb population growth before they must choose between mass starvation and coercive measures that severely restrict human freedom.

## 12-5 CUTTING GLOBAL POPULATION GROWTH

In 1994, the United Nations held its third once-in-a-decade Conference on Population and Development in Cairo, Egypt. One of the conference's goals was to encourage action to stabilize the world's population at 7.8 billion by 2050 instead of the projected 9.3 billion (Figure 12-11). The major goals of the resulting population plan, endorsed by 180 governments, are to do the following by 2015:

■ Provide universal access to family planning services and reproductive health care

■ Improve the health care of infants, children, and pregnant women (Solutions, p. 244)

■ Encourage development and implementation of national population policies as part of social and economic development policies

■ Bring about more equitable relationships between men and women, with emphasis on improving the status of women and expanding education and job opportunities for young women

■ Increase access to education, especially for girls and women

■ Increase the involvement of men in child-rearing responsibilities and family planning

■ Take steps to eradicate poverty

■ Reduce and eliminate unsustainable patterns of production and consumption

At the conference, developing countries agreed to cover two-thirds of the $17 billion annual cost, with developed countries paying the remainder. By 2002, developing countries had provided about 70% of their Cairo commitment, but developed countries had provided only about 40% of their commitment. Because of the funding shortfall, the United Nations estimated that by 2002 there were 122 million pregnancies and 41 million abortions that could have been prevented.

The *good news* is that the experience of Japan, Thailand (p. 255), South Korea, Taiwan, Iran, and China indicates that a country can achieve or come close to replacement-level fertility within 15–30 years. Such experience also suggests that the best way to slow population growth is a combination of (1) investing in family planning, (2) reducing poverty, and (3) elevating the status of women.

*Our numbers expand but Earth's natural systems do not.*
LESTER R. BROWN

## REVIEW QUESTIONS

1. Define the boldfaced terms in this chapter.

2. How did Thailand reduce its birth rate?

3. How is population change calculated? What are the *crude birth rate* and the *crude death rate*? About how many people are added to the world's population each year and each day? How is the *annual rate of population change* calculated? What three countries have the world's largest populations?

4. Distinguish between *replacement-level fertility* and *total fertility rate*. Explain why replacement-level fertility is higher than 2. Explain why reaching replacement-level fertility does not mean an immediate halt in population growth.

5. How have fertility rates and birth rates changed in the United States since 1910? How rapidly is the U.S. population growing?

6. List 10 factors that affect birth rates and fertility rates.

7. List five reasons why the world's death rate has declined over the past 100 years.

8. Distinguish between *life expectancy* and *infant mortality rate*. Why is infant mortality the best measure of a society's quality of life? List three factors that keep the U.S. infant mortality higher than it could be.

9. What is the *age structure* of a population? Explain why the current age structure of the world's population means the world's population will keep growing for at least another 50 years even if the replacement-level rate of 2.1 is somehow reached globally tomorrow.

10. Draw the general shape of an age structure diagram for a country undergoing **(a)** rapid population growth, **(b)** slow population growth, **(c)** zero population growth, and **(d)** population decline.

11. What percentage of population is under age 15 in **(a)** the world, **(b)** developed countries, and **(c)** developing countries? Explain how age structure diagrams can be used to make population and economic projections.

12. What are the benefits and potentially harmful effects of rapid population decline?

13. List the major arguments for and against reducing birth rates globally.

14. Describe immigration in the United States in terms of numbers, and list the pros and cons of reducing immigration limits.

15. What is the *demographic transition,* and what are its four phases? What factors might keep many developing countries from making the demographic transition?

16. What is *family planning,* and what are the advantages of using this approach to reduce the birth rate?

17. Explain how empowering women can help reduce birth rates.

18. What economic rewards and penalties have some countries used to reduce birth rates? What four conditions increase the success of using such economic rewards and penalties?

19. Briefly describe and compare the success China and India have had in reducing their birth rates.

20. List the eight goals of the current UN plan to stabilize the world's population at 7.8 billion by 2050, instead of the projected 9.3 billion.

## CRITICAL THINKING

1. Why is a drop in the birth rate not necessarily a reliable indicator of future population growth?

2. Why is it rational for a poor couple in a developing country such as India to have four or five children? What changes might induce such a couple to consider their behavior irrational?

3. List what you consider to be a major local, national, or global environmental problem, and describe the role of population growth in this problem.

4. Suppose that all women in the world today began bearing children at replacement-level fertility rates of 2.1 children per woman. Explain why this would not immediately stop global population growth. About how long would it take for population growth to stabilize?

5. What do you believe is the world's **(a)** maximum human population and **(b)** optimum human population?

6. Do you believe the population of **(a)** your own country and **(b)** the area where you live is too high? Explain.

7. Evaluate the claims made by those opposing a reduction in births and those promoting a reduction in births, as discussed on p. 267. Which position do you support, and why?

8. Explain why you agree or disagree with each of the following proposals:
   a. The number of legal immigrants and refugees allowed into the United States each year should be reduced sharply.
   b. Illegal immigration into the United States should be decreased sharply. If you agree, how would you go about achieving this?
   c. Families in the United States should be given financial incentives to have more children to prevent eventual population decline.
   d. The United States should adopt an official policy to stabilize its population and reduce unnecessary resource waste and consumption as rapidly as possible.
   e. Everyone should have the right to have as many children as they want.

9. Some people have proposed that the earth could solve its population problem by shipping people off to space colonies, each containing about 10,000 people. Assuming

we could build such large-scale, self-sustaining space stations, how many people would have to be shipped off each day to provide living spaces for the 79 million people being added to the earth's population each year? Current space shuttles can handle about 6 to 8 passengers. If this capacity could be increased to 100 passengers per shuttle, how many shuttles would have to be launched per day to offset the 79 million people being added each year? According to your calculations, determine whether this proposal is a logical solution to the earth's population problem.

**10.** Some people believe the most important goal is to sharply reduce the rate of population growth in developing countries, where 95% of the world's population growth is expected to take place. Some people in developing countries agree that population growth in these countries can cause local environmental problems. However, they contend that the most serious environmental problem the world faces is disruption of the global life-support system by high levels of resource consumption per person in developed countries, which use 80% of the world's resources. What is your view on this issue? Explain.

**11.** Some analysts contend that we have enough food and resources for everyone but these resources are not distributed equitably. To them, poverty, hunger, overpopulation, and environmental degradation are caused mainly by a lack of *social justice*. What is your view on this issue? Explain.

**12.** Suppose the cloning of human beings becomes possible without any serious health effects for cloned individuals. What effect might this have on the world's population size and growth rate? Explain.

**13.** Why has China been more successful than India in reducing its rate of population growth? Do you agree with China's current population control policies? Explain. What alternatives, if any, would you suggest?

**14.** Congratulations! You are in charge of the world. List the three most important features of your population policy.

## PROJECTS

**1.** Survey members of your class to determine how many children they plan to have. Tally the results and compare them for men and women.

**2.** Assume your entire class (or manageable groups of your class) is charged with coming up with a plan for halving the world's population growth rate within the next 20 years. Develop a detailed plan that would achieve this goal, including any differences between policies in developing countries and developed countries. Justify each part of your plan. Predict what problems you might face in implementing the plan, and devise strategies for dealing with these problems.

**3.** Prepare an age structure diagram for your community. Use the diagram to project future population growth and economic and social problems.

**4.** Use the library or the Internet to find bibliographic information about *Theodore Roosevelt, Paul Hawken,* and *Lester R. Brown,* whose quotes appear at the beginning and end of this chapter.

**5.** Make a concept map of this chapter's major ideas, using the section heads and subheads and the key terms (in boldface). See material on the website for this book about how to prepare concept maps.

## INTERNET STUDY RESOURCES AND RESOURCES FOR FURTHER READING AND RESEARCH

The website for this book contains helpful study aids and many ideas for further reading and research. Log on to

**www.info.brookscole.com/miller13**

and click on the Chapter-by-Chapter area. Choose Chapter 12 and select a resource:

■ Flash Cards allows you to test your mastery of the Terms and Concepts to Remember for this chapter.

■ Tutorial Quizzes provides a multiple-choice practice quiz.

■ Student Guide to InfoTrac will lead you to Critical Thinking Projects that use InfoTrac College Edition as a research tool.

■ References lists the major books and articles consulted in writing this chapter.

■ Hypercontents takes you to an extensive list of sites with news, research, and images related to individual sections of the chapter.

## INFOTRAC COLLEGE EDITION

Improve your skills with InfoTrac College Edition, a searchable online database of articles from more than 700 periodicals. Log on to

**http://www.infotrac-college.com**

or access InfoTrac through the website for this book. Try to find the following articles:

**1.** Brown, R. W. 1999. When we hit the wall: The lesson is likely to be painful. *Free Inquiry* 19: 23. *Keywords:* "world population" and "exponential growth." This article discusses some of the social and ecological implications of the rapidly expanding human population, even though fertility rates are declining.

**2.** McMichael, A. J. 2002. Population, environment, disease, and survival: Past patterns, uncertain futures. *The Lancet* 359: 1145. *Keywords:* "human population" and "environment." Even though human populations are adversely affecting the environment, human life span continues to increase. This article looks at the relationship between human societies and their impacts on the environment and on individual survival.

# 13 FOOD RESOURCES

## Perennial Crops on the Kansas Prairie

When you think about farms in Kansas, you probably picture seemingly endless fields of wheat or corn plowed up and planted each year. By 2040, the picture might change, thanks to pioneering research at the nonprofit Land Institute near Salina, Kansas (Figure 13-1).

The institute, headed by plant geneticist Wes Jackson, is experimenting with an ecological approach to agriculture on the midwestern prairie. This approach relies on planting a mixture of different crops in the same area, a technique called *polyculture*. The goal is to grow food crops by planting a mix of (1) perennial grasses (Figure 13-1, left), (2) legumes (a source of nitrogen fertilizer, Figure 13-1, right), (3) sunflowers, (4) grain crops, and (5) plants that provide natural insecticides in the same field.

The institute's goal is to raise food by mimicking many of the natural conditions of the prairie without losing fertile grassland soil (Figure 10-15, top right, p. 215). Institute researchers believe that *perennial polyculture* can be blended with *modern monoculture* to reduce its harmful environmental effects.

Because these plants are perennials, the soil does not have to be plowed up and prepared each year to replant them. This takes much less labor than conventional monoculture or diversified organic farms that grow annual crops. It also reduces (1) soil erosion because the unplowed soil is not exposed to wind and rain, (2) pollution caused by chemical fertilizers and pesticides, and (3) the need for irrigation because the deep roots of such perennials retain more water than annuals.

Thirty years of research by the institute have shown that various mixtures of perennials grown in parts of the midwestern prairie could be used as important sources of food. One such mix of perennial crops includes (1) *eastern gamma grass* (a warm season grass that is a relative of corn with three times as much protein as corn and twice as much as wheat; Figure 13-1, left), (2) *mammoth wildrye* (a cool season grass that is distantly related to rye, wheat, and barley), (3) *Illinois bundleflower* (a wild nitrogen-producing legume that can enrich the soil and whose seeds can serve as livestock feed; Figure 13-1, right), and (4) *Maximilian sunflower* (which produces seeds with as much protein as soybeans).

These discoveries may help us come closer to producing and distributing enough food to meet everyone's basic nutritional needs without degrading the soil, water, air, and biodiversity that support all food production.

**Figure 13-1** The Land Institute in Salina, Kansas, is a farm, a prairie laboratory, and a school dedicated to changing the way we grow food. It advocates growing a diverse mixture (polyculture) of edible perennial plants to supplement traditional annual monoculture crops. Two of these perennial crops are (1) eastern gamma grass (above) and (2) the Illinois bundleflower (right).

This chapter addresses the following questions:

- How is the world's food produced?
- How are green revolution and traditional methods used to raise crops?
- How much has food production increased, how serious is malnutrition, and what are the environmental effects of producing food?
- How can we increase production of **(a)** crops, **(b)** meat, and **(c)** fish and shellfish?
- How do government policies affect food production?
- How can we design and shift to more sustainable agricultural systems?

## 13-1 HOW IS FOOD PRODUCED?

**What Three Systems Provide Us with Food? Some Good and Bad News** Historically, humans have depended on three systems for their food supply: **(1)** *croplands* (mostly for producing grains, which provide about 76% of the world's food), **(2)** *rangelands* (for producing meat mostly from grazing livestock, which supply about 17% of the world's food), and **(3)** *oceanic fisheries* (which supply about 7% of the world's food).

Some *good news* is that

- Since 1950 there has been a staggering increase in global food production from all three systems.
- This phenomenal growth in food productivity occurred because of technological advances such as **(1)** increased use of tractors and farm machinery and high-tech fishing boats and gear, **(2)** inorganic chemical fertilizers, **(3)** irrigation, **(4)** pesticides, **(5)** high-yield varieties of wheat, rice, and corn, **(6)** densely populated feedlots and enclosed pens for raising cattle, pigs, and chickens, and **(7)** aquaculture ponds and ocean cages for raising some types of fish and shellfish.

To feed the world's 9.3 billion people projected by 2050, we must **(1)** produce and equitably distribute more food than has been produced since agriculture began about 10,000 years ago and **(2)** do this in an environmentally sustainable manner. Some analysts believe we can continue expanding the use of industrialized agriculture to produce the necessary food.

Some *bad news* is that other analysts contend that **(1)** environmental degradation, **(2)** pollution, **(3)** lack of water for irrigation, **(4)** overgrazing by livestock, **(5)** overfishing, and **(6)** loss of vital ecological services (Figure 4-34, p. 92) may limit future food production as human activities continue to take over or degrade more of the planet's *net primary productivity* (Figure 4–26, p. 82), which supports all life. The rest of this chapter analyzes **(1)** the pros and cons of the world's crop, meat, and fish production systems and **(2)** how these systems can be made more sustainable.

**What Plants and Animals Feed the World?** Although the earth has perhaps 30,000 plant species with parts that people can eat, only 15 plant and 8 terrestrial animal species supply an estimated 90% of our global intake of calories. Just three grain crops—*wheat, rice,* and *corn*—provide more than half the calories people consume. These three grains, and most other food crops, are *annuals*, whose seeds must be replanted each year.

Two-thirds of the world's people survive primarily on traditional grains (mainly rice, wheat, and corn), mostly because they cannot afford meat. As incomes rise, people consume more grain, but indirectly in the form of meat (mostly beef, pork, and chicken), eggs, milk, cheese, and other products of grain-eating domesticated livestock.

Fish and shellfish are an important source of food for about 1 billion people, mostly in Asia and in coastal areas of developing countries. But on a global scale fish and shellfish supply only **(1)** 7% of the world's food, **(2)** less than 6% of the protein in the human diet, and **(3)** 1% of the energy in the human diet.

**What Are the Major Types of Food Production?** All crop production involves replacing species-rich late successional communities such as mature grasslands (Figure 6-30, p. 131) and forests (Figure 6-38, p. 138) with an early successional community (Figure 8-15, p. 181) consisting of a single crop (*monoculture,* Figure 6-31, p. 132) or a mixture of crops (*polyculture*).

The two major types of agricultural systems are industrialized and traditional. **Industrialized agriculture,** or **high-input agriculture,** uses large amounts of fossil fuel energy, water, commercial fertilizers, and pesticides to produce huge quantities of single crops (monocultures) or livestock animals for sale. Practiced on about 25% of all cropland, mostly in developed countries (Figure 13-2), high-input industrialized agriculture has spread since the mid-1960s to some developing countries.

**Plantation agriculture** is a form of industrialized agriculture practiced primarily in tropical developing countries. It involves growing cash crops (such as bananas, coffee, soybeans, sugarcane, cocoa, and veg-

| Industrialized agriculture | Plantation agriculture | Intensive traditional agriculture |
| Shifting cultivation | Nomadic herding | No agriculture |

**Figure 13-2** Locations of the world's principal types of food production. Excluding Antarctica and Greenland, agricultural systems cover almost one-third of the earth's land surface and account for an annual output of food worth about $1.3 trillion.

etables) on large monoculture plantations, mostly for sale in developed countries.

An increasing amount of livestock production in developed countries is industrialized. Large numbers of cattle are brought to densely populated feedlots, where they are fattened up for about 4 months before slaughter. Most pigs and chickens in developed countries spend their entire lives in densely populated pens and cages and are fed mostly grain grown on cropland.

*Traditional agriculture* consists of two main types, which together are practiced by about 2.7 billion people (44% of the world's people) in developing countries and provide about 20% of the world's food supply. **Traditional subsistence agriculture** typically uses mostly human labor and draft animals to produce only enough crops or livestock for a farm family's survival. Examples of this very low-input type of agriculture include numerous forms of shifting cultivation in trop-

ical forests (Figure 2-2, p. 23) and nomadic livestock herding (Figure 13-2).

In **traditional intensive agriculture,** farmers increase their inputs of human and draft labor, fertilizer, and water to get a higher yield per area of cultivated land to produce enough food to feed their families and to sell for income. Figure 13-3 (p. 280) shows the relative inputs of land, human and animal labor, fossil fuel energy, and financial capital needed to produce one unit of food energy in various types of food production systems. In North America, only 2.4% of the labor force is engaged directly in food production, compared to 45–65% in developing countries. Figure 13-4 (p. 280) shows the estimated input of fossil fuel energy required to produce various foods.

Croplands, like natural ecosystems, provide ecological and economic services (Figure 13-5, p. 281). The food, fiber, and animal feed produced throughout the world is worth more than $1.3 trillion.

**Figure 13-3** Relative inputs of land, labor, financial capital, and fossil fuel energy in four agricultural systems. An average of 60% of the people in developing countries are involved directly in producing food, compared with only 8% in developed countries (2% in the United States).

**Figure 13-4** Estimated fossil fuel energy required for production of various foods. (Data from Malcolm Beveridge)

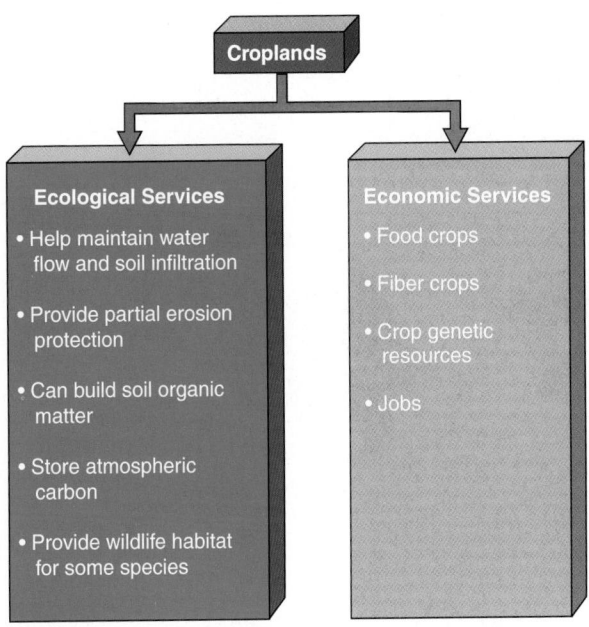

**Figure 13-5** Ecological and economic services provided by croplands.

## 13-2 PRODUCING FOOD BY GREEN REVOLUTION AND TRADITIONAL TECHNIQUES

**How Have Green Revolutions Increased Food Production? High-Input Monocultures in Action**   Farmers can produce more food by **(1)** farming more land or **(2)** getting higher yields per unit of area from existing cropland. Since 1950, most of the increase in global food production has come from increased yields per unit of area of cropland in a process called the **green revolution.**

This green revolution involves three steps:

■   Developing and planting monocultures (Figure 6-31, p. 132) of selectively bred or genetically engineered high-yield varieties of key crops such as rice, wheat, and corn

■   Producing high yields by using large inputs of fertilizer, pesticides, and water on crops

■   Increasing the number of crops grown per year on a plot of land through *multiple cropping.*

This high-input approach dramatically increased crop yields in most developed countries between 1950 and 1970 in what is called the *first green revolution* (Figure 13-6, p. 282).

A *second green revolution* has been taking place since 1967 (Figure 13-6, p. 282), by introducing fast-growing dwarf varieties of rice and wheat, specially bred for tropical and subtropical climates, into several developing countries. With enough fertile soil and fertilizer, water, and pesticides, yields of these new plants (Figure 13-7, p. 282) can be two to five times those of traditional wheat and rice varieties. The fast growth also allows farmers to grow two or even three crops a year (multiple cropping) on the same land. Producing more food on less land is also an important way to protect biodiversity by saving large areas of forests, grasslands, wetlands, and easily eroded mountain terrain from being used to grow food.

These yield increases depend not only on fertile soil and ample water but also on high inputs of fossil fuels to **(1)** run machinery, **(2)** produce and apply inorganic fertilizers and pesticides, and **(3)** pump water for irrigation. All told, high-input green revolution agriculture uses about 8% of the world's oil output.

**Case Study: Food Production in the United States**   Since 1940, U.S. farmers have used green revolution techniques to more than double crop production without cultivating more land. This strategy has kept large areas of forests, grasslands, wetlands, and easily erodible land from being converted to farmland. Figure 13-8 (p. 283) shows the various uses of land in the United States.

Farming has become *agribusiness* as big companies and larger family-owned farms have taken control of almost three-fourths of U.S. food production. Only about 650,000 Americans (2% of the population) are full-time farmers. However, about 9% of the population is involved in the U.S. agricultural system, from growing and processing food to distributing it and selling it at the supermarket.

In terms of total annual sales, agriculture is bigger than the automotive, steel, and housing industries combined. It generates about 18% of the country's gross national product and 19% of all jobs in the private sector, employing more people than any other industry.

The U.S. agricultural system is highly productive. With only 0.3% of the world's farm labor force, U.S. farms produce about 17% of the world's grain (most consumed by U.S. livestock) and nearly half of the world's grain exports. U.S. residents spend an average of only 10–12% of their income on food (down from 21% in 1940), compared to 18% in Japan and 40–70% in most developing countries.

This industrialization of agriculture has been made possible by the availability of cheap energy, most of it from oil. Agriculture consumes about 17% of all commercial energy in the United States each year (Figure 13-9, p. 283). Most plant crops in the United States provide more food energy than the energy used to grow them. However, if we include livestock, the U.S. food production system uses about three units of fossil fuel energy to produce one unit of food energy.

First green revolution
(developed countries)

Second green revolution
(developing countries)

● Major international agricultural
research centers and seed banks

**Figure 13-6** Countries whose crop yields per unit of land area increased during the two green revolutions. The first (blue) took place in developed countries between 1950 and 1970; the second (green) has occurred since 1967 in developing countries with enough rainfall or irrigation capacity. Several agricultural research centers and gene or seed banks (red dots) play a key role in developing high-yield crop varieties.

**Figure 13-7** A high-yield, semidwarf variety of rice called IR-8 (left), a part of the second green revolution, was produced by crossbreeding two parent strains of rice: PETA from Indonesia (center) and DGWG from China (right). The shorter and stiffer stalks of the new variety allow the plants to support larger heads of grain without toppling over and increase the benefit of applying more fertilizer.

**Figure 13-8** General uses of land in the United States. (Data from U.S. Geological Survey and U.S. Department of Agriculture)

**Cropland**
**Irrigated farmland**
**Rangeland**
**Pasture**
**Forest**
**Barren land**
**Wetland**
**Urban area**

Energy efficiency is much lower if we look at the whole U.S. food system. Considering the energy used to grow, store, process, package, transport, refrigerate, and cook all plant and animal food, *about 10 units of nonrenewable fossil fuel energy are needed to put 1 unit of food energy on the table.* By comparison, every unit of energy from human labor in traditional subsistence farming provides at least 1 unit of food energy and up to 10 units of food energy using traditional intensive farming.

| 4% | 2% | 6% | 5% |
|---|---|---|---|
| Crops | Livestock | Food processing | Food distribution and preparation |

Food production

17% of total U.S. commercial energy use

**Figure 13-9** In the United States, industrialized agriculture uses about 17% of all commercial energy. On average, a piece of food eaten in the United States has traveled 2,100 kilometers (1,300 miles).

**What Growing Techniques Are Used in Traditional Agriculture? Low-Input Agrodiversity in Action** Traditional farmers in developing countries today grow about 20% of the world's food on about 75% of its cultivated land. Many traditional farmers simultaneously grow several crops on the same plot, a practice known as **interplanting.** Such crop diversity reduces the chance of losing most or all of the year's food supply to pests, bad weather, and other misfortunes.

Common interplanting strategies found throughout the world, mostly in developing countries, include the following:

- **Polyvarietal cultivation,** in which a plot is planted with several varieties of the same crop.

- **Intercropping,** in which two or more different crops are grown at the same time on a plot (for example, a carbohydrate-rich grain that uses soil nitrogen and a protein-rich legume that puts it back).

- **Agroforestry,** or **alley cropping,** in which crops and trees are planted together (Figure 10-26c, p. 224).

- **Polyculture,** a more complex form of intercropping in which many different plants maturing at various times are planted together. Advantages of this low-input approach include (1) less need for fertilizer and water because root systems at different depths in the soil capture nutrients and moisture efficiently, (2) protection from wind and water erosion because the soil is covered with crops year round, (3) little or no need for insecticides because multiple habitats are created for natural predators of crop-eating insects, (4) little or no need for herbicides because weeds have trouble competing with the multitude of crop plants, and (5) insurance against bad weather because of the diversity of crops raised. Wes Jackson is using this technique to grow perennial crops on prairie land in the United States (p. 277).

Recent ecological research on crop yields of 14 artificial ecosystems found that on average low-input polyculture (with four or five different crop species) produces higher yields per hectare of land than high-input monoculture. This finding has important implications for developing high-yield sustainable agriculture in developing countries by combining the techniques of traditional high-yield interplanting with increased inputs of organic fertilizer and irrigation. In 2001, ecologists Peter Reich and David Tilman found that carefully controlled polyculture plots with 16 different species of plants consistently outproduced plots with 9, 4, or only 1 type of plant species.

Traditional farmers in arid and semiarid areas with low natural soil fertility have developed innovative methods to boost crop production. For example, in the African countries of Niger and Burkina Faso a farmer innovation called *tassas* has tripled yields on at least 100,000 hectares (250,000) acres of unproductive land. *Tassas* are small pits dug in the soil, filled with manure, and then planted with crops once they fill with infrequent rain.

## 13-3 FOOD PRODUCTION, NUTRITION, AND ENVIRONMENTAL EFFECTS

**How Much Has Food Production Increased?** Figure 13-10 illustrates the success of using high-input monoculture farming to produce food and ward off sharp rises in hunger, malnutrition, and food prices. Here is some *good news*:

- Between 1950 and 1990, world grain production almost tripled (Figure 13-10, left), and per capita grain production rose by about 36% (Figure 13-10, right).

- According to a 2001 World Bank study, the average inflation-adjusted price of all major types of food in 2000 was less than one-third of its price in 1957.

**Figure 13-10** Total worldwide grain production of wheat, corn, and rice (left), and per capita grain production (right), 1950–2001. In order, the world's three largest grain-producing countries in 2001 were China, the United States, and India. (Data from U.S. Department of Agriculture, Worldwatch Institute, and UN Food and Agriculture Organization)

Despite these impressive achievements in food production, there is some *bad news:*

- Population growth is outstripping food production and distribution in areas that support about 2 billion people, especially in parts of (1) Africa with extreme poverty and very high population growth rates and (2) the former Soviet Union where economic growth, food production, and living standards have dropped sharply since 1990.

- Since 1985, global grain production has leveled off (Figure 13-10, left), and per capita grain production has declined (Figure 13-10, right).

There is controversy over why grain yields leveled off during the 1990s. According to some analysts, this occurred for economic and political reasons because (1) more efficient food production lowered the price that some farmers get for grain and reduced their incentive to grow more food and (2) grain yields per hectare dropped sharply in the former Soviet Union during the 1990s after its breakup.

Other analysts attribute much of this leveling off of grain production to environmental factors such as (1) limits on the amounts of water, fertilizer, and pesticides that green revolution crops can tolerate in some areas, and (2) loss of productivity from erosion and salinization of soil and lack of irrigation water in some areas, especially Africa.

### What Is Undernutrition and Malnutrition?
To maintain good health and resist disease, people need (1) fairly large amounts of *macronutrients* such as protein, carbohydrates, and fats, and (2) smaller amounts of *micronutrients* consisting of various vitamins (such as A, C, and E) and minerals (such as iron, iodine, and calcium).

People who cannot grow or buy enough food to meet their basic energy needs suffer from **undernutrition.** *Chronically undernourished* people consume between 100 and 400 fewer kilocalories per day than they need to maintain body weight and undertake light activity. Children in this category are likely to (1) suffer from mental retardation and stunted growth and (2) be much more susceptible to infectious diseases (such as measles and diarrhea).

People who are forced to live on a low-protein, high-carbohydrate diet consisting only of grains such as wheat, rice, or corn often suffer from **malnutrition:** deficiencies of protein and other key nutrients. Many of the world's desperately poor people, especially children, suffer from both undernutrition and malnutrition.

The two most common nutritional deficiency diseases are marasmus and kwashiorkor. *Marasmus* (from the Greek word *marasmos*, "to waste away") occurs when a diet is low in both calories and protein (see figure in Connections, p. 8). Most victims are either nursing infants of malnourished mothers or children who do not get enough food after being weaned from breast-feeding. If the child is treated in time with a balanced diet, most of these effects can be reversed.

*Kwashiorkor* (meaning "displaced child" in a West African dialect) is a severe protein deficiency occurring in infants and children ages 1–3, usually after the arrival of a new baby deprives them of breast milk. The displaced child's diet changes to grain or sweet potatoes, which provide enough calories but not enough protein. If it is caught soon enough, most of the harmful effects can be cured with a balanced diet. Otherwise, children who survive their first year or two suffer from stunted growth and mental retardation.

Chronically undernourished and malnourished people are disease prone and adults are too weak to work productively or think clearly. As a result, their children also tend to be underfed, malnourished, and susceptible to disease. If these children survive to adulthood, many are locked in a malnutrition and poverty cycle (Figure 13-11, p. 286) that can continue for generations.

### How Serious Are Undernutrition and Malnutrition?
Here is some *good news.* Despite population growth, according to the UN Food and Agriculture Organization (FAO),

- The average daily food intake in calories per person in the world and in developing countries rose sharply between 1961 and 2000, and is projected to continue rising through 2030 (Figure 13-12, p. 287).

- The estimated number of chronically undernourished or malnourished people fell from 918 million in 1970 to 826 million in 2000—792 million of them in developing countries (especially in Asia and Africa) and 34 million in developed countries.

- The estimated number of chronically undernourished or malnourished people in developing countries is projected to fall to 680 million by 2010 and 400 million by 2030.

- The percentage of the world's people suffering from chronic undernourishment or malnourishment fell (1) from 35% in 1970 to 17% in 2000, and (2) is projected to decline to 12% by 2010 and 6% by 2030.

However, according to the FAO, World Bank, and WHO some *bad news* is that

- About one of every six people in developing countries (including about one of every three children below age 5) is chronically undernourished or malnourished. This is an unacceptably high number in a world with the affluence and means to virtually eliminate poverty and hunger.

- The 1996 World Food Summit goal of cutting the number of undernourished and malnourished people

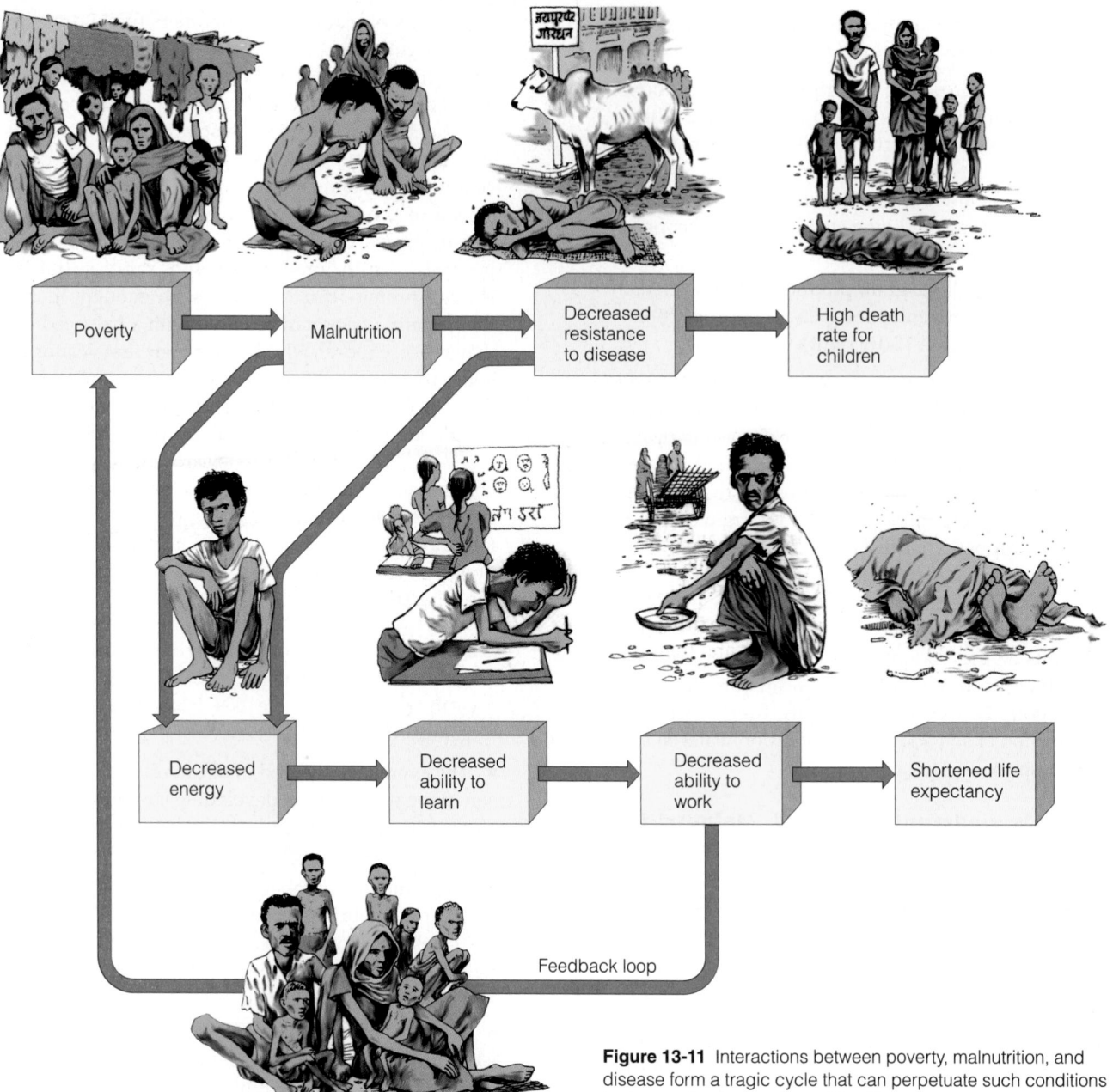

**Figure 13-11** Interactions between poverty, malnutrition, and disease form a tragic cycle that can perpetuate such conditions in succeeding generations of families.

Diagram labels: Poverty → Malnutrition → Decreased resistance to disease → High death rate for children; Decreased energy → Decreased ability to learn → Decreased ability to work → Shortened life expectancy; Feedback loop

to 400 million by 2015 is not expected to be achieved before 2030—15 years late. According to the FAO, hungry people cannot wait another 15 years.

■ Each year at least 10 million people, half of them children under age 5, die prematurely from **(1)** undernutrition, **(2)** malnutrition, **(3)** increased susceptibility to normally nonfatal infectious diseases such as measles and diarrhea because of their weakened condition from malnutrition, and **(4)** infectious diseases caused by drinking contaminated water.

■ Disease and premature death from undernutrition and malnutrition is a "silent and invisible global emergency with a massive impact on children" that could be prevented (Solutions, p. 289).

**How Serious Are Micronutrient Deficiencies?**
According to the WHO, about 2 billion people—about one out of three people—suffer from a deficiency of one or more vitamins and minerals. The most widespread micronutrient deficiencies in developing countries involve *vitamin A, iron,* and *iodine.*

The *bad news* that that 100–140 million children in developing countries are deficient in vitamin A. This puts them at risk for **(1)** blindness (about 500,000 cases per year) and **(2)** premature death because even mild vitamin A deficiency reduces children's resistance to infectious diseases such as diarrhea and measles.

Some *good news* is that Swiss scientists recently spliced genes into rice to make it rich in beta-carotene, the source of vitamin A. According to the

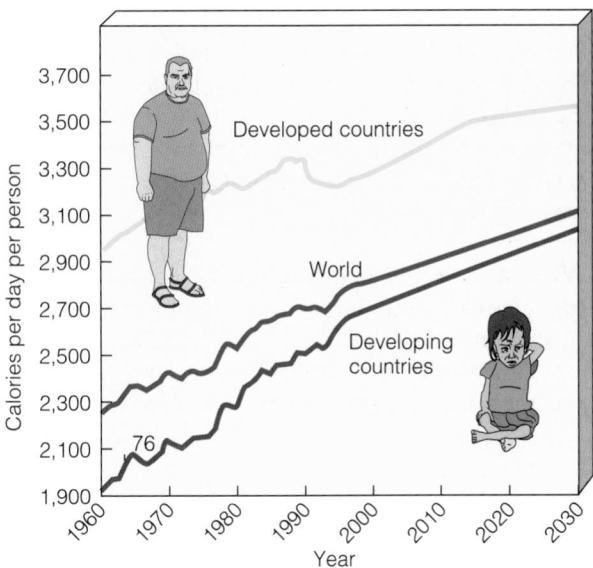

**Figure 13-12** The average daily food intake in calories per person in the world, developing countries, and developed countries: 1961–2000 and projected increases to 2030. The average adult male needs about 2,500 calories per day for good health. (Data from UN Food and Agriculture Organization)

United Nations Children's Fund (UNICEF), improved vitamin A nutrition through use of this vitamin-fortified rice, called Golden Rice, could prevent 1–2 million premature deaths per year among children under age 5.

Some *bad news* is that **(1)** the average person would have to consume about 9 kilograms (20 pounds) of cooked rice per day to get the necessary amount of vitamin A, and **(2)** beta carotene can be converted to vitamin A only in the body of a well-nourished person.

Other nutritional deficiency diseases are caused by the lack of minerals. Too little *iron* (a component of hemoglobin that transports oxygen in the blood) causes anemia. Iron is found in whole grains, green leafy vegetables, and meat. Iron deficiency **(1)** causes fatigue, **(2)** makes infection more likely, **(3)** increases a woman's chances of dying in childbirth, **(4)** increases an infant's chances of dying of infection during its first year of life, and **(5)** cripples efforts to improve primary school education because developing brains need adequate iron to learn. According to a 1999 survey by the WHO, one of every three people, mostly women and children in tropical developing countries, suffers from iron deficiency.

Elemental *iodine,* found in seafood and crops grown in iodine-rich soils, is essential for the functioning of the thyroid gland, which produces a hormone that controls the body's rate of metabolism. Lack of iodine can cause **(1)** stunted growth, **(2)** mental retardation, and **(3)** goiter (an abnormal enlargement of the thyroid gland that can lead to deafness).

Some *good news* is that WHO and UNICEF programs to get countries to add iodine to salt slashed the percentage of the world's people with iodine deficiency from 29% to 12% between 1994 and 1999. Some *bad news* is that this still leaves at least 740 million people in developing countries—2.5 times the U. S. population—with too little iodine in their diet.

**How Serious Is Overnutrition?** About one out of seven adults in developed countries (one out of five in the United States) suffers from **overnutrition,** a condition in which food energy intake exceeds energy use and causes excess body fat (obesity). Too many calories (Figure 13-12, top curve), too little exercise, or both can cause overnutrition.

People who are underfed and underweight and those who are overfed and overweight face similar health problems: **(1)** lower life expectancy, **(2)** greater susceptibility to disease and illness, and **(3)** lower productivity and life quality.

Overnutrition is the second leading cause of preventable deaths after smoking (p. 228), mostly from heart disease, cancer, stroke, and diabetes. An estimated 300,000 Americans die prematurely each year as a result of being overweight. This death toll is roughly equivalent to two fully loaded jumbo (400-passenger) jets crashing accidentally every day with no survivors.

A study of thousands of Chinese villagers indicates that the healthiest diet for humans is largely vegetarian, with only 10–15% of calories coming from fat. This is in contrast to the typical meat-based diet, in which 40% of the calories come from fat.

About 61% of the U.S. adult population is overweight and 27% is obese—the highest percentage of any developed country. The $36 billion Americans spend each year trying to lose weight is almost twice the $19 billion needed to eliminate undernutrition and malnutrition in the world.

Some nutrition analysts, including Yale University professor Kelly Brownell, advocate discouraging consumption of unhealthful foods by

- Regulating advertising of junk foods.

- Taxing food based on its nutrient value per calorie. Sugary and fatty foods low in nutrients would be taxed the most, and fruits and vegetables would not be taxed.

- Using the resulting tax revenues to promote **(1)** healthful diets, **(2)** nutrition education, and **(3)** exercise programs in schools and communities.

**Do We Produce Enough Food to Feed the World's People?** The *good news* is that according to the FAO **(1)** we produce more than enough food to meet the basic nutritional needs of every person on the earth today and **(2)** there should be more food for more people in the future (Figure 13-12). If distributed equally, the grain currently produced worldwide is enough to give everyone a meatless subsistence diet.

The *bad news* for the one out of eight people not getting enough to eat is that food is not distributed equally among the world's people because of differences in **(1)** soil, **(2)** climate, **(3)** political and economic power, and **(4)** average per capita income throughout the world (Figure 1-3, p. 5).

Most agricultural experts agree that *the principal cause of hunger and malnutrition is and will continue to be*

*poverty,* which prevents poor people from growing or buying enough food regardless of how much is available. For example, according to the United Nations, in the 1990s nearly 80% of all malnourished children lived in countries with food surpluses. Thus *poverty, not lack of food production, is the real food problem for about one out of eight people.*

**What Are the Environmental Effects of Producing Food?** Agriculture has significant harmful effects on air, soil, water, and biodiversity (Figure 13–13). Ecologist David Pimentel has estimated that the harmful environmental costs not included in

**Biodiversity Loss**

Loss and degradation of habitat from clearing grasslands and forests and draining wetlands

Fish kills from pesticide runoff

Killing of wild predators to protect livestock

Loss of genetic diversity from replacing thousands of wild crop strains with a few monoculture strains

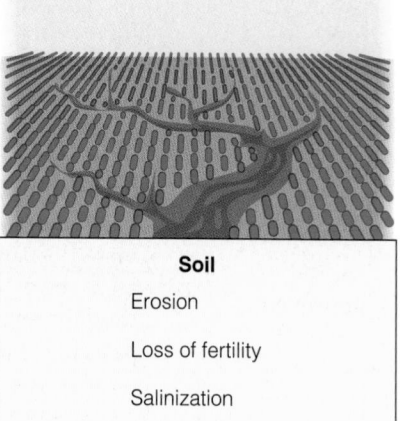

**Soil**

Erosion

Loss of fertility

Salinization

Waterlogging

Desertification

**Air Pollution**

Greenhouse gas emissions from fossil fuel use

Other air pollutants from fossil fuel use

Pollution from pesticide sprays

**Water**

Aquifer depletion

Increased runoff and flooding from land cleared to grow crops

Sediment pollution from erosion

Fish kills from pesticide runoff

Surface and groundwater pollution from pesticides and fertilizers

Overfertilization of lakes and slow-moving rivers from runoff of nitrates and phosphates from fertilizers, livestock wastes, and food processing wastes

**Human Health**

Nitrates in drinking water

Pesticide residues in drinking water, food, and air

Contamination of drinking and swimming water with disease organisms from livestock wastes

Bacterial contamination of meat

**Figure 13-13** Major environmental effects of food production. According to UN studies, land degradation reduced cumulative food production worldwide by about 13% on cropland and 4% on pastureland between 1950 and 2000.

## Saving Children

According to the World Health Organization, 7 out of 10 of the deaths of children under age 5 in developing countries can be attributed to one or a combination of five main causes: malnutrition, pneumonia, diarrhea, measles, and malaria.

According to the United Nations Children's Fund (UNICEF), one-half to two-thirds of childhood deaths from nutrition-related causes could be prevented at an average annual cost of only $5–10 per child, or only 10–19¢ per week. This life-saving program would involve the following measures:

- Immunizing children against childhood diseases such as measles
- Encouraging breast-feeding (except for mothers with AIDS)
- Preventing dehydration from diarrhea by giving infants a mixture of sugar and salt in a glass of water
- Preventing blindness by giving people a vitamin A capsule twice a year at a cost of about 75¢ per person or fortifying common foods with vitamin A and other micronutrients at a cost of about 10¢ per person annually

- Providing family planning services to help mothers space births at least 2 years apart
- Increasing education for women, with emphasis on nutrition, drinking water sterilization, and child care

### Critical Thinking

How much money (if any) would you be willing to spend each year to help implement such a program for saving children? Why has insufficient money been allocated for such a program?

---

the prices of food in the United States are $150–200 billion per year.

According to Norman Myers (Guest Essay, p. 108), the future ability to produce more food will be limited by a combination of (1) soil erosion (Figure 10-19, p. 218), (2) desertification (Figure 10-20, p. 220), (3) salinization and waterlogging of irrigated lands (Figure 10-22, p. 221), (4) water deficits and droughts, (5) loss of wild species that provide the genetic resources for improved forms of foods, and (6) the effects of global warming (Figure 13-14).

According to a 2000 study by the UN-affiliated International Food Policy Research Institute, nearly 40% of the world's cropland is seriously degraded (including 75% in Central America, 20% in Africa, and 11% in Asia). Other studies indicate that 10–20% of the world's cropland suffers from degradation, with 7–14% seriously degraded (25% in developing countries). Such environmental factors may limit food production in India and China (Case Study, p. 293), the world's two most populous countries.

| Advantages | | Disadvantages |
|---|---|---|
| Increased crop yields in some areas |  | Lower crop yields in some areas |
| Increased precipitation in some dry areas | | Decreased precipitation is some areas |
| Longer growing seasons in currently cool areas | | Shorter growing seasons in some areas |
| Less precipitation in some areas with too much precipitation | | More unpredictable farming conditions |
| Increased yields of warm-water fish | | Increased pest populations in warmer areas |
| Expanded growing area | | Loss of wetlands and fertile coastal land from rising sea levels |
| | | Changes in distribution of fish supplies |

**Figure 13-14** Some affects of projected global warming on growing crops and catching fish.

## 13-4 INCREASING WORLD CROP PRODUCTION

**How Can Crossbreeding Be Used to Develop Genetically Improved Crop Strains?** For centuries, farmers and scientists have used traditional methods of *crossbreeding* through artificial selection to develop genetically improved varieties of crop strains and livestock (Spotlight, p. 100). For example, two crop plants such as a variety of a pear and of an apple can be crossbred with the goal of producing a pear with a more reddish color (Figure 13-15, p. 290). This is repeated for a number of generations until the desired trait in the pear predominates.

Agricultural experts expect most future increases in food yields per hectare on existing cropland to result from improved crossbred strains of plants and from expansion of green revolution technology to new parts of the world.

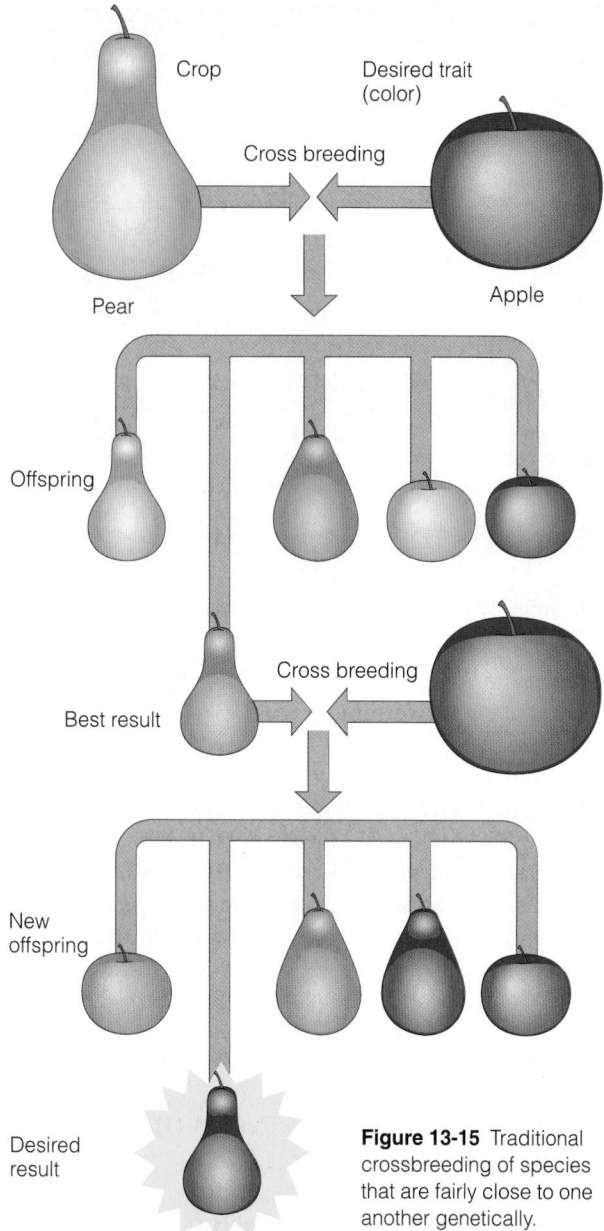

Crop

Desired trait
(color)

Cross breeding

Pear

Apple

Offspring

Best result

Cross breeding

New
offspring

Desired
result

**Figure 13-15** Traditional crossbreeding of species that are fairly close to one another genetically.

However, traditional crossbreeding **(1)** is a slow process, typically taking 15 years or more to produce a commercially valuable new variety, **(2)** can combine traits only from species that are close to one another genetically, and **(3)** provides varieties that are useful for only about 5–10 years before pests and diseases reduce their effectiveness.

**Is Genetic Engineering the Answer?** Scientists are working to create new green revolutions—actually *gene revolutions*—by using genetic engineering and other forms of biotechnology to develop new genetically improved strains of crops. **Genetic engineering,** or **gene splicing,** of food crops is the insertion of an alien gene into a commercially valuable plant (or animal) to give it new beneficial genetic

traits. Such organisms are called **genetically modified organisms (GMOs).**

In comparison to traditional crossbreeding (Figure 13-15), gene splicing **(1)** takes about half as much time to develop a new crop or animal variety, **(2)** cuts costs, and **(3)** allows the insertion of genes from almost any other organism into crop or animal cells. Figure 13-16 outlines the steps involved in developing a genetically modified or transgenic plant.

Scientists are also using the following techniques:

- *Advanced tissue culture techniques* to produce only the desired parts of a plant such as its oils or fruits.

- *Transgenomics* in which an artificially created DNA sequence is introduced into a plant's DNA to stimulate a mutation that activates genes that provide the desired trait. If successful, **(1)** scientists will be able to speed up the rate of beneficial mutations that is a major driving force in biological evolution (p. 100), and **(2)** sidestep some of the current critics of biotechnology.

Ready or not, the world is entering the *age of genetic engineering.* Nearly two-thirds of the food products on U.S. supermarket shelves contain genetically engineered crops, and the proportion is increasing rapidly. The United States, Canada, and Argentina contain about 98% of the world's land currently planted with genetically engineered crops.

Controversy is growing over the use of *genetically modified food* (GMF). Such food is seen as a potentially sustainable way to solve world food problems by its producers and investors and called potentially dangerous "Frankenfood" by its critics. Figure 13-17 (p. 292) summarizes the pros and cons of this new technology.

Critics recognize the potential benefits of genetically modified crops but say **(1)** we know far too little about the potential harm from widespread use of such crops to human health and ecosystems, and **(2)** genetically modified organisms cannot be recalled if they cause harmful genetic and ecological effects. They call for **(1)** more controlled field experiments, **(2)** more research and long-term safety testing to better understand the risks, **(3)** stricter regulation of this technology, and **(4)** mandatory labeling of such foods to provide consumers with a choice (now required in Japan, Europe, South Korea, Canada, Australia, and New Zealand and favored by 81% of Americans polled in 1999). Industry representatives oppose this because **(1)** they claim the foods are not substantially different from conventional foods and **(2)** labeling such foods would hurt sales by arousing unwarranted suspicion.

According to a 2002 study by the U.S. National Academy of Sciences,

- There is no strong evidence suggesting that genetically engineered crops cause environmental harm.

- This lack of evidence does not necessarily mean that these crops do not cause environmental damage

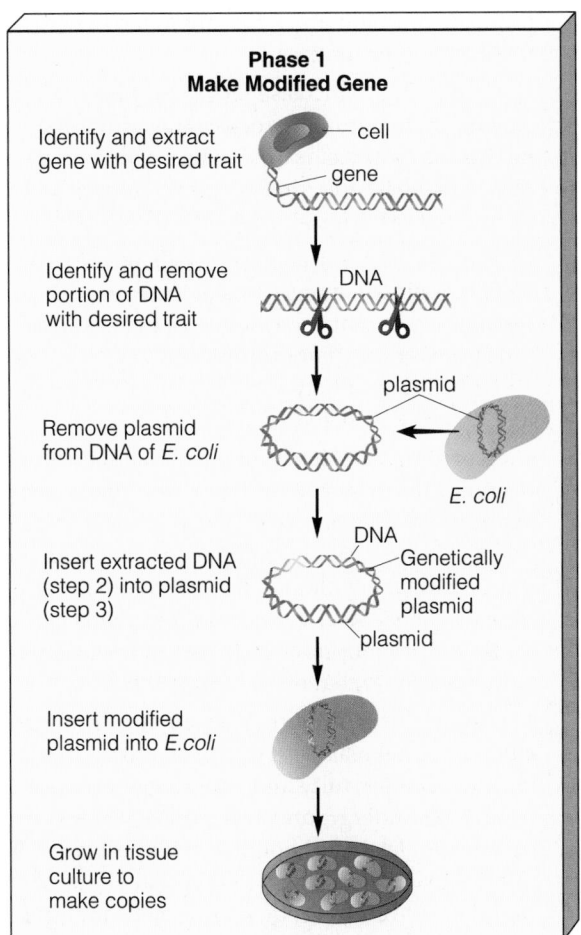

**Phase 1
Make Modified Gene**

Identify and extract gene with desired trait

cell

gene

Identify and remove portion of DNA with desired trait

DNA

Remove plasmid from DNA of *E. coli*

plasmid

*E. coli*

Insert extracted DNA (step 2) into plasmid (step 3)

DNA

Genetically modified plasmid

plasmid

Insert modified plasmid into *E.coli*

Grow in tissue culture to make copies

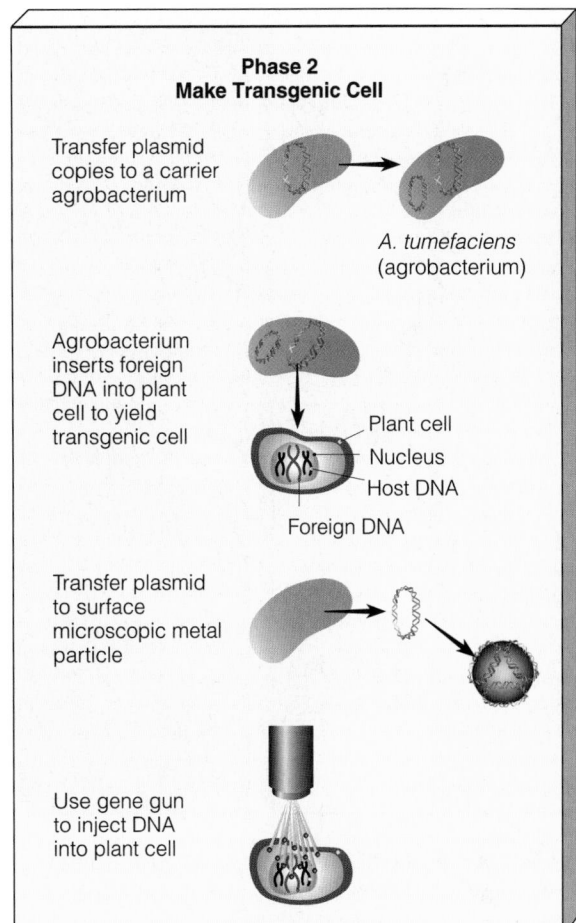

**Phase 2
Make Transgenic Cell**

Transfer plasmid copies to a carrier agrobacterium

*A. tumefaciens* (agrobacterium)

Agrobacterium inserts foreign DNA into plant cell to yield transgenic cell

Plant cell

Nucleus

Host DNA

Foreign DNA

Transfer plasmid to surface microscopic metal particle

Use gene gun to inject DNA into plant cell

because the United States does not have in place a system for systematic monitoring of agricultural and natural ecosystems.

There is also concern about the future use of genetic engineering to

■ Use bioengineered pathogens to devastate a country's crops during warfare or as an act of terrorism. For example, the United States has developed a bioengineered pathogen to kill coca plants (used to produce cocaine) in Colombia in South America.

■ Develop crop seed varieties that contain *terminator genes*. Such genes would prevent the seeds from a crop planted one year from reproducing in subsequent years unless the gene is unlocked by applying certain chemicals or antibiotics sold by the seed company. Thus terminator gene technology provides a seed company with control over any farmer who adopts it.

In 2001, member states of the FAO adopted an international treaty that affirms the right of farmers to **(1)** save, use, exchange, and sell farm-saved seed for 64 crops and **(2)** limits the genetic materials of plants biotechnology companies can patent in countries that ratify the treaty.

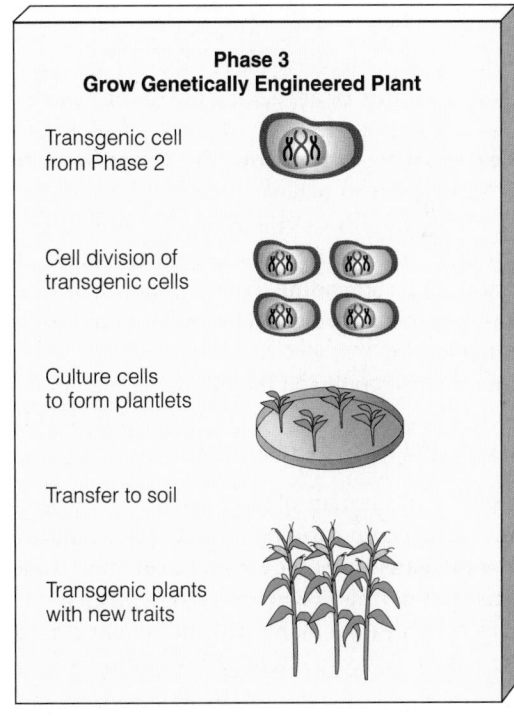

**Phase 3
Grow Genetically Engineered Plant**

Transgenic cell from Phase 2

Cell division of transgenic cells

Culture cells to form plantlets

Transfer to soil

Transgenic plants with new traits

**Figure 13-16** Steps in genetically modifying a plant.

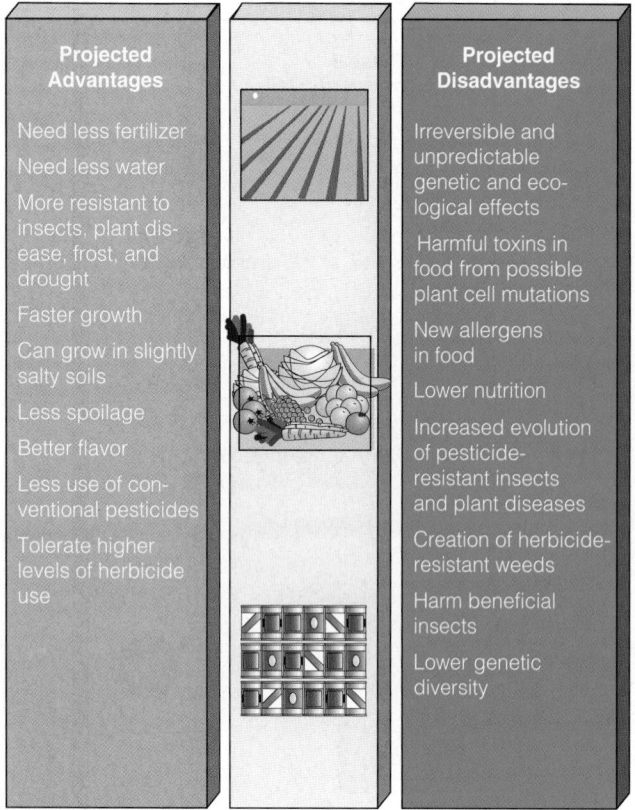

| Projected Advantages | Projected Disadvantages |
|---|---|
| Need less fertilizer | Irreversible and unpredictable genetic and ecological effects |
| Need less water | |
| More resistant to insects, plant disease, frost, and drought | Harmful toxins in food from possible plant cell mutations |
| Faster growth | New allergens in food |
| Can grow in slightly salty soils | Lower nutrition |
| Less spoilage | Increased evolution of pesticide-resistant insects and plant diseases |
| Better flavor | |
| Less use of conventional pesticides | Creation of herbicide-resistant weeds |
| Tolerate higher levels of herbicide use | Harm beneficial insects |
| | Lower genetic diversity |

**Figure 13-17** Projected advantages and disadvantages of genetically modified crops and foods.

Growing numbers of food manufacturers and retailers, first in Europe and now in the United States, have stopped selling GMFs. As a result, some major food biotech companies have made biotech crop operations a lower priority or are getting out of the business.

**Can We Continue Expanding the Green Revolution?** Many analysts believe it is possible to produce enough food to feed the 9.3 billion people projected by 2050 through **(1)** new advances in gene-splicing technology and **(2)** by spreading the use of new and existing high-yield green revolution techniques throughout most of the world.

Other analysts point to the following factors that have limited the success of the green and gene revolutions to date and may continue to do so:

- Without huge amounts of fertilizer and water, most green revolution crop varieties produce yields that are no higher (and are sometimes lower) than those from traditional strains; this is why the second green revolution has not spread to many arid and semiarid areas such as much of Africa and Australia (Figure 13-6).

- Green revolution and genetically engineered crop strains and their needed inputs of water, fertilizer, and pesticides cost too much for most subsistence farmers in developing countries.

- Continuing to increase fertilizer, water, and pesticide inputs eventually produces no additional increase in crop yields but we do not know when these biological and physiological limits on yields will be reached in various parts of the world.

- The *good news* is that grain yields per hectare are still increasing in many parts of the world. The *disturbing news* is that such yields are increasing at a much slower rate. For example, grain yields rose about 2.1% a year between 1950 and 1990 but dropped to 1.1% per year between 1990 and 2000.

- According to Indian economist Vandana Shiva, overall gains in crop yields from new green and gene revolution varieties may be much lower than claimed. The yields are based on comparisons between the output per hectare of old and new *monoculture* varieties rather than between the even higher yields per hectare for *polyculture* cropping systems and the new monoculture varieties that often replace them.

- Crop yields may start dropping for a number of environmental reasons: **(1)** the soil erodes, loses fertility, and becomes salty and waterlogged (Figure 10-22, p. 221), **(2)** underground and surface water supplies become depleted and polluted with pesticides and nitrates from fertilizers, and **(3)** populations of rapidly breeding pests develop genetic immunity to widely used pesticides. We do not know how close we are to such environmental limits in various parts of the world.

- Increased loss of biodiversity can limit the genetic raw material needed for future green and gene revolutions (Spotlight, p. 295).

**Will People Try New Foods?** Some analysts recommend greatly increased cultivation of less widely known plants to supplement or replace such staples as wheat, rice, and corn. One of many possibilities is the *winged bean,* a protein-rich legume now common only in New Guinea and Southeast Asia. This fast-growing plant produces so many different edible parts that it has been called a supermarket on a stalk. It also needs little fertilizer because of nitrogen-fixing nodules in its roots.

Insects—called *microlivestock*—are also important potential sources of protein, vitamins, and minerals in many parts of the world. There are about 1,500 edible insect species. Some are important food items in many parts of the world. Examples include **(1)** black ant larvae (served in tacos in Mexico), **(2)** giant waterbugs (crushed into vegetable dip in Thailand), **(3)** *Mopani,* or emperor moth caterpillars (eaten in South Africa), **(4)** cockroaches (eaten by Kalahari desert dwellers), **(5)** lightly toasted butterflies (a favorite food in Bali),

## Can China's Population Be Fed?

Since 1970, China has made significant progress in feeding its people and slowing its rate of population growth (p. 273). Despite such efforts, China is projected to add about 275 million people between 2000 and 2030—about as many people as live in the United States today.

There is concern that crop yields may not be able to keep up with demand. A basic problem is that with 21% of the world's people, China has only (1) 7% of the world's cropland and fresh water, (2) 4% of its forests, and (3) 2% of its oil.

China depends on irrigated land to produce 70% of the grain for its population. According to projections by the Worldwatch Institute and the U.S. Central Intelligence Agency, China's grain production could fall by at least 20% between 1990 and 2030, mostly because of (1) water shortages, (2) degraded cropland, and (3) diversion of water from cropland to cities.

A growing amount of China's cropland is irrigated by withdrawing groundwater from aquifers faster than they are naturally recharged. An example is the heavily irrigated North China Plain, which produces over half of China's wheat and a third of its corn. According to a 2001 study by the Geological Environmental Monitoring Institute in Beijing, the water table under this plain is falling faster than thought.

As such groundwater deficits worsen, China's options are to (1) take land out of irrigation, (2) switch to less thirsty crops, (3) irrigate more efficiently, (4) divert water in rivers from the south to the north, and (5) import more grain.

As incomes in China have risen, so has meat consumption. The Chinese now equal Americans in consumption of pork and are now concentrating on increasing beef production.

Even if China's currently booming economy resulted in no increases in meat consumption, the 20% projected drop in grain production would mean that by 2030 China would need to import more than all of the world's current grain exports (roughly half from the United States).

However, if the increased demand for meat led to a rise in per capita grain consumption equal to the current level in Taiwan (one-half the current U.S. level), China would need to import more than the entire current grain output of the United States .

As pressures on grazing land increased, Japan began getting most of its animal protein from the ocean. If China—with 10 times more people—did this, its annual seafood consumption would be equal to the entire world fish catch.

The Worldwatch Institute and the U.S. Central Intelligence Agency warn that if either of these scenarios is correct, no country or combination of countries has the potential to

supply even a small fraction of China's potential food supply deficit. This does not take into account the huge grain deficits that are projected in other parts of the world by 2030, especially in Africa and India.

However, other analysts disagree with this assessment. For example,

- According to a 1997 study by the International Food Policy Institute, China should be able to feed its population and begin exporting grain again by 2020 if the government invests in (1) expanding irrigation, (2) using more water-efficient forms of irrigation, and (3) increasing agricultural research.

- Recent satellite surveys show that China has about 40% more potential cropland than previously thought.

- The World Bank concluded in 1997 that China's domestic food production should keep up with its population growth for the next two or three decades without having to import large amounts of grain.

### Critical Thinking

If the scenarios about China's future dependence on greatly increased food imports are accurate, how might this affect (a) world food prices and (b) your life? What actions, if any, do you suggest for dealing with this potential problem?

and (6) fried ants (sold on the streets of Bogota, Colombia). Most of these insects are 58–78% protein by weight—three to four times as protein rich as beef, fish, or eggs. Two problems are (1) getting farmers to take the financial risk of cultivating new types of food crops and (2) convincing consumers to try new foods.

Some plant scientists believe we should rely more on polycultures of perennial crops, which are better adapted to regional soil and climate conditions than most annual crops (p. 277). Using perennials would also (1) eliminate the need to till soil and replant seeds

each year, (2) greatly reduce energy use, (3) save water, and (4) reduce soil erosion and water pollution from eroded sediment. However, large seed companies that make their money selling farmers seeds each year for annual crops generally oppose this idea.

**Is Irrigating More Land the Answer?** About 40% of the world's food production comes from the 18% of the world's cropland that is irrigated. Irrigated land produces about 70% of the grain harvest in China, 50% in India, and 15% in the United States.

Some *good news* is that between 1950 and 2002, the world's irrigated area tripled, with most of the growth occurring from 1950 to 1978. Some *bad news* is that since 1978, the amount of irrigated land per person has been falling and is projected to fall much more between 2000 and 2050 (Figure 13-18). Reasons for this downward trend include the following:

- World population has grown faster than irrigated agriculture since 1978.

- Water is being pumped more rapidly than it is replaced from aquifers in many of the world's food-growing areas.

- Irrigation water is used inefficiently.

- Crop productivity is decreased by soil salinization (Figure 10-23, p. 222) on irrigated cropland.

- Increasing urbanization puts city dwellers and farmers in competition for limited water supplies.

- Global warming may disrupt water supplies in some food-growing areas.

- The majority of the world's farmers do not have enough money to irrigate their crops. Thus rainfall is the source of water for 83% of the world's cropland.

Key methods for using water more sustainably in crop production are **(1)** increasing irrigation efficiency, **(2)** shifting to crops that need less water (for example, depending less on water-thirsty rice and sugarcane and more on wheat and sorghum), and **(3)** withdrawing water from aquifers no faster than they are replenished.

**Figure 13-18** World irrigated area of cropland per person, 1900–2001, with projections to 2050. (Data from United Nations Food and Agriculture Organization, U.S. Census Bureau, and the Worldwatch Institute)

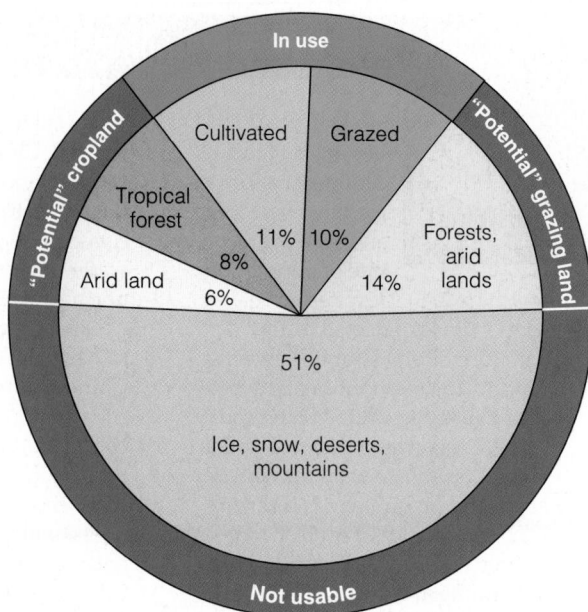

**Figure 13-19** Classification of the earth's land. Theoretically, we could double the amount of cropland by clearing tropical forests and irrigating arid lands. However, converting these lands into cropland would **(1)** destroy valuable forest resources, **(2)** reduce the earth's biodiversity, **(3)** affect water quality and quantity, and **(4)** cause other serious environmental problems, usually without being cost effective.

**Is Cultivating More Land the Answer?**
Theoretically, the world's cropland could be more than doubled by clearing tropical forests and irrigating arid land (Figure 13-19). But much of this is *marginal land* with poor soil fertility, steep slopes, or both. Cultivation of such land is unlikely to be sustainable.

Most of the land cleared in tropical rain forests has nutrient-poor soils (Figure 10-15, lower left, p. 215) and cannot support crop growth for more than a couple of years. In addition, potential cropland in savanna and other semiarid land in Africa cannot be used for farming or livestock grazing. The reason is the presence of 22 species of the tsetse fly, which transmits a protozoan parasite that causes incurable sleeping sickness in humans and a fatal disease in livestock.

Some researchers hope to develop new methods of intensive cultivation in tropical areas. Other scientists argue that it makes more ecological and economic sense to combine ancient methods of shifting cultivation (Figure 2-2, p. 23) with various forms of polyculture.

Much of the world's potentially cultivable land lies in dry areas, especially in Australia and Africa. Large-scale irrigation in these areas would **(1)** require large, expensive dam projects with a mixture of beneficial and harmful impacts, **(2)** use large inputs of fossil fuel to pump water long distances, **(3)** deplete ground-water supplies by removing water faster than it is replenished, and **(4)** require expensive efforts to prevent erosion, groundwater contamination, salinization, and waterlogging, all of which reduce crop productivity.

Thus much of the world's new cropland that could be developed would be on land that is marginal for raising crops and requires expensive inputs of fertilizer, water, and energy. Furthermore, these potential increases in cropland would not offset the projected loss of almost one-third of today's cultivated cropland caused by erosion, overgrazing, waterlogging, salinization, and urbanization.

Such expansion in cropland would also reduce wildlife habitats and thus the world's biodiversity. According to the FAO, cultivating all potential cropland in developing countries would reduce forests, woodlands, and permanent pasture by 47%. Clearing these forests would also release a huge amount of carbon dioxide into the atmosphere and accelerate global warming, which is expected to cause shifts in the areas where crops could be grown.

Thus *many analysts believe that significant expansion of cropland is unlikely over the next few decades.* For example, the International Food Policy Institute and FAO estimate that 80% of projected increase in food production between 1993 and 2020 will come from increased yields per hectare and only 20% from expansion of cropland, If such assessments are correct, the world's grainland area per person, which dropped by half between 1950 and 1998 (because population growth grew seven times faster than expansion of grainland), is expected to decline further (Figure 13-20).

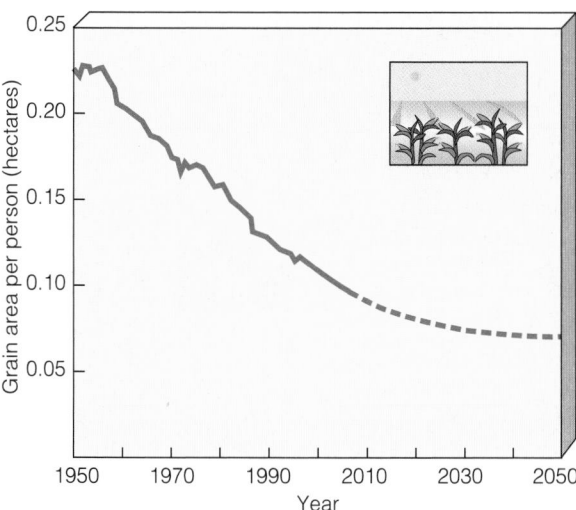

**Figure 13-20** Average grain area per person worldwide, 1950–2001, with projections to 2030. (Data from U.S. Department of Agriculture and Worldwatch Institute)

# Shrinking the World's Genetic Plant Library

**SPOTLIGHT**

The UN Food and Agriculture Organization estimates that by 2000, two-thirds of all seeds planted in developing countries were of uniform strains. Such genetic uniformity increases the vulnerability of food crops to pests, diseases, and harsh weather. Many biologists argue that this decreased variability, plus growing extinction rates of plant species, can limit the genetic raw material available to support future green and gene revolutions.

For example, in the mid-1970s, a valuable wild corn species, the only known perennial strain of corn, was barely saved from extinction. Cross-breeding this perennial strain with commercial varieties could reduce the need for yearly plowing and sowing, which would reduce soil erosion and save water and energy. Even more important, this wild corn **(1)** has a built-in genetic resistance to four of the eight major corn viruses and **(2)** grows better in cooler and damper habitats than established commercial strains. Overall, the economic benefits of cultivating this wild plant could total several billion dollars per year.

Wild varieties of the world's most important plants can be collected and stored in **(1)** gene or seed banks, **(2)** agricultural research centers, and **(3)** botanical gardens. However, space and money severely limit the number of species that can be preserved.

Other limitations include **(1)** inability to successfully store seeds of many plants (such as potatoes), **(2)** irreversible loss of stored seeds because of power failures, fires, or unintentional disposal, **(3)** death of stored seeds unless they are periodically planted (germinated) and then stored again, and **(4)** difficulty in reintroducing stored plants and seeds into changed habitats because they do not evolve during storage.

Because of these limitations, ecologists and plant scientists warn that the only effective way to preserve the genetic diversity of most plant and animal species is to protect representative ecosystems throughout the world from agriculture and other forms of development.

## Critical Thinking

What are the major advantages and disadvantages of relying on a shrinking number of crop varieties? Why do seed companies favor this approach?

To some analysts this drop in grainland area per person is not particularly harmful because it reduces the pressure on the earth's biodiversity by increasing yields per hectare. But environmentalists warn that this is true only if there is a decrease in the harmful environmental effects associated with modern industrialized agriculture (Figure 13-13).

**Can We Grow More Food in Urban Areas?** Food experts believe that people in urban areas could live more sustainably and save money by growing food in empty lots, on rooftops and balconies, and in their own backyards and by raising fish in tanks and sewage lagoons. Currently, about 800 million urban gardens provide about 15% of the world's food.

More food could be grown in urban areas. A study by the UN Center for Human Settlements estimated that up to 50% of the total area in many cities in developing countries is vacant public land that could be used to produce food.

## 13-5   PRODUCING MORE MEAT

**What Are Rangeland and Pasture?** About 40% of the earth's ice-free land is **rangeland** that is too dry, too steeply sloped, or too infertile to grow crops. This type of land supplies forage or vegetation for grazing (grass-eating) and browsing (shrub-eating) animals.

About 3.3 billion cattle, sheep, and goats graze on about 42% of the world's rangeland (Figure 13-21). Much of the rest is too dry, cold, or remote from population centers to support large numbers of livestock. About 29% of the total U.S. land area is rangeland, most of it short-grass prairie in the arid and semiarid western half of the country (Figure 13-8). Livestock also graze in **pastures:** managed grasslands or enclosed meadows usually planted with domesticated grasses or other forage (Figure 13-8).

Livestock can be raised **(1)** on *open ranges* where rainfall is low but fairly regular and **(2)** by *nomadic herding* where rainfall is sparse and irregular and herders must move livestock to find ample grass and prevent overgrazing (Figure 13-21).

**What Is the Ecology of Rangeland Plants?** Most rangeland grasses have deep and complex root systems (Figure 10-15, top right, p. 215) that **(1)** help anchor the plants, **(2)** extract underground water so plants can withstand drought, and **(3)** store nutrients so plants can grow again after a drought or fire.

Blades of rangeland grass grow from the base, not the tip. Thus, as long as only its upper half—called its *metabolic reserve*—is eaten and its lower half remains, rangeland grass is a renewable resource that can be grazed again and again (Figure 13-22, top). The exposed metabolic reserve of a grass plant is where photosynthesis takes place to provide food for the deep

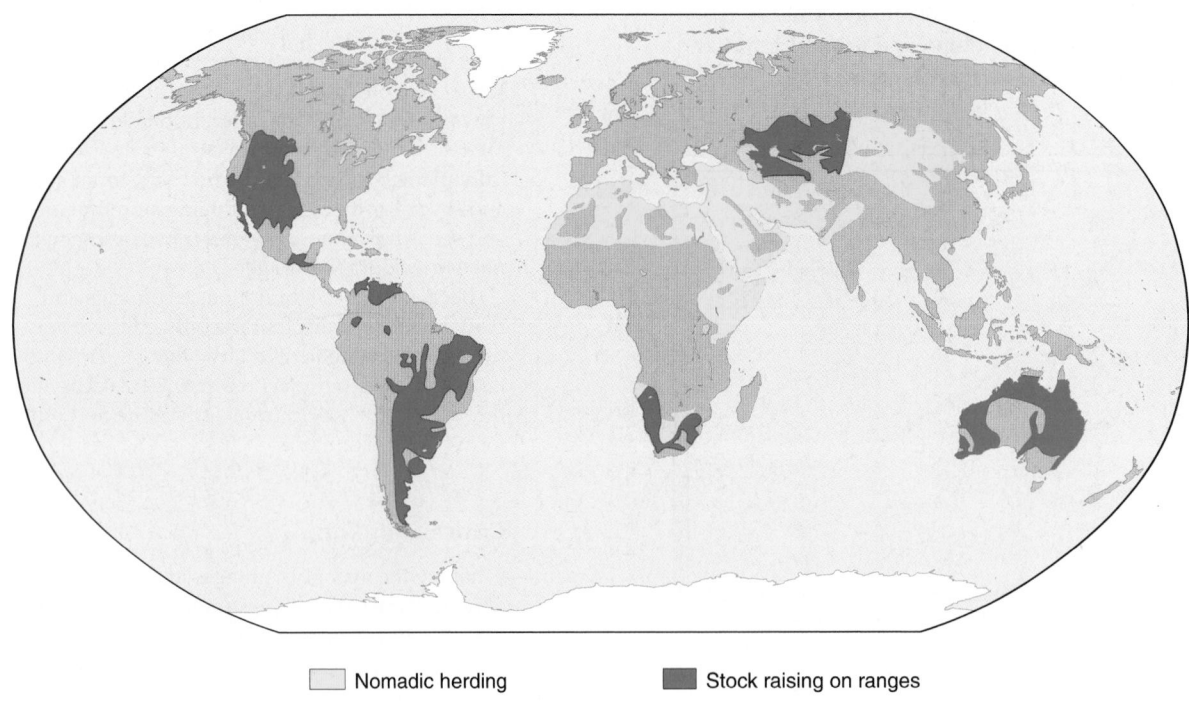

☐ Nomadic herding      ■ Stock raising on ranges

**Figure 13-21** Arid and semiarid regions of the world in which livestock (mostly cattle, sheep, and goats) can be raised **(1)** on open ranges where rainfall is low but fairly regular and **(2)** by nomadic herding where rainfall is so sparse and irregular that livestock must be moved to find adequate grass.

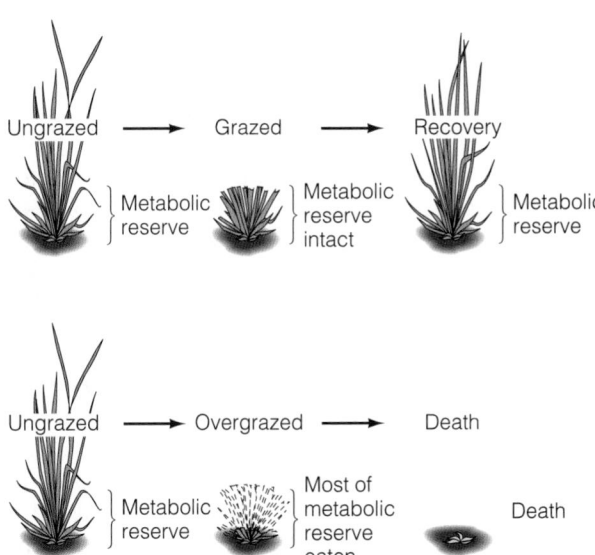

**Figure 13-22** Rangeland grasses grow from the bottom up and are renewable as long as the bottom half of the plant (metabolic reserve), where photosynthesis takes place, is not eaten (top). If the metabolic reserve is eaten, the plant is weakened and can die (bottom). (From Chiras, *Environmental Science*, 5th ed., p. 208. Copyright © 1998 by Wadsworth)

roots of rangeland grasses. If all or most of the lower half (metabolic reserve) of the plant is eaten, the plant is weakened and can die (Figure 13-22, bottom).

Rangeland plants vary in their ability to recover from stresses such as fire, drought, and excessive grazing (Figure 13-23). When native plant species disappear from a rangeland, weedy invader plants move in and gradually decrease the nutritional value of the available forage (Figure 13-23, bottom).

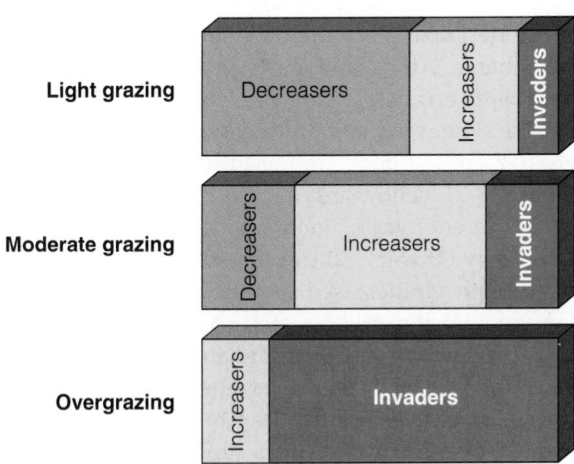

**Figure 13-23** Effects of various degrees of grazing on the relative amounts of three major types of grassland plants: **(1)** *decreasers* that decline in abundance with moderate grazing, **(2)** *increasers* that increase with moderate to heavy grazing pressure, and **(3)** *invaders* that colonize an area because of overgrazing or other changes in rangeland conditions. (From Chiras, *Environmental Science*, 5th ed., p. 208. Copyright © 1998 by Wadsworth)

**How Is Meat Produced, and What Are Its Environmental Consequences?** Between 1950 and 2000, world meat production increased nearly fivefold, and per capita meat production more than doubled. Globally, animal products provide about 15% of the energy and 30% of the protein in the human diet. According to Worldwatch Institute estimates, the world's meat production is likely to more than double between 2000 and 2050 as affluence rises in middle-income developing countries and people begin consuming more meat.

About 80% of the world's cattle, sheep, and goats are raised on rangeland by open grazing or nomadic herding (Figure 13-21). These animals are **ruminants,** which have complex digestive systems that enable them to convert grass and other roughage into beef, mutton, and milk. These ruminants also supply us with leather and wool. Worldwide, about 180 million people try to make a living as *pastoralists* who tend cattle, sheep, and goats grazing on rangeland.

Some analysts expect most future increases in meat production to come from densely populated *feedlots*, where animals are fattened for slaughter by feeding on grain grown on cropland or meal produced from fish. Feedlots account for about 40% of the world's meat production and more than half of the world's poultry and pork. In the United States, most production of cattle, pigs, and poultry is concentrated in increasingly large, factorylike production facilities in only a few states (Figure 13-24, p. 298).

Most of the world's beef and mutton is still produced on rangeland, however. Even in the United States, which has most of the world's beef feedlots, a typical steer is fed in a feedlot only for a few months before being slaughtered.

This industrialized approach increases meat productivity. However, it also

- Concentrates pollution problems such as **(1)** foul odors, **(2)** water pollution when lagoons storing animal wastes collapse or are flooded, and **(3)** contamination of drinking water wells by nitrates from animal wastes.

- Increases pressure on the world's **(1)** grain supply because feedlot livestock consume grain produced on cropland instead of feeding on natural grasses and **(2)** fish supply because fish are diverted to feed livestock instead of being consumed directly by people.

- Requires increased inputs of fossil fuel (Figure 13-4).

- Increases the spread of infectious livestock diseases such as **(1)** *mad cow disease,* which since 1985 has infected cows in 12 European nations and killed more than 80 people in Great Britain and several people in France and Ireland, and **(2)** *highly infectious hoof-and-mouth disease,* which since 2000 has infected large numbers of cattle, pigs, and sheep in Europe and Brazil.

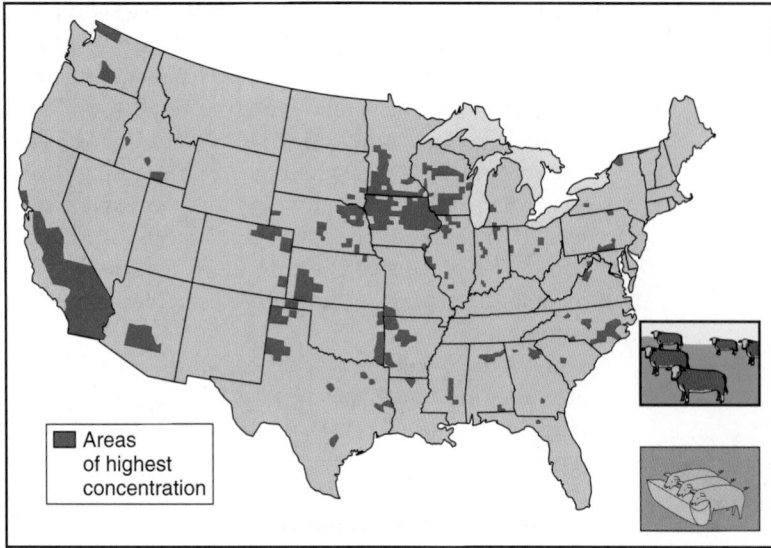

**Figure 13-24** Large-scale, factorylike production of livestock—mostly cattle, pigs, and poultry—in the United States and the resulting pollution problems are concentrated mostly in a few states. (Data from the U.S. Department of Agriculture)

Livestock and fish vary widely in the efficiency with which they convert grain into animal protein (Figure 13-25). A more sustainable form of agriculture would involve shifting from less grain-efficient forms of animal protein, such as beef or pork, to more grain-efficient ones, such as poultry or farmed fish (Figure 13-25). Livestock production also has an enormous environmental impact (Connections, p. 299).

**How Can We Raise Meat Production by Recycling Crop Residues?** One way to increase yields of meat and milk without consuming more grain is to feed livestock ruminants crop residues such as wheat straw, rice straw, and corn stalks. Such roughage-based livestock feeding programs work only at the

**Kilograms of grain needed per kilogram of body weight**

**Figure 13-25** Efficiency of converting grain into animal protein. Data in kilograms of grain per kilogram of body weight added. (Data from U.S. Department of Agriculture)

local level because roughage is too bulky and expensive to transport long distances.

This productive way to use crop residues is being employed in China and India to increase meat and milk productivity and reduce pressure on rangelands. However, some ecologists argue that it makes more sense to allow such residues to decompose naturally to increase soil fertility.

**What Are the Effects of Overgrazing and Undergrazing?** Overgrazing can also limit livestock production. **Overgrazing** occurs when too many animals graze for too long and exceed the carrying capacity of a grassland area. Excessive numbers of domestic livestock feeding for too long in a particular area causes most overgrazing.

Such overgrazing **(1)** lowers the net primary productivity of grassland vegetation (Figure 4-25, p. 81), **(2)** reduces grass cover and exposes the soil to erosion by water and wind (Figure 13-26), **(3)** compacts the soil (which diminishes its capacity to hold water), **(4)** enhances invasion of exposed land by woody shrubs such as mesquite and prickly pear cactus (Figure 13-23, bottom), and **(5)** is a major cause of desertification (Figure 10-20, p. 220).

Some grassland can suffer from **undergrazing,** where absence of grazing for long periods (at least 5 years) can reduce the net primary productivity of grassland vegetation and grass cover. Moderate grazing of such areas removes accumulation of standing dead material and stimulates new biomass production.

Undergrazing is more likely in *arid* areas (such as sub-Saharan Africa and parts of the Mediterranean area) with erratic rainfall and wide, largely unpredictable swings in plant productivity. These are mostly areas where livestock are raised by nomadic herding (Figure 13-21, yellow areas).

In recent years, nomadic herding has been reduced by **(1)** wars, **(2)** travel restrictions, **(3)** population growth, **(4)** increased crop growing and urbanization, and **(5)** the drilling of fairly inexpensive tube-wells (narrow wells drilled into an aquifer to provide water for livestock). However, the resulting reduced movement of livestock can lead to loss of grass cover through overgrazing in areas around the wells and through undergrazing in other areas.

**What Is the Condition of the World's Range-lands?** *Range condition* usually is classified as **(1)** *excellent* (containing more than 75% of its potential forage production), **(2)** *good* (51–75%), **(3)** *fair* (26–50%),

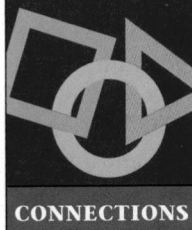

# Some Environmental Consequences of Meat Production

**CONNECTIONS**

The meat-based diet of affluent people in developed and developing countries has the following environmental effects:

- More than half of the world's cropland (19% in the United States) is used to produce livestock feed grain (mostly field corn, sorghum, and soybeans).

- Livestock and fish raised for food consume about 36% of the world's grain. This includes 65% of grain production in the United States compared to 25% in China and 4% in India.

- Livestock use more than half the water withdrawn from rivers and aquifers each year, mostly to **(1)** irrigate crops fed to livestock and **(2)** wash away manure from crowded livestock pens and feedlots.

- Manure washing off the land or leaking from lagoons used to store animal wastes is a significant source of water pollution that kills fish by depleting dissolved oxygen.

- About 14% of U.S. topsoil loss is directly associated with livestock grazing.

- Overgrazing of sparse vegetation and trampling of the soil by too many livestock is the major cause of desertification in arid and semiarid areas (Figure 10-20, p. 220).

- Cattle belch out about 16% of the methane (a greenhouse gas that is about 25 times more potent than carbon dioxide) released into the atmosphere.

- Some of the nitrogen in commercial inorganic fertilizer used to grow livestock feed is converted to nitrous oxide, a greenhouse gas released from the soil into the atmosphere.

- More than one-third of all raw materials and fossil fuels consumed in the United States are used in animal production.

- Livestock in the United States produce at least 20 times more waste (manure) than is produced by the country's human population. Only about half of this nutrient-rich livestock waste is recycled into the soil.

Some environmentalists have called for reducing livestock production (especially cattle) to decrease its environmental effects and to feed more people. This would decrease the environmental impact of livestock production, but it would not free up much land or grain to feed more of the world's hungry people.

Cattle and sheep that graze on rangeland use a resource (grass) that humans cannot eat, and most of this land is not suitable for growing crops. Moreover, because of poverty, insufficient economic aid, and the nature of global economic and food distribution systems, very little if any additional grain grown on land used to raise livestock or livestock feed would reach the world's hungry people.

### Critical Thinking

Would you be willing to eat less meat or not eat any meat? Explain.

USDA, Natural Resources Conservation Service

**Figure 13-26** Rangeland: overgrazed (left) and lightly grazed (right).

or **(4)** *poor* (0–25%). Limited data from surveys in various countries indicate that overgrazing by livestock has caused as much as 20% of the world's rangeland to lose productivity, mostly by desertification (Figure 10-20, p. 220).

Most of the rangeland in the United States is in the West (Figures 13-8 and 13-21). About 60% is privately owned and the rest is public land managed by the Bureau of Land Management (BLM) and the U.S. Forest Service. Only about 2% of the 120 million cattle and 10% of the 20 million sheep raised in the United States graze on public rangelands.

According to a 2000 survey by the Bureau of Land Management, about 64% of the nonarctic U.S. public rangeland it managed was in unsatisfactory (fair or poor) condition, compared with 84% in 1936. This represents a great improvement, but there is still a long way to go. Conservation biologists and some range experts also point out that surveys of U.S. rangeland condition neglect the damage that livestock inflict on vital riparian zones (Spotlight, p. 300, and Figure 13-27, top, p. 300).

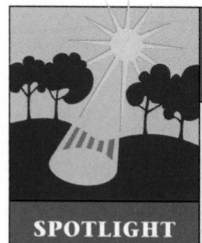

## Endangered Riparian Zones

**SPOTLIGHT**

According to some wildlife and rangeland experts, estimates of rangeland condition do not take into account severe damage to heavily grazed thin strips of lush vegetation along streams called **riparian zones.** Because cattle need lots of water, they **(1)** congregate near riparian zones, **(2)** feed there, and **(3)** trample and overgraze riparian vegetation (Figure 13-27, top).

These ecologically important zones **(1)** help prevent floods, **(2)** help keep streams from drying out during droughts by storing and releasing water slowly from spring runoff and summer storms, and **(3)** provide habitats, food, water, and shade for wildlife in the arid and semiarid western lands.

Studies indicate that 65–75% of the wildlife in the western United States totally depends on riparian habitats. According to a 1999 study in the *Journal of Soil and Water Conservation*, livestock grazing has damaged approximately 80% of stream and riparian ecosystems in the United States.

Riparian areas can be restored by **(1)** using fencing to restrict access to degraded areas and **(2)** developing off-stream watering sites for livestock (Figure 13-27, bottom). Sometimes protected areas can recover in a few years.

### Critical Thinking

Do you believe that riparian zones on public rangelands in the United States should receive stronger protection? Explain. If so, how would you see that such protection is provided?

**How Can Rangelands Be Managed Sustainably to Produce More Meat?** The primary goal of sustainable rangeland management is to maximize livestock productivity without overgrazing or undergrazing rangeland vegetation. *Rangeland management* methods include **(1)** controlling the number, types, and distribution of livestock grazing on land, **(2)** deferred grazing, and **(3)** rangeland restoration and improvement.

The most widely used method for sustainable rangeland management is controlling the number of grazing animals and the duration of their grazing in a given area so the carrying capacity of the area is not exceeded. However, determining the carrying capacity of a range site is difficult and costly. In addition, carrying capacity varies with factors such as **(1)** climatic conditions (especially drought), **(2)** past grazing use,

**(3)** soil type, **(4)** invasions by new species, **(5)** kinds of grazing animals, and **(6)** intensity of grazing.

Livestock tend to aggregate around natural water sources and stock ponds. As a result, areas around water sources tend to be overgrazed and other areas can be undergrazed. Managers can prevent this tendency and help promote more uniform use of rangeland by **(1)** fencing off damaged rangeland and riparian zones (Figure 13-27, bottom), **(2)** moving livestock from one grazing area to another, **(3)** providing supplemental feed at selected sites, and **(4)** situating water holes and tanks and salt blocks in strategic places.

One method used to help sustain rangeland grasses is *deferred grazing* (Figure 13-28). With this

**Figure 13-27** Cattle on a riparian zone of a public rangeland along Arizona's San Pedro River (top) in the mid-1980s just before this section of waterway was protected by banning domestic livestock grazing for 15 years, eliminating sand and gravel operations and water pumping rights in nearby areas, and limiting access by off-highway vehicles. The bottom photo shows the recovery of this riparian area at the same time of year after 10 years of protection.

| Pasture A | | | | | |
|-----------|-----------|-----------|-----------|-----------|-----------|
| First year | Second year | Third year | Fourth year | Fifth year | Sixth year |
| Deferred | Grazed last | Grazed second | Grazed first | Grazed first | Grazed second |

| Pasture B | | | | | |
|-----------|-----------|-----------|-----------|-----------|-----------|
| First year | Second year | Third year | Fourth year | Fifth year | Sixth year |
| Grazed first | Grazed second | Deferred | Grazed last | Grazed second | Grazed first |

| Pasture C | | | | | |
|-----------|-----------|-----------|-----------|-----------|-----------|
| First year | Second year | Third year | Fourth year | Fifth year | Sixth year |
| Grazed second | Grazed first | Grazed first | Grazed second | Deferred | Grazed last |

**Figure 13-28** Deferred grazing plan in which during a 6-year rotation cycle each fenced-in field gets nearly a 2-year rest from grazing. (From Chiras, *Environmental Science*, 5th ed., p. 210. Copyright © 1998 by Wadsworth)

approach, livestock are rotated on a regular schedule from one fenced area to another so over a 6-year period each area is protected from grazing for 2 years to allow recovery. However, protecting areas too long (more than 5 years) can lead to undergrazing.

A more expensive and less widely used method of rangeland management involves suppressing the growth of unwanted plants (mostly invaders, Figure 13-23, bottom) by herbicide spraying, mechanical removal, or controlled burning. A cheaper way to discourage unwanted vegetation is controlled, short-term trampling by large numbers of livestock.

Replanting barren areas with native grass seeds and applying fertilizer can increase growth of desirable vegetation and reduce soil erosion. Reseeding is an excellent way to restore severely degraded rangeland, but it is expensive.

## 13-6 CATCHING AND RAISING MORE FISH

**How Are Fish and Shellfish Harvested?** The world's third major food-producing system consists of **fisheries:** concentrations of particular aquatic species

suitable for commercial harvesting in a given ocean area or inland body of water. Some commercially important marine species of fish and shellfish are shown in Figure 13-29 (p. 302).

The world's commercial fishing industry is dominated by industrial fishing fleets using (1) satellite positioning equipment, (2) sonar, (3) huge nets, (4) spotter planes, and (5) factory ships that can process and freeze their catches. About 55% of the annual commercial catch of fish and shellfish comes from the ocean using harvesting methods shown in Figure 13-30 (p. 303). They include using

- *Trawler fishing* to catch demersal (mostly bottom dwelling) fish and shellfish (especially shrimp) by dragging a funnel-shaped net held open at the neck along the ocean bottom (Figure 13-30). This scrapes up almost everything that lies on it and often destroys bottom habitats (Figure 7-18, right, p. 156). Newer trawling nets are large enough to swallow 12 jumbo jets in a single gulp, and even larger ones are on the way. The large mesh of the net allows most small fish to escape but can capture and kill other species such as seals and endangered and threatened sea turtles. Only the large fish are kept, with most of the fish and

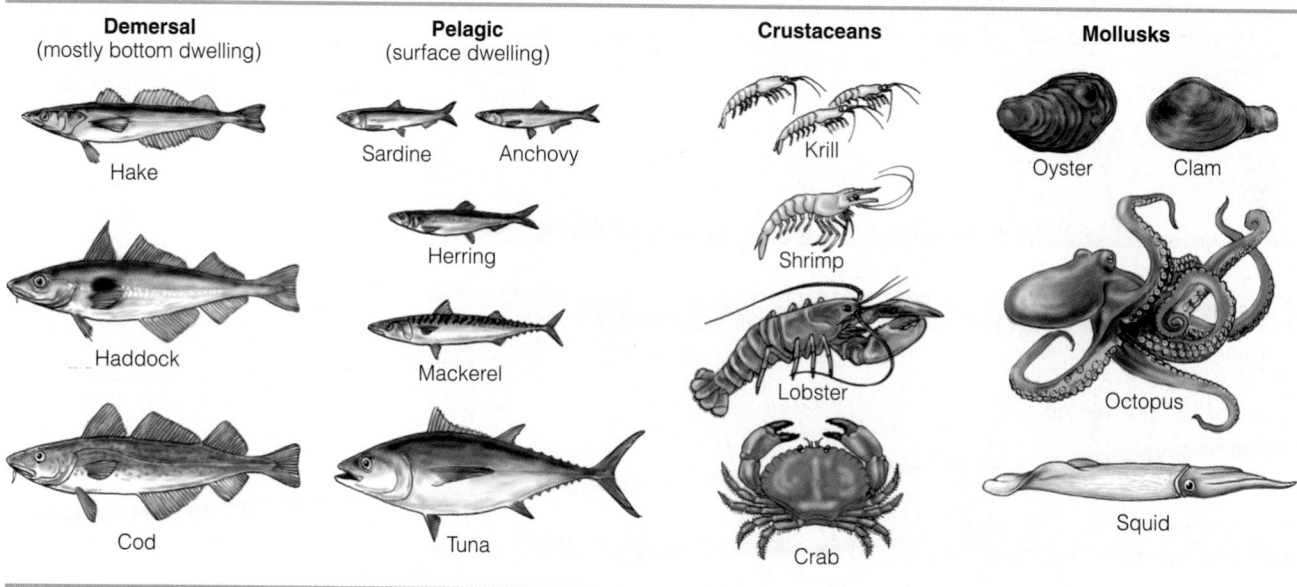

**Fish**

**Demersal**
(mostly bottom dwelling)

Hake

Haddock

Cod

**Pelagic**
(surface dwelling)

Sardine    Anchovy

Herring

Mackerel

Tuna

**Shellfish**

**Crustaceans**

Krill

Shrimp

Lobster

Crab

**Mollusks**

Oyster    Clam

Octopus

Squid

**Figure 13-29** Some major types of commercially harvested marine fish and shellfish.

other aquatic species (called *bycatch*) thrown back into the ocean dead or dying. For commercially valuable shrimp, the bycatch can be up to eight times the weight of the shrimp that are kept.

- *Purse-seine fishing* (Figure 13-30) to catch pelagic (surface dwelling) species such as tuna, which feed in schools near the surface or in shallow areas. Once located, a tuna school is surrounded by a large purse-seine net, which is closed like a drawstring purse to trap the fish. Nets used to capture yellowfin tuna in the eastern tropical Pacific Ocean have killed large numbers of dolphins, which swim on the surface above schools of the tuna.

- *Longlining* in which fishing vessels put out lines up to 130 kilometers (80 miles) long, hung with thousands of baited hooks (Figure 13-30), to catch open-ocean fish species such as swordfish, tuna, and sharks (Case Study, p. 176). Longlines also hook pilot whales, dolphins, endangered sea turtles, and sea-feeding albatross.

- *Drift-net fishing* in which fish are caught by huge drifting nets (Figure 13-30). Nets can hang as much as 15 meters (50 feet) below the surface and be up to 55 kilometers (34 miles) long. This method can **(1)** lead to overfishing of the desired species and **(2)** trap and kill large quantities of unwanted fish and marine mammals (such as dolphins, porpoises, and seals), marine turtles, and seabirds. Since 1992, a UN ban on the use of drift nets longer than 2.5 kilometers (1.6 miles) in international waters has sharply reduced this harvesting technique. But **(1)** compliance is voluntary, **(2)** it is

difficult to monitor fishing fleets over vast ocean areas, and **(3)** the decrease has led to increased use of longlines, which often have similar effects on marine wildlife.

About 55% of the annual commercial catch of fish and shellfish comes from the ocean. About 99% of this catch is taken from plankton-rich coastal waters, but this vital coastal zone is being disrupted and polluted (p. 155).

The rest of the annual catch comes from using **(1)** aquaculture to raise marine and freshwater fish in ponds and underwater cages (33%) and **(2)** from inland freshwater fishing from lakes, rivers, reservoirs, and ponds (12%). About one-third of the world fish harvest (mostly small pelagic species such as anchovy, herring, and menhaden) is used as animal feed, fish meal, and oils. Figure 13-31 shows the estimated fossil fuel energy needed for harvesting or raising various species of oceanic fish or shellfish.

**Can We Harvest More Fish and Shellfish?** The *good news* is that between 1950 and 1982, **(1)** the annual commercial fish catch (marine plus freshwater harvest) increased almost fivefold (Figure 13-32, left, p. 304), and **(2)** the per capita seafood catch more than doubled (Figure 13-32, right).

The *bad news* is that **(1)** the commercial fish catch has increased little since 1982 (Figure 13-32, left), **(2)** the per capita commercial fish catch has been falling since 1982 (Figure 13-32, right) and may continue to decline because of overfishing, pollution, habitat loss,

**Figure 13-30**
Major commercial fishing methods used to harvest various marine species.

Spotter airplane

Fish farming in cage

Trawler fishing

Purse-seine fishing

trawl flap

sonar

trawl lines

fish school

trawl bag

Drift-net fishing

fish caught by gills

float    buoy

Long line fishing

lines with hooks

| Seafood Type | Kilocalories of fossil fuel input per kilocalorie of protein output |
|---|---|
| **Marine Fisheries** | |
| Shrimp | 3–98 |
| Salmon | 18–52 |
| Cod | 20 |
| **Ocean Aquaculture** | |
| Salmon cage culture | 50 |
| Salmon ranching | 7–12 |
| Seaweed | 1 |

**Figure 13-31** Estimated fossil fuel energy required for harvesting or raising various ocean species. (Data from Malcolm Beveridge)

**Figure 13-32** World fish catch (left) and world fish catch per person (right), 1950–2000. Worldwide per capita fish catch did not rise much between 1968 and 1989 and has dropped since then. The total catch and per capita catches since 1990 are probably about 10% lower than shown here because of the discovery in 2002 that since 1990 China had apparently been inflating its fish catches. (Data from UN Food and Agriculture Organization and Worldwatch Institute)

and population growth, and **(3)** the total catch and per capita catches are both estimated 10% lower than those shown in Figure 13-32 because in 2002 it was discovered that since 1990 China has apparently been inflating its fish catches.

**Connections: How Are Overfishing and Habitat Degradation Affecting Fish Harvests?** Fish are renewable resources as long as the annual harvest leaves enough breeding stock to renew the species for the next year. Ideally, an annual **sustainable yield**—the size of the annual catch that could be harvested indefinitely without a decline in the population of a species—should be established for each species to avoid depleting the stock.

However, determining sustainable yields is difficult because **(1)** it is hard to estimate mobile aquatic populations, and **(2)** sustainable yields shift from year to year because of changes in climate, pollution, and other factors. Furthermore, sustainably harvesting the entire annual surplus of one species may severely reduce the population of other species that rely on it for food.

**Overfishing** is the taking of so many fish that too little breeding stock is left to maintain numbers; that is, overfishing is a harvest of a species that exceeds its sustainable yield. Prolonged overfishing leads to **commercial extinction,** when the population of a species declines to the point at which it is no longer profitable to hunt for them. Fishing fleets then move to a new species or a new region, hoping the overfished species will recover eventually.

High levels of *bycatch* (the nontarget fish that are caught in nets and then thrown back into the sea) also deplete fisheries. Nearly one-fourth of the annual global fish catch is bycatch that depletes marine biodiversity and does not provide food for people.

According to a 2001 report by the UN Food and Agriculture Organization, about 75% of the world's 200 commercially valuable marine fish species are either overfished or fished to their estimated sustainable yield. The primary cause of this depletion of fish stocks is too many fishing boats pursuing too few fish—another example of the tragedy of the commons (Connections, p. 305). This decline in available fish in many areas helps explain why there are more than 100 disputes over rights to marine fisheries between countries.

The stocks of some marine fisheries have fallen dramatically.

- In 1992, the Newfoundland cod fishery collapsed and put some 40,000 Canadian fishers and fish processors out of work. Despite a ban on additional fishing, by 2002 the fishery had not recovered.

- In the Atlantic Ocean, the bluefin tuna has been heavily overfished primarily for use as sushi in Tokyo's restaurants. As a result, the stock of this fishery has dropped by 94%. Even if no more of these commercially valuable fish are caught, it will take decades for this long-lived species to recover.

According to the U.S. National Fish and Wildlife Foundation, 14 major commercial fish species in U.S. waters (accounting for one-fifth of the world's annual catch and half of all U.S. stocks) are so depleted that even if all fishing stopped immediately it would take up to 20 years for stocks to recover (Figure 13-33). A 2001 report by the U.S. Department of Commerce found that 107 out of 127 species taken in U.S. marine waters were in jeopardy of being overfished.

Degradation, destruction, and pollution of wetlands, estuaries, coral reefs, salt marshes, and mangroves also threaten populations of fish and shellfish. An estimated 80–90% of the global commercial marine

## Commercial Fishing and the Tragedy of the Commons

**CONNECTIONS**

In the 1970s and 1980s, extensive investment in fishing fleets, aided by government and international development agency subsidies, helped boost the fish catch significantly (Figure 13-32, left). Since 1975, however, the size of the industrial fishing fleet has expanded twice as fast as the rise in catches.

Thus too many boats now fish for a declining number of fish. This leads to overfishing, an example of the tragedy of the commons (Connections, p. 11).

In a 1998 study, Daniel Pauly warned that the current harvesting of species at increasingly lower trophic levels in ocean food webs can lead to **(1)** decreased chances for recovery of species at the top of

ocean food webs by reducing stocks of the smaller fish they feed on, **(2)** collapse of marine ecosystems, **(3)** a drop in aquatic biodiversity, and **(4)** a loss of high-quality protein for humans.

Because of overfishing and the overcapacity of the fishing fleet, it costs the global fishing industry about $125 billion a year to catch $70 billion worth of fish. Government subsidies such as fuel tax exemptions, price controls, low-interest loans, and grants for fishing gear make up most of the $55 billion annual deficit of the industry.

Critics contend that such subsidies promote overfishing. They argue that eliminating or significantly lowering these subsidies would reduce the size of the fishing fleet by encouraging free-market competition and would allow some of the

economically and biologically depleted stocks to recover.

Eliminating these subsidies will cause a loss of jobs for some fishers and fish processors in coastal communities. However, to fishery biologists the alternative is worse. Continuing to subsidize excess fishing allows fishers to keep their jobs a little longer while making less and less money until the fishery collapses. Then all jobs are gone, and fishing communities suffer even more.

### Critical Thinking

Do you believe government subsidies for the fishing industry should be eliminated or sharply reduced? Explain. How would you feel about eliminating such subsidies if your livelihood depended on fishing?

---

catch comes from coastal waters within 320 kilometers (200 miles) of the shoreline.

Projected global warming over the next 50–100 years is also a threat to the global fish catch. Warmer ocean water can degrade or **(1)** destroy highly productive coral reefs (p. 144) and **(2)** enhance the harmful ef-

fects of habitat degradation and pollution on fish populations. The thinning of the ozone layer in the lower stratosphere (Figure 4-8, p. 69) can also damage surface-dwelling marine species by leading to increased penetration of harmful UV radiation into ocean waters. Fish populations also are affected by shorter-term climatic changes such as El Niño–Southern Oscillations (ENSOs, Figure 6-14, p. 119).

**Is Aquaculture the Answer?** Aquaculture, in which fish and shellfish are raised for food, supplies about 33% of the world's commercial fish harvest, with production increasing fivefold between 1984 and 2001. China is the world leader in aquaculture (producing about 68% of the world's output), followed by India and Japan.

There are two basic types of aquaculture:

- **Fish farming,** which involves **(1)** cultivating fish in a controlled environment—often a coastal or inland pond, lake, reservoir, or rice paddy—and **(2)** harvesting them when they reach the desired size.

- **Fish ranching,** which involves **(1)** holding anadromous species such as salmon (that live part of their lives in fresh water and part in salt water) in captivity for the first few years of their lives (usually in fenced-in areas or floating cages in coastal lagoons and estuaries; Figure 13-30), **(2)** releasing them, and then **(3)** harvesting the adults when they return to spawn (Figure 13-34, p. 306).

**Figure 13-33** The harvest of groundfishes (yellowtail flounder, haddock, and cod) in the Georges Bank off the coast of New England in the North Atlantic, once one of the world's most productive fishing grounds, has declined sharply since 1965. Stocks dropped to such low levels that since December 1994 the National Marine Fisheries Services has banned fishing of these species in the Georges Bank. (Data from U.S. National Marine Fisheries Service)

**Figure 13-34** Normal life cycle of wild salmon (left) and human-modified life cycle of hatchery-raised salmon (right). Salmon spend part of their lives in fresh water and part in salt water.

Species cultivated in developing countries (mostly in inland aquaculture ponds and rice paddies) include carp (especially in China and India), catfish (in the United States), tilapia, milkfish, clams, and oysters. These species feed on phytoplankton and other aquatic plants and thus eat low on the food chain.

China has developed a fish polyculture in which four types of carp feed at different trophic levels in a food chain. They include **(1)** *silver carp* (a filter feeder eating phytoplankton), **(2)** *bighead carp* (a filter feeder eating zooplankton), **(3)** *grass carp* (feeding on aquatic vegetation), and **(4)** *common carp* (feeding on detritus that settles to the bottom). Fish polyculture is also widely used in India. Most aquaculture in China is

integrated with agriculture. This allows farmers to use pig manure and other agricultural wastes to fertilize aquaculture ponds and thus promote the growth of phytoplankton to feed aquaculture species.

In developed countries and some rapidly developing countries in Asia, aquaculture is used mostly to stock lakes and streams with game fish or to raise expensive fish and shellfish such as oysters, catfish, crayfish, rainbow trout, shrimp, and salmon—mostly for export to Japan, Europe, and North America. Aquaculture now produces **(1)** 90% of all oysters, **(2)** 40% of all salmon (75% in the United States), **(3)** 50% of internationally traded shrimp and prawns, and **(4)** 65% of freshwater fish sold in the global marketplace.

Catfish are the leading aquacultural product in the United States. Most are produced in ponds in Mississippi, Louisiana, Arkansas, and Alabama.

Figure 13-35 lists the major advantages and disadvantages of aquaculture. Some analysts project that freshwater and saltwater aquaculture production could double during the next 10 years. Other analysts warn that the harmful environmental effects of aquaculture (Figure 13-35) could limit future production.

Aquaculture has been promoted as a way to boost the global seafood harvest while taking the pressure off the world's overharvested marine fisheries. But a 2000 study by Stanford University researcher Rosamond Taylor found that increased use of aquaculture has stressed marine fisheries by **(1)** raising the demand for some ocean fish such as anchovies that are ground into fish meal and fed to some aquaculture species and **(2)** creating vast amounts of animal waste that have fouled coastal areas, which are important sources of fish and shellfish.

Intensive farming of large carnivorous fish whose wild populations have been decimated by overfishing is replacing traditional aquaculture in which farmed fish eat plants and detritus. This increases overfishing of smaller marine species used to feed farmed carnivorous species. If kept up, this depleting the seas to feed aquaculture farms could cause the collapse of both marine fisheries and carnivorous aquaculture.

Aquaculture proponents point to new trends and research that may help decrease the harmful effects of aquaculture. They include the following:

- Abandonment of most attempts to raise shrimp and other species by clearing mangrove forests (Figure 7-2, p. 145, and 7-9, p. 149) and converting them to large aquaculture ponds.

- Relying more on smaller, more intensively managed aquaculture ponds. Recent research shows that warm water species can be intensively cultivated in small stirred ponds **(1)** in which bacteria are used to provide food for phytoplankton needed to feed the aquaculture species, and **(2)** the same water remains in the pond, which eliminates water pollution from dumping pond water on the land or into nearby aquatic systems.

- Increased use of intensive farming of some aquaculture species (such as salmon and cobia) in deeply submerged ocean cages that can be thought of as stationary fish schools. The cages **(1)** are located below wave action, **(2)** protect the species being raised from predators, **(3)** can be cleaned by species such as starfish, and **(4)** allow dispersion of the wastes produced by natural dilution in the surrounding ocean. Attached tubes can be used to feed the species as needed.

Even under the most optimistic projections, increasing both the wild catch and aquaculture will not increase world food supplies significantly. The reason is that currently fish and shellfish supply only about 1% of the energy and 6% of the protein in the human diet.

## 13-7 GOVERNMENT AGRICULTURAL POLICY

**How Do Government Agricultural Policies Affect Food Production?** Agriculture is a financially risky business. Whether farmers have a good year or a bad year depends on factors over which they have little control: weather, crop prices, crop pests and diseases, interest rates, and the global market. Because of the need for reliable food supplies despite fluctuations in these factors, most governments provide various forms of assistance to farmers and consumers.

Here are three approaches:

- *Keep food prices artificially low.* This makes consumers happy but means that farmers may not be able to make a living.

- *Give farmers subsidies to keep them in business and encourage them to increase food production.* Globally, government price supports and other subsidies for agriculture total more than $500 billion per year (including $100 billion per year in the United States).

| Advantages | Disadvantages |
|---|---|
| Highly efficient | Large inputs of land, feed, and water needed |
| High yield in small volume of water | Produces large and concentrated outputs of waste |
| Increased yields through crossbreeding and genetic engineering | Destroys mangrove forests |
| Can reduce overharvesting of conventional fisheries | Increased grain production needed to feed some species |
| Little use of fuel | Fish can be killed by pesticide runoff from nearby cropland |
| Profits not tied to price of oil | Dense populations vulnerable to disease |
| High profits | Tanks too contaminated to use after about 5 years |

**Figure 13-35** Advantages and disadvantages of aquaculture.

If government subsidies are too generous and the weather is good, farmers may produce more food than can be sold. The resulting surplus depresses food prices, which reduces the financial incentive for farmers in developing countries to increase domestic food production. Moreover, the taxes paid by citizens in developed countries to provide agricultural subsidies can offset the lower food prices they enjoy.

- *Eliminate most or all price controls and subsidies and let farmers and fishers respond to market demand without government interference.* However, some analysts urge that any phaseout of farm and fishery subsidies should be coupled with increased aid for the poor and the lower middle class, who would suffer the most from any increase in food prices.

Many environmentalists believe that instead of eliminating all subsidies, we should use them to reward farmers and ranchers who (1) protect the soil, (2) conserve water, (3) reforest degraded land, (4) protect and restore wetlands, (5) conserve wildlife, and (6) practice more sustainable agriculture and fishing.

## 13-8 SOLUTIONS: SUSTAINABLE AGRICULTURE

**What Is Sustainable Agriculture?** As we have seen in this chapter, the two major ways to increase the world's food production are to increase crop yields per hectare or increase the amount of land used to grow crops.

The total area of cropland is unlikely to expand because of a lack of affordable and environmentally sustainable land, however. In addition, increasing the yields per area of existing cropland may be limited because of (1) a lack of water for irrigation (Figure 13-18), (2) reduced genetic diversity (Spotlight, p. 295), (3) a leveling off of yields per hectare as biological and physiological limits of crop productivity are reached, and (4) the environmental effects of food production, which degrade existing cropland (Figure 13-13).

If these projections are correct, the three main tools in trying to reduce hunger and malnutrition and the harmful environmental effects of agriculture will be (1) slowing population growth (Section 12-3, p. 267), (2) reducing poverty so that people can grow or buy enough food for their survival and good health, and (3) developing and phasing in systems of **sustainable agriculture** or **low-input agriculture** (also called **organic farming**) over the next three decades.

Gordon Conway, president of the Rockefeller Foundation, calls this a new *doubly green revolution* that will (1) increase crop yields in an environmentally sustainable manner and (2) benefit the poor more directly than the first two green revolutions.

Currently, organic farming is used on less than 1% of the world's cropland (0.2% in the United States) but on 6–10% of the cropland in many European countries. However, this type of farming is growing rapidly, and in 2000 it was a $25 billion global market.

Under U.S. Department of Agriculture regulations, foods labeled *organic* (1) must be produced without synthetic pesticides, fungicides, and herbicides, and (2) cannot include genetically engineered foods, be irradiated, or be grown on soil fertilized by sewage sludge. In addition to these restrictions, organic meat and dairy products must be (1) produced from 100% organically grown feed, (2) given access to outdoor range or pasture, and (3) produced without use of hormones and antibiotics.

Figure 13-36 lists the major components of more sustainable, low-input agriculture. Studies have shown that low-input organic farming (1) produces equivalent yields with lower carbon dioxide emissions, (2) uses about 50% less energy than conventional farming, (3) improves soil fertility, (4) provides more habitats for wild plant and animal species, and (5) generally is more profitable for the farmer than high-input farming.

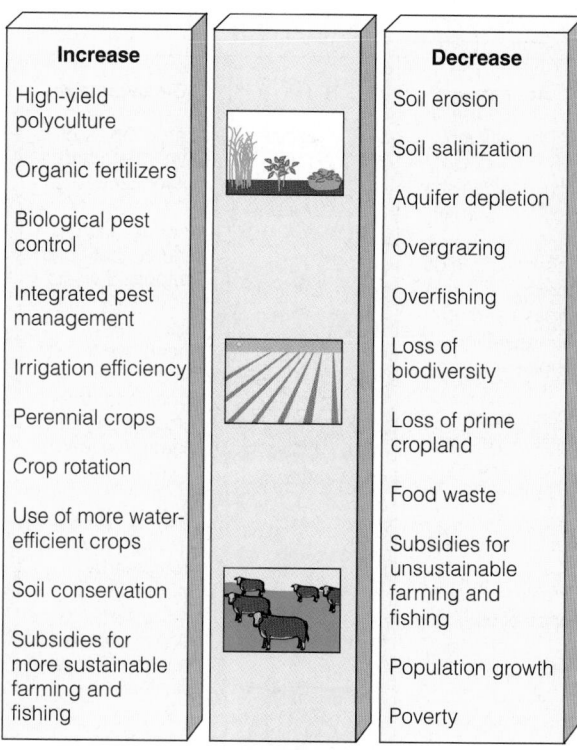

| **Increase** | **Decrease** |
|---|---|
| High-yield polyculture | Soil erosion |
| Organic fertilizers | Soil salinization |
| Biological pest control | Aquifer depletion |
| Integrated pest management | Overgrazing |
| Irrigation efficiency | Overfishing |
| Perennial crops | Loss of biodiversity |
| Crop rotation | Loss of prime cropland |
| Use of more water-efficient crops | Food waste |
| Soil conservation | Subsidies for unsustainable farming and fishing |
| Subsidies for more sustainable farming and fishing | Population growth |
| | Poverty |

**Figure 13-36** Components of more sustainable, low-throughput agriculture.

Most proponents of more sustainable agriculture are not opposed to high-yield agriculture. Instead, they see it as vital for protecting the earth's biodiversity by reducing the need to cultivate new and often marginal land. They call for using environmentally sustainable forms of both high-yield polyculture and high-yield monoculture for growing crops.

**Can We Make the Transition to More Sustainable Agriculture?** A growing number agricultural analysts believe that over the next 30 years we must make a transition from unsustainable and environmentally harmful agriculture (Figure 13-13) to more sustainable forms of agriculture (Figure 13-36).

In developed countries, even a partial shift to more environmentally sustainable food production will not be easy. It will be opposed by **(1)** agribusiness, **(2)** successful farmers with large investments in unsustainable forms of industrialized agriculture, **(3)** specialized farmers unwilling to learn the more demanding art of farming sustainably, and **(4)** many consumers unwilling or unable to pay higher prices for food when more of agriculture's harmful environmental and health costs (Figure 13-13) are included in the market prices of food.

To help farmers make the transition to more sustainable agriculture, analysts call for

- Greatly increasing research on sustainable agriculture and improving human nutrition.

- Setting up demonstration projects throughout each country so farmers can see how sustainable agricultural systems work.

- Increasing agricultural aid to developing countries (which, when adjusted for inflation, declined by about 50% between 1982 and 1999), with emphasis on developing more sustainable, low-input agriculture.

- Establishing training programs in sustainable agriculture for farmers and government agricultural officials and encouraging the creation of college curricula in sustainable agriculture and human nutrition.

Sustainable agriculture involves applying the four principles of sustainability (Solutions, p. 201) to producing food. The goal is to feed the world's people while sustaining and restoring the earth's natural capital (Figure 4-34, p. 92). See the website material for this chapter for some actions you can take to help promote more sustainable agriculture.

*The need to bring birth rates well below death rates, increase food production while protecting the environment, and distribute food to all who need it is the greatest challenge our species has ever faced.*

PAUL AND ANNE EHRLICH

## REVIEW QUESTIONS

**1.** Define the boldfaced terms in this chapter.

**2.** What are *perennial crops*? What advantages do they have over conventional annual crops?

**3.** What are the three main systems that supply our food? What three crops provide most of the world's food?

**4.** Distinguish among *industrialized agriculture, plantation agriculture, traditional subsistence agriculture,* and *traditional intensive agriculture.*

**5.** What is a *green revolution,* and what three steps does it involve? Distinguish between the first and second green revolutions.

**6.** Explain how producing more food on less land can help protect biodiversity.

**7.** Describe the nature and importance of the agricultural industry in the United States. How energy efficient is industrialized agriculture in the United States?

**8.** Distinguish among *interplanting, polyvarietal cultivation, intercropping, agroforestry,* and *polyculture.* What are the major advantages and disadvantages of polyculture?

**9.** List two pieces of *good* news about world food production since 1950. List two pieces of *bad* news about present and future food production.

**10.** Distinguish among *undernutrition, malnutrition,* and *overnutrition.* What are the two most common nutritional deficiency diseases, and how do they differ? What are the effects of deficiencies of **(a)** vitamin A, **(b)** iron, and **(c)** iodine?

**11.** About how many chronically malnourished people are there in the world? About how many people die each year from undernutrition, malnutrition, diseases worsened by malnutrition, and drinking contaminated water? List six major ways to reduce sickness and premature death of children from malnutrition. What is the primary cause of hunger in the world?

**12.** List the major harmful environmental effects of producing food.

**13.** What are China's major food problems? How could lower food production in China affect the rest of the world?

**14.** Describe how genetically improved crop strains are developed by **(a)** *crossbreeding* and **(b)** *genetic engineering.*

**15.** List the pros and cons of growing more food by **(a)** increasing crop yields through green revolutions, **(b)** genetically modifying crops and foods, **(c)** getting people to switch to new types of foods, **(d)** irrigating more cropland, **(e)** cultivating more land, and **(f)** growing more food in urban areas.

**16.** List seven factors that could limit greatly increased food production through green revolution and genetic engineering techniques. Why should we be concerned about loss of genetic diversity in agricultural crop strains?

17. What is *rangeland*? Explain how rangeland grass can be a renewable resource for livestock and wild herbivores. How is meat produced in developed and developing countries? What are the advantages and disadvantages of raising livestock in factorylike production facilities?

18. Distinguish between *overgrazing* and *undergrazing*. What are three major effects of overgrazing? Describe the general condition of rangelands throughout the world and in the United States. Describe three ways to manage rangelands more sustainably for meat production. What are *riparian areas*, and why are they important?

19. What are some of the harmful environmental effects of meat production?

20. What are *fisheries*? Distinguish among *trawling, purse-seine, longlining,* and *drift-net* methods for harvesting fish. Describe trends in the world's total fish catch and per capita fish catch since 1950, and explain why the per capita catch is expected to decline.

21. What is the *sustainable yield* of a fishery? Distinguish between *overfishing* and *commercial extinction* of a fish species. About what percentage of the world's fish stocks are in decline because of overfishing and pollution?

22. Distinguish between *fish farming* and *fish ranching*. What are the pros and cons of aquaculture?

23. List three policy types that governments use to affect food production. List the pros and cons of each approach.

24. What is *sustainable agriculture*, why is it important, and what are its major components?

## CRITICAL THINKING

1. Summarize the major economic and ecological advantages and limitations of each of the following proposals for increasing world food supplies and reducing hunger over the next 30 years: (a) cultivating more land by clearing tropical forests and irrigating arid lands, (b) catching more fish in the open sea, (c) producing more fish and shellfish with aquaculture, and (d) increasing the yield per area of cropland.

2. Why should it matter to people in developed countries that many people in developing countries are malnourished and hungry? What are the three most important actions you believe should be taken to reduce hunger (a) in the country where you live and (b) in the world?

3. Some people argue that starving people could get enough food by eating nonconventional plants and insects; others point out that most starving people do not know what plants and insects are safe to eat and cannot take a chance on experimenting when even the slightest illness could kill them. If you had no money to grow or buy food, would you collect and eat protein-rich grasshoppers, moths, beetles, or other insects?

4. What could happen to energy-intensive agriculture in the United States and other industrialized countries if world oil prices rose sharply?

5. Some have suggested that some rangelands could be used to raise wild grazing animals for meat instead of conventional livestock. Others consider it unethical to raise and kill wild herbivores for food. What do you think? Explain.

6. Should (a) all price supports and other government subsidies paid to farmers be eliminated, and (b) governments phase in agricultural tax breaks and subsidies to encourage farmers to switch to more sustainable farming? Explain your answers. Try to consult one or more farmers in answering these questions.

7. What are the economic and ecological advantages and disadvantages of relying more on (a) a small number of genetic varieties of major crops and livestock, (b) genetically modified food, and (c) perennial food crops? Explain why you support or oppose each of these approaches.

8. Suppose you live near a coastal area and a company wants to use a fairly large area of coastal marshland for an aquaculture operation. If you were an elected local official, would you support or oppose such a project? Explain. What safeguards or regulations would you impose on the operation?

9. How could knowledge about (a) secondary ecological succession (Figure 8-15, p. 181) and (b) the intermediate disturbance hypothesis (Figure 8-17, p. 184) be used to make agriculture more sustainable?

10. Congratulations! You are in charge of the world. List the three most important features of your agricultural policy.

## PROJECTS

1. If possible, visit both a conventional industrialized farm and an organic or low-input farm. Compare (a) soil erosion and other forms of land degradation, (b) use and costs of energy, (c) use and costs of pesticides and inorganic fertilizer, (d) use and costs of natural pest control and organic fertilizer, (e) yields per hectare for the same crops, and (f) overall profit per hectare for the same crops.

2. Evaluate cattle grazing on private and public rangeland and pastures in your local area. Try to document any harmful environmental impacts. Have the economic benefits to the community outweighed any harmful environmental effects?

3. Gather information from your local planning office to determine how much cropland in your area has been lost to urbanization since 1980. What policies, if any, do your state and local community have for promoting cropland preservation?

4. Try to gather data evaluating the harmful environmental effects of nearby agriculture on your local community. What is being done to reduce these effects?

5. Use health and other local government records to estimate how many people in your community suffer from

undernutrition or malnutrition. Has this problem increased or decreased since 1980? What are the basic causes of this hunger problem, and what is being done to alleviate it? Share the results of your study with local officials, and present your own plan for improving efforts to reduce hunger in your community.

**6.** Use the library or the Internet to find out what controls now exist on genetically engineered organisms in the United States (or the country where you live) and how well such controls are enforced.

**7.** Make a survey in the nearest urban area to estimate what percentage of the food is grown by urban dwellers. Survey unused land and use it to estimate how much it could contribute to urban food production. Use these data to draw up a plan for increasing urban food production and present it to city officials.

**8.** Use the library or the Internet to find bibliographic information about *Aldo Leopold* and *Paul* and *Anne Ehrlich,* whose quotes appear at the beginning and end of this chapter.

**9.** Make a concept map of this chapter's major ideas, using the section heads and subheads and the key terms (in boldface type). Look on the website for this book for information about making concept maps.

## INTERNET STUDY RESOURCES AND RESOURCES FOR FURTHER READING AND RESEARCH

The website for this book contains helpful study aids and many ideas for further reading and research. Log on to

www.info.brookscole.com/miller13

and click on the Chapter-by-Chapter area. Choose Chapter 13 and select a resource:

- Flash Cards allows you to test your mastery of the Terms and Concepts to Remember for this chapter.

- Tutorial Quizzes provides a multiple-choice practice quiz.

- Student Guide to InfoTrac will lead you to Critical Thinking Projects that use InfoTrac College Edition as a research tool.

- References lists the major books and articles consulted in writing this chapter.

- Hypercontents takes you to an extensive list of sites with news, research, and images related to individual sections of the chapter.

## INFOTRAC COLLEGE EDITION

Improve your skills with InfoTrac College Edition, a searchable online database of articles from more than 700 periodicals. Log on to

http://www.infotrac-college.com

or access InfoTrac through the website for this book. Try to find the following articles:

**1.** Snell, M. B. 2001. Against the grain. *Sierra* 86: 30. *Keywords:* "transgenic crops" and "developing countries." Genetically engineered food crops may seem like a boon to the hungry populations in developing countries, but many of these countries are concerned about the overall environmental effects of these foods.

**2.** Finneran, K. 2001. What's food got to do with it? *Issues in Science and Technology* 17: 24. *Keyword:* "genetically modified food." This article looks at the debate over genetically modified foods, not so much from the standpoint of whether the technology is good or bad but from the point of view of human psychology.

# 14 WATER RESOURCES

## Water and Grain Import Wars in the Middle East

Future wars between countries in the Middle East could be fought over water. Most water in this dry region comes from three shared river basins: the Nile, Jordan, and Tigris-Euphrates (Figure 14-1).

Ten countries share water from the Nile River basin (Figure 14-1), but three countries—Egypt, Sudan, and Ethiopia—use most of the water. Egypt, where it rarely rains, is mostly desert and would not exist without irrigation water from the Nile.

Because of water scarcity, Egypt already has to import 40% of its grain to feed its current population of 71 million. Yet by 2050, its population is expected to increase to 115 million, greatly increasing its demand for already scarce water.

Most of the precipitation that feeds 85% of the Nile's flow falls in Ethiopia. With a total fertility rate of 5.9 children, its population is projected to increase from 68 million in 2002 to 173 million by 2050, roughly tripling its water needs. To meet these needs and help lift its people out of poverty, Ethiopia plans to divert more water from the Nile.

Sudan also plans to divert more of the Nile's water to help feed its population, which is expected to increase from 33 million to 64 million between 2002 and 2050. This will at least double its water needs.

Such upstream diversions by Ethiopia and Sudan would reduce the amount of water available to water-short Egypt. Its options are to (1) go to war with Sudan and Ethiopia to obtain more water, (2) cut population growth, (3) improve irrigation efficiency, (4) spend $2 billion to build the world's longest concrete canal and pump water out of Lake Nasser (the reservoir created from the Nile by the Aswan High Dam) to create more irrigated farmland in the middle of the desert, (5) import more grain to reduce the need for irrigation water, (6) work out water-sharing agreements with other countries, or (7) suffer the harsh human and economic consequences of extreme hydrological poverty.

The Jordan basin is by far the most water-short region, with fierce competition for its water among Jordan, Syria, Palestine (Gaza and the West Bank), and Israel (Figure 14-1). The combined populations of these already water-short countries are projected to more than double from 33 million to 69 million between 2002 and 2050. Some *good news* is that in 1994, Israel and Jordan signed a peace treaty that addressed

**Figure 14-1** The Middle East, whose countries have some of the highest population growth rates in the world. Because of the dry climate, food production depends heavily on irrigation. Existing conflicts between countries in this region over access to water may soon overshadow both long-standing religious and ethnic clashes and attempts to take over valuable oil supplies.

their disputes over water from the Jordan River basin.

Syria plans to build dams and withdraw more water from the Jordan River, decreasing the downstream water supply for Jordan and Israel. Israel warns that it will consider destroying the largest dam that Syria plans to build.

Turkey, located at the headwaters of the Tigris and Euphrates Rivers, controls how much water flows downstream to Syria and Iraq before emptying into the Persian Gulf (Figure 14-1). Turkey is building 24 dams along the upper Tigris and Euphrates Rivers to (1) generate huge quantities of electricity, (2) irrigate a large area of land, and (3) generate several million jobs for its 67 million people.

If completed, these dams will reduce the flow of water downstream to Syria and Iraq by up to 35% in normal years and much more in dry years. Syria also plans to build a large dam along the Euphrates River to divert water arriving from Turkey. This will leave little water for Iraq and could lead to war between Syria and Iraq.

Resolving these water distribution problems will require a combination of (1) regional cooperation in allocating water supplies, (2) slowed population growth, (3) improved efficiency in water use, (4) increased water prices to encourage water conservation and improve irrigation efficiency, and (5) increased grain imports to reduce water needs.

Instead of water military wars we could have grain-import economic wars. Water-short countries able to pay for imported grain instead of those that are the strongest militarily may win the competition for scarce water and food.

Thus the availability of water and food in water-short countries is connected to the interlocking problems of (1) *population growth and control* and *water conservation* to reduce water needs and (2) *environmentally sustainable economic growth* to provide enough money to reduce water needs through grain imports.

*Our liquid planet glows like a soft blue sapphire in the hard-edged darkness of space. There is nothing else like it in the solar system. It is because of water.*

JOHN TODD

This chapter addresses the following questions:

- What are water's unique physical properties?

- How much fresh water is available to us, and how much of it are we using?

- What causes freshwater shortages, and what can be done about this problem?

- What are the pros and cons of using dams and reservoirs to supply more water?

- What are the pros and cons of transferring large amounts of water from one place to another?

- What are the pros and cons of withdrawing groundwater and converting salt water to fresh water?

- How can we waste less water?

- What are the causes of flooding, and what can be done to reduce the risk of flooding and flood damage?

- How can we use the earth's water more sustainably?

## 14-1 WATER'S IMPORTANCE AND UNIQUE PROPERTIES

**Why Is Water So Important?** We live on the water planet, with a precious film of water—most of it salt water—covering about 71% of the earth's surface (Figure 7-5, p. 147). All organisms are made up mostly of water; a tree is about 60% water by weight, and most animals are about 50–65% water.

Each of us needs only about a dozen cupfuls of water per day to survive, but huge amounts of water are needed to supply us with food, shelter, and our other needs and wants. Water also plays a key role in **(1)** sculpting the earth's surface, **(2)** moderating climate, and **(3)** diluting pollutants.

**What Are Some Important Properties of Water?** Water is a remarkable substance with a unique combination of properties:

- *There are strong forces of attraction (called hydrogen bonds, Appendix 2, Figure 4) between molecules of water.* These attractive forces are the major factor determining water's unique properties.

- *Water exists as a liquid over a wide temperature range because of the strong forces of attraction between water molecules.* Its high boiling point of 100°C (212°F) and low freezing point of 0°C (32°F) mean that water remains a liquid in most climates on the earth.

- *Liquid water changes temperature very slowly because it can store a large amount of heat without a large change in temperature.* This high heat capacity **(1)** helps protect living organisms from temperature fluctuations, **(2)** moderates the earth's climate, and **(3)** makes water an excellent coolant for car engines, power plants, and heat-producing industrial processes.

- *It takes a lot of heat to evaporate liquid water because of the strong forces of attraction between its molecules.* Water absorbs large amounts of heat as it changes into water vapor and releases this heat as the vapor condenses back to liquid water. This is a primary factor in distributing heat throughout the world (Figure 6-10, p. 117) and thus plays an important role in determining the climates of various areas. This property also makes water evaporation an effective cooling process, which is why you feel cooler when perspiration or bathwater evaporates from your skin.

- *Liquid water can dissolve a variety of compounds.* This enables it to **(1)** carry dissolved nutrients into the tissues of living organisms, **(2)** flush waste products out of those tissues, **(3)** serve as an all-purpose cleanser, and **(4)** help remove and dilute the water-soluble wastes of civilization. Water's superiority as a solvent also means that water-soluble wastes pollute it easily.

- *Water molecules can break down (ionize) into hydrogen ions ($H^+$) and hydroxide ions ($OH^-$), which help maintain a balance between acids and bases in cells, as measured by the pH of water solutions* (Figure 3-5, p. 49).

- *Water filters out wavelengths of ultraviolet radiation* (Figure 3-9, p. 52) *that would harm some aquatic organisms.*

- *The strong attractive forces between the molecules of liquid water cause its surface to contract (high surface tension) and to adhere to and coat a solid (high wetting ability).* These cohesive forces pull water molecules at the surface layer together so strongly that it can support small insects. The combination of high surface tension and wetting ability allow water to rise through a plant from the roots to the leaves (capillary action).

- *Unlike most liquids, water expands when it freezes.* This means that ice has a lower density (mass per unit of volume) than liquid water. Thus ice floats on water. Without this property, lakes and streams in cold climates would freeze solid and lose most of their current forms of aquatic life. Because water expands upon freezing, it can also **(1)** break pipes, **(2)** crack a car's engine block (which is why we use antifreeze), **(3)** break up streets, and **(4)** fracture rocks (thus forming soil).

Water is the lifeblood of the biosphere. It connects us to one another, to other forms of life, and to the entire planet. Despite its importance, water is one of our most poorly managed resources. We waste it and pollute it. We also charge too little for making it available. This encourages still greater waste and pollution of this resource, for which we have no substitute.

## 14-2 SUPPLY, RENEWAL, AND USE OF WATER RESOURCES

**How Much Fresh Water Is Available?** Only a tiny fraction of the planet's abundant water is available to us as fresh water (Figure 14-2). About 97.4 % by volume is found in the oceans and is too salty for drinking, irrigation, or industry (except as a coolant).

Most of the remaining 2.6% that is fresh water is **(1)** locked up in ice caps or glaciers or **(2)** in groundwater too deep or salty to be used (Figure 14-2).

Thus only about 0.014% of the earth's total volume of water is easily available to us as soil moisture, usable groundwater, water vapor, and lakes and streams (Figure 14-2). If the world's water supply were only 100 liters (26 gallons), our usable supply of fresh water would be only 0.014 liter (2.5 teaspoons).

Some *good news* is that the available fresh water amounts to a generous supply. Moreover, this water is continuously collected, purified, recycled, and distributed in the solar-powered *hydrologic cycle* (Figure 4-27, p. 83) as long as we do not **(1)** overload it with slowly degradable and nondegradable wastes or **(2)** withdraw it from underground supplies faster than it is replenished. The *bad news* is that in parts of the world we are doing both.

Differences in average annual precipitation divide the world's countries and people into water *haves* and *have-nots*. For example, Canada, with only 0.5% of the world's population, has 20% of the world's fresh water, whereas China, with 21% of the world's people, has only 7% of the supply.

As population, irrigation, and industrialization increase, water shortages in already water-short regions will intensify and heighten regional tensions between and within countries. Examples of such areas include **(1)** the Middle East, (p. 312), **(2)** sub-Saharan Africa, **(3)** South Asia, and **(4)** northern China. Global warming can **(1)** increase global rates of evaporation, **(2)** shift precipitation patterns, and **(3)** disrupt water supplies and thus food supplies. Some areas will get more precipitation and some less. Some river flows will change.

**What Is Surface Water?** Precipitation that does not infiltrate the ground or return to the atmosphere by evaporation (including transpiration) is called **surface runoff,** which flows into streams, lakes, wetlands, and reservoirs.

About two-thirds of the world's annual runoff is lost by seasonal floods and is not available for human use. The remaining one-third is **reliable runoff,** which generally we can count on as a stable source of water from year to year..

A **watershed,** also called a **drainage basin,** is a region from which water drains into a stream, lake, reservoir, wetland, or other body of water.

**What Is Groundwater?** Some precipitation infiltrates the ground and percolates downward through voids (pores, fractures, crevices, and other spaces) in soil and rock (Figure 14-3). The water in these voids is called **groundwater.**

Close to the surface, the voids have little moisture in them. However, below some depth, in the **zone of saturation,** the voids are completely filled with water.

The **water table** is located at the top of the zone of saturation. It falls in dry weather and rises in wet weather. An unsaturated zone, or **zone of aeration,** lies above the water table. In this zone, pores of rock and soil contain air and may be moist but not saturated with water.

Porous, water-saturated layers of sand, gravel, or bedrock through which groundwater flows are called **aquifers** (Figure 14-3). Aquifers are like large elongated sponges through which groundwater seeps. Any

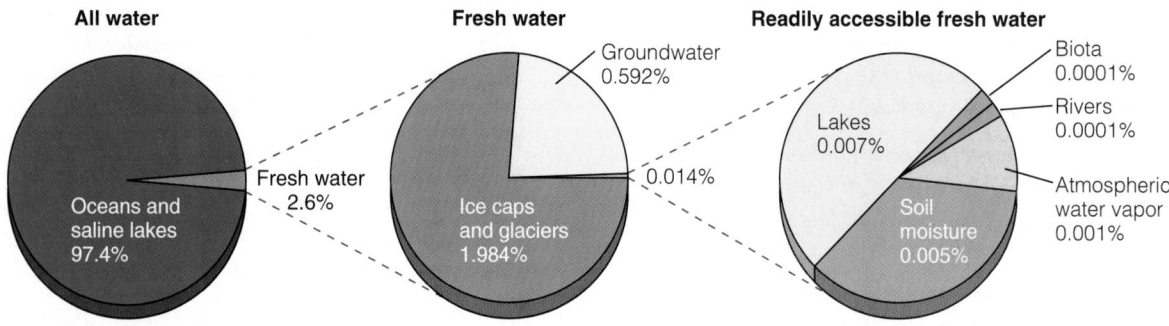

**Figure 14-2** The planet's water budget. Only a tiny fraction by volume of the world's water supply is fresh water available for human use.

**Figure 14-3** The groundwater system. An *unconfined aquifer* is an aquifer with a water table. A *confined aquifer* is bounded above and below by less permeable beds of rock. Groundwater in this type of aquifer is confined under pressure.

area of land through which water passes downward or laterally into an aquifer is called a **recharge area.**

Aquifers are replenished naturally by precipitation that percolates downward through soil and rock in what is called **natural recharge,** but some are recharged from the side by *lateral recharge.* Groundwater moves from the *recharge area* through an aquifer and out to a *discharge area* (well, spring, lake, geyser, stream, or ocean) as part of the hydrologic cycle (Figure 4-27, p. 83). Groundwater normally moves from (1) points of high elevation and pressure to (2) points of lower elevation and pressure. This movement is quite slow, typically only a meter or so (about 3 feet) per year and rarely more than 0.3 meter (1 foot) per day.

Some aquifers get very little (if any) recharge and on a human time scale are nonrenewable resources. They are often found fairly deep underground and were formed tens of thousands of years ago. Withdrawals from such aquifers amount to *water mining* that, if kept up, will deplete these ancient deposits of water.

**How Much of the World's Reliable Water Supply Are We Withdrawing?** Since 1900, global water withdrawal has increased about ninefold and

per capita withdrawal has quadrupled, with irrigation accounting for the largest increase in water withdrawal (Figure 14-4, p. 316). As a result, humans now withdraw about 35% of the world's reliable runoff. At least another 20% of this runoff is left in streams to (1) transport goods by boats, (2) dilute pollution, and (3) sustain fisheries and wildlife.

Thus we directly or indirectly withdraw more than half of the world's reliable runoff. Because of increased population growth and economic development, global withdrawal rates of surface water are projected to (1) at least double in the next two decades and (2) exceed the reliable surface runoff in a growing number of areas.

Nature's water delivery does not match up with the distribution of much of the world's population. For example, Asia, with 61% of the world's people, has only 36% of the earth's reliable annual runoff. In contrast, South America, with 26% of the earth's reliable runoff, has only 6% of the world's people.

**How Do We Use the World's Fresh Water?** Uses of withdrawn water vary from one region to another and from one country to another (Figure 14-5).

**Figure 14-4** Global water withdrawal, 1900–2000. Between 2000 and 2050, the world's population is expected to increase by about 3.3 billion people and greatly increase the demand for water. (Data from World Commission on Water Use in the 21st Century)

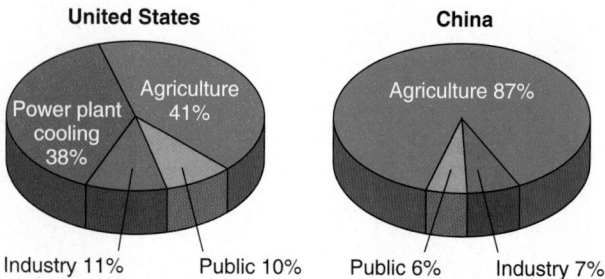

**Figure 14-5** Use of water withdrawn in the United States and China. The United States has the world's highest per capita use of water, amounting to an average of 4,800 liters (1,280 gallons) per person per day in 1999. Between 1980 and 1999, total water use in the United States decreased by 10% despite a 17% increase in population, mostly because of more efficient irrigation. (Data from Worldwatch Institute and World Resources Institute)

Worldwide, about 70% of all water withdrawn each year from rivers, lakes, and aquifers is used to **(1)** irrigate 18% of the world's cropland and **(2)** produce about 40% of the world's food.

Industry uses about 20% of the water withdrawn each year, and cities and residences use the remaining 10%. Agriculture and manufacturing use large amounts of water (Figure 14-6).

Some of the water withdrawn from a source may be returned to that source for reuse. *Consumptive water use* occurs when water withdrawn becomes unavailable for reuse in the basin from which it was removed—mostly because of losses such as evaporation or contamination.

**Case Study: Freshwater Resources in the United States** The United States has plenty of fresh water. However, much of it is **(1)** in the wrong place at the wrong time or **(2)** contaminated by agricultural and industrial practices. The eastern states usually have ample precipitation, whereas many western states have too little (Figure 14-7, top).

In the East, the largest uses for water are for energy production, cooling, and manufacturing. The largest use by far in the West is for irrigation (which accounts for about 85% of all water use).

In many parts of the eastern United States, the most serious water problems are **(1)** flooding, **(2)** occasional urban shortages, and **(3)** pollution.

For example, the 3 million residents of Long Island, New York, get most of their water from an increasingly contaminated aquifer.

The major water problem in the arid and semiarid areas of the western half of the country is a shortage of runoff, caused by **(1)** low precipitation (Figure 14-7, top), **(2)** high evaporation, and **(3)** recurring prolonged drought. Water tables in many areas are dropping rapidly as farmers and cities deplete aquifers faster than they are recharged.

In the United States, many major urban centers (especially those in the West and Midwest) are located in areas that do not have enough water (Figure 14-7, bottom). Water experts project that conflicts over

**Figure 14-6** Amount of water needed to produce some common agricultural and manufactured products. (Data from U.S. Geological Survey)

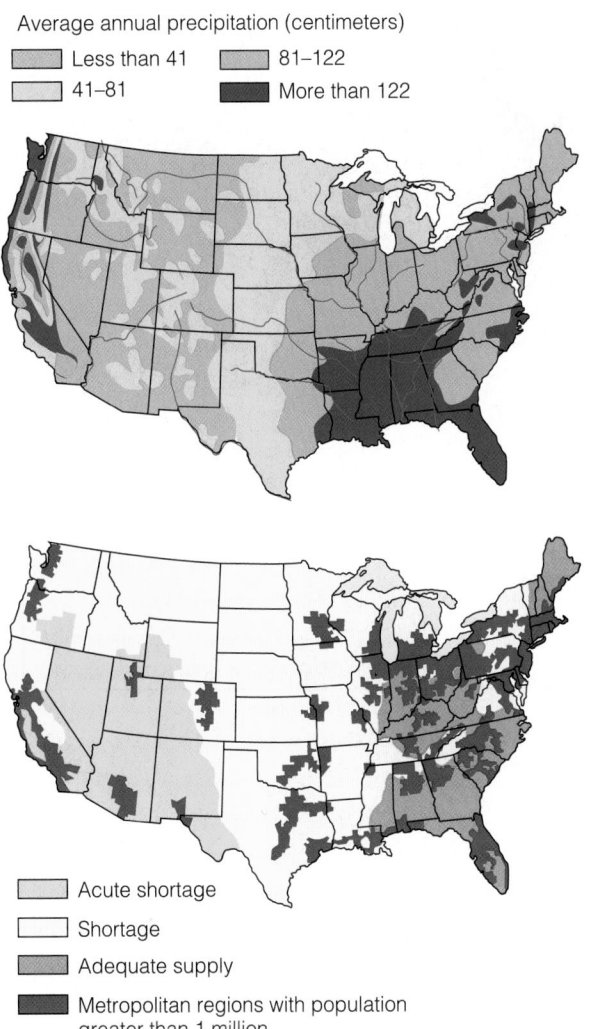

Average annual precipitation (centimeters)

[ ] Less than 41    [ ] 81–122
[ ] 41–81           [ ] More than 122

[ ] Acute shortage

[ ] Shortage

[ ] Adequate supply

[ ] Metropolitan regions with population greater than 1 million

**Figure 14-7** Average annual precipitation and major rivers (top) and water-deficit regions in the continental United States and their proximity to metropolitan areas having populations greater than 1 million (bottom). (Data from U.S. Water Resources Council and U.S. Geological Survey)

water supplies within and between states will intensify as more industries and people migrate west and compete with farmers for scarce water.

## 14-3 TOO LITTLE WATER

**What Causes Freshwater Shortages?** According to water expert Malin Falkenmark, the four causes of water scarcity are **(1)** a *dry climate* (Figure 6-7, p. 116), **(2)** *drought* (a period of 21 days or longer in which precipitation is at least 70% lower and evaporation is higher than normal), **(3)** *desiccation* (drying of the soil because of such activities as deforestation and over-

grazing by livestock), and **(4)** *water stress* (low per capita availability of water caused by increasing numbers of people relying on limited runoff levels).

Figure 14-8 (p. 318) shows the degree of stress on the world's major river systems, based on comparing the amount of water available with the amount used by humans. A country is said to be:

- *Water stressed* when the volume of its reliable runoff per person drops to below about 1,700 cubic meters (60,000 cubic feet) per year.

- Suffering from *water scarcity* when yearly per capita water availability falls below 1,000 cubic meters (35,000 cubic feet)

According to the United Nations, currently about 500 million people live in countries that are water-scarce or water-stressed. By 2025, there may be 2.4–3.4 billion people in such countries. Income level and location determine how many of these people have access to a reliable and safe water supply.

Some areas have lots of water, but the largest rivers (which carry most of the runoff) are far from agricultural and population centers. For example, South America has the largest annual water runoff of any continent, but 60% of the runoff flows through the Amazon River in remote areas where few people live.

In some areas, overall precipitation may be plentiful but **(1)** most arrives during short periods or **(2)** cannot be collected and stored because of a lack of water storage capacity. For example, only a few hours of rain provide over half of India's rainfall during a four-month monsoon season.

Even when a plentiful supply of water exists, most of the 1.2 billion poor people living on less than $1 a day cannot afford a safe supply of drinking water and live in hydrological poverty. Most are cut off from municipal water supplies and **(1)** must collect water from unsafe sources or **(2)** buy water (often coming from polluted rivers) from private vendors at high prices. In developing countries, people not connected to municipal water supplies on average pay 12 times more per liter of water than people connected to such systems, and in some areas they pay up to 100 times as much.

Since the 1970s, water scarcity intensified by prolonged drought has killed more than 24,000 people per year and created millions of environmental refugees. In water-short rural areas in developing countries, many women (Figure 12-27, p. 271) and children must walk long distances each day, carrying heavy jars or cans, to get a meager and sometimes contaminated supply of water.

A number of analysts believe that *access to water resources, already a key foreign policy and environmental and economic security issue for water-short countries*

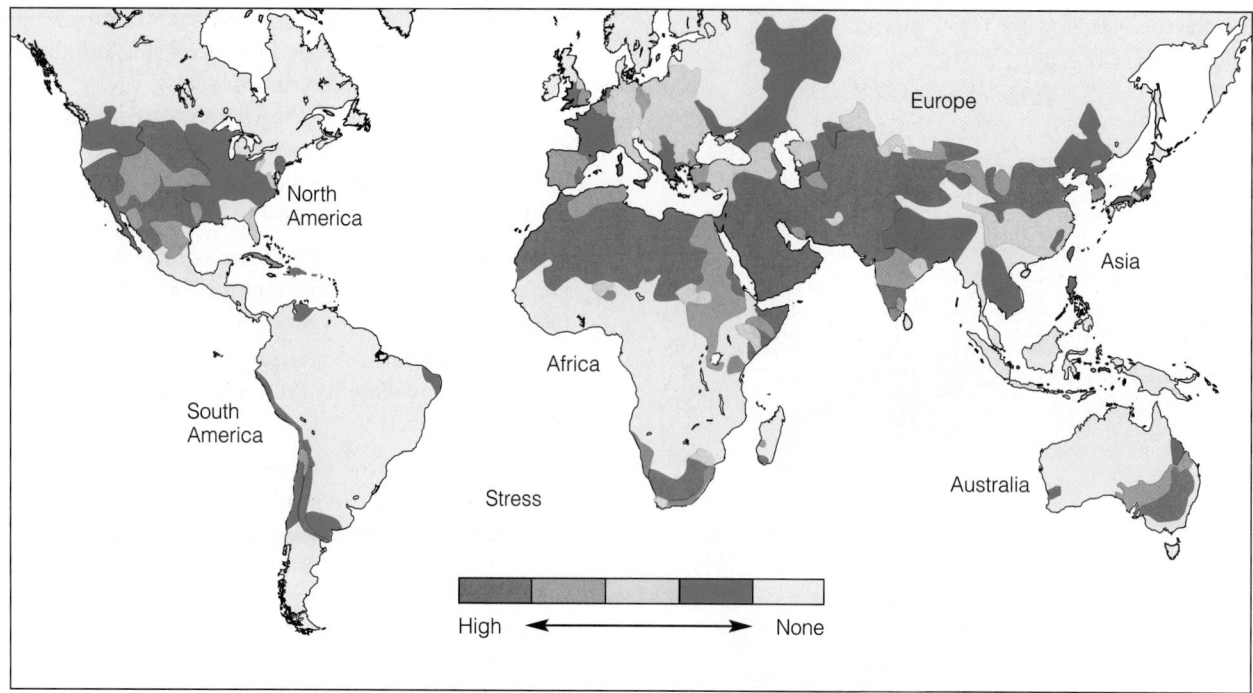

**Figure 14-8** Stress on the world's major river basins, based on a comparison of the amount of water available with the amount used by humans. (Data from World Commission on Water Use in the 21st Century)

(p. 312), *will become even more important over the next 10–25 years.*

**How Can We Increase Freshwater Supplies?**
Six ways to increase the supply of fresh water in a particular area are to **(1)** build dams and reservoirs to store runoff, **(2)** bring in surface water from another area, **(3)** withdraw groundwater, **(4)** convert salt water to fresh water (desalination), **(5)** waste less water, and **(6)** import food to reduce water use.

In *developed countries*, people tend to live where the climate is favorable and then bring in water from another watershed. For example, since 1900 the United States has spent at least $400 billion—mostly as government subsidies—in building dams, reservoirs, aqueducts, pipelines, and flood control levees to manage and supply farmers and cities with low-cost water and hydroelectric power.

In *developing countries*, most people (especially the rural poor) must settle where the water is and try to capture the precipitation they need. Millions of the more than 820 million undernourished people live in poor farm families in Asia and Africa, where long dry seasons make crop production difficult or impossible without irrigation. But conventional irrigation techniques are too expensive for many of these rural poor people. *Poverty is the principal cause of hunger, malnutri-*

*tion, and lack of access to sufficient water, regardless of how much water is available.*

Thirty-six water-stressed countries in Asia, Africa, and the Middle East (Figure 14-8) account for 26% of global grain imports. As water stress increases in coming decades, such imports are likely to rise.

## 14-4 USING DAMS AND RESERVOIRS TO SUPPLY MORE WATER

**What Are the Pros and Cons of Large Dams and Reservoirs?** Large dams and reservoirs have benefits and drawbacks (Figure 14-9 and Case Study, p. 321). The main purpose is to capture and store runoff and release it as needed for **(1)** controlling floods, **(2)** producing hydroelectric power, and **(3)** supplying water for irrigation and for towns and cities. Reservoirs also provide recreational activities such as swimming, fishing, and boating.

Between 1950 and 2000, the number of large dams (more than 15 meters or 49 feet high) has increased nearly sevenfold, from about 5,700 to more than 45,000. In the United States, more than 70,000 dams are capable of capturing and storing half of the country's entire river flow.

As a result, many rivers resemble an elaborate plumbing system, with multiple dams used to control

Large losses of water through evaporation

Flooded land destroys forests or cropland and displaces people

Downstream flooding is reduced

Downstream cropland and estuaries are deprived of nutrient-rich silt

Provides water for year-round irrigation of cropland

Reservoir is useful for recreation and fishing

Can produce cheap electricity (hydropower)

Migration and spawning of some fish are disrupted

**Figure 14-9** Main advantages (green) and disadvantages (orange) of large dams and reservoirs. The world's 45,000 large dams now impound about 14% of the world's runoff.

the timing and flow of water, like water from a faucet. This engineering approach to river management often impairs the important ecological services that rivers provide (Figure 14-10). For example, according to water-resource expert Peter H. Gleck, more than 24% of the world's freshwater fish species are threatened or endangered, primarily because dams and water withdrawals have destroyed the free-flowing river ecosystems (Figure 7-23, p. 160) where they once thrived.

Some *good news* is that these dams have increased the annual runoff available for human use by nearly one-third. Some *bad news* is that a series of dams on a

river, especially in arid areas, can reduce downstream flow to a trickle and prevent it from reaching the sea as a part of the hydrologic cycle. According to the World Commission on Water in the 21st Century, half of the world's major rivers either **(1)** run dry part of the year and fail to reach the ocean or **(2)** have little water left in them when they get to the sea. Causes include a combination of **(1)** prolonged drought in some areas, **(2)** dams, and **(3)** increased diversion of water for irrigation and for cities.

Major rivers that run dry and do not reach the sea anymore during the dry season include the **(1)** Colorado in the southwestern United States (Figure 14-11, p. 320 and Case Study, p. 322), **(2)** Rio Grande along the border between Texas and Mexico, **(3)** Yellow in northern China, **(4)** Nile in the Middle East (Figure 14-1), **(5)** Ganges and Indus in South Asia, and **(6)** Amu Darya and Syr Darya in five counties that once were part of the Soviet Union.

**Figure 14-10** Some ecological services provided by rivers. Currently, the services are given little or no monetary value when the costs and benefits of dam and reservoir projects are assessed. According to environmental economists, attaching even crudely estimated monetary values to these ecosystem services would help sustain them.

• **Deliver nutrients to the sea, which helps to sustain coastal fisheries**

• **Deposit silt that maintains deltas**

• **Purify water**

• **Renew and nourish wetlands**

• **Provide habitats for aquatic life**

• **Conserve species diversity**

A small number of countries have taken some steps to remove the old, dangerous, or environmentally harmful dams. In 1998 and 1999, for example, two dams in France's Loire River basin were demolished to help restore the region's fisheries. In 1999, a dam on Maine's Kennebac River was dismantled to open up a 29-kilometer(18-mile) stretch of the river for fish spawning. It is one of 500 dams that have been removed from U.S. rivers in the past few years.

**Figure 14-11** *The Colorado River basin.* The area drained by this basin is equal to more than one-twelfth of the land area of the lower 48 states.

supposed to be completed by 2009 at an estimated cost of $25–65 billion.

According to Chinese officials, this superdam, with the electric output of 20 large coal-burning or nuclear power plants, will

- Generate almost 10% of China's electricity for use by industries and about 150 million people.

- Help China reduce its dependence on coal, which causes severe air pollution and releases enormous amounts of the greenhouse gas carbon dioxide into the atmosphere.

- Hold back the Yangtze River's floodwaters, which have killed more than 500,000 people during the past 100 years including 4,000 people in 1998. According to Chinese officials, the 15 million people living in the Yangtze River Valley will benefit from such flood protection. This greatly exceeds the 1.9 million people who will be relocated from the area to be flooded to form a gigantic 600-kilometer-long (370-mile-long) reservoir behind the dam (Figure 14-12, right).

- Reduce flooding and silting of the river by eroded soil.

**Case Study: China's Three Gorges Dam**  When completed, China's Three Gorges project on the mountainous upper reaches of the Yangtze River (Figure 14-12) will be the world's largest hydroelectric dam and reservoir. This 2-kilometer-(1.2-mile-) long dam is

**Figure 14-12** Site of the Three Gorges dam—the world's largest dam— on China's Yangtze River.

## Egypt's Aswan High Dam: Blessing or Disaster?

The Aswan High Dam on the Nile River in Egypt and its Lake Nasser reservoir (Figure 14-1) were built in the 1960s and demonstrate the mix of advantages and disadvantages of such projects.

The project's major benefits include the following:

- Supplying about one-half of Egypt's electrical power and reducing electricity prices.

- Storing and releasing water for irrigation, which is used to grow all of Egypt's food. This saved Egypt's rice and cotton crops during severe droughts in the 1970s and 1980s and helped avert massive famines. To many Egyptians, this more than paid for the cost of the dam.

- Increasing food production by allowing year-round irrigation of land in the lower Nile basin. Since 1970, this has helped increase Egypt's agricultural income by about 200%.

- Improving navigation along the river.

- Providing flood control for the lower Nile basin.

However, the project has also produced the following harmful ecological and economic effects:

- Ending the yearly flooding that for thousands of years had fertilized the Nile's floodplain with silt, most of it washed down from the Ethiopian highlands. Now the river's silt accumulates behind the dam, filling Lake Nasser and eventually will make the dam useless.

- Necessitating the use of commercial fertilizer on cropland in the Nile Delta basin at an annual cost of more than $100 million to make up for plant nutrients once available at no cost. The country's new fertilizer plants use up much of the electrical power produced by the dam.

- Increasing salinization (Figure 10-22, p. 221) because there is no natural annual flooding to flush salts from the irrigated soil. This has offset about three-fourths of the gain in food production from new land irrigated by water from the reservoir.

- Eliminating 94% of Nile water that once reached the Mediterranean Sea each year and upsetting the ecology of waters near the mouth of the Nile.

- Eliminating the annual sediment discharge where the Nile reaches the sea. This has **(1)** caused the coastal delta to erode and advance inland and **(2)** reduced productivity on large areas of agricultural land.

- Eradicating most of Egypt's sardine, mackerel, shrimp, and lobster fishing industries because nutrient-rich silt no longer reaches the river's mouth. This has led to losses of **(1)** approximately 30,000 jobs, **(2)** millions of dollars annually, and **(3)** an important source of protein for Egyptians. However, a new fishing industry taking bass, catfish, and carp from Lake Nasser has offset some of these losses.

- Uprooting 125,000 people when land was flooded to create Lake Nasser and changing nomadic grazing patterns.

In 1997, the Egyptian government **(1)** opened a new canal to transfer Nile water under the Suez Canal to irrigate land in the Sinai desert and **(2)** began a 20-year project to divert Nile water upstream from Lake Nasser and transport it hundreds of kilometers to irrigate land in Egypt's southwestern desert. This will open up land for human settlement to relieve population pressures in the crowded Nile valley.

These plans are threatened because about 80% of the water flowing into Lake Nasser comes from Ethiopia (Figure 14-1), which plans to build dams for irrigation and hydropower projects. This may not leave enough water in the Nile to support Egypt's plans for increased irrigation and could increase tension between the two countries.

Some analysts believe the Aswan dam's benefits outweigh its economic and ecological costs. Other analysts consider it an economic and ecological disaster. Time will tell who is right.

### Critical Thinking

**1.** Do you believe the benefits of the Aswan High Dam outweigh its drawbacks? Explain.

**2.** List two principles for designing and building large dams based on lessons from the Aswan High Dam.

---

Critics point to a number of drawbacks of the Yangtze dam and reservoir project:

- Forming the huge reservoir will **(1)** flood large areas of productive farmland and forests and **(2)** displace about 1.9 million people from their homes.

- The region's entire ecosystem will be radically changed.

- Water pollution will increase because of the river's reduced water flow.

- If the reservoir fills up with sediment and overflows (especially if the reservoir is kept filled at a high level, as planned, to provide maximum hydroelectric power), half a million people will be exposed to severe flooding.

- Annual deposits of nutrient-rich sediments below the dam will be reduced.

- The reduced downstream water flow will promote saltwater intrusion into drinking water supplies near the mouth of the river.

## The Colorado River Basin

The Colorado River flows 2,300 kilometers (1,400 miles) from the mountains of central Colorado to the Mexican border and eventually to the Gulf of California (Figure 14-11, p. 320). During the past 50 years, this once free-flowing river has been tamed by a gigantic plumbing system consisting of (1) 14 major dams and reservoirs (Figure 14-11), (2) hundreds of smaller dams, and (3) a network of aqueducts and canals that supply water to farmers, ranchers, and cities.

Today, this domesticated river provides (1) electricity (from hydroelectric plants at major dams), (2) water for more than 25 million people in seven states, (3) water used to produce about 15% of the nation's produce and livestock, and (4) a multibillion-dollar recreation industry of whitewater rafting, boating, fishing, camping, and hiking enjoyed by more than 15 million people a year.

Take away this tamed river and (1) Las Vegas, Nevada, would be a mostly uninhabited desert area, (2) San Diego, California (which gets 70% of its water from the Colorado), could not support its present population, and (3) California's Imperial Valley (which grows a major portion of the nation's vegetables) would consist mostly of cactus and mesquite plants.

However, three major problems are associated with use of this river's water:

- The Colorado River basin includes some of the driest lands in the United States and Mexico (Figure 14-7).

- Legal pacts in 1922 and 1944 allocated more water to the states in the river's *upper basin* (Wyoming, Utah, Colorado, and New Mexico) and *lower basin* (Arizona, Nevada, and California; Figure 14-11) and to Mexico than now flows through the river, even in years without a drought.

- Because of so many withdrawals, the river rarely makes it to the Gulf of California. Instead, it fizzles into a trickle that disappears into the Mexican desert or (in drought years) the Arizona desert. This (1) threatens the survival of species that spawn in the river, (2) destroys estuaries that serve as breeding grounds for numerous aquatic species, and (3) increases saltwater contamination of aquifers near coasts.

Legal battles are increasing over how much of the river's limited water can be withdrawn and used by (1) cities, (2) farmers, (3) ranchers, and (4) Native Americans (who as senior owners of water rights dating back to the mid-1880s have the law on their side and have been winning legal battles to withdraw more water).

Environmentalists have initiated mostly unsuccessful attempts to keep more of the river wild by (1) not building so many large dams and (2) removing some of the existing dams to help protect the river's ecological services (Figure 14-10).

Traditionally, about 80% of the water withdrawn from the Colorado has been used to irrigate crops and raise cattle because ranchers and farmers (after Native Americans) got there first and established legal rights to use a certain amount of water each year. This large-scale use of water for agriculture was made possible because the government (1) paid for the dams and reservoirs and (2) under long-term contracts has supplied many of the farmers and ranchers with water at a very low price. This has led to inefficient use of irrigation water and growing crops such as rice, cotton, and alfalfa (for cattle feed) that need a lot of water.

Some cities (such as Tucson, Arizona, and Colorado Springs, Colorado) have been buying up the legal water rights of nearby farmers and ranchers. Others are paying farmers to install less wasteful irrigation systems (Figure 14-18, p. 330) so more water will be available to support urban areas. It is estimated that improving overall irrigation efficiency by about 10–15% would provide enough water to support projected urban growth in the areas served by the river to 2020.

These controversies illustrate the problems that governments and people in semiarid regions with shared river systems face as population and economic growth place increasing demands on limited supplies of surface water.

### Critical Thinking

1. What are the pros and cons of reducing or eliminating government subsidies that provide U. S. farmers, ranchers, and cities with cheap water from the Colorado River?

2. If the legal system allowed it, put the following users in order of how much water you would allocate to them from the Colorado River: farmers, ranchers, cities, Native Americans, and Mexico. Explain your choices.

## 14-5 TRANSFERRING WATER FROM ONE PLACE TO ANOTHER

**What Are the Pros and Cons of Large-Scale Water Transfers?** Tunnels, aqueducts, and underground pipes can transfer stream runoff collected by dams and reservoirs from water-rich areas to water-poor areas. Although such transfers have benefits, they also create environmental problems (Case Study, p. 324). Indeed, most of the world's dam projects and large-scale water transfers illustrate the important ecological principle that *you cannot do just one thing.*

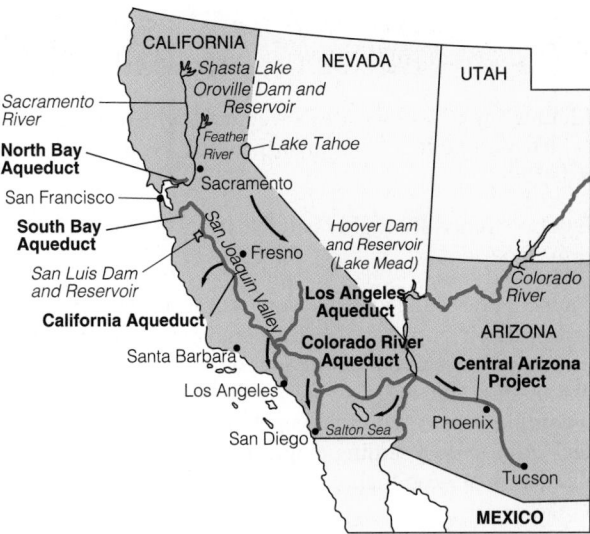

**Figure 14-13** The California Water Project and the Central Arizona Project involve large-scale water transfers from one watershed to another. Arrows show the general direction of water flow.

One of the world's largest watershed transfer projects is the *California Water Project*. In California, the basic water problem is that 75% of the population lives south of Sacramento, but 75% of the state's rain occurs north of Sacramento.

The California Water Project uses a maze of giant dams, pumps, and aqueducts to transport water from water-rich northern California to heavily populated areas and to arid and semiarid agricultural regions, mostly in southern California (Figure 14-13).

For decades, northern and southern Californians have been feuding over how the state's water should be allocated under this project. Southern Californians say they need more water from the north to support Los Angeles, San Diego, and other growing urban areas and to grow more crops. Agriculture uses 74% of the water withdrawn in California, much of it for water-thirsty crops. For example, alfalfa, one of the most water-intensive crops, is grown in the southern California desert. It uses about one-fourth of California's irrigation water but makes up only 0.1% of the state's economy.

Opponents in the north say that sending more water south would **(1)** degrade the Sacramento River, **(2)** threaten fisheries, and **(3)** reduce the flushing action that helps clean San Francisco Bay of pollutants. They also argue that **(1)** much of the water sent south is wasted unnecessarily and **(2)** making irrigation just 10% more efficient would provide enough water for domestic and industrial uses in southern California. However, if water supplies in northern California and in the Colorado River basin (Figure 14-11) drop sharply because of global warming, the amount of

water delivered by the huge distribution system will plummet.

Pumping out more groundwater is not the answer because groundwater is already being withdrawn faster than it is replenished throughout much of California. To most analysts, quicker and cheaper solutions are **(1)** improving irrigation efficiency and **(2)** allowing farmers to sell their legal rights to withdraw certain amounts of water from rivers.

**Case Study: The James Bay Watershed Transfer Project** Another major watershed transfer project is Canada's James Bay project. It is a $60-billion 50-year scheme to harness the wild rivers that flow into Quebec's James and Hudson Bays to produce electric power for Canadian and U.S. consumers (Figure 14-14).

If completed, this megaproject would **(1)** construct 600 dams and dikes that will reverse or alter the flow of 19 giant rivers covering a watershed three times the size of New York State, **(2)** flood an area of boreal forest and tundra equal in area to Washington State or Germany, and **(3)** displace thousands of indigenous Cree and Inuit, who for 5,000 years have lived off James Bay by subsistence hunting, fishing, and trapping.

After 20 years, the $16-billion phase I has been completed. The second and much larger phase was

**Figure 14-14** If completed, the James Bay project in northern Quebec will alter or reverse the flow of 19 major rivers and flood an area the size of the state of Washington to produce hydropower for consumers in Quebec and the United States, especially in New York State. Phase I of this 50-year project is completed.

## The Aral Sea Water Transfer Disaster

**CASE STUDY**

The shrinking of the Aral Sea (see figure) is a result of a large-scale water transfer project in an area of the former Soviet Union with the driest climate in central Asia. Since 1960, enormous amounts of irrigation water have been diverted from the inland Aral Sea and its two feeder rivers to create one of the world's largest irrigated areas. The irrigation canal, the world's longest, stretches over 1,300 kilometers (800 miles).

This water diversion project (coupled with droughts) and high evaporation rates in this hot, dry climate has caused a regional ecological, economic, and health disaster. Problems caused by this massive water-diversion project include:

- Tripling of the sea's salinity.

- Decreasing the sea's surface area by 54% (see figure) and its volume by 75%.

- Reducing the sea's two supply rivers to mere trickles.

- Converting about 36,000 square kilometers (14,000 square miles) of former lake bottom to a human-made desert covered with glistening white salt.

- Causing the presumed extinction of 20 of the area's 24 native fish species as the salt concentrations in the sea's water have increased. This has devastated the area's fishing industry, which once provided work for more than 60,000 people. Fishing villages and boats once on the sea's coastline now are in the middle of a salt desert and have been abandoned.

- Eliminating 85% of the area's wetlands, which along with increased pollution has greatly reduced waterfowl populations.

- Disappearance of roughly half the area's bird and mammal species.

- Causing one of the world's worst salinization problems. Winds pick up the salty dust that encrusts the lake's now-exposed bed and blow it onto fields as far as 300 kilometers (190 miles) away. As the salt spreads, it kills wildlife, crops, and other vegetation and pollutes water. Aral Sea dust settling on glaciers in the Himalayas is causing them to melt at a faster than normal rate.

- Increasing groundwater and surface water pollution. To raise yields, farmers have increased inputs of herbicides, insecticides, fertilizers, and irrigation water on some crops. Many of these chemicals have percolated downward and accumulated to dangerous levels in the groundwater, from which most of the region's drinking water comes. The lower river flows have also concentrated salts, pesticides, and other toxic chemicals, making surface water supplies hazardous to drink.

- Alteration of the area's climate. The once-huge sea acted as a thermal buffer that moderated the heat of summer and the extreme cold of winter. Now **(1)** there is less rain, **(2)** summers are hotter and drier, **(3)** winters are colder, and **(4)** the growing season is shorter.

- Reduction of crop yields by 20–50% from a combination of climate change and severe salinization of almost a

---

postponed indefinitely in 1994 because of **(1)** an excess of power generated, **(2)** opposition by the Cree (whose ancestral hunting grounds would have been flooded) and Canadian and U.S. environmentalists, and **(3)** New York State's cancellation of two contracts to buy electricity produced by phase II.

## 14-6 TAPPING GROUNDWATER, CONVERTING SALT WATER TO FRESH WATER, SEEDING CLOUDS, AND TOWING ICEBERGS

**What Are the Advantages of Withdrawing Groundwater?** Pumping groundwater from aquifers has several advantages over tapping more erratic flows from streams. Groundwater **(1)** can be removed as needed year round, **(2)** is not lost by evap-

oration, and **(3)** usually is less expensive to develop than surface water systems.

Aquifers provide drinking water for almost one-third of the world's people. In Asia alone, more than 1 billion people depend on groundwater for drinking. In the United States, water pumped from aquifers supplies about **(1)** 51% of the drinking water (96% in rural areas and 20% in urban areas) and **(2)** 43% of irrigation water.

 **What Are the Disadvantages of Withdrawing Groundwater?** Withdrawing groundwater from aquifers faster than it is replenished can cause or intensify several problems: **(1)** *water table lowering* (Figure 14-15, p. 326), **(2)** *aquifer depletion* (Figure 14-16, top, p. 326), **(3)** *aquifer subsidence* (sinking of land when groundwater is withdrawn, Figure 14-16, bottom),

KAZAKHSTAN

2000

1989

1960

ARAL SEA

Syr Dar'ya

UZBEKISTAN

Amu Dar'ya

TURKMENISTAN

Once the world's fourth largest freshwater lake, the Aral Sea has been shrinking and getting saltier since 1960 because most of the water from the rivers that replenish it has been diverted to grow cotton and food crops. As the lake shrinks, it leaves behind a salty desert, economic ruin, increasing health problems, and severe ecological disruption.

number of the 58 million people living in the Aral Sea's watershed. Such problems include abnormally high rates of **(1)** infant mortality, **(2)** tuberculosis, **(3)** anemia, **(4)** respiratory illness (one of the world's highest), **(5)** eye diseases (from salt dust), **(6)** throat cancer, **(7)** kidney and liver diseases (especially cancers), **(8)** arthritic diseases, **(9)** typhoid fever, and **(10)** hepatitis.

Can the Aral Sea be saved, and can the area's serious ecological and human health problems be reduced? Since 1999, the United Nations and the World Bank have spent about $600 million to **(1)** purify drinking water, **(2)** upgrade irrigation and drainage systems to improve irrigation efficiency, flush salts from croplands, and boost crop productivity, and **(3)** construct wetlands and artificial lakes to help restore aquatic vegetation, wildlife, and fisheries. However, this process will take decades and will not prevent the shrinkage of the Aral Sea into a few brine lakes.

### Critical Thinking

What ecological and economic lessons can we learn from the Aral Sea tragedy?

third of the area's cropland. More water could be withdrawn to flush out and lessen the area's acute salt problem. But Russian scientists estimate that freeing up this much water would mean retiring about half of the area's irrigated cropland, an unthinkable solution considering the region's already dire economic conditions.

- Greatly increased health problems from a combination of toxic dust, salt, and contaminated water for a growing

**(4)** *intrusion of salt water into aquifers,* **(5)** *drawing of chemical contamination in groundwater toward wells,* and **(6)** *reduced stream flow* because of diminished flows of groundwater into streams. Also, industrial and agricultural activities, septic tanks, and other sources can contaminate groundwater.

According to Earth Policy Institute and the World Resources Institute, water tables are falling in many areas as the rate of water pumping exceeds the rate of recharge from precipitation. Such unsustainable *water mining* from overpumping aquifers produces about 8% of the world's current grain harvest. This is causing water tables to fall in

- The North China Plain, which produces more than half of China's wheat and a third of its corn. A 2001 survey found that the aquifer under North China's plain is falling faster than previously thought.

- Agricultural areas in **(1)** parts of the southern Great Plains of the United States, which are served by the gigantic but essentially nonrenewable Ogallala aquifer (Case Study, p. 327) and **(2)** in parts of the arid southwestern United States (Figure 14-7, top), especially California's Central Valley, which supplies about half the country's vegetables and fruits.

- Much of India, especially the Punjab. This jeopardizes as much as one-fourth of India's grain production.

- Parts of **(1)** Saudi Arabia, **(2)** northern Africa (especially Libya and Tunisia), **(3)** southern Europe, **(4)** the Middle East, and **(5)** Mexico, Thailand, and Pakistan.

According to water resource expert Sandra Postel, about 480 million of the world's 6.2 million people are being fed with grain produced with eventually unsustainable water mining from aquifers. This example of

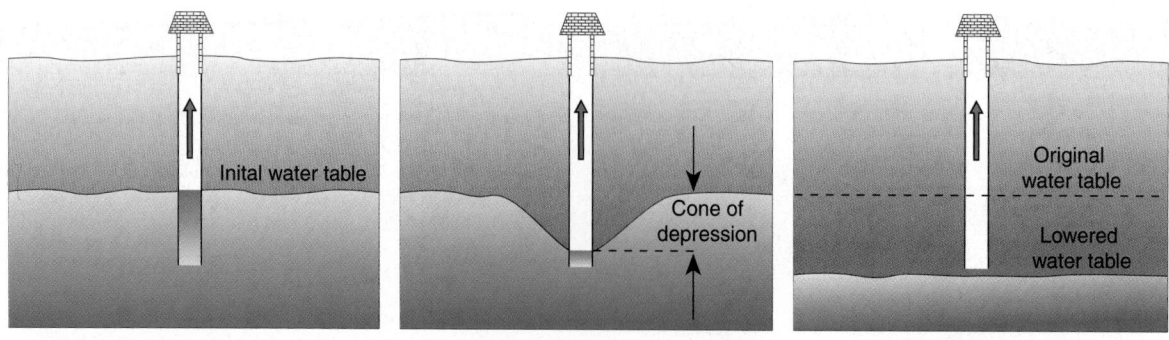

**Figure 14-15** Lowering of the water table when a well is drilled into an aquifer (left). A cone of depression (middle) in the water table forms if groundwater is pumped to the surface faster than it can flow through the aquifer to the well. If this excessive water removal continues, the water table falls (right).

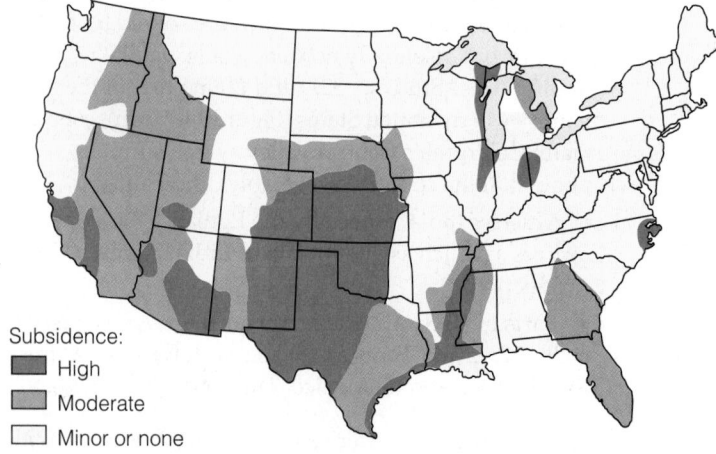

**Figure 14-16** Areas of greatest aquifer depletion from groundwater overdraft (top) and ground subsidence (bottom) in the continental United States. Aquifer depletion is also high in Hawaii and Puerto Rico (not shown on map). (Data from U.S. Water Resources Council and U.S. Geological Survey)

the tragedy of the commons (Connections, p. 11) is expected to increase as irrigated areas are expanded to help feed the 3.1 billion more people projected to join the ranks of humanity between 2002 and 2050.

Overpumping is a new phenomenon that has largely occurred since 1950 because of the development of increasingly powerful electric and diesel pumps that can remove water from an aquifer faster than it is renewed by precipitation. With water worth up to 70 times more in industry and cities as in agriculture, farmers almost always lose in the competition for scarce water.

In addition to limiting future food production, overpumping aquifers is increasing the gap between the rich and poor in some areas. As water tables drop, farmers must **(1)** drill deeper wells, **(2)** buy larger pumps to bring the water to the surface, and **(3)** use more electricity to run the pumps. Poor farmers cannot afford to do this and end up losing their land and either working for richer farmers or hoping to survive by migrating to cities.

When fresh water from an aquifer near a coast is withdrawn faster than it is recharged, salt water intrudes into the aquifer (Figure 14-17, p. 328). Such intrusion can contaminate drinking water supplies of many towns and cities along coastal areas.

Ways to prevent or slow groundwater depletion include **(1)** controlling population growth, **(2)** not planting water-intensive crops such as cotton and sugarcane in dry areas, **(3)** shifting to crops that need less water in dry areas, **(4)** developing crop strains that need less water and are more resistant to heat stress, **(5)** wasting less irriga-

## Mining Groundwater: The Shrinking Ogallala Aquifer

Large amounts of water have been pumped from the Ogallala, the world's largest known aquifer (see figure). This has helped transform vast areas of arid high plains prairie land into one of the largest and most productive agricultural regions in the United States.

Mostly because of irrigated farming, this region produces 20% of U.S. agricultural output (including 40% of its feedlot beef), valued at $32 billion per year. This has brought prosperity to many farmers and merchants in this region. But the largely hidden environmental and economic cost has been increasing aquifer depletion in some areas.

Although this aquifer is gigantic, it is essentially nonrenewable (stored during the retreat of the last ice age about 15,000–30,000 years ago) with an extremely slow recharge rate. In some areas, water is being pumped out of the aquifer 8–10 times faster than the aquifer's natural recharge rate.

The northernmost states (Wyoming, North Dakota, South Dakota, and parts of Colorado) still have ample supplies. However, supplies in parts of the southern states, where the aquifer is thinner (see figure), are being depleted rapidly, with about two-thirds of the aquifer's depletion taking place in the Texas high plains.

Water experts project that at the current rate of withdrawal, one-fourth of the aquifer's original supply will be depleted by 2020 and much sooner in areas where it is shallow. It will take thousands of years to replenish the aquifer.

Government subsidies designed to increase crop production also increase depletion of the Ogallala by **(1)** encouraging farmers to grow water-thirsty cotton in the lower basin, **(2)** providing crop-disaster payments, and **(3)** providing tax breaks in the form of groundwater depletion allowances, with larger breaks for heavier groundwater use.

Depletion of this essentially nonrenewable water resource can be delayed if farmers **(1)** use more efficient forms of irrigation (Figure 14-18, p. 330), **(2)** switch to crops that need less water, or **(3)** irrigate less land.

Cities using this groundwater can also implement policies and technologies to reduce their water use and waste. People enjoying the benefits of this aquifer can help by **(1)** installing water-saving toilets and showerheads and **(2)** converting their lawns to plants that can survive in an arid climate with little watering (Figure 14-21, p. 332).

### Critical Thinking

**1.** What are the pros and cons of giving government subsidies to farmers and ranchers using water withdrawn from the Ogallala to grow crops and raise livestock that need large amounts of irrigation water? How do you benefit from such subsidies?

**2.** Should these government subsidies be reduced or eliminated and replaced with subsidies that encourage farmers to use more efficient forms of irrigation and switch to crops that need less water? Explain.

Saturated thickness of Ogallala Aquifer

Less than 61 meters (200 ft.)

61–183 meters (200–600 ft.)

More than 183 meters (600 ft.)
(as much as 370 meters or 1,200 ft. in places)

The Ogallala is the world's largest known aquifer. If the water in this aquifer were above ground, it could cover all 50 states with 0.5 meter (1.5 feet) of water. Water withdrawn from this aquifer is used to grow crops, raise cattle, and provide cities and industries with water. As a result, this aquifer, which is renewed very slowly, is being depleted (especially at its thin southern end in parts of Texas, New Mexico, Oklahoma, and Kansas). (Data from U.S. Geological Survey)

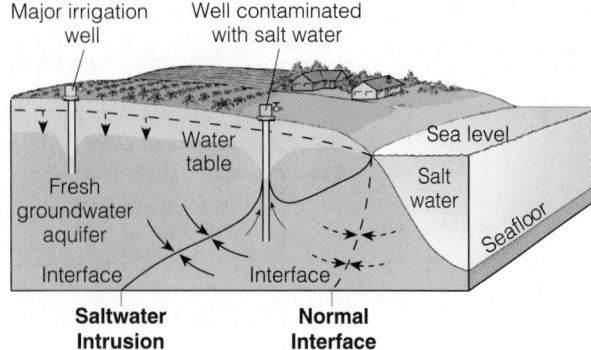

**Major irrigation well**  **Well contaminated with salt water**

Water table

Sea level

Salt water

Fresh groundwater aquifer

Seafloor

Interface  Interface

**Saltwater Intrusion**    **Normal Interface**

**Figure 14-17** Saltwater intrusion along a coastal region. When the water table is lowered, the normal interface (dashed line) between fresh and saline groundwater moves inland (solid line), making groundwater drinking supplies unusable.

tion water, and **(6)** importing grain, with each imported metric ton of grain saving roughly 1,000 metric tons of water needed to produce the grain.

**How Useful Is Desalination?**   Removing dissolved salts from ocean water or from brackish (slightly salty) groundwater, called **desalination,** is another way to increase supplies of fresh water. The two most widely used methods are:

- *Distillation,* which involves heating salt water until it evaporates (and leaves behind salts in solid form) and condenses as fresh water.

- *Reverse osmosis,* in which salt water is pumped at high pressure through a thin membrane whose pores allow water molecules, but not dissolved salts, to pass through. In effect, high pressure is used to push freshwater out of salt water.

About 13,300 desalination plants in 120 countries (especially in the arid, desert nations in the Middle East, North Africa, the Caribbean, and the Mediterranean) meet less than 0.2% of the world's water needs. Desalination would have to increase 25-fold just to supply 5% of current world water use.

This is unlikely because desalination has two major disadvantages:

- *It is expensive because it takes large amounts of energy.* Desalinating water costs 2–3 times as much as the conventional purification of fresh water.

- *It produces large quantities of wastewater (brine) containing high levels of salt and other minerals.* Dumping the concentrated brine into the ocean near the plants increases the local salt concentration and threatens food resources in estuary waters, and dumping it on land could contaminate groundwater and surface water.

Desalination can provide fresh water for coastal cities in arid countries (such as sparsely populated Saudi Arabia and Israel), where the cost of getting fresh water by any method is high. In the United States, desalination plants are used to meet some of the water needs along coastal areas of Florida, southern California, Virginia, North Carolina, and Texas.

Scientists are working to develop new membranes for reverse osmosis that can separate water from salt more efficiently and under less pressure. If successful, this strategy could help bring down the cost of using desalinization to produce drinking water. However, desalinated water probably will not be cheap enough to irrigate conventional crops or meet much of the world's demand for fresh water unless **(1)** affordable solar-powered distillation plants can be developed, and **(2)** someone can figure out what to do with the resulting mountains of salt.

**Can Cloud Seeding and Towing Icebergs Improve Water Supplies?**   For decades, several countries, particularly the United States, have been experimenting with seeding clouds with tiny particles of chemicals (such as silver iodide). The particles form water condensation nuclei and thus produce more rain over dry regions and more snow over mountains.

However, cloud seeding **(1)** is not useful in very dry areas, where it is most needed, because rain clouds rarely are available there and **(2)** would introduce large amounts of the cloud-seeding chemicals into soil and water systems, possibly harming people, wildlife, and agricultural productivity.

Another obstacle to cloud seeding is legal disputes over the ownership of water in clouds. During the 1977 drought in the western United States, the attorney general of Idaho accused officials in neighboring Washington of "cloud rustling" and threatened to file suit in federal court.

Some have proposed towing huge icebergs to arid coastal areas (such as Saudi Arabia and southern California) and then pumping the fresh water from the melting bergs ashore. But the technology for doing this is not available and the costs may be too high, especially for water-short developing countries.

## 14-7 USING WATER MORE EFFICIENTLY

**What Are the Benefits of Reducing Water Waste?**   Mohamed El-Ashry of the World Resources Institute estimates that *65–70% of the water people use throughout the world is lost through evaporation, leaks, and other losses.* The United States, the world's largest user of water, does slightly better but still loses about 50% of

## Water Rights in the United States

**SPOTLIGHT**

Laws regulating access to and use of surface water differ in the eastern and western parts of the United States. In most of the East, water use is based on the *doctrine of riparian rights*.

Basically, this system of water law gives anyone whose land adjoins a flowing stream the right to use water from the stream as long as some is left for downstream landowners. However, as population and water-intensive land uses grow, there is often too little water to meet the needs of all the people along a stream.

In the arid and semiarid West, the riparian system does not work because large amounts of water are needed in areas far from major surface water sources. In most of this region, the *principle of prior appropriation* regulates water use.

In this first-come, first-served approach, the first user of water

from a stream establishes a legal right for continued use of the amount originally withdrawn. If a shortage occurs, later users are cut off in order until enough water is available to satisfy the demands of the earlier users. Some states have a combination of riparian and prior appropriation water rights.

Most groundwater use in the United States is based on *common law*, which holds that subsurface water belongs to whoever owns the land above such water. This allows landowners to withdraw as much groundwater as they want. Because the largest users have little incentive to conserve, this can deplete the aquifer for everyone and create a tragedy of the commons (Connections, p. 11).

A system of legally protected water rights allows individuals owning rights to **(1)** sell, trade, or lease them to make money, **(2)** ease water shortages, or **(3)** protect the ecosystem services of rivers

(Figure 14-10). For example, some water-short cities in the western United States are paying nearby farmers to install more efficient irrigation methods in exchange for the water the farmers save.

Private organizations and government agencies are also buying up water rights and using them to help restore aquatic environments by returning the water to rivers and wetlands. However, water markets must be regulated to avoid excessive water prices (especially for the poor) and inequalities in water distribution.

### Critical Thinking

What are the advantages and disadvantages of **(a)** the principles of riparian rights and prior appropriation for access to surface water and **(b)** the common law approach to groundwater use in the United States? If you disagree with these approaches, how would you divide up water rights?

the water it withdraws. El-Ashry believes it is economically and technically feasible to reduce such water losses to 15%, thereby meeting most of the world's water needs for the foreseeable future.

Accomplishing this will require greatly increased use of water-saving technologies and practices. It will **(1)** decrease the burden on wastewater plants, **(2)** reduce the need for expensive dams and water transfer projects that destroy wildlife habitats and displace people, **(3)** slow depletion of groundwater aquifers, and **(4)** save energy and money.

**Why Do We Waste So Much Water?** According to water resource experts, there are three major causes of water waste. One is *water subsidy policies.* Governments and international lending agencies often provide subsidies for development of water supply projects such as dams and large-scale water transfer schemes. This creates artificially low water prices that help water users but discourage improvements in water efficiency. Similar subsidies for improving water efficiency are rare. According to water resource expert Sandra Postel, "By heavily subsidizing water, governments give out the false message that it is abundant

and can afford to be wasted—even as rivers are drying up, aquifers are being depleted, fisheries are collapsing, and species are going extinct."

Government-subsidized irrigation water in the western United States costs U.S. taxpayers an estimated $2–2.5 billion per year. However, farmers, industries, and others benefiting from government water subsidies argue that they **(1)** promote settlement and agricultural production in arid and semiarid areas, **(2)** stimulate local economies, and **(3)** help lower prices of food, manufactured goods, and electricity for consumers.

Water prices may rise as water supplies are being rapidly privatized worldwide. Transnational corporations are buying large supplies of water in dozens of water-short countries for resale at huge profit. Two byproducts of this lucrative business are **(1)** decreased ability of poor farmers and city dwellers to buy enough water to meet their needs and **(2)** political control by such large corporations over any country that imports privately owned water from outside its borders.

A second cause of water waste is *water laws* that determine the legal rights of water users in countries such as the United States (Spotlight, above).

Water is also wasted because of *fragmented watershed management*. The Chicago, Illinois, metropolitan area, for example, has 349 water supply systems divided among some 2,000 local units of government over a six-county area. Water saved by government planning and regulations in one area of a watershed can be offset by lack of such policies in other areas.

**Solutions: How Can We Waste Less Water in Irrigation?** About 57% of the irrigation water applied throughout the world does not reach the targeted crops. Most irrigation systems distribute water from a groundwater well or a surface water source and allow it to flow by gravity through unlined ditches in crop fields so the water can be absorbed by crops (Figure 14-18, left). This *flood irrigation* method **(1)** delivers far more water than needed for crop growth and **(2)** typically allows only 60% of the water to reach crops because of evaporation, seepage, and runoff.

Some *good news* is that more efficient and environmentally sound irrigation technologies exist that could reduce water demands and waste on farms by up to 50%. Here are some examples:

- *Center-pivot low-pressure sprinklers* (Figure 14-18, right), which typically allow 80% of the water input to reach crops and reduce water use over conventional gravity flow systems by 20–25%.

- *Low-energy precision application (LEPA) sprinklers.* This form of center-pivot irrigation allows 90–95% of the water input to reach crops by spraying it closer to the ground and in larger droplets than the center-pivot low-pressure system. LEPA sprinklers use 20–30% less energy than low-pressure sprinklers and typically use 37% less water than conventional gravity flow systems.

- *Using surge or time-controlled valves on conventional gravity flow irrigation systems* (Figure 14-18, left). These valves send water down irrigation ditches in pulses instead of in a continuous stream, which can raise irrigation efficiency to 80% and reduce water use by 25%.

- *Using soil moisture detectors to water crops only when they need it.* For example, some farmers in Texas bury a $1 cube of gypsum, the size of a lump of sugar, at the root zone of crops. Wires embedded in the gypsum are run back to a small portable meter that indicates soil moisture. Farmers using this technique can use 33–66% less irrigation water.

- *Drip irrigation systems* (Figure 14-18, center, and Solutions, p. 333)

Other ways to reduce water waste in irrigating crops are listed in Figure 14-19. Since 1950, water-short Israel has used many of these techniques to slash irrigation water waste by about 84% while irrigating 44% more land. Israel now treats and reuses 30% of its municipal sewage water for crop production and plans to increase this to 80% by 2025. The government also **(1)** gradually removed most government water subsidies to raise the price of irrigation water to one of the highest in the world, **(2)** imports most of its water-intensive wheat and meat, and **(3)** concentrates on growing fruits, vegetables, and flowers that need less

**Gravity Flow**
(efficiency 60% and 80% with surge valves)

Water usually comes from an aqueduct system or a nearby river.

**Drip Irrigation**
(efficiency 90–95%)

Above- or below-ground pipes or tubes deliver water to individual plant roots.

**Center Pivot**
(efficiency 80% with low-pressure sprinkler and 90–95% with LEPA sprinkler)

Water usually pumped from underground and sprayed from mobile boom with sprinklers.

**Figure 14-18** Major irrigation systems. Because of high initial costs, center-pivot irrigation and drip irrigation are used on only about 1% of the world's irrigated cropland each. However, this may change because of the development of new low-cost drip irrigation systems (Solutions, p. 333).

- Lining canals bringing water to irrigation ditches
- Leveling fields with lasers
- Irrigating at night to reduce evaporation
- Using soil and satellite sensors and computer systems to monitor soil moisture and add water only when necessary
- Polyculture
- Organic farming
- Growing water efficient crops using drought-resistant and salt-tolerant crop varieties
- Irrigating with treated urban waste water
- Importing water intensive crops and meat

**Figure 14-19** Methods for reducing water waste in irrigation.

water. In 2001, China announced a policy to raise water prices gradually over a 5-year period to cut down water waste and help prevent a looming water shortage crisis.

Some *bad news* is that more efficient sprinklers are used on only 10% and drip irrigation on just over 1% of the world's irrigated cropfields. This could change with **(1)** development of cheaper sprinkler and drip irrigation technologies (Solutions, p. 333) and **(2)** increased government subsidies for farmers using more efficient irrigation methods.

Many of the world's poor farmers cannot afford to use most of the modern technological methods for increasing irrigation and irrigation efficiency. These farmers increase irrigation by using small-scale and low-cost traditional technologies such as **(1)** pedal-powered treadle pumps to move water through irrigation ditches (widely used in Bangladesh), **(2)** animal-powered irrigation pumps, **(3)** buckets with holes for drip irrigation, **(4)** small dams, ponds, and tanks to collect rainwater for irrigation, **(5)** terracing (Figure 10-26a, p. 224) to reduce water loss on crops grown on steep terrain, and **(6)** cultivating seasonally waterlogged wetlands, delta lands, and valley bottoms.

Paul Polak, a pioneer in low-cost irrigation technologies and president of International Development Enterprises, believes that a realistic goal for the next 15 years is to reduce hunger and poverty for 150 million of the world's poorest rural people by spreading the use of these and other low-cost irrigation techniques for small farms.

**Solutions: How Can We Waste Less Water in Industry, Homes, and Businesses?** Figure 14-20 lists ways to use water more efficiently in industries,

homes, and businesses. Many homeowners and businesses in water-short areas are replacing green lawns in arid and semiarid regions with vegetation adapted to a dry climate (Figure 14-21, p. 332). This form of landscaping, called *xeriscaping* (pronounced "ZER-i-scaping"), reduces water use by 30–85% and sharply reduces inputs of labor, fertilizer, and fuel and the production of polluted runoff, air pollution, and yard wastes.

In Boulder, Colorado, introducing water meters reduced water use by more than one-third. About one-fifth of all U.S. public water systems do not have water meters and charge a single low rate for almost unlimited use of high-quality water. Many apartment dwellers have little incentive to conserve water because their water use is included in their rent.

Because of laws requiring water conservation, the desert city of Tucson, Arizona, consumes half as much water per person as Las Vegas, a desert city with even less rainfall and less emphasis on water conservation (Spotlight, p. 334).

About 50–75% of the water from bathtubs, showers, bathroom sinks, and clothes washers in a typical house could be stored and reused as *gray water* for irrigating lawns and nonedible plants. In the United States, California has become the first state to legalize reuse of gray water to irrigate landscapes. About 65% of the wastewater in Israel is reused in this way. See the website for this chapter for ways you can reduce your personal water use and waste.

- Redesign manufacturing processes
- Landscape yards with plants that require little water
- Use drip irrigation
- Fix water leaks
- Use water meters and charge for all municipal water use
- Raise water prices
- Require water conservation in water-short cities
- Use water-saving toilets, showerheads, and front-loading clothes washers
- Collect and reuse household water to irrigate lawns and nonedible plants
- Purify and reuse water for houses, apartments, and office buildings

**Figure 14-20** Methods of reducing water waste in industries, homes, and businesses.

**Figure 14-21** *Xeriscaping.* This technique can reduce water use by as much as 85% by landscaping with rocks and plants that need little water and are adapted to the growing conditions in arid and semiarid areas. The term Xeriscape® was first used 1978 in Denver, Colorado, and means "water conservation through creative landscaping."

## 14-8 TOO MUCH WATER

**What Are the Causes and Effects of Flooding?** Heavy rain or rapid melting of snow is the major cause of natural flooding by streams. This causes water in a stream to overflow its normal channel and flood the adjacent area, called a **floodplain** (Figure 14-22). Floodplains, which include highly pro-

ductive wetlands (Figure 7-25, p. 162), provide important ecological and economic services by helping to (1) provide natural flood and erosion control, (2) maintain high water quality, and (3) recharge groundwater.

People have settled on floodplains since the beginnings of agriculture. They have many advantages, including (1) fertile soil, (2) ample water for irrigation, (3) flat land suitable for crops, buildings, highways, and railroads, and (4) availability of nearby rivers for transportation and recreation. In the United States, 10 million households and businesses with property valued at $1 trillion are located in flood-prone areas.

Floods are a natural phenomenon and have several benefits. They (1) provide the world's most productive farmland because they are regularly covered with nutrient-rich silt left after floodwaters recede, (2) recharge groundwater, and (3) refill wetlands.

Floods, like droughts, usually are considered natural disasters, but since the 1960s human activities have contributed to the sharp rise in flood deaths and damages. Three ways humans increase the severity of flood damage are by (1) removing water-absorbing vegetation, especially on hillsides (Figure 14-23), (2) draining wetlands that absorb floodwaters and reduce the severity of flooding, and (3) living on floodplains (Connections, p. 335). Urbanization also increases flooding by replacing water-absorbing vegetation, soil, and wetlands with highways, parking lots, and buildings that cannot absorb rainwater.

In developed countries, people deliberately settle on floodplains and then expect dams, levees, and other devices to protect them from floodwaters. However,

**Figure 14-22** Land in a natural floodplain (left) often is flooded after prolonged rains. When the floodwaters recede, deposits of silt are left behind, creating a nutrient-rich soil. To reduce the threat of flooding (and thus allow people to live in floodplains), rivers have been **(1)** dammed to create reservoirs that store and release water as needed, **(2)** narrowed and straightened (channelization), and **(3)** equipped with protective levees and walls (middle). These alterations can give a false sense of security to floodplain dwellers living in high-risk areas. In the long run, such measures can greatly increase flood damage because they can be overwhelmed by prolonged rains (right), as happened along the Mississippi River in the midwestern United States during the summer of 1993.

Oxygen released by vegetation

Diverse ecological habitat

Evapotranspiration

Trees reduce soil erosion from heavy rain and wind

Agricultural land

Steady river flow

Leaf litter improves soil fertility

Tree roots stabilize soil and aid water flow

Vegetation releases water slowly and reduces flooding

**Forested Hillside**

Tree plantation

Roads destabilize hillsides

Evapotranspiration decreases

Ranching accelerates soil erosion by water and wind

Winds remove fragile topsoil

Agricultural land is flooded and silted up

Gullies and landslides

Heavy rain leaches nutrients from soil and erodes topsoil

Silt from erosion blocks rivers and reservoirs and causes flooding downstream

Rapid runoff causes flooding

**After Deforestation**

**Figure 14-23** A hillside before and after deforestation. Once a hillside has been deforested for timber and fuel-wood, livestock grazing, or unsustainable farming, water from precipitation **(1)** rushes down the denuded slopes, **(2)** erodes precious topsoil, and **(3)** floods downstream areas. A 3,000-year-old Chinese proverb says, "To protect your rivers, protect your mountains."

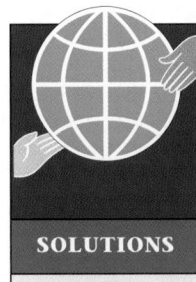

## The Promise of Drip Irrigation

**SOLUTIONS**

The development of inexpensive, weather-resistant, and flexible plastic tubing after World War II paved the way for a new form of micro-irrigation called *drip irrigation* (Figure 14-18, middle, p. 330). It consists of a network of perforated plastic tubing, installed at or below the ground surface. The small holes or emitters in the tubing deliver drops of water at a slow and steady rate close to plant roots.

This technique, developed in Israel in the 1960s and now used by half of the country's farmers, has a number of advantages, including the following:

- *Adaptability.* The tubing system can easily be fitted to match the patterns of crops in a field and left in place or moved to different locations.

- *Efficiency*, with 90–95% of the water input reaching crops.

- *Lower operating costs* because 37–70% less energy is needed to pump this water at low pressure, and less labor is needed to move sprinkler systems.

- *Ability to apply fertilizer solutions in precise amounts,* which reduces **(1)** fertilizer use and waste, **(2)** salinization, and **(3)** water pollution from fertilizer runoff.

- *An increase in crop yields of 20–90% by getting more crop growth per drop of water.*

- *Healthier plants and higher yields* because plants are neither underwatered nor overwatered.

Despite these advantages, drip irrigation is used on less than 1% of the world's irrigated area. The capital cost of conventional drip irrigation systems is too high for most poor farmers and for use on low-value row crops. However, drip irrigation is economically feasible for high-profit fruit, vegetable, and orchard crops and for home gardens.

Some *good news* is that the capital cost of a new drip irrigation system is one-tenth as much per hectare as conventional drip systems. Another innovation is DRiWATER®, called "drip irrigation in a box." It consists of 1-liter (1.1-quart) packages of gel-encased water that is released slowly into the soil after being buried near plant roots. It wastes almost no water and lasts about 3 months. Egypt is using it to help grow 17 million trees in a desert community.

These and other low-cost drip irrigation systems could bring about a revolution in more sustainable irrigated agriculture that would **(1)** increase food yields, **(2)** reduce water use and waste, and **(3)** lessen some of the environmental problems associated with agriculture (Figure 13-13, p. 288).

### Critical Thinking

Should governments provide subsidies to farmers who use drip irrigation based on how much water they save? Explain.

when heavier-than-normal rains occur, these devices do not work. In many developing countries, the poor have little choice but to try to survive in flood-prone areas (Connections, p. 335). Between 1985 and 2001, floods prematurely killed about 300,000 people, 96% of them in developing countries.

## Solutions: How Can We Reduce Flood Risks?

Ways humans can reduce the risk from flooding include

- *Straightening and deepening streams* (channelization, Figure 14-22, middle). Channelization can reduce upstream flooding, but the increased flow of water can also **(1)** increase upstream bank erosion and downstream flooding and sediment deposition and **(2)** reduce habitats for aquatic wildlife by removing bank vegetation and increasing stream velocity.

- *Building levees* (Figure 14-22, middle). Levees contain and speed up stream flow but **(1)** increase the water's capacity for doing damage downstream and **(2)** do not protect against unusually high and powerful floodwaters, as occurred in 1993 when two-thirds of the levees built along the Mississippi River were damaged or destroyed.

- *Building dams*. A flood control dam built across a stream can reduce flooding by storing water in a reservoir and releasing it gradually. Dams have a number of advantages and disadvantages (Figure 14-9).

- *Restoring wetlands* to take advantage of the natural flood control provided by floodplains.

- *Identifying and managing flood-prone areas* (Figure 14-24). Such actions include **(1)** prohibiting certain

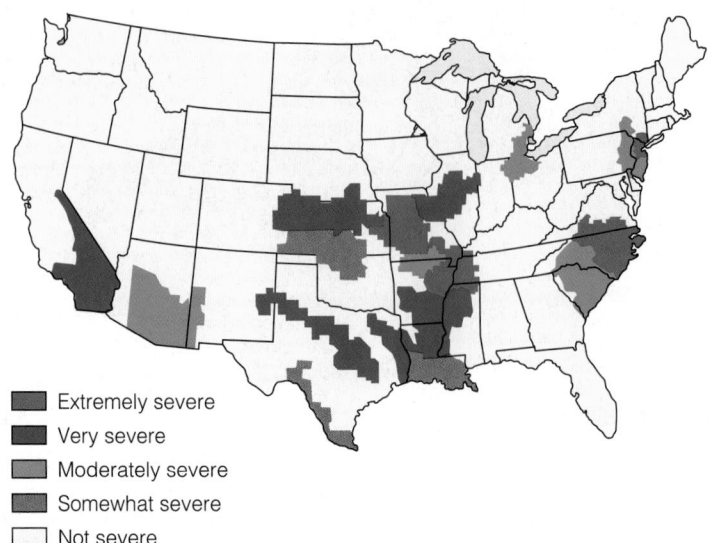

| | |
|---|---|
| ▓ | Extremely severe |
| ▓ | Very severe |
| ▓ | Moderately severe |
| ▒ | Somewhat severe |
| □ | Not severe |

**Figure 14-24** Generalized map of f*lood-prone areas* in the United States. State boundaries are shown in black. More detailed state and local maps are used to show the likelihood and severity of floods within these general areas. Flood frequency data and maps of flood-prone areas do not tell us when floods will occur, but they give a general idea of how often and where floods might occur, based on an area's history. (Data from U.S. Geological Survey)

---

## Running Short of Water in Las Vegas, Nevada

**SPOTLIGHT**

Las Vegas, Nevada, located in the Mojave Desert, is an artificial aquatic wonderland of large trees, green lawns and golf courses, waterfalls, and swimming pools. The city is also one of the fastest growing cities in the United States, with its population more than doubling from 550,000 in 1985 to 1.4 million in 2001. It is estimated that the city uses more water per person than any other city in the world.

Tucson, Arizona, in the Sonora Desert, gets only 30 centimeters (12 inches) of rainfall a year, and Las Vegas averages only 10 centimeters (4 inches). Tucson, now a model of water conservation, began a strict water conservation program in 1976, including raising water rates 500% for some residents.

In contrast, Las Vegas only recently started to encourage water conservation by **(1)** raising water rates sharply (but they are still less than half those in Tucson) and **(2)** encouraging replacement of lawns with rocks and native plants that survive on little water (Figure 14-21, p. 332).

Water experts project that even if these recent water conservation efforts are successful, Las Vegas should begin running short of water by 2007.

### Critical Thinking

**1.** If you were an elected official in charge of Las Vegas, what three actions would you take to improve water conservation? What might be the political implications of instituting such a program?

**2.** If water shortages by 2007 limit the growth of the population of Las Vegas, would you consider this outcome good or bad? Explain.

Bangladesh (Figure 12-7, p. 257) is one of the world's **(1)** most densely populated countries, with 134 million people packed into an area roughly the size of Wisconsin, and **(2)** poorest countries, with an average per capita GNI PPP of about $1,590, or $4.36 per day.

The people of Bangladesh depend on moderate annual flooding during the summer monsoon season. They need these seasonal floodwaters to grow rice and help maintain soil fertility in the delta basin by receiving an annual deposit of eroded Himalayan soil.

However, excessive flooding can be disastrous. In the past, great floods occurred every 50 years or so, but since the 1970s they have come about every 4 years.

Bangladesh's increased flood problems begin in the Himalayan watershed. A combination of rapid population growth, deforestation, overgrazing, and unsustainable farming on steep, easily erodible mountain slopes has greatly diminished the soil's ability to absorb water. Instead of being absorbed and released slowly, water from the monsoon rains runs off the denuded Himalayan foothills, carrying vital topsoil with it (Figure 14-23, p. 333).

This runoff, combined with heavier-than-normal monsoon rains, has increased the severity of flooding along Himalayan rivers and downstream in Bangladesh. For example, a disastrous flood in 1998 **(1)** covered two-thirds of Bangladesh's land area for 9 months, **(2)** leveled 2 million homes, **(3)** drowned at least 2,000 people, **(4)** left 30 million people homeless, **(5)** destroyed more than one-fourth of the country's crops, which caused thousands of people to die of starvation, and **(6)** caused at least $3.4 billion in damages.

Living on Bangladesh's coastal floodplain also carries dangers from storm surges and cyclones. Since 1961, 17 devastating cyclones have slammed into Bangladesh. In 1970, as many as 1 million people drowned in one storm, and another surge killed an estimated 139,000 people in 1991.

In their struggle to survive, the poor in Bangladesh have cleared many of the country's coastal mangrove forests (Figures 7-2, p. 145, and 7-9, p. 149) for fuelwood, farming, and aquaculture ponds for raising shrimp. This has led to more severe flooding because these coastal wetlands shelter Bangladesh's low-lying coastal areas from storm surges and cyclones. Damages and deaths from cyclones in areas of Bangladesh still protected by mangrove forests have been much lower than in areas where the forests have been cleared.

### Critical Thinking

**1.** Bangladesh's population is growing rapidly and expected to increase from 134 million to 178 million between 2002 and 2025. How could slowing its rate of population growth help reduce poverty and the harmful impacts of excessive flooding?

**2.** How could reforestation in the upstream countries of Bhutan, China, India, and Nepal reduce flooding in those countries and in Bangladesh?

types of buildings or activities in high-risk flood zones, **(2)** elevating or otherwise floodproofing buildings that are allowed on legally defined floodplains, and **(3)** constructing a floodway that allows floodwater to flow through the community with minimal damage. This *prevention,* or *precautionary,* approach to reducing flood damage is based on thousands of years of experience that can be summed up in one idea: *Sooner or later the river (or the ocean) always wins.*

## 14-9 SOLUTIONS: ACHIEVING A MORE SUSTAINABLE WATER FUTURE

Sustainable water use is based on the commonsense principle stated in an old Inca proverb: "The frog does not drink up the pond in which it lives." Figure 14-25 (p. 336) lists ways to implement this principle.

The challenge in developing such a *blue revolution* is to implement a mix of strategies built around **(1)** irrigating crops more efficiently, **(2)** using water-saving technologies in industries and homes, and **(3)** improving and integrating management of water basins and groundwater supplies.

Accomplishing such a revolution in water use and management will be difficult and controversial. However, water experts contend that not developing such strategies will eventually lead to **(1)** economic and health problems, **(2)** increased environmental degradation and loss of biodiversity, **(3)** heightened tensions and perhaps armed conflicts or economic competition over water supplies and food imports (p. 312), and **(4)** larger numbers of environmental refugees from water-scarce areas.

*It is not until the well runs dry that we know the worth of water.*

BENJAMIN FRANKLIN

- Not depleting aquifers

- Preserving ecological health of aquatic systems

- Preserving water quality

- Integrated watershed management

- Agreements among regions and countries sharing surface water resources

- Outside party mediation of water disputes between nations

- Marketing of water rights

- Wasting less water

- Decreasing government subsides for supplying water

- Increasing government subsides for reducing water waste

- Slowing population growth

**Figure 14-25** Methods for achieving more sustainable use of the earth's water resources.

## REVIEW QUESTIONS

1. Define the boldfaced terms in this chapter.

2. Explain why there is a danger of water wars or economic competition between countries for food imports in the Middle East.

3. List nine unique properties of water and explain the importance of each property.

4. What percentage of the earth's total volume of water is available for use by us? How might global warming alter the hydrologic cycle?

5. Distinguish among *surface runoff, reliable runoff, watershed, groundwater, zone of saturation, water table, aquifer, recharge area,* and *natural recharge.* Explain how the water in some aquifers can be depleted.

6. Since 1900, how much has the total use and per capita use of water by humans increased? About what percentage of the world's reliable surface runoff is used by humanity?

7. About what percentage of the water we withdraw each year is used for **(a)** irrigation, **(b)** industry, and **(c)** residences and cities?

8. What are the major water uses and problems of **(a)** the eastern United States and **(b)** the western United States?

9. List four causes of water scarcity. What is *water stress?* How can growth in the number of water-stressed countries affect **(a)** global grain exports and prices, **(b)** hunger and malnutrition in developing countries, **(c)** the number of environmental refugees, and **(d)** the daily workload of many poor women and children?

10. List six ways to increase the supply of fresh water in a particular area.

11. List six ecological services that rivers provide.

12. List the major pros and cons of building large dams and reservoirs to supply fresh water. List the pros and cons of **(a)** Egypt's Aswan High Dam project, **(b)** building numerous dams along the Colorado River basin, and **(c)** China's Three Gorges dam project.

13. List the major pros and cons of supplying water by transferring it from one watershed to another. List the pros and cons of **(a)** the California Water Project, **(b)** the James Bay project in Canada, and **(c)** the Aral Sea water transfer project in central Asia.

14. List the pros and cons of supplying more water by withdrawing groundwater. Explain why excessive groundwater withdrawal can be viewed as an example of the tragedy of the commons and how it can increase the gap between the world's rich and poor. Summarize the problems of withdrawing groundwater from the Ogallala Aquifer in the United States. List five ways to prevent or slow groundwater depletion.

15. List the pros and cons of increasing supplies of fresh water by **(a)** desalination of salt water, **(b)** cloud seeding, and **(c)** towing icebergs to water-short areas.

16. What percentage of the water used by people throughout the world is wasted? List four benefits of conserving water. List three major causes of water waste.

17. Define and give the pros and cons of **(a)** the *doctrine of riparian rights,* **(b)** the *principle of prior appropriation* used to govern legal rights to surface water, and **(c)** the *common law* approach used to govern legal rights to groundwater in the United States. How can such rights promote **(a)** water waste and **(b)** water conservation?

18. List ways to reduce water waste in **(a)** irrigation and **(b)** industry, homes, and businesses. List six advantages of *drip irrigation,* and explain how it could help bring about a revolution in improving water efficiency.

19. What is a *floodplain?* What three major ecological and economic services does it provide? List four reasons why so many people live on floodplains. List the major benefits and disadvantages of floods. List three ways in which humans increase the damages from floods. Describe the nature and causes of the flooding problems in Bangladesh.

20. List the pros and cons of trying to reduce flood risks by **(a)** stream channelization, **(b)** building levees, **(c)** building dams, and **(d)** managing floodplains.

21. List 11 ways to use the world's water more sustainably and 4 disadvantages of not implementing such strategies.

## CRITICAL THINKING

1. What would happen to your body if suddenly your water molecules no longer formed hydrogen bonds with one another (Appendix 2, Figure 4)?

2. How do human activities increase the harmful effects of prolonged drought? How can we reduce these effects?

3. Explain how dams and reservoirs can cause more flood damage than they prevent. Should all proposed large dam and reservoir projects be scrapped? Explain.

4. Do you believe the projected benefits of China's Three Gorges dam and reservoir project on the Yangtze River will outweigh its potential drawbacks? Explain. What are the alternatives?

5. What role does population growth play in water supply problems?

6. Explain why you are for or against (a) gradually phasing out government subsidies of irrigation projects in the western United States (or in the country where you live) to raise the price of water and promote using water more efficiently and (b) providing government subsidies to farmers for improving irrigation efficiency.

7. Should the prices of water for all uses be raised sharply to include more of its environmental costs and to encourage water conservation? Explain. What harmful and beneficial effects might this have on (a) business and jobs, (b) your lifestyle and the lifestyles of any children or grandchildren you might have, (c) the poor, and (d) the environment?

8. Should we use up slowly renewable underground water supplies such as the Ogallala aquifer (Case Study, p. 327) or save them for future generations? Explain.

9. Calculate how many liters and gallons of water are wasted in 1 month by a toilet that leaks 2 drops of water per second (1 liter of water equals about 3,500 drops and 1 liter equals 0.265 gallon).

10. List five major ways to conserve water for personal use (see website material for this chapter). Which, if any, of these practices do you now use or intend to use?

11. How do human activities contribute to flooding and flood damage? How can these effects be reduced?

12. Congratulations! You are in charge of managing the world's water resources. What are the three most important things you would do?

## PROJECTS

1. In your community,
   a. What are the major sources of the water supply?
   b. How is water use divided among agricultural, industrial, power plant cooling, and public uses?
   c. Who are the biggest consumers of water?
   d. What has happened to water prices (adjusted for inflation) during the past 20 years? Are they too low to encourage water conservation and reuse?
   e. What water supply problems are projected?
   f. How is water being wasted?

2. Use the library or the Internet to discover (a) which industries in the country where you live use the most water and (b) which industries have done the most to improve water-use efficiency in the last 20 years.

3. Develop a water conservation plan for your school and submit it to school officials.

4. Consult with local officials to identify any floodplain areas in your community. Develop a map showing these areas and the types of activities (such as housing, manufacturing, roads, and recreational use) found on these lands.

5. Use the library or the Internet to find bibliographic information about *John Todd* and *Benjamin Franklin*, whose quotes appear at the beginning and end of this chapter.

6. Make a concept map of this chapter's major ideas, using the section heads and subheads and the key terms (in boldface type). See material on the website for this book about how to prepare concept maps.

## INTERNET STUDY RESOURCES AND RESOURCES FOR FURTHER READING AND RESEARCH

The website for this book contains helpful study aids and many ideas for further reading and research. Log on to

www.info.brookscole.com/miller13

and click on the Chapter-by-Chapter area. Choose Chapter 14 and select a resource:

■ Flash Cards allows you to test your mastery of the Terms and Concepts to Remember for this chapter.

■ Tutorial Quizzes provides a multiple-choice practice quiz.

■ Student Guide to InfoTrac will lead you to Critical Thinking Projects that use InfoTrac College Edition as a research tool.

■ References lists the major books and articles consulted in writing this chapter.

■ Hypercontents takes you to an extensive list of sites with news, research, and images related to individual sections of the chapter.

## INFOTRAC COLLEGE EDITION

Improve your skills with InfoTrac College Edition, a searchable online database of articles from more than 700 periodicals. Log on to

http://www.infotrac-college.com

or access InfoTrac through the website for this book. Try to find the following articles:

1. University of California at Irvine. 2002. Satellite data on underground aquifer levels can be vital to water resource management, UC Irvine hydrologist finds; Use of NASA technology seen as breakthrough to understanding water availability, movement. *Ascribe Higher Education News Service* (June 10). Keywords: "satellite," "aquifer," and "levels." A new satellite now allows hydrologists to asses more accurately the condition of the world's aquifers. This has important implications for water management.

2. Postel, S. 1999. When the world's wells run dry. *World Watch* 12: 30. Keywords: "aquifer" and "depletion." This article represents a good summary of groundwater-use issues, including sustainability, conservation, and government policy.

# 15 GEOLOGIC RESOURCES: NONRENEWABLE MINERAL AND ENERGY RESOURCES

## Bitter Lessons from Chernobyl

*Chernobyl* is a chilling word recognized around the globe as the site of a major nuclear disaster (Figure 15-1). On April 26, 1986, a series of explosions in one of the reactors in a nuclear power plant in Ukraine (then part of the Soviet Union) blew the massive roof off the reactor building and flung radioactive debris and dust high into the atmosphere. A huge radioactive cloud spread over much of Belarus, Russia, Ukraine, and other parts of Europe and eventually encircled the planet.

According to various UN studies, here are some consequences of this disaster, caused by poor reactor design and human error:

- By the year 2000, an estimated 8,000 people had died prematurely from radiation-related diseases because of the accident. The Ukrainian Health Ministry says that 125,000 people have died and 3.5 million people have become ill because of the accident.

- Almost 400,000 people had to leave their homes. Most were not evacuated until at least 10 days after the accident.

- Some 160,000 square kilometers (62,000 square miles)—about the size of the state of Florida—of the former Soviet Union remains highly contaminated with radioactivity.

- Despite the danger, between 100,000 and 200,000 people either illegally remained or have returned to live inside this highly radioactive zone.

- More than half a million people were exposed to dangerous levels of radioactivity. About 2,000 people have been diagnosed with thyroid cancer and 8,000–10,000 additional thyroid cancer cases are expected between 2000 and 2010.

- The total cost of the accident will reach at least $358 billion, many times more than the value of all the nuclear electricity ever generated in the former Soviet Union.

The environmental refugees evacuated from the Chernobyl region had to leave their possessions behind and say good-bye to **(1)** lush green wheat fields and blossoming apple trees, **(2)** land their families had farmed for generations, **(3)** cows and goats that would be shot because the grass they ate was radioactive, and **(4)** their radioactivity-poisoned cats and dogs. They will not be able to return without exposing themselves to potentially harmful doses of ionizing radiation. In 2002—16 years after the accident—the Chernobyl power plant remains one of the most dangerous places on the earth.

Chernobyl taught us that *a major nuclear accident anywhere is a nuclear accident everywhere.*

**Figure 15-1** Major events leading to the Chernobyl nuclear power plant accident on April 26, 1986, in the former Soviet Union. The accident happened because **(1)** engineers turned off most of the reactor's automatic safety and warning systems (to keep them from interfering with an unauthorized safety experiment), **(2)** the safety design of the reactor was inadequate (there was no secondary containment shell, as in Western-style reactors), and **(3)** a design flaw led to unstable operation at low power. After the reactor exploded, crews exposed themselves to lethal levels of radiation to put out fires and encase the shattered reactor in a hastily constructed concrete tomb. This 19-story concrete tomb is sagging and full of holes that allow water to seep in and radioactive dust to drift out. Building a new tomb for the reactor will cost at least $1.5 billion—money the Ukrainian government does not have.

**2** Almost all control rods were removed from the core during experiment.

**Crane for moving fuel rods**

**1** Emergency cooling system was turned off to conduct an experiment.

**3** Automatic safety devices that shut down the reactor when water and steam levels fall below normal and turbine stops were shut off because engineers didn't want systems to "spoil" experiment.

**Cooling pond**

**Steam generator**

**Turbines**

**Radiation shields**

**Reactor**

**Water pumps**

**5** Reactor power output was lowered too much, making it too difficult to control.

**4** Additional water pump to cool reactor was turned on. But with low power output and extra drain on system, water didn't actually reach reactor.

*Mineral resources are the building blocks on which modern society depends. Knowledge of their physical nature and origins, the web they weave between all aspects of human society and the physical earth, can lay the foundations for a sustainable society.*

ANN DORR

This chapter addresses the following questions:

- What are nonrenewable mineral resources, and how are they formed?
- How do we find and extract nonrenewable mineral and energy resources from the earth's crust?
- What are the environmental effects of extracting and using mineral resources?
- How fast are nonfuel mineral supplies being used up?
- How can we increase supplies of key nonfuel minerals?
- How should we evaluate energy alternatives?
- What are the advantages and disadvantages of oil?
- What are the advantages and disadvantages of natural gas?
- What are the advantages and disadvantages of coal?
- What are the advantages and disadvantages of conventional nuclear fission, breeder nuclear fission, and nuclear fusion?

## 15-1 NATURE AND FORMATION OF MINERAL RESOURCES

**What Are Mineral Resources?** A **mineral resource** is a concentration of naturally occurring material in or on the earth's crust that can be extracted and processed into useful materials at an affordable cost. Over millions to billions of years, the earth's internal and external geologic processes (Section 10-2, p. 205, and Figure 10-8, p. 210) have produced numerous nonfuel mineral resources and fossil fuel energy resources. Because they take so long to produce, they are classified as *nonrenewable resources*.

We know how to find and extract more than 100 nonrenewable minerals from the earth's crust. They include **(1)** *metallic mineral resources* (iron, copper, aluminum), **(2)** *nonmetallic mineral resources* (salt, clay, sand, phosphates, and soil), and **(3)** *energy resources* (coal, oil, natural gas, and uranium).

**Ore** is rock containing enough of one or more metallic minerals to be mined profitably. We convert about 40 metals extracted from ores into many everyday items that we either **(1)** use and discard (Figure 3-20, p. 60) or **(2)** learn to reuse, recycle, or use less wastefully (Figure 3-21, p. 61).

The U.S. Geological Survey (USGS) divides nonrenewable mineral resources into several categories (Figure 15-2):

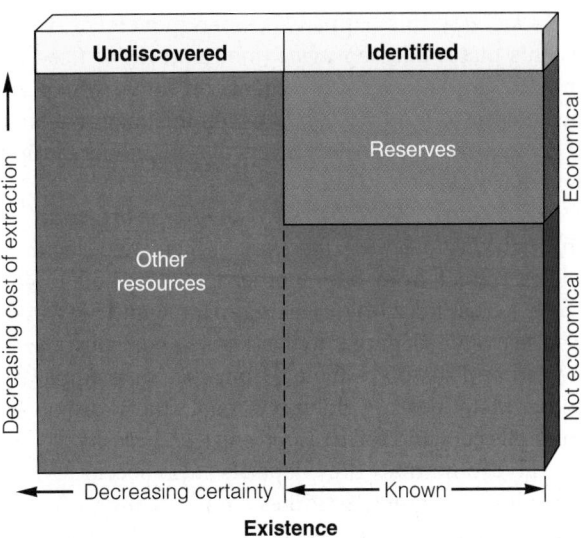

**Figure 15-2** General classification of mineral resources. (The area shown for each class does not represent its relative abundance.) In theory, all mineral resources classified as *other resources* could become reserves because of rising mineral prices or improved mineral location and extraction technology. In practice, geologists expect only a fraction of other resources to become reserves.

- **Identified resources**: deposits of a nonrenewable mineral resource **(1)** with a *known* location, quantity, and quality, or **(2)** whose existence is based on direct geological evidence and measurements.

- **Undiscovered resources**: potential supplies of a nonrenewable mineral resource assumed to exist on the basis of geologic knowledge and theory but with unknown specific locations, quality, and amounts.

- **Reserves**: identified resources from which a usable nonrenewable mineral can be extracted profitably at current prices.

- **Other resources**: identified and undiscovered resources not classified as reserves.

Most published estimates of the supply of a given nonrenewable resource refer to *reserves*. Reserves can increase when **(1)** new deposits are found or **(2)** price increases or improved mining technology make it profitable to extract deposits that previously were too expensive to extract. Theoretically, all of the *other resources* could eventually be converted to reserves, but this is highly unlikely.

**How Do Ores Form from Magma?** Ores form as a result of several internal and external geologic processes. Plate tectonics (Figure 10-4, p. 206, and Figure 10-5b, p. 207) **(1)** shapes the earth's crust as the earth's plates collide, retreat, and slide across one another at the boundaries between them (Figure 10-6, p. 208) and **(2)** determines where the earth's richest mineral deposits form.

One way this happens is when movement of the earth's plates allows *magma* (molten rock) to flow up into the earth's crust at divergent and convergent plate boundaries (Figure 10-6, p. 208). As this magma cools, it crystallizes into various layers of mineral-containing igneous rocks.

The most common way ore deposits form is through *hydrothermal processes*. When two tectonic plates retreat from one another, gaps created in the earth's crust fill with upwelling magma and seawater. The seawater seeping into these cracks becomes superheated and dissolves metals from rock or magma. As these metal-bearing solutions cool, their dissolved minerals cool and form *hydrothermal ore deposits*.

Hydrothermal ore deposits also occur when upwelling magma solidifies into chimney-shaped *black smokers* (Figure 15-3) in volcanically active regions of the ocean floor near spreading oceanic centers (Figure 10-4, p. 206). These smokers are miniature volcanoes that shoot out jets of hot, black, mineral-rich water through vents in solidified magma on the sea-

floor. As the hot water comes into contact with cold seawater, black particles of various metal sulfides precipitate out and accumulate as chimneylike structures near the hot water vents (Figure 15-3). These ore deposits are especially rich in copper, lead, zinc, silver, gold, and other minerals.

Because they are so rich in nutrients (especially sulfur), these hydrothermal deposits on the dark ocean floor support colonies of bacteria that **(1)** produce food through *chemosynthesis* and **(2)** support a variety of animals such as red tube worms, clams, crustaceans, and other forms of marine life (Figure 15-3).

Another potential source of metals from the ocean floor is *manganese nodules* that cover about 25–50% of the Pacific Ocean floor. These cherry- to potato-sized rocks contain **(1)** 30–40% manganese by weight and **(2)** small amounts of other important metals such as iron, copper, and nickel. Geologists believe these modules crystallized from hot solutions arising from volcanic activity at midoceanic ridges, perhaps by black smokers.

### How Do Ores and Other Minerals Form from Sedimentary and Weathering Processes?

As sediments settle they can form ore deposits by *sedimentary sorting* and *precipitation*. For example, many streams carry a mixture of silt, sand, gravel, and occasional small grains of gold. When the stream current slows down, these minerals settle out on the basis of their density. Because gold is denser than any other mineral, it falls to the bottom of a stream first in this *sedimentary sorting* process. Over time, fairly rich deposits of settled gold particles, called *placer deposits*, concentrate near bedrock or coarse gravel in streams. Miners use pans or sieves to scoop up such streambed material and sort out the gold particles.

In deserts, groundwater flows can form lakes with no outlets to the sea. Some of the mineral-containing groundwater flowing into these lakes (or into enclosed seas) evaporates. This causes the concentrations of the dissolved salts to increase to the point where they precipitate to form *evaporite mineral deposits*. Important minerals formed this way include table salt, borax, and sodium carbonate.

Ore deposits can also form because of the *weathering* of rock by water. Torrents of water dissolve and remove most soluble metal ions from rock and soil near the earth's surface. This weathering process leaves ions of insoluble compounds in the soil to form *residual deposits* of metal ores such as iron and aluminum (bauxite ore).

**Figure 15-3** Hydrothermal ore deposits form when mineral-rich, superheated water shoots out of vents in solidified magma on the ocean floor. After mixing with cold seawater, black particles of metal ore precipitate out and build up as chimneylike ore deposits around the vents. A variety of organisms, supported by bacteria producing food by chemosynthesis, exist in the dark ocean around the black smokers.

## 15-2 FINDING AND REMOVING NONRENEWABLE MINERAL RESOURCES

**How Are Buried Mineral Deposits Found?** Mining companies use several methods to find promising mineral deposits. They include

- Using aerial photos and satellite images to reveal protruding rock formations (outcrops) associated with certain minerals.

- Using planes equipped with **(1)** *radiation-measuring equipment* to detect deposits of radioactive metals such as uranium and **(2)** a *magnetometer* to measure changes in the earth's magnetic field caused by magnetic minerals such as iron ore.

- Using a *gravimeter* to measure differences in gravity because the density of an ore deposit usually differs from that of the surrounding rock.

- Drilling a deep well and extracting core samples.

- Putting sensors in existing wells to detect electrical resistance or radioactivity to pinpoint the location of oil and natural gas.

- Making *seismic surveys* on land and at sea by **(1)** detonating explosive charges and **(2)** analyzing the resulting shock waves to get information about the makeup of buried rock layers.

- Performing *chemical analysis* of water and plants to detect deposits of underground minerals that **(1)** have leached into nearby bodies of water or **(2)** have been absorbed by plant tissues.

After suitable mineral deposits are located, several different types of mining techniques are used to remove the deposits, depending on their location and type. Shallow deposits are removed by **surface mining** (Figure 15-4), and deep deposits are removed by **subsurface mining** (Figure 15-5, p. 342).

In surface mining, mechanized equipment strips away the **overburden** of soil and rock and usually

**(a)** Open Pit Mine

**(b)** Dredging

**(c)** Area Strip Mining

**(d)** Contour Strip Mining

**Figure 15-4** Major mining methods used to extract surface deposits of solid mineral and energy resources.

**Figure 15-5** Major mining methods used to extract underground deposits of solid mineral and energy resources (primarily coal); **(a)** mine shafts and tunnels are dug and blasted out; **(b)** in *room-and-pillar* mining, machinery is used to gouge out coal and load it onto a shuttle car in one operation, and pillars of coal are left to support the mine roof; and **(c)** in *longwall coal mining*, movable steel props support the roof and cutting machines shear off the coal onto a conveyor belt. As the mining proceeds, roof supports are moved forward and the roof behind is allowed to fall (often causing the land above to sink or subside).

**(a)** Underground Coal Mine

**(b)** Room-and-Pillar

**(c)** Longwall Mining of Coal

discards it as waste material called **spoils.** In the United States, surface mining extracts about **(1)** 90% of the nonfuel mineral and rock resources and **(2)** 60% of the coal by weight.

The type of surface mining used depends on the resource being sought and on local topography. Methods include the following:

- **Open-pit mining** (Figure 15-4a), in which machines dig holes and remove ores (such as iron and copper) sand, gravel, and stone (such as limestone and marble).

- **Dredging** (Figure 15-4b), in which chain buckets and draglines scrape up underwater mineral deposits.

- **Area strip mining** (Figure 15-4c), used where the terrain is fairly flat. An earthmover strips away the overburden, and a power shovel digs a cut to remove the mineral deposit. After the mineral is removed, the trench is filled with overburden and a new cut is made parallel to the previous one. The process is repeated over the entire site. If the land is not restored, area strip mining leaves a wavy series of highly erodible hills of rubble called *spoil banks*.

- **Contour strip mining** (Figure 15-4d), used on hilly or mountainous terrain. A power shovel cuts a series of terraces into the side of a hill. An earthmover removes the overburden, a power shovel extracts the coal, and the overburden from each new terrace is dumped onto the one below. Unless the land is restored, a wall of dirt is left in front of a highly erodible bank of soil and rock called a *highwall*.

- **Mountaintop removal.** This method uses explosives, massive shovels, and even larger machinery called draglines to remove the top of a mountain and expose seams of coal underneath. This form of surface mining—increasingly used in West Virginia—causes considerable environmental damage. In 2002, the Bush administration changed a government rule to allow rock and dirt from mountaintop strip mining of coal to be dumped into the streams and valleys below.

Although surface-mined land can be restored (except in arid and semiarid areas), it is expensive and not done in many countries. In the United States, the *Surface Mining Control and Reclamation Act of 1977*

- Requires mining companies to restore most surface-mined land so it can be used for the same purpose as it was before it was mined.

- Levied a tax on mining companies to restore land that was disturbed by surface mining before the law was passed.

*Subsurface mining* (Figure 15-5) is used to remove coal and various metal ores that are too deep to be extracted by surface mining. Miners (1) dig a deep vertical shaft, (2) blast subsurface tunnels and chambers to get to the deposit, and (3) use machinery to remove the ore or coal and transport it to the surface.

Subsurface mining (1) disturbs less than one-tenth as much land as surface mining and (2) usually produces less waste material. But it leaves much of the resource in the ground and is more dangerous and expensive than surface mining. Hazards include (1) collapse of roofs and walls of underground mines, (2) explosions of dust and natural gas, and (3) lung diseases caused by prolonged inhalation of mining dust.

## 15-3 ENVIRONMENTAL EFFECTS OF EXTRACTING, PROCESSING, AND USING MINERAL RESOURCES

**What Are the Environmental Impacts of Using Mineral Resources?** The mining, processing, and use of mineral resources takes enormous amounts of energy and often causes land disturbance, soil erosion, and air and water pollution (Figure 15-6).

Mining can affect the environment in the following ways:

- Scarring and disruption of the land surface (Figures 15-4 and 15-7, p. 344). The Department of the Interior estimates that about 500,000 mines dot the U.S. landscape, mostly in the West. Cleanup costs are estimated in the tens of billions of dollars.

- Collapse or subsidence of land above underground mines, which can cause (1) houses to tilt, (2) sewer lines to crack, (3) gas mains to break, and (4) groundwater systems to be disrupted.

- Wind- or water-caused erosion of toxin-laced mining wastes. The EPA estimates that mining has polluted 40% of Western watersheds.

- Acid mine drainage, when rainwater seeping through a mine or mine wastes (1) carries sulfuric acid

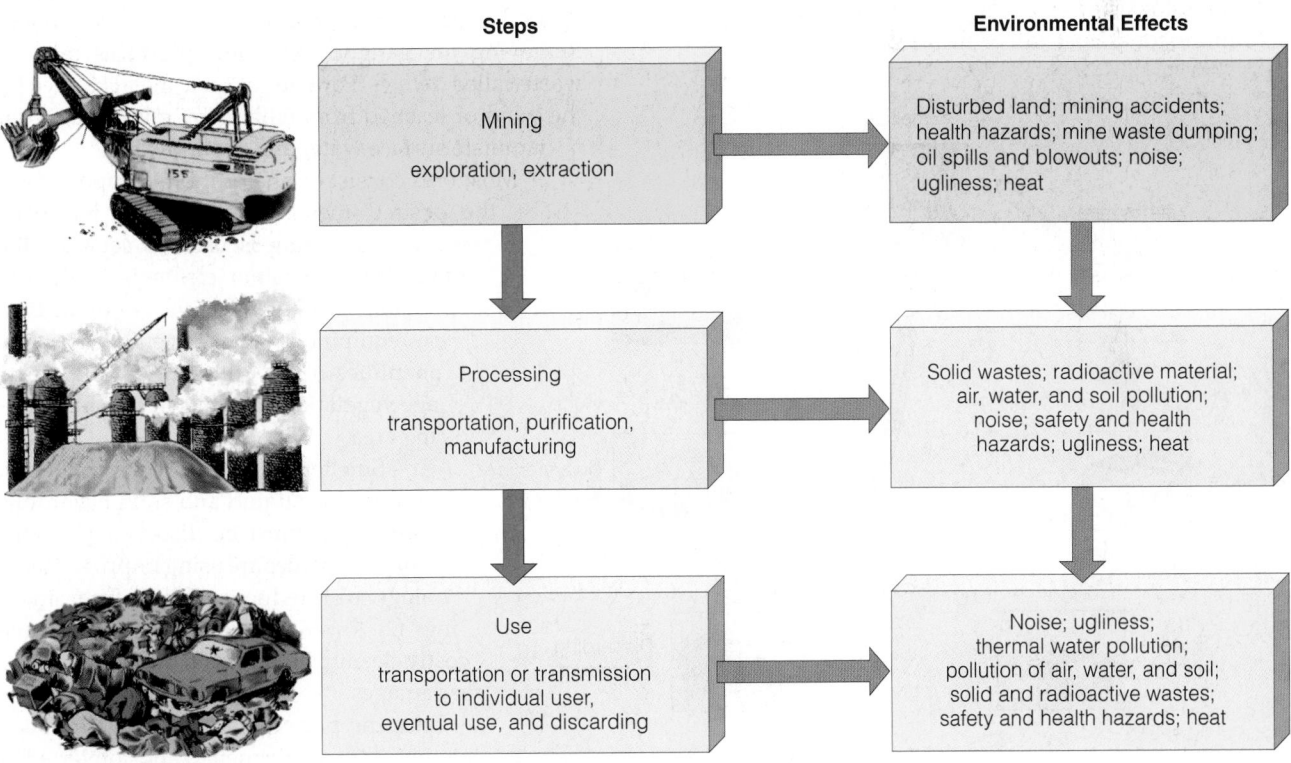

| Steps | Environmental Effects |
|---|---|
| Mining — exploration, extraction | Disturbed land; mining accidents; health hazards; mine waste dumping; oil spills and blowouts; noise; ugliness; heat |
| Processing — transportation, purification, manufacturing | Solid wastes; radioactive material; air, water, and soil pollution; noise; safety and health hazards; ugliness; heat |
| Use — transportation or transmission to individual user, eventual use, and discarding | Noise; ugliness; thermal water pollution; pollution of air, water, and soil; solid and radioactive wastes; safety and health hazards; heat |

**Figure 15-6** Some harmful environmental effects of extracting, processing, and using nonrenewable mineral and energy resources. The energy used to carry out each step causes additional pollution and environmental degradation.

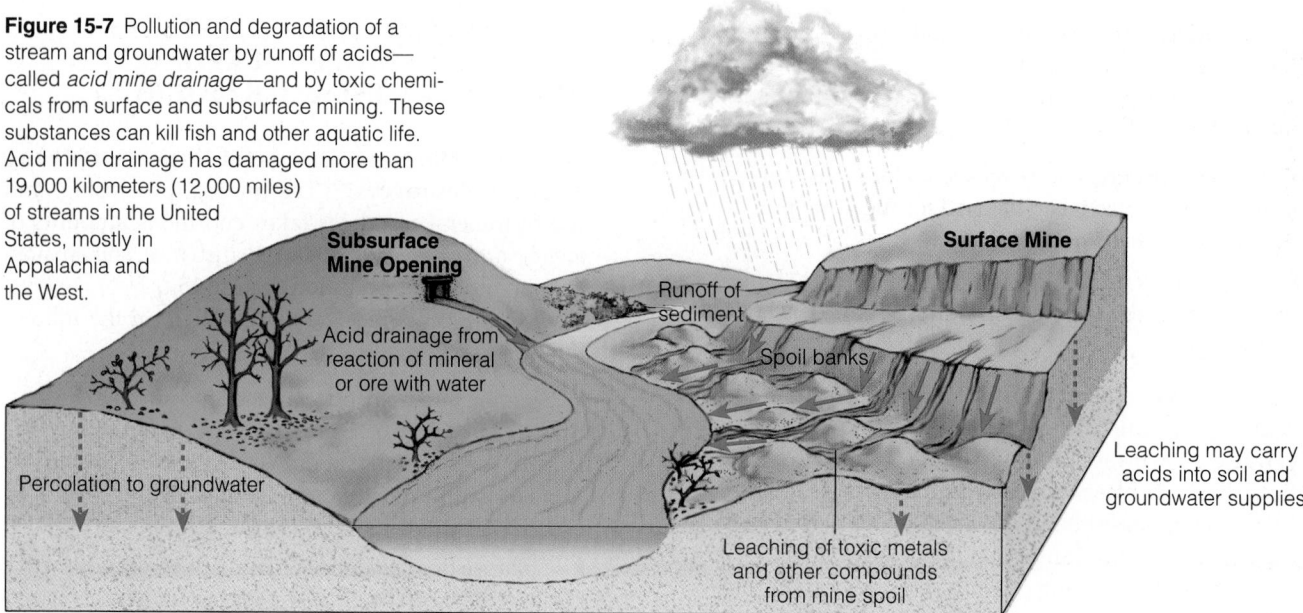

**Figure 15-7** Pollution and degradation of a stream and groundwater by runoff of acids—called *acid mine drainage*—and by toxic chemicals from surface and subsurface mining. These substances can kill fish and other aquatic life. Acid mine drainage has damaged more than 19,000 kilometers (12,000 miles) of streams in the United States, mostly in Appalachia and the West.

Subsurface Mine Opening

Surface Mine

Acid drainage from reaction of mineral or ore with water

Runoff of sediment

Spoil banks

Percolation to groundwater

Leaching may carry acids into soil and groundwater supplies

Leaching of toxic metals and other compounds from mine spoil

($H_2SO_4$, produced when aerobic bacteria act on iron sulfide minerals in spoils) to nearby streams and groundwater (Figure 15-7), **(2)** contaminates water supplies, and **(3)** destroys aquatic life.

- Emission of toxic chemicals into the atmosphere. In the United States, the mining industry produces more toxic emissions than any other industry (typically accounting for almost half of such emissions).

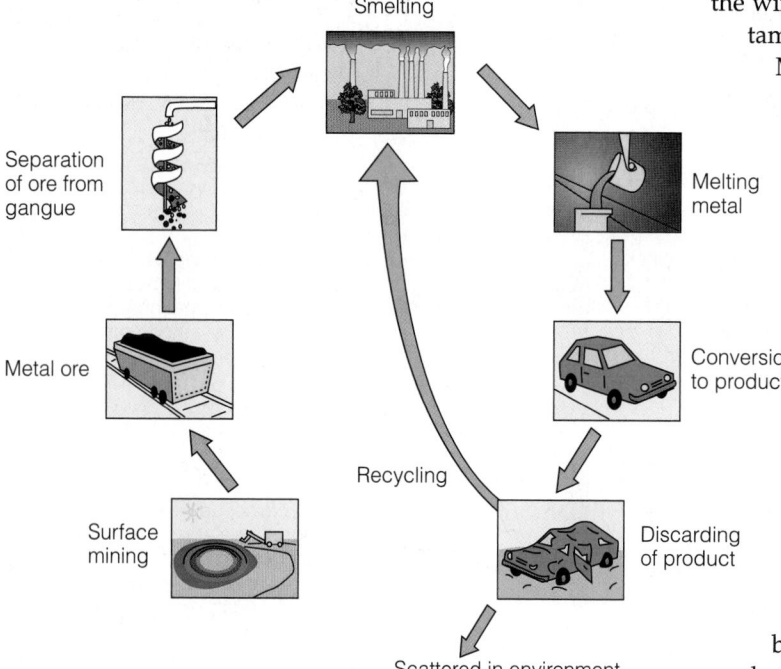

Smelting

Separation of ore from gangue

Melting metal

Metal ore

Conversion to product

Recycling

Surface mining

Discarding of product

Scattered in environment

**Figure 15-8** Typical *life cycle of a metal resource*. Each step in this process uses energy and produces some pollution and waste heat.

- Exposure of wildlife to toxic mining wastes stored in holding ponds and leakage of toxic wastes from such ponds.

Figure 15-8 shows the typical life cycle of a metal resource. Ore extracted from the earth's crust typically has two components: **(1)** the *ore mineral* containing the desired metal and **(2)** waste material called *gangue*. Removing the gangue from ores produces piles of waste called *tailings*. Particles of toxic metals blown by the wind or leached from tailings by rainfall can contaminate surface water and groundwater.

Most ores consist of one or more compounds of the desired metal. After gangue has been removed, **smelting** is used to separate the metal from the other elements in the ore mineral. Without effective pollution control equipment, smelters emit enormous quantities of air pollutants, which damage vegetation and soils in the surrounding area.

Smelters also cause water pollution and produce liquid and solid hazardous wastes that must be disposed of safely. Some companies are using improved technology to **(1)** reduce pollution from smelting, **(2)** lower production costs, **(3)** save costly cleanup bills, and **(4)** decrease liability for damages.

Once the pure metal has been produced by smelting, it is usually melted and converted to desired products, which are then used and discarded or recycled (Figure 15-8). Removing and processing ores to produce metals uses enormous amounts of energy, which pollutes the air and water and adds

## Some Environmental Effects of Gold Mining

Gold miners typically remove ore equal to the weight of 50 automobiles to extract an amount of gold that would fit inside your clenched fist. Most newlyweds would be surprised to know that about 5.5 metric tons (6 tons) of mining waste was created to make their two gold wedding rings.

The solid waste remaining after gold is extracted from its ore is left piled near the mine sites and can pollute the air, surface water (Figures 15-6 and 15-7), and groundwater. In South Africa, each metric ton of gold that is mined kills an average of 1 worker and seriously injures 11 others.

In Australia and North America, a mining technology called *cyanide heap leaching* is cheap enough to allow mining companies to level entire mountains containing very low-grade gold ore. To extract the gold, miners spray a cyanide solution (which reacts with gold) onto huge open-air piles of crushed ore. They then **(1)** collect the solution in leach beds and overflow ponds, **(2)** recirculate it a number of times, and **(3)** extract gold from it.

A problem is that cyanide is extremely toxic to birds and mammals drawn to cyanide solution collection ponds as a source of water. Cyanide leach pads and collection ponds can also leak or overflow, posing threats to underground drinking water supplies and wildlife (especially fish) in lakes and streams.

Special liners beneath the ore heaps and in the collection ponds can prevent leaks, but some have failed. According to the EPA, all such liners will leak eventually.

On January 30, 2000, snow and heavy rains washed out an earthen dam containing an aboveground cyanide leach pond at an Australian-operated gold mine in Romania. The dam's collapse released large amounts of water laced with cyanide and toxic metals into the Tisza and Danube Rivers flowing through parts of Romania, Hungary, and Yugoslavia.

Several hundred thousand people living along these rivers were told not to fish or to drink or extract water from affected rivers or from wells along the rivers. Food industries and paper mills were shut down. Thousands of fish and other forms of aquatic life were killed. The accident and another one that occurred in January 2001 could have been prevented if the mine had installed a stronger containment dam and a backup collection pond to prevent leakage into nearby surface water.

Some gold mining companies take care to avoid environmental damage, but other companies do not. A glaring example is the Summitville gold mine site in the San Juan Mountains of southern Colorado. A Canadian company used the 1872 mining law (Pro/Con, p. 347) to buy the land from the federal government for only $7,000, spent $1 million developing the site, and then removed more than $130 million worth of gold.

Shoddy construction allowed acids and toxic metals to leak from the site and poison a 27-kilometer (17-mile) stretch of the Alamosa River, the source of irrigation water for farms and ranches in Colorado's San Luis Valley.

The company then declared bankruptcy and abandoned the property, but only after being allowed to retrieve $2.5 million of the $7.5 million reclamation bond it had posted with the state. Summitville is now on the country's list of highly toxic (Superfund) sites, with the EPA spending $40,000 a day to contain the site's toxic wastes. Ultimately, the EPA expects to spend about $232 million on the cleanup.

Since 1980, millions of miners have streamed into tropical forests and other areas in search of gold. These small-scale miners use destructive mining techniques such as **(1)** digging large pits by hand, **(2)** river dredging, and **(3)** hydraulic mining (a technique, outlawed in the United States, in which water jets wash entire hillsides into sluice boxes).

Highly toxic mercury usually is used to extract the gold from the other materials. In the process, much of the mercury ends up contaminating water supplies and fish consumed by people. Just one teaspoon of mercury in a 1-hectare (2.5-acre) lake can make its fish unfit for human consumption.

### Critical Thinking

What regulations, if any, would you impose on gold mining operations?

---

greenhouse gases to the atmosphere. For example, the U.S. steel industry uses as much electricity each year as the country's 90 million homes.

### Are There Environmental Limits to Resource Extraction and Use?

Some environmentalists and resource experts believe the greatest danger from the world's continually increasing consumption of nonrenewable mineral resources is not exhaustion of their supplies but the environmental damage caused by

their extraction, processing, and conversion to products (Figure 15-6).

The mineral industry accounts for 5–10% of world energy use. This makes it a major contributor to air and water pollution and to emissions of greenhouse gases such as carbon dioxide ($CO_2$). The environmental impacts from mining an ore are affected by its percentage of metal content, or *grade* (Case Study, above).

Usually more accessible and higher-grade ores are exploited first. As they are depleted, it takes more money, energy, water, and other materials to exploit lower-grade ores. This in turn increases land disruption, mining waste, and pollution.

Currently, most of the harmful environmental costs of mining and processing minerals are not included in the prices for processed metals and consumer products produced from such minerals. This gives mining companies and manufacturers little incentive to reduce resource waste and pollution because they can pass many of the harmful environmental costs of their production on to society and future generations.

## 15-4 SUPPLIES OF MINERAL RESOURCES

**Will There Be Enough Mineral Resources?** The future supply of nonrenewable minerals depends on two factors: **(1)** the actual or potential supply and **(2)** the rate at which that supply is used. We never completely run out of any mineral. However, a mineral becomes *economically depleted* when it costs more to find, extract, transport, and process the remaining deposit than it is worth. At that point, there are five choices: **(1)** recycle or reuse existing supplies, **(2)** waste less, **(3)** use less, **(4)** find a substitute, or **(5)** do without.

**Depletion time** is the time it takes to use up a certain proportion (usually 80%) of the reserves of a mineral at a given rate of use (Figure 1-7, p. 10). When experts disagree about depletion times, they are often using different assumptions about supply and rate of use (Figure 15-9).

A traditional measure of the projected availability of nonrenewable resources is the **reserve-to-production ratio:** the number of years that proven reserves of a particular nonrenewable mineral will last at current annual production rates. Reserve estimates are continually changing because **(1)** new deposits often are discovered, and **(2)** new mining and processing can allow some of the minerals classified as other resources (Figure 15-2) to be converted to reserves. Under these circumstances, the reserve-to-production ratio is the best available projection of the current estimated supply and its estimated depletion time.

The shortest depletion time assumes no recycling or reuse and no increase in reserves (curve A, Figure 15-9). A longer depletion time assumes that recycling will stretch existing reserves and that better mining technology, higher prices, and new discoveries will increase reserves (curve B, Figure 15-9). An even longer depletion time assumes that new discoveries will further expand reserves and that recycling, reuse, and reduced consumption will extend supplies (curve C, Figure 15-9). Finding a substitute for a resource leads to a new set of depletion curves for the new resource.

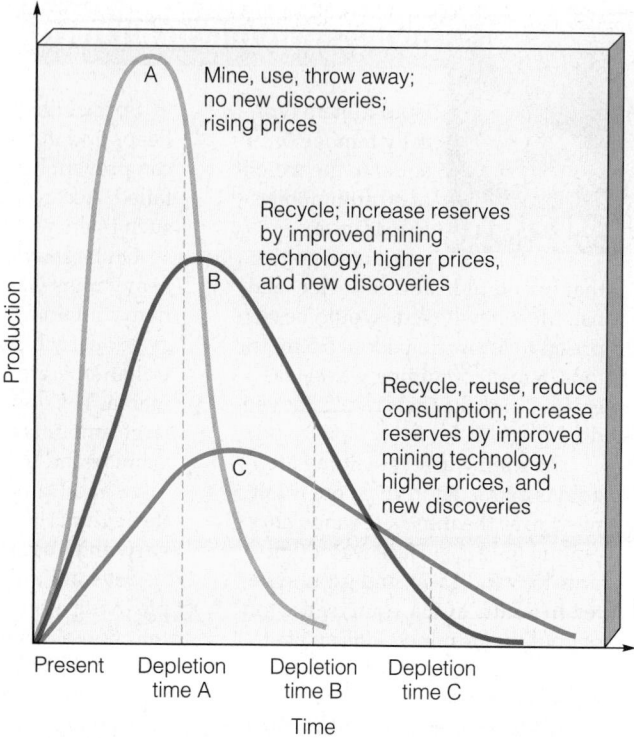

**Figure 15-9** *Depletion curves* for a nonrenewable resource (such as aluminum or copper) using three sets of assumptions. Dashed vertical lines represent times when 80% depletion occurs.

**How Does Economics Affect Mineral Resource Supplies?** Geologic processes determine the quantity and location of a mineral resource in the earth's crust, but economics determines what part of the known supply is extracted and used.

According to standard economic theory, in a competitive free market a plentiful mineral resource is cheap when its supply exceeds demand. However, when a resource becomes scarce its price rises. This can **(1)** encourage exploration for new deposits, **(2)** stimulate development of better mining technology, **(3)** make it profitable to mine lower-grade ores, **(4)** encourage a search for substitutes, and **(5)** promote conservation.

However, according to some economists, this theory may no longer apply to most developed countries. One reason is that industry and government in such countries control the supply, demand, and prices of minerals to such an extent that a truly competitive free market does not exist.

Most mineral prices are low because governments subsidize development of their domestic mineral resources to help promote economic growth and national security. In the United States, for instance, mining companies **(1)** get depletion allowances amounting to 5–22% of their gross income (depending on the mineral) and **(2)** can reduce the taxes they pay by deducting much of their costs for finding and developing mineral deposits. In addition, hardrock mining

**PRO/CON**

Some people have gotten rich by using the little known General Mining Law of 1872. This law was designed to **(1)** encourage mineral exploration and mining of gold, silver, copper, zinc, nickel, uranium, and other *hardrock minerals* on U.S. public lands and **(2)** help develop the then sparsely populated West.

Under this 1872 law, a person or corporation can assume legal ownership of parcels of land on essentially all U.S. public land except parks and wilderness areas by *patenting* it. This involves **(1)** declaring the belief that the land contains valuable hardrock minerals, **(2)** spending $500 to improve the land for mineral development, **(3)** filing a claim, **(4)** paying an annual fee of $100 for each 8 hectares (20 acres) to maintain the claim whether or not a mine is in operation, and, if desired, **(5)** paying the federal government $6–12 per hectare ($2.50–5.00 an acre) for the land. Once purchased, the land can be used, leased, or sold for essentially any purpose.

So far, public lands containing an estimated $240–385 billion (adjusted for inflation) of publicly owned mineral resources have been transferred to private interests at 1872 prices. Domestic and foreign mining companies operating under this law remove mineral resources worth at least $2–3 billion per year on once-public land they bought at very low prices.

In addition, the Congressional Budget Office estimates that mining companies remove hardrock minerals worth at least $650 million per year from public land that has not been transferred to private ownership.

*Hardrock mining companies also pay no royalties on the minerals they extract from such lands.* In contrast, **(1)** oil and natural gas companies pay a gross royalty of 12.5% and **(2)** coal companies a gross royalty of 8–12.5% on the wholesale price of the resources they remove from public lands. Congress has also given hardrock mining companies tax breaks worth an estimated $823 million between 2002 and 2012.

No provision in the 1872 law requires mining companies to pay for environmental cleanup of any damage they cause to these lands and nearby water resources. Cleanup costs for land and streams damaged by 557,000 abandoned hardrock mines (Case Study, p. 345) and open pits (mostly in the West) will cost U.S. taxpayers an estimated $33–72 billion.

Mining companies defend the 1872 law. They point out that

■ They must invest large sums of money (often $100 million or more) to locate and develop an ore site before they make any profits from mining hardrock minerals.

■ Their mining operations **(1)** provide high-paying jobs to miners, **(2)** supply vital resources for industry, **(3)** stimulate the national and local economies, **(4)** reduce trade deficits, and **(5)** save American consumers money on products produced from such minerals.

■ Paying royalties on their profits and requiring them to pay cleanup costs would force them to move their mining operations to other countries.

For decades, environmentalists have been trying, without success, to have this law revised to protect taxpayers and the environment by

■ Permanently banning the patenting (sale) of public lands but allowing 20-year leases of designated public land for hardrock mining.

■ Requiring mining companies to pay a *gross* royalty of 8–12% on the wholesale value of all minerals removed from public land—similar to what oil, natural gas, and coal companies pay. Hardrock mining companies want to **(1)** continue paying no royalties or **(2)** if the law is changed pay no more than a 5% *net* royalty based on gross sales minus production costs—a system that would yield a much lower return on sales of these minerals owned jointly by all taxpayers.

■ Making mining companies legally and financially responsible for environmental cleanup and restoration of each site or charging them an additional mining fee to help pay for cleanup costs. Currently, mining companies are required to post bonds to cover 100% of the estimated cleanup costs in case they go bankrupt.

Canada, Australia, South Africa, and other countries that are major extractors of hardrock minerals have laws with such requirements.

### Critical Thinking

Do you support or oppose the three major changes that environmentalists believe should be made in the U.S. General Mining Law of 1872? Explain.

---

companies operating in the United States can buy public land at 1872 prices and pay no royalties to the government on the minerals they extract (Pro/Con, above).

Between 1982 and 2001, U.S. mining companies received more than $6 billion in government subsidies. Critics argue that taxing rather than subsidizing the extraction of nonfuel mineral resources would **(1)** provide governments with revenue, **(2)** create incentives for more efficient resource use, **(3)** promote waste reduction and pollution prevention, and **(4)** encourage recycling and reuse.

Mining company representatives say they need subsidies and low taxes to **(1)** keep the prices of minerals low for consumers and **(2)** encourage them not to move their mining operations to other countries without such taxes and less stringent mining regulations.

Two other economic problems hinder the development of new supplies of mineral resources:

■ Mineral scarcity does not raise the market price of products very much because the cost of mineral resources is only a small part of the final cost of goods.

■ Exploring for new mineral resources takes a lot of increasingly scarce investment capital and is a risky financial venture. Typically, if geologists identify 10,000 possible deposits of a given resource, only 1,000 sites are worth exploring; only 100 justify drilling, trenching, or tunneling; and only 1 becomes a producing mine or well.

**Should More Mining Be Allowed on Public Lands in the United States?** About one-third of the land in the United States is public land owned jointly by all U.S. citizens. This land, consisting of national forests, parks, resource lands, and wilderness, is managed by various government agencies under laws passed by Congress. About 72% of this public land is in Alaska, and 22% is in western states (where 60% of all land is public land).

For decades, resource developers, environmentalists, and conservationists have argued over how this land should be used. Mineral resource extractors of mineral resources complain that three-fourths of the country's vast public lands, with many areas containing rich deposits of mineral resources, are off limits to mining.

In recent decades, they have stepped up efforts to have Congress **(1)** open up most of these lands to mineral development, **(2)** sell off mineral-rich public lands to private interests, or **(3)** turn their management over to state and local governments that usually can be more readily influenced by mining and development interests. In 2002, the Bush administration proposed using a mix of these three approaches for management of mineral and timber resources on U.S. public lands.

Conservation biologists and environmentalists strongly oppose such efforts. They argue that this would increase environmental degradation and decrease biodiversity.

**Can We Get Enough Minerals by Mining Lower-Grade Ores?** Some analysts contend that all we need to do to increase supplies of a mineral is to extract lower grades of ore. They point to the development of **(1)** new earth-moving equipment, **(2)** improved techniques for removing impurities from ores, and **(3)** other technological advances in mineral extraction and processing.

In 1900, for instance, the average copper ore mined in the United States was about 5% copper by weight. Today it is 0.5%, and copper costs less (ad-

justed for inflation). New methods of mineral extraction may allow even lower-grade ores of some metals to be used (Solutions, p. 349).

However, the mining of lower-grade ores can be limited by **(1)** increased cost of mining and processing larger volumes of ore, **(2)** availability of fresh water needed to mine and process some minerals (especially in arid and semiarid areas), and **(3)** the environmental impact of the increased land disruption, waste material, and pollution produced during mining and processing (Figure 15-6).

**Can We Get Enough Minerals by Mining the Oceans?** Ocean mineral resources are found in **(1)** seawater, **(2)** sediments and deposits on the shallow continental shelf (Figure 7-7, p. 148), **(3)** hydrothermal ore deposits (Figure 15-3), and **(4)** manganese-rich nodules on the deep-ocean floor.

Most of the chemical elements found in seawater occur in such low concentrations that recovering them takes more energy and money than they are worth. Only magnesium, bromine, and sodium chloride are abundant enough to be extracted profitably at current prices with existing technology.

Deposits of minerals (mostly sediments) along the continental shelf and near shorelines are significant sources of sand, gravel, phosphates, sulfur, tin, copper, iron, tungsten, silver, titanium, platinum, and diamonds.

Rich deposits of gold, silver, zinc, and copper are found as sulfide deposits in the deep-ocean floor and around black smokers (Figure 15-3). Currently, it is too expensive to extract these minerals even though some of these deposits contain large concentrations of important metals.

Manganese-rich nodules found on the deep-ocean floor at various sites may be a future source of manganese and other key metals. They might be **(1)** sucked up from the ocean floor by giant vacuum pipes or **(2)** scooped up by buckets on a continuous cable operated by a mining ship.

So far these nodules and resource-rich mineral beds in international waters have not been developed because of high costs and squabbles over who owns these common-property resources and how any profits from extracting them should be distributed among the world's nations. Some of these issues may be resolved by the international Law of the Sea Treaty.

Some environmentalists believe seabed mining probably would cause less environmental harm than mining on land. But they are concerned that removing seabed mineral deposits and dumping back unwanted material will **(1)** stir up ocean sediments, **(2)** destroy seafloor organisms, and **(3)** have potentially harmful effects on poorly understood ocean food webs and marine biodiversity.

## Mining with Microbes

One way to improve mining technology is to use microorganisms for in-place (*in situ*, pronounced "in-SY-too") mining. This biological approach to mining would **(1)** remove desired metals from ores while leaving the surrounding environment undisturbed, **(2)** reduce air pollution associated with the smelting of metal ores, and **(3)** reduce water pollution associated with using hazardous chemicals such as cyanides and mercury to extract gold (Case Study, p. 345).

Once a commercially viable ore deposit has been identified, wells are drilled into it and the ore is fractured. Then the ore is inoculated with natural or genetically engineered bacteria to extract the desired metal. Next the well is flooded with water, which is pumped to the surface, where the desired metal is removed. Then the water is recycled.

This technique permits economical extraction from low-grade ores, which are increasingly being used as high-grade ores are depleted. Since 1958, the copper industry has been using natural strains of the bacterium *Thiobacillus ferroxidans* to remove copper from low-grade copper ore. Currently, more than 30% of all copper produced worldwide, worth more than $1 billion a year, comes from such *biomining*. If naturally occurring bacteria cannot be found to extract a particular metal, genetic engineering techniques could be used to produce such bacteria.

However, microbiological ore processing is slow. It can take decades to remove the same amount of material that conventional methods can remove within months or years. So far, biological mining methods are economically feasible only with low-grade ore (such as gold and copper) for which conventional techniques are too expensive.

### Critical Thinking

**1.** If you had a large sum of money to invest, would you invest it in the microbiological mining of aluminum ore? Explain.

**2.** Are the ecological and human health risks from using genetically engineered organisms to mine metals likely to be higher or lower than those of genetically engineered organisms in food (Figure 13-16, p. 291, and Figure 13-17, p. 292)? Explain.

---

**Can We Find Substitutes for Scarce Nonrenewable Mineral Resources? The Materials Revolution** Some analysts believe that even if supplies of key minerals become very expensive or scarce, human ingenuity will find substitutes. They point to the current *materials revolution* in which silicon and new materials, particularly ceramics and plastics, are being developed and used as replacements for metals.

Ceramics have many advantages over conventional metals. They are harder, stronger, lighter, and longer lasting than many metals, and they withstand intense heat and do not corrode. Within a few decades we may have high-temperature ceramic superconductors in which electricity flows without resistance. Such a development may lead to faster computers, more efficient power transmission, and affordable electromagnets for propelling high-speed magnetic levitation trains.

Plastics also have advantages over many metals. High-strength plastics and composite materials strengthened by lightweight carbon and glass fibers are likely to transform the automobile and aerospace industries. They **(1)** cost less to produce than metals because they take less energy, **(2)** do not need painting, and **(3)** can be molded into any shape. New plastics and gels also are being developed to provide super-insulation without taking up much space. One new plastic can withstand extremely high temperatures and is not even affected by exposure to the most intense laser beams.

Substitutes undoubtedly can be found for many scarce mineral resources. But finding substitutes for some key materials may be difficult or impossible. Examples are **(1)** helium, **(2)** phosphorus for phosphate fertilizers, **(3)** manganese for making steel, and **(4)** copper for wiring motors and generators.

In addition, some substitutes are inferior to the minerals they replace. For example, aluminum could replace copper in electrical wiring. But producing aluminum takes much more energy than producing copper and aluminum wiring is a greater fire hazard than copper wiring.

## 15-5 EVALUATING ENERGY RESOURCES

**What Types of Energy Do We Use?** *Some 99% of the energy used to heat the earth and all of our buildings comes directly from the sun* (see photo on p. 253). Without this direct input of essentially inexhaustible solar energy, the earth's average temperature would be $-240°C$ ($-400°F$), and life as we know it would not exist.

This incoming solar energy is based on the nuclear fusion of hydrogen atoms that make up the sun's mass

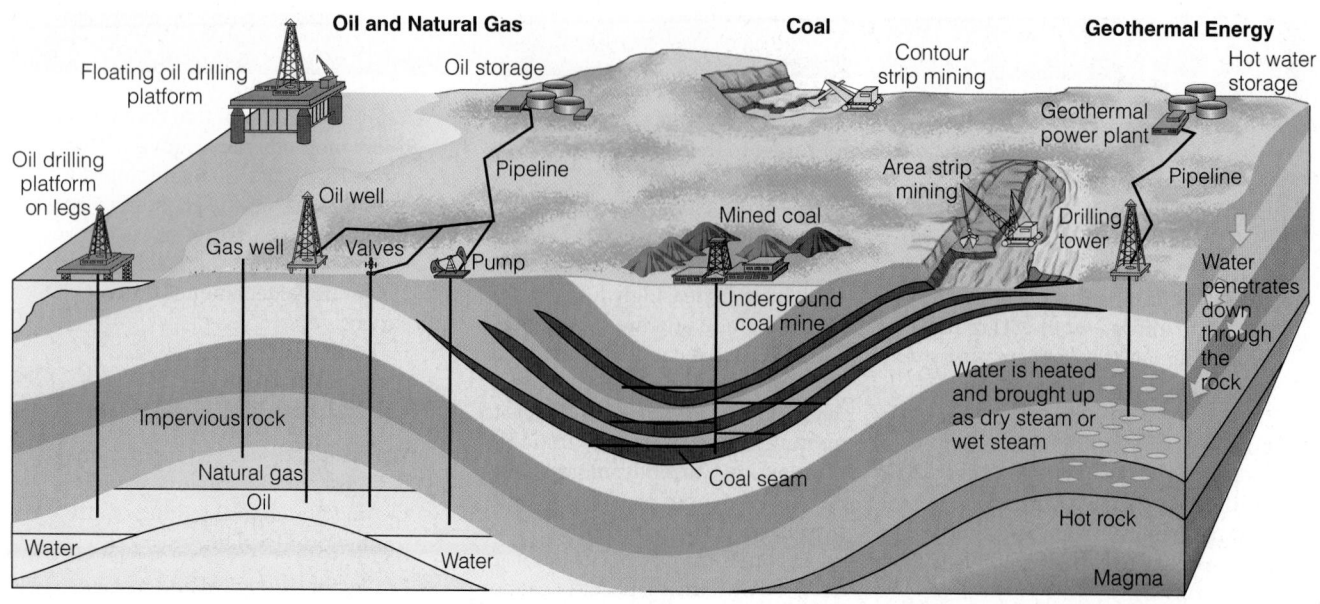

**Figure 15-10** Important *nonrenewable energy resources* that can be removed from the earth's crust are coal, oil, natural gas, and some forms of geothermal energy. Nonrenewable uranium ore is also extracted from the earth's crust and then processed to increase its concentration of uranium-235, which can be used as a fuel in nuclear reactors to produce electricity.

(Figure 3-18, p. 58). Thus *life on earth is made possible by a gigantic nuclear fusion reactor safely located about 150 million kilometers (93 million miles) away.*

This direct input of solar energy also produces several other *indirect forms of renewable solar energy:* (1) wind, (2) falling and flowing water (hydropower), and (3) biomass (solar energy converted to chemical energy stored in chemical bonds of organic compounds in trees and other plants).

*Commercial energy* sold in the marketplace makes up the remaining 1% of the energy we use to supplement the earth's direct input of solar energy. Most commercial energy comes from extracting and burning *nonrenewable mineral resources* obtained from the earth's crust, primarily carbon-containing fossil fuels (oil, natural gas, and coal; Figure 15-10).

**What Types of Energy Does the World Depend On, and How Might This Change?** Over the past 60,000 years, major cultural changes (Section 2-1, p. 22) and technological advances have greatly increased energy use per person (Figure 15-11). As a result of such advances, about 82% of the commercial energy consumed in the world comes from *nonrenewable* energy resources (76% from fossil fuels and 6% from nuclear power; Figure 15-12, left).

Figure 15-13 shows the world's increase in consumption of oil, coal, and natural gas between 1950 and 2000, and Figure 15-14 (p. 352) shows past and projected future trends in the use of nuclear power to produce electricity.

Here are some important trends in the use of fossil fuels, nuclear power, and biomass (mostly from wood):

■ Between 1996 and 2000, global use of *coal* declined by 7% (Figure 15-13) and in the long run is expected to continue to decline because it is the world's most polluting and climate-disrupting fossil fuel. China, the world's second largest user of coal, after the United

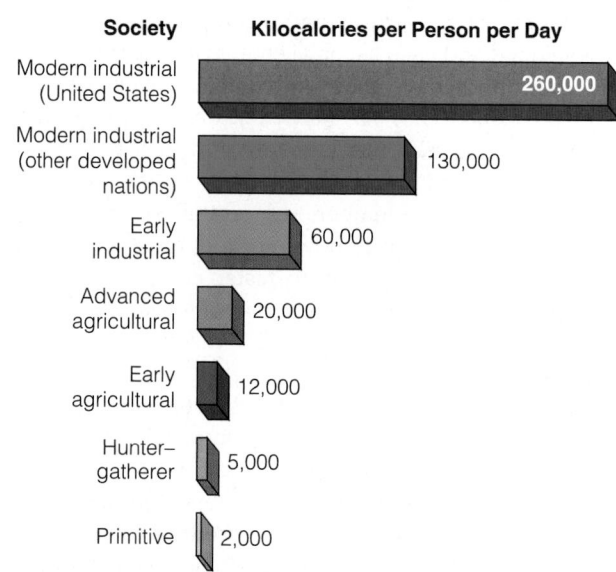

**Figure 15-11** Average direct and indirect daily energy use per person at various stages of human cultural development. A typical citizen in a modern industrial society uses 65–130 times as much energy per day as a hunter–gatherer.

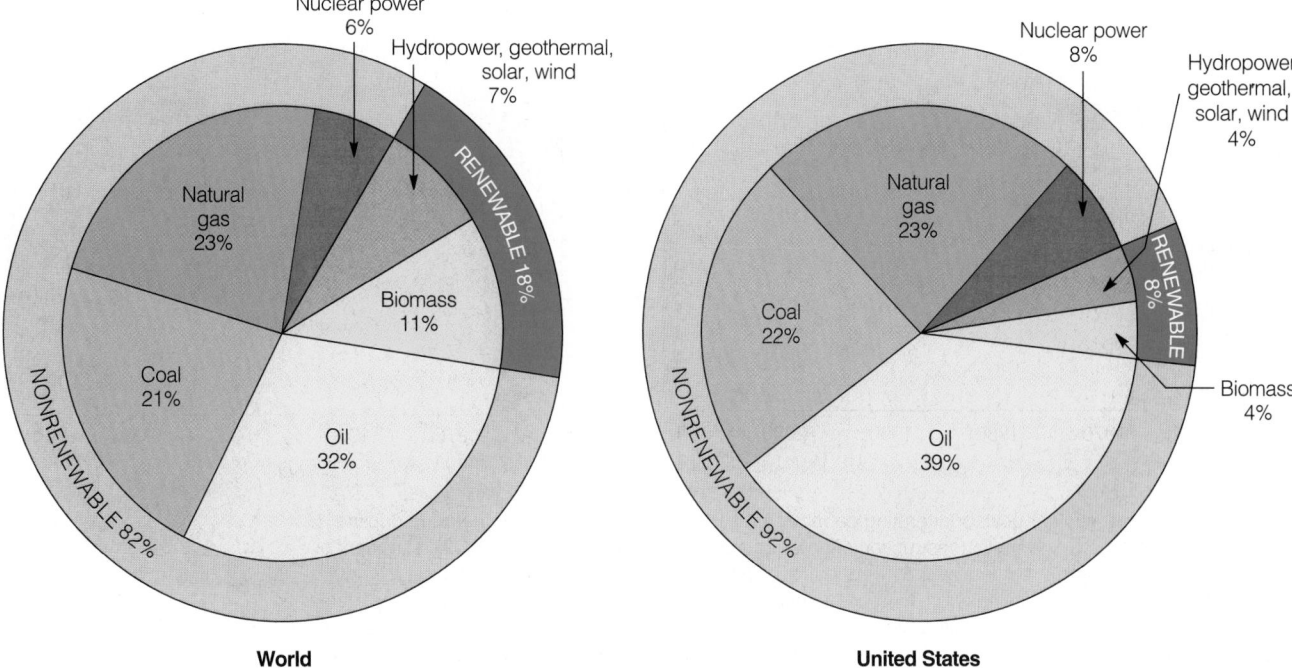

**World**

Nuclear power
6%

Hydropower, geothermal,
solar, wind
7%

Natural
gas
23%

Biomass
11%

RENEWABLE 18%

Coal
21%

Oil
32%

NONRENEWABLE 82%

**United States**

Nuclear power
8%

Hydropower
geothermal,
solar, wind
4%

Natural
gas
23%

Coal
22%

RENEWABLE 8%

Biomass
4%

Oil
39%

NONRENEWABLE 92%

**Figure 15-12** Commercial energy use by source for the world (left) and the United States (right) in 2000. Commercial energy amounts to only 1% of the energy used in the world; the other 99% is direct solar energy received from the sun and is not sold in the marketplace. (Data from U.S. Department of Energy, British Petroleum, and Worldwatch Institute)

States, reduced its coal use by an estimated 14% between 1996 and 2000.

▪ Use of *oil* continues to climb by about 1% a year (Figure 15-13), primarily because of its **(1)** abundance, **(2)** low price (bolstered by huge government subsidies and failure to include its environmental costs in its market price), and **(3)** ease of use as a motor vehicle fuel. Global oil production is expected to peak between 2010 and 2030 and then begin declining.

▪ Natural gas use is increasing by about 2% per year. Since 1999, it has produced more of the world's

energy than coal (Figure 15-13) mostly because of ample supplies and because it is the cleanest and least climate disrupting of the three major fossil fuels.

▪ Global production of electricity by nuclear power plants has leveled off since 1989 (Figure 15-14). Without greatly increased government subsidies, it is projected to decline as aging reactors wear out and are retired.

▪ In developing countries, the main source of energy for heating and cooking for roughly half the world's population is renewable energy from *biomass* (mostly fuelwood and charcoal made from fuelwood)—as long as wood supplies are not harvested faster than they are replenished. Some *bad news* is many of the world's people in developing countries **(1)** face a fuelwood shortage that is expected to get worse because of unsustainable harvesting, **(2)** die prematurely from breathing particles emitted by burning wood indoors in open fires and poorly designed primitive stoves, and **(3)** cannot afford to use fossil fuels.

**What Types of Energy Does the United States Depend On, and How Might That Change?** The United States is the world's largest energy user. With only 4.6% of the population, it uses 24% of the world's commercial energy. This is more energy than the combined total used by the next four largest energy-consuming countries—China, Russia, Japan,

**Figure 15-13** Global consumption of fossil fuels—oil, coal, and natural gas—1950–2000. (Data from Worldwatch Institute)

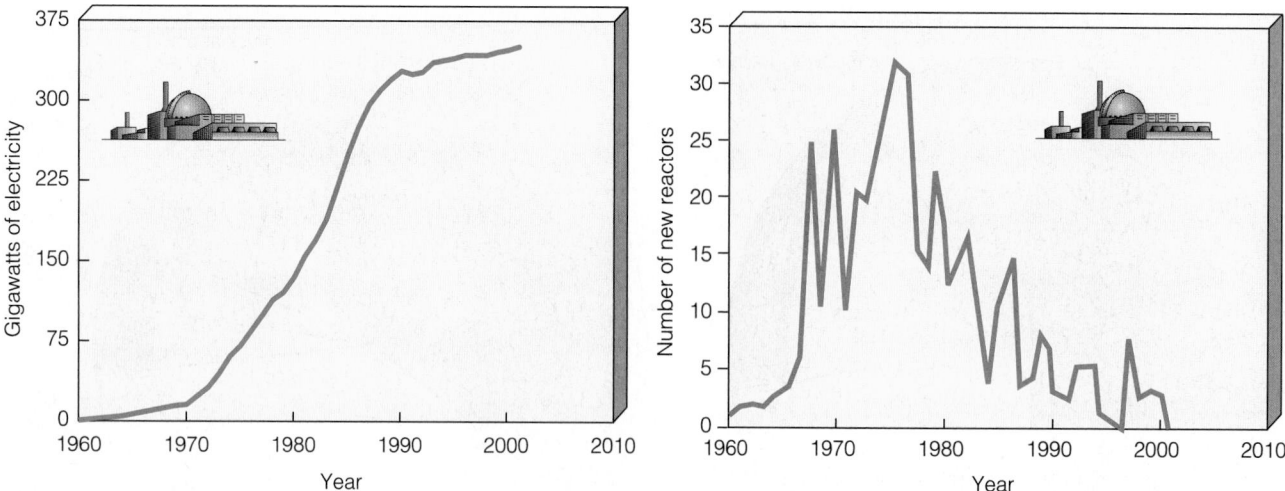

**Figure 15-14** Global nuclear power generating capacity peaked in the 1990s and is projected to decline because of the **(1)** sharp decline in construction of new nuclear reactors since 1975 (right), **(2)** retirement of many of the world's existing reactors as they wear out or cost too much to run, **(3)** lower projected electricity demand because of energy savings from increased energy efficiency, and **(4)** increased availability of safer, easier, quicker to install, and less costly ways to produce electricity from alternatives such as turbines burning natural gas, wind power, and solar cells (as prices continue to fall). (Data from U.S. Department of Energy and the Worldwatch Institute)

and Germany. In contrast, India, with 16% of the world's people, uses about 3% of the world's commercial energy.

About 92% of the commercial energy used in the United States comes from *nonrenewable* energy resources (84% from fossil fuels and 8% from nuclear power; Figure 15-12, right). Energy use per person in the United States and Canada is **(1)** about twice as high as in Japan, Germany, France, and the United Kingdom and **(2)** at least 100 times as high as that in China and India. According to Maurice Strong, secretary-general of the 1992 United Nations (UN) Earth Summit, "Typical citizens of advanced industrialized nations each consume as much energy in six months as typical citizens in developing countries consume during their entire life."

Figure 15-15 shows energy consumption by fuel in the United States from 1970 to 2000, with projections to 2020. Note that the main projected trends between 2000 and 2020 are increased use of oil and natural gas and a leveling off of coal use.

An important environmental, economic, and political issue is what energy resources the United States might be using by 2050 and 2100. Figure 15-16 shows shifts in use of various sources of energy in the United States since 1800 and one scenario showing projected changes to a solar-hydrogen energy age by 2100.

Current global and U.S. dependence on nonrenewable fossil fuels (Figures 15-12 and 15-13) is the primary cause of **(1)** air and water pollution, **(2)** land disruption, and **(3)** greenhouse gas emissions. According to many energy experts, the need to use cleaner and less cli-

mate-disrupting forms of energy—not the depletion of fossil fuels—is the driving force behind the projected global transition to a solar-hydrogen energy age in the United States and other parts of the world before the end of this century (Figure 15-16).

Whether this shift occurs depends primarily on a combination of technological developments and what energy resources the U.S. government decides to **(1)** *promote* by use of subsidies and tax breaks and **(2)** *dampen* by reducing subsidies and tax breaks and taxing energy use for fuels that cause environmental harm or produce $CO_2$. This is primarily a political decision made by elected officials with pressure from officials of energy companies and citizens.

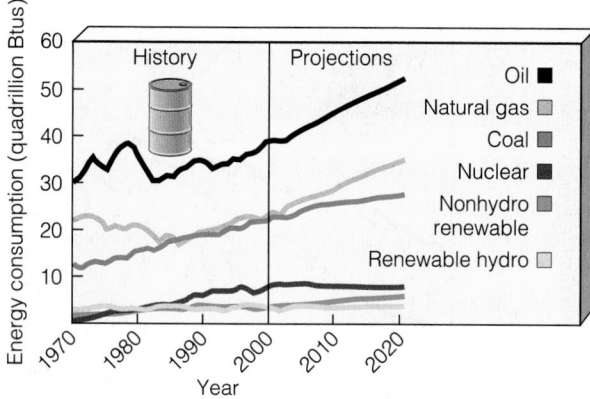

**Figure 15-15** Energy consumption by fuel in the United States, 1970–2000, with projections to 2020. (Data from U.S. Department of Energy, *Annual Energy Review, 2002*)

**Figure 15-16** Shifts in the use of commercial energy resources in the United States since 1800, with projected changes to 2100. Shifts from wood to coal and then from coal to oil and natural gas have each taken about 50 years. The projected shift to 2100 is only one of many possible scenarios depending on a variety of assumptions. (Data from U.S. Department of Energy)

**How Can We Decide Which Energy Resources to Use?** There is intense scientific, economic, and political controversy over which energy resources we should rely on now and in the future. As you will learn in this chapter and the one that follows, each energy resource has advantages and disadvantages that must be carefully evaluated.

Energy policies need to be developed with the future in mind because experience shows that it usually takes at least 50 years and huge investments to phase in new energy alternatives to the point where they provide 10–20% of total energy use. Making projections such as those in Figure 15-16 involves answering the following questions for *each* energy alternative:

- How much of the energy source will be available in the **(1)** near future (the next 15–25 years) and **(2)** long term (the next 25–50 years)?

- What is this source's net energy yield?

- How much will it cost to develop, phase in, and use this energy resource?

- What government research and development subsidies and tax breaks will be provided for each energy resource to spur or hinder its development?

- How will dependence on each energy resource affect national and global economic and military security?

- How vulnerable is each source of energy to terrorism?

- How will extracting, transporting, and using the energy resource affect the environment, human health, and the earth's climate? Should these harmful costs be included in the market prices of each energy resource

through a combination of taxes and phasing out environmentally harmful subsidies (full-cost pricing)?

**What Is Net Energy? The Only Energy That Really Counts** It takes energy to get energy. For example, oil must be **(1)** found, **(2)** pumped up from beneath the ground or ocean floor, **(3)** transferred to a refinery and converted to useful fuels (such as gasoline, diesel fuel, and heating oil), **(4)** transported to users, and **(5)** burned in furnaces and cars before it is useful to us. Each of these steps uses energy, and the second law of thermodynamics (p. 59) tells us that each time we use high-quality energy (Figure 3-12, p. 53) to perform a task, some of it is always wasted and degraded to lower-quality energy.

The usable amount of *high-quality energy* (Figure 3-12, p. 53) available from a given quantity of an energy resource is its **net energy:** the total amount of energy available from an energy resource minus the energy needed to find, extract, process, and get that energy to consumers. It is calculated by estimating the total energy available from the resource over its lifetime minus the amount of energy **(1)** used (the first law of thermodynamics), **(2)** automatically wasted (the second law of thermodynamics), and **(3)** unnecessarily wasted in finding, processing, concentrating, and transporting the useful energy to users.

Net energy is like your net spendable income (your wages minus taxes and other deductions). For example, suppose that for every 10 units of energy in oil in the ground we have to use and waste 8 units of energy to find, extract, process, and transport the oil to users. Then we have only 2 units of *useful energy* available from every 10 units of energy in the oil.

We can express net energy as the ratio of useful energy produced to the useful energy used to produce it. In the example just given, the *net energy ratio* would be 10/8, or 1.25. The higher the ratio, the greater the net energy. When the ratio is less than 1, there is a net energy loss.

Figure 15-17 (p. 354) shows estimated net energy ratios for **(1)** various types of space heating, **(2)** high-temperature heat for industrial processes, and **(3)** transportation. Currently, oil has a high net energy ratio because much of it comes from large, accessible, and cheap-to-use deposits such as those in the Middle East. When those sources are depleted, the net energy ratio of oil will decline and prices will rise. Then more money and high-quality fossil fuel energy will be needed to find, process, and deliver new oil from **(1)** deposits that are small and widely dispersed, buried deep in the earth's crust, and located in remote areas or further and further offshore, and **(2)** extracting and processing shale oil.

Conventional nuclear energy has a low net energy ratio because large amounts of energy are needed to

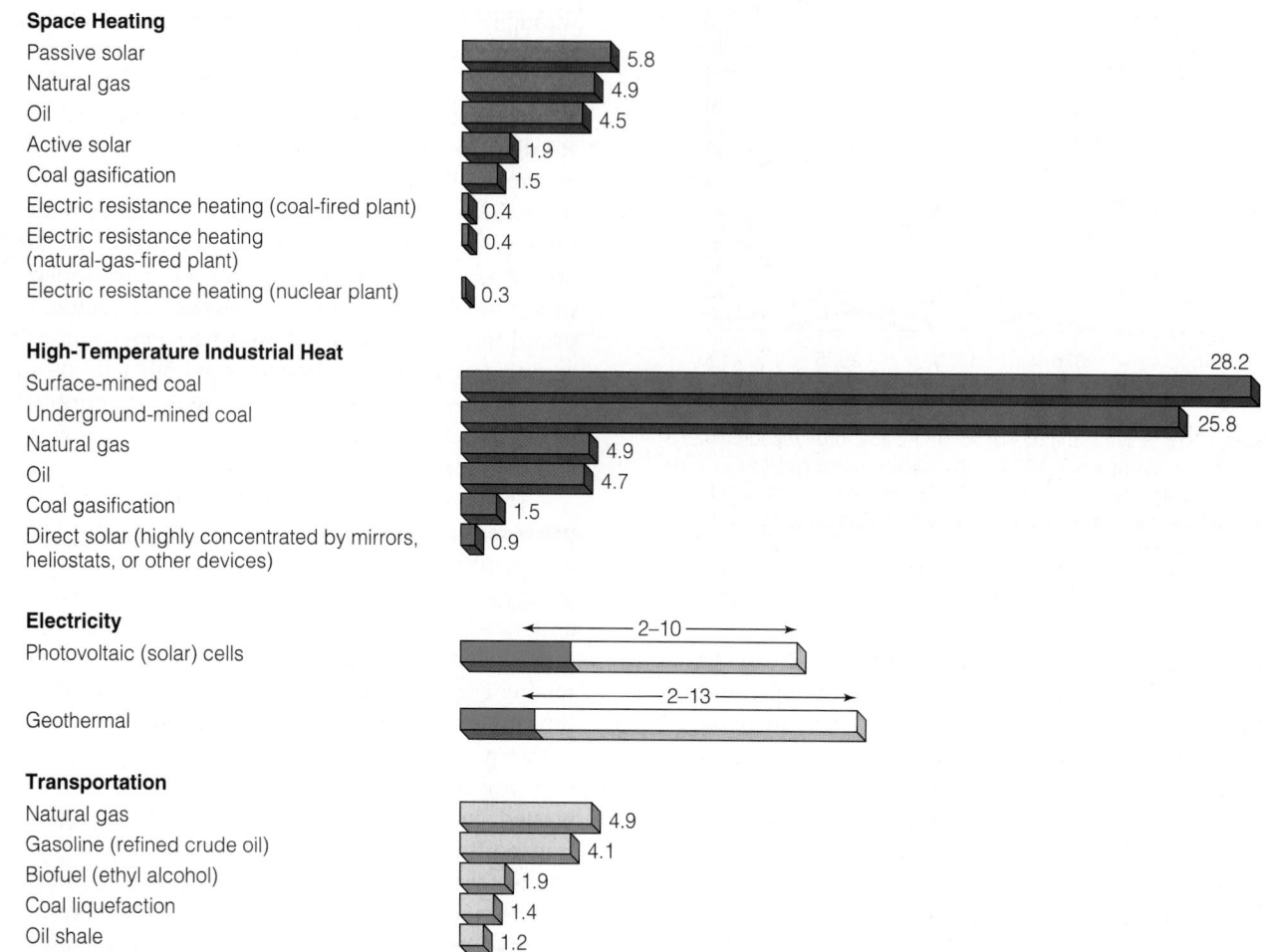

**Space Heating**

Passive solar — 5.8
Natural gas — 4.9
Oil — 4.5
Active solar — 1.9
Coal gasification — 1.5
Electric resistance heating (coal-fired plant) — 0.4
Electric resistance heating (natural-gas-fired plant) — 0.4
Electric resistance heating (nuclear plant) — 0.3

**High-Temperature Industrial Heat**

Surface-mined coal — 28.2
Underground-mined coal — 25.8
Natural gas — 4.9
Oil — 4.7
Coal gasification — 1.5
Direct solar (highly concentrated by mirrors, heliostats, or other devices) — 0.9

**Electricity**

Photovoltaic (solar) cells — 2–10
Geothermal — 2–13

**Transportation**

Natural gas — 4.9
Gasoline (refined crude oil) — 4.1
Biofuel (ethyl alcohol) — 1.9
Coal liquefaction — 1.4
Oil shale — 1.2

**Figure 15-17** *Net energy ratios* for various energy systems over their estimated lifetimes. The higher the net energy ratio, the greater the net energy available. (Data from U.S. Department of Energy and Colorado Energy Research Institute, *Net Energy Analysis*, 1976; and Howard T. Odum and Elisabeth C. Odum, *Energy Basis for Man and Nature*, 3rd ed., New York: McGraw-Hill, 1981)

(1) extract and process uranium ore, (2) convert it into a usable nuclear fuel, (3) build and operate nuclear power plants, (4) dismantle the highly radioactive plants after their 15–60 years of useful life, and (5) store the resulting highly radioactive wastes safely for thousands of years.

## 15-6 OIL

**What Is Crude Oil, and How Is It Extracted and Processed?** **Petroleum,** or **crude oil** (oil as it comes out of the ground), is a thick liquid consisting of hundreds of combustible hydrocarbons along with small amounts of sulfur, oxygen, and nitrogen impurities. This fossil fuel was produced by the decomposition of dead organic matter from plants (primarily plankton) and animals that were (1) buried under lake and ocean sediments 2–140 million years ago and (2) subjected to high temperatures and pressures over millions of years as part of the carbon cycle (Figure 4-28, p. 84).

Deposits of crude oil and natural gas often are trapped together under a dome deep within the earth's crust on land or under the seafloor (Figure 15-10). The crude oil is dispersed in pores and cracks in underground rock formations, somewhat like water saturating a sponge. A well can be drilled. Then we can pump out the crude oil that is drawn by gravity out of the rock pores and into the bottom of the well.

On average, producers get only about 35% of the oil out of an oil deposit. They then abandon the well because the remaining *heavy crude oil* is too difficult or expensive to recover. As oil prices rise, it can become economical to remove about 10–25% of this remaining heavy oil by flushing the well with steam and water. But the net energy yield for such recovered oil is lower because it takes the energy in one-third of a barrel of refined oil to retrieve each barrel of heavy crude oil.

Drilling for oil causes only moderate damage to the earth's land because the wells occupy fairly little land area. However, oil drilling always involves (1) some oil spills on land and in aquatic systems and **(2)** the harmful environmental effects associated with the extraction, processing, and use of any nonrenewable resource from the earth's crust (Figure 15-6).

Some *good news* is that new drilling technologies allow oil and natural gas producers to **(1)** drill deeper on land and the ocean bottom, **(2)** use fewer drilling rigs (derricks) by using one rig to drill several gas or oil pockets at the same time (multilateral drilling), and **(3)** remove oil or gas from distances as far away as 8 kilometers (5 miles) by drilling at angles of 90 degrees or more (slant drilling). According to oil producers, these improved extraction technologies can increase oil production without despoiling environmentally sensitive areas.

When prices for conventional oil rise and range from $30–40 per barrel, it may become economically feasible to extract enough of the heavy crude oil left in existing wells to increase the world's identified oil reserves by 50%. However, at that price it may be cheaper to depend more on natural gas and other energy resources such as wind and eventually hydrogen (Figure 15-16)

Once crude oil has been extracted, it is transported to a *refinery* by pipeline, truck, or ship (oil tanker). There it is heated and distilled in gigantic columns to separate it into components with different boiling points (Figure 15-18). Some of the products of oil distillation, called **petrochemicals,** are used as raw materials in industrial organic chemicals, pesticides, plastics, synthetic fibers, paints, medicines, and many other products.

**Who Has the World's Oil Supplies?**    Oil *reserves* are identified deposits from which oil can be extracted profitably at current prices with current technology. The 11 countries that make up the Organization of Petroleum Exporting Countries (OPEC)* have 67% of the world's crude oil reserves, which explains why OPEC is expected to have long-term control over world oil supplies and prices.

Saudi Arabia, with 26%, has by far the largest proportion of the world's crude oil reserves, followed by Iraq, Kuwait, Iran, and United Arab Emirates, each with 9–10%.

The remaining global crude oil reserves are found in **(1)** Latin America (9%, mostly in Venezuela and Mexico), **(2)** Africa (7%), **(3)** the former Soviet Union (6%), **(4)** Asia (4%, with 3% in China), **(5)** the United States (3%), and **(6)** western Europe (2%). Figure 15-19

*OPEC was formed in 1960 so developing countries with much of the world's known and projected oil supplies could get a higher price for this resource. Today its members are Algeria, Indonesia, Iran, Iraq, Kuwait, Libya, Nigeria, Qatar, Saudi Arabia, United Arab Emirates, and Venezuela.

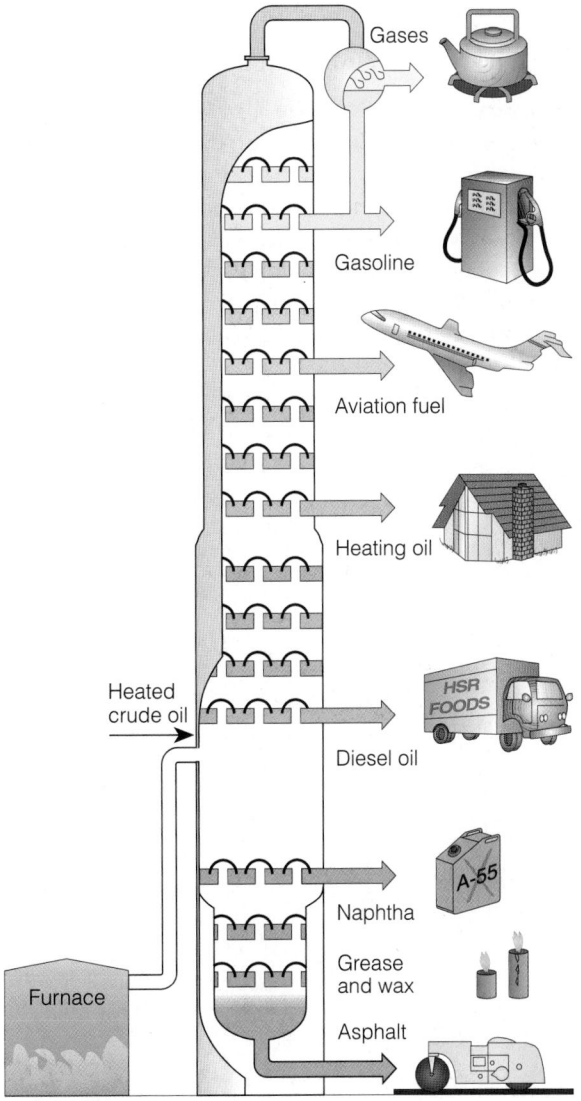

**Figure 15-18** Refining crude oil. Based on their boiling points, components are removed at various levels in a giant distillation column. The most volatile components with the lowest boiling points are removed at the top of the column.

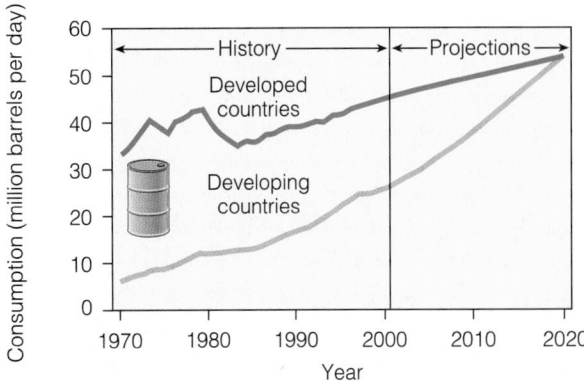

**Figure 15-19** Oil consumption in developed and developing regions, 1970–2020. (U.S. Department of Energy)

shows the projected increase in oil consumption in developed and developing countries.

**Case Study: Oil Use in the United States** Figure 15-20 shows the locations of the major known deposits of fossil fuels (oil, natural gas, and coal) in **(1)** the United States and Canada and **(2)** ocean areas where more crude oil and natural gas might be found. In 2001, about 25% of U.S. domestic oil production came from offshore drilling and 17% from Alaska's North Slope. Currently, about 93% of all U.S. offshore drilling takes place in the Gulf of Mexico, primarily off the coasts of Texas and Louisiana (Figure 15-21).

The United States has only 3% of the world's oil reserves. However, it uses about 26% of the crude oil extracted worldwide each year (68% of it for transportation), mostly because oil is an abundant and convenient fuel to use and is cheap (Figure 15-22). Despite an upsurge in exploration and test drilling, U.S. oil extraction has declined since 1985, and most geologists do not expect a significant increase in domestic supplies (Figure 15-23).

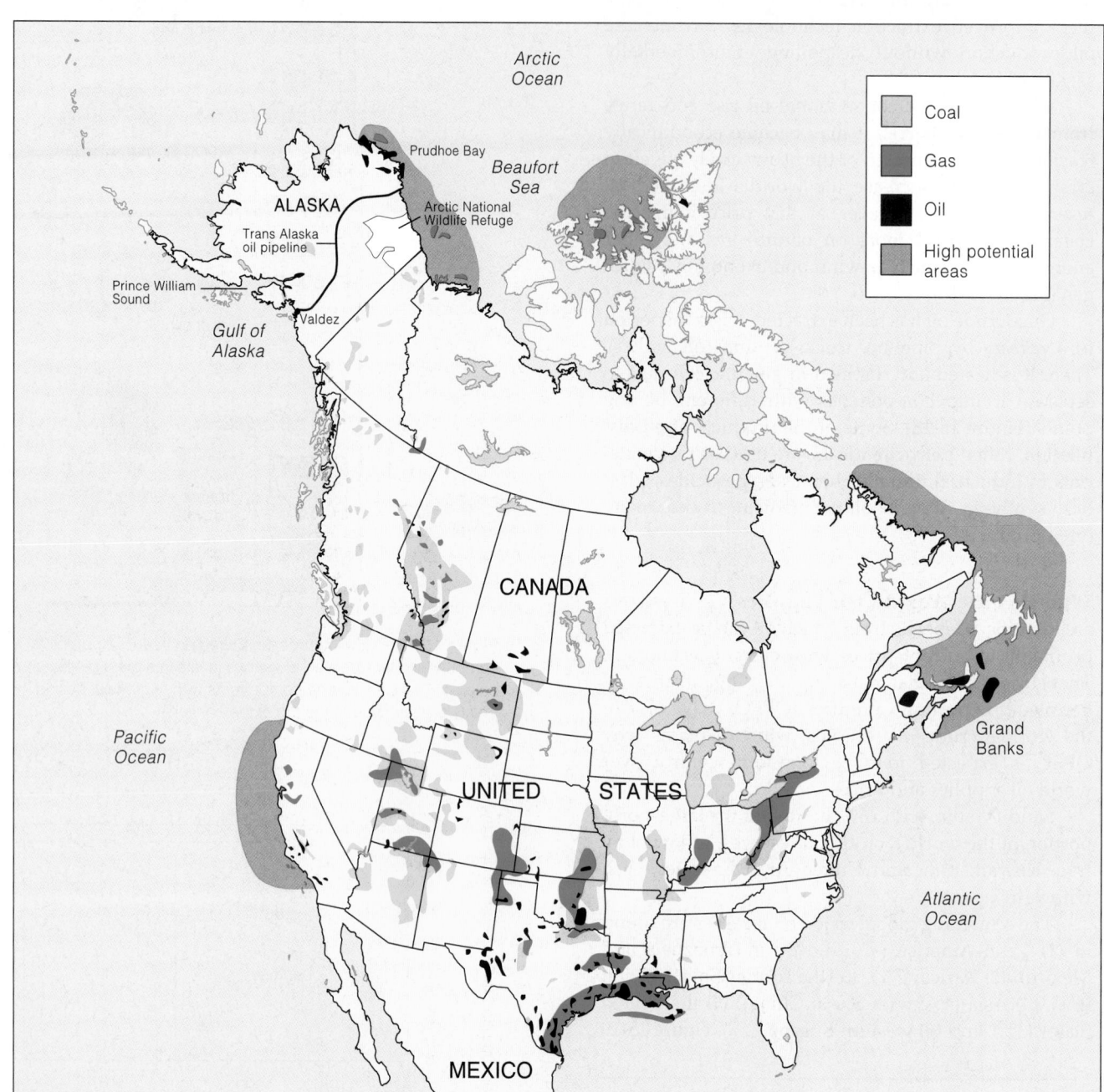

**Figure 15-20** Locations of the major known deposits of oil, natural gas, and coal in North America and offshore areas where more crude oil and natural gas might be found. Geologists do not expect to find very much new oil and natural gas in North America. (Data from Council on Environmental Quality and U.S. Geological Survey)

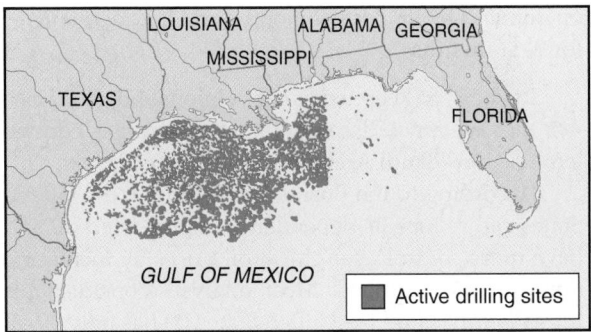

**Figure 15-21** Offshore drilling for oil accounts for about 26% of U.S. oil production. About 93% of this oil comes from the Gulf of Mexico where there are 4,000 oil drilling platforms and 53,000 kilometers (33,000 miles) of underwater pipeline. (U.S. Geological Survey)

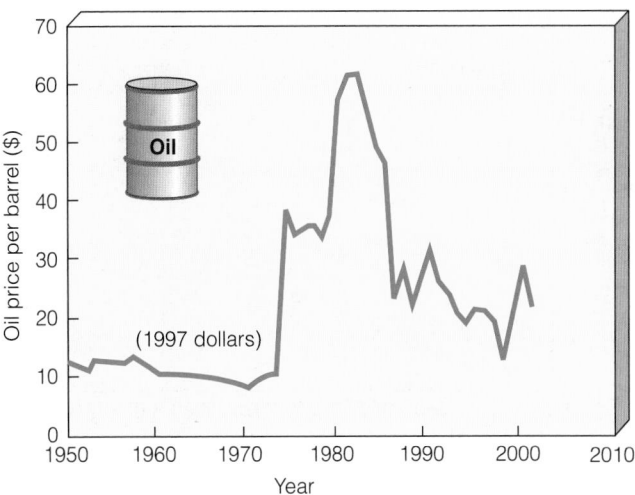

**Figure 15-22** Inflation-adjusted price of oil, 1950–2001. When adjusted for inflation, oil costs about the same as it did in 1975. Although low oil prices have stimulated economic growth, they have discouraged **(1)** improvements in energy efficiency and **(2)** increased use of renewable energy resources. (Data from U.S. Department of Energy and Department of Commerce)

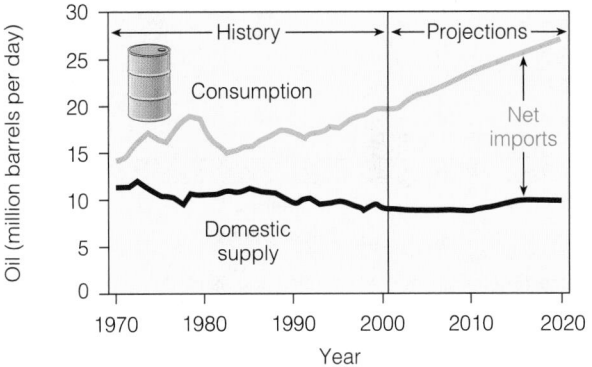

**Figure 15-23** U.S. petroleum supply, consumption, and imports, 1970–2000, with projections to 2020. (U.S. Department of Energy)

In 2001, the United States imported about 55% of the oil it used (up from 36% in 1973 during the OPEC oil embargo), mostly because of declining domestic oil reserves, higher production costs for domestic oil than for most sources of imported oil, and increased oil use. About 23% of this oil came from countries in the Persian Gulf, mainly Saudi Arabia (14%), Iraq (7%), and Kuwait (3%); 27% from Canada (15%) and Mexico (12%); and 20% from the OPEC nations of Venezuela (13%) and Nigeria (7%). In 2001, the U.S. bill for oil imports was about $100 billion—an average of $11 million per hour. According to the Department of Energy (DOE), the United States could be importing 61% or more of the oil it uses by 2010 (Figure 15-23).

**How Long Will Oil Supplies Last, and What Are the Pros and Cons of Oil?** It is important to understand that *we are not currently running out of oil— or natural gas or coal.* Like all nonrenewable resources, the world's oil supplies are eventually expected to decline (Spotlight, p. 359). This will occur gradually when **(1)** affordable supplies of oil decrease as demand exceeds production and prices rise and **(2)** other energy resources become economically and environmentally acceptable substitutes for oil.

Since 1800 the primary energy resource for the world has shifted from wood to coal to oil and is projected to shift to natural gas and perhaps hydrogen by 2100 (Figure 15-16). Each of these shifts has taken at least 50 years so the search for replacements for oil is under way.

In 1999, Mike Bowling, CEO of ARCO Oil said at an energy conference in Houston, Texas, "We are embarked on the beginning of the last days of the Age of Oil." He then went on to discuss the need for the world to shift from a carbon-based to a hydrogen-based energy economy during this century (Figure 15-16).

Production of the world's estimated oil reserves is expected to peak between 2010 and 2030 (Figure 15-24, top, p. 358), and production of estimated U.S. reserves peaked in 1975 (Figure 15-23 and Figure 15-24, bottom).

*Identified* global reserves of oil should last about 53 years at the current usage rate, and 42 years if usage increases exponentially by about 2% per year. Undiscovered oil that is thought to exist might add another 20–40 years to global oil supplies, probably at higher prices. Thus *known and projected supplies of oil are expected to be 80% depleted within 42–93 years depending on the annual rate of use* (Spotlight, p. 359).

U.S. oil reserves should last about **(1)** 15–24 years (Figure 15-24, bottom) at current consumption rates and **(2)** 10–15 years if consumption increases as projected. However, potential reserves might yield an additional 24 years of production. Thus *U.S. oil supplies are projected to be 80% depleted within 10–48 years, depending on the annual rate of use* (Spotlight, p. 359).

**Figure 15-24** Petroleum production curves for the world (top) and the United States (bottom). (Data from U.S. Geological Survey)

Some analysts contend that rising oil prices (when oil consumption exceeds oil production) will stimulate exploration and lead to enough new reserves to meet future demand through the next century or longer. Other analysts argue that such projections ignore the consequences of the high (1–5% per year) exponential growth in oil consumption (Figure 15-19).

Assuming that we use oil at the current rate,

- Saudi Arabia, with the world's largest crude oil reserves, could supply world oil needs for about 10 years.

- The estimated reserves under Alaska's North Slope (the largest ever found in North America) would meet current world demand for only 6 months or U.S. demand for 3 years.

- The estimated reserves in Alaska's Arctic National Wildlife Refuge would met current oil demand for only 1–5 months and U.S. oil demand for 7–24 months (Pro/Con, p. 360).

- Estimated oil reserves on other federal lands on Alaska's North Slope would meet the current world

oil demand for 10 days–2 months and U.S. demand for 2–11 months.

In short, to keep using conventional oil at the *current rate*, we must discover global oil reserves equivalent to a new Saudi Arabian supply *every 10 years*.

According to the Bush administration, the United States can reduce its dependence on imported oil and have more control over global oil prices by increasing domestic oil supplies. Most analysts consider this unrealistic because the United States **(1)** has only 3% of the world's oil reserves, **(2)** uses 26% of the world's annual oil production, and **(3)** produces most of its dwindling supply of oil at a high cost of $5–7.50 per barrel compared to production costs of less than $1.50 per barrel in Persian Gulf countries. Thus opening all of the U.S. coastal water, forests, and wild places to drilling would hardly put a dent in world oil prices or meet much of the growing U.S. demand for oil.

Critics also urge the government to force the oil companies to **(1)** stop shorting taxpayers by about $100 million a year on oil royalty payments for oil extracted from public lands and **(2)** pay the several billion dollars they owe in back bills for underpayment of oil royalties. According to sworn government and court evidence, the oil industry shorts taxpayers in annual oil royalty payments by **(1)** falsifying prices, **(2)** using phony bills of sale, and **(3)** deliberately classifying high-quality oil as low-quality oil.

The problem is that the current system allows the oil industry great leeway in deciding **(1)** how to measure the amount of oil removed from public lands and **(2)** how much it should pay the government for the oil. This is like going to a gas station and being allowed to bring your own gauge to measure how much gasoline you pump into your car and then decide how much it is worth.

Burning any carbon-containing fossil fuel releases $CO_2$ into the atmosphere and thus can promote global warming. Figure 15-25 compares the relative amounts

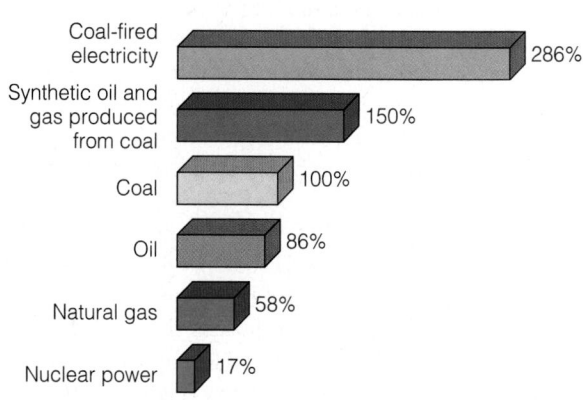

**Figure 15-25** $CO_2$ emissions per unit of energy produced by various fuels, expressed as percentages of emissions produced by coal.

## A Brief History of Oil

In 1859, the world's first commercial oil well was drilled in Titusville, Pennsylvania. This was the beginning of the *Age of Oil*, which now supplies most of the world's energy (Figure 15-12, left). *We are not running out of oil, but many energy experts expect that by 2059—some 200 years after oil was discovered—we will probably begin shifting to increased dependence on natural gas and possibly hydrogen by 2100 (Figure 15-16).*

Here are some milestones in the Age of Oil:

- **1905:** Oil supplies 10% of U.S. energy.

- **1925:** United States produces 71% of the world's oil.

- **1930:** Because of an oil glut, oil sells for 10¢ a barrel.

- **1953:** U.S. oil companies account for about half of the world's oil production and the United States is the world's leading oil exporter.

- **1955:** United States has 20% of the world's estimated oil reserves.

- **1960:** OPEC formed so developing countries, with most of the world's known oil and projected oil supplies, can get a higher price for their oil.

- **1961:** U.S.-proven oil reserves reach a peak and begin to decline.

- **1970:** U.S. oil production peaks and begins to decline.

- **1973:** United States uses 30% of the world's oil, imports 36% of this oil, and has only 5% of the world's proven oil reserves.

- **1973–1974:** OPEC reduces oil imports to the West and bans oil exports to the U.S. because of its support for Israel in the 18-day Yom Kippur War with Egypt and Syria. World oil prices rise sharply (Figure 15-22) and lead to **(1)** double-digit inflation in the United States and many other countries and **(2)** a global economic recession.

- **1975:** Production of estimated U.S. oil reserves peaks.

- **1979:** Iran's Islamic Revolution shuts down most of Iran's oil production and reduces world oil production.

- **1981:** Iran–Iraq war pushes global oil prices to a historic high (Figure 15-22).

- **1983:** Facing an oil glut, OPEC cuts its oil prices.

- **1985:** U.S. domestic oil production begins to decline. Domestic production is not expected to increase enough to **(1)** affect the global price of oil or **(2)** reduce U.S. dependence on oil imports (unless the demand decreases through a combination of reducing oil waste and shifting to other energy resources).

- **August 1990–June 1991:** United States and its allies fight the Persian Gulf War to protect Saudi Arabia and Kuwait oil supplies after Iraq invades Kuwait.

- **2001:** OPEC has 67% of world oil reserves and produces 40% of the world's oil. U.S. has only 3% of oil reserves, used 26% of the world's oil production, and imported 55% of its oil.

- **2010:** U.S. could be importing at least 61% of the oil it uses as consumption continues to exceed production (Figure 15-23).

- **2010–2030:** Production of oil from the world's estimated oil reserves is expected to peak. Oil prices expected to increase gradually as the demand for oil increasingly exceeds the supply—unless the world decreases demand by **(1)** wasting less energy and **(2)** shifting to other sources of energy.

- **2010–2048:** Domestic U.S. oil supplies projected to be 80% depleted.

- **2042–2083:** Gradual decline in dependence on oil (Figure 15-16) unless the world decreases demand for oil by **(1)** wasting less energy and **(2)** shifting to other sources of energy.

### Critical Thinking

What are the three most likely effects of decreased dependence on oil on **(a)** the country where you live, **(b)** your life, and **(c)** the life of any child you might have?

---

of $CO_2$ emitted per unit of energy by the major fossil fuels and nuclear power. Currently, burning oil mostly as gasoline and diesel fuel for transportation accounts for 43% of global $CO_2$ emissions.

Figure 15-26 (p. 361) lists the pros and cons of using conventional crude oil as an energy resource. We are heavily dependent on oil today because it has a high energy content and net energy yield, low cost (as long as supplies exceed demand), and is easy to transport within and between countries.

### How Useful Are Heavy Oils from Oil Shale and Tar Sands?
*Oil shale* is a fine-grained sedimentary rock (Figure 15-27, left, p. 361) containing a solid combustible organic material called *kerogen*. This material can be distilled from oil shale by heating it in a large container to yield *shale oil* (Figure 15-27, right). Before the thick shale oil can be sent by pipeline to a refinery, it must be **(1)** heated to increase its flow rate and **(2)** processed to remove sulfur, nitrogen, and other impurities.

Some *good news* is that estimated potential global supplies of shale oil are about 240 times larger than estimated global supplies of conventional oil. The *bad news* is most deposits of oil shale are of such a low grade that with current oil prices and technology it

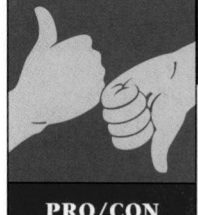

# Should Oil and Gas Development Be Allowed in the Arctic National Wildlife Refuge?

The Arctic National Wildlife Refuge (ANWR) on Alaska's North Slope (Figure 15-20) contains more than one-fifth of all the land in the U.S. National Wildlife Refuge System and has been called the crown jewel of the system. The refuge's coastal plain, its most biologically productive part, is the only stretch of Alaska's arctic coastline not open to oil and gas development.

The Alaskan National Interest Lands Conservation Act of 1980 requires specific authorization from Congress before drilling or other development can take place on this coastal plain. For years, U.S. oil companies have been lobbying Congress to grant them permission to carry out exploratory drilling in the coastal plain because they believe this area might contain oil and natural gas deposits.

Some oil company officials, with the support of the Bush administration and members of the powerful congressional delegation from Alaska (which gets 80% of its general revenue from oil royalties), argue that

- Possible oil and natural gas in ANWR's coastal plain could **(1)** increase U.S. oil and natural gas supplies, **(2)** reduce U.S. dependence on oil imports, and **(3)** lower energy prices.

- They seek to open to oil and gas development on about 800 hectares (2,000 acres) of the coastal plain region.

- They have developed Alaska's Prudhoe Bay oil fields without significant harm to wildlife.

- They can develop this area in an environmentally responsible manner with little lasting environmental impact by using new oil-drilling technology. These advances **(1)** greatly reduce the area covered by gravel drilling pads, buildings, and equipment and **(2)** inject drilling wastes deep into the ground instead of into huge surface pits.

Environmentalists, many biologists, and some economists oppose this proposal. They contend that

- The Department of Interior estimates there is only a 19% chance of finding as much economically recoverable oil in ANWR as the United States consumes every 7–24 months. This will have no effect on oil prices or oil imports because **(1)** the potential supply is too little (no more than 1% of the world's oil for a few years) and **(2)** Persian Gulf oil is much cheaper to produce.

- It would take at least 10 years for any oil or natural gas from the refuge to become available and another 15 years for the field to reach peak production level.

- Improving fuel efficiency is a much faster, cheaper, cleaner, and more secure way to save far more oil. For example, refining the projected peak oil output from ANWR would provide enough gasoline to run only 2% of American cars and light trucks—an amount that could be supplied much more quickly and cheaply from improving the fuel efficiency of these vehicles by only 0.2 kilometers per liter (0.4 miles per gallon). In addition, requiring new SUVs and light trucks used in the United States to have the same average fuel efficiency as new cars would save more oil in 10 years than would ever be produced from the ANWR.

- The 800 hectares (2,000 acres) to be developed would be spread across 35 separate and far-flung drilling sites that would require construction of a network of roads and pipelines, spanning a much larger area.

- Between 1996 and 2001, more than 400 oil spills or oil-related pollution incidents per year have occurred at Alaska's Prudhoe Bay, including the huge 1989 oil spill from the tanker *Exxon Valdez* in Alaska's Prince William Sound. A 2001 study by British Petroleum revealed large and growing maintenance problems and safety valve failures at its giant oil field in Prudhoe Bay.

- The Trans-Alaska Pipeline System and other oil distribution facilities in Alaska are highly vulnerable to sabotage and hard to repair.

- Potential degradation of any portion of this irreplaceable wildlife area is not worth the risk. A 1995 study by the Department of the Interior concluded that long-lasting ecological harm would be caused by oil drilling in the refuge's fragile tundra ecosystem.

- Carrying out any sort of drilling or exploration there will disqualify the refuge from being added to the U.S. wilderness system.

- Even if drilling in the Arctic National Wildlife Refuge posed no environmental threats, it still could not be justified on economic and national security grounds.

- Improvements in slant drilling technology may enable oil companies someday to drill the refuge from outside its boundaries.

## Critical Thinking

**1.** Do you believe oil companies should be allowed to explore and remove oil and natural gas from this wildlife refuge? Why or why not?

**2.** Use the library or Internet to find out the political fate of this wildlife refuge.

| Advantages | | Disadvantages |
|---|---|---|
| Ample supply for 42–93 years | | Need to find substitute within 50 years |
| Low cost (with huge subsidies) | | Artificially low price encourages waste and discourages search for alternatives |
| High net energy yield | | |
| Easily transported within and between countries | | Air pollution when burned |
| Low land use | | Releases $CO_2$ when burned |
| Technology is well developed | | Moderate water pollution |
| Efficient distribution system | | |

**Figure 15-26** Advantages and disadvantages of using conventional oil as an energy resource.

takes more energy and money to mine and convert the kerogen to crude oil than the resulting fuel is worth. However, as oil prices rise it may become economically feasible to exploit reserves of oil shale.

*Tar sand* (or oil sand) is a mixture of clay, sand, water, and a combustible organic material called *bitumen* (a thick and heavy oil with a high sulfur content). Most deposits are too deep underground to be mined at a profit, but some deposits are close enough to the earth's surface to be removed by surface mining. The bitumen is removed, purified, and chemically upgraded into a synthetic crude oil suitable for refining.

**Figure 15-27** Oil shale (left) and the shale oil (right) extracted from it. Big U.S. oil shale projects have been canceled because of excessive cost.

The world's largest known deposits of tar sands, the Athabasca Tar Sands, lie in northern Alberta, Canada. About 10% of these deposits lie close enough to the surface to be surface mined. In Canada, oil has been extracted from tar sands since 1978. Currently, these deposits supply about 21% of Canada's oil needs with prices dropping from $28 per barrel in 1978 to about $11 per barrel today—less than half the current cost of conventional oil.

These deposits could supply all of Canada's projected oil needs for about 33 years at its current consumption rate, but they would last the world only about 2 years. Other large deposits of tar sands are in Utah, Venezuela, Colombia, and Russia. According to the U.S. Department of Energy, exploitation of tar sands could increase the global oil reserves **(1)** by 50% within 25 years if the price of conventional oil rises above $30 per barrel and **(2)** fivefold if the price of oil rises above $40 per barrel.

Figure 15-28 lists the pros and cons of using heavy oil from oil shale and tar sand as energy resources. Because of low net energy yields and the high costs needed to develop and process them, neither of these resources is expected to provide much of the world's energy in the near future. However, as oil prices rise it may become economically feasible to exploit these two sources of heavy oil unless supplies of natural gas and other energy resources cost less to develop and produce fewer harmful environmental effects.

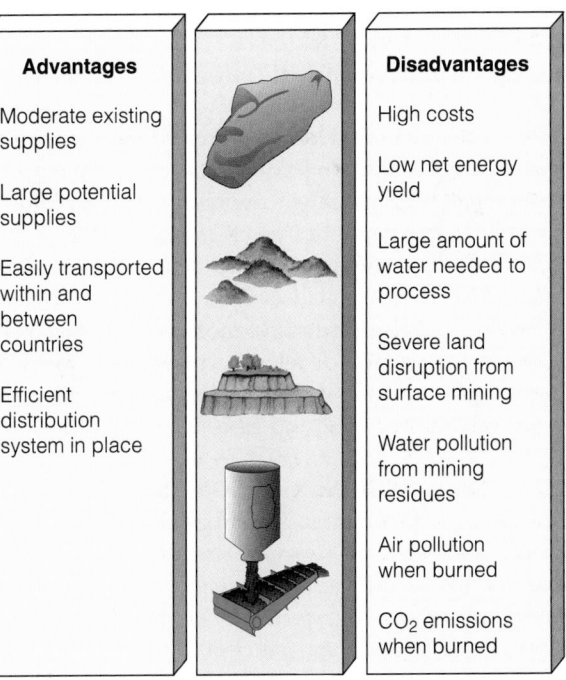

| Advantages | | Disadvantages |
|---|---|---|
| Moderate existing supplies | | High costs |
| Large potential supplies | | Low net energy yield |
| Easily transported within and between countries | | Large amount of water needed to process |
| Efficient distribution system in place | | Severe land disruption from surface mining |
| | | Water pollution from mining residues |
| | | Air pollution when burned |
| | | $CO_2$ emissions when burned |

**Figure 15-28** Advantages and disadvantages of using heavy oils from oil shale and tar sand as energy resources.

## 15-7 NATURAL GAS

**What Is Natural Gas?** In its underground gaseous state, **natural gas** is a mixture of **(1)** 50–90% by volume of methane ($CH_4$), the simplest hydrocarbon, **(2)** smaller amounts of heavier gaseous hydrocarbons such as ethane ($C_2H_6$), propane ($C_3H_8$), and butane ($C_4H_{10}$), and **(3)** small amounts of highly toxic hydrogen sulfide ($H_2S$), a by-product of naturally occurring sulfur in the earth.

*Conventional natural gas* lies above most reservoirs of crude oil and like oil formed from fossil deposits of plants (mostly phytoplankton) and animals buried on the seafloor for millions of years (Figure 15-10). *Unconventional natural gas* is found by itself in other underground sources. One such source is *methane hydrate*, which is composed of small bubbles of natural gas trapped in ice crystals deep under the arctic permafrost and beneath deep-ocean sediments. So far it costs too much to get natural gas from such unconventional sources, but the extraction technology is being developed rapidly.

When a natural gas field is tapped, propane and butane gases are liquefied and removed as **liquefied petroleum gas (LPG).** LPG is stored in pressurized tanks for use mostly in rural areas not served by natural gas pipelines. The rest of the gas (mostly methane) is **(1)** dried to remove water vapor, **(2)** cleansed of poisonous hydrogen sulfide and other impurities, and **(3)** pumped into pressurized pipelines for distribution. At a very low temperature of $-184°C$ ($-300°F$), natural gas can be converted to **liquefied natural gas (LNG).** This highly flammable liquid can then be shipped to other countries in refrigerated tanker ships.

**Who Has the World's Natural Gas Supplies?** Russia and Kazakhstan have about 42% of the world's natural gas reserves. Other countries with large known natural gas reserves are Iran (15%), Qatar (5%), Saudi Arabia (4%), Algeria (4%), the United States (3%), Nigeria (3%), and Venezuela (3%).

Geologists expect to find more natural gas, especially in unexplored developing countries. Most U.S. natural gas reserves are located in the same places as crude oil (Figures 15-10 and 15-20).

**How Long Will Natural Gas Supplies Last?** The outlook for natural gas supplies is much better than for oil. *At the current consumption rate, known reserves and undiscovered, potential reserves of conventional natural gas are expected to last the world for 125 years and the United States for 65–80 years.*

Geologists estimate that *conventional* supplies of natural gas, plus *unconventional* supplies available at higher prices, will last at least **(1)** 200 years at the current consumption rate and **(2)** 80 years if usage rates rise 2% per year. Thus *global supplies of conventional and*

*unconventional natural gas should last 205–325 years, depending on how rapidly natural gas is used.*

**What Is the Future of Natural Gas?** Figure 15-29 lists the pros and cons of natural gas as an energy resource. Energy experts project greatly increased global use of natural gas during this century (Figure 15-16) because of its abundant supply, low production costs, and lower pollution and $CO_2$ per unit of energy than other fossil fuels.

In *combined-cycle natural gas systems*, natural gas is burned in combustion turbines, which are essentially giant jet engines bolted to the ground. This system can **(1)** produce electricity more efficiently than burning coal or oil or using nuclear power, **(2)** produce much less $CO_2$ (Figure 15-25) and smog-causing nitrogen oxides per unit of energy than coal-burning power plants, and **(3)** provide backup power for solar energy and wind power systems. Smaller combined-cycle natural gas units being developed could supply the heat and electricity needs of an apartment or office building.

In 2001, natural gas was burned to provide 53% of the heat in U.S. homes and 16% of the country's electricity. By 2020, the DOE projects that natural gas will be burned to produce 32% of the country's electricity. However, this will require considerable expansion of the country's natural gas pipeline distribution system.

A major problem is that U.S. production of natural gas has been declining for a long time, and experts do

| Advantages | Disadvantages |
|---|---|
| Ample supplies (125 years) | Nonrenewable resource |
| High net energy yield | Releases $CO_2$ when burned |
| Low cost (with huge subsidies) | Methane (a greenhouse gas) can leak from pipelines |
| Less air pollution than other fossil fuels | Difficult to transfer from one country to another |
| Lower $CO_2$ emissions than other fossil fuels | Shipped across ocean as highly explosive LNG |
| Moderate environmental impact | Sometimes burned off and wasted at wells because of low price |
| Easily transported by pipeline | Requires pipelines |
| Low land use | |
| Good fuel for fuel cells and gas turbines | |

**Figure 15-29** Advantages and disadvantages of using conventional natural gas as an energy resource.

not believe this situation will be reversed. More natural gas could be obtained from Canada and Alaska's North Slope. But the pipeline for bringing this gas to the lower 48 states—assuming that it is ever built—will take 7–10 years to complete. More liquified natural gas could be imported by ship. But this requires cooling the gas to $-184°C$ $(-300°F)$, shipping it in special tankers and building special LNG receiving terminals.

Because of its advantages over oil, coal, and nuclear energy, some analysts see natural gas as the best fuel to help make the transition to improved energy efficiency and greater use of solar energy and hydrogen over the next 50 years (Figures 15-15 and 15-16).

## 15-8 COAL

**What Is Coal, and How Is It Extracted and Processed?** Coal is a solid fossil fuel formed in several stages as buried remains of land plants that lived 300–400 million years ago were subjected to intense heat and pressure over many millions of years (Figure 15-30). Coal contains **(1)** small amounts of sulfur (released into the atmosphere as $SO_2$ when coal is burned) and **(2)** trace amounts of mercury and radioactive materials (also released into the atmosphere when coal is burned). Anthracite, about 98% carbon, is the most desirable type of coal because of its high heat content and low sulfur content (Figure 15-30). However, because it takes much longer to form, it is less common and therefore more expensive than other types of coal.

Some coal is extracted underground (Figure 15-5) by miners working in tunnels and shafts. Such mining is one of the world's most dangerous occupations because of accidents and black lung disease (caused by prolonged inhalation of coal dust particles). When coal lies close to the earth's surface, it is extracted by *area strip mining* (Figure 15-4c) on flat terrain and *contour strip mining* (Figure 15-4d) on hilly or mountainous terrain. In some cases, entire mountaintops are removed to expose seams of coal under the mountains.

After coal is removed, it is transported (usually by train) to a processing plant, where it is broken up, crushed, and then washed to remove impurities. The coal is then dried and shipped (again usually by train) to users, mostly power plants and industrial plants.

**How Is Coal Used, and Where Are the Largest Supplies?** Coal provides about 21% of the world's commercial energy (22% in the United States). It is burned to generate 62% of the world's electricity (52% in the United States) and make 75% of its steel.

About 66% of the world's proven coal reserves and 85% of the estimated undiscovered coal deposits are located in the United States (with 24% of global reserves), Russia, China, and India. Half of global coal consumption takes place in the United States (26%) and China (24%).

**How Long Will Coal Supplies Last?** Coal is the world's most abundant fossil fuel. *Identified* world reserves of coal should last at least **(1)** 225 years at the current usage rate and **(2)** 65 years if usage rises 2% per year. The world's *unidentified* coal reserves are projected to last about **(1)** 900 years at the current consumption rate and **(2)** 149 years if the usage rate increases 2% per year. Thus *identified and unidentified supplies of coal could last the world for 214–1,125 years, depending on the rate of usage.*

China, with 11% of the world's reserves, has enough coal to last 300 years at its current rate of consumption. Identified U.S. coal reserves should also last about 300 years at the current consumption rate, and unidentified U.S. coal resources could extend those supplies for perhaps 100 years, at a higher cost.

**What Is the Future of Coal?** Figure 15-31 (p. 364) lists the pros and cons of using coal as an energy resource. Although coal is very abundant it has the highest environmental impact of any

| Peat (not a coal) | Lignite (brown coal) | Bituminous Coal (soft coal) | Anthracite (hard coal) |
|---|---|---|---|
| Partially decayed plant matter in swamps and bogs; low heat content | Low heat content; low sulfur content; limited supplies in most areas | Extensively used as a fuel because of its high heat content and large supplies; normally has a high sulfur content | Highly desirable fuel because of its high heat content and low sulfur content; supplies are limited in most areas |

**Figure 15-30** Stages in coal formation over millions of years. Peat is a soil material made of moist, partially decomposed organic matter. Lignite and bituminous coal are sedimentary rocks, whereas anthracite is a metamorphic rock (Figure 10-8, p. 210).

| Advantages | | Disadvantages |
|---|---|---|
| Ample supplies (225–900 years) | | Very high environmental impact |
| High net energy yield | | Severe land disturbance, air pollution, and water pollution |
| Low cost (with huge subsidies) | | High land use (including mining) |
| Mining and combustion technology well-developed | | Severe threat to human health |
| Air pollution can be reduced with improved technology (but adds to cost) | | High $CO_2$ emissions when burned |
| | | Releases radioactive particles and mercury into air |

**Figure 15-31** Advantages and disadvantages of using coal as an energy resource.

fossil fuel from (1) land disturbance (Figures 15-4 and 15-6), (2) air pollution, (3) $CO_2$ emissions (Figure 15-25, accounting for about 36% of the world's annual emissions), (4) release of particles of toxic mercury when burned, (5) release of thousands of times more radioactive particles into the atmosphere per unit of energy produced than a normally operating nuclear power plant, and (6) water pollution (Figure 15-7). Each year in the United States alone, air pollutants from coal burning (1) kill thousands of people (with estimates ranging from 65,000 to 200,000), (2) cause at least 50,000 cases of respiratory disease, and (3) result in several billion dollars of property damage.

Coal is also difficult and expensive to transport very far because it is heavy and bulky. Thus most coal is used fairly close to where it is mined—with only about 10% of the coal produced exported compared to 60% of the oil produced.

Energy costs from a new coal power plant in the United States are low (around 4¢ per kilowatt-hour*), mostly because of large governmental subsidies. However, according to a 2001 study by Stanford University researchers, this cost doubles to around 8¢ per kilowatt-hour if health and environmental costs are included. In contrast, the average cost of wind energy in the United States—including its environmental and health costs—is about 4¢ per kilowatt-hour.

New ways, such as *fluidized-bed combustion* (Figure 15-32), and *coal gasification* have been developed to burn coal more cleanly and efficiently. With large gov-

---

*A *kilowatt-hour* (kwh), a basic unit of electricity, is equal to the energy consumed by a 100-watt lightbulb burning for 10 hours.

ernment subsidies, these technologies may be phased in over the next several decades. But they do little to reduce $CO_2$ emissions that are considered the major culprit in projected global warming and a major drawback of coal as an energy resource.

In 2001, the Bush administration (1) scuttled U.S. participation in the Kyoto treaty designed to reduce global $CO_2$ emissions and later proposed that business voluntarily reduce their $CO_2$ emissions (a policy strongly opposed by supporters of the Kyoto treaty throughout much of the world), (2) proposed a $2 billion government subsidy program for research into cleaner coal technologies (such as fluidized-bed combustion and coal gasification), (3) supported exemption of older and highly polluting U.S. coal burning plants from the latest Clean Air Act standards for another 10 years, (4) allowed already heavily subsidized coal-fired power plants to qualify for government renewable energy subsidies merely by mixing small amounts of biomass such as wood chips or agriculture waste with the coal they burn (called an obvious scam by environmentalists), and (5) asked Congress to reduce government research and development subsidies for energy efficiency by 30% and renewable energy by 40%.

**What Are the Pros and Cons of Converting Solid Coal into Gaseous and Liquid Fuels?** Solid coal can be converted into **synthetic natural gas (SNG)** by **coal gasification** (Figure 15-33) or into a liquid fuel such

**Figure 15-32** *Fluidized-bed coal combustion.* A stream of hot air is blown into a boiler to suspend a mixture of powdered coal and crushed limestone. This method (1) removes most of the sulfur dioxide, (2) sharply reduces emissions of nitrogen oxides, and (3) burns the coal more efficiently and cheaply than conventional combustion methods. However, it does little to reduce $CO_2$ emissions.

**Figure 15-33** *Coal gasification.* Generalized view of one method for converting solid coal into synthetic natural gas (methane).

as methanol or synthetic gasoline by **coal liquefaction.** Figure 15-34 lists the pros and cons of using these *synfuels* produced from coal.

Unless it receives huge government subsidies, most analysts expect coal gasification to play only a minor role as an energy resource in the next 20–50 years mostly because

- **(1)** $CO_2$ emissions from gasifying coal and burning the gas are higher than those from burning the coal itself or natural gas (Figure 15-25) and **(2)** using wind to produce electricity emits virtually no $CO_2$ or other pollutants.

- Construction and operating costs per kilowatt are much higher than producing electricity from natural gas, conventional coal, and wind.

| Advantages | | Disadvantages |
|---|---|---|
| Large potential supply | | Low to moderate net energy yield |
| Vehicle fuel | | Higher cost than coal |
| Moderate cost (with large government subsidies) | | High environmental impact |
| | | Increased surface mining of coal |
| Lower air pollution when burned than coal | | High water use |
| | | Higher $CO_2$ emissions than coal |

**Figure 15-34** Advantages and disadvantages of using synthetic natural gas (SNG) and liquid synfuels produced from coal.

## 15-9 NUCLEAR ENERGY

**How Does a Nuclear Fission Reactor Work?** To evaluate the pros and cons of nuclear power, we must know how a conventional nuclear power plant and its accompanying nuclear fuel cycle work. In a nuclear fission chain reaction, neutrons split the nuclei of atoms such as uranium-235 (Figure 3-17, p. 58) and plutonium-239 and release energy mostly as high-temperature heat. In the reactor of a nuclear power plant, the rate of fission is controlled and the heat generated is used to produce high-pressure steam, which spins turbines that generate electricity.

*Light-water reactors (LWRs)* like the one diagrammed in Figure 15-35 (p. 366) produce about 85% of the world's nuclear-generated electricity (100% in the United States). An LWR has the following key parts:

- *Core,* containing 35,000–70,000 long, thin fuel rods, each packed with fuel pellets. Each pellet is about one-third the size of a cigarette and contains the energy equivalent of 0.9 metric tons (1 ton) of coal.

- *Uranium oxide fuel,* consisting of about 97% nonfissionable uranium-238 and 3% fissionable uranium-235. To create a suitable fuel, the concentration of uranium-235 in the ore is increased (enriched) from 0.7% (its natural concentration in uranium ore) to 3% by removing some of the uranium-238.

- *Control rods,* which are moved in and out of the reactor core to absorb neutrons and thus regulate the rate of fission and amount of power the reactor produces.

- *Moderator,* which slows down the neutrons emitted by the fission process so the chain reaction can be kept going. This is a material such as **(1)** liquid water (75% of the world's reactors, called *pressurized water reactors,*

Small amounts of
radioactive gases

Uranium fuel input
(reactor core)

Containment shell

Emergency core
cooling system

Control
rods

Steam

Waste heat

Electrical power

Turbine

Generator

Heat
exchanger

Useful energy
25 to 30%

Hot coolant

Hot water output

Pump

Coolant

Condenser

Pump

Cool water input

Moderator

Pump

Coolant
passage

Water

Waste
heat

Pressure
vessel

Pump

Shielding

Waste
heat

Water source
(river, lake, ocean)

Periodic removal
and storage of
radioactive wastes
and spent fuel assemblies

Periodic removal
and storage of
radioactive liquid wastes

**Figure 15-35** Light-water–moderated and –cooled
nuclear power plant with a pressurized water reactor.

Figure 15-35), **(2)** solid graphite (20% of reactors), or **(3)** heavy water ($D_2O$; 5% of reactors). Graphite-moderated reactors can also produce fissionable plutonium-239 for nuclear weapons.

■ *Coolant*, usually water, which circulates through the reactor's core to remove heat (to keep fuel rods and other materials from melting) and produce steam for generating electricity.

Nuclear power plants, each with one or more reactors, are only one part of the nuclear fuel cycle (Figure 15-36). *In evaluating the safety and economic feasibility of nuclear power, energy experts and economists caution us to look at this entire cycle, not just the nuclear plant itself.*

**What Happened to Nuclear Power?** Studies indicate that U.S. utility companies began developing nuclear power plants in the late 1950s for three reasons:

■ The Atomic Energy Commission (which had the conflicting roles of promoting and regulating nuclear

power) promised utility executives that nuclear power would produce electricity at a much lower cost than coal and other alternatives. Indeed, President Dwight D. Eisenhower declared in a 1953 speech that nuclear power would be "too cheap to meter."

■ The government paid about one-fourth of the cost of building the first group of commercial reactors and guaranteed there would be no cost overruns.

■ After insurance companies refused to insure nuclear power, Congress passed the Price-Anderson Act to protect the U.S. nuclear industry and utilities from significant liability to the general public in case of accidents.*

In the 1950s, researchers predicted that by the year 2000, at least 1,800 nuclear power plants would supply

---

*This act limits the nuclear industry's liability in case of an accident to $9.5 billion, with the government (taxpayers) paying most of this. According to the U.S. Nuclear Regulatory Commission, a worst-case accident would cause more than $300 billion in damages.

Fuel assemblies → Reactor → Spent fuel assemblies

(conversion of enriched UF$_6$ to UO$_2$
and fabrication of fuel assemblies)

Fuel fabrication

Enriched UF$_6$

Plutonium-239 as PuO$_2$

Interim storage under water

Enrichment

UF$_6$

Uranium-235 as UF$_6$

Spent fuel assemblies

Spent fuel reprocessing

Decommissioning of reactor

Conversion of U$_3$O$_8$ to UF$_6$

Uranium tailings (low level but long half-life)

High-level radioactive waste or spent fuel assemblies

Processed uranium ore

Uranium mines and mills
Ore and ore concentrate (U$_3$O$_8$)

Geologic disposal of moderate- and high-level radioactive wastes

**Front end**

**Back end**

⟵ Open fuel cycle today
◄ - - Prospective "closed" end fuel cycle

**Figure 15-36** The nuclear fuel cycle.

21% of the world's commercial energy (25% in the United States) and most of the world's electricity.

However, after almost 50 years of development, enormous government subsidies, and an investment of $2 trillion, these goals have not been met. Instead,

- By 2001, 436 commercial nuclear reactors in 32 countries were producing 6% of the world's commercial energy and 16% of its electricity.

- Since 1989, the growth in electricity production from nuclear power has essentially leveled off (Figure 15-14, left). The U.S. Department of Energy expect its capacity to decline between 2003 and 2020 as existing plants wear out and are retired (Figure 15-14 and Figure 15-15).

- Germany (with 31% of its electricity from nuclear power) and Sweden (with 39%) plan to phase out nuclear power over the next 20–30 years.

- Nuclear power is losing some of its appeal in France, Japan, and China—all once solid supporters of its increased use. France and China (which has 3 reactors and is building 10 more) have put a moratorium on building new nuclear plants, and France has cut its long-term target for building new reactors in half.

- No new nuclear power plants have been ordered in the United States since 1978, and all 120 plants ordered since 1973 have been canceled. In 2001, there were 103 licensed and operating commercial nuclear power reactors in 31 states—most in the eastern half of the country (Figure 15-37, p. 368). These reactors generated about 20% of the country's electricity and 8% of its total energy use. This percentage is expected to decline over the next two decades as existing plants wear out and are retired (decommissioned) (Figure 15-15).

According to energy analysts and economists, the major reasons for the failure of nuclear power to grow as projected are (1) multibillion-dollar construction cost overruns, (2) stricter government safety regulations, (3) higher operating costs and more malfunctions than expected, (4) poor management, (5) public concerns about safety after the 1986 Chernobyl (p. 338) and 1979 Three Mile Island (Pennsylvania) accidents, and (6) investor concerns about the economic feasibility of nuclear power.

**What Are the Pros and Cons of Nuclear Power?**
Figure 15-38 (p. 369) lists the major advantages and disadvantages of nuclear power. Using nuclear power to produce electricity has some important advantages over coal-burning power plants (Figure 15-39, p. 369).

**How Safe Are Nuclear Power Plants and Other Nuclear Facilities?** *Because of the built-in safety features, the risk of exposure to radioactivity from nuclear power plants in the United States and most other developed countries is extremely low.* However, a partial or complete meltdown or explosion is possible, as accidents at the Chernobyl (p. 338) nuclear power plant in Ukraine and the Three Mile Island plant in Pennsylvania have taught us.

The U.S. Nuclear Regulatory Commission (NRC) estimates there is a 15–45% chance of a complete core meltdown at a U.S. reactor during the next 20 years.

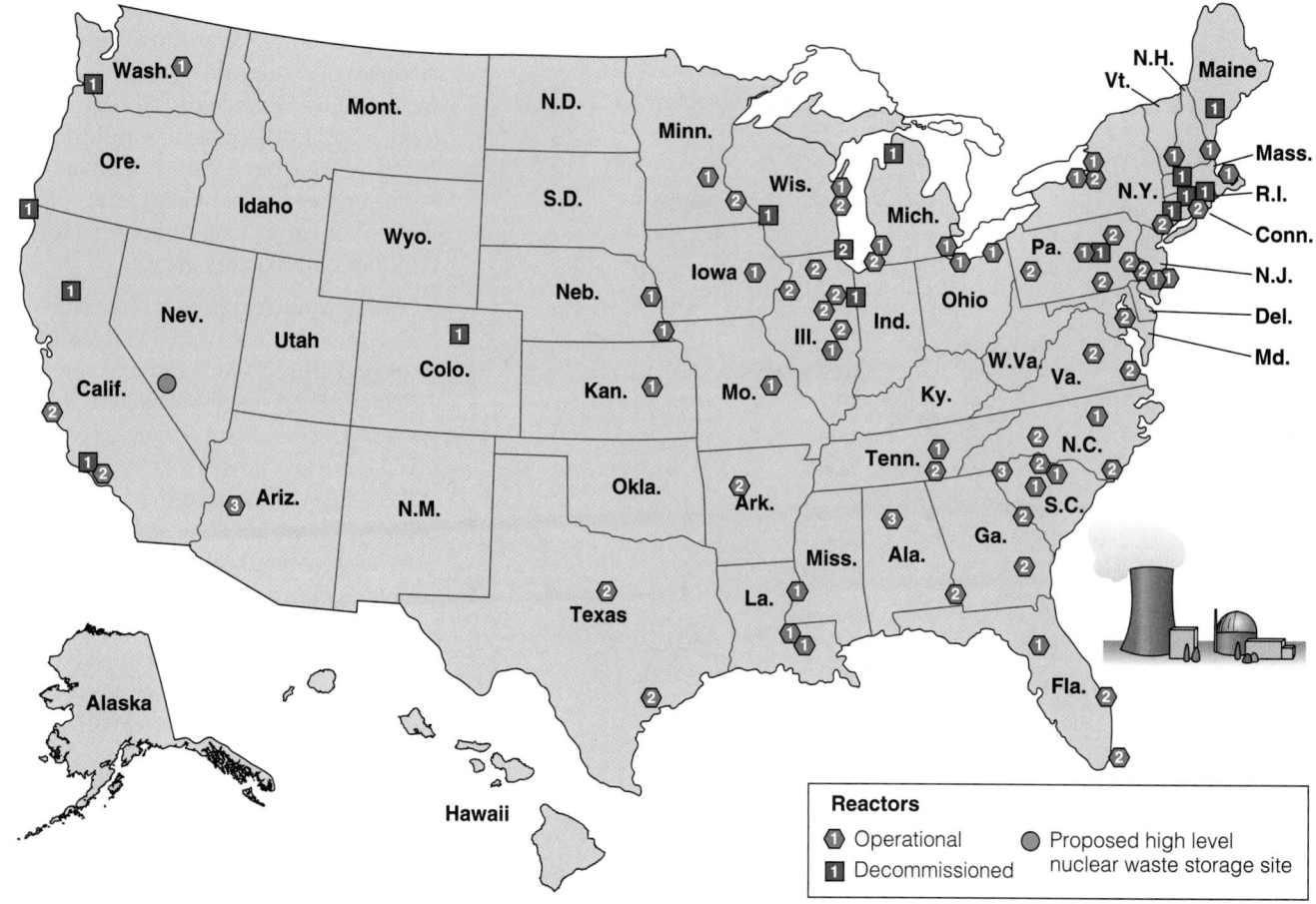

**Figure 15-37** Locations in the United States of **(1)** its 103 operating commercial nuclear power plant reactors, **(2)** 13 decommissioned reactors (with highly radioactive used fuel stored on site), and **(3)** the recently approved site in Nevada for storage of highly radioactive used fuel from operating and decommissioned nuclear reactors. Numbers refer to the number of reactors at each nuclear power plant site. (Data from U.S. Nuclear Regulatory Commission and U.S. Department of Energy)

The NRC also found that 39 U.S. reactors have an 80% chance of failure in the containment shell from a meltdown or an explosion of gases inside the containment structures.

In 2002, the NRC found that boric acid, produced as a byproduct in a pressurized water nuclear reactor, had eaten two cavities in the heavy stainless steel device that covers the fuel rods in a reactor near Toledo, Ohio. This head is used for corrosion protection and to help contain the enormous pressure that builds up inside the reactor. The NRC is investigating whether the corrosion could weaken the head enough for it to shatter and create a serious *loss of coolant* accident at the Toledo reactor and 69 similar reactors in the United States.

Another concern is that 27 of 57 operating nuclear power plants in the United States failed mock, ground-based terrorist security tests made by the Nuclear Regulatory Commission prior to 1998. The NRC contends that the security weaknesses revealed by these tests have been corrected. But many nuclear power

analysts are unconvinced and note that the government has stopped staging mock attacks on nuclear plants that reveal security shortcomings.

The 2001 destruction of New York City's two World Trade Center towers by terrorist attacks has suggested that a similar attack by a large plane loaded with fuel could **(1)** break open a reactor's containment shell (Figure 15-35) and **(2)** set off a reactor meltdown that could create a major radioactive disaster (p. 338). Nuclear officials believe that U.S. plants could survive such an attack. But a 2002 study by the Nuclear Control Institute found that the plants were not designed to withstand the crash of a large jet traveling at the impact speed of the two highjacked airliners that hit the World Trade Center.

According to 2002 report by Rep. Ed Markey (D-Mass) based on analysis of NRC data,

■ Guards at U.S. nuclear plants are underpaid, undertrained, and incapable of repelling a serious ground attack by terrorists.

- Twenty-one U.S. nuclear reactors are within 8 kilometers (5 miles) of an airport.

- A small or large aircraft or ground attack that cut off electrical power to a reactor could cause a core meltdown within about two hours without crashing into the reactor.

In 2002, David Freeman, President Jimmy Carter's energy advisor and CEO of several major power companies, warned that "The danger of penetration into a nuclear reactor—which is difficult but not impossible—is so horrendous that we've got to put out of our minds the building of any more nuclear power plants."

Throughout the world, nuclear scientists and government officials urge the shutdown of 35 poorly designed and poorly operated nuclear reactors in some republics of the former Soviet Union and in eastern Europe. This is unlikely without economic aid from the world's developed countries.

In the United States, there is widespread public distrust in the ability of the NRC and the Department of Energy (DOE) to enforce nuclear safety in commercial (NRC) and military (DOE) nuclear facilities. Congressional hearings in 1987 uncovered evidence that high-level NRC staff members **(1)** destroyed documents and obstructed investigations of criminal wrongdoing

**Figure 15-39** Comparison of the risks of using nuclear power and coal-burning plants to produce electricity.

by utilities, **(2)** suggested ways utilities could evade commission regulations, and **(3)** provided utilities and their contractors with advance notice of so-called surprise inspections. In 1996, George Galatis, a respected senior nuclear engineer, said, "I believe in nuclear power but after seeing the NRC in action I'm convinced a serious accident is not just likely, but inevitable. . . . They're asleep at the wheel."

The nuclear power industry claims that nuclear power plants in the United States have not killed anyone and cause far less environmental harm than coal-burning plants (Figure 15-39). However, according to U.S. National Academy of Sciences estimates, U.S. nuclear plants cause 6,000 premature deaths and 3,700 serious genetic defects each year. If correct, this annual death toll is much smaller than the 65,000–200,000 deaths per year caused by coal-burning plants in the United States. But critics point out that the estimated annual deaths from both of these types of plants are unacceptable, given the availability of much less harmful alternatives such as combined-cycle natural gas turbines and wind power and eventually solar cells and hydrogen.

**What Do We Do with Low-Level Radioactive Waste?** Each part of the nuclear fuel cycle (Figure 15-36) produces low-level and high-level solid,

**Figure 15-38** Advantages and disadvantages of using nuclear power to produce electricity. This evaluation includes the entire nuclear fuel cycle (Figure 15-36).

liquid, and gaseous radioactive wastes with various half-lives (Table 3-2, p. 56). Wastes classified as *low-level radioactive wastes* give off small amounts of ionizing radiation and must be stored safely for 100–500 years before decaying to safe levels.

From the 1940s to 1970, most low-level radioactive waste produced in the United States (and most other countries) was put into steel drums and dumped into the ocean; the United Kingdom and Pakistan still dispose of their low-level radioactive wastes in this way.

Today, low-level waste materials from commercial nuclear power plants, hospitals, universities, industries, and other producers in the United States are put in steel drums and shipped to the two remaining regional landfills run by federal and state governments. Attempts to build new regional dumps for low-level radioactive waste using improved technology (Figure 15-40) have met with fierce public opposition.

**What Should We Do with High-Level Radioactive Waste?** *High-level radioactive wastes* give off large amounts of ionizing radiation (Figure 3-13, p. 56) for a short time and small amounts for a long time. Such wastes must be stored safely for at least 10,000 years and about 240,000 years if plutonium-239 (with a half-life of 24,000 years) is not removed by reprocessing (Figure 15-36).

Most high-level radioactive wastes are **(1)** spent fuel rods from commercial nuclear power plants (now being stored in barrels immersed in pools of water or in dry-storage casks at plant sites; Figure 15-37) and **(2)** an assortment of wastes from plants that produce plutonium and tritium for nuclear weapons. There is concern

that some of the pools and casks used to stored spent fuel rods at various nuclear power plants are vulnerable to sabotage by terrorist attacks (Case Study, p. 371).

After 50 years of research, scientists still do not agree on whether there is any safe method of storing these wastes. Some scientists believe the long-term safe storage or disposal of high-level radioactive wastes is technically possible. Others disagree, pointing out it is impossible to demonstrate that any method will work for the 10,000–240,000 years of fail-safe storage needed for such wastes.

Here are some of the proposed methods and their possible drawbacks:

■ *Bury it deep underground* (Figure 15-41, p. 372, and Case Study, p. 374). This favored strategy is under study by all countries producing nuclear waste. In 2001, the U.S. National Academy of Sciences concluded that the geological repository option is the only scientifically credible long-term solution for safely isolating such wastes. However, according to an earlier 1990 report by the U.S. National Academy of Sciences, "Use of geological information to pretend to be able to make very accurate predictions of long-term site behavior is scientifically unsound."

■ *Shoot it into space or into the sun.* Costs would be very high, and a launch accident, like the explosion of the space shuttle *Challenger*, could disperse high-level radioactive wastes over large areas of the earth's surface. This strategy has been abandoned for now.

■ *Bury it under the Antarctic ice sheet or the Greenland ice cap.* The long-term stability of the ice sheets is not known. They could be destabilized by heat from the

**Figure 15-40** Proposed design of a state-of-the-art *low-level radioactive waste landfill.* According to the EPA, all landfills eventually leak. The best designed landfills may not leak for several decades, after which the companies running them would no longer be liable for leaks and problems. Then any problems would be passed on to taxpayers and future generations. (Data from U.S. Atomic Industrial Forum)

## How Safe Are Radioactive Wastes Stored at Nuclear Power Plants?

Highly radioactive spent-fuel rods are stored underwater and in dry casks at many U.S. nuclear power plants (Figure 15-37). Spent-fuel pools typically hold 5–10 times more long-lived radioactivity than the radioactive core inside a plant's reactor. Unlike the reactor core, many of these pools and dry casks have little protective cover.

At about one-third of U.S. power plants the reactor is in one building and the spent-fuel pool is in a separate building with a thin corrugated metal roof and walls. At the rest of the plants, the spent-fuel pool is in a concrete building attached to the reactor building.

The NRC acknowledges that with enough explosives a spent-fuel pool or a spent-fuel dry cask can be penetrated. If a spent-pool loses its water or a dry storage cask is ruptured, the exposed and thermally hot fuel rods can catch fire, release large amounts of radioactive materials into the atmosphere, and render large areas uninhabitable for generations. These pools have back-up cooling systems to help prevent such a fire but these systems could malfunction or be destroyed by a terrorist attack.

A 1997 report prepared by the Brookhaven National Laboratory for the Nuclear Regulatory Commission estimated that a severe fire in a typical spent-fuel pool could **(1)** render about 487 square kilometers (188 square miles) uninhabitable for decades, **(2)** cause as many as 28,000 premature deaths from radiation-induced cancers, and **(3)** result in up to $59 billion in damages.

According to a 2002 study by the Institute for Resource and Security Studies,

- Ground-level sabotage or a small plane could penetrate or blow up the corrugated buildings that house spent-fuel pools and perhaps destroy the back-up cooling system. This could start a fire and release radioactive material into the environment. After the September 11 attacks in 2001, the Federal Aviation Administration banned small planes from flying over most U.S. nuclear plants, but these restrictions were lifted on November 6, 2001.

- A similar accident could be caused by the crash of a larger plane or jet into a concrete building used to store spent fuel rods.

- An accident or sabotage that released all of radioactive material in the spent-fuel rods in the storage pool at the Millstone Unit 3 reactor in Connecticut would **(1)** put five times more radioactive material into the atmosphere than the 1986 Chernobyl accident (p. 338) and **(2)** make about 145,000 square kilometers (55,900 square miles)—more than the area of New York state—uninhabitable for at least 30 years because of radioactive contamination.

- If all of the fuel in two spent-fuel storage pools at the Sharon Harris Nuclear Plant near Raleigh, North Carolina, burned, enough radioactive material would be released to contaminate an area larger than the entire state for at least 30 years.

- At some nuclear plants, some of the spent-fuel rods have been removed from the pool and stored in lead-lined concrete casks. An

explosion or airplane crash could split open the casks and allow the rods to catch fire. However, these casks are probably less vulnerable to such an attack than spent fuel stored in pools.

- Spent fuel is stored away from nuclear plants at some sites which are sometimes guarded by only one person.

- Decommissioned nuclear power plants (Figure 15-37) may be even more vulnerable to sabotage because they store large amounts of spent fuel and have fewer security personnel than operating plants.

Nuclear power officials, **(1)** consider such events to be highly unlikely worst-case scenarios, **(2)** question some of the estimates, **(3)** consider nuclear power facilities to be very safe from such attacks, and **(4)** consider this a reason to store all spent-fuel rods in a national underground storage site as soon as possible.

Other analysts contend that using trucks or trains to make thousands of shipments of spent fuel across much of the United States to a central storage facility in Nevada (Figure 15-37) makes the shipments highly vulnerable to sabotage.

### Critical Thinking

You are in charge of security for nuclear power plants and nuclear waste materials stored at such plants in the United States. How would you protect against release of radioactive materials by sabotage from **(1)** spent fuel rods stored in pools or casks at plant sites or **(2)** transportation of dry casks to a central waste storage facility?

---

wastes, and retrieving the wastes would be difficult or impossible if the method failed. This strategy is prohibited by international law.

- *Dump it into descending subduction zones in the deep ocean* (Figure 10-6, middle, p. 208). However, **(1)** wastes eventually might be spewed out somewhere else by volcanic activity, **(2)** containers might leak and contaminate the ocean before being carried

downward, and **(3)** retrieval would be impossible if the method did not work. This strategy is prohibited by international law.

- *Bury it in thick deposits of mud on the deep-ocean floor in areas that tests show have been geologically stable for 65 million years.* The waste containers eventually would corrode and release their radioactive contents. This approach is prohibited by international law.

**Figure 15-41** Proposed general design for deep underground permanent storage of high-level radioactive wastes from commercial nuclear power plants in the United States. (U.S. Department of Energy)

- *Change it into harmless, or less harmful, isotopes.* Currently no way exists to do this. Even if a method was developed, **(1)** costs probably would be very high, and **(2)** the resulting toxic materials and low-level (but very long-lived) radioactive wastes would still need to be disposed of safely.

**How Widespread Are Contaminated Radioactive Sites?** In 1992, the EPA estimated that as many as 45,000 sites in the United States may be contaminated with radioactive materials, 20,000 of them belonging to the DOE and the Department of Defense. Since 1992, the DOE has spent $60 billion on cleanups and estimates that the cleanup will cost taxpayers another $200 billion over the next 70 years (with some analysts estimating a cost of $400–900 billion). According to a 2000 DOE report, more than two-thirds of 144 highly contaminated sites used to produce nuclear weapons will never be completely cleaned up and will have to be protected and monitored for centuries. Some critics question spending so much money on a problem ranked by scientific advisers to the EPA as a low-risk ecological problem and not among the top high-risk human health problems (Figure 11-15, p. 246).

The radioactive contamination situation in the United States pales in comparison to the post–Cold War legacy of nuclear waste and contamination in the republics of the former Soviet Union. Land in various parts of the former Soviet Union is dotted with **(1)** areas severely contaminated by nuclear accidents, **(2)** 25 op-

erating nuclear power plants with flawed and unsafe designs, **(3)** nuclear waste dump sites, **(4)** radioactive waste-processing plants, **(5)** contaminated nuclear test sites, and **(6)** coastal waters where nuclear wastes and retired nuclear-powered submarines were dumped.

A 1957 explosion of a nuclear waste storage tank at Mayak, a plutonium production facility in southern Russia, spewed 2.5 times as much radiation into the atmosphere as the Chernobyl accident. Because of radioactive contamination, **(1)** no one can live within about 2,600 square kilometers (1,000 square miles) of the surrounding area, and **(2)** nearby Lake Karachay (which was a dump site for the facility's radioactive wastes between 1949 and 1967) is so radioactive that standing on its shores for about an hour would be fatal.

**What Can We Do with Worn-Out Nuclear Plants?** After approximately 15–40 years of operation, a nuclear reactor becomes dangerously contaminated with radioactive materials, and many of its parts are worn out. Unless the plant's life can be extended by expensive renovation, it must be *decommissioned* or retired (the last step in the nuclear fuel cycle, Figure 15-36) This can be done by **(1)** dismantling it and storing its large volume of highly radioactive materials in high-level nuclear waste storage facilities which currently do not exist (Figure 15-41), **(2)** putting up a physical barrier and setting up full-time security for 30–100 years before the plant is dismantled, or **(3)** enclosing the entire plant in a tomb that must last for several thousand years.

At least 228 large commercial reactors worldwide (20 in the United States) are scheduled for retirement by 2012. By 2033, all U.S. reactors will have to be retired, based on the life of their original 40-year operating licenses.

Decommissioning costs for large commercial U.S. reactors range from $300–500 million depending on the site. U.S. utilities have been setting aside funds for decommissioning more than 100 reactors, but to date these funds fall far short of the estimated costs. If sufficient funds are not available for decommissioning, the balance of the costs could be passed along to ratepayers and taxpayers.

Some utility companies and the Bush administration have proposed extending the life of current reactors to 50–60 years. By 2000, five U.S. nuclear reactors had obtained 20-year license extensions, and 30 other plants may apply for such extensions by 2005. Opponents contend that extending the life of reactors could increase the risk of nuclear accidents in aging reactors.

**What Is the Connection Between Nuclear Reactors and the Spread of Nuclear Weapons?** Currently, 60 countries—1 of every 3 in the world—have nuclear weapons or the knowledge and ability to build them. Information and fuel needed to build these nuclear weapons have come mostly from the research and commercial nuclear reactors that the United States and 14 other countries have been giving away and selling in the international marketplace for decades.

Some *good news* is that between 1986 and 2000, the number of nuclear warheads held by the world's five largest nuclear powers declined by 55% and further declines are expected by 2012. The *bad news* is that **(1)** this still leaves enough nuclear weapons to kill everyone in the world at least 30 times and **(2)** greatly increases the amount of bomb-grade plutonium-239 removed from retired nuclear warheads that must be kept secure from use in nuclear weapons.

**What Is the Threat From "Dirty" Radioactive Bombs?** There is growing concern, especially after the September 11, 2001, terrorist attack in New York City, about threats from explosions of so-called *"dirty" radioactive bombs*. A *dirty bomb* consists of an explosive such as dynamite mixed with some form of radioactive material that is not difficult or expensive to obtain. Such a conventional bomb with a small amount of radioactive material (that often would fit in a coffee cup) is fairly easy to assemble.

Examples of radioactive materials for use in such bombs include **(1)** *irridium-192* (half-life 74 days), **(2)** *cobalt-60* (half-life 5.3 years), **(3)** *cesium-137* (half-life 30 years), and **(4)** *americium-241* (half-life 433 years).

Such materials can be stolen from thousands of loosely guarded and difficult to protect sources or bought on the black market. Sources include **(1)** hospitals, using radioisotopes to treat cancer, diagnose various diseases, and sterilize some types of medical equipment, **(2)** university research labs, **(3)** industries using radioisotopes to detect leaks in underground pipes, irradiate food, examine mail and other materials, and detect flaws in pipe welds, boilers, and concrete, and **(4)** smoke detectors (americium-241).

Detonating a dirty bomb at street level or on a rooftop does not cause a nuclear blast. But depending on the amount of TNT used it could

- Kill a dozen to 1,000 people in densely populated cities from the blast and subsequent cancers.

- Spread radioactive material over several to hundreds of blocks.

- Contaminate buildings and soil in the affected area for up to 10 times the half-life of the isotope used unless areas are cleaned up at great expense (billions of dollars). Cleanup would involve sandblasting or demolishing buildings, digging up asphalt and sidewalks, removing topsoil, and transporting the radioactive material to safe storage sites.

- Require long-term evacuation of affected areas, shut down businesses and government agencies, and discourage businesses and agencies from reopening in such areas.

- Cause intense psychological terror and panic—the primary objective of terrorism.

According to simulations by the Federation of American Scientists and the Center for Strategic and International Studies (a Washington think tank), detonating a dirty bomb

- In Manhattan using a small piece of cobalt-60 stolen from a food irradiation plant would spread contamination over about 300 city blocks, kill up to 1,000 people, and render much of New York City uninhabitable for decades.

- Using 4.5 kilograms (10 pounds) of TNT and containing a pea-size piece of cesium-137 (which is fairly easy to steal from medical equipment) on the mall in Washington, D.C., near the National Gallery of Art would kill about 20 people and contaminate a 1.6-kilometer (1-mile) swath of land that includes the U.S. Capitol, Supreme Court, and Library of Congress buildings.

- Containing 1,800 kilograms (4,000 pounds) of TNT and a small amount of cesium-137 in an empty school bus on Washington's mall would kill several hundred people, contaminate a much larger area, shut down official Washington, close nearby airports, cause immense panic and long-term economic damage, and

# Underground Storage of High-Level Radioactive Wastes in the United States

In 1985, the U.S. Department of Energy (DOE) announced plans to build a repository for underground storage of high-level radioactive wastes from commercial nuclear reactors on federal land in the Yucca Mountain desert region, 160 kilometers (100 miles) northwest of Las Vegas, Nevada (green dot in Figure 15-37).

By 2002, the federal government had spent about $7 billion evaluating the site as a permanent underground repository. The proposed facility (Figure 15-41), expected to cost at least $58 billion to build (financed by a tax on nuclear power), is scheduled to open by 2010.

Some scientists argue that it should never be allowed to open, mostly because **(1)** rock fractures may allow water to leak into the site and corrode radioactive waste storage casks, **(2)** an active volcano is located nearby, and **(3)** there are 32 active earthquake fault lines running through the site—an unusually high number. In 1998, Jerry Szymanski, formerly the DOE's top geologist at Yucca Mountain and now an outspoken opponent of the site, said that if water flooded the site it could cause an explosion so large that "Chernobyl would be small potatoes."

However, in 1999 and 2002, scientists working on the site released a report finding nothing to disqualify the site as a safe place to store high-level radioactive wastes.

Other scientists and energy analysts disagree with this assessment. For example,

- According to a December 2002 report by Congress's General Accounting Office, any decision to officially approve the site would be "premature" because 293 scientific questions about safety have not been answered.

- A January 2002 review by the Nuclear Waste Technical Review Board pointed to numerous scientific uncertainties in basic assumptions and computer models used to project how well the site should protect the wastes. The Board said these uncertainties make it impossible to ensure that the wastes would remain safe for the thousands of years necessary to protect the environment and human health.

Despite such concerns, in January 2002, the U.S. Energy Secretary **(1)** found that the site is scientifically sound and **(2)** recommended to President Bush and Congress that that highly radioactive waste from the nation's nuclear power plants be deposited under Nevada's Yucca Mountain far from population centers. The Secretary cited this as an important way to help protect wastes now stored at nuclear plants from possible terrorist attacks (Case Study, p. 371). However, according to the DOE, the Yucca Mountain site will not solve the nuclear waste storage problem unless its size is doubled. By 2036 when the site is expected to be filled, there will be about as much nuclear waste stored at plant sites as exists today.

This decision raised a storm of protest from Nevada elected officials and citizens (80% of them opposed to the site) and others concerned about the safety of this approach. Critics point out that shipping high-level nuclear waste in casks to the Nevada site by truck or rail from nuclear plants scattered throughout 39 states in the United States (Figure 15-37) poses a much greater security risk than beefing up protection of the wastes at nuclear power plants.

However, nuclear plant officials want to pass on more of their onsite waste storage and security costs to taxpayers. Critics say that this and the desire to restart a de-

probably require the President to declare martial law in Washington.

Since 1986, the NRC has recorded 1,700 incidents in the United States in which radioactive materials used by industrial, medical, or research facilities have been stolen or lost—an average of about 100 incidents per year. Since 1991, the International Atomic Energy Agency (IAEA) has detected 671 incidents of illicit trafficking in dirty-bomb materials.

## Can Nuclear Power Reduce Dependence on Oil?

Proponents of nuclear power in the United States claim it will help reduce dependence on imported oil. However, other analysts point out that use of nuclear power has little effect on U.S. oil use because **(1)** oil produces only about 2–3% of the electricity in the United States, and **(2)** the major use for oil is in transportation, which would not be affected by increasing nuclear power production.

## Can We Afford Nuclear Power?

Experience has shown that nuclear power is an expensive way to boil water to produce electricity, even when huge government subsidies partially shield it from free-market competition with other energy sources.

Costs rose dramatically in the 1970s and 1980s because of unanticipated safety problems and stricter regulations after the Three Mile Island and Chernobyl accidents. Estimates of the costs of producing nuclear power vary widely because of different variables used to make such calculations. However, current costs are typically 2–3 times higher per kilowatt-hour than for using coal, natural gas, and wind power to produce electricity.

In 1995, the World Bank said that nuclear power is too costly and risky. *Forbes* business magazine has called the failure of the U.S. nuclear power program "the largest managerial disaster in U.S. business history, involving $1 trillion in wasted investment and $10 billion in direct losses to stockholders."

clining industry are major reasons why the nuclear power industry donated $13.8 million to candidates from both parties for federal office in the 2000 elections and spent another $25 million in 2000 to lobby elected officials.

Drawing lines between each reactor site and the Nevada site reveals that at least 56,000 truckloads (or rail car loads) of nuclear waste will be traveling over much of the United States, especially in the eastern half where most nuclear reactors are found (Figure 15-37). This amounts to an average of six shipments a day for 30 years. According to the DOE, possible highway and rail routes will pass through 109 cities of 100,000 population or more—with Atlanta, Georgia, bearing much of the waste traffic.*

Nevada's Senator Harry Reid, calls a truck carrying waste to the site "a dirty nuclear bomb on 18 wheels waiting to happen." Others call such trucks or rail cars "rolling Chernobyls."

The DOE estimates that a nuclear waste shipment accident could cost $20–50 billion in damages and cleanup costs and lead to an unknown number of premature cancer deaths from exposure to radioactivity. The DOE and nuclear power proponents say the risks of an accident are negligible. Opponents believe the risks are underestimated, especially after the events of September 11, 2001.

Opponents contend that *the waste site should not be opened because it greatly decreases national security* by

---

*Anyone can go to the website, www.mapscience.org, type in an address, and view a map showing how close that area is to probable nuclear waste transportation routes to be used for at least 36 years after the site opens.

(1) making about 56,000 shipments of wastes over much of the country for 30 years in trucks and rail cars that are extremely difficult to protect and (2) still having about the same amount of wastes stored in pools and casks at the country's nuclear plant sites because the plants will be producing new wastes about as fast as the old wastes are shipped out.

The National Academy of Sciences and collaboration between Harvard and University of Tokyo scientists urge the government to slow down and rethink the nuclear waste storage process. They contend that storing spent-fuel rods in dry-storage casks in well-protected buildings at nuclear plant sites is an adequate solution for a number of decades in terms of safety and security. This would buy time (1) to carry out more research on this complex problem and (2) to evaluate other sites that might be more acceptable scientifically and politically.

Despite many objections from scientists and citizens, during the summer of 2002, Congress approved Yucca Mountain as the official site for the country's commercial nuclear wastes.

### Critical Thinking

1. What do you believe should be done with high-level radioactive wastes? Explain.

2. Would you favor having high-level nuclear waste transported by truck or train through the area where you live to the Yucca Mountain site? Explain. Use the website in the footnote (left) to see how close such shipments might come to the area where you live for at least 36 years after the site is opened.

---

In recent years, the operating cost of many U.S. nuclear power plants has dropped mostly because of less downtime. However, environmentalists and economists point out that the cost of nuclear power must be based on the entire nuclear fuel cycle, not merely the operating cost of individual plants. This includes mining and producing nuclear fuel, nuclear waste disposal, and decommissioning of worn-out plants. When these costs are included, the overall cost of nuclear power is very high (even with huge government subsidies) compared to many other energy alternatives.

**Can We Develop New and Safer Types of Nuclear Reactors?** The U.S. nuclear industry hopes to persuade the federal government and utility companies to build hundreds of smaller second-generation plants using standardized designs, which they claim are safer and can be built more quickly (in 3–6 years). These *advanced light-water reactors (ALWRs)*

have built-in *passive safety features* designed to make explosions or the release of radioactive emissions almost impossible. However, according to *Nucleonics Week*, an important nuclear industry publication, "Experts are flatly unconvinced that safety has been achieved—or even substantially increased—by the new designs."

One proposed new design is called a *pebble bed modular reactor (PBMR)* (Figure 15-42, p. 376). About 10,000 uranium oxide fuel particles, each the size of a pencil point, are encapsulated into a microsphere ball (Figure 15-42). Designers say the balls are meltdown-proof. To make this reactor affordable, they contend there is no need for an emergency core cooling system and an airtight containment dome used in light-water reactors (Figure 15-35). Germany, South Africa, and China have built small-scale pebble bed reactors to help evaluate and improve this technology.

Edwin Lyman and several other nuclear physicists oppose the pebble bed reactor. They contend that

Each pebble contains about 10,000 uranium dioxide particles the size of a pencil point.

Pebble detail

Silicon carbide

Pyrolytic carbon

Porous buffer

Uranium dioxide

Graphite shell

Helium

Turbine

Generator

Pebble

Core

Hot water output

Cool water input

Reactor vessel

Recuperator

Water cooler

**Figure 15-42** *Pebble bed modular reactor (PBMR).* This is one of several new and smaller reactor designs that some nuclear engineers say should improve the safety of nuclear power and reduce its costs. This design reduces chances of a runaway chain reaction by encapsulating uranium fuels in tiny heat-resistant ceramic spheres instead of packing large numbers of fuel pellets into long metal rods.

■ A crack in the reactor could expose the graphite protective coatings to air. At a high temperature the graphite could burn and release massive amounts of radioactivity—similar to what happened at Chernobyl (Figure 15-1).

■ It is an old design that has been rejected in England and Germany for safety reasons.

■ This technology would create about 10 times the volume of high-level radioactive waste per unit of electricity as a conventional nuclear reactor.

■ A lack of a containment shell would make it easier for terrorists to enter such reactor facilities and **(1)** steal nuclear fuel material that could be used to make nuclear weapons or **(2)** blow it up to release large amounts of radioactivity.

■ This approach does not eliminate the expense and hazards of long-term radioactive waste storage and power plant decommissioning.

**Is Breeder Nuclear Fission a Feasible Alternative?** Some nuclear power proponents urge the development and widespread use of **breeder nuclear fission reactors,** which generate more nuclear fuel than they consume by converting nonfissionable uranium-

238 into fissionable plutonium-239. Because breeders would use more than 99% of the uranium in ore deposits, the world's known uranium reserves would last at least 1,000 years, and perhaps several thousand years.

However, if the safety system of a breeder reactor fails, the reactor could lose some of its liquid sodium coolant, which ignites when exposed to air and reacts explosively if it comes into contact with water. This could cause a runaway fission chain reaction and perhaps a nuclear explosion powerful enough to blast open the containment building and release a cloud of highly radioactive gases and particulate matter. Leaks of flammable liquid sodium can also cause fires, which has happened with all experimental breeder reactors built so far.

In addition, existing experimental breeder reactors produce plutonium so slowly, it would take 100–200 years for them to produce enough to fuel a significant number of other breeder reactors. In 1994, the United States ended government-supported research for breeder technology after providing about $9 billion in research and development funding.

In December 1986, France opened a commercial-size breeder reactor. It was so expensive to build and operate that after spending $13 billion, the government spent another $2.75 billion to shut it down permanently in 1998. Because of this experience, other countries have abandoned their plans to build full-size commercial breeder reactors.

**Is Nuclear Fusion a Feasible Alternative?** Scientists hope that controlled nuclear fusion will provide an almost limitless source of high-temperature heat and electricity. Research has focused on the D–T nuclear fusion reaction, in which two isotopes of hydrogen—deuterium (D) and tritium (T)—fuse at about 100 million degrees (Figure 3-18, p. 58).

After 50 years of research and huge expenditures of mostly government funds, controlled nuclear fusion is still in the laboratory stage. None of the approaches tested so far have produced more energy than they use.

In 1989, two chemists claimed to have achieved deuterium–deuterium (D–D) nuclear fusion at room temperature using a simple apparatus, but subsequent experiments have not substantiated their claim. Some scientists still hope to develop low-temperature nuclear fusion, but most nuclear physicists are skeptical that it can be done.

If researchers can eventually get more energy out of nuclear fusion than they put in, the next step would be to build a small fusion reactor and then scale it up to commercial size. This is an extremely difficult engineering problem. The estimated cost of a commercial fusion reactor is several times that of a comparable conventional fission reactor.

Proponents contend that with greatly increased federal funding, a commercial nuclear fusion power plant might be built by 2030. However, many energy experts do not expect nuclear fusion to be a significant energy source until 2100, if then.

**What Should Be the Future of Nuclear Power in the United States?**   Since 1948, nuclear energy (fission and fusion) has received about 58% of all federal energy research and development funds in the United States (compared to 22% for fossil fuels, 11% for renewable energy, and 8% for energy efficiency and conservation). Some analysts call for (1) phasing out all or most government subsides and tax breaks for nuclear power and (2) using such funds to subsidize and accelerate the development of promising newer energy technologies.

To these analysts, nuclear power is a complex, expensive, inflexible, and centralized way to produce electricity that is too vulnerable to terrorist attack. They believe it is a technology whose time has passed in a world where electricity will increasingly be provided by small, decentralized, easily expandable power plants such as natural gas turbines, wind turbines, arrays of solar cells, and fuel cells. According to investors and World Bank economic analysts, nuclear power simply cannot compete in today's increasingly open and unregulated energy market.

Proponents of nuclear power, including the Bush administration, argue that governments should continue funding research and development and pilot plant testing of potentially safer and cheaper reactor designs (Figure 15-42) along with breeder fission and nuclear fusion. They argue that we need to keep these nuclear options available for use in the future if natural gas turbines, improved energy efficiency, hydrogen-powered fuel cells, wind turbines, and other renewable energy options fail to (1) keep up with electricity demands and (2) reduce $CO_2$ emissions to acceptable levels.

*The question is not whether there will be an energy revolution. It is already under way. The only questions are how rapidly it will unfold, whether it will move fast enough to prevent climate change from getting out of hand, and who will benefit most from the transition.*

LESTER R. BROWN

## REVIEW QUESTIONS

**1.** Define the boldfaced terms in this chapter.

**2.** Describe the causes and effects of the 1986 Chernobyl nuclear power plant accident in the former Soviet Union.

**3.** Distinguish between a *mineral resource* and an *ore*. Distinguish among *identified resources, undiscovered resources, reserves,* and *other resources.* List two factors that can increase the reserves of a mineral resource.

**4.** Describe how mineral deposits are formed by *magma flows, hydrothermal processes, sedimentary sorting, precipitation,* and *rock weathering.*

**5.** List seven ways mining companies find mineral deposits. Distinguish among (a) *overburden* and *spoils,* (b) *surface mining* and *subsurface mining,* and (c) *open-pit mining, dredging, area strip mining,* and *contour strip mining.*

**6.** List five major environmental impacts of mining, processing, and using mineral resources. Describe the life cycle of a metal resource. Distinguish among *ore mineral, gangue,* and *tailings.* What is *smelting,* and what are its major environmental impacts? What three environmental limits are associated with extracting and using mineral resources?

**7.** What is *economic depletion* of a mineral resource? When such depletion occurs, what five choices are available? Distinguish between *depletion time* and the *reserve-to-production ratio* for a mineral resource. How can the estimated depletion time for a resource be extended?

**8.** Explain how a competitive free market should increase supplies of a scarce mineral resource. List three reasons why this idea may not be effective under today's economic conditions.

**9.** Describe the basic features of the 1872 Mining Law in the United States and list its pros and cons.

**10.** List the pros and cons of allowing more mineral exploration and mining on public lands in the United States.

**11.** List the pros and cons of increasing supplies of mineral resources by (a) mining lower-grade ores, (b) mining the oceans, and (c) finding substitutes for scarce nonrenewable mineral resources.

**12.** List the pros and cons of (a) current methods used to mine gold in developed and developing countries and (b) using bacteria to extract metals from ores.

**13.** What supplies 99% of the energy we use? What percentage of the remaining 1% of the energy we use comes from nonrenewable and from renewable energy in (a) the world, and (b) the United States?

**14.** Summarize the trends since 1950 in the global use of (a) coal, (b) oil, (c) natural gas, (d) nuclear power to produce electricity, and (e) wood to provide heat and cook food in developing countries.

**15.** How long does it usually take to phase in a new energy alternative to the point where it accounts for 10–20% of total energy use? What seven questions should we try to answer about each energy resource?

**16.** What is *net energy,* and why is it important in evaluating an energy resource? Why is the net energy for oil from the Middle East high and that for nuclear power low?

**17.** What is *petroleum,* or *crude oil*? How is oil extracted from the earth's crust?

**18.** What happens to crude oil at a refinery? What are *petrochemicals*?

**19.** Summarize the history of the Age of Oil.

**20.** Who has most of the world's oil reserves? What percentage of the world's oil reserves is found in the United States? What percentage of the world's oil does the United States use? What percentage of the oil used in the United States is imported?

**21.** How long are known and projected supplies of conventional oil expected to last in **(a)** the world and **(b)** the United States? List the pros and cons of drilling for oil and natural gas in Alaska's Arctic National Wildlife Refuge.

**22.** What are the pros and cons of using conventional oil as an energy resource?

**23.** What are the pros and cons of using heavy oil from shale oil and tar sand as energy resources?

**24.** What is *natural gas*? Who has most of the world's reserves of natural gas? What is *methane hydrate*? Distinguish between *liquefied petroleum gas (LPG)* and *liquefied natural gas (LNG)*.

**25.** How long are known and projected supplies of natural gas expected to last in **(a)** the world and **(b)** the United States? What is a *combined-cycle natural gas turbine system*, and why is its use rising rapidly?

**26.** What are the pros and cons of using natural gas as an energy resource?

**27.** What is *coal*, and how is it formed? Distinguish among *lignite*, *bituminous*, and *anthracite* coal. How is coal extracted from the earth's crust? How is coal used? What four countries have the largest coal reserves?

**28.** How long are known and projected supplies of coal expected to last **(a)** in the world and **(b)** in the United States?

**29.** What are the pros and cons of using coal as an energy resource? What are the pros and cons of converting solid coal into gaseous and liquid fuels?

**30.** Describe how a *nuclear fission reactor* works. What are the five major components of a *light-water nuclear reactor*, and what role does each play? What is the *nuclear fuel cycle*?

**31.** List three reasons why commercial nuclear power plants were developed in the United States after World War II. List six factors that have contributed to the leveling off of the use of nuclear power plants to produce electricity.

**32.** List the major advantages and disadvantages of using conventional nuclear fission to produce electricity. Compare the advantages and disadvantages of using nuclear power and burning coal to produce electricity.

**33.** How safe are nuclear power plants?

**34.** What is being done with *low-level radioactive waste* produced by the nuclear fuel cycle? What are the options for dealing with *high-level radioactive waste*? Describe the threat from terrorist attacks on high-level radioactive wastes stored in pools of water or in dry casks at most nuclear power plants in the United States.

**35.** List the pros and cons of the proposed site for storing high-level nuclear wastes at Yucca Mountain in Nevada. How widespread are contaminated radioactive waste sites in **(a)** the United States and **(b)** the former Soviet Union?

**36.** What are the three options for retiring (decommissioning) worn-out nuclear power plants?

**37.** What is the relationship between the development of commercial nuclear power and the spread of nuclear weapons throughout much of the world? Describe the threat from terrorists stealing or buying radioactive materials used in medicine, industry, and research facilities and using the materials to make dirty radioactive bombs.

**38.** How useful is nuclear power in reducing U.S. dependence on oil imports?

**39.** What are the pros and cons of new reactor designs such as the pebble bed nuclear reactor?

**40.** What are the pros and cons of using **(a)** breeder nuclear fission and **(b)** nuclear fusion as an energy resource? What are the pros and cons of continuing large-scale government subsidies for research and development of conventional nuclear power, breeder fission, and nuclear fusion?

## CRITICAL THINKING

**1.** Use the second law of thermodynamics (p. 59) to analyze the scientific and economic feasibility of each of the following processes: **(a)** extracting most minerals dissolved in seawater, **(b)** mining increasingly lower-grade deposits of minerals, **(c)** using inexhaustible solar energy to mine minerals, and **(d)** continuing to mine, use, and recycle minerals at increasing rates.

**2.** Explain why you support or oppose each of the following proposals concerning extraction of hardrock minerals on public land in the United States: **(a)** not granting title to public lands in the United States for actual or claimed hardrock mining, **(b)** requiring mining companies to pay a royalty of 8–12% on the *gross* revenues they earn from hardrock minerals they extract from public lands, and **(c)** making hardrock mining companies legally responsible for restoring the land and cleaning up environmental damage caused by their activities.

**3.** List the pros and cons of including the environmental and health costs caused by mining, processing, and producing mineral resources (Figure 15-6) in the prices of metals to manufacturers and in the prices of consumer products. Do you favor including environmental costs in the prices of products? Explain. How would you institute such a policy?

**4.** Just to continue using oil at the current rate (not the projected higher exponential increase in its annual use), we must discover and add to global oil reserves the equivalent of a new Saudi Arabia supply (the world's largest) *every 10 years*. Do you believe this is possible? If not, what effects might this have on your life and on the life of a child or grandchild you might have?

**5.** If you were trying to find new deposits of oil, would you search primarily in formations of igneous rock, sedimentary rock, or metamorphic rock? Explain.

6. List five actions you can take to reduce your dependence on oil and resources such as gasoline and most plastics derived from oil (see website material for this chapter). Which of these things do you actually plan to do?

7. The United States now imports 55% of the oil it uses and could be importing at least 61% of its oil by 2010. Explain why you are for or against continuing to increase oil imports. What do you believe are the three best ways to reduce dependence on oil imports?

8. Explain why you agree or disagree with the following proposals by various energy analysts to solve U.S. energy problems: (a) find and develop more domestic supplies of oil, (b) place a heavy federal tax on gasoline and imported oil to help reduce the waste of oil resources, (c) increase dependence on nuclear power, and (d) phase out all nuclear power plants by 2020.

9. Explain why you agree or disagree with each of the following proposals made by the U.S. nuclear power industry: (a) provide at least $100 billion in government subsidies to build a large number of better designed nuclear fission power plants (Figure 15-42) to reduce dependence on imported oil and slow global warming, (b) prevent the public from participating in hearings for licensing nuclear power plants and the Yucca Mountain high-level waste depository (Figure 15-41) and on safety issues at the nation's nuclear reactors, (c) restore government subsidies to develop a breeder nuclear fission reactor program, and (d) greatly increase federal subsidies for developing nuclear fusion.

10. If you had to choose, would you rather live next door to a coal-fired power plant or a nuclear plant? Explain.

11. Should the United States and other developed countries provide economic and technical aid for closing 35 poorly designed and poorly operated nuclear reactors in some republics of the former Soviet Union and in eastern Europe? Explain.

## PROJECTS

1. What mineral resources are extracted in your local area? What mining methods are used, and what have been their environmental impacts? How has mining these resources benefited the local economy?

2. How is the electricity in your community produced? How has the cost of that electricity changed since 1970 compared to general inflation?

3. Write a two-page scenario of what your life might be like without oil. Compare and discuss the scenarios developed by members of your class.

4. Use the library or the Internet to find out information about the accident that took place at the Three Mile Island (TMI) nuclear power plant near Harrisburg, Pennsylvania, in 1979. According to the nuclear power industry, the TMI accident showed that its safety systems work because the accident caused no known deaths. Other analysts dispute this claim and argue the accident was a wake-up call about the potential dangers of nuclear power plants that led to tighter and better safety regulations. Use the information you find to determine

which of these positions you support, and defend your choice.

5. Use the library or the Internet to find bibliographic information about *Ann Dorr* and *Lester R. Brown*, whose quotes appear at the beginning and end of this chapter.

6. Make a concept map of this chapter's major ideas, using the section heads and subheads and the key terms (in boldface). Look on the website for this book for information about making concept maps.

## INTERNET STUDY RESOURCES AND RESOURCES FOR FURTHER READING AND RESEARCH

The website for this book contains helpful study aids and many ideas for further reading and research. Log on to

www.info.brookscole.com/miller13

and click on the Chapter-by-Chapter area. Choose Chapter 15 and select a resource:

■ Flash Cards allows you to test your mastery of the Terms and Concepts to Remember for this chapter.

■ Tutorial Quizzes provides a multiple-choice practice quiz.

■ Student Guide to InfoTrac will lead you to Critical Thinking Projects that use InfoTrac College Edition as a research tool.

■ References lists the major books and articles consulted in writing this chapter.

■ Hypercontents takes you to an extensive list of sites with news, research, and images related to individual sections of the chapter.

## INFOTRAC COLLEGE EDITION

Improve your skills with InfoTrac College Edition, a searchable online database of articles from more than 700 periodicals. Log on to

http://www.infotrac-college.com

or access InfoTrac through the website for this book. Try to find the following articles:

1. Geiselman, B. 2002. Yucca Mountain foes quake over plan; Tremor won't dissuade energy officials. (Brief article) *Waste News* 8: 1. *Keywords:* "Yucca Mountain" and "earthquake." Nevada's proposed Yucca Mountain nuclear waste repository has been controversial for a number of years, but as the government prepares to make the site the official US nuclear waste dump, the area's geologic stability is being questioned.

2. Kerlin, K. 2001. Diamonds aren't forever. *E* 12: 54. *Keywords:* "diamonds" and "environmental problems." Diamonds, gold, and other precious materials often come from not-so-friendly places and at high environmental costs.

# 16 ENERGY EFFICIENCY AND RENEWABLE ENERGY

## The Coming Energy-Efficiency and Renewable-Energy Revolution

Energy experts Hunter and Amory Lovins (Guest Essay, p. 384) have built a large, passively heated, superinsulated, partially earth-sheltered home and office in Snowmass, Colorado (Figure 16-1), where winter temperatures can drop to $-40°C$ ($-40°F$).

This structure, which also houses the research center for the Rocky Mountain Institute, an office used by 40 people, **(1)** gets 99% of its space and water heating and 95% of its daytime lighting from the sun and **(2)** uses one-tenth the usual amount of electricity for a structure of its size.

With today's superinsulating windows a house can have large numbers of windows without much heat loss in cold weather or heat gain in hot weather. Thinner insulation material now being developed will allow roofs and walls to be insulated far better than in today's best superinsulated houses.

A small but growing number of people in developed and developing countries are getting their elec-tricity from *solar cells* that convert sunlight directly into electricity. They can be attached like shingles to a roof, used as a roof material, or applied to window glass as a coating. Solar-cell prices are high but are falling.

Many scientists and executives of oil and automobile companies believe we are in the beginning stages of a *solar–hydrogen revolution* to be phased in during this century as the Age of Oil begins winding down (Spotlight, p. 359, and Figure 15-16, p. 353). Electricity produced by large banks of solar cells or farms of wind turbines could be passed through water to make hydrogen gas ($H_2$), which could be used to fuel vehicles, industries, and buildings. Another solution is to burn hydrogen in energy-efficient *fuel cells* that produce electricity to **(1)** run cars and appliances, **(2)** heat water, and **(3)** heat and cool buildings.

Burning hydrogen made by decomposing water produces water vapor and no carbon dioxide ($CO_2$). Thus shifting to hydrogen as our primary energy resource during this century would eliminate most of the world's air pollution and greatly slow global warming—as long as the hydrogen is produced from water and not fossil fuels or other carbon-containing compounds.

Robert Millman/Rocky Mountain Institute

**Figure 16-1** The Rocky Mountain Institute in Colorado. This facility is a home and a center for the study of energy efficiency and sustainable use of energy and other resources. It is also an example of energy-efficient passive solar design.

This chapter addresses the following questions:

- What are the advantages and disadvantages of improving energy efficiency?
- What are the advantages and disadvantages of using solar energy to **(1)** heat buildings and water and **(2)** produce electricity?
- What are the advantages and disadvantages of using flowing water (hydropower) to produce electricity?
- What are the advantages and disadvantages of using wind to produce electricity?
- What are the advantages and disadvantages of burning plant material (biomass) to **(1)** heat buildings and water, **(2)** produce electricity, and **(3)** propel vehicles (biofuels)?
- What are the advantages and disadvantages of producing hydrogen gas and using it to **(1)** produce electricity, **(2)** heat buildings and water, and **(3)** propel vehicles?
- What are the advantages and disadvantages of extracting heat from the earth's interior (geothermal energy)?
- What are the advantages and disadvantages of using smaller, decentralized micropower sources to heat buildings and water, produce electricity, and propel vehicles?
- How can we make a transition to a more sustainable energy future?

## 16-1 THE IMPORTANCE OF IMPROVING ENERGY EFFICIENCY

**What Is Energy Efficiency? Doing More with Less** Energy efficiency is the percentage of total energy input into an energy conversion device or system that **(1)** does useful work and **(2)** is not converted to low-quality, essentially useless heat. Improving the energy efficiency of a car motor, home heating system, or other energy conversion device involves using less energy to do more useful work.

**How Much Energy Do We Waste?** You may be surprised to learn that *84% of all commercial energy used in the United States is wasted* (Figure 16-2). About 41% of this energy is wasted automatically because of the degradation of energy quality imposed by the second

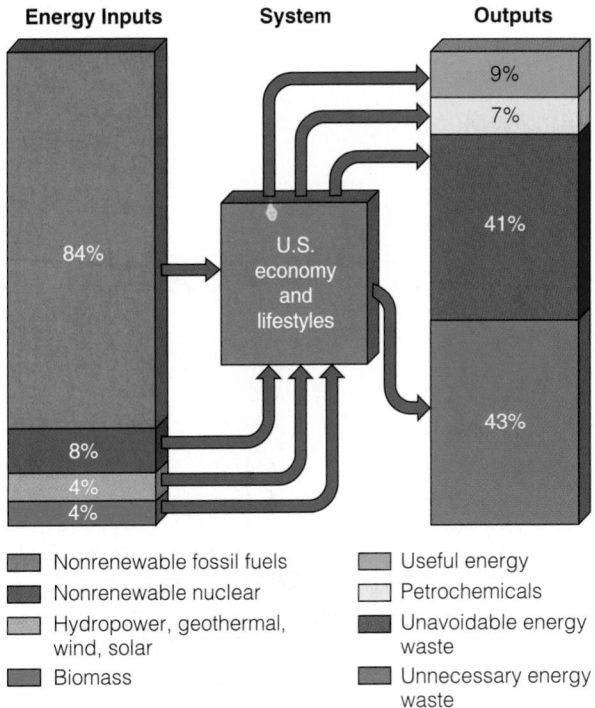

**Figure 16-2** Flow of commercial energy through the U.S. economy. Note that only 16% of all commercial energy used in the United States ends up performing useful tasks or being converted to petrochemicals; the rest is either automatically and unavoidably wasted because of the second law of thermodynamics (41%) or wasted unnecessarily (43%).

law of thermodynamics (p. 59). However, about 43% is wasted unnecessarily, mostly by **(1)** using fuel-wasting motor vehicles, furnaces, and other devices and **(2)** living and working in leaky, poorly insulated, poorly designed buildings (Guest Essay, p. 384).

According to the U.S. Department of Energy (DOE), the United States unnecessarily wastes as much energy as two-thirds of the world's population consumes. Improvements in energy efficiency since the OPEC oil embargo in 1973 (Figure 2-9, p. 31, and Spotlight, p. 359) have cut U.S. energy bills by $275 billion a year. But unnecessary energy waste still costs the United States about $300 billion per year—an average of $570,000 per minute. Reducing energy waste has a number of economic and environmental advantages (Figure 16-3, p. 382).

**What Are the Energy Efficiencies of Common Devices?** The energy conversion devices we use vary in their energy efficiencies (Figure 16-4, p. 382). We can save energy and money by buying more energy-efficient cars, lighting, heating systems, water heaters, air conditioners, and appliances. Some energy-efficient models may cost more initially, but in the long

Prolongs fossil
fuel supplies

Reduces oil
imports

Very high net
energy

Low cost

Reduces pollution
and environmental
degradation

Buys time to
phase in
renewable energy

Less need for
military protection
of Middle East oil
resources

Improves local
economy by
reducing flow of
money out to
pay for energy

Creates local jobs

INSULATION

**Figure 16-3** Advantages of reducing energy waste. Global improvements in energy efficiency could save the world about $1 trillion per year—an average of $11.4 million per hour.

H$_2$O    H$_2$    O$_2$    KOH

Fuel cell
60%

Steam turbine
45%

Human body
20–25%

Fluorescent light
22%

Internal combustion
engine
(gasoline) 10%

Incandescent light
5%

**Figure 16-4** Energy efficiency of some common energy conversion devices.

run they usually save money by having a lower **life cycle cost:** initial cost plus lifetime operating costs.

Perhaps the three least efficient energy-using devices in widespread use today are **(1)** incandescent lightbulbs (which waste 95% of the energy input), **(2)** vehicles with internal combustion engines (which waste 86–90% of the energy in their fuel), and **(3)** nuclear power plants producing electricity for space heating or water heating (which waste 86% of the energy in their nuclear fuel and probably 92% when the energy needed to deal with radioactive wastes and retired nuclear plants is included). Energy experts call for us to replace these devices or greatly improve their energy efficiency over the next few decades.

Coal-burning power plants also are big energy wasters. About 34% of the energy in coal burned in a typical electric power plant is used to produced electricity, and the remaining 66% ends up as waste heat that flows into the environment. As a result, U.S. coal-burning power plants throw away as much heat as all the energy used by Japan.

**What Is Net Energy Efficiency?** Recall that the only energy that really counts is *net energy* (p. 353). The *net energy efficiency* of the entire energy delivery process for a space heater, water heater, or car is determined by the efficiency of each step in the energy conversion process.

Figure 16-5 shows the net energy efficiency for heating two well-insulated homes, **(1)** one with electricity produced at a nuclear power plant, transported by wire to the home, and converted to heat (electric resistance heating) and **(2)** the other heated passively, with an input of direct solar energy through high-efficiency windows facing the sun, with heat stored in heat-absorbing materials for slow release.

This analysis shows that the process of **(1)** converting the high-quality energy in nuclear fuel to high-quality heat at several thousand degrees in the power plant, **(2)** converting this heat to high-quality electricity, **(3)** transmitting the electricity to users, and **(4)** using the electricity to provide low-quality heat for warming a house to only about 20°C (68°F) is very wasteful of high-quality energy (Figure 3-12, p. 53). Burning coal or any fossil fuel at a power plant to supply electricity and transmitting it long distances to heat water or space is also inefficient.

This example illustrates two general principles for saving energy:

■ *Keep the number of steps in an energy conversion process as low as possible.* Each time we convert energy from one form to another or transmit it some useful energy is lost.

■ *Strive to have the highest possible energy efficiency for each step in an energy conversion process.*

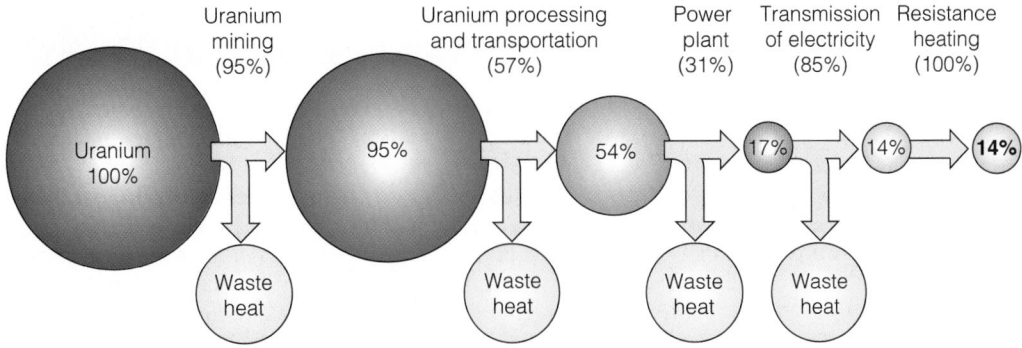

Uranium mining (95%)   Uranium processing and transportation (57%)   Power plant (31%)   Transmission of electricity (85%)   Resistance heating (100%)

Uranium 100% → 95% → 54% → 17% → 14% → **14%**

Waste heat   Waste heat   Waste heat   Waste heat

**Electricity from Nuclear Power Plant**

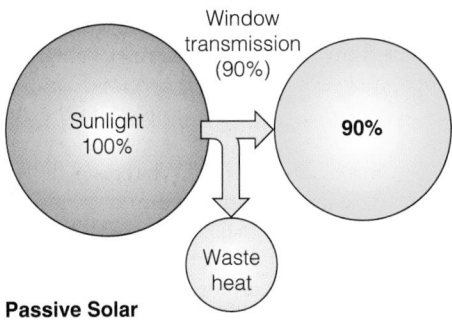

Window transmission (90%)

Sunlight 100% → **90%**

Waste heat

**Passive Solar**

**Figure 16-5** Comparison of net energy efficiency for two types of space heating. The cumulative net efficiency is obtained by multiplying the percentage shown inside the circle for each step by the energy efficiency for that step (shown in parentheses). Because of the second law of thermodynamics, in most cases the greater the number of steps in an energy conversion process, the lower its net energy efficiency. About 86% of the energy used to provide space heating by electricity produced at a nuclear power plant is wasted. If the additional energy needed to deal with nuclear wastes and to retire highly radioactive nuclear plants after their useful life is included, then the net energy yield for a nuclear plant is only about 8% (or 92% waste). By contrast, with passive solar heating, only about 10% of incoming solar energy is wasted.

## 16-2 WAYS TO IMPROVE ENERGY EFFICIENCY

**How Can We Use Waste Heat?** Could we save energy by recycling energy? No. The second law of thermodynamics (p. 59) tells us that we cannot recycle energy. But we can slow the rate at which waste heat flows into the environment when high-quality energy is degraded.

For a house, the best way to do this is to **(1)** insulate it thoroughly, **(2)** eliminate air leaks (Figure 16-6), and **(3)** equip it with an air-to-air heat exchanger to prevent buildup of indoor air pollutants.

In office buildings and stores, waste heat from lights, computers, and other machines can be collected and distributed to reduce heating bills during cold weather. During hot weather, the collected heat can be vented outdoors to reduce cooling bills or to

**Figure 16-6** An infrared photo (thermogram) showing heat loss (red, white, and orange) around the windows, doors, roofs, and foundations of houses and stores in Plymouth, Michigan. Many homes and buildings in the United States (and in most other countries) are so full of leaks that their heat loss in cold weather and heat gain in hot weather are equivalent to having a large window-sized hole in the wall of the house.

## Technology Is the Answer (But What Was the Question?)

*Amory B. Lovins*

**GUEST ESSAY**

*Physicist and energy consultant Amory B. Lovins is one of the world's most respected experts on energy strategy. In 1989, he received the Delphi Prize for environmental work; in 1990, the* Wall Street Journal *named him one of the 39 people most likely to change the course of business in the 1990s. He is research director at Rocky Mountain Institute, a nonprofit resource policy center that he and Hunter Lovins founded in Snowmass, Colorado, in 1982. He has served as a consultant to more than 200 utilities, private industries, and international organizations, and to many national, state, and local governments. He is active in energy affairs in more than 35 countries and has published several hundred papers and a dozen books on energy strategies and policies.*

It is fashionable to suppose that we're running out of energy and ask how can we get more of it. However, the more important questions are **(1)** How much energy do we need and **(2)** What are the cheapest and least environmentally harmful ways to meet these needs?

How much energy it takes to make steel, run a car, or keep ourselves comfortable in our houses depends on how cleverly we use energy. For example, it is now cheaper to double the efficiency of most industrial electric motor drive systems than to fuel existing power plants to make electricity. Just this one saving can more than replace the entire U.S. nuclear power program. We know how to make **(1)** lights five times as efficient as those currently in use and **(2)** household appliances that give us the same work as now but use one-fifth as much energy (saving money in the process).

There are at least 50 good-sized, peppy, safe prototype cars averaging 30–60 kpl (70–140 mpg) on the market. Within a decade automakers could have cars getting 64–128 kpl (150–300 mpg) on the road if consumers demanded such cars.

We know today how to make new buildings (and many old ones) so heat-tight (but still well ventilated) that they need essentially no outside energy to maintain comfort year-round, even in severe climates. In fact, I live and work in one [Figure 16-1].

These energy-saving measures are all cheaper than going out and getting more energy. However, the old view of the energy problem included a worse mistake than forgetting to ask how much energy we needed: It sought more energy, in any form, from any source, at any price, as if all kinds of energy were alike.

Just as there are different kinds of food, so there are many different forms of energy whose different prices and qualities suit them to different uses [Figure 3-12, p. 53]. After all, there is no demand for energy as such; nobody wants raw kilowatt-hours or barrels of sticky black goo. People instead want energy services: comfort, light, mobility, hot showers, cold beverages, and the ability to cook food and make cement. In developing energy resources we should start by asking, "What tasks do we want energy for, and what amount, type, and source of energy will do each task most cheaply?"

The real question is, "What is the cheapest way to do low-temperature heating and cooling?" The answer is weather-stripping, insulation, heat exchangers, greenhouses, superwindows (which have as much insulating value as the outside wall of a typical house), roof overhangs, trees, and so on. These measures generally cost the equivalent of buying electricity at about 0.5¢–2¢ per kilowatt-hour, the lowest-cost way by far to supply energy.

If we need more electricity, we should get it from the cheapest sources first. In approximate order of increasing price, these include

- Converting to efficient lighting equipment. This would save the United States electricity equal to the output of 120 large power plants, plus $30 billion a year in fuel and maintenance costs.

- Using more efficient electric motors to save up to half the energy used by motor systems. This would save electricity equal to the output of another 150 large power plants and repay the cost in about a year.

drive a type of air conditioner called an *absorption chiller.*

**How Can We Save Energy in Industry?** Here are three important ways to save energy and money in industry:

- **Cogeneration,** or *combined heat and power (CHP)* systems, in which two useful forms of energy (such as steam and electricity) are produced from the same fuel source. These systems **(1)** have an efficiency of up to 80% (compared to about 30–40% for coal-fired boilers and nuclear power plants) and **(2)** emit two-thirds less $CO_2$ per unit of energy produced than conventional coal-fired boilers. Cogeneration has been widely used in western Europe for years. Its use in the United States (now producing only 9% of the country's electricity) and China is growing. In Germany, small cogeneration units that run on natural gas or liquefied petroleum gas (LPG) supply restaurants, apartment buildings, and houses with all their energy. In 6–8 years, they pay for themselves in saved fuel and electricity.

- *Replacing energy-wasting electric motors.* Running electric motors (mostly in industry) consumes about half of the electricity produced in the United States. Most of these motors are inefficient because they run

- Displacing the electricity now used for water heating and for space heating and cooling with good architecture, weatherization, insulation, and mostly passive solar techniques.

- Improving the energy efficiency of appliances, smelters, and the like.

Just these four measures can quadruple U.S. electrical efficiency, making it possible to run today's economy with no changes in lifestyles and using no power plants, whether old or new or fueled with oil, gas, coal, uranium, or solar energy. We would need only the present hydroelectric capacity, readily available small-scale hydroelectric projects, and a modest amount of wind power.

If we still wanted more electricity, the next cheapest sources would include **(1)** cogenerating electricity and heat in industrial plants and power plants, **(2)** using low-temperature heat engines run by industrial waste heat or by solar ponds, **(3)** filling empty turbine bays and upgrading equipment in existing big dams, **(4)** using modern wind turbines or small-scale hydroelectric turbines in good sites, **(5)** using combined-cycle natural gas turbines, and perhaps **(6)** using recently developed more efficient solar cells when their price is reduced by mass production.

Only after exhausting all these cheaper opportunities should we even consider building a new central power station of any kind—the slowest and costliest known way to get more electricity (or to save oil).

To emphasize the importance of starting with energy end uses rather than energy sources, consider a story from France. In the mid-1970s, energy conservation planners in the French government found that their biggest need for energy was to heat buildings and that even with good heat pumps, electricity would be the costliest way to do this. So they had a fight with their government-owned and -run utility company; they won, and electric heating was supposed to be discouraged or even phased out because it was so wasteful of money and fuel.

Meanwhile, down the street, the energy supply planners (who were far more numerous and influential in the French government) said, "Look at all that nasty imported oil coming into our country. We must replace that oil with some other source of energy. Voilà! Nuclear reactors can give us energy, so we'll build them all over the country." However, they paid little attention to who would use that extra energy and no attention to relative prices.

Thus, these two groups of the French energy establishment went on with their respective solutions to two different, indeed contradictory, French energy problems: *more energy of any kind* versus *the right kind to do each task in the most inexpensive way.* It was only in 1979 that these conflicting perceptions collided. The supply-side planners suddenly realized that the only thing they would be able to sell all that nuclear electricity for would be electric heating, which they had just agreed not to do.

Every industrial country is in this embarrassing position. Supply-oriented planners think the problem boils down to whether to build coal or nuclear power stations (or both). Energy-use planners realize that *no* kind of new power station can be an economic way to meet the needs for using electricity to provide low- and high-temperature heat and for the vehicular liquid fuels that are 92% of our energy problem.

So if we want to provide energy services at the lowest cost, we need to begin by determining what we need the energy for!

## Critical Thinking

**1.** The author argues that building more nuclear, coal, or other electrical power plants to supply electricity for the United States is unnecessary and wasteful of energy and money. List your reasons for agreeing or disagreeing with this viewpoint.

**2.** Explain why you agree or disagree that increasing the supply of energy, instead of improving energy efficiency, is the wrong answer to our energy problems.

only at full speed with their output throttled to match the task. Each year a heavily used electric motor consumes 10 times its purchase cost in electricity—equivalent to using $200,000 worth of gasoline each year to fuel a $20,000 car. The costs of replacing such motors with new adjustable-speed drive motors would **(1)** be paid back in about 1 year and **(2)** save an amount of energy equal to that generated by 150 large (1,000-megawatt) power plants.

- *Switching to high-efficiency lighting.*

## How Can We Save Energy in Transportation?
According to most energy analysts, the best way to save energy (especially oil) and money in transportation is to *increase the fuel efficiency of motor vehicles.*

Some *good environmental news* is that between 1973 and 1985, the average fuel efficiency rose sharply for new cars sold in the United States and to a lesser degree for pickup trucks, minivans, and sport utility vehicles (SUVs) (Figure 16-7, p. 386). This occurred because of the government-mandated *Corporate Average Fuel Economy (CAFE)* standards.

Some *bad environmental news* is that between 1985 and 2001, the average fuel efficiency for new motor vehicles sold in the United States leveled off or declined slightly (Figure 16-7). This occurred because of **(1)** the increased popularity of energy-inefficient sport utility

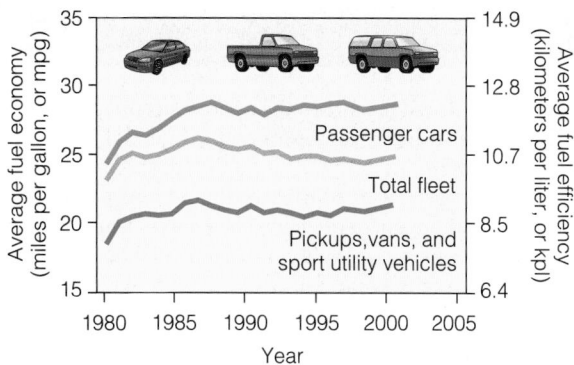

**Figure 16-7** Average fuel economy of new vehicles sold in the United States, 1975–2001. (Data from U.S. Environmental Protection Agency and National Highway Traffic Safety Administration)

vehicles (SUVs), minivans, light trucks, and large autos that also produce about 20% of U.S. emissions of $CO_2$ and **(2)** failure of elected officials to raise CAFE standards because of opposition from automakers.

According to a 2001 study by the American Council for an Energy-Efficient Economy (ACEEE), increasing the fuel economy of new vehicles in the United States by just 5% a year for 10 years would **(1)** save 10–20 times more oil than the projected supply from the Arctic

**Figure 16-8** Real price of gasoline (in 1993 dollars) in the United States, 1920–2001. The 225 million motor vehicles in the United States use about 40% of the world's gasoline. Gasoline is one of the cheapest items American consumers buy and is less expensive than bottled water. (U.S. Department of Energy)

National Wildlife Refuge (Pro/Con, p. 360) and **(2)** more than three times the oil in the nation's current proven oil reserves.

Suppose that in 1991 the first Bush administration and Congress had established a policy of requiring that the average car in the United States get 14 kilometers per liter (32 miles per gallon) by 2001. According to energy analysts, doing this would have saved enough oil to eliminate all current oil imports to the United States from the Persian Gulf. A similar action by the second Bush administration and Congress could significantly reduce U.S. dependence on imported oil within 10 years.

There are about 50 models of cars that get more than 15 kpl (35 mpg) on the market in the United States. However, they account for less than 1% of all car sales mostly because **(1)** the inflation-adjusted price of gasoline today in the United States is low (Figure 16-8 and Connections, p. 388), and **(2)** two-thirds of U.S. consumers prefer SUVs, pickup trucks, minivans, and other large, inefficient vehicles.

In Europe, where gasoline costs 80¢–$1.30 per liter ($3–5 per gallon), small subcompact cars are in much greater use—especially for urban trips. For example, Volkswagen has a four-seater subcompact car that gets 33 kpl (78 mpg) and has begun producing a smaller model that gets 100 kpl (235 mpg).

According to a 2001 study by the Natural Resources Defense Council (NRDC), a well-designed small car can be safer than a large gas guzzler. For example, U.S. government safety authorities gave **(1)** the General Motors Jimmy SUV an overall safety rating of only one star and the smaller Honda Accord five stars and **(2)** the Jeep Cherokee three stars in side-impact collisions and the much smaller Volkswagen Beetle five stars.

**Are Hybrid-Electric Cars the Answer?** There is rapidly growing interest in developing *superefficient cars* that could eventually get 34–128 kpl (80–300 mpg). One type of highly efficient car uses **(1)** a small *hybrid-electric internal combustion engine* that runs on gasoline, diesel fuel, or natural gas and **(2)** a small battery (recharged by the internal combustion engine) to provide the energy needed for acceleration and hill climbing (Figure 16-9).

In 2002, fuel-efficient hybrid-engine cars included the **(1)** *Toyota Prius* (a five-seater) that gets 21 kpl (49 mpg), **(2)** *Honda Insight* (a two-seater) that gets 29 kpl (67 mpg), and **(3)** *Honda Civic Hybrid* (a five-seater) that gets 21 kpl (49 mpg). These cars, priced at about $20,000, are selling well, and new buyers can get a federal tax deduction of up to $2,000 through 2003.

Carmakers are projected to introduce up to 20 hybrid models, including cars, trucks, SUVs, and vans, in the next 4–5 years. Sales are expected to reach 500,000 a year by 2006.

**A** **Combustion engine:**
Small, efficient internal combustion engine powers vehicle with low emissions.

**B** **Fuel tank:**
Liquid fuel such as gasoline, diesel, or ethanol runs small combustion engine.

**C** **Electric motor:**
Traction drive provides additional power, recovers braking energy to recharge battery.

**D** **Battery bank:**
High-density batteries power electric motor for increased power.

**E** **Regulator:**
Controls flow of power between electric motor and battery bank.

**F** **Transmission:**
Efficient 5-speed automatic transmission.

**Figure 16-9** General features of a car powered by a *hybrid gas–electric engine*. A small internal combustion engine recharges the batteries, thus reducing the need for heavy banks of batteries and solving the problem of the limited range of conventional electric cars. The bodies of future models of such cars probably will be made of lightweight composite plastics that **(1)** offer more protection in crashes, **(2)** do not need to be painted, **(3)** do not rust, **(4)** can be recycled, and **(5)** have fewer parts than conventional cars. (Concept information from DaimlerChrysler, Ford, Honda, and Toyota)

→ Fuel
→ Electricity

**Are Fuel-Cell Cars the Answer?** Another type of superefficient car is an electric vehicle that uses a *fuel cell* that burns hydrogen ($H_2$) fuel to produce the electricity (Figure 16-10). In the cell, the hydrogen fuel ($H_2$) combines with oxygen ($O_2$) in the air to produce **(1)** electrical energy to power the car and **(2)** water vapor ($H_2O$), which is emitted into the atmosphere.

Most major automobile companies have developed prototype fuel-cell cars and hope to begin marketing them within a few years using several different approaches:

- An *onboard liquid reformer system* that strips hydrogen from available carbon-containing fuels such as gasoline, methanol, or natural gas. However, the use of carbon-containing fuels to produce the hydrogen adds $CO_2$ to the atmosphere. The amount of $CO_2$ emitted per kilometer traveled varies with the carbon

**1** Cell splits $H_2$ into protons and electrons. Protons flow across catalyst membrane.

**2** React with oxygen ($O_2$).

**3** Produce electrical energy (flow of electrons) to power car.

**4** Emits water ($H_2O$) vapor.

**H₂** Hydrogen gas

**A** **Fuel cell stack:**
Hydrogen and oxygen combine chemically to produce electricity.

**B** **Fuel tank:**
Hydrogen gas or liquid or solid metal hydride stored on board or made from gasoline or methanol.

**C** **Turbo compressor:**
Sends pressurized air to fuel cell.

**D** **Traction inverter:**
Module converts DC electricity from fuel cell to AC for use in electric motor.

**E** **Electric motor / transaxle:**
Converts electrical energy to mechanical energy to turn wheels.

**Figure 16-10** General features of an electric car powered by a *fuel cell* running on hydrogen gas. The hydrogen can be produced **(1)** onboard the vehicle from gasoline or methanol **(2)** or offboard for transfer to the vehicle from natural gas or by using renewable energy sources such as solar cells or wind turbines to decompose water into hydrogen and oxygen gas. Several automobile companies have developed prototypes and are working to get costs down. Early models could be on the road by 2003–2004. (Concept information from DaimlerChrysler, Ford, Ballard, Toyota, and Honda)

→ Fuel
→ Electricity

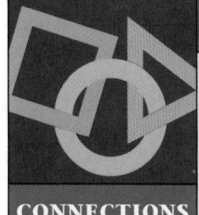

## The Real Cost of Gasoline in the United States

Economists and environmentalists point out that gasoline costs U.S. consumers much more than it appears. This is because the real cost of gasoline is not paid directly at the pump.

According to a 1998 study by the International Center for Technology Assessment, the hidden costs of gasoline to U.S. consumers is about $1.30–3.70 per liter ($5–14 per gallon), depending on how the costs are estimated. These hidden costs include the following:

- Government subsidies and tax breaks for oil companies and road builders.
- Pollution cleanup.

- Military protection of oil supplies in the Middle East.
- Environmental, health, and social costs such as increased medical bills and insurance premiums, time wasted in traffic jams, noise pollution, increased mortality from air and water pollution, urban sprawl, and harmful effects on wildlife species and habitats.

Economists point out that if these harmful costs were included as taxes in the market price of gasoline, we would have much more energy-efficient and less polluting cars. However, gasoline and car companies benefit financially by being able to pass these hidden costs on to consumers and future generations.

This is basically an education and political problem. Most con-

sumers are unaware that they are paying these harmful costs and do not connect them with gasoline use. Also, politicians running on a platform of raising gasoline prices in the United States 3–11-fold would be committing political suicide.

### Critical Thinking

Some economists have suggested that U.S. consumers might be willing to pay much more for gasoline if (1) they understood they are already paying these hidden costs indirectly and (2) the tax revenues from gasoline sales were used to reduce taxes on wages, income, and wealth and provide a safety net for low- and middle-class consumers. Would you support or oppose such a proposal? Explain.

---

compounds used to produce the hydrogen fuel (Figure 16-11).

- DamlierChrysler has developed a prototype minivan fueled with an *onboard* system that converts *solid sodium borohydride* into a mixture of borax (a nontoxic compound used in laundry detergent), water, and hydrogen gas (used to power a fuel cell). When the vehicle is refueled with sodium borohydride, the borax solution can be pumped out and discarded or recycled to make more sodium borohydride. This system does not require a large fuel tank to store hydrogen or a large, hot, dirty reformer and does not emit $CO_2$. In addition, the sodium borohydride fuel is not flammable.

| Engine System | Grams of $CO_2$ emitted per kilometer traveled |
|---|---|
| Gasoline internal combustion engine | 250 |
| $H_2$ produced onboard from gasoline | 175 |
| $H_2$ produced onboard from methanol | 160 |
| $H_2$ produced offboard from natural gas | 70 |

**Figure 16-11** Comparison of $CO_2$ emissions from a conventional gasoline-powered internal combustion engine (red bar) and a hydrogen-powered fuel-cell engine, with the hydrogen produced from various options (green bars). (Data from Pembina Institute, Drayton Valley, Alberta, Canada)

- General Motors and Honda use a chemical process to store hydrogen fuel produced *offboard* in a *solid metal hydride* compound that can be heated to provide $H_2$ and replaced as needed at fueling stations.

Which is best: hybrid-electric or fuel-cell cars? It is too early to know. The answer will depend primarily on (1) how rapidly the technologies for both systems are developed, (2) the amount automobile and fuel-cell companies are willing to invest in developing each approach, (3) the comparative costs of each type of vehicle, and (4) the amount of government research and development subsidies and tax breaks that are available for each approach. Currently, fuel cells are very expensive but automakers hope to bring the costs down.

A 2001 MIT study tentatively concluded that

- In the short run, gasoline-powered hybrid-electric cars are expected to have better fuel economies and lower $CO_2$ and air pollution emissions than fuel-cell cars producing their hydrogen fuel from carbon-based gasoline, methanol, or natural gas (methane).

- After 2020, fuel-cell cars may have fuel economy and environmental advantages if their hydrogen fuel can be produced economically by using various forms of renewable energy to decompose water molecules into hydrogen and oxygen gas. Cars would be fueled from a network of hydrogen fueling stations. Because of the potential of these new technologies, William Ford, CEO of Ford Motor Company, said in 1998 that he expects to preside over the demise of the conventional internal combustion engine.

**How Can Electric Bicycles and Scooters Reduce Energy Use and Waste?** For urban trips, some people may begin using *electric bicycles* powered by a small electric motor. These bicycles, now being sold by several companies, **(1)** cost $500–1,100, **(2)** travel at up to 32 kilometers per hour (20 miles per hour), **(3)** go about 48 kilometers (30 miles) without pedaling on a full electric charge, and **(4)** produce no pollution during operation (and only a small amount for the electricity used in recharging them).

In 2003, an electric bicycle powered by a small fuel cell became available for about $1,500–2000. A small metal container (similar to a propane gas container) that can be easily disconnected and refilled within seconds supplies the hydrogen.

Another alternative is an *electric scooter.* One model, the Nova Cruz Voloci, has a range of about 81 kilometers (50 miles), can travel at a top speed of 48 kph (30 mph), and costs about $2,500.

**How Can We Save Energy in Buildings?** Atlanta's 13-story Georgia Power Company building uses 60% less energy than conventional office buildings of the same size. The largest surface of the building faces south to capture solar energy. Each floor extends out over the one below it, blocking out the higher summer sun to reduce air conditioning costs but allowing warming by the lower winter sun. Energy-efficient lights focus on desks rather than illuminating entire rooms.

If phased in over 2–3 decades, the Georgia Power model and other existing cost-effective commercial building technologies could **(1)** reduce energy use by 75% in U.S. buildings, **(2)** cut $CO_2$ emissions in half, and **(3)** save more than $130 billion per year in energy bills—an average of $15 million an hour.

A number of ways are available to improve the energy efficiency of houses, some of them discussed in

**Figure 16-12** Major features of a *superinsulated house.* Such a house is so heavily insulated and so airtight that it can be warmed by heat from direct sunlight, appliances, and human bodies, with little or no need for a backup heating system. An air-to-air heat exchanger prevents buildup of indoor air pollution.

the opening of this chapter (p. 380). One is a *superinsulated house* (Figure 16-12). Such houses typically cost 5% more to build than conventional houses of the same size. But this extra cost is paid back by energy savings within about 5 years and can save a home owner $50,000–100,000 over a 40-year period.

Since the mid-1980s there has been growing interest in building superinsulated houses called *strawbale houses.* Their walls consist of compacted bales of certain types of straw (available at a low cost almost everywhere) covered with plaster or adobe (Figure 16-13). By 2002, more than 1,200 such homes had been built or were under construction in the United States (Guest Essay, p. 390). Using straw, an

**Figure 16-13** An energy-efficient, environmentally healthy, and affordable Victorian-style *strawbale house* designed and built by Alison Gannett in Crested Butte, Colorado. The left photo is during construction, and the right photo is the completed house. Depending on the thickness of the bales, plastered strawbale walls have an insulating value of R-35–R-60, compared to R-12–R-19 in a conventional house. (The R-value is a measure of resistance to heat flow.)

## Living Lightly on the Earth at Round Mountain Organics

*Nancy Wicks*

GUEST ESSAY

*Nancy Wicks is an eco-pioneer trying to live her ideals. She grew up in a small town in Iowa and did undergraduate studies in a village in Nepal. Both of these life experiences inspired her to live more sustainably by creating Round Mountain Organics, an organic garden at an altitude of 1.6 kilometers (8,500 feet) in the Rocky Mountains near Crested Butte, Colorado. Nancy lives in a passive solar strawbale house, which is powered by the wind and sun. She is a fanatic reuser, recycler, and composter. She received the "Sustainable Business of the Year 2000" award from the High Country Citizen's Alliance.*

After studying in Nepal, where sustainability is a do or die situation, I have tried to incorporate as many sustainable practices into my life as possible at my house and organic garden business called Round Mountain Organics. This includes being a member of a buying coop (where buying in bulk not only saves resources but also saves money), reusing everything from plastic and paper bags to trays and pots for garden plants, and composting food waste (which saves money on trash bills and fertilizes the soil).

After moving onto the land that is now home to Round Mountain Organics, I spent 4 years planning and building an octagonal strawbale house with a stucco exterior—the first such house to be built in the county. I chose to build with straw because **(1)** straw is a natural building material and renewable resource, **(2)** there is a surplus of straw after harvesting grains such as wheat (which I used), oats, barley, and rice, **(3)** its insulation value of R-54 comes in handy when you live in an area where winter temperatures can dip to 40°F below zero, and **(4)** they are easy to build (with only 1 week needed to put up the strawbale walls). Since the 1980s strawbale houses have also been built in Arizona and New Mexico to beat the heat.

I used a passive solar design by orienting the house to the south to take advantage of Colorado's abundant sunshine. During the day the insulated window covers are drawn up and the sun shines onto flagstone tiles covering a cement slab that stores and releases heat slowly to keep the house comfortably warm or cool regardless of outside conditions. At night the window covers are let down to hold the heat in.

Because I live in one of the world's sunniest places, I decided not to get hooked up to the electrical grid and instead get my electricity from a small wind turbine and panels of solar cells. The electricity is stored in a bank of 12 batteries and an inverter converts the stored direct current (DC) electricity to ordinary 120-volt alternating current (AC).

If it's cloudy and not windy for a couple of days (which is rare), I fire up a small gas generator to charge the batteries. I also use some propane to provide hot water with a small on-demand water heater. Only a small pilot light stays lit until the hot water faucet is turned on. Then a large flame is ignited that the water is piped through. This way, I do not use energy to keep a tank of water hot around the clock.

I use many energy-saving devices. They include compact florescent lightbulbs, an oversized pressure tank so the well pump does not have to kick on every time the faucet turns on, and a superinsulated energy-efficient DC refrigerator.

I use organic gardening to grow flowers, herbs, and vegetables for my own use and for sale to local residents and restaurants. I incorporate some pioneering organic gardening techniques such as Rudolph Steiner's biodynamics (developed in 1924) and Bill Mollison's permaculture (developed in 1978).

Insect pests are picked off by hand and beneficial insects such as ladybugs are used to eat harmful insects such as aphids. Compost, aged animal manure, and cover crops that are plowed in as green manure are used to add nutrients to the soil. Crop rotation is used so as not to deplete the soil of nutrients.

Cold frames (a type of mini-greenhouse) are used to extend the growing season to 150 days in the cold climate where there are only about 90 days without a killing frost. Recently I built a passively heated strawbale greenhouse to extend the short growing season further and raise heat-loving plants such as tomatoes, cucumbers, and zucchinis. The chicken coop is in the northeast corner of the greenhouse, with the heat given off by the chickens helping to warm the greenhouse.

Now I am working on starting a nonprofit, Round Mountain Institute, Inc., to educate people on how they can live in harmony with the earth.

### Critical Thinking

Would you like to live a lifestyle similar to that of Nancy Wicks? Explain. Why do you think more people do not try to live more sustainably, as she does? List three ways to help encourage people to adopt such a lifestyle.

*annually* renewable agricultural residue often burned as a waste product, for the walls reduces the need for wood and thus slows deforestation. The main problem is getting banks and other moneylenders to recognize the potential of this and other unconventional types of housing and provide home owners with construction loans.

Eco-roofs covered with plants have been used in Germany and in other parts of Europe for about 25 years. These plant-covered roof gardens **(1)** provide

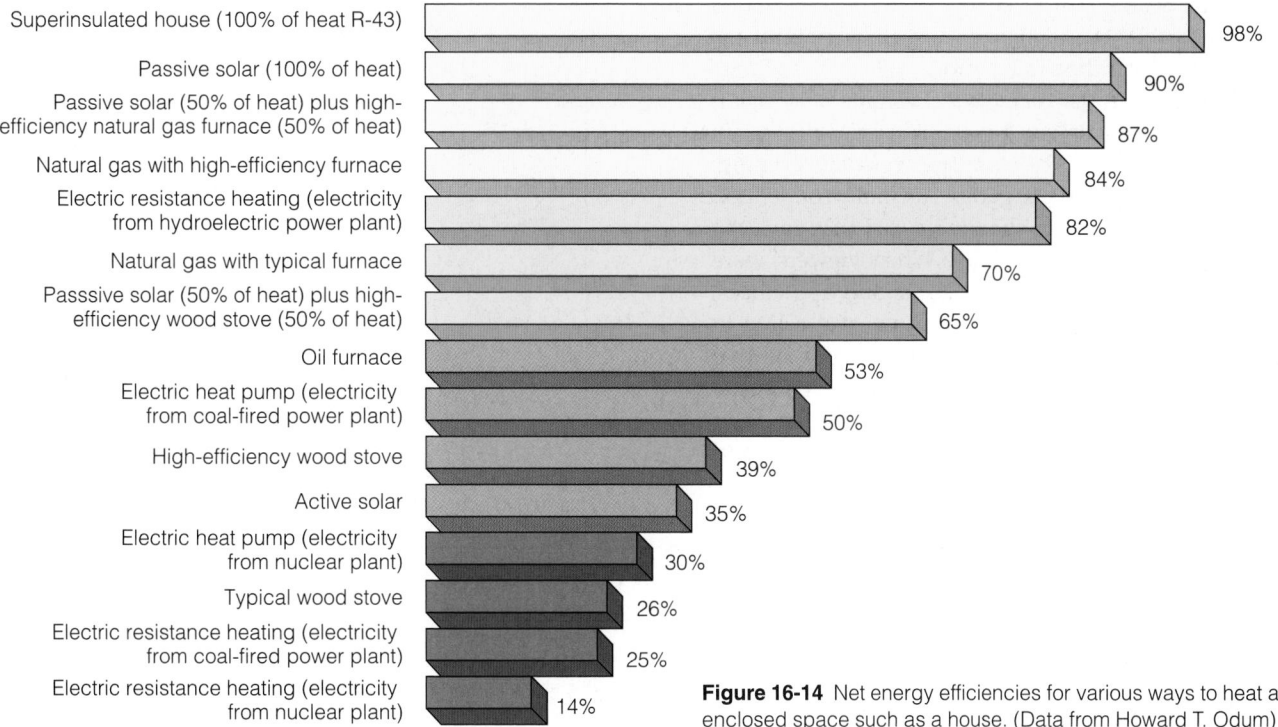

**Net Energy Efficiency**

Superinsulated house (100% of heat R-43) — 98%
Passive solar (100% of heat) — 90%
Passive solar (50% of heat) plus high-efficiency natural gas furnace (50% of heat) — 87%
Natural gas with high-efficiency furnace — 84%
Electric resistance heating (electricity from hydroelectric power plant) — 82%
Natural gas with typical furnace — 70%
Passsive solar (50% of heat) plus high-efficiency wood stove (50% of heat) — 65%
Oil furnace — 53%
Electric heat pump (electricity from coal-fired power plant) — 50%
High-efficiency wood stove — 39%
Active solar — 35%
Electric heat pump (electricity from nuclear plant) — 30%
Typical wood stove — 26%
Electric resistance heating (electricity from coal-fired power plant) — 25%
Electric resistance heating (electricity from nuclear plant) — 14%

**Figure 16-14** Net energy efficiencies for various ways to heat an enclosed space such as a house. (Data from Howard T. Odum)

good insulation, **(2)** absorb storm water, and **(3)** outlast conventional roofs.

Another way to save energy is to *use the most energy-efficient ways to heat houses* (Figure 16-14). The most energy-efficient ways to heat space are **(1)** a superinsulated house, **(2)** passive solar heating, **(3)** heat pumps in warm climates (but not in cold climates because at low temperatures they automatically switch to costly electric resistance heating), and **(4)** a high-efficiency (85–98%) natural gas furnace. The most wasteful and expensive way is to use electric resistance heating with the electricity produced by a coal-fired or nuclear power plant.

*The energy efficiency of existing houses and buildings can be improved significantly by* **(1)** *adding insulation,* **(2)** *plugging leaks, and* **(3)** *installing energy-saving windows and lighting.* About one-third of heated air in U.S. homes and buildings escapes through closed windows and holes and cracks (Figure 16-6)—equal to the energy in all the oil flowing through the Alaska pipeline every year. During hot weather these windows and cracks also let heat in, increasing the use of air conditioning.

Replacing all windows in the United States with low-E (low-emissivity) windows would cut these expensive losses by two-thirds and reduce $CO_2$ emissions. Widely available superinsulating windows insulate as well as 8–12 sheets of glass. Although they cost 10–15% more than double-glazed windows, this

cost is paid back rapidly by the energy they save. Even better windows will reach the market soon.

Simply wrapping a water heater in a $20 insulating jacket can save $45 a year and reduce $CO_2$ emissions. Leaky ducts allow 20–30% of a home's heating and cooling energy to escape and draw unwanted moisture and heat into the home. Careful sealing can reduce this loss. Some designs for new homes keep the ducts inside the home's thermal envelope so that escaping hot or cool air leaks into the living space.

An energy-efficient way to heat hot water for washing and bathing is to use *tankless instant water heaters* (about the size of a small suitcase) fired by natural gas or LPG (Guest Essay, p. 390). These devices, widely used in many parts of Europe, **(1)** heat water instantly as it flows through a small burner chamber, **(2)** provide hot water only when it is needed, and **(3)** use about 20% less energy than traditional water heaters.*

A well-insulated, conventional natural gas or LPG water heater is fairly efficient. But all conventional natural gas and electric resistance heaters **(1)** waste energy by keeping a large tank of water hot all day and night and **(2)** can run out after a long shower or two.

Using electricity produced by any type of power plant is the most inefficient and expensive way to heat

---

*They work great. I used them in a passive solar office and living space for 15 years. Models are available for $500–1,000 from companies such as Rinnai, Bosch, Takagi, and Envirotech.

water for washing and bathing. A $425 electric water heater can cost $5,900 in energy over its 20-year life, compared to about $4,000 for a comparable natural gas water heater over the same period.

*Cutting off lights, computers, TVs, and other appliances when they are not needed can make a big difference in energy use and bills.* At 9 P.M. one weekday evening, major TV stations in Bangkok, Thailand, cooperated with the government in showing a dial that gave the city's current use of electricity. When viewers were asked to turn off unnecessary lights and appliances, they watched the dial register a 735 megawatt drop in electricity use—a drop equal to the output of two medium-sized coal-burning power plants. This visual experience showed individuals that reducing their unnecessary electricity use could cut their bills and collectively close down power plants.

*Setting higher energy-efficiency standards for new buildings would also save energy.* Building codes could require that all new houses use 60–80% less energy than conventional houses of the same size, as has been done in Davis, California. Because of tough energy-efficiency standards, the average Swedish home consumes about one-third as much energy as the average American home of the same size.

Another way to save energy is to *buy the most energy-efficient appliances and lights.* Since 1978, the Department of Energy (DOE) has set federal energy-efficiency standards for more than 20 appliances used in the United States. A 2001 study by the National Academy of Sciences found that **(1)** between 1978 and 2000, the $7 billion spent by the DOE on this program saved consumers more than $30 billion in energy costs and provided environmental benefits valued conservatively at $60–80 billion, and **(2)** the program is expected to save U.S. consumers another $46 billion in energy costs between 2000 and 2020.* Programs like these exist in 43 other countries.

Energy-efficient lighting could save U.S. businesses and homes about $30 billion per year in electricity bills. Replacing a standard incandescent bulb with an energy-efficient compact fluorescent bulb (Figure 16-15) saves about $48–70 per bulb over its 10-year life. Thus replacing 25 incandescent bulbs (in a house or building) with energy-efficient fluorescent bulbs saves $1,250–1,750. Students in Brown University's environmental studies program showed that the school could save more than $40,000 per year just by replacing the incandescent lightbulbs in exit signs with compact fluorescent bulbs.

---

*Each year the American Council for an Energy-Efficient Economy (ACEEE) publishes a list of the most energy-efficient major appliances mass produced for the U.S. market. A copy can be obtained from the council at 1001 Connecticut Avenue NW, Suite 801, Washington, DC 20036, or on their website at http://www.aceee.org/consumerguide/index.htm.

**Figure 16-15** Cost of electricity for comparable lightbulbs used for 10,000 hours. Because conventional incandescent bulbs are only 5% efficient and last only 1,500 hours, they waste enormous amounts of energy and money and add to the heat load of houses during hot weather. Socket-type fluorescent lights use one-fourth as much electricity as conventional bulbs. Although these bulbs cost $6–15 per bulb, they last up to 100,000 hours (60–70 times longer than conventional incandescent bulbs and 25 times longer than halogen bulbs), saving a lot of money (compared with less efficient incandescent and halogen bulbs) over their long life. Between 1998 and 2001, global sales of compact fluorescent bulbs rose from 45 million to 606 million per year—with 80% of them made in China. (Data from Electric Power Research Institute)

Despite their advantages, less than 10% of U.S. homes use these energy- and money-saving bulbs, which pay for themselves in 2–4 years. Reasons for their low use are **(1)** their high initial cost, **(2)** lack of information and education about life-cycle costing, **(3)** initial lack of suitable light fixtures for these larger bulbs (light fixtures and smaller bulbs are now available), and **(4)** dissatisfaction with the color and intensity of the light produced compared with incandescent bulbs (corrected with newer bulbs).

In 2001, researchers at the Lawrence Berkeley National Laboratory developed a very efficient high-intensity fluorescent table lamp. It uses two independently controllable and fully dimmable compact fluorescent bulbs, one directed downward and the other upward. The lamp can eliminate the need for overhead room lighting, provide down lighting for reading and other tasks, and help decrease use of highly inefficient halogen bulbs (which can also start fires and increase air conditioning needs because of the intense heat they produce). In 2002, scientists at Sandia National Laboratories developed a new type of incandescent lightbulb that raises the efficiency of such bulbs from 5% to about 60%.

If all households in the United States used the most efficient frost-free refrigerator now available,

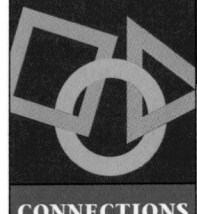
## Using the Internet to Save Energy and Paper and Reduce Global Warming

According to a 2000 report by researchers at the Center for Energy and Climate Solutions, increasing use of the Internet is saving energy and material resources by

- Allowing more employees to work at home.

- Allowing a reduction in retail, manufacturing, warehouse, and commercial office space. Some online companies keep no merchandise in warehouses and have it shipped to customers directly from manufacturers. For example, Amazon.com uses 1/16 as much energy per unit of floor space to sell a book as a regular store.

- Using less energy to get products from sellers to consumers. Sending a package by overnight air uses about 40% less fuel than driving round trip to the mall to get the product. Shipping by

rail saves even more energy. However, shipping a larger number of packages to individuals instead of bulk shipments to businesses causes a huge increase in packaging.

- Reducing the energy, paper, and materials used to produce, package, and market consumer items such as computer software and music CDs by downloading them.

- Reducing energy used in transporting goods by using Internet-based systems to auction off empty shipping space on trucks, aircraft, and trains.

The resulting energy savings also reduce air pollution and $CO_2$ emissions by reducing fossil fuel use. Paper production (a highly energy- and resource-intensive industry) is expected to decrease as **(1)** consumers use the Internet to download software and view magazines, newspapers, research articles, telephone directories, encyclopedias, and books, **(2)** con-

sumers and businesses send more e-mail and less mail and reports by using envelopes and packages, and **(3)** easily updated online catalogs replace paper catalogs.

Although this book is printed on paper, I used no paper in preparing it for the publisher. Instead, the manuscript was sent to the publisher electronically as attachments to e-mail messages. Copyediting of the manuscript was also done via e-mail attachments.

This and other books are still being printed on paper. However, we can envision a day not too far away when we can read and interact with most textbooks on websites maintained by book publishers or individual authors.

### Critical Thinking

What types of environmental harm might be increased by greatly expanded use of the Internet to sell more and more goods in the global marketplace?

---

18 large (1,000-megawatt) power plants could close. Microwave ovens can cut electricity use for cooking by 25–50% (but not if used for defrosting food). Clothes dryers with moisture sensors cut energy use by 15%, and front-loading washers use 50% less energy than top-loading models but cost about the same. Increased use of the Internet for business and shopping transactions reduces energy use and decreases emissions of $CO_2$ and other air pollutants (Connections, above).

**Why Are We Not Doing More to Reduce Energy Waste?** According to Amory Lovins (Guest Essay, p. 384), energy-efficient improvements since 1975 now save the United States each year energy equal to **(1)** more than five times the country's annual domestic oil production, **(2)** two times the energy in all current oil imports, and **(3)** twelve times the energy in all oil imported from the Persian Gulf. Even though improving energy efficiency is the country's cheapest energy option, its potential has barely been tapped.

With such an impressive array of benefits (Figure 16-3), why isn't there more emphasis on improving energy efficiency? The major reasons are as follows:

- A glut of low-cost oil (Figure 15-22, p. 357) and gasoline (Figure 16-8). As long as energy is cheap, people are more likely to waste it and not make investments in improving energy efficiency.

- Lack of sufficient tax breaks and other economic incentives for consumers and businesses to invest in improving energy efficiency.

- Lack of information about the availability of energy-saving devices and the amount of money such items can save consumers by using *life cycle cost* analysis.

## 16-3 USING SOLAR ENERGY TO PROVIDE HEAT AND ELECTRICITY

**What Are the Major Advantages and Disadvantages of Solar Energy?** Figure 16-16 (p. 394) lists some of the advantages and disadvantages of making a shift to greatly increased use of direct solar energy and indirect forms of solar energy such as wind. Like fossil fuels and nuclear power (Chapter 15), each renewable energy alternative has a mix of advantages and disadvantages, as discussed in the remainder of this chapter.

| Advantages | | Disadvantages |
|---|---|---|
| Save money (wind) |  | Making solar cells produces toxic chemicals |
| Reduce air pollution (99% less than coal) | | Solar systems last only 30–40 years |
| Greatly reduce $CO_2$ emissions | | Solar cells and solar thermal take large amounts of land because of diffuse nature of sunlight |
| Reduce dependence on imported oil | | |
| Last as long as coal and nuclear plants (30–40 years) | | Can damage fragile desert ecosystems used to collect solar energy |
| Land use less than for coal | | Need backup systems at night and during cloudy and rainy weather |
| Low land use with new solar cell and window glass system | | |
| Backup and storage devices available (such as gas turbines, batteries, and flywheels) | | Solar cells and solar thermal systems still too costly |
| Backup need reduced by distributing and storing solar-produced hydrogen gas | | |

**Figure 16-16** Major advantages and disadvantages of using direct and indirect solar energy systems to produce heat and electricity. Specific advantages and disadvantages of different direct and indirect solar and other renewable energy systems are discussed in this chapter.

Here is some *good news* about the increased use of renewable energy:

- In 2001, the European Union (EU) adopted a law requiring its member countries to get 12% of their total energy and 22% of their electricity from renewable energy by 2010.

- A 2001 joint study by the American Council for an Energy Efficient Economy, the Tellus Institute, and the Union of Concerned Scientists showed how renewable energy could provide 20% of U.S. energy and save consumers $440 billion by 2020.

- In 2001, voters overwhelmingly approved a $100 million bond issue aimed at **(1)** making San Francisco, California, the nation's top urban producer of solar power and wind power and **(2)** using these renewable forms of energy to supply about 25% of the energy used by the city's schools and government buildings.

- According to Royal Dutch Shell International Petroleum, renewable energy could account for 50% of the world's energy production by 2050.

The *bad news* is that solar and wind power currently provide only about 1% of the world's commercial energy—mostly because they have received and continue to receive much lower government tax breaks, subsidies, and research and development funding than fossil fuels and nuclear power.

**How Can We Use Solar Energy to Heat Houses and Water?** Buildings and water can be heated by solar energy using two methods: passive and active (Figure 16-17). A **passive solar**

**Figure 16-17** Passive and active solar heating for a home.

**Direct Gain**
Ceiling and north wall heavily insulated

Hot air

Super insulated windows

Warm air

Cool air

Summer sun

Winter sun

Earth tubes

**Earth Sheltered**

Earth

Reinforced concrete, carefully waterproofed walls and roof

Flagstone floor for heat storage

Triple-paned or superwindows

**Greenhouse, Sunspace, or Attached Solarium**

Summer cooling vent

Warm air

Insulated windows

Cool air

**Figure 16-18** Three examples of *passive solar design* for houses.

heating system absorbs and stores heat from the sun directly within a structure (Figure 16-1, Figure 16-17, left, Figure 16-18, and Guest Essay, p. 390).

Energy-efficient windows and attached greenhouses face the sun to collect solar energy by direct gain. Walls and floors of concrete, adobe, brick, stone, salt-treated timber, and water in metal or plastic containers store much of the collected solar energy as heat and release it slowly throughout the day and night. A small backup heating system such as a vented natural gas or propane heater may be used but is not necessary in many climates.

On a life cycle cost basis, good passive solar and superinsulated design is the cheapest way to heat a home or small building in regions where ample sunlight is available during the daytime (Figure 16-19, p. 396). Such a system usually adds 5–10% to the construction cost, but the life cycle cost of operating such a house is 30–40% lower. The typical payback time for passive solar features is 3–7 years.

In an **active solar heating system,** collectors absorb solar energy, and a fan or a pump supplies part of a building's space-heating or water-heating needs (Figure 16-17, right). Several connected collectors usually are mounted on the roof with an unobstructed exposure to the sun. Some of the heat can be used directly, and the rest can be stored in insulated tanks containing rocks, water, or a heat-absorbing chemical

for release as needed. Active solar collectors can also supply hot water. Most analysts do not expect widespread use of active solar collectors for heating houses because of **(1)** high costs, **(2)** maintenance requirements, and **(3)** unappealing appearance.

Figure 16-20 (p. 396) lists the major advantages and disadvantages of using passive or active solar energy for heating buildings. Passive solar cannot be used to heat existing homes and buildings **(1)** not oriented to receive sunlight and **(2)** whose access to sunlight is blocked by other buildings and structures.

**How Can We Cool Houses Naturally?** Ways to make a building cooler include the following:

- Using superinsulation and superinsulating windows.

- Blocking the high summer sun with deciduous trees, window overhangs, or awnings (Figure 16-18, top left).

- Using windows and fans to take advantage of breezes and keep air moving.

- Suspending reflective insulating foil in an attic to block heat from radiating down into the house.

- Placing plastic *earth tubes* 3–6 meters (10–20 feet) underground where the earth is cool year round and using a tiny fan to pipe cool and partially dehumidified air into an energy-efficient house (Figure 16-18, top left).*

- Using solar-powered evaporative air conditioners (which work well only in dry climates and cost too much for residential use).

---

*They work. I used them in a passively heated and cooled office and home for 15 years. People allergic to pollen and molds should add an air purification system, but this is also necessary with a conventional cooling system.

Figure 16-19 Map of *global solar energy availability.* Areas with more than 3.5 kilowatt-hours per square meter per day (see scale) are good candidates for passive and active solar heating systems and use of solar cells to produce electricity. (Data from U.S. Department of Energy)

2   3   4   5   6   6.8

Kilowatt-hours per square meter per day

| Advantages | | Disadvantages |
|---|---|---|
| Energy is free | | Need access to sun 60% of time |
| Net energy is moderate (active) to high (passive) | | Blockage of sun access by other structures |
| Quick installation | | Need heat storage system |
| No $CO_2$ emissions | | High cost (active) |
| Very low air and water pollution | | Active system needs maintenance and repair |
| Very low land disturbance (built into roof or window) | | Active collectors unattractive |
| Moderate cost (passive) | | |

Figure 16-20 Advantages and disadvantages of heating a house with passive or active solar energy.

**How Can We Use Solar Energy to Generate High-Temperature Heat and Electricity?** Several so-called *solar thermal systems* collect and transform radiant energy from the sun into high-temperature thermal energy (heat), which can be used directly or converted to electricity (Figure 16-21). Examples include the following:

- A *central receiver system,* called a *power tower,* in which huge arrays of computer-controlled mirrors called *heliostats* track the sun and focus sunlight on a central heat collection tower (Figure 16-21a).

- A *solar thermal plant* or *distributed receiver system,* in which sunlight is collected and focused on oil-filled pipes running through the middle of curved solar collectors (Figure 16-21b). This concentrated sunlight can generate temperatures high enough for industrial processes or for producing steam to run turbines and generate electricity. At night or on cloudy days, high-efficiency combined-cycle natural gas turbines can supply backup electricity as needed.

- A distributed receiver system which uses *parabolic dish collectors* (which look somewhat like TV satellite

**(a)** Solar Power Tower

**(b)** Solar Thermal Plant

**(c)** Nonimaging Optical Solar Concentrator

**(d)** Solar Cooker

**Figure 16-21** Several ways to collect and concentrate solar energy to produce high-temperature heat and electricity. Because of their high costs (except for solar ovens), such systems are not expected to provide much of the world's energy.

dishes) instead of parabolic troughs. These collectors can track the sun along two axes and generally are more efficient than troughs. A pilot plant is being built in northern Australia. The DOE projects that within 10–20 years, parabolic dishes with a natural gas turbine backup should be able to produce electrical power costing about the same as that from coal-burning plants.

■ A *nonimaging optical solar concentrator* which intensifies incoming solar energy about 80,000 times (Figure 16-21c).

■ Inexpensive *solar cookers*, which can focus and concentrate sunlight and cook food, especially in rural villages in sunny developing countries. They can be made by fitting an insulated box big enough to hold three

or four pots with a transparent, removable top (Figure 16-21d). Solar cookers reduce **(1)** deforestation for fuelwood, **(2)** the time and labor needed to collect firewood, and **(3)** indoor air pollution from smoky fires.

Figure 16-22 (p. 398) lists the advantages and disadvantages of concentrating solar energy to produce high-temperature heat or electricity. Most analysts do not expect widespread use of such technologies over the next few decades because of **(1)** their high costs, **(2)** lack of sufficient tax breaks and government research and development funding, and **(3)** the availability of much cheaper ways to produce electricity such as combined-cycle natural gas turbines and wind turbines.

| Advantages | | Disadvantages |
|---|---|---|
| Moderate net energy | | Low efficiency |
| Moderate environmental impact | | High costs |
| No $CO_2$ emissions | | Needs backup or storage system |
| Fast construction (1–2 years) | | Need access to sun most of the time |
| Costs reduced with natural gas turbine backup | | High land use |
| | | May disturb desert areas |

**Figure 16-22** Advantages and disadvantages of using solar energy to generate high-temperature heat and electricity.

**How Can We Produce Electricity with Solar Cells?** Solar energy can be converted directly into electrical energy by **photovoltaic (PV) cells,** commonly called **solar cells** (Figure 16-23). A solar cell is a transparent wafer containing a *semiconductor* material with a thickness ranging from less than that of a human hair to that of a sheet of paper. Sunlight energizes and causes electrons in the semiconductor to flow, creating an electrical current.

Because a single solar cell produces only a tiny amount of electricity, many cells are wired together in modular panels to produce the amount of electricity needed. The resulting direct current (DC) electricity can be **(1)** stored in batteries and used directly or

**(2)** converted to conventional alternating-current (AC) electricity by a separate inverter or an inverter built into the cells (Guest Essay, p. 390).

Traditional-looking solar-cell roof shingles and roofing material (developed in Japan) reduce the cost of solar-cell installations by saving on roof costs (Figure 16-23). Glass walls and windows of buildings can also have built-in solar cells. With this technology, the roof and glass walls and windows become a building's power plant.

Easily expandable banks of solar cells can be used to **(1)** provide electricity for 1.7 billion people in rural villages of developing countries who have no electricity, **(2)** produce electricity at a small power plant, using combined-cycle natural gas turbines to provide backup power when the sun is not shining, and **(3)** convert water to hydrogen gas that can be distributed to energy users by pipeline, as natural gas is. With financing from the World Bank, India (the world's number-one market for solar cells) is installing solar-cell systems in 38,000 villages, and Zimbabwe is bringing solar electricity to 2,500 villages.

Oberlin College in Ohio recently built a new environmental studies center incorporating major elements of *green design,* including use of passive solar energy and solar cells (Figure 16-24). David Orr (head of Oberlin's environmental studies program) designed the building with the help of more than 250 students, faculty, and townspeople.

Figure 16-25 (p. 400) lists the advantages and disadvantages of solar cells. By 2001, about 1 million homes in the world (200,000 in the United States) were getting some or all of their electricity from solar cells. About 700,000 of these homes were located in villages in developing countries.

**Figure 16-23** Photovoltaic (PV) (solar) cells can provide electricity for a house or building using new solar-cell roof shingles or PV panel roof systems that look like metal roofs. Small and easily expandable arrays of such cells can provide electricity for urban villages throughout the world without large power plants or power lines. Large banks of such cells can also produce electricity at a small power plant for direct use or for converting water to hydrogen fuel. As the price of such electricity drops, usage is expected to increase dramatically.

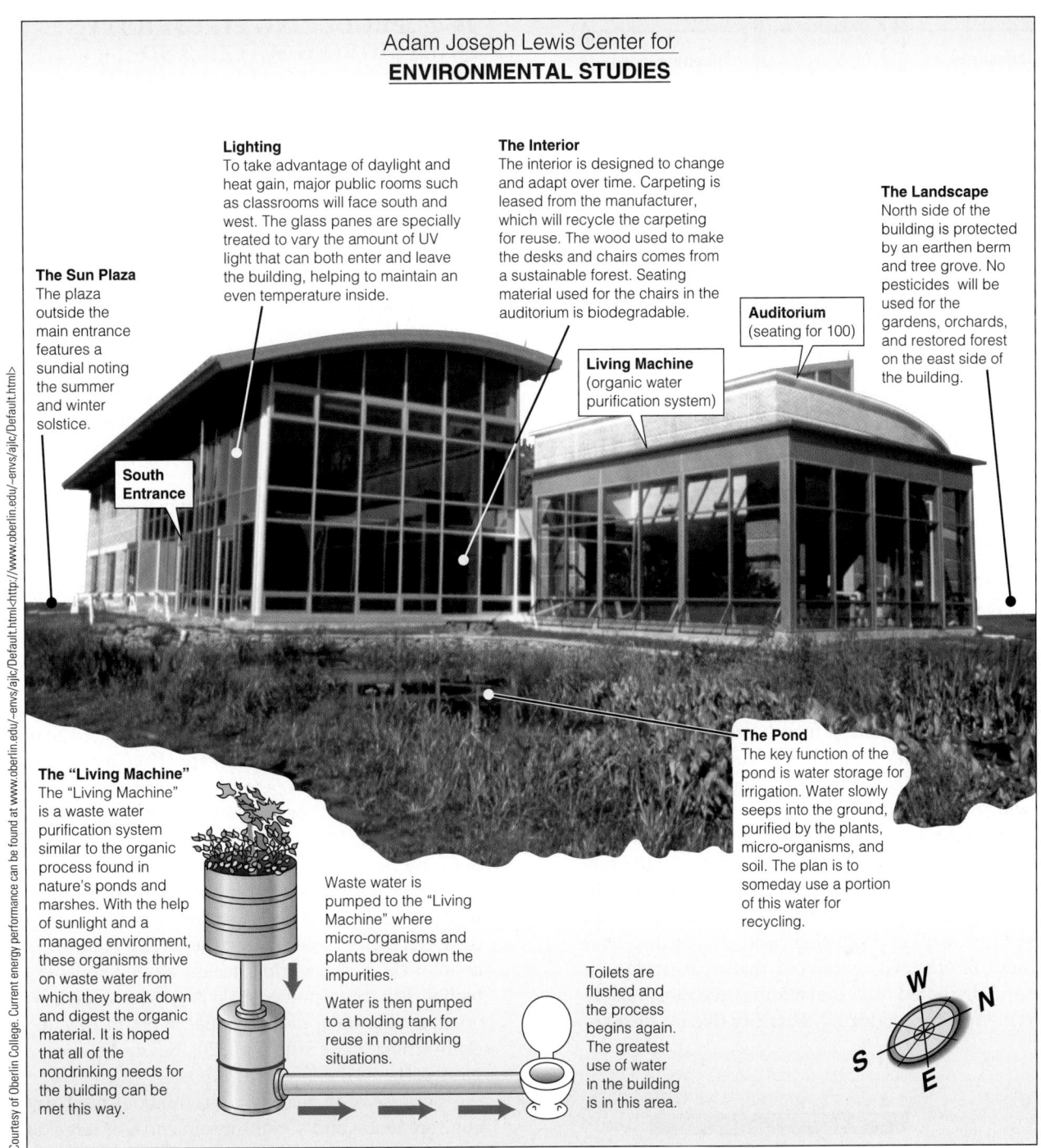

**Figure 16-24** Major elements of green design in the Adam Joseph Lewis Center for Environmental Studies at Oberlin College in Ohio. There were no waste products as a result of the construction and no use of toxic materials. The building is the brainchild of David Orr (head of Oberlin's Environmental Studies program) and a number of students, faculty, and townspeople. In North Carolina, Catawba College's Center for the Environment is also a model of green design.

Current costs of producing electricity from solar cells are high, but costs are expected to drop because of **(1)** greatly increased research by major corporations and many governments in solar-cell design (based on use of very thin films of cheap amorphous silicon and possibly carbon-based polymers) and manufacturing technology and **(2)** savings from mass production of solar cells. Researchers are developing ways to make solar cells out of thin and flexible plastic materials that can be stuck on windows and and can be mixed and painted onto houses, cars, and other surfaces.

Currently solar cells supply less than 1% of the world's electricity. With a strong push from governments and private investors, by 2050 they could

| Advantages | | Disadvantages |
|---|---|---|
| Fairly high net energy | | Need access to sun |
| Work on cloudy days | | Low efficiency |
| Quick installation | | Need electricity storage system or backup |
| Easily expanded or moved | | |
| No $CO_2$ emissions | | High land use (solar cell power plants) could disrupt desert areas |
| Low environmental impact | | |
| Last 20–40 years | | High costs (but should be competitive in 5–15 years) |
| Low land use (if on roof or built into walls or windows) | | |
| Reduces dependence on fossil fuels | | DC current must be converted to AC |

**Figure 16-25** Advantages and disadvantages of using solar cells to produce electricity.

provide up to 25% of the world's electricity (at least 35% in the United States). If such projections are correct, the production, sale, and installation of solar cells could become one of the world's largest and fastest growing businesses.

Critics of solar energy contend that producing electricity using large banks of solar cells, solar thermal plants (Figure 16-21b), and wind farms (see photo in table of contents, p. xx) uses too much land. However, these three ways of producing electricity use less land per unit of electricity produced than coal (including the land disrupted from coal mining), the most widely used method for producing electricity (Figure 16-26).

Coal (including mining)  3,640
Solar thermal  3,560
Solar cells  3,240
Wind  1,340
Geothermal  404

**Figure 16-26** Approximate land use of various systems for producing electricity in the United States. Numbers give the land occupied in square meters per gigawatt-hour of electricity produced for 30 years. (Data from Worldwatch Institute).

## 16-4 PRODUCING ELECTRICITY FROM MOVING WATER AND FROM HEAT STORED IN WATER

**How Can We Produce Electricity Using Hydropower Plants?** Electricity can be produced from flowing water by

- *Large-scale hydropower,* in which a high dam is built across a large river to create a reservoir (Figure 14-9, p. 319). Some of the water stored in the reservoir is allowed to flow through huge pipes at controlled rates, spinning turbines and producing electricity.

- *Small-scale hydropower,* in which a low dam with no reservoir (or only a small one) is built across a small stream, and the stream's flow of water is used to spin turbines and produce electricity.

- *Pumped-storage hydropower,* in which pumps using surplus electricity from a conventional power plant pump water from a lake or a reservoir to another reservoir at a higher elevation. When more electricity is needed, water in the upper reservoir is released, flows through turbines, and generates electricity on its return to the lower reservoir.

Hydropower supplies about **(1)** 6% of the world's total commercial energy (3–4% in the United States), **(2)** 20% of the world's electricity (10% in the United States but about 63% of the power used along the West Coast), and **(3)** 99% of the electricity in Norway, 75% in New Zealand, 50% in developing countries, and 25% in China.

Figure 16-27 lists the advantages and disadvantages of using large-scale hydropower plants to produce electricity. According to the United Nations, only about 13% of the world's technically exploitable potential for hydropower has been developed, with much of this untapped potential in South Asia (especially China, Case study, p. 320), South America, and parts of the former Soviet Union.

Because of increasing concern about the harmful environmental and social consequences of large dams (Figure 14-9, p. 319), there has been growing pressure on the World Bank and other development agencies to stop funding new large-scale hydropower projects. In 2000, the World Commission on Dams published a study indicating that hydropower is a major emitter of greenhouse gases. This occurs because reservoirs that power the dams can trap rotting vegetation, which can emit greenhouse gases such as $CO_2$ and $CH_4$.

Small-scale hydropower projects eliminate most of the harmful environmental effects of large-scale projects, but they can **(1)** threaten recreational activities and aquatic life, **(2)** disrupt the flow of wild and

| Advantages | Disadvantages |
|---|---|
| Moderate to high net energy | High construction costs |
| High efficiency (80%) | High environmental impact |
| Low-cost electricity | High $CO_2$ emissions from biomass decay in shallow tropical reservoirs |
| Long life span | |
| No $CO_2$ emissions during operation | Floods natural areas |
| May provide flood control below dam | Converts land habitat to lake habitat |
| Provides water for year-round irrigation of crop land | Danger of collapse |
| | Uproots people |
| Reservoir is useful for fishing and recreation | Decreases fish harvest below dam |
| | Decreases flow of natural fertilizer (silt) to land below dam |

**Figure 16-27** Advantages and disadvantages of using large dams and reservoirs to produce electricity.

scenic rivers, and **(3)** destroy wetlands. In addition, their electrical output can vary with seasonal changes in stream flow.

**Is Producing Electricity from Tides and Waves a Useful Option?** Twice a day in high and low tides, water that flows into and out of coastal bays and estuaries can spin turbines to produce electricity. Two large tidal energy facilities are currently operating, one at La Rance in France and the other in Canada's Bay of Fundy. However, most analysts expect tidal power to make only a tiny contribution to world electricity supplies because of a lack of suitable sites and high construction costs.

The kinetic energy in ocean waves, created primarily by wind, is another potential source of electricity. Most analysts expect wave power to make little contribution to world electricity production, except in a few coastal areas with the right conditions (such as western England).

**How Can We Produce Electricity from Heat Stored in Water?** Japan and the United States have been evaluating the use of the large temperature differences (between the cold deep waters and the sun-warmed surface waters) of tropical oceans for pro-

ducing electricity. If economically feasible, this would be done in *ocean thermal energy conversion* (*OTEC*) plants anchored to the bottom of tropical oceans in suitable sites. However, most energy analysts believe the large-scale extraction of energy from ocean thermal gradients may never compete economically with other energy alternatives.

*Saline solar ponds,* usually located near inland saline seas or lakes in areas with ample sunlight, can be used to produce electricity. Heat accumulated during the day in the denser bottom layer can be used to produce steam that spins turbines, generating electricity. A small experimental saline solar pond power plant on the shore of the Israeli side of the Dead Sea operated for several years but was closed in 1989 because of high operating costs.

*Freshwater solar ponds* can be used to heat water and space. A shallow hole is dug and lined with concrete. A number of large black plastic bags, each filled with several centimeters of water, are placed in the hole and then covered with fiberglass insulation panels. The panels let sunlight in but keep most of the heat stored in the water during the daytime from being lost to the atmosphere. When the water in the bags has reached its peak temperature in the afternoon, a computer turns on pumps to transfer hot water from the bags to large insulated tanks for distribution.

Saline and freshwater solar ponds **(1)** use no energy storage and backup systems, **(2)** emit no air pollution, and **(3)** have a moderate net energy yield. Freshwater solar ponds can be built in almost any sunny area and have moderate construction and operating costs. However, saline and freshwater solar ponds are expected to make little contribution to global energy supplies in the foreseeable future.

## 16-5 PRODUCING ELECTRICITY FROM WIND

**What Is the Status of Wind Power?** In 2001, wind turbines (Figure 16-28, p. 402) worldwide produced almost 25,000 megawatts of electricity, enough to meet the needs of about 7 million homes. About 70% of the world's wind power is produced in Europe, especially in Germany, Spain, and Denmark.

In 2001, the price of electricity produced by wind at prime sites in the United States was about 4¢ per kilowatt-hour (down from 38¢ per kilowatt-hour in the early 1980s). This is **(1)** almost equal to the cost of electricity produced by new coal-fired power plants and half the cost if coal's health and environmental costs are included and **(2)** about half the cost of nuclear power if all nuclear fuel cycle costs (Figure 15-36, p. 367) are taken into account.

Wind Turbine

Wind Farm

**Figure 16-28** Wind turbines can be used to produce electricity individually or in clusters called wind farms. Since 1990, wind power has been the world's fastest growing source of energy.

The global wind power industry was a $7 billion business in 2001. Increased investments in wind power by governments and large corporation should reduce its costs further from technological innovations and savings from mass production of wind turbines.

**What Areas Have the Greatest Potential for Wind Power?** In 2001, Western European countries produced 2% of their electricity from wind (18% in Denmark). These countries expect to get at least 10% of their electricity from onshore and offshore wind turbines within 10 years. The German government plans to get 25% of its electricity from wind power by 2025, much of it from building offshore wind farms in the Baltic and the North Sea.

Wind power also is being developed rapidly in India (the world's number-two market for wind energy), and China could easily double its wind-generating capacity.

Figure 16-29 shows the potential areas for use of wind power in the United States. The DOE calls the midwestern United States the "Saudi Arabia of wind." The Dakotas and Texas alone have enough wind resources to meet all the nation's electricity needs.

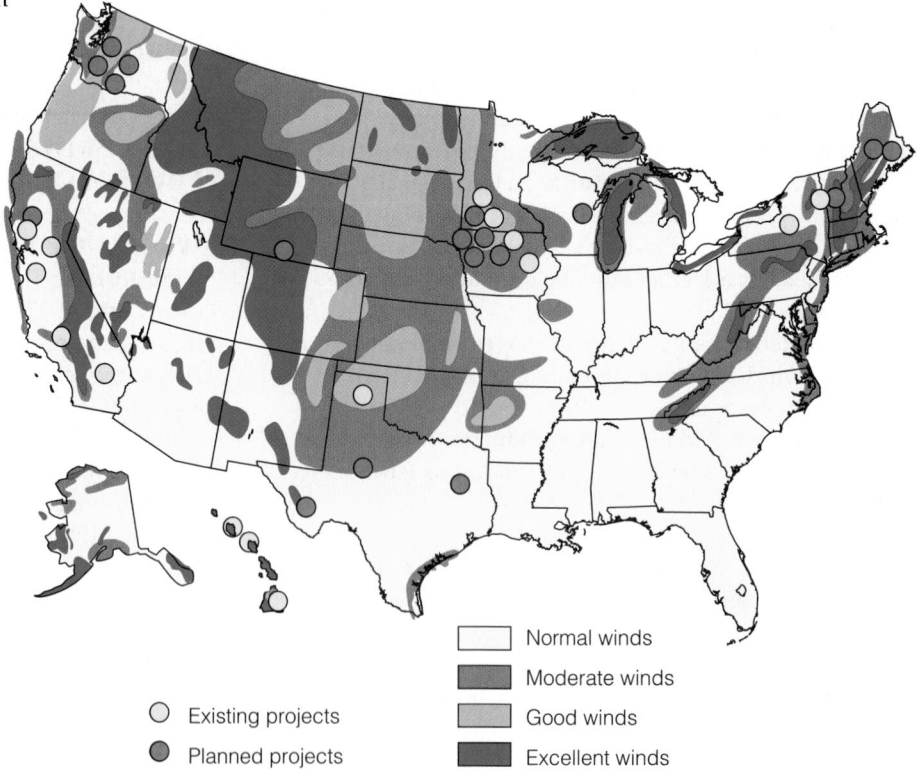

**Figure 16-29** Potential for use of wind power in the United States. In principle, exploiting the wind potential of just three states—North Dakota, South Dakota, and Texas—could provide all the power needs of the United States. (Data from U.S. Department of Energy)

○ Existing projects
● Planned projects

☐ Normal winds
☐ Moderate winds
☐ Good winds
☐ Excellent winds

A growing number of U.S. farmers and ranchers are boosting their income by leasing some of their cropland or ranchland for wind turbines while still growing crops or grazing cattle around the turbines. Currently, a U.S. farmer or rancher who leases 0.10 hectare (0.25 acre) of cropland or rangeland to the local utility as a site for a wind turbine can easily get $2,000 a year in royalties from providing the local community with electricity worth $100,000. Some are making more money by leasing their land for wind power production than from growing crops or raising cattle. This explains why many U.S. farmers and ranchers are joining environmentalists and wind industry executives in urging political leaders to increase government research and development and tax breaks for wind power. Because most money from wind power stays in local communities, using this resource can boost the economies of rural areas in the United States and elsewhere.

In the 1980s, the United States led the world in the development of wind power. But the country frittered away its lead by meager government research and development funds and tax credits compared to most Western European countries and to those available for fossil fuels and nuclear power. In 2001, wind produced only 0.3% of U.S. electricity. A modest wind power tax credit enacted by the U.S. Congress expired at the end of 2001 and has not been renewed. In addition, the Bush administration proposed cutting already modest federal research and development funds for wind power in 2002 and 2003 in half while greatly increasing research funds and tax breaks for coal and nuclear power.

**What Are the Major Advantages and Disadvantages of Wind Power?** Figure 16-30 lists the advantages and disadvantages of using wind to produce electricity. Some critics have alleged that wind turbines suck large numbers of birds into their wind stream. However, studies have shown that much larger numbers of birds die when they **(1)** are sucked into jet engines, **(2)** crash into skyscrapers, plate glass windows, communications towers, and car windows and **(3)** are killed by domesticated and feral cats. As long as wind farms are not located along bird migration routes most birds learn to fly around them.

In addition, much larger numbers of birds, fish, and other forms of wildlife are killed by oil spills, air pollution, water pollution, and release of toxic wastes from use of fossil fuels such as coal and oil. The key questions are **(1)** which types of energy resources lead to the lowest loss of wildlife and **(2)** how loss of wildlife from use of any energy resource can be minimized.

In the long run, electricity from large wind farms in remote areas might be used to make hydrogen gas from water during off-peak periods—thus storing electricity from excess wind capacity in a useful fuel. The hydrogen could then be fed into a pipeline and

Figure 16-30 Advantages and disadvantages of using wind to produce electricity. Wind power experts project that by 2020 wind power could supply more than 10% of the world's electricity and 10–25% of the electricity used in the United States.

storage system for fuel cells or gas turbines used to power cars, homes, and buildings.

Increasingly, many governments and corporations are recognizing that wind is a vast, climate-benign, renewable energy resource that can supply both electricity and hydrogen fuel at an affordable cost. If its current growth rate continues, wind power could produce 10% of the world's electricity by 2020.

## 16-6 PRODUCING ENERGY FROM BIOMASS

**How Useful Is Burning Solid Biomass?** Biomass is plant materials and animal wastes used as sources of energy. Biomass comes in many forms and can be burned directly as a solid fuel or converted into gaseous or liquid **biofuels** (Figure 16-31, p. 404).

Most biomass is burned **(1)** directly for heating, cooking, and industrial processes or **(2)** indirectly to drive turbines and produce electricity. Burning wood and manure for heating and cooking supplies about 11% of the world's energy and about 30% of the energy used in developing countries. Almost 70% of the people living in developing countries heat their homes and cook their food by burning wood or charcoal. However, about 2.7 billion people in these countries cannot find or are too poor to buy enough fuelwood to meet their needs.

In the United States, biomass is used to supply about 4% of the country's commercial energy and 2%

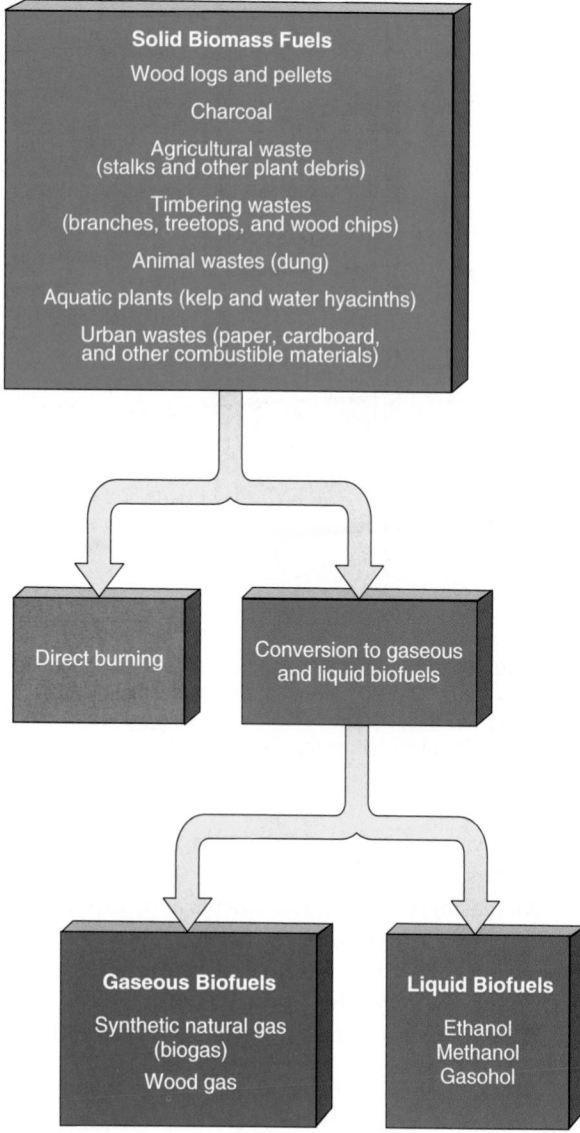

**Figure 16-31** Principal types of biomass fuel.

the United States, without irrigation and without competing with food crops for land. Some ecologists argue that it makes more sense to use animal manure as a fertilizer and crop residues to feed livestock, retard soil erosion, and fertilize the soil.

Figure 16-32 lists the general advantages and disadvantages of burning solid biomass as a fuel. One problem is that burning biomass produces $CO_2$. However, if the rate of use of biomass does not exceed the rate at which it is replenished by new plant growth (which takes up $CO_2$), there is no net increase in $CO_2$ emissions.

**Is Producing Gaseous and Liquid Fuels from Solid Biomass a Useful Option?** Bacteria and various chemical processes can convert some forms of biomass into gaseous and liquid biofuels (Figure 16-31). Examples include **(1)** *biogas,* a mixture of 60% methane and 40% $CO_2$, **(2)** *liquid ethanol* (ethyl, or grain, alcohol), and **(3)** *liquid methanol* (methyl, or wood alcohol).

In China, anaerobic bacteria in more than 6 million *biogas digesters* convert plant and animal wastes into methane fuel for heating and cooking. These simple devices can be built for about $50 including labor. After the biogas has been separated, the solid residue is used as fertilizer on food crops or, if contaminated, on trees. When they work, biogas digesters are very

of its electricity (produced by about 350 biomass power plants). The U.S. government has a goal of increasing the use of biomass energy to 9% of the country's total commercial energy by 2010.

One way to produce biomass fuel is to plant, harvest, and burn large numbers of **(1)** fast-growing trees (especially cottonwoods, poplars, sycamores, willows, and leucaenas), **(2)** shrubs, **(3)** perennial grasses (such as switchgrass), and **(4)** water hyacinths in *biomass plantations.*

In agricultural areas, *crop residues* (such as sugarcane residues, rice husks, cotton stalks, and coconut shells) and *animal manure* can be collected and burned or converted into biofuels. According to a 1999 study by the Union of Concerned Scientists, energy crops and crop wastes from the Midwest alone could theoretically provide about 16% of the electricity used in

**Figure 16-32** General advantages and disadvantages of burning solid biomass as a fuel.

efficient. However, they are also slow and unpredictable, a problem that could be corrected by developing more reliable models.

Some analysts believe liquid ethanol and methanol produced from biomass could replace gasoline and diesel fuel when oil becomes too scarce and expensive. *Ethanol* can be made from sugar and grain crops (sugarcane, sugar beets, sorghum, sunflowers, and corn) by fermentation and distillation. Gasoline mixed with 10–23% pure ethanol makes *gasohol*, which can be burned in conventional gasoline engines and is sold as super unleaded or ethanol-enriched gasoline.

Another alcohol, *methanol*, is made mostly from natural gas but also can be produced at a higher cost from wood, wood wastes, agricultural wastes (such as corncobs), sewage sludge, garbage, and coal. Some of the first generation of cars using hydrogen-powered fuel cells (Figure 16-10) will use reformers to convert carbon-containing natural gas, gasoline, or methanol to hydrogen. The advantages and disadvantages of using ethanol, methanol, and several other fuels as alternatives to gasoline are summarized in Table 16-1, p. 406. According to a 1997 analysis by David Pimentel and two other researchers, "Large-scale biofuel production is not an alternative to the current use of oil and is not even an advisable option to cover a significant fraction of it."

## 16-7 THE SOLAR–HYDROGEN REVOLUTION

**What Can We Use to Replace Oil? Goodbye Oil and Smog, Hello Hydrogen**   When oil is gone (or when what is left costs too much to use), how will we fuel vehicles, industry, and buildings? Many scientists and executives of major oil companies and automobile companies say the fuel of the future is hydrogen gas ($H_2$) (Table 16-1, p. 406)—envisioned in 1874 by science fiction writer Jules Verne in his book *The Mysterious Island.*

When hydrogen gas burns in air, it combines with oxygen gas in the air and produces nonpolluting water vapor ($2H_2 + O_2 \longrightarrow 2H_2O$).* Widespread use of this fuel would **(1)** eliminate most of the air pollution problems we face today and **(2)** greatly reduce the threats from global warming by emitting no $CO_2$ (as long as the hydrogen is not produced from fossil fuels or other carbon-containing compounds).

The *bad news* is that although hydrogen is all around us it is chemically locked up in water and organic compounds such as methane and gasoline. But

the *good news* is that we can produce it from something we have plenty of: *water.* Water can be split by electricity (electrolysis) or high temperatures (thermolysis) into gaseous hydrogen and oxygen (Figure 16-33, p. 407). Hydrogen can also be produced **(1)** by *reforming,* in which high temperatures and chemical processes are used to separate hydrogen from carbon atoms in organic chemicals (hydrocarbons) found in conventional carbon-containing fuels such as natural gas, gasoline, or methanol, **(2)** from gasification of coal (Figure 15-33, p. 365) or biomass, and **(3)** by some types of algae and bacteria (Spotlight, p. 408). These various sources of hydrogen could become, as some scientists put it, "tomorrow's oil" and be used to provide most of the energy need to run an economy (Figure 16-34, p. 407).

**What Is the Catch?**   If you think using $H_2$ as our major energy source sounds too good to be true, you are right. Several problems must be solved to make hydrogen one of our primary energy resources, but scientists are making rapid progress in finding solutions to these challenges.

One problem is that it takes energy (and thus money) to produce this fuel. We could burn coal to produce high-temperature heat or use electricity from coal-burning and nuclear power plants to split water and produce hydrogen. However, doing this **(1)** subjects us to the harmful environmental effects associated with using these fuels (Figure 15-31, p. 364; Figure 15-38, p. 369; and Figure 15-39, p. 369), and **(2)** costs more than the hydrogen fuel is worth. We can also produce hydrogen by coal gasification or from carbon-containing methane (natural gas), gasoline, or methanol, but this adds $CO_2$ to the atmosphere.

Most proponents of using hydrogen gas believe that if we are to get its very low pollution benefits, the energy needed to produce $H_2$ by decomposing water must come from renewable energy, probably in the form of electricity generated by solar cells, wind farms, hydropower, and geothermal energy (p. 409) or by bacteria and algae through *biolysis* (Spotlight, p. 408). The type of renewable energy used would vary in different parts of the world depending on its local and regional availability.

If scientists and engineers can learn how to use various forms of direct and indirect solar energy to decompose water cheaply enough, they will set in motion a *solar–hydrogen revolution* over the next 50 years and change the world as much as the agricultural and industrial revolutions did. In effect, the world would shift from carbon-based *fossil fuel economies* (Figure 15-12, p. 351) to decarbonized *hydrogen economies* powered increasingly by using solar energy to produce hydrogen gas from water (Figure 15-16, p. 353). By using renewable solar energy, such an economy would

---

*Water vapor is a potent greenhouse gas. However, because there is already so much of it in the atmosphere, human additions of this gas are insignificant.

## Table 16-1  Evaluation of Alternatives to Gasoline

| Advantages | Disadvantages |
|---|---|
| **Compressed Natural Gas** | |
| Fairly abundant, inexpensive domestic and global supplies | Large fuel tank needed; one-fourth the range |
| Low hydrocarbon, CO, and $CO_2$ emissions | Expensive engine modification needed ($2,000) |
| Vehicle development advanced; well suited for fleet vehicles | New filling stations needed |
| Reduced engine maintenance | Nonrenewable resource |
| **Electricity** | |
| Renewable if not generated from fossil fuels or nuclear power | Limited range and power |
| Zero vehicle emissions | Batteries expensive |
| Electric grid in place | Slow refueling (6–8 hours) |
| Efficient and quiet | Power plant emissions if generated from coal or oil |
| **Reformulated Gasoline (Oxygenated Fuel)** | |
| No new filling stations needed | Nonrenewable resource |
| Low to moderate CO emissions reduction | Dependence on imported oil perpetuated |
| No engine modification needed | No $CO_2$ emission reduction |
| | Higher cost |
| | Groundwater contaminated by leakage and spills (especially by MTBE, a possible human carcinogen) |
| | No longer needed because of improved emission control system |
| **A-55 (55% water, 45% naphtha)** | |
| Can be sold in conventional filling station | Not yet widely available |
| Much lower emissions of nitrogen oxide and particulates than diesel fuel | Independent tests needed to verify pollution reduction claims |
| Cannot explode or catch fire | Refineries may limit supply or drive up price of less-profitable naphtha (Figure 15-18, p. 355) |
| Lower cost (25–50%) | Large amounts of water needed to produce |
| Naphtha produces 90% less pollution at refineries than gasoline or diesel fuel | |
| Low-cost engine modification ($300 for cars, $1,000 for trucks and buses | |
| Modified engine can run A-55, gasoline, or diesel | |
| **Methanol** | |
| High octane | Large fuel tank needed; one-half the range |
| Reduction of $CO_2$ emissions (total amount depends on method of production) | Corrosive to metal, rubber, plastic |
| Reduced total air pollution (30–40%) | Increased emissions of potentially carcinogenic formaldehyde |
| Can be made from natural gas | High $CO_2$ emissions if generated by coal |
| | High capital cost to produce |
| | Hard to start in cold weather |
| **Ethanol** | |
| High octane | Large fuel tank needed; lower range |
| Reduction of $CO_2$ emissions (total amount depends on distillation process and efficiency of crop growing) | Cannot be shipped in multifuel pipelines |
| Reduction of CO emissions | Much higher cost |
| Potentially renewable | Corn supply limited |
| | Competition with food growing for cropland |
| | Higher emissions of smog-forming compounds |
| | Higher emissions of NO |
| | Corrosive |
| | Hard to start in cold weather |
| **Solar–Hydrogen** | |
| Renewable if produced using solar energy | Nonrenewable if generated by fossil fuels or nuclear power |
| High-energy fuel | Large fuel tank needed |
| Lower flammability than gasoline | No distribution system in place |
| Potentially unlimited supply if produced from water | Engine redesign needed |
| Virtually emission-free | Currently expensive |
| No emissions of $CO_2$ | |
| Nontoxic | |

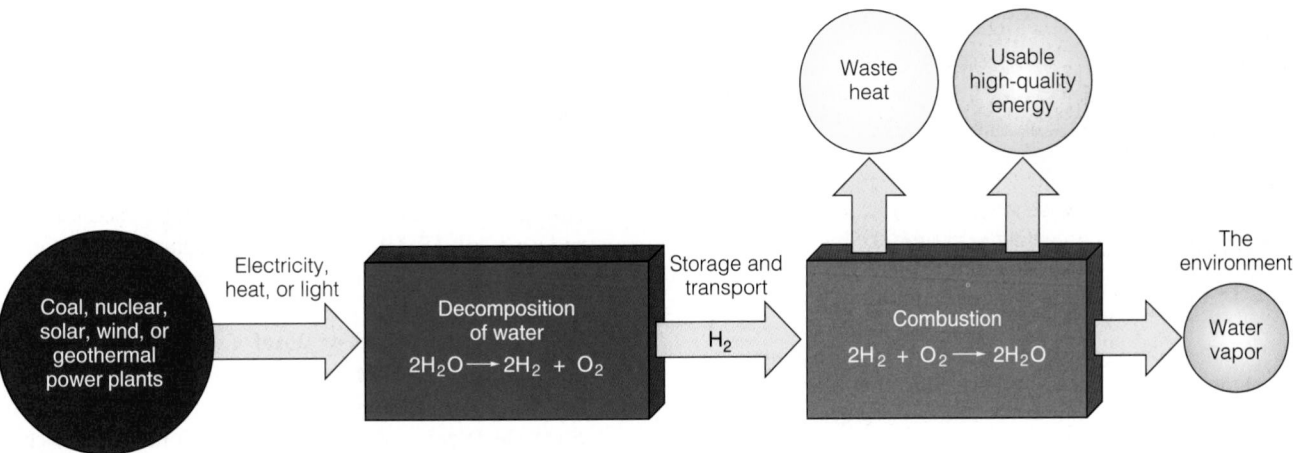

**Figure 16-33** Hydrogen gas as an energy source. Producing hydrogen gas takes electricity, heat, or solar energy to decompose water, thus leading to a negative net energy yield. However, hydrogen is a clean-burning fuel that can replace oil, other fossil fuels, and nuclear energy. Using solar energy (probably solar cells and wind turbines) to produce hydrogen from water could eliminate most air pollution and greatly reduce the threat of global warming.

follow the first of the four principles of sustainability based on observing how the earth sustains itself (Solutions, p. 201).

Methane from natural gas may be used to produce hydrogen in the transition to a true renewable hydrogen system because of its **(1)** large supply (p. 362) and **(2)** lower production of air pollutants and $CO_2$ (Figure 15-25, p. 358) compared to other fossil fuels.

**How Can We Store Hydrogen?** Once produced, $H_2$ can be stored (Figure 16-34)

- In *compressed gas storage tanks,* either above or below ground or aboard motor vehicles. The technology is

available, but the costs of tanks and compression are high. Storage tanks are too heavy and large for use in cars but can be used in buses and large trucks.

- As *liquid hydrogen.* Condensing hydrogen gas into more dense liquid form allows a larger quantity of hydrogen to be stored in stationary containers or aboard motor vehicles. However, the liquid hydrogen must be stored at very low temperatures below −250°C (−420°F), which is costly, takes a large input of energy (as much as 30% of the hydrogen's original fuel energy), and requires a large amount of insulation. Liquid hydrogen could be transported in refrigerated tankers from one country to another, just as liquefied propane gas (LPG) is today.

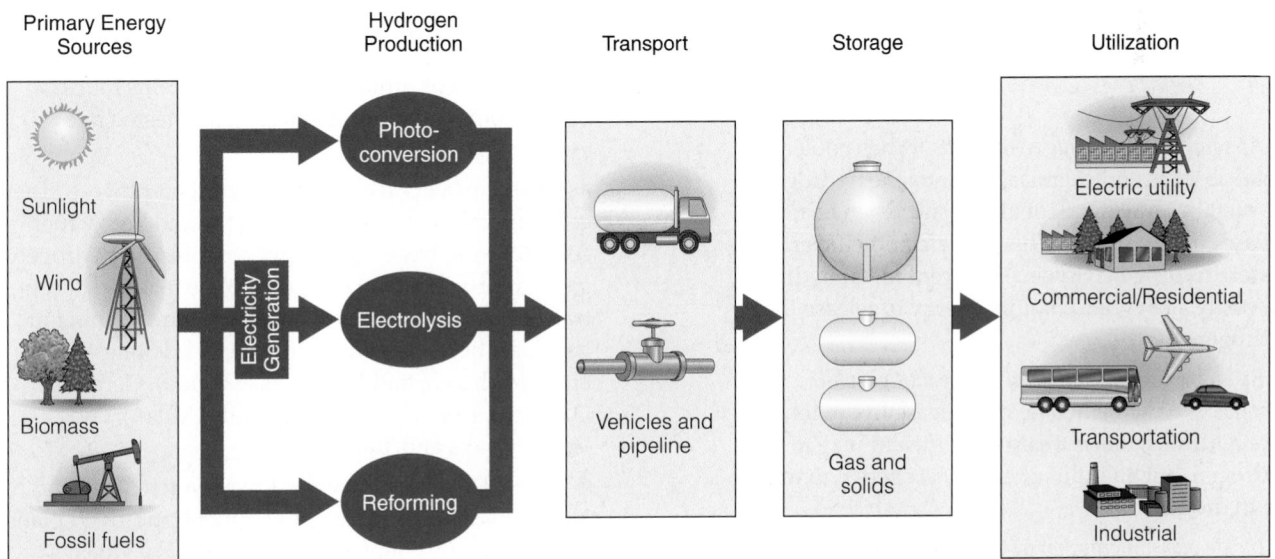

**Figure 16-34** A hydrogen energy system. (Data from U.S. Department of Energy and the Worldwatch Institute)

## Producing Hydrogen from Green Algae Found in Pond Scum

In a few decades we may be able to use large-scale cultures of green algae to produce hydrogen gas. This simple plant grows all over the world and is commonly found in pond scum.

When living in ordinary air and sunlight, green algae carry out photosynthesis like other plants and produce carbohydrates and oxygen gas. However, in 2000, Tasios Melis, a researcher at the University of California at Berkeley, found a way to make these algae produce bubbles of hydrogen rather than oxygen.

First, he grew cultures of hundreds of billions of the algae in the normal way with plenty of sunlight, nutrients, and water. Then he cut off their supply of two key nutrients: sulfur and oxygen. Within 20 hours, the plant cells underwent a metabolic change and switched from an oxygen-producing to a hydrogen-producing metabolism, allowing the researcher to collect hydrogen gas bubbling from the culture.

Melis believes he can increase the efficiency of this hydrogen-producing process tenfold. If so, sometime in the future a biological hydrogen plant might cycle a mixture of algae and water through a system of clear tubes exposed to sunlight to produce hydrogen. The gene responsible for producing the hydrogen might even be transferred to other plants to produce hydrogen.

### Critical Thinking

What might be some ecological problems related to the widespread use of this method for producing hydrogen?

---

- *As solid metal hydride compounds.* When cooled, the metal absorbs and chemically bonds the hydrogen in the metal's latticework of atoms and when heated releases the hydrogen. This is a safe and efficient way to store hydrogen. However, current metal hydrides are costly, heavy, and require energy to release the hydrogen.

- *By absorption on activated charcoal or graphite nanofibers,* which when heated release hydrogen gas. Like hydrides, this is a safe and efficient way to store hydrogen, but an input of energy is needed to release the hydrogen.

- *Inside glass microspheres.* Currently, tiny glass spheres are being developed for this purpose.

Some *good news* is that metal hydrides (including sodium borohydride), charcoal powders, graphite nanofibers, and glass microspheres containing hydrogen will not explode or burn if a vehicle's tank is ruptured in an accident.

The *bad news* is that so far it is difficult to store enough hydrogen gas in a car as a compressed gas, liquid, or a solid for it to run very far. Scientists and engineers are seeking solutions to this problem.

**What Is the Role of Fuel Cells in the Solar–Hydrogen Revolution?** In a *fuel cell* (Figures 16-4 and 16-10), hydrogen and oxygen gas combine to produce electrical current. Various versions of such cells can be used to power a car or bus and meet the heating, cooling, and electrical needs of buildings.

Fuel cells **(1)** have energy efficiencies of 65–95% (several times the efficiency of conventional gasoline-powered engines and electric cars and at least twice the efficiency of coal-burning and nuclear power plants), **(2)** have no moving parts, **(3)** are quiet, **(4)** emit only water and heat but some $CO_2$ if the hydrogen is produced from carbon-containing substances such as gasoline, natural gas, propane, or methanol, and **(5)** are more reliable than the traditional electricity grid because they are not as susceptible to lightning strikes, fallen trees, and terrorist or military attacks.

Some fuel cells are tiny enough to fit into a cellular phone. Others are big enough to power a large building or factory and are currently used to provide electricity for buildings such as a police station in New York City's Central Park and a postal facility in Alaska. Smaller fuel cells can power bicycles, vacuum cleaners, laptop computers, lawn mowers, leaf blowers, and other devices.

With hydrogen-powered fuel cells, people would have their own personal power plant to run their lights, appliances, and car and to heat and cool their house. Progress toward this goal is being made:

- A number of prototype fuel-cell systems for cars, buses, homes, and buildings are being tested and evaluated.

- Buses are a good choice for hydrogen-powered fuel cells because they can **(1)** carry large and heavy fuel cells, **(2)** store large amounts of compressed hydrogen gas in roof-mounted tanks, and **(3)** be refueled at centralized facilities. Fleets of such buses are running in various cities of the world in the United States (Dearborn, Michigan, and Las Vegas, Nevada), Germany (Munich), Iceland (Reykjavik), Italy (Milan), and Japan (Osaka and Takamatsu).

- In 1999, DaimlerChrysler, Royal Dutch Shell, and Norsk Hydro announced government-approved plans to turn the tiny country of Iceland into the world's first "hydrogen economy" by 2030–2040—the brainchild of chemist Bragi Árnason, known as "Professor Hydrogen." The country's abundant renewable geothermal energy, hydropower, and offshore winds will be used to produce hydrogen from seawater with the $H_2$ used to run its buses, passenger cars, fishing vessels, and factories. Royal Dutch Shell is already opening hydrogen filling stations in parts of Europe and plans to open a chain of such stations in Iceland.

The key problem with fuel cells so far is cost. For widespread use the price of fuel cells must be sharply reduced by improved technology and mass production. With greatly increased private and government-funded research and tax breaks, some analysts see this happening within 10 years. They envision fuel cells being used first by electric utilities, followed in order by midsize buildings, homes and small buildings, and motor vehicles.

**What Are the Pros and Cons of Hydrogen as an Energy Resource?** Figure 16-35 lists the pros and cons of using hydrogen as an energy resource. The U.S. Department of Energy has a goal of hydrogen energy providing 10% of all U.S. energy consumption by 2025.

Citizens and local and state officials can promote the transition to a hydrogen economy by creating *hydrogen cities* and regional *hydrogen utility districts*. Emphasis would be on **(1)** converting municipal buses and fleets of taxis, police vehicles, and other govern-

ment vehicles to run on hydrogen, **(2)** establishing hydrogen refueling facilities along heavily traveled routes, and **(3)** using stationary fuel cells to power local schools, airports, and police stations and other government buildings.

## 16-8 GEOTHERMAL ENERGY

**How Can We Tap the Earth's Internal Heat?** Heat contained in underground rocks and fluids is an important source of energy. Over millions of years, this **geothermal energy** from the earth's mantle (Figure 10-3, p. 205, and Figure 10-4, p. 206) has been transferred to underground reservoirs of **(1)** *dry steam* (steam with no water droplets), **(2)** *wet steam* (a mixture of steam and water droplets), and **(3)** *hot water* trapped in fractured or porous rock at various places in the earth's crust.

If such geothermal sites are close to the surface, wells can be drilled to extract the dry steam, wet steam

| Advantages | | Disadvantages |
|---|---|---|
| Can be produced from water | | Not found in nature |
| Low environmental impact | | Energy is needed to produce fuel |
| No $CO_2$ emissions | | Negative net energy |
| Good substitute for oil | | Nonrenewable if generated by fossil fuels or nuclear power |
| Competitive price if environmental and social costs are included in cost comparisons | | High costs (but expected to come down) |
| Easier to store than electricity | | Short driving range for current fuel cell cars |
| Safer than gasoline and natural gas | | No distribution system in place |
| High efficiency (65–95%) in fuel cells | | |

**Figure 16-35** Advantages and disadvantages of using hydrogen as a fuel for vehicles and for providing heat and electricity.

**Figure 16-36** Tapping the earth's internal heat or *geothermal energy* in the form of wet steam to produce electricity.

**Figure 16-37** Known global reservoirs of moderate- to high-temperature geothermal energy. (Data from Canadian Geothermal Resources Council)

(Figure 16-36), or hot water. This thermal energy can be used to heat homes and buildings and to produce electricity. For example, geothermal energy is used to heat about 85% of Iceland's buildings.

Figure 16-37 shows the locations of the world's known reservoirs of moderate- to high-temperature geothermal energy. Currently, about 22 countries (most of them in the developing world) are extracting energy from geothermal sites to produce about 1% of the world's electricity. Japan, with an abundance of geothermal energy, could get an estimated 30% of its electricity from this energy resource.

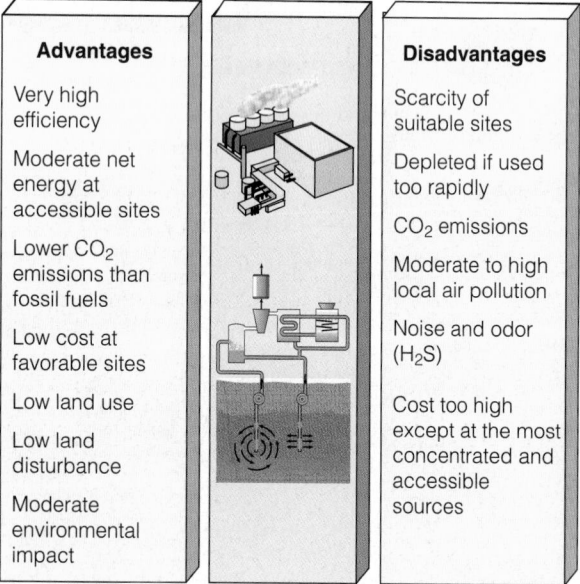

| Advantages | Disadvantages |
|---|---|
| Very high efficiency | Scarcity of suitable sites |
| Moderate net energy at accessible sites | Depleted if used too rapidly |
| Lower $CO_2$ emissions than fossil fuels | $CO_2$ emissions |
| Low cost at favorable sites | Moderate to high local air pollution |
| Low land use | Noise and odor ($H_2S$) |
| Low land disturbance | Cost too high except at the most concentrated and accessible sources |
| Moderate environmental impact | |

**Figure 16-38** Advantages and disadvantages of using geothermal energy for space heating and to produce electricity or high-temperature heat for industrial processes.

However, geothermal reservoirs can be depleted if heat is removed faster than natural processes renew it. Thus geothermal resources can be nonrenewable on a human time scale, but the potential supply is so vast that it is usually classified as a renewable energy resource.

Geothermal electricity meets the electricity needs of 6 million Americans and supplies 6% of California's electricity. The world's largest operating geothermal system, called *The Geysers*, extracts energy from a dry steam reservoir north of San Francisco, California. But heat is being withdrawn from this geothermal site about 80 times faster than it is being replenished, converting this potentially renewable resource to a nonrenewable source of energy. In 1999, Santa Monica, California, became the first city in the world to get all its electricity from geothermal energy.

Three other nearly nondepletable sources of geothermal energy are **(1)** *molten rock* (magma), **(2)** *hot dry-rock zones*, where molten rock that has penetrated the earth's crust heats subsurface rock to high temperatures, and **(3)** low- to moderate-temperature *warm-rock reservoir deposits*, which could be used to preheat water and run heat pumps for space heating and air conditioning. Research is being carried out in several countries to see whether hot dry-rock zones, which can be found almost anywhere about 8–10 kilometers (5–6 miles) below the earth's surface, can provide affordable geothermal energy.

Figure 16-38 lists the pros and cons of using geothermal energy. Currently, the cost of tapping geothermal energy is too high for all but the most concentrated and accessible sources. In 2000, the U.S. Department of Energy launched a program to have geothermal energy produce 10% of the electricity used in the western United States by 2020.

## 16-9 ENTERING THE AGE OF DECENTRALIZED MICROPOWER

**What Is Micropower?** According to the director of energy supply policy for the Edison Electric Institute, Chuck Linderman, the era of big central power plant systems (Figure 16-39) is over. Most energy analysts believe the chief feature of electricity production over the next few decades will be *decentralization* to dispersed, small-scale, **micropower systems** that generate 1–10,000 kilowatts of power (Figure 16-40). This shift

**Central power plants**

**Figure 16-39** *Centralized power system* in which electricity produced mainly by a fairly small number of **(1)** large coal-burning and nuclear power plants (producing 600,000–1 million kilowatts of power) and **(2)** natural gas turbines (producing about 200,000 kilowatts of power) is distributed by a system of high-voltage wires to users. Such centralized systems are easy targets and make a country more vulnerable to widespread power outages and releases of radioactivity from terrorist or military attacks.

**Transmission and distribution system**

**Residential**

**Commercial**

**Industrial**

**Wind farm**

**Small solar cell power plants**

**Bioenergy power plants**

**Fuel cells**

**Rooftop solar cell arrays**

**Solar cell rooftop systems**

**Fuel cells**

**Small wind turbine**

**Transmission and distribution system**

**Commercial**

**Residential**

**Industrial**

**Microturbines**

**Figure 16-40** *Decentralized power system* in which electricity is produced by a large number of dispersed, small-scale *micro-power systems* (producing 1–10,000 kilowatts of power). Some would produce power on site and others would feed the power they produce into a conventional electrical distribution system. Over the next few decades, many energy and financial analysts expect a shift to this type of power system.

from centralized *macropower* to dispersed *micropower* is analogous to the computer industry's shift from large centralized mainframes to increasingly smaller, widely dispersed PCs, laptops, and handheld computers.

Examples of micropower systems include energy-efficient **(1)** natural gas–burning *microturbines* for commercial buildings and residences (5–10,000 kilowatts), **(2)** *wind turbines* (1–3,000 kilowatts), **(3)** *Stirling engines* (0.1–100 kilowatts), **(4)** *fuel cells* (1–10,000 kilowatts), and **(5)** household *solar panels and solar roofs* (1–1,000 kilowatts; Figures 16-23 and 16-24). Figure 16-41 lists some of the advantages of decentralized micropower systems over traditional macropower systems.

The potential for financial gain by companies and investors in micropower systems is huge, with a $10- trillion market projected for the global energy supply between 2000 and 2020. Decentralized micropower systems could also allow 2 billion people in isolated villages in developing countries to leapfrog over more expensive centralized power systems.

## 16-10 SOLUTIONS: A SUSTAINABLE ENERGY STRATEGY

**What Are the Best Energy Alternatives?**    Many scientists and energy experts who have evaluated energy alternatives have come to the following general conclusions:

- *We are not running out of energy and we have a variety of available nonrenewable and renewable energy resources,* each with certain advantages and disadvantages.

- *There will be a gradual shift from centralized macropower systems (Figure 16-39) to smaller, decentralized micropower systems (Figures 16-40 and 16-41).*

- *The best alternatives are a combination of improved energy efficiency and using natural gas as a fuel to make the transition to increased use of a variety of small-scale, decentralized, locally available renewable energy resources.*

- *Because not enough money is available to develop all energy alternatives, governments and private companies must choose carefully which alternatives to support.*

- *Over the next 50 years, the choice is not between using nonrenewable fossil fuels and various types of renewable energy.* Because of their supplies and low prices, fossil fuels will continue to be used in large quantities (Figure 15-15, p. 352, and Figure 15-16, p. 353). The key questions are **(1)** how we can reduce the harmful environmental impacts of widespread fossil fuel use (especially to reduce air pollution and slow projected global warming) and **(2)** what roles improving energy efficiency and depending more on some forms of renewable energy can play in achieving these goals.

**What Role Does Economics Play in Energy Resource Use?**    To most analysts the key to making a shift to more sustainable energy resources and societies is not technology but economics and politics. Governments can use three basic economic and political strategies to help stimulate or dampen the short-term and long-term use of a particular energy resource:

- *Allowing all energy resources to compete in a free market without any government interference.* This is rarely politically feasible because of well-entrenched government intervention into the marketplace in the form of subsidies, taxes, and regulations. Furthermore, the free-market approach, with its emphasis on short-

Small modular units

Fast factory production

Fast installation
(hours to days)

Can add or remove
modules as needed

High energy efficiency
(60–80%)

Low or no $CO_2$
emissions

Low air pollution
emissions

Reliable

Easy to repair

Much less vulnerable
to power outages

Useful anywhere

Especially useful
in rural areas in
developing countries
with no power

Can use locally
available renewable
energy resources

Easily financed
(costs included in
mortgage and
commercial loan)

**Figure 16-41** Some advantages of micropower systems.

term profit, can inhibit development of new energy resources, which can rarely compete economically in their early stages without government support.

■ *Trying to keep energy prices artificially low to encourage use of selected energy resources.* This is done mostly by **(1)** providing research and development subsidies and tax breaks and **(2)** enacting regulations that help stimulate the development and use of energy resources receiving such support. For decades, this approach has been used to help stimulate the development and use of fossil fuels and nuclear power in the United States (Figure 16-42) and most other developed countries. This has created an uneven economic playing field that **(1)** encourages energy waste and rapid depletion of a nonrenewable energy resource and **(2)** discourages the development of energy alternatives such as energy efficiency and renewable energy (Figures 16-42 and 16-43) that are not getting at least the same level of subsidies and tax breaks.

■ *Keeping energy prices artificially high to discourage use of a resource.* Governments can raise the price of an energy resource by **(1)** withdrawing existing tax breaks and other subsidies, **(2)** enacting restrictive regulations, or **(3)** adding taxes on its use. This **(1)** increases government revenues, **(2)** encourages improvements in energy efficiency, **(3)** reduces dependence on imported energy, and **(4)** decreases use of an energy resource that has a limited future supply.

Many economists favor *increasing taxes on fossil fuels* as a way to reduce air and water pollution and slow global warming. The tax revenues would be used to **(1)** reduce income taxes on wages and profits, **(2)** improve energy efficiency, **(3)** encourage use of renewable energy resources, and **(4)** provide energy assistance to the poor and lower middle class. Some economists believe the public might accept these higher taxes if income and payroll taxes were lowered as gasoline or other fossil fuel taxes were raised.

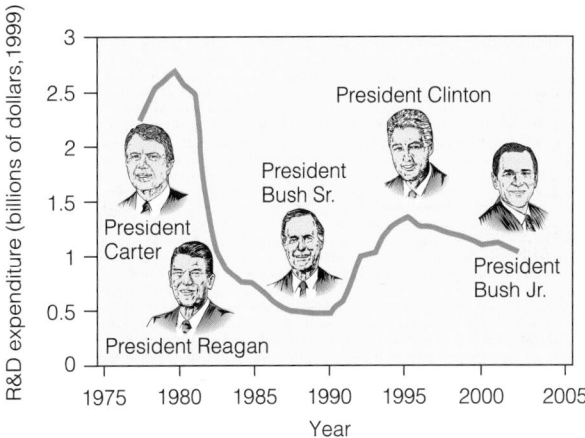

**Figure 16-43** U.S. government research and development (R & D) spending on renewable energy and energy efficiency, 1978–2002. (Data from U.S. Department of Energy and Worldwatch Institute)

**How Can We Develop a More Sustainable Energy Future?** Figure 16-44 (p. 414) lists strategies for making the transition to a more sustainable energy future over the next few decades.

Energy experts estimate that implementing policies such as those shown in Figure 16-44 over the next 20–30 years could **(1)** save money, **(2)** create a net gain in jobs, **(3)** reduce greenhouse gas emissions, **(4)** sharply reduce air and water pollution, and **(5)** increase national security by reducing dependence on imported oil and decreasing dependence on large nuclear power and coal plants that are vulnerable to terrorist attacks.

Some *great news* is that we have technology, creativity, and wealth to make the transition to a more sustainable energy future. The *challenging news* is that making this happen depends primarily on politics—which depends largely on pressure individuals put on elected officials. See this chapter's website for actions you can take to promote this transition.

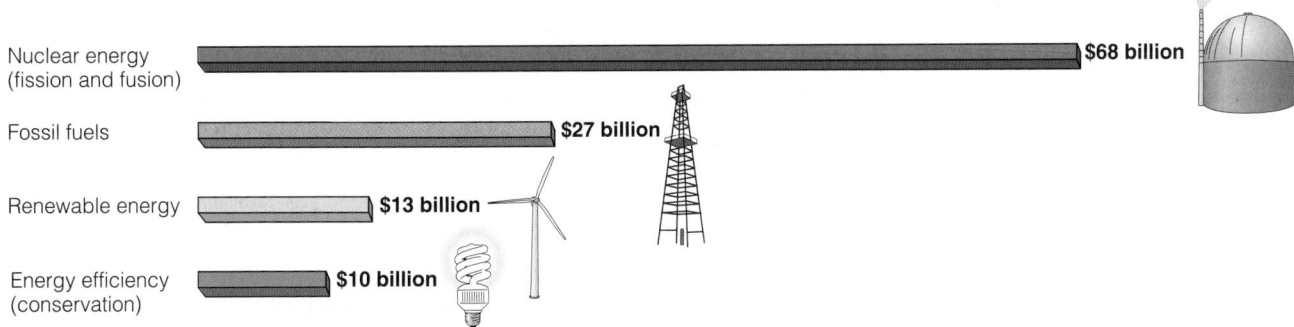

**Figure 16-42** U.S. Department of Energy research and development (R & D) funding for various sources of energy, 1948–1998. If other government subsidies and tax breaks were included, the figures for nuclear power and fossil fuels would be much higher. (Data from Congressional Research Office)

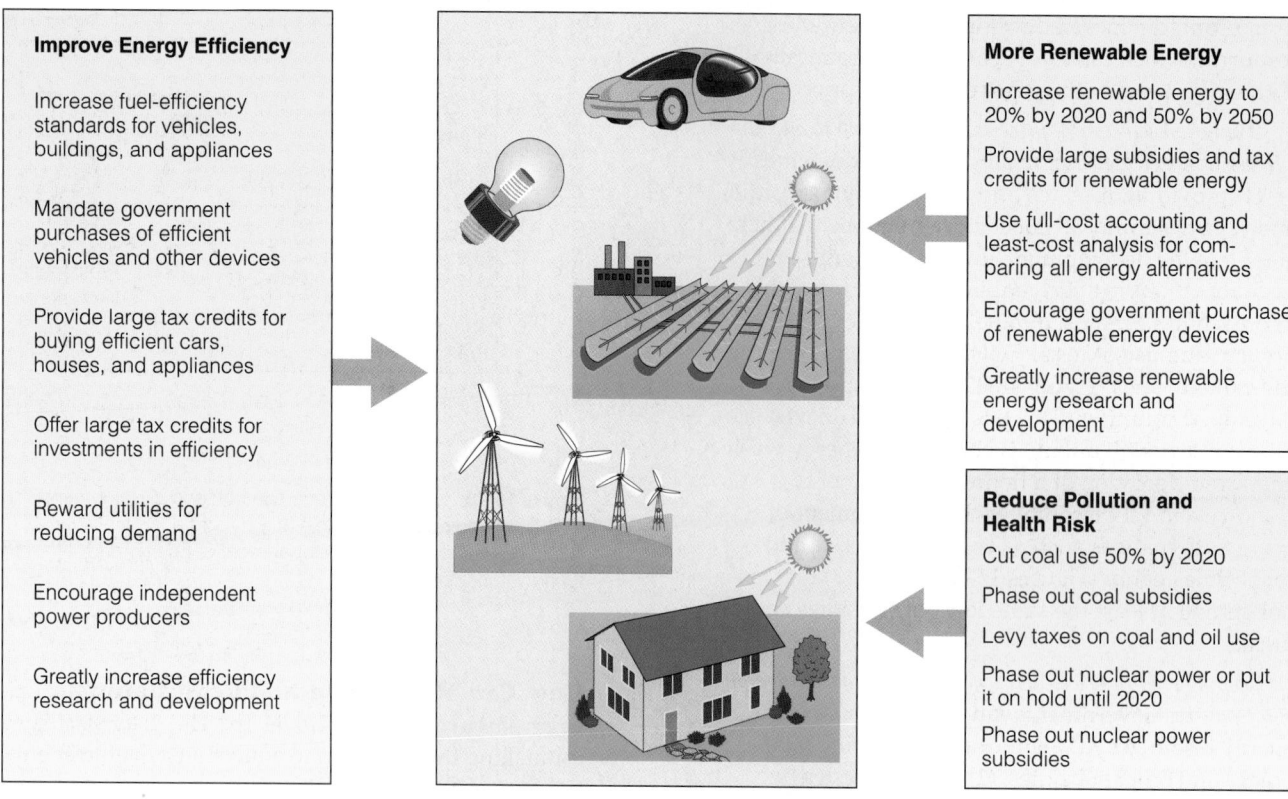

**Improve Energy Efficiency**

Increase fuel-efficiency standards for vehicles, buildings, and appliances

Mandate government purchases of efficient vehicles and other devices

Provide large tax credits for buying efficient cars, houses, and appliances

Offer large tax credits for investments in efficiency

Reward utilities for reducing demand

Encourage independent power producers

Greatly increase efficiency research and development

**More Renewable Energy**

Increase renewable energy to 20% by 2020 and 50% by 2050

Provide large subsidies and tax credits for renewable energy

Use full-cost accounting and least-cost analysis for comparing all energy alternatives

Encourage government purchase of renewable energy devices

Greatly increase renewable energy research and development

**Reduce Pollution and Health Risk**

Cut coal use 50% by 2020

Phase out coal subsidies

Levy taxes on coal and oil use

Phase out nuclear power or put it on hold until 2020

Phase out nuclear power subsidies

**Figure 16-44** *Solutions:* suggestions of various analysts to help make the transition to a more sustainable energy future.

*A transition to renewable energy is inevitable, not because fossil fuel supplies will run out—large reserves of oil, coal, and gas remain in the world—but because the costs and risks of using these supplies will continue to increase relative to renewable energy.*

MOHAMED EL-ASHRY

## REVIEW QUESTIONS

**1.** Define the boldfaced terms in this chapter.

**2.** What is *energy efficiency?* How much of the energy used in the United States is wasted? What percentage is wasted because of the second law of thermodynamics, and what percentage is wasted unnecessarily? What is *life cycle cost?* What are three of the least efficient energy-using devices?

**3.** Explain why we cannot recycle energy. List three ways to slow down the flow of heat from **(a)** a house and **(b)** an office building.

**4.** What are the advantages of saving energy?

**5.** What is *cogeneration,* and how efficient is it compared with producing electricity by a conventional coal-burning or nuclear power plant? List two other ways to save energy in industry.

**6.** What do most experts believe is the best way to save energy in transportation?

**7.** List the pros and cons of using **(a)** hybrid cars, **(b)** fuel-cell cars, and **(c)** electric bicycles.

**8.** Describe how we can save energy in homes by using **(a)** superinsulated houses and **(b)** strawbale houses. What are the four most efficient ways to heat a house? Describe ways to make an existing house more energy efficient. What are the most efficient and least efficient ways to heat water for washing and bathing? List the pros and cons of switching from inefficient incandescent and halogen lightbulbs to efficient compact fluorescent lightbulbs.

**9.** Describe how using the Internet can save energy and help reduce $CO_2$ emissions.

**10.** List three reasons why there is little emphasis on saving energy in the United States, despite its important benefits.

**11.** What are the major advantages and disadvantages of relying more on direct and indirect renewable energy from the sun?

**12.** Distinguish between a *passive solar heating system* and an *active solar heating system,* and list the pros and cons of each system.

**13.** Describe three ways to cool houses naturally.

**14.** Distinguish among the following solar systems used to generate high-temperature heat and electricity: **(a)** power tower, **(b)** solar thermal plant, **(c)** parabolic dish collection system, and **(d)** nonimaging optical solar concentrator. List the advantages and disadvantages of concentrating solar energy to produce high-temperature heat or electricity.

**15.** What is a *solar cell?* List the advantages and disadvantages of using solar cells to produce electricity.

**16.** Distinguish among *large-scale hydropower, small-scale-hydropower,* and *pumped-storage hydropower* systems. List the advantages and disadvantages of using hydropower to produce electricity.

**17.** List the advantages and disadvantages of using the following systems for storing heat in water to produce electricity: **(a)** ocean thermal energy conversion (OTEC), **(b)** saline solar ponds, and **(c)** freshwater solar ponds.

**18.** List the advantages and disadvantages of using wind to produce electricity.

**19.** List the advantages and disadvantages of **(a)** burning solid biomass as a source of energy and **(b)** producing gaseous and liquid fuels from solid biomass.

**20.** What is the *solar–hydrogen revolution?* What is a *fuel cell,* and what are the advantages and disadvantages of using this technology? List the advantages and disadvantages of using hydrogen as a source of energy.

**21.** What is *geothermal energy?* Describe three types of geothermal reservoirs. List the advantages and disadvantages of using geothermal energy to produce heat and electricity.

**22.** What is *micropower,* and what are its advantages over macropower electricity systems? Describe five types of micropower systems.

**23.** What five conclusions have energy experts reached about possible future energy alternatives?

**24.** Summarize the three different economic approaches that can be used to stimulate or dampen the use of a particular energy resource. List the pros and cons of each approach.

**25.** What major ways have various analysts suggested to help make the transition to a more sustainable energy future?

## CRITICAL THINKING

**1.** A home builder installs electric baseboard heat and claims "it is the cheapest and cleanest way to go." Apply your understanding of the second law of thermodynamics to evaluate this claim.

**2.** Someone tells you we can save energy by recycling it. How would you respond?

**3.** Should the Corporate Average Fuel Economy (CAFE) standards for motor vehicles used in the United States be increased, left at 1985 levels (the current situation), or eliminated? Explain. Should the CAFE standards for light trucks, vans, and sport utility vehicles be increased to the same level as for cars? Explain. List the positive and negative effects on your health and lifestyle if CAFE standards are **(a)** increased or **(b)** eliminated.

**4.** What are the five most important actions an individual can take to save energy at home and in transportation (see website for this chapter)? Which, if any, of these do you currently do? Which, if any, do you plan to do?

**5.** Congratulations! You have won $250,000 to build a house of your choice anywhere you want. What type of house would you build? Where would you locate it? What types of materials would you use? What types of materials would you *not* use? How would you heat and cool your house? How would you heat your water? Considering fuel and energy efficiency, what sort of lighting, stove, refrigerator, washer, and dryer would you use? Which of these appliances could you do without?

**6.** Explain why you agree or disagree with the following proposals by various energy analysts: **(a)** federal subsidies for all energy alternatives should be eliminated so all energy choices can compete in a true free-market system, **(b)** all government tax breaks and other subsidies for conventional fuels (oil, natural gas, coal), synthetic natural gas and oil, and nuclear power (fission and fusion) should be phased out and replaced with subsidies and tax breaks for improving energy efficiency and developing solar, wind, geothermal, hydrogen, and biomass energy alternatives, and **(c)** development of solar, wind, and hydrogen energy should be left to private enterprise and receive little or no help from the federal government, but nuclear energy and fossil fuels should continue to receive large federal subsidies.

**7.** Explain why you agree or disagree with the proposals suggested in Figure 16-44 as ways to promote a more sustainable energy future.

**8.** Congratulations! You are in charge of the world. List the five most important features of your energy policy.

## PROJECTS

**1.** Make a study of energy use in your school and use the findings to develop an energy-efficiency improvement program. Present your plan to school officials.

**2.** Learn how easy it is to produce hydrogen gas from water using a battery, some wire for two electrodes, and a dish of water. Hook a wire to each of the poles of the battery, immerse the electrodes in the water, and observe bubbles of hydrogen gas being produced at the negative electrode and bubbles of oxygen at the positive electrode. Carefully add a small amount of battery acid to the water and notice that this increases the rate of hydrogen production.

**3.** Use the library or the Internet to find bibliographic information about *Amory B. Lovins* and *Mohamed El-Ashry,* whose quotes appear at the beginning and end of this chapter.

**4.** Make a concept map of this chapter's major ideas, using the section heads and subheads and the key terms (in boldface). Look on the website for this book for information about making concept maps.

## INTERNET STUDY RESOURCES AND RESOURCES FOR FURTHER READING AND RESEARCH

The website for this book contains helpful study aids and many ideas for further reading and research. Log on to

www.info.brookscole.com/miller13

and click on the Chapter-by-Chapter area. Choose Chapter 16 and select a resource:

- Flash Cards allows you to test your mastery of the Terms and Concepts to Remember for this chapter.

- Tutorial Quizzes provides a multiple-choice practice quiz.

- Student Guide to InfoTrac will lead you to Critical Thinking Projects that use InfoTrac College Edition as a research tool.

- References lists the major books and articles consulted in writing this chapter.

- Hypercontents takes you to an extensive list of sites with news, research, and images related to individual sections of the chapter.

## INFOTRAC COLLEGE EDITION

Improve your skills with InfoTrac College Edition, a searchable online database of articles from more than 700 periodicals. Log on to

http://www.infotrac-college.com

or access InfoTrac through the website for this book. Try to find the following articles:

**1.** Nanney, J. 2002. How motor efficiencies affect system designs. *Plant Engineering* 56: 46. *Keywords:* "motor efficiencies" and "system designs." Electric motors are ubiquitous in America's manufacturing plants. They are also notoriously inefficient. This article describes how revamping the motors in a manufacturing plant can help the "watts per part" of a company's bottom line.

**2.** Fairley, P. 2002. Wind power for pennies: A lightweight wind turbine is finally on the horizon and it just might be the breakthrough needed to give fossil fuels a run for their money. *Technology Review* 105: 40. *Keywords:* "wind power" and "fossil fuels." Using the wind as a way to generate electricity seems to be always just out of reach on a large scale, but advances in turbine design may make wind power a windfall for electricity users.

# PART IV

## ENVIRONMENTAL QUALITY AND POLLUTION

*In our every deliberation, we must consider the impact of our decisions on the next seven generations.*

IROQUOIS CONFEDERATION, 18TH CENTURY

# 17 AIR AND AIR POLLUTION

## When Is a Lichen Like a Canary?

Nineteenth-century coal miners took canaries with them into the mines—not for their songs but for the moment when they stopped singing. Then the miners knew it was time to get out of the mine because the air contained methane, which could ignite and explode.

Today we use sophisticated equipment to monitor air quality, but living things such as lichens (Figure 17-1) still can warn us of bad air. A lichen consists of a fungus and an alga living together, usually in a mutually beneficial (mutualistic) partnership.

These hearty pioneer species are good air pollution detectors because they are always absorbing air as a source of nourishment. Certain lichen species are sensitive to specific air-polluting chemicals. Old man's beard (*Usnea trichodea*) (Figure 17-1, right) and yellow *Evernia* lichens, for example, sicken or die in the presence of too much sulfur dioxide.

Because lichens are widespread, long lived, and anchored in place, they can also help track pollution to its source. The scientist who discovered sulfur dioxide pollution on Isle Royale in Lake Superior (Case Study, p. 197), where no car or smokestack had ever intruded, used *Evernia* lichens to point the finger northward to coal-burning facilities at Thunder Bay, Canada.

Radioactive particles spewed into the atmosphere by the Chernobyl nuclear power plant disaster (p. 338) fell to the ground over much of northern Scandinavia and were absorbed by lichens that carpet much of Lapland. The area's Saami people depend on reindeer meat for food, and the reindeer feed on lichens. After Chernobyl, more than 70,000 reindeer had to be killed and the meat discarded because it was too radioactive to eat. Scientists helped the Saami identify which of the remaining reindeer to move by analyzing lichens (which absorbed some of the radioactive fallout) to pinpoint the most contaminated areas.

Last but not least, lichens can replace electronic monitoring stations that cost more than $100,000 each. This is not so much a triumph of nature over technology as a partnership between the two, for technicians use highly sophisticated methods to analyze lichens for pollution and measure their rates of photosynthesis.

We all must breathe air from a global atmospheric commons in which air currents and winds can transport some pollutants long distances (p. 110). Lichens can alert us to the danger, but as with all forms of pollution, the best solution is prevention.

Kenneth W. Fink/Ardea, London

**Figure 17-1** Red and yellow crustose lichens growing on slate rock in the foothills of the Sierra Nevada near Merced, California (left), and *Usnea trichodea* lichen growing on a branch of a larch tree in Gifford Pinchot National Park, Washington (right). The vulnerability of various lichen species to specific air pollutants can help researchers detect levels of these pollutants and track down their sources.

*I thought I saw a blue jay this morning. But the smog was so bad that it turned out to be a cardinal holding its breath.*

MICHAEL J. COHEN

This chapter addresses the following questions:

- What layers are found in the atmosphere?

- What are the major outdoor air pollutants, and where do they come from?

- What are two types of smog?

- What is acid deposition, and how can it be reduced?

- What are the harmful effects of air pollutants?

- How can we prevent and control air pollution?

## 17-1 THE ATMOSPHERE

**What Is the Troposphere? Weather Breeder**  We live at the bottom of a sea of air called the **atmosphere.** This sea of life-sustaining gases surrounding the earth is divided into several spherical layers (Figure 17-2). Each layer is characterized by abrupt changes in temperature, the result of differences in the absorption of incoming solar energy.

About 75–80% of the mass of the earth's air is found in the atmosphere's innermost layer, the **troposphere,** which extends only about 17 kilometers (11 miles) above sea level at the equator and about 8 kilometers (5 miles) over the poles. If the earth were the size of an apple, this lower layer containing the air we breathe would be no thicker than the apple's skin. This thin and turbulent layer of rising and falling air currents and winds is the planet's *weather breeder.*

During several billion years of chemical and biological evolution, the composition of the earth's atmosphere has varied (Spotlight, p. 99). Today, about 99% of the volume of the air you inhale consists of two gases: nitrogen (78%) and oxygen (21%). The remainder consists of (1) water vapor (varying from 0.01% at the frigid poles to 4% in the humid tropics), (2) slightly less than 1% argon (Ar), (3) 0.037% carbon dioxide ($CO_2$), and (4) trace amounts of several other gases.

**What Is the Stratosphere? Earth's Global Sunscreen**  The atmosphere's second layer is the **stratosphere,** which extends from about 17 to 48 kilometers (11–30 miles) above the earth's surface (Figure 17-2). Although the stratosphere contains less matter than the troposphere, its composition is similar, with two notable exceptions: (1) its volume of water vapor is

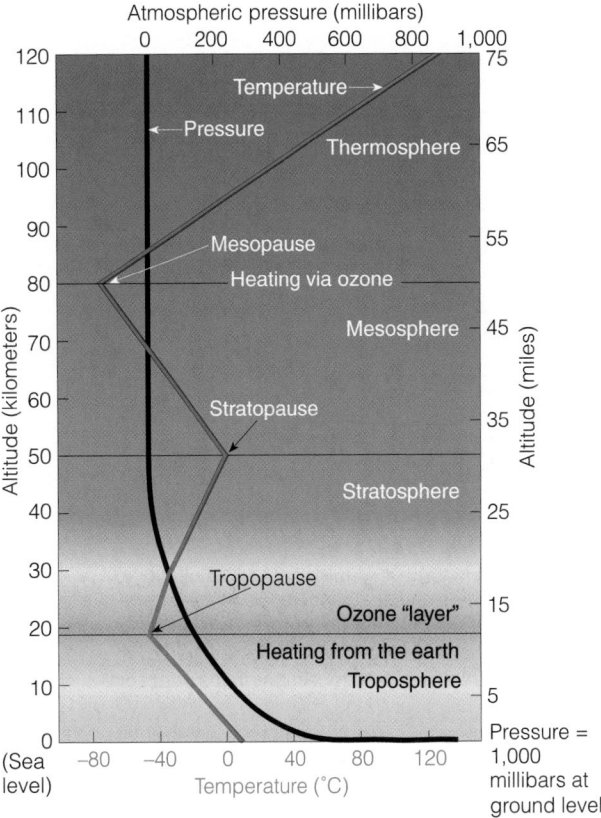

**Figure 17-2**  The earth's current atmosphere consists of several layers. The average temperature of the atmosphere varies with altitude (red line). The average temperature of the atmosphere at the earth's surface is determined by a combination of (1) *natural heating* by incoming sunlight and certain greenhouse gases that release absorbed energy as heat into the lower troposphere (the natural *greenhouse effect;* Figure 6-17, p. 121) and (2) *natural cooling* by surface evaporation of water and convection processes that transfer heat to higher altitudes and latitudes (Figure 6-10, p. 117, and Figure 6-11, p. 118). Most UV radiation from the sun is absorbed by ozone ($O_3$), found primarily in the stratosphere in the *ozone layer* 17–26 kilometers (10–16 miles) above sea level.

about 1/1,000 as much, and (2) its concentration of ozone is much higher (Figure 17-3, p. 420).

Stratospheric ozone is produced when some of the oxygen molecules there interact with ultraviolet (UV) radiation emitted by the sun. This "global sunscreen" of ozone in the stratosphere keeps about 95% of the sun's harmful UV radiation from reaching the earth's surface. This UV filter (1) allows humans and other forms of life to exist on land, (2) helps protect us from sunburn, skin and eye cancer, cataracts, and damage to the immune system, and (3) prevents much of the oxygen in the troposphere from being converted to photochemical ozone, a harmful air pollutant (Figure 17-3, p. 420).

**Figure 17-3** Average distribution and concentrations of ozone in the troposphere and stratosphere. *Beneficial ozone* that forms in the stratosphere protects life on earth by filtering out most of the incoming harmful ultraviolet radiation emitted by the sun. *Harmful* or *photochemical* ozone forms in the troposphere when various air pollutants undergo chemical reactions under the influence of sunlight. Ozone in this portion of the atmosphere near the earth's surface damages plants, lung tissues, and some materials such as rubber.

Much evidence indicates that some human activities are (1) *decreasing* the amount of beneficial ozone in the stratosphere and (2) *increasing* the amount of harmful ozone in the troposphere—especially in some urban areas.

## 17-2 OUTDOOR AIR POLLUTION

**What Are the Major Types and Sources of Air Pollution?** **Air pollution** is the presence of one or more chemicals in the atmosphere in sufficient quantities and duration to (1) cause harm to us, other forms of life, and materials or (2) alter climate. The effects of airborne pollutants range from annoying to lethal. Air pollution is not new (Spotlight, p. 423).

Table 17-1 lists the major classes of pollutants commonly found in outdoor (ambient) air. Such air pollutants come from both natural sources and human (anthropogenic) activities. Examples of natural sources include (1) dust and other forms of suspended particulate matter from windstorms and soil (Figure 6-1, p. 110), (2) sulfur oxides and particulate matter from volcanoes, (3) carbon oxides, nitrogen oxides, and particulates from forest fires, (4) hydrocarbons and pollen from live plants, (5) methane and hydrogen sulfide from decaying plants, and (6) salt particulates from the sea.

Most natural sources of air pollution are spread out and, except for those from volcanic eruptions and some forest fires, rarely reach harmful levels. Most outdoor pollutants in urban areas enter the atmosphere from the burning of fossil fuels in power plants and factories (*stationary sources*) and motor vehicles (*mobile sources*).

Scientists distinguish between primary and secondary air pollutants in outdoor air. **Primary pollutants** are those emitted directly into the troposphere in a potentially harmful form. While in the tropo-

| Table 17-1 Major Classes of Air Pollutants | |
|---|---|
| **Class** | **Examples** |
| Carbon oxides | Carbon monoxide (CO) and carbon dioxide ($CO_2$) |
| Sulfur oxides | Sulfur dioxide ($SO_2$) and sulfur trioxide ($SO_3$) |
| Nitrogen oxides | Nitric oxide (NO), nitrogen dioxide ($NO_2$), nitrous oxide ($N_2O$) (NO and $NO_2$ often are lumped together and labeled $NO_x$) |
| Volatile organic compounds (VOCs) | Methane ($CH_4$), propane ($C_3H_8$), chlorofluorocarbons (CFCs) |
| Suspended particulate matter (SPM) | Solid particles (dust, soot, asbestos, lead, nitrate, and sulfate salts), liquid droplets (sulfuric acid, PCBs, dioxins, and pesticides) |
| Photochemical oxidants | Ozone ($O_3$), peroxyacyl nitrates (PANs), hydrogen peroxide ($H_2O_2$), aldehydes |
| Radioactive substances | Radon-222, iodine-131, strontium-90, plutonium-239 (Table 3-2, p. 56) |
| Hazardous air pollutants (HAPs), which cause health effects such as cancer, birth defects, and nervous system problems | Carbon tetrachloride ($CCl_4$), methyl chloride ($CH_3Cl$), chloroform ($CHCl_3$), benzene ($C_6H_6$), ethylene dibromide ($C_2H_2Br_2$), formaldehyde ($CH_2O_2$) |

**Primary Pollutants**

CO    $CO_2$

$SO_2$   NO   $NO_2$

Most hydrocarbons

Most suspended
particles

**Secondary Pollutants**

$SO_3$

$HNO_3$    $H_2SO_4$

$H_2O_2$    $O_3$    PANs

Most $NO_3^-$ and $SO_4^{2-}$ salts

Natural

**Sources**

Stationary

Mobile

**Figure 17-4** Sources and types of air pollutants. Human inputs of air pollutants may come from *mobile sources* (such as cars) and *stationary sources* (such as industrial and power plants). Some *primary air pollutants* may react with one another or with other chemicals in the air to form *secondary air pollutants.*

sphere, some of these primary pollutants may react with one another or with the basic components of air to form new pollutants, called **secondary pollutants** (Figure 17-4).

With their large concentrations of cars and factories, cities normally have higher air pollution levels than rural areas. However, prevailing winds can spread long-lived primary and secondary air pollutants emit-

ted in urban and industrial areas to the countryside and to other downwind urban areas.

Winds and air currents can spread some long-lived air pollutants across much of the earth. In 2000, a NASA spacecraft that circles the earth 16 times a day began tracking air pollutants (such as carbon monoxide) from large forest fires and the burning of fossil fuels as they flow across continents and oceans (Figure 17-5).

**March 10, 2000**      **March 12, 2000**      **March 13, 2000**      **March 15, 2000**

**Figure 17-5** Since 2000, a NASA Terra spacecraft, which circles the globe 16 times a day, has been tracking the air pollutant carbon monoxide (CO) as it flows across continents and oceans. In these images, CO from fires and industrial sources in Southeast Asia crosses the Pacific Ocean during March 2000. Red indicates the highest levels of CO at 450 parts per million.

Indoor pollutants come from **(1)** infiltration of polluted outside air and **(2)** various chemicals used or produced inside buildings, as discussed in more detail in Section 17-5, p. 434. Experts in risk analysis rate indoor air pollution and outdoor air pollution as high-risk human health problems (Figure 11-15, left, p. 246).

According to the World Health Organization (WHO), more than 1.1 billion people live in urban areas where the air is unhealthy to breathe. Most live in densely populated cities in developing countries where air pollution control laws do not exist or are poorly enforced.

In the United States (and in most other developed countries), government-mandated standards set maximum allowable atmospheric concentrations for six *criteria air pollutants* commonly found in outdoor air (Table 17-2). The *good news* is that this has helped sharply reduce levels of these pollutants in most of these countries.

---

**Table 17-2  Common Criteria Air Pollutants in the United States***

**CARBON MONOXIDE (CO)**

**Description:** Colorless, odorless gas that is poisonous to air-breathing animals; forms during the incomplete combustion of carbon-containing fuels ($2C + O_2 \longrightarrow 2CO$).

**Major human sources:** Cigarette smoking (p. 228), incomplete burning of fossil fuels. About 77% (95% in cities) comes from motor vehicle exhaust.

**Health effects:** Reacts with hemoglobin in red blood cells and reduces the ability of blood to bring oxygen to body cells and tissues. This impairs perception and thinking; slows reflexes; causes headaches, drowsiness, dizziness, and nausea; can trigger heart attacks and angina; damages the development of fetuses and young children; and aggravates chronic bronchitis, emphysema, and anemia. At high levels it causes collapse, coma, irreversible brain cell damage, and death.

**NITROGEN DIOXIDE (NO₂)**

**Description:** Reddish-brown irritating gas that gives photochemical smog its brownish color; in the atmosphere can be converted to nitric acid ($HNO_3$), a major component of acid deposition.

**Major human sources:** Fossil fuel burning in motor vehicles (49%) and power and industrial plants (49%).

**Health effects:** Lung irritation and damage; aggravates asthma and chronic bronchitis; increases susceptibility to respiratory infections such as the flu and common colds (especially in young children and older adults).

**Environmental effects:** Reduces visibility; acid deposition of $HNO_3$ can damage trees, soils, and aquatic life in lakes.

**Property damage:** $HNO_3$ can corrode metals and eat away stone on buildings, statues, and monuments; $NO_2$ can damage fabrics.

**SULFUR DIOXIDE (SO₂)**

**Description:** Colorless, irritating; forms mostly from the combustion of sulfur-containing fossil fuels such as coal and oil ($S + O_2 \longrightarrow SO_2$); in the atmosphere can be converted to sulfuric acid ($H_2SO_4$), a major component of acid deposition.

**Major human sources:** Coal burning in power plants (88%) and industrial processes (10%).

**Health effects:** Breathing problems for healthy people; restriction of airways in people with asthma; chronic exposure can cause a permanent condition similar to bronchitis. According to the WHO, at least 625 million people are exposed to unsafe levels of sulfur dioxide from fossil fuel burning.

**Environmental effects:** Reduces visibility; acid deposition of $H_2SO_4$ can damage trees, soils, and aquatic life in lakes.

**Property damage:** $SO_2$ and $H_2SO_4$ can corrode metals and eat away stone on buildings, statues, and monuments; $SO_2$ can damage paint, paper, and leather.

**SUSPENDED PARTICULATE MATTER (SPM)**

**Description:** Variety of particles and droplets (aerosols) small and light enough to remain suspended in atmosphere for short periods (large particles) to long periods (small particles; Figure 17-8, p. 426); cause smoke, dust, and haze.

**Major human sources:** Burning coal in power and industrial plants (40%), burning diesel and other fuels in vehicles (17%), agriculture (plowing, burning off fields), unpaved roads, construction.

**Health effects:** Nose and throat irritation, lung damage, and bronchitis; aggravates bronchitis and asthma; shortens life; toxic particulates (such as lead, cadmium, PCBs, and dioxins) can cause mutations, reproductive problems, cancer.

**Environmental effects:** Reduces visibility; acid deposition of $H_2SO_4$ droplets can damage trees, soils, and aquatic life in lakes.

**Property damage:** Corrodes metal; soils and discolors buildings, clothes, fabrics, and paints.

**OZONE (O₃)**

**Description:** Highly reactive, irritating gas with an unpleasant odor that forms in the troposphere as a major component of photochemical smog (Figures 17-3 and 17-6, p. 424).

**Major human sources:** Chemical reaction with volatile organic compounds (VOCs, emitted mostly by cars and industries) and nitrogen oxides to form photochemical smog (Figure 17-6, p. 424).

**Health effects:** Breathing problems; coughing; eye, nose, and throat irritation; aggravates chronic diseases such as asthma, bronchitis, emphysema, and heart disease; reduces resistance to colds and pneumonia; may speed up lung tissue aging.

**Environmental effects:** Ozone can damage plants and trees; smog can reduce visibility.

**Property damage:** Damages rubber, fabrics, and paints.

**LEAD**

**Description:** Solid toxic metal and its compounds, emitted into the atmosphere as particulate matter.

**Major human sources:** Paint (old houses), smelters (metal refineries), lead manufacture, storage batteries, leaded gasoline (being phased out in developed countries).

**Health effects:** Accumulates in the body; brain and other nervous system damage and mental retardation (especially in children); digestive and other health problems; some lead-containing chemicals cause cancer in test animals.

**Environmental effects:** Can harm wildlife.

*Data from U.S. Environmental Protection Agency.

## Air Pollution in the Past: The Bad Old Days

Modern civilization did not invent air pollution. It probably began when humans discovered fire and used it to burn wood in poorly ventilated caves.

During the Middle Ages, a haze of wood smoke hung over densely packed urban areas. The industrial revolution brought even worse air pollution as coal was burned to power factories and heat homes. By the 1850s, London had become well known for its "pea soup" fog, a mixture of coal smoke and fog that blanketed the city. In 1880, a prolonged coal fog killed an estimated 2,200 people. Another in 1911 killed more than 1,100 Londoners. The authors of a report on this disaster coined the word *smog* for the deadly mixture of smoke and fog that enveloped the city.

In 1952, an even worse yellow fog lasted for 5 days and killed 4,000 Londoners, prompting Parliament to pass the Clean Air Act of 1956. Additional air pollution disasters in 1956, 1957, and 1962 killed 2,500 more people. Because of strong air pollution laws, London's air today is much cleaner, and "pea soup" fogs are a thing of the past.

The industrial revolution, powered by coal-burning factories and homes, brought air pollution to the United States. Large industrial cities such as Pittsburgh, Pennsylvania, and St. Louis, Missouri, were known for their smoky air. By the 1940s, the air over some cities was so polluted that people had to use their automobile headlights during the day.

The first documented air pollution disaster in the United States occurred during October 1948, at the town of Donora in Pennsylvania's Monongahela River Valley south of Pittsburgh. Pollutants from the area's industries became trapped in a fog that stagnated over the valley for 5 days. After several days the fog was so dense that people could not see well enough to drive, even at noon with their headlights on. About 7,000 of the town's 14,000 inhabitants became sick, and 22 of them died. This killer fog resulted from a combination of mountainous terrain surrounding the valley and weather conditions that trapped and concentrated deadly pollutants emitted by the community's steel mill, zinc smelter, and sulfuric acid plant.

In 1963, high concentrations of air pollutants accumulated in the air over New York City, killing about 300 people and injuring thousands. Other episodes in New York, Los Angeles, and other large cities in the 1960s led to much stronger air pollution control programs in the 1970s.

Congress passed the original version of the Clean Air Act in 1963, but it did not have much effect until a stronger version of this law was enacted in 1970. The Clean Air Act of 1970 empowered the federal government to set air pollution emission standards (with an adequate safety margin) for automobiles and industries that each state was required to enforce. Even stricter emission standards were imposed by amendments to the Clean Air Act in 1977 and 1990. Mostly as a result of these laws and actions by states and local areas, the United States has not had any more Donora or New York City incidents.

### Critical Thinking

Explain why you agree or disagree with the statement that air pollution in the United States should not be a major concern because of the significant progress in reducing outdoor air pollution since 1970.

## 17-3 PHOTOCHEMICAL AND INDUSTRIAL SMOG

 **What Is Photochemical Smog? Brown-Air Smog** Any chemical reaction activated by light is called a *photochemical reaction*. Air pollution known as **photochemical smog** is a mixture of primary and secondary pollutants formed under the influence of sunlight (Figure 17-6, p. 424). The resulting mixture of more than 100 chemicals is dominated by *photochemical ozone,* a highly reactive gas that harms most living organisms (Figure 17-3).

Here is a simplified version of the complex chemistry of photochemical smog formation. It begins when nitrogen and oxygen in air react at the high temperatures found inside automobile engines and the boilers in coal-burning power and industrial plants to pro-

duce colorless nitric oxide ($N_2 + O_2 \longrightarrow 2NO$). Once in the troposphere, the nitric oxide slowly reacts with oxygen to form nitrogen dioxide, a yellowish-brown gas with a choking odor ($2NO + O_2 \longrightarrow 2NO_2$). The $NO_2$ is responsible for the brownish haze that hangs over many cities during the afternoons of sunny days, explaining why photochemical smog sometimes is called *brown-air smog.*

Some of the $NO_2$ reacts with water vapor in the atmosphere to form nitric acid vapor and nitric oxide ($3NO_2 + H_2O \longrightarrow 2HNO_3 + NO$). When the remaining $NO_2$ is exposed to ultraviolet radiation from the sun, some of it is converted to nitric oxide and oxygen atoms ($NO_2 + UV\ radiation \longrightarrow NO + O$). The highly reactive oxygen atoms then react with $O_2$ to produce ozone ($O_2 + O \longrightarrow O_3$). Both the oxygen atoms and ozone then react with volatile organic compounds

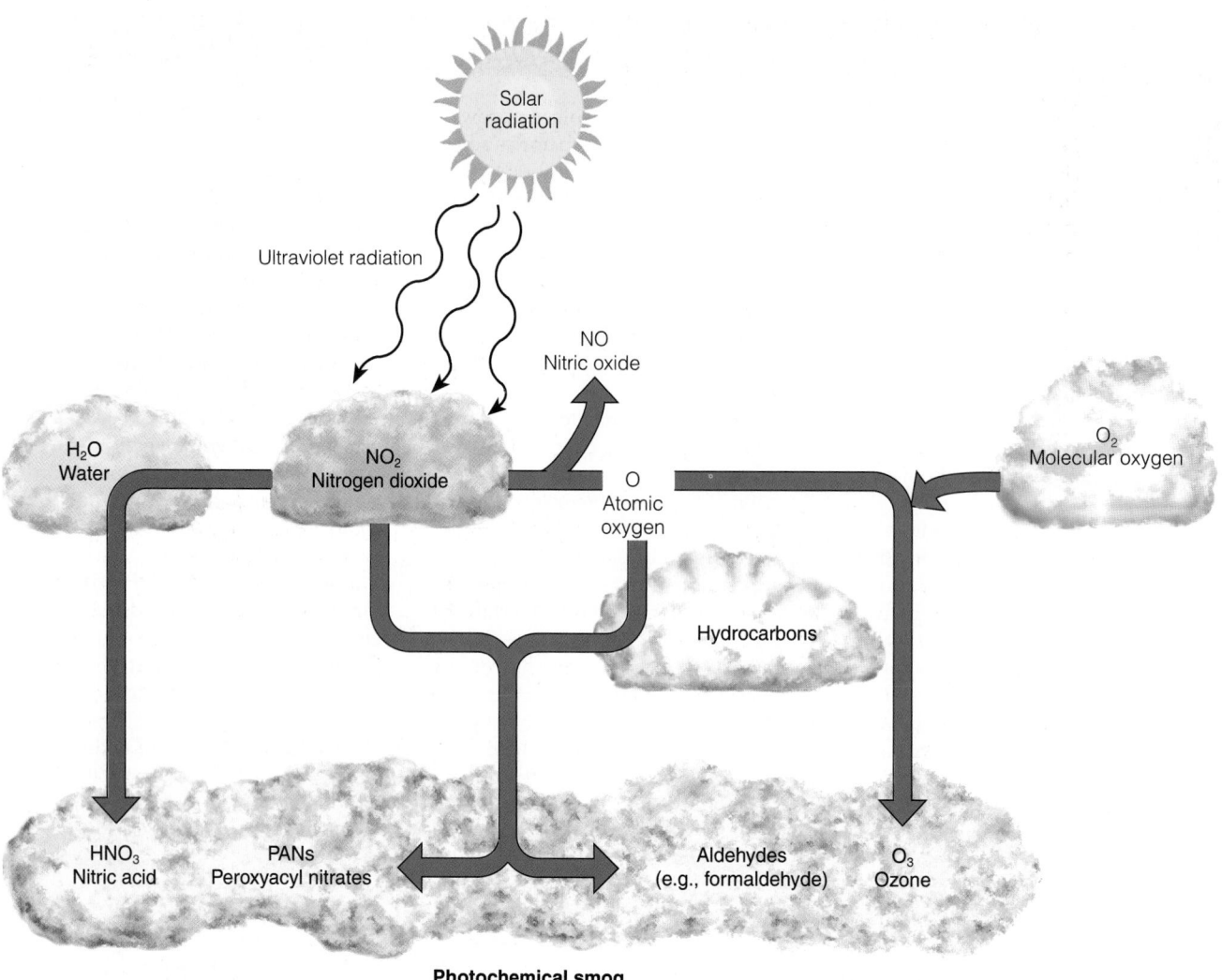

**Figure 17-6** Simplified scheme of the formation of photochemical smog. The severity of smog generally is associated with atmospheric concentrations of ozone at ground level.

(mostly hydrocarbons released by vegetation, vehicles, gas stations, oil refineries, and dry cleaners) to produce aldehydes. In addition, hydrocarbons, oxygen, and nitrogen dioxide react to produce peroxyacyl nitrates, or PANs (hydrocarbons + $O_2$ + NO $\longrightarrow$ PANs).

Collectively, $NO_2$, $O_3$, and PANs are called *photochemical oxidants* because they can react with and oxidize certain compounds in the atmosphere (or inside your lungs) that normally are not oxidized. Mere traces of these photochemical oxidants (especially ozone) and aldehydes in photochemical smog can irritate the respiratory tract and damage crops and trees.

Hotter days lead to higher levels of ozone and other components of photochemical smog. As traffic increases in the morning, levels of $NO_x$ and unburned hydrocarbons rise and begin reacting in the presence of sunlight to produce photochemical smog. On a

sunny day the photochemical smog (dominated by $O_3$) builds up to peak levels by early afternoon, irritating people's eyes and respiratory tracts (Figure 17-7).

According to atmospheric chemist Sherwood Rowland, since 1900 the concentration of photochemical ozone near the earth's surface has increased by a factor of **(1)** 5–8 during summer in the northern hemisphere, **(2)** 2–4 during the winter in the northern hemisphere, and **(3)** 2–5 during winter and summer in the southern hemisphere.

All modern cities have photochemical smog, but it is much more common in cities with sunny, warm, dry climates and lots of motor vehicles. Examples of such cities are Los Angeles, California; Denver, Colorado; and Salt Lake City, Utah, in the United States, as well as Sydney, Australia; Mexico City, Mexico; and São Paulo and Buenos Aires in Brazil. According to a 1999

**Figure 17-7** Typical daily pattern of changes in concentrations of air pollutants that lead to development of photochemical smog in a city such as Los Angeles, California.

article in *Geophysical Research Letters*, if 400 million Chinese drive cars by 2050 as projected, the resulting photochemical smog could cover the entire western Pacific in ozone, extending to the United States.

**What Is Industrial Smog? Gray-Air Smog** Fifty years ago, cities such as London, England, and Chicago and Pittsburgh in the United States burned large amounts of coal and heavy oil (which contain

sulfur impurities) in power plants and factories and for space heating. During winter, people in such cities were exposed to **industrial smog** consisting mostly of **(1)** sulfur dioxide, **(2)** suspended droplets of sulfuric acid (formed from sulfur dioxide, Figure 17-4), and **(3)** a variety of suspended solid particles and droplets (called aerosols; Figure 17-8, p. 426).

The chemistry of industrial smog is fairly simple. When burned, the carbon in coal and oil is converted to carbon dioxide ($C + O_2 \longrightarrow CO_2$) and carbon monoxide ($2C + O_2 \longrightarrow 2CO$). Some of the unburned carbon also ends up in the atmosphere as suspended particulate matter (soot).

The sulfur compounds in coal and oil also react with oxygen to produce sulfur dioxide, a colorless, suffocating gas ($S + O_2 \longrightarrow SO_2$). Sulfur dioxide also is emitted into the troposphere when metal sulfide ores (such as lead sulfide, PbS) are roasted or smelted to convert the metal ore to the free metal (Figure 15-8, p. 344).

In the troposphere, some of the sulfur dioxide reacts with oxygen to form sulfur trioxide ($2SO_2 + O_2 \longrightarrow 2SO_3$), which then reacts with water vapor in the air to produce tiny suspended droplets of sulfuric acid ($SO_3 + H_2O \longrightarrow H_2SO_4$). Some of these droplets react with ammonia in the atmosphere to form solid particles of ammonium sulfate ($2NH_3 + H_2SO_4 \longrightarrow (NH_4)_2SO_4$). The tiny suspended particles of such salts and carbon (soot) give the resulting industrial smog a gray color, explaining why it is sometimes called *gray-air smog*.

Urban industrial smog is rarely a problem today in most developed countries because coal and heavy oil are burned only in large boilers with reasonably good pollution control or with tall smokestacks (which transfer the pollutants to downwind areas). However, industrial smog is a problem in industrialized urban areas of China, India, Ukraine, and some eastern European countries, where large quantities of coal are burned with inadequate pollution controls. According to a recent UN study, 13 of the world's 15 cities with the world's worst air pollution are found in Asia (10 of them in China)—mostly from burning coal and leaded gasoline.

**What Factors Influence the Formation of Photochemical and Industrial Smog?** The frequency and severity of smog in an area depend on **(1)** local climate and topography, **(2)** population density, **(3)** the amount of industry, and **(4)** the fuels used in industry, heating, and transportation.

Air pollution can be reduced by

- *Rain and snow,* which help cleanse the air of pollutants. This explains why cities with dry climates are

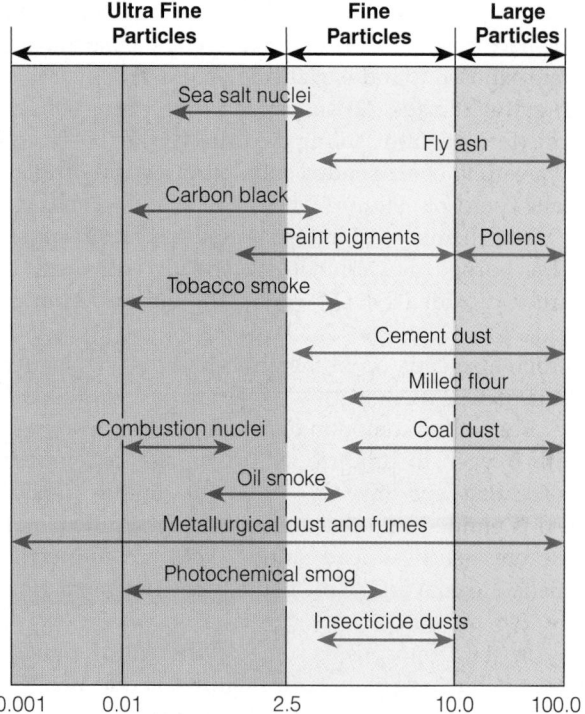

| Ultra Fine Particles | Fine Particles | Large Particles |
|---|---|---|

Sea salt nuclei

Fly ash

Carbon black

Paint pigments          Pollens

Tobacco smoke

Cement dust

Milled flour

Combustion nuclei          Coal dust

Oil smoke

Metallurgical dust and fumes

Photochemical smog

Insecticide dusts

0.001     0.01          2.5          10.0     100.0

Average particle diameter (micrometers or microns)

**Figure 17-8** Suspended particulate matter consists of particles of solid matter and droplets of liquid that are small and light enough to remain suspended in the atmosphere for short periods (large particles) to long periods (small particles). Suspended particles are found in a wide variety of types and sizes, ranging in diameter from 0.001 micrometer to 100 micrometers (a micrometer, or micron, is one millionth of a meter, or about 0.00004 inches). Since 1987, the EPA has focused on *fine particles* smaller than 10 microns (known as *PM-10*). In 1997, the agency began focusing on reducing emissions of *ultrafine particles* with diameters less than 2.5 microns (known as *PM-2.5*) because these particles are small enough to reach the lower part of human lungs and contribute to respiratory diseases.

more prone to photochemical smog than ones with wet climates.

- *Winds,* which **(1)** help sweep pollutants away, **(2)** dilute pollutants by mixing them with cleaner air, and **(3)** bring in fresh air. However, these pollutants are blown somewhere else or are deposited from the sky onto surface waters, soil, and buildings.

A 2000 study of clean and dirty clouds over three countries by atmospheric scientist Daniel Rosenfield indicated that air pollution can reduce the rain and snowfall that help cleanse the air of pollutants. He found that clean clouds hold large droplets of water that can easily be converted into rain or snow. However, dirty clouds contain small water droplets that are less likely to bump into each other and stick together in large enough clumps to form air-cleansing raindrops and snowflakes.

Three factors that can increase air pollution are

- *Urban buildings,* which can slow wind speed and reduce dilution and removal of pollutants.

- *Hills and mountains,* which tend to reduce the flow of air in valleys below them and allow pollutant levels to build up at ground level.

- *High temperatures,* which promote the chemical reactions leading to photochemical smog formation.

**What Are Temperature Inversions?** During daylight, the sun warms the air near the earth's surface. Normally, this warm air and most of the pollutants it contains rises to mix with the cooler air above it. This mixing of warm and cold air creates turbulence, which disperses the pollutants.

Under certain atmospheric conditions, however, a layer of warm air can lie atop a layer of cooler air nearer the ground, a situation known as a **temperature inversion.** Because the cooler air is denser than the warmer air above it, the air near the surface does not rise and mix with the air above it. Pollutants can concentrate in this stagnant layer of cool air near the ground.

There are two types of temperature inversions:

- A **subsidence temperature inversion,** which occurs when a large mass of warm air moves into a region at a high altitude and floats over a mass of colder air near the ground. This keeps the air over a city stagnant and prevents vertical mixing and dispersion of air pollutants. Normally such conditions do not last long, but sometimes warmer air masses can remain over cooler air below for days and allow pollutants to build up to harmful levels.

- A **radiation temperature inversion,** which typically occurs at night as the air near the ground cools faster than the air above it. As the sun rises and warms the earth's surface, a radiation inversion normally disappears by noon and disperses the pollutants built up during the night.

Under certain conditions, radiation or subsidence temperature inversions can last for several days and allow pollutants to build up to dangerous concentrations. Areas with two types of topography and weather conditions are especially susceptible to prolonged temperature inversions (Figure 17-9).

One such area is a town or city located in a valley surrounded by mountains that experiences cloudy and cold weather during part of the year (Figure 17-9, top). In such cases, the surrounding mountains block out the winter sun needed to reverse the nightly radiation temperature inversion. As long as these stagnant conditions persist, concentrations of pollutants in the valley below will build up to harmful and even lethal concentrations. This is what happened during the 1948

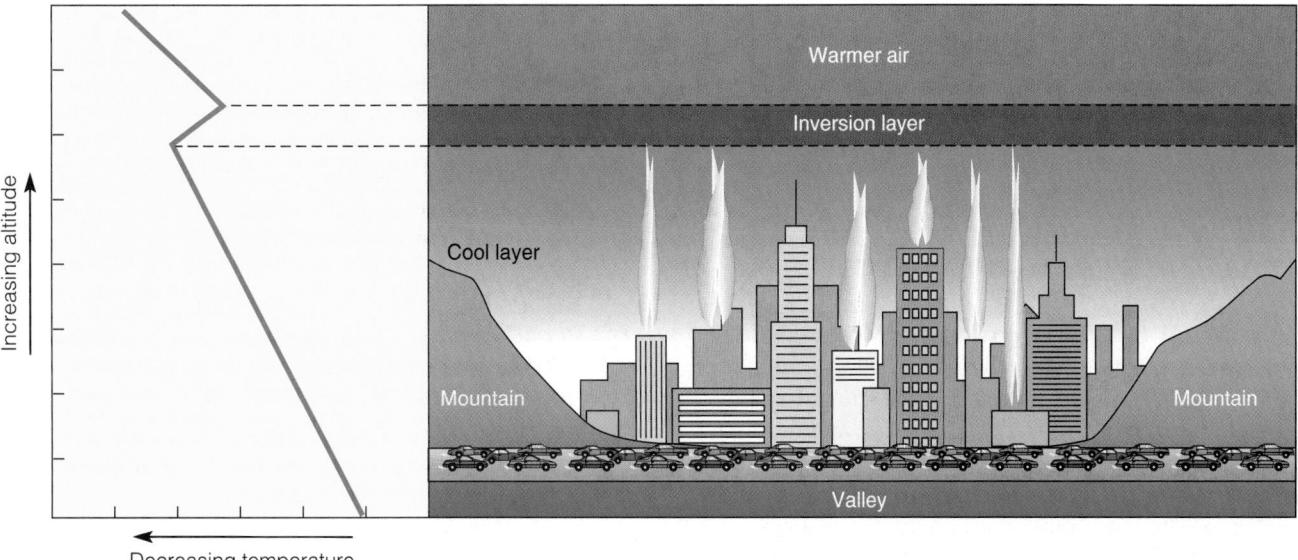

Increasing altitude

Decreasing temperature

Warmer air

Inversion layer

Cool layer

Mountain

Mountain

Valley

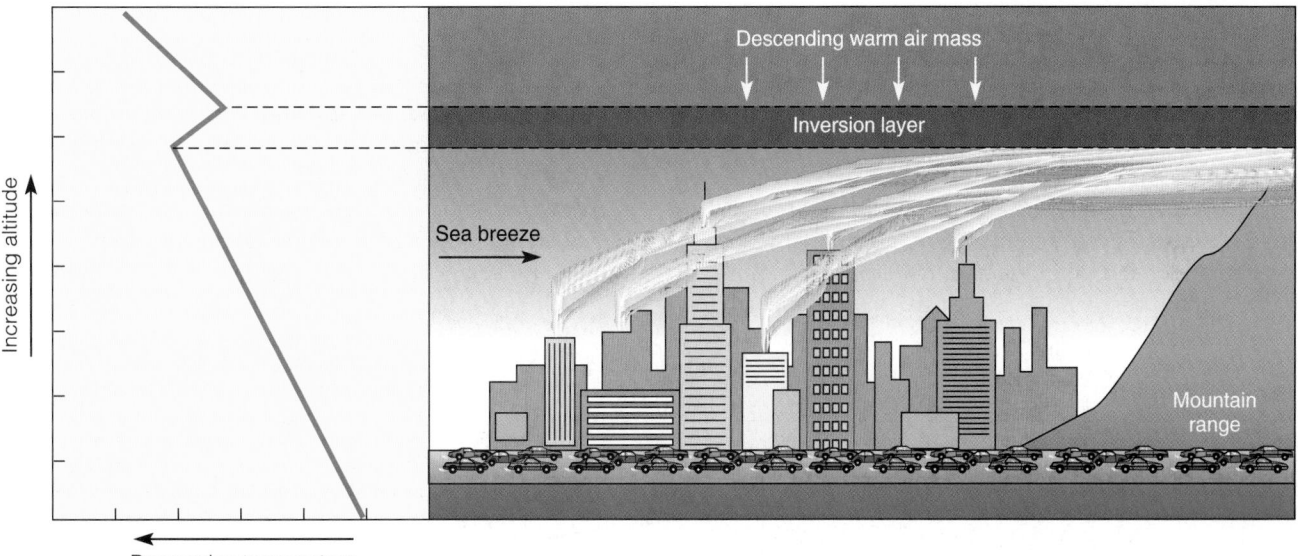

Increasing altitude

Decreasing temperature

Descending warm air mass

Inversion layer

Sea breeze

Mountain range

**Figure 17-9** Topography and weather conditions that can create more frequent and prolonged *radiation temperature inversions*, in which a layer of warm air sits atop a cooler layer of air near the ground. In such cases, pollutant concentrations in the air near the earth's surface can build up to harmful levels. The top figure shows how air pollutants can build up in the air near the ground in a valley surrounded by mountains. The bottom figure shows how frequent and prolonged radiation temperature inversions can occur in an area (such as Los Angeles, California) with a sunny climate, light winds, mountains on three sides, and the ocean on the other. The layer of descending warm air (bottom) prevents ascending air currents from dispersing and diluting pollutants from the cooler air near the ground. Because of their topography, Los Angeles in the United States and Mexico City in Mexico have frequent thermal inversions, many of them prolonged during the summer.

air pollution disaster in the valley town of Donora, Pennsylvania (Spotlight, p. 423).

A city with several million people and motor vehicles in an area with a **(1)** sunny climate, **(2)** light winds, **(3)** mountains on three sides, and **(4)** the ocean on the other has ideal conditions for photochemical smog worsened by frequent subsidence thermal inversions

(Figure 17-9, bottom). This describes California's heavily populated Los Angeles basin, which has prolonged subsidence temperature inversions at least half of the year, mostly during the warm summer and fall. High-pressure air off the coast of California much of the year creates a descending warm air mass that sits atop an air mass below that is cooled by the nearby ocean.

When this subsidence thermal inversion persists throughout the day, the surrounding mountains prevent the polluted surface air from being blown away by sea breezes (Figure 17-9, bottom).

## 17-4 REGIONAL OUTDOOR AIR POLLUTION FROM ACID DEPOSITION

**What Is Acid Deposition?** Most coal-burning power plants, ore smelters, and other industrial plants in developed countries use tall smokestacks to emit sulfur dioxide, suspended particles, and nitrogen oxides above the inversion layer (Figure 17-9, top), where mixing, dilution, and removal by wind are more effective. Thus tall smokestacks reduce *local* air pollution but increase *regional* air pollution downwind.

The primary pollutants, sulfur dioxide and nitrogen oxides, emitted into the atmosphere above the inversion layer are transported as much as 1,000 kilometers (600 miles) by prevailing winds. During their trip, they form secondary pollutants such as **(1)** nitric acid vapor, **(2)** droplets of sulfuric acid, and **(3)** particles of acid-forming sulfate and nitrate salts (Figure 17-4).

These acidic substances remain in the atmosphere for 2–14 days, depending mostly on prevailing winds, precipitation, and other weather patterns. During this period they descend to the earth's surface in two forms: **(1)** *wet deposition* (as acidic rain, snow, fog, and cloud vapor with a pH less than 5.6) and **(2)** *dry deposition* (as acidic particles). The resulting mixture is called **acid deposition** (Figure 17-10), sometimes termed *acid rain*. Most dry deposition occurs within about 2–3 days fairly near the emission sources, whereas most wet deposition takes place in 4–14 days in more distant downwind areas (Figure 17-10).

**What Areas Are Most Affected by Acid Deposition?** Acid deposition is a regional problem in the eastern United States (Figure 17-11) and in other parts of the world (Figure 17-12). Most of these regions are downwind from coal-burning power plants, smelters, or factories or are major urban areas with large numbers of motor vehicles.

In the United States, coal-burning power and industrial plants in the Ohio Valley (Figure 17-11) emit the largest quantities of sulfur dioxide and other acidic pollutants. Mostly as a result of these emissions, typical precipitation in the eastern United States has a pH of 4.2–4.7 (Figure 17-11). This is 10 or more times the acidity of natural precipitation with a pH of 5.6. Some mountaintop forests in the eastern United States and east of Los Angeles, California, are bathed in fog and dews as acidic as lemon juice, with a pH of 2.3—about 1,000 times the acidity of normal precipitation.

In some areas, soils contain basic compounds such as calcium carbonate ($CaCO_3$) or limestone that

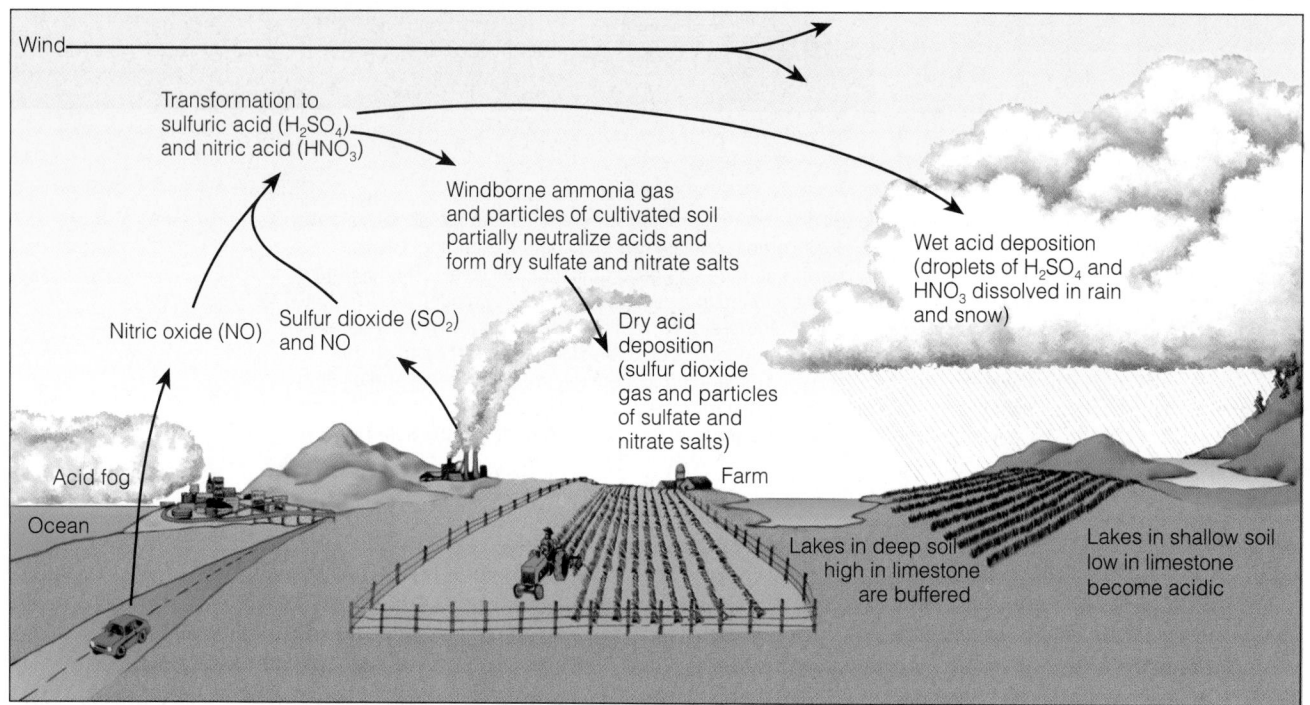

**Figure 17-10** *Acid deposition*, which consists of rain, snow, dust, or gas with a pH lower than 5.6, is commonly called acid rain. Soils and lakes vary in their ability to buffer or remove excess acidity.

Major coal-burning power and industrial plants

| | | | |
|---|---|---|---|
| ≥5.3 | 5.0–5.1 | 4.7–4.8 | 4.4–4.5 |
| 5.2–5.3 | 4.9–5.0 | 4.6–4.7 | 4.3–4.4 |
| 5.1–5.2 | 4.8–4.9 | 4.5–4.6 | <4.3 |

**Figure 17-11** pH values from field measurements in 48 states in 1998. Red dots show major sources of sulfur dioxide ($SO_2$) emissions, mostly large coal-burning power plants. In the eastern United States, the primary component of acid deposition is $H_2SO_4$ (formed from $SO_2$ emitted by coal-burning plants). In the western United States, $HNO_3$ predominates (formed mostly from $NO_x$ emissions from motor vehicles). According to the EPA, about 66% of the $SO_2$ and 25% of the $NO_x$ that are the primary causes of acid deposition come from coal-burning power plants. (National Atmospheric Deposition Program [NRSP-3]/National Trends Network, 1998. NADP Program Office, Illinois State Water Survey, 2204 Griffith Dr., Champaign, IL 61820)

can neutralize, or *buffer,* some inputs of acids. Hydrogen ions in acids percolating through soils derived from limestone rock are neutralized (buffered) when they react with $CaCO_3$ ($CaCO_3 + 2H^+ \longrightarrow Ca^{2+} + CO_2 + H_2O$).

The areas most sensitive to acid deposition are **(1)** those containing thin acidic soils derived mostly from granite rock without such natural buffering (Figure 17-12, green and most red areas) and **(2)** those in which the buffering capacity of soils has been depleted by decades of acid deposition (some red areas in Figure 17-12).

**Figure 17-12** Regions where acid deposition is now a problem (red) and regions with the potential to develop this problem (yellow and green). Such regions **(1)** have large inputs of air pollution (mostly from power plants, industrial plants, and ore smelters; red dots in Figure 17-11), or **(2)** are sensitive areas with soils and bedrock that cannot neutralize (buffer) inputs of acidic compounds (green areas and most red areas). (Data from World Resources Institute and U.S. Environmental Protection Agency)

Potential problem areas because of sensitive soils

Potential problem areas because of air pollution: emissions leading to acid deposition

Current problem areas (including lakes and rivers)

Many of the acid-producing chemicals generated by power plants, factories, smelters, and cars in one country are exported to other countries by prevailing winds. Here are some examples:

- Acidic emissions from industrialized areas of western Europe (especially the United Kingdom and Germany) and eastern Europe blow into Norway, Switzerland, Austria, Sweden, the Netherlands, and Finland.

- Some $SO_2$ and other emissions from the Ohio Valley of the United States (Figure 17-11) end up in Southeastern Canada (Figure 17-12).

- Some acidic fallout onto parts of the eastern United States have been traced to emissions from two large metal smelters in southeastern Canada

- Some acidic emissions in China end up in Japan and North and South Korea.

The worst acid deposition is in Asia, especially in China, which gets about 59% of its energy from burning coal. Acid deposition is also a growing problem in eastern Europe, Russia, Nigeria, Venezuela, and Colombia (Figure 17-12).

In 1999, researchers at California's Scripps Institution of Oceanography found a thick brown haze of air pollution covering much of the Indian Ocean during winter (Figure 17-13). The haze-covered area is about the size of the continental United States and rises as high as 3,000 meters (10,000 feet). During the late spring and summer, when prevailing winds reverse, some of the haze can be blown back onto the land, where it can combine with monsoon rains and fall as acid deposition.

### What Are the Effects of Acid Deposition on Human Health, Materials, and the Economy?
Acid deposition

- Contributes to human respiratory diseases such as bronchitis and asthma (discussed in Section 17-6).

- Can leach toxic metals such as lead and copper from water pipes into drinking water.

- Damages statues, buildings, metals, and car finishes. Limestone and marble (which is a form of limestone) are especially susceptible because they dissolve even in weak acid solutions ($CaCO_3 + 2H^+ \longrightarrow Ca^{2+} + CO_2 + H_2O$).

- Decreases atmospheric visibility (mostly because of sulfate particles).

- Can lower profits and cause job losses because of lower productivity in fisheries, forests, and farms.

### What Are the Effects of Acid Deposition on Aquatic Ecosystems?
Acid deposition has many harmful ecological effects when the pH of most aquatic

**Figure 17-13** A thick brown haze of air pollution occurs over much of the Indian Ocean during winter. This air pollution comes from burning fossil fuels for transportation and industry in China, Southeast Asia, and India. These pollutants are blown out over the ocean during the winter monsoon season when prevailing winds flow down from the Himalayas and out to sea. In the late spring and summer, the winds reverse. This can blow some of the haze back across the land, where it can combine with monsoon rains and fall as acid deposition. (Data from Veerabhadran Ramanathan, Scripps Institution of Oceanography)

systems falls below 6 and especially below 5 (Figure 17-14). These effects include

- Loss of essentially all fish populations below a pH of 4.5 (Figure 17-14).

- Release of aluminum ions ($Al^{3+}$) attached to minerals in nearby soil into lakes, where they can kill many kinds of fish by stimulating excessive mucus formation. This asphyxiates the fish by clogging their gills.

Much of the damage to aquatic life in sensitive areas with little buffering capacity (Figure 17-12) is a result of *acid shock.* This is caused by the sudden runoff of large amounts of highly acidic water and aluminum ions into lakes and streams, when snow melts in the spring or after unusually heavy rains.

Because of excess acidity,

- In Norway and Sweden, at least 16,000 lakes contain no fish, and 52,000 more lakes have lost most of their acid-neutralizing capacity.

- In Canada, some 14,000 acidified lakes contain few if any fish, and some fish populations in 150,000 more lakes are declining because of increased acidity.

- In the United States, about 9,000 lakes (most in the Northeast and upper Midwest; Figure 17-11) are threatened with excess acidity, one-third of them seriously. According to the Environmental Protection Agency's National Surface Water Survey (NSWS), acid deposition causes about 75% of the acidic lakes and about 50% of the acidic streams in the United States.

### What Are the Effects of Acid Deposition on Plants and Soil Chemistry?

Acid deposition (often along with other air pollutants such as ozone) can harm forests and crops, especially when the soil pH falls below 5.1. Effects of acid deposition on trees and other plants are caused by chemical interactions in forest and cropland soils (Figure 17-15, p. 432) and include

- Damaging leaves and needles directly.

- Leaching essential plant nutrients such as calcium and magnesium salts from soils. This reduces plant productivity and the ability of the soils to buffer or neutralize acidic inputs.

**Figure 17-14** Fish and other aquatic organisms vary in their sensitivity to acidity. The figure shows the lowest pH (highest acidity) at which the various species can survive. Note that the greatest effects occur when the pH drops below 5.5.

- Releasing aluminum ions ($Al^{3+}$) attached to insoluble soil compounds, which can hinder uptake and use of soil nutrients and water by plants.

- Dissolving insoluble soil compounds and releasing ions of metals such as lead, cadmium, and mercury that can be absorbed by plants and are highly toxic to plants and animals.

- Promoting the growth of acid-loving mosses that can kill trees by (1) holding so much water that feeder roots are drowned, (2) eliminating air from the soil, and (3) killing mycorrhizal fungi that help tree roots absorb nutrients (Figure 8-12c and d, p. 179).

- Weakening trees and other plants so they become more susceptible to other types of damage such as (1) severe cold, (2) diseases, (3) insect attacks, (4) drought, and (5) harmful mosses.

It is important to note that *most of the world's forests and lakes are not being destroyed or seriously harmed by acid deposition.* Instead, acid deposition is a regional problem that can harm forests and lakes downwind

Emissions

Acid deposition

$SO_2$    $NO_x$
$H_2O_2$    $O_3$
PANs    Others

Direct damage to leaves and bark

Reduced photosynthesis and growth

Increased susceptibility to drought, extreme cold, insects, mosses, and disease organisms

Soil acidification

Leaching of soil nutrients

Acids

Release of toxic metal ions

Root damage

Reduced nutrient and water uptake

Tree death

Lake

Groundwater

**Figure 17-15** Air pollutants are one of several interacting stresses that can damage, weaken, or kill trees.

from **(1)** power plants, smelters, and industrial plants that burn coal without modern air pollution equipment and **(2)** large car-dominated cities without adequate controls on emissions of nitrogen oxides ($NO_x$) from motor vehicles. Mountaintop forests are the terrestrial areas hardest hit by acid deposition because **(1)** they tend to have thin soils without much buffering capacity, and **(2)** trees on mountaintops (especially conifers such as red spruce and balsam fir that keep their leaves year round) are bathed almost continuously in very acidic fog and clouds.

For example, scientists have analyzed decades of data on nutrient losses from soils at Yale University's Hubbard Brook Experimental Forest in New Hampshire. They found that since 1960 acid deposition has leached out more than 50% of the available

calcium in the generally alkaline (and thus buffering) soils found in this research forest. As a result, no net tree growth has occurred since the 1980s.

**How Serious Is Acid Deposition in the United States?** Since 1980, the federal government has sponsored the National Acid Precipitation Assessment Program (NAPAP) to **(1)** coordinate government acid deposition research, **(2)** assess the costs, benefits, and effectiveness of the country's acid deposition legislation and control program, and **(3)** report its findings to Congress. This study involved about 700 scientists and has cost more than a half a billion dollars.

In its 1998 report to Congress, the NAPAP and a 2001 article by Charles T. Driscoll and other researchers provided both good and bad news.

Here is the *good news*:

- Reductions in $SO_2$ and $NO_x$ emissions from previously unregulated coal-fired power plants required by Phase I of the 1990 amendments to the Clean Air Act have been met. Although $SO_2$ emissions dropped between 1990 and 1999, $NO_x$ emissions have remained roughly the same (mostly because of emissions from motor vehicles). Phase II (which began in 2000) requires further reduction in both pollutants from a larger number of sources.

- Declines have been noted in the acidity and sulfate concentrations in precipitation in the Midwest and Northeast.

- Dissolved concentrations of sulfate (a major cause of acidification) have dropped in monitored lakes and streams.

- Epidemiological studies suggest that decreased emissions of $SO_2$, $NO_x$, and particulate matter (especially fine particles) could reduce premature deaths from cardiovascular and respiratory causes.

- Acid deposition has not led to a decline in overall tree growth in the vast majority of forests in the United States and Canada.

- The benefits for human health and visibility resulting from $SO_2$ reductions could exceed the costs of complying with the 1990 amendments to the Clean Air Act (but the report provides no cost-benefit calculations).

Here is some *bad news*:

- Deposition of sulfur and nitrogen compounds has caused adverse impacts on highly sensitive forest ecosystems in the United States.

- Acidic deposition has accelerated the leaching of important plant nutrients—such as ions of calcium and magnesium—from soils in some areas.

- Adverse impacts from acidic deposition could develop in other forest ecosystems through chronic long-term exposure.

- Atmospheric nitrate concentrations have not decreased.

- Although sulfate levels in many lakes have declined, no decline has been noted in the acidity or acid-neutralizing capacity of sensitive aquatic systems, the key to a recovery of aquatic life.

- Acid deposition has increased the toxic forms of Al in soil waters, lakes, and streams.

- According to 2001 study by Gene Likens and nine other leading acid deposition researchers, an additional 80% reduction in $SO_2$ emissions from coal-burning power and industrial plants in the midwestern United States will be needed for northeastern lakes,

forests, and streams to recover from the effects of acid deposition. This amounts to a 44% reduction in total U.S. $SO_2$ emissions.

In other words, the *good news* is that the 1990 amendments to the Clean Air Act have helped reduce some of the harmful impacts of acid deposition in the United States. However, the *bad news* is there is still a long way to go.

**Solutions: What Can Be Done to Reduce Acid Deposition?** Figure 17-16 summarizes ways to reduce acid deposition. According to most scientists studying acid deposition, the best solutions are *prevention approaches* that reduce or eliminate emissions of $SO_2$, $NO_x$, and particulates, as discussed in Section 17-7.

Controlling acid deposition is a difficult political problem because **(1)** the people and ecosystems it affects often are quite distant from those who cause the problem, **(2)** countries with large supplies of coal (such as China, India, Russia, and the United States) have a strong incentive to use it as a major energy resource, and **(3)** owners of coal-burning power plants say the costs of adding equipment to reduce air pollution, using low-sulfur coal, or removing sulfur from coal are too high and would increase the cost of electricity for consumers.

Environmentalists respond that **(1)** much cleaner and affordable ways are available to produce electricity—including wind turbines (p. 401) and burning

| Prevention | | Cleanup |
|---|---|---|
| Reduce air pollution by improving energy efficiency | | Add lime to neutralize acidified lakes |
| Reduce coal use | | Add phosphate fertilizer to neutralize acidified lakes |
| Increase natural gas use | | |
| Increase use of renewable resources | | |
| Burn low-sulfur coal | | |
| Remove $SO_2$ particulates, and $NO_x$ from smokestack gases | | |
| Remove $NO_x$ from motor vehicular exhaust | | |
| Tax emissions of $SO_2$ | | |

**Figure 17-16** *Solutions:* methods for reducing acid deposition.

natural gas in turbines (p. 362), **(2)** the health and environmental costs of burning coal are twice its market cost, and **(3)** these costs should be included in the price of producing electricity from coal (full-cost pricing) so consumers have more realistic knowledge about the effects of using coal to produce electricity.

Large amounts of limestone or lime can be used to neutralize acidified lakes or surrounding soil—the only cleanup approach now being used. However, liming presents several problems.

It is an expensive and temporary remedy that usually must be repeated annually. Using lime to reduce excess acidity in U.S. lakes would cost at least $8 billion per year.

It can kill some types of plankton and aquatic plants and can harm wetland plants that need acidic water.

It is difficult to know how much of the lime to put where (in the water or at selected places on the ground).

Researchers in England found that adding a small amount of phosphate fertilizer can neutralize excess acidity in a lake. However, the effectiveness of this approach is still being evaluated.

## 17-5 INDOOR AIR POLLUTION

**What Are the Types and Sources of Indoor Air Pollution?** If you are reading this book indoors, you may be inhaling more air pollutants with each breath than if you were outside (Figure 17-17). According to EPA studies, in the United States

Levels of 11 common pollutants generally are **(1)** two to five times higher inside homes and commercial buildings than outdoors and **(2)** as much as 100 times higher in some cases.

Levels of fine particles (Figure 17-8), which can contain toxins and metals such as lead and cadmium, can be as much as 60% higher indoors than outdoors.

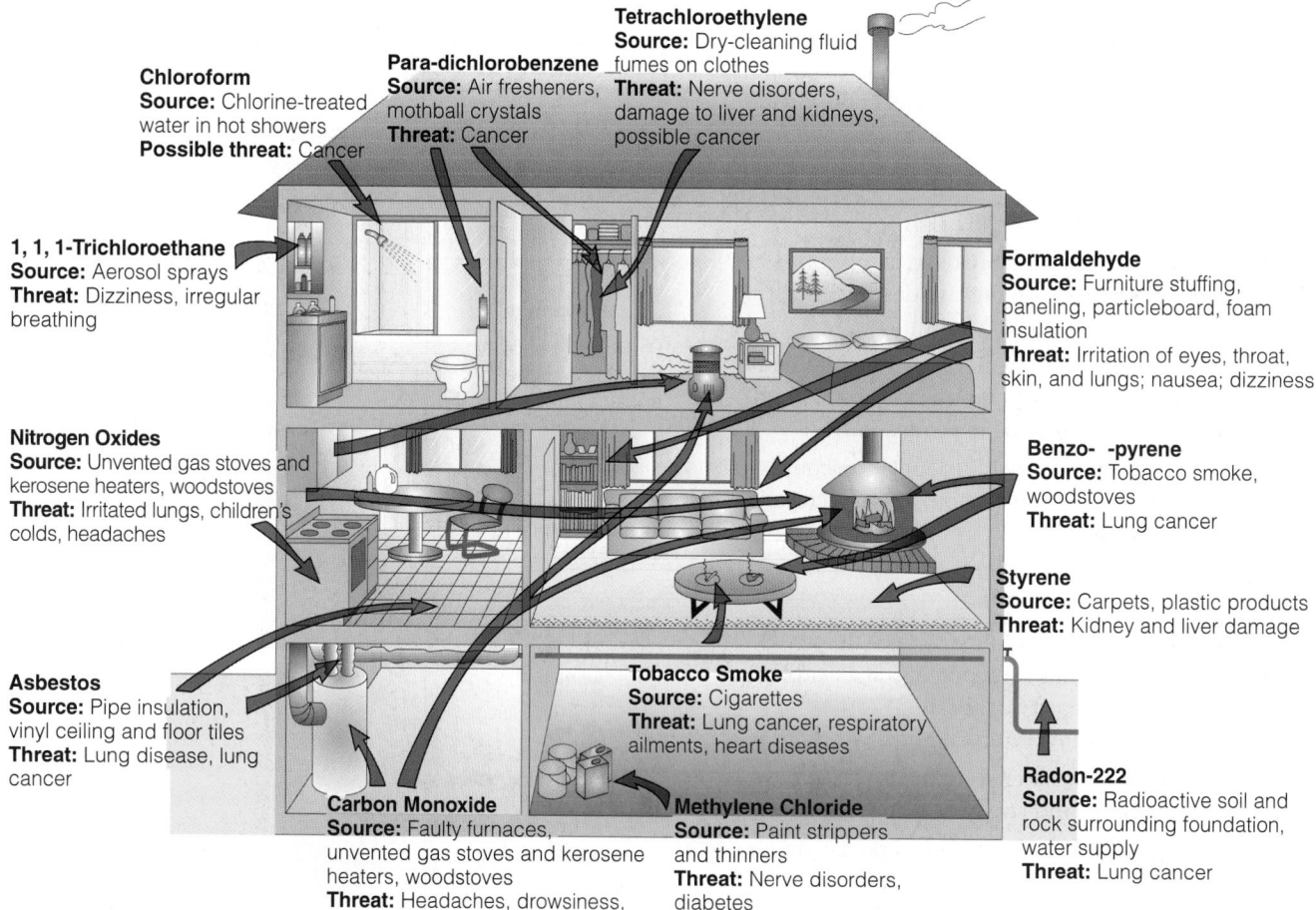

**Figure 17-17** Some important indoor air pollutants. (Data from U.S. Environmental Protection Agency)

- Concentrations of several pesticides (such as chlordane), approved for outdoor use only, were 10 times greater inside than outside monitored homes (some coming from pesticide dust tracked in on shoes).

- Pollution levels inside cars in traffic-clogged urban areas can be up to 18 times higher than those outside the vehicles.

The health risks from exposure to such chemicals are magnified because people typically spend 70–98% of their time indoors or inside vehicles. In 1990, the EPA placed indoor air pollution at the top of the list of 18 sources of cancer risk, and it is rated by risk analysis scientists as a high-risk health problem for humans (Figure 11-15, left, p. 246).

According to the EPA, more than 3,000 cases of cancer per year in the United States may be caused by exposure to indoor air pollutants. At greatest risk are **(1)** smokers, **(2)** infants and children under age 5, **(3)** the old, **(4)** the sick, **(5)** pregnant women, **(6)** people with respiratory or heart problems, and **(7)** factory workers.

Danish and U.S. EPA studies have linked pollutants found in buildings to dizziness, headaches, coughing, sneezing, nausea, burning eyes, chronic fatigue, and flulike symptoms, known as the *sick-building syndrome.* New buildings are more commonly "sick" than old ones because of **(1)** reduced air exchange (to save energy) and **(2)** chemicals released from new carpeting and furniture. According to the EPA, at least 17% of the 4 million commercial buildings in the United States are considered "sick" (including EPA headquarters). Indoor air pollution in the United States costs an estimated $100 billion per year in **(1)** absenteeism, **(2)** reduced productivity, and **(3)** health-care costs. Mostly because of differences in genetic makeup, some individuals can be acutely sensitive to one or a number of indoor air pollutants (Figure 11-3, p. 230).

According to the EPA and public health officials, the three most dangerous indoor air pollutants are **(1)** cigarette smoke (p. 228), **(2)** formaldehyde, and **(3)** radioactive radon-222 gas.

Worker exposure to asbestos fibers in mines and in factories making asbestos material also is a serious indoor air pollution problem, especially in developing countries. A number of research studies on laboratory animals have also identified tiny fibers of *fiberglass* as a widespread and potentially potent carcinogen in indoor air.

The chemical that causes most people difficulty is *formaldehyde,* a colorless, extremely irritating gas widely used to manufacture common household materials. As many as 20 million Americans suffer from chronic breathing problems, dizziness, rash, headaches, sore throat, sinus and eye irritation, wheezing, and nausea caused by daily exposure to low levels of formaldehyde emitted (outgassed) from common household materials. These include **(1)** building materials (such as plywood, particleboard, paneling, and high-gloss wood used in floors and cabinets), **(2)** furniture, **(3)** drapes, **(4)** upholstery, **(5)** adhesives in carpeting and wallpaper, **(6)** urethane-formaldehyde insulation, **(7)** fingernail hardener, and **(8)** wrinkle-free coating on permanent-press clothing (Figure 17-17). The EPA estimates that as many as 1 of every 5,000 people who live in manufactured homes for more than 10 years will develop cancer from formaldehyde exposure.

In developing countries, the burning of wood, dung, crop residues, and coal in open fires or in unvented or poorly vented stoves for cooking and heating exposes inhabitants (especially women and young children) to very high levels of particulate air pollution.

**Case Study: Is Your Home Contaminated with Radon Gas?** Radon-222, a naturally occurring radioactive gas that you cannot see, taste, or smell, is produced by the radioactive decay of uranium-238. Small amounts of uranium-238 are found in most soil and rock, but this isotope is much more concentrated in underground deposits of minerals such as uranium, phosphate, granite, and shale.

When radon gas from such deposits seeps upward through the soil and is released outdoors, it disperses quickly in the atmosphere and decays to harmless levels. However, radon gas can enter buildings above such deposits through **(1)** cracks in foundations and walls, **(2)** openings around sump pumps and drains, and **(3)** hollow concrete blocks (Figure 17-18, p. 436). It can build up to high levels, especially in unventilated lower levels of homes and buildings.

Radon-222 gas quickly decays into solid particles of other radioactive elements that, if inhaled, expose lung tissue to a large amount of ionizing radiation from alpha particles (Figure 3-13, p. 56). This exposure can damage lung tissue and lead to lung cancer over the course of a 70-year lifetime. Your chances of getting lung cancer from radon depend mostly on **(1)** how much radon is in your home, **(2)** how much time you spend in your home, and **(3)** whether you are a smoker or have ever smoked.

In 1998, the National Academy of Science estimated that prolonged exposure for a lifetime of 70 years to low levels of radon or radon acting together with smoking is responsible for 15,000–22,000 (or 12%) of the lung cancer deaths each year in the United States. This makes radon the second leading cause of lung cancer after smoking (p. 228). Most of the deaths are among smokers or former smokers, with about 2,100–2,900 deaths among nonsmokers.

Outlet vents for furnaces and dryers

**Figure 17-18** Sources and paths of entry for indoor radon-222 gas. (Data from U.S. Environmental Protection Agency)

These estimates assume that (1) there is no safe threshold dose for radon exposure (Figure 11-6, left, p. 233), and (2) the incidence of lung cancer in uranium miners exposed to high levels of radon in mines can be extrapolated to estimate lung cancer deaths for people in homes exposed to much lower levels of radon. Some scientists question these assumptions and say these estimates are too high. They also point to the contradictory results of several epidemiological studies on the risks of lung cancer from radon exposure.

EPA indoor radon surveys suggest that 4–5 million U.S. homes may have annual radon levels above 4 picocuries* per liter of air and that 50,000–100,000 homes may have levels above 20 picocuries per liter. If the 4 picocuries per liter standard is adopted (as proposed by the EPA), the cost of testing and correcting the problem could run about $50 billion, with a 15–20% reduction in radon-related deaths. Some researchers argue that it makes more sense to spend perhaps only $500 million to find and fix homes and buildings with radon levels above 20 picocuries per liter until more reliable data are available on the threat from exposure to lower levels of radon.

Because radon hot spots can occur almost anywhere, it is impossible to know which buildings have unsafe levels of radon without conducting tests. In 1988, the EPA and the U.S. Surgeon General's Office recommended that everyone living in a detached house, a town house, a mobile home, or on the first three floors of an apartment building test for radon. Ideally, radon levels should be monitored continuously in the main living areas (not basements or crawl spaces) for 2 months to a year. By 2001, only about 6% of U.S. households had conducted radon tests (most lasting only 2–7 days and costing $20–100 per home).

For information about radon testing visit the EPA website at www.epa.gov/iaq/radon. According to the EPA, radon control could add $350–500 to the cost of a new home, and correcting a radon problem in an existing house could run $800–2,500.

**Case Study: What Should Be Done About Asbestos?** *Asbestos* refers to several different fibrous forms of silicate minerals. For decades it was widely used in the United States as a building material and for large water pipelines because of its strength, flexibility, and low cost. Unless completely sealed within a product, asbestos crumbles easily into a dust of fibers tiny enough to become suspended in the air and inhaled deep into the lungs, where they remain for many years.

Prolonged exposure to asbestos fibers can cause (1) *asbestosis* (a chronic, sometimes fatal disease that makes breathing very difficult and was recognized as a hazard among asbestos workers as early as 1924), (2) *lung cancer,* and (3) *mesothelioma* (a fatal cancer of the lung's lining). Epidemiological studies have shown that smokers exposed to asbestos fibers have a much greater chance of dying from lung cancer than do nonsmokers exposed to such fibers.

Most of these diseases occur in workers exposed for years to high levels of asbestos fibers. This group includes asbestos miners, insulators, pipefitters, shipyard employees, and workers in asbestos-producing factories. Family members who breathe asbestos dust brought home in the clothes and hair of asbestos workers also have higher than expected cancer rates, as do people who live near asbestos manufacturing plants with inadequate control of asbestos emissions.

According to health officials, asbestos fibers caused the premature cancer deaths of almost 172,000 asbestos workers in the United States between 1967 and 2000, the worst U.S. occupational health disaster of the 20th century. An additional 119,000 premature cancer deaths among U.S. asbestos workers are predicted between 2000 and 2025, mostly from workers exposed to unsafe conditions before working conditions were improved. A 2001 study by Tillinghast-Towers Perrin, a consultant firm to the financial services industry, estimated that settlements to individuals exposed to asbestos in the United States and related expenses ultimately will reach $200 billion.

According to health experts, the major health risk from asbestos today is occurring among asbestos min-

---

*A *picocurie* is a trillionth of a curie, which is the amount of radioactivity emitted by a gram of radium.

ers and workers in developing countries (especially Russia, China, Brazil, India, and Thailand), where the use of asbestos as an inexpensive building material is growing rapidly. Experts say that 90% of the worker deaths from asbestos exposure can be prevented by **(1)** using a good-fitting face mask, **(2)** wetting asbestos to control dust, and **(3)** changing clothes before and after handling asbestos.

## 17-6 EFFECTS OF AIR POLLUTION ON LIVING ORGANISMS AND MATERIALS

**How Does the Human Respiratory System Help Protect Us from Air Pollution?**   Table 17-2 listed the major health effects from the six most common (criteria) outdoor air pollutants. Your respiratory system (Figure 17-19) has a number of mechanisms that help protect you from such air pollution, including

- Hairs in your nose, which filter out large particles.

- Sticky mucus in the lining of your upper respiratory tract, which captures smaller (but not the smallest) particles and dissolves some gaseous pollutants.

- Sneezing and coughing, which expel contaminated air and mucus when pollutants irritate your respiratory system.

- Hundreds of thousands of tiny mucus-coated hair-like structures called *cilia,* which line your upper respiratory tract. They continually wave back and forth and transport mucus and the pollutants they trap to your throat (where they are swallowed or expelled).

Years of smoking and exposure to air pollutants can overload or break down these natural defenses, causing or contributing to respiratory diseases such as **(1)** *lung cancer,* **(2)** *asthma* (typically an allergic reaction causing sudden episodes of muscle spasms in the bronchial walls, resulting in acute shortness of breath), **(3)** *chronic bronchitis* (persistent inflammation and damage to the cells lining the bronchi and bronchioles, causing mucus buildup, painful coughing, and shortness of breath), and **(4)** *emphysema* (irreversible damage to air sacs or alveoli leading to abnormal dilation of air spaces, loss of lung elasticity, and acute shortness of breath (Figure 17-20, p. 438). Older adults, infants, pregnant women, and people with heart disease, asthma, or other respiratory diseases are especially vulnerable to air pollution.

**How Many People Die Prematurely from Air Pollution?**   It is difficult to estimate by risk analysis how many people die prematurely from respiratory or cardiac problems caused or aggravated by air pollution because people are exposed to so many different pollutants over their lifetimes.

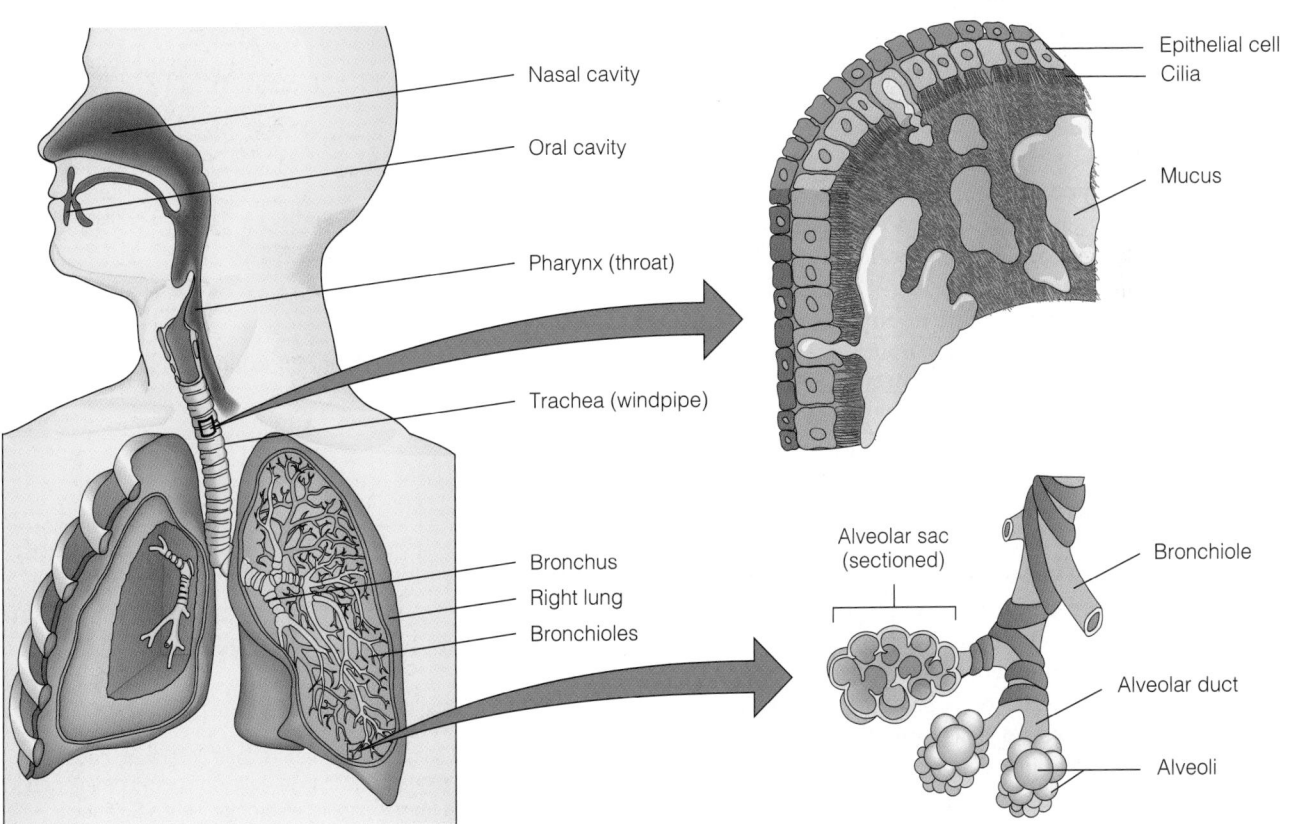

**Figure 17-19** Major components of the human respiratory system.

**Figure 17-20** Normal human lungs (left) and the lungs of a person who died of emphysema (right). Prolonged smoking and exposure to air pollutants can cause emphysema in anyone, but about 2% of emphysema cases result from a defective gene that reduces the elasticity of the air sacs in the lungs. Anyone with this hereditary condition, for which testing is available, should not smoke and should not live or work in a highly polluted area.

O. Auerbach/Visuals Unlimited

In the United States, the EPA estimates that annual deaths related to outdoor air pollution range from 65,000 to 200,000 (most from exposure to fine particles; Spotlight, p. 440). If we include indoor air pollution, estimated annual deaths from air pollution in the United States range from 150,000 to 350,000 people—equivalent to 1–2 fully loaded 400-passenger jumbo jets crashing accidentally *each day* with no survivors.

Millions more become ill and lose work time. A 2000 study by state and local air pollution officials estimated that each year more than 125,000 Americans (120,000 of them in urban areas) get cancer from breathing diesel fumes from buses, trucks, and other diesel engines. According to the EPA and the American Lung Association, air pollution in the United States costs at least $150 billion annually in health care and lost work productivity, with $100 billion of that caused by indoor air pollution.

According to a 1999 study by Australia's Commonwealth Science Council, worldwide at least 3 million people (most of them in Asia) die prematurely each year from the effects of air pollution—an average of 8,200 deaths per day. About 2.8 million of these deaths are from *indoor* air pollution, and 200,000 are from *outdoor* pollution (Figure 17-21). This explains why the World Health Organization and the World Bank consider indoor air pollution one of the world's most crucial environmental problems.

**How Are Plants Damaged by Air Pollutants?**
The effects of exposure of trees to a combination of air pollutants may not become visible for several decades, when large numbers of trees suddenly begin dying (see photo on p. 417) because of **(1)** soil nutrient depletion and **(2)** increased susceptibility to pests, diseases, fungi, and drought (Figure 17-15). This phenomenon has degraded areas of forests downwind of coal-burning facilities and some large urban areas.

The greatest harm occurs to downwind coniferous forests at high altitudes whose needles are exposed to air pollution year round. In the United States, the most seriously affected areas are high-elevation spruce trees that populate the ridges of the Appalachian Mountains from Maine to Georgia, including the Shenandoah and Great Smoky Mountain national parks.

Air pollution, mostly by ozone, also **(1)** threatens some crops (especially corn, wheat, and soybeans) and

**Indoor Exposure**

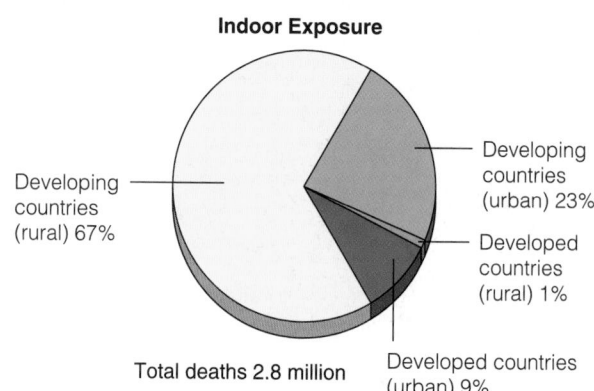

Developing countries (rural) 67%

Developing countries (urban) 23%

Developed countries (rural) 1%

Developed countries (urban) 9%

Total deaths 2.8 million

**Outdoor Exposure**

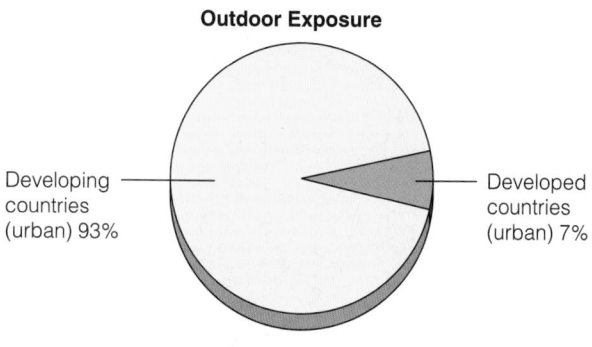

Developing countries (urban) 93%

Developed countries (urban) 7%

Total deaths 0.2 million

**Figure 17-21** Estimated premature deaths per year caused by indoor and outdoor air pollution in developing and developed countries. (Data from Australia's Commonwealth Science Council, 1999)

**(2)** reduces U.S. food production by 5–10%. In the United States, estimates of agricultural losses as a result of air pollution (mostly by ozone) range from $2 to $6 billion per year, with an estimated $1 billion of damages in California alone.

**What Are the Harmful Effects of Air Pollutants on Materials?** Each year, air pollutants cause billions of dollars in damage to various materials we use (Table 17-3). The fallout of soot and grit on buildings, cars, and clothing necessitates costly cleaning. Air pollutants break down exterior paint on cars and houses, and they deteriorate roofing materials. Irreplaceable marble statues, historic buildings, and stained glass windows around the world have been pitted, gouged, and discolored. The EPA estimates damage to buildings in the United States from acid deposition alone at $5 billion per year.

## 17-7 SOLUTIONS: PREVENTING AND REDUCING AIR POLLUTION

**How Have Laws Been Used to Reduce Air Pollution in the United States?** The U.S. Congress passed Clean Air Acts in 1970, 1977, and 1990. With these laws the federal government establishes air pollution regulations that are enforced by each state and by major cities.

Congress directed the EPA to establish *national ambient air quality standards* (*NAAQS*) for six outdoor criteria pollutants (Table 17-2). The EPA regulates these chemicals by using *criteria* developed from risk assessment methods (Section 11-2, p. 232) to set maximum permissible levels in outdoor air.

One limit, called a *primary standard*, is set to protect human health, and another, called a *secondary standard*, is intended to prevent environmental and property damage. Each standard specifies the maximum allowable level, averaged over a specific period, for a certain pollutant in outdoor (ambient) air.

The EPA has also established national emission standards for more than 100 different toxic air pollutants known to cause or suspected of causing cancer or other adverse health effects.

Here is some *great news.* According to the EPA,

- Between 1970 and 2000, national total emissions of the six criteria pollutants declined 29% while U.S. population increased 32%, gross domestic product increased 158%, and vehicle miles traveled rose 143%.

- Between 1970 and 2000, mean concentrations of five of six criteria air pollutants in the troposphere decreased by **(1)** 98% for lead, **(2)** 93% for volatile organic compounds (VOCs), **(3)** 88% for suspended particulate matter (10 micrometers or less in diameter), **(4)** 44% for sulfur dioxide, and **(5)** 26% for carbon monoxide.

- The mean estimated human health and environmental benefits from air pollution regulations between 1970 and 1990 amounted to $6.8 trillion, compared to $436 million (in 1990 dollars) spent to implement all federal, state, and local air pollution regulations. Thus the net economic benefit of the Clean Air Act between 1970 and 1990 was $6.4 trillion. During this 20-year period, the act prevented an estimated 1.6 million premature deaths and 300 million cases of respiratory disease.

- Between 1990 and 2010, the 1990 amendments to the Clean Air Act should provide four times more health and environmental benefits than the estimated compliance costs to industries and consumers. By 2010, the 1990 amendments should prevent 23,000 Americans from dying prematurely and avert 1.7 million asthma attacks per year.

| Table 17-3 Harmful Effects of Air Pollution on Materials | | |
|---|---|---|
| **Material** | **Effects** | **Principal Air Pollutants** |
| Stone and concrete | Surface erosion, discoloration, soiling | Sulfur dioxide, sulfuric acid, nitric acid, particulate matter |
| Metals | Corrosion, tarnishing, loss of strength | Sulfur dioxide, sulfuric acid, nitric acid, particulate matter, hydrogen sulfide |
| Ceramics and glass | Surface erosion | Hydrogen fluoride, particulate matter |
| Paints | Surface erosion, discoloration, soiling | Sulfur dioxide, hydrogen sulfide, ozone, particulate matter |
| Paper | Embrittlement, discoloration | Sulfur dioxide |
| Rubber | Cracking, loss of strength | Ozone |
| Leather | Surface deterioration, loss of strength | Sulfur dioxide |
| Textiles | Deterioration, fading, soiling | Sulfur dioxide, nitrogen dioxide, ozone, particulate matter |

Here is some *bad news.*

- Between 1970 and 2000, emissions of nitrogen oxides ($NO_x$) increased 20%.

- Between 1990 and 2000, ground-level concentrations of ozone increased, especially in the southern and northeastern regions of the United States.

- Despite continued improvements in air quality, in 2002 areas in which approximately 142 million people lived did not meet the primary standards for one or more of the six criteria pollutants during part of the year.

## How Can U.S. Air Pollution Laws Be Improved?

The Clean Air Act of 1990 was an important step in the right direction, but many environmentalists point to the following deficiencies in this law:

- *Continuing to rely mostly on pollution cleanup rather than prevention.* In the United States, the air pollutant with the largest drop (98% between 1970 and 2000) in its atmospheric level was lead, which was largely banned in gasoline.

- *Failing to increase fuel-efficiency standards for cars and light trucks* (Figure 16-7, p. 386). According to environ-mental scientists, increased standards would **(1)** reduce air pollution more quickly and effectively than any other method, **(2)** reduce $CO_2$ emissions, **(3)** save energy (p. 385), and **(4)** save consumers enormous amounts of money.

- *Not adequately regulating emissions from inefficient two-cycle gasoline engines* These engines are used in lawn mowers, leaf blowers, chain saws, and personal marine engines used to power jet skis, outboard motors, and personal watercraft. According to the California Air Resources Board, **(1)** a 1-hour ride on a typical jet ski creates more air pollution than the average U.S. car does in a year, **(2)** operating a 100-horsepower marine engine for 7 hours emits more air pollutants than a new car driven 160,000 kilometers (100,000 miles). Some *good news* is that in 2001 the EPA announced plans to reduce emissions from most of these sources by 2004 and establish even stricter emissions by 2007.

- *Doing too little to reduce emissions of carbon dioxide and other greenhouse gases.*

Executives of companies affected by implementing such policies strongly oppose such changes in air pollution laws. They claim that implementing such

---

## SPOTLIGHT

## Health Dangers from Fine Particles

Research indicates that invisible particles—especially *fine particles* with diameters less than 10 microns (PM-10) and *ultrafine particles* with diameters less than 2.5 microns (PM-2.5)—pose a significant health hazard. Such particles are emitted by incinerators, motor vehicles, radial tires, wind erosion, wood-burning fireplaces, and power and industrial plants (Figure 17-8).

Such tiny particles **(1)** are not effectively captured by modern air pollution control equipment, **(2)** are small enough to penetrate the respiratory system's natural defenses against air pollution (Figure 17-19), and **(3)** can bring with them droplets or other particles of toxic or cancer-causing pollutants that become attached to their surfaces.

Once they are lodged deep within the lungs, these fine particles can cause chronic irritation that can **(1)** trigger asthma attacks, **(2)** aggra-vate other lung diseases, **(3)** cause lung cancer, and **(4)** interfere with the blood's ability to take in oxygen and release $CO_2$, which strains the heart and increases the risk of death from heart disease.

Several recent studies of air pollution in U.S. cities have indicated that fine and ultrafine particles prematurely kill 65,000–200,000 Americans each year. There is no known threshold level below which the harmful effects of fine particles disappear.

Exposure to particulate air pollution is much worse in most developing countries, where urban air quality has generally deteriorated. The World Bank estimates that if particulate levels were reduced globally to WHO guidelines, 300,000–700,000 premature deaths per year could be prevented.

In 1997, the EPA announced stricter emission standards for ul-trafine particles with diameters less than 2.5 microns (PM-2.5). The EPA estimates the cost of implementing the standards at $7 billion per year, with the resulting health and other benefits estimated at $120 billion per year.

According to industry officials, the new standard is based on flimsy scientific evidence, and its implementation will cost $200 billion per year. EPA officials say that their review of the scientific evidence—one of the most exhaustive ones ever undertaken by the agency—supports the need for the new standard for ultrafine particles. Furthermore, a 2000 study by the Health Effects Institute of 90 large American cities supported the link between fine and ultrafine particles and higher rates of death and disease.

### Critical Thinking

Are you for or against the stricter standard for emissions of ultrafine particles? Explain. Use the library or Internet to determine whether stricter standards for ultrafine particles have been implemented.

---

changes would cost too much, harm economic growth, and cost jobs.

Proponents contend that history has shown that most industry estimates of implementing various air pollution control standards in the United States were many times the actual cost of implementation. In addition, implementing such standards has helped increase economic growth and create jobs by stimulating companies to develop new technologies for reducing air pollution emissions. Many of these technologies are sold in the international marketplace.

**Should We Use the Marketplace to Reduce Pollution?** To help reduce $SO_2$ emissions, the Clean Air Act of 1990 allows an *emissions trading policy,* which enables the 110 most polluting power plants in 21 states (primarily in the Midwest and East; Figure 17-11) to buy and sell $SO_2$ pollution rights.

Each year a power plant is given a certain number of pollution credits or rights that allow it to emit a certain amount of $SO_2$. A utility that emits less $SO_2$ than its limit receives more pollution credits. It can use these credits **(1)** to avoid reductions in $SO_2$ emissions from some of its other facilities, **(2)** bank them for future plant expansions, or **(3)** sell them to other utilities, private citizens, or environmental groups. Proponents of this system argue that it allows the marketplace to determine the cheapest, most efficient way to get the job done instead of having the government dictate how to control pollution.

Some environmentalists see this *cap-and-trade* market approach as an improvement over the regulatory approach, as long as it achieves a net reduction in $SO_2$ pollution. This would be accomplished by limiting the total number of credits and gradually lowering the annual number of credits. However, this reduction in the cap is not required by the 1990 amendments to the Clean Air Act and currently is not being done.

Some environmentalists contend that marketing pollution

- Allows utilities with older, dirtier power plants to buy their way out and keep on emitting unacceptable levels of $SO_2$.

- Creates incentives to cheat because air quality regulation is based largely on self-reporting of emissions and pollution monitoring is incomplete and imprecise.

Here is some *good news*. Between 1990 and 2000, the emission trading system helped reduce $SO_2$ emissions in the United States by 30%. The cost of doing this was less than one-tenth the cost projected by industry because this market-based system motivated companies to reduce emissions in more efficient ways.

In 1997, the EPA proposed a voluntary emissions trading program involving smog-forming nitrogen oxides ($NO_x$) for 22 eastern states and the District of Columbia. Emissions trading may also be implemented for particulate emissions and volatile organic compounds.

In 2002, the Bush administration and Congress were evaluating a new clear sky cap-and-trade program to control three substances emitted by coal-burning power plants at the same time instead of regulating them one pollutant at a time. The idea is to **(1)** place an upper cap on the combined emissions of $SO_2$ $NO_x$, and mercury (Hg) and **(2)** allow utilities to trade emissions to reduce levels of these pollutants.

Environmentalists caution that the success of this or any emissions trading approach depends on **(1)** how low the initial cap is and **(2)** requiring phased-in reduction of the cap to promote continuing innovation in air pollution prevention and control. They contend that the cap proposed in the Bush administration's Blue Sky program is **(1)** much too high to be effective and **(2)** about twice the cap value proposed to the White House by the EPA. There is also no plan for future reduction of the cap.

**How Can We Reduce Outdoor Air Pollution?** Figure 17-22 summarizes ways to reduce emissions of sulfur oxides, nitrogen oxides, and particulate matter from stationary sources (such as electric power plants and industrial plants that burn coal). Until recently, emphasis has been on **(1)** dispersing and diluting the pollutants by using tall smokestacks or **(2)** adding equipment that removes some of the particulate pollutants after they are produced (Figure 17-23, p. 442). However, under the sulfur reduction requirements of the 1990 amendments to the Clean Air Act, more utilities are switching to low-sulfur coal to reduce $SO_2$ emissions. Environmentalists call for greater emphasis on such prevention methods.

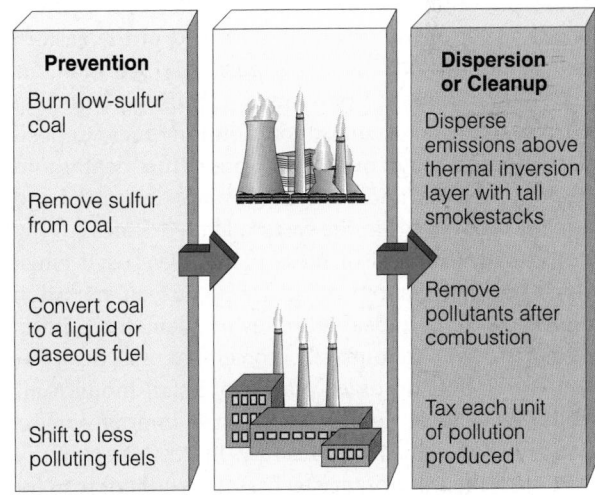

**Figure 17-22** *Solutions:* methods for reducing emissions of sulfur oxides, nitrogen oxides, and particulate matter from stationary sources such as coal-burning electric power plants and industrial plants.

**Figure 17-23** *Solutions:* four commonly used methods for removing particulates from the exhaust gases of electric power and industrial plants. Of these, only baghouse filters remove many of the more hazardous fine particles. All these methods produce hazardous materials that must be disposed of safely, and except for cyclone separators, all of them are expensive. The wet scrubber can also reduce sulfur dioxide emissions.

a. Electrostatic Precipitator

b. Baghouse Filter

c. Cyclone Separator

d. Wet Scrubber

There has been much controversy over requiring better pollution control for 17,000 older coal-burning plants, most of the larger ones located in the eastern half of the United States (Figure 17-11). These plants and several thousand older manufacturing plants that burn coal **(1)** make a major contribution to acid deposition, **(2)** cause large numbers of premature deaths and health problems, and **(3)** degrade many terrestrial and aquatic ecosystems in the eastern United States.

Owners of most of these plants have used emissions trading to avoid having to reduce air pollution emissions. To help deal with this problem, the Clinton administration announced enforcement of a Clean Air Act rule requiring older plants to install modern air pollution control devices when they improve or expand their facilities significantly. In 2000, a study by Abt Associates (a primary technical consultant firm for the EPA) estimated that reducing emissions from older coal-fired plants could prevent 18,700 premature deaths per year and 3 million lost work days annually from respiratory illness.

The affected utility and manufacturing companies vigorously opposed enforcement of this rule, arguing that it would cost them too much money, raise electricity prices, and cause them to shut down some of their older plants. In 2002, the Bush administration said it would not enforce this rule. In protest of this decision, Eric Schaeffer resigned his job as chief of Civil Enforcement for the EPA. He said that the Abt Associates report "shows how the Bush administration's failure to enforce the Clean Air Act is a serious threat to public health."

Six eastern states and several large cities (including Chicago and New York), fed up with dirty power plants and the lack of desire of elected officials to do much about them, are taking matters into their own hands. They are studying ways to reduce pollution from such plants or have passed legislation or implemented policies to accomplish this.

Figure 17-24 lists ways to reduce emissions from motor vehicles, the primary culprits in producing photochemical smog. Use of alternative vehicle fuels

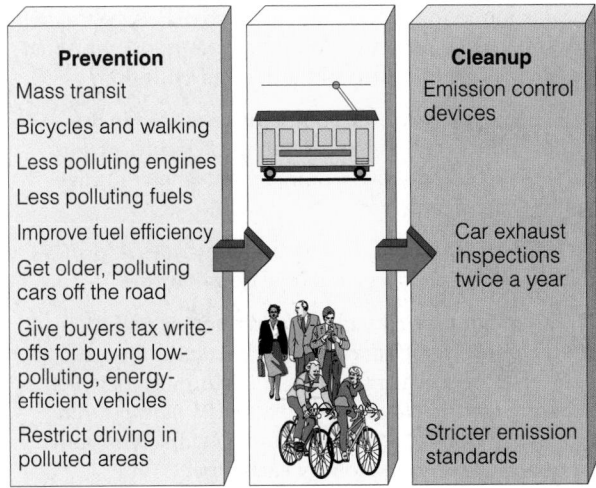

| Prevention | | Cleanup |
|---|---|---|
| Mass transit | | Emission control devices |
| Bicycles and walking | | |
| Less polluting engines | | |
| Less polluting fuels | | |
| Improve fuel efficiency | | Car exhaust inspections twice a year |
| Get older, polluting cars off the road | | |
| Give buyers tax write-offs for buying low-polluting, energy-efficient vehicles | | |
| Restrict driving in polluted areas | | Stricter emission standards |

**Figure 17-24** *Solutions:* methods for reducing emissions from motor vehicles.

to reduce air pollution is evaluated in Table 16-1, p. 406.

An important way to make significant reductions in air pollution is to get older, high-polluting vehicles off the road. According to EPA estimates, 10% of the vehicles on the road in the United States emit 50–70% of the pollutants. But people who cannot afford to buy a newer car often own old cars. One suggestion would be to pay people to take their old cars off the road, which would result in huge savings in health and air pollution control costs.

Here is some *good news.* During the past 30 years, outdoor air quality in Tokoyo, in Japan, and in most western European cities has improved. The *bad news* is that outdoor air quality has remained about the same or has gotten worse in most rapidly growing urban areas in developing countries.

**How Can We Reduce Indoor Air Pollution?** To reduce indoor air pollution, it is not necessary to impose indoor air quality standards and monitor the more than 100 million homes and buildings in the United States. Instead, air pollution experts suggest that indoor air pollution can be reduced by several means (Figure 17-25). Another possibility for cleaner indoor air in high-rise buildings is rooftop greenhouses through which building air can be circulated.

In developing countries, indoor air pollution from open fires and leaky and inefficient stoves that burn wood, charcoal, or coal (and the resulting high levels of respiratory illnesses) could be reduced if governments **(1)** gave people simple stoves that burn biofuels more efficiently (which would also reduce deforestation) and that are vented outside or **(2)** provided them with simple solar cookers (Figure 16-21d, p. 397).

**What Is the Next Step? Individuals Matter** It is very encouraging that since 1970 most of the world's

developed countries have enacted laws and regulations that have significantly reduced outdoor air pollution. However, without strong political pressure by individuals and organized groups of individuals on elected officials in the 1970s and 1980s these laws and regulations would not have been enacted, funded, and implemented. In turn these laws and regulations spurred companies, scientists, and engineers to come up with better ways to control outdoor pollution.

These laws and regulations are a useful *output approach* to controlling pollution. To environmentalists, however, the next step is to shift to *preventing air pollution*. With this approach, the question is not *"What can we do about the air pollutants we produce?"* but *"How can we not produce such pollutants in the first place?"*

Burning fossil fuels is the major cause of most outdoor air pollution. Thus preventing such pollution over the next 40–50 years involves the following steps:

- *Integrating government policies for energy and air pollution.*

| Prevention | | Cleanup or Dilution |
|---|---|---|
| Cover ceiling tiles and lining of AC ducts to prevent release of mineral fibers | | Use adjustable fresh air vents for work spaces |
| Ban smoking or limit it to well-ventilated areas | | Increase intake of outside air |
| Set stricter formaldehyde emissions standards for carpet, furniture, and building materials | | Change air more frequently |
| | | Circulate building's air through rooftop greenhouses |
| Prevent radon infiltration | | Use exhaust hoods for stoves and appliances burning natural gas |
| Use office machines in well-ventilated areas | | |
| Use less polluting substitutes for harmful cleaning agents, paints, and other products | | Install efficient chimneys for wood-burning stoves |

**Figure 17-25** *Solutions:* ways to prevent and reduce indoor air pollution.

- *Improving energy efficiency to reduce the use and waste of fossil fuels* (Section 16-1, p. 381)
- *Relying more on lower-polluting and more climate-benign natural gas* (Figures 15-25, p. 358 and 15-29, p. 362) *than on oil and coal.*
- *Increasing use of renewable energy, especially solar cells* (Figure 16-25, p. 400), *wind* (Figure 16-30, p. 403), and *solar-produced hydrogen* (Figure 16-35, p. 409)
- *Regulating air quality for an entire region or airshed with primary emphasis on prevention*
- *Transferring the latest energy-efficiency, renewable-energy, pollution prevention, and pollution control technologies to developing countries*

In terms of human health, the most serious problem is indoor air pollution (Figure 11-15, left, p. 246). This is caused primarily by **(1)** burning of wood, charcoal, dung, and crop wastes in open fires or inefficient stoves in developing countries, **(2)** poverty, which is the primary reason people in developing countries cannot afford less polluting ways to cook and heat their dwellings and water (Figures 11-17, p. 247, and 11-18, p. 248), and **(3)** indoor smoking in developed and developing countries (p. 228 and Figure 11-18, p. 248).

Thus, the most important ways to reduce and prevent indoor air pollution are the following:

- *Greatly reducing poverty*
- *Distributing cheap and efficient cookstoves and solar cookstoves in developing countries*
- *Greatly reducing or banning indoor smoking*

Like the shift to *controlling air pollution* between 1970 and 2000, this new shift to *preventing air pollution* will not take place without political pressure on elected officials by individual citizens and groups of such citizens. See the website material for this chapter for ways you can reduce your exposure to indoor and outdoor pollutants.

*Turning the corner on air pollution requires moving beyond patchwork, end-of-pipe approaches to confront pollution at its sources. This will mean reorienting energy, transportation, and industrial structures toward prevention.*

HILARY F. FRENCH

## REVIEW QUESTIONS

**1.** Define the boldfaced terms in this chapter.

**2.** How can lichens be used to detect air pollutants?

**3.** Briefly describe the history of air pollution in Europe and the United States.

**4.** Distinguish among *atmosphere, troposphere,* and *stratosphere*. What key role does the stratosphere play in maintaining life on the earth?

**5.** Distinguish among *air pollution, primary air pollutants,* and *secondary air pollutants*. List the major classes of pollutants found in outdoor air. Distinguish between *stationary* and *mobile* sources of pollution for outdoor air. What are the two major sources of indoor air pollution?

**6.** List the six *criteria* air pollutants regulated in the United States (and in most developed countries). For each of these pollutants, summarize its major human sources and health effects.

**7.** What is *photochemical smog,* and how does it form? What is *industrial smog,* and how does it form?

**8.** List major factors that can **(a)** reduce air pollution and **(b)** increase air pollution. What is a *temperature inversion,* and what are its harmful effects? Distinguish between a *subsidence thermal inversion* and a *radiation temperature inversion*. What types of places are most likely to suffer from prolonged inversions of each type?

**9.** What is *acid deposition,* and what are its major components and causes? Distinguish among *acid deposition, wet deposition,* and *dry deposition*. What areas tend to be affected by acid deposition? What is a *buffer,* and what types of geologic areas can neutralize or buffer some inputs of acidic chemicals? What two types of areas are most sensitive to acid deposition?

**10.** What are the major harmful effects of acid deposition on **(a)** human health, **(b)** materials, **(c)** soils, **(d)** aquatic life, **(e)** trees and other plants, and **(f)** some forms of wildlife?

**11.** Summarize the major *good news* and *bad news* about acid deposition in the United States.

**12.** List eight ways to prevent acid deposition and two ways to clean it up.

**13.** How serious is indoor air pollution, and what are some of its sources? What is the *sick-building syndrome?* According to the EPA, what are the three most dangerous indoor air pollutants in the United States? What is the most dangerous indoor air pollutant in most developing countries?

**14.** Summarize the problems of indoor pollution from **(a)** formaldehyde, **(b)** radioactive radon gas, and **(c)** asbestos fibers.

**15.** List four defenses of your body against air pollution. What are the major harmful health effects of **(a)** carbon monoxide, **(b)** suspended particulate matter, **(c)** sulfur dioxide, **(d)** nitrogen oxides, and **(e)** ozone (see Table 17-2, p. 422) Describe the health dangers from inhaling fine particles.

**16.** About how many people die prematurely each year from exposure to air pollutants in **(a)** the United States and **(b)** the world? What percentage of these deaths occurs in developing countries? What percentage of these deaths is the result of indoor air pollution?

**17.** What is the Clean Air Act, and how has it helped reduce outdoor air pollution in the United States? Distinguish among *national ambient air quality standards, primary standards,* and *secondary standards*.

**18.** Summarize the major *good news* and *bad news* about the effectiveness of the Clean Air Act in reducing outdoor air pollution in the United States. According to environmentalists, what are four weaknesses of the current Clean Air Act in the United States?

**19.** What is an *emission trading policy,* and what are the pros and cons of using this approach to help reduce air pollution?

**20.** List the major prevention and cleanup methods for dealing with air pollution from **(a)** emissions of sulfur oxides, nitrogen oxides, and particulate matter from stationary sources, **(b)** automobile emissions, **(c)** indoor air pollution in developed countries, and **(d)** indoor air pollution in developing countries.

**21.** Why do environmentalists believe that we must now put much greater emphasis on preventing air pollution? List six ways to prevent outdoor air pollution and three ways to prevent indoor air pollution.

## CRITICAL THINKING

**1.** Evaluate the pros and cons of the following statement: "Because we have not proven absolutely that anyone has died or suffered serious disease from nitrogen oxides, current federal emission standards for this pollutant should be relaxed."

**2.** Identify climate and topographic factors in your local community that **(a)** intensify air pollution and **(b)** help reduce air pollution.

**3.** Should all tall smokestacks be banned? Explain.

**4.** Explain how sulfur in coal can increase the acidity of rainwater.

**5.** Suppose you become trapped in your car during a snowstorm and you have your engine and heater running to keep warm. Explain why you should roll down one of your windows just a little.

**6.** Why are most severe air pollution episodes associated with subsidence temperature inversions rather than radiation temperature inversions?

**7.** Should annual government-held auctions of marketable trading permits be used as a primary way to control and reduce air pollution? Explain. What conditions, if any, would you put on this approach?

**8.** Do you agree or disagree with the possible weaknesses of the U.S. Clean Air Act listed on p. 440? Defend each of your choices. Can you identify other weaknesses?

**9.** Congratulations! You are in charge of reducing air pollution in the country where you live. List the three most important features of your policy.

## PROJECTS

**1.** Evaluate your exposure to some or all of the indoor air pollutants in Figure 17-17 (p. 434) in your school, workplace, and home. Come up with a plan for reducing your exposure to these pollutants.

**2.** Have buildings at your school been tested for radon? If so, what were the results? What has been done about areas with unacceptable levels? If this testing has not

been done, talk with school officials about having it done.

**3.** Use the library or the Internet to find bibliographic information about *Michael J. Cohen* and *Hilary F. French,* whose quotes appear at the beginning and end of this chapter.

**4.** Make a concept map of this chapter's major ideas, using the section heads and subheads and the key terms (in boldface). Look on the website for this book for information about making concept maps.

## INTERNET STUDY RESOURCES AND RESOURCES FOR FURTHER READING AND RESEARCH

The website for this book contains helpful study aids and many ideas for further reading and research. Log on to

www.info.brookscole.com/miller13

and click on the Chapter-by-Chapter area. Choose Chapter 17 and select a resource:

- Flash Cards allows you to test your mastery of the Terms and Concepts to Remember for this chapter.

- Tutorial Quizzes provides a multiple-choice practice quiz.

- Student Guide to InfoTrac will lead you to Critical Thinking Projects that use InfoTrac College Edition as a research tool.

- References lists the major books and articles consulted in writing this chapter.

- Hypercontents takes you to an extensive list of sites with news, research, and images related to individual sections of the chapter.

## INFOTRAC COLLEGE EDITION

Improve your skills with InfoTrac College Edition, a searchable online database of articles from more than 700 periodicals. Log on to

http://www.infotrac-college.com

or access InfoTrac through the website for this book. Try to find the following articles:

**1.** Becker, R. and V. Henderson. 2000. Effects of air quality regulations on polluting industries. *Journal of Political Economy* 108: 379. *Keywords:* "air quality regulations" and "polluting." Air pollution regulations can have a significant effect on how and where industry can build manufacturing plants.

**2.** Spake, A. 2002. Don't breathe the air. (Brief article) *U.S. News and World Report* (July 1): 36. *Keyword:* "ozone pollution." Ground-level ozone is quickly becoming the primary air quality concern in many parts of the country. It could potentially have a great impact on the development of respiratory diseases in children.

# 18 CLIMATE CHANGE AND OZONE LOSS

## A.D. 2060: Green Times on Planet Earth

Mary Wilkins sat in the living room of the solar-powered and earth-sheltered house (Figure 18-1) she shared with her daughter Jane and her family. It was July 4, 2060: Independence Day.

She got up and walked into the greenhouse that provided much of her home's heat. There she heard the hum of solar-powered pumps trickling water to rows of organically grown vegetables and glanced at the fish in the aquaculture and waste treatment tanks.

Mary returned to the coolness of her earth-sheltered house and began putting the finishing touches on her grandchildren's costumes for this afternoon's pageant in Rachel Carson Park. It would honor earth heroes who began the Age of Ecology in the 20th century and those who continued this tradition in the 21st century.

She was delighted that her 12-year-old grandson Jeffrey had been chosen to play Aldo Leopold (Figure 2-12, p. 36), who in the late 1940s began urging people to work with the earth (Case Study, p. 36). Her pride swelled when her 10-year-old granddaughter Lynn was chosen to play Rachel Carson (p. 33), who in the 1960s warned us about threats from our increasing exposure to pesticides and other harmful chemicals (Individuals Matter, p. 33). Her neighbor's son Manuel had been chosen to play biologist Edward O. Wilson, who in the last third of the 20th century alerted us to the need to preserve the earth's biodiversity.

Even in her most idealistic dreams, she never guessed she would see the loss of global biodiversity slowed to a trickle. Most air pollution gradually disappeared when energy from the sun (p. 393), wind (p. 401), and hydrogen (p. 405) had replaced most use of fossil fuels by 2040. Most food was now grown by more sustainable agriculture (Figure 13-36, p. 308).

Preventing pollution and reducing resource waste had become important money-saving priorities for businesses and households based on the four *R*s of resource consumption: *reduce, reuse, recycle,* and *refuse.* Walking and bicycling had increased in cities and towns designed as vibrant communities for people instead of cars. Low-polluting and safe eco-cars (pp. 386–388) got up to 128 kilometers per liter (300 miles per gallon), and most places had bike paths and efficient mass transportation.

World population had stabilized at 8 billion in 2028 and then had begun a slow decline. The threat of climate change from atmospheric warming enhanced by human activities and air pollution lessened as the use of fossil fuels declined. International treaties enacted in the 1990s effectively banned the chemicals that had begun depleting ozone in the stratosphere during the last quarter of the 20th century. By 2050, ozone levels in the stratosphere had returned to 1980 levels.

Two hours later, Mary, her daughter Jane, and her son-in-law Gene watched with pride as 40 beautiful children honored the leaders of the Age of Ecology. At the end, Lynn stepped forward and said, "Today we have honored many earth heroes, but the real heroes are the ordinary people in this audience and around the world who worked to help sustain the earth's life-support systems for us and other species. Thank you, Grandma, Mom, Dad, and everyone here for giving us such a wonderful gift. We promise to leave the earth even better for our children and grandchildren and all living creatures."

**Figure 18-1** An *earth-sheltered house* in the United States. Solar cells on the roof provide most of the house's electricity. About 13,000 families across the United States have built such houses. Mary Wilkins's fictional house in 2060 could be similar to this one.

*We are embarked on the most colossal ecological experiment of all time—doubling the concentration in the atmosphere of an entire planet of one of its most important gases—and we really have little idea of what might happen.*

PAUL A. COLINVAUX

This chapter addresses the following questions:

- How has the earth's climate changed in the past?

- How might the earth's climate change in the future?

- What factors can affect changes in the earth's average temperature?

- What are some possible effects of climate change from a warmer earth?

- What can we do to slow or adapt to projected climate change caused by natural processes, human activities, or both?

- Are human activities depleting ozone in the stratosphere, and why should we care?

- What can we do to slow and eventually reverse ozone depletion in the stratosphere caused by human activities?

## 18-1 PAST CLIMATE CHANGE AND THE NATURAL GREENHOUSE EFFECT

**How Have the Earth's Temperature and Climate Changed in the Past?** Climate change is neither new nor unusual. The earth's average surface temperature and climate have been changing throughout the world's 4.7-billion-year history, sometimes gradually (over hundreds to millions of years) and at other times fairly quickly (over a few decades). Figure 18-2 shows how the *estimated* average global temperature of the atmosphere near the earth's surface has changed during four time scales in the past: **(1)** 900,000 years, **(2)** 22,000 years, **(3)** 1,000 years, and **(4)** 130 years.

Over the past 900,000 years, the average temperature of the atmosphere near the earth's surface has undergone prolonged periods of *global cooling* and *global warming* (Figure 18-2, top). During each cold period, thick glacial ice covered much of the earth's surface for about 100,000 years. Each of these glacial periods was followed by a *warmer interglacial period* lasting 10,000–12,500 years, during which most of the ice melted. For the past 10,000 years, we have had the good fortune to live in an interglacial period with a fairly stable climate and average global surface temperature (Figure 18-2, top middle).

However, even during this generally stable period, significant changes have occurred in regional climates.

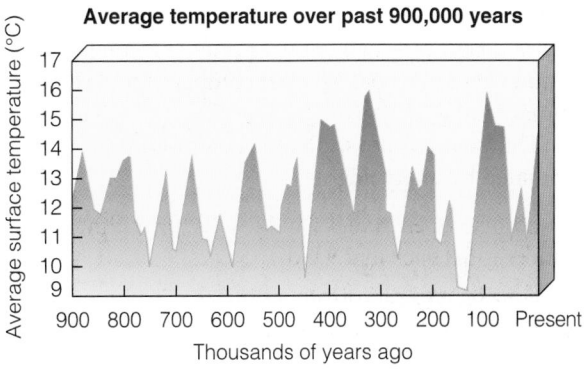

Average temperature over past 900,000 years

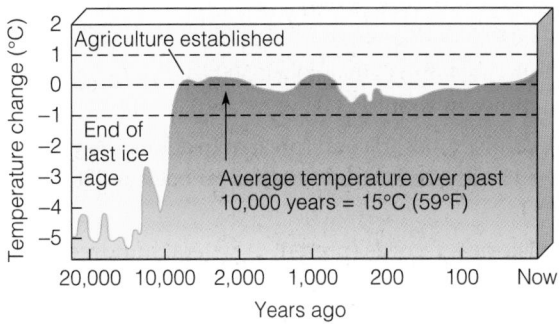

Temperature change over past 22,000 years

Temperature change over past 1,000 years

Average temperature over past 130 years

**Figure 18-2** Estimated changes in the average global temperature of the atmosphere near the earth's surface over different periods of time. (Data from Goddard Institute for Space Studies, Intergovernmental Panel on Climate Change, National Academy of Sciences, National Aeronautics and Space Agency, National Center for Atmospheric Research, and National Oceanic and Atmospheric Administration)

For example, about 7,000 years ago, most of the current Sahara desert received annual rainfall of more than 20 centimeters (8 inches) per year compared to its current annual rainfall of less than 1.3 centimeters (0.5 inch).

The past temperature changes in Figure 18-2 are estimated by analyzing

- Radioisotopes in rocks and fossils (providing information as far back as 2.9 billion years).

- Plankton and radioisotopes in ocean sediments (20,000–180 million years ago).

- Pollen from lake bottoms, bogs, and volcanic ash (present to several million years ago).

- Ice cores from ancient glaciers (present–440,000 years ago).

- Tree rings (typically present 500–700 years ago but sometimes to about 11,000 years ago).

- Radioisotopes in coral (present to about 400 years ago but with some large corals as far back as 130,000 years).

- Historical records (present to several hundred years ago).

- Temperature measurements (1861–present).

**What Is the Greenhouse Effect?** For the earth and its atmosphere to remain at a constant temperature, incoming solar energy must be balanced by an equal amount of outgoing energy (Figure 4-8, p. 69). Although the overall average temperature of the atmosphere is constant, its average temperature at various altitudes varies (Figure 17-2, p. 419, red line).

In addition to incoming sunlight, a natural process called the *greenhouse effect* (Figure 6-17, p. 121) warms the earth's lower troposphere and surface. Recall that it occurs because molecules of certain atmospheric gases, called *greenhouse gases,* warm the lower atmosphere by absorbing some of the infrared radiation (heat) radiated by the earth's surface. This causes their molecules to vibrate and transform the absorbed energy into longer wavelength infrared radiation (heat) in the troposphere (Figure 6-17, p. 121).*

Actually, the atmosphere does not behave like a real greenhouse (or a car with its windows closed). The primary reason air heats up in a greenhouse (or car interior) is that the closed windows keep the air from being carried away by convection (Figure 6-10, p. 117)

---

*To say the earth's atmosphere *traps* heat or *reradiates* heat it has absorbed back toward the earth's surface is scientifically incorrect. Molecules of greenhouse gases absorb various wavelengths of infrared radiation and transform them into infrared radiation with different (longer) wavelengths. Because the originally absorbed wavelengths of infrared radiation no longer exist, it is incorrect to say they have been trapped or reradiated.

to the outside air. By contrast, heat released by molecules of greenhouse gases in the atmosphere is spread through the atmosphere by convection. A more scientifically accurate term for this phenomenon would be *tropospheric heating effect.* However, the term *greenhouse effect* is widely used and accepted.

Swedish chemist Svante Arrhenius first recognized this natural tropospheric heating effect in 1896. Since then it **(1)** has been confirmed by numerous laboratory experiments and measurements of atmospheric temperatures at different altitudes and **(2)** is one of the most widely accepted theories in the atmospheric sciences.

If the natural greenhouse effect acted by itself, the average surface temperature of the earth would be about 54°C (130°F). However, a *natural cooling process* also takes place at the earth's surface. This occurs when **(1)** large quantities of heat are absorbed by the evaporation of liquid surface water, and **(2)** the water vapor molecules rise, condense to form droplets in clouds, and release their stored heat higher in the atmosphere (Figure 6-10, p. 117). Because of the combined effects of these natural heating and cooling effects, the earth's average surface temperature is about 15°C (59°F) instead of a frigid +18°C (0°F).

The two greenhouse gases with the largest concentrations in the atmosphere are **(1)** *water vapor* controlled by the hydrologic cycle (Figure 4-27, p. 83) and **(2)** *carbon dioxide* ($CO_2$) controlled by the carbon cycle (Figure 4-28, p. 84). Table 18-1 shows the major sources, average time in the troposphere, and the relative warming potential of various greenhouse gases present in the troposphere.

Analysis of gases in bubbles trapped at various depths in ancient glacial ice shows that over the past 160,000 years, levels of tropospheric water vapor (the dominant greenhouse gas) have remained fairly constant. However, during most of this period, $CO_2$ levels have fluctuated between 190 and 290 parts per million. These estimated changes in tropospheric $CO_2$ levels correlate fairly closely with estimated variations in the atmosphere's average global temperature near the earth's surface during the past 160,000 years (Figure 18-3).

## 18-2 CLIMATE CHANGE AND HUMAN ACTIVITIES

**What Is Global Warming?** Since the beginning of the industrial revolution around 1750 (and especially since 1950), there has been a sharp rise in **(1)** the use of fossil fuels (Figure 15-13, p. 351), which release large amounts of the greenhouse gases $CO_2$ and $CH_4$ into the troposphere, **(2)** deforestation and clearing and burning of grasslands to raise crops, which

**Table 18-1 Major Greenhouse Gases from Human Activities**

| Greenhouse Gas | Human Sources | Average Time in the Troposphere | Relative Warming Potential (compared to $CO_2$) |
|---|---|---|---|
| Carbon dioxide ($CO_2$) | Fossil fuel burning, especially coal (70–75%), deforestation, and plant burning | 50–120 years | 1 |
| Methane ($CH_4$) | Rice paddies, guts of cattle and termites, landfills, coal production, coal seams, and natural gas leaks from oil and gas production and pipelines | 12–18 years | 23 |
| Nitrous oxide ($N_2O$) | Fossil fuel burning, fertilizers, live-stock wastes, and nylon production | 114–120 years | 296 |
| Chlorofluorocarbons (CFCs)* | Air conditioners, refrigerators, plastic foams | 11–20 years (65–110 years in the stratosphere) | 900–8,300 |
| Hydrochloro-fluorocarbons (HCFCs) | Air conditioners, refrigerators, plastic foams | 9–390 | 470–2,000 |
| Hydrofluorocarbons (HFCs) | Air conditioners, refrigerators, plastic foams | 15–390 | 130–12,700 |
| Halons | Fire extinguishers | 65 | 5,500 |
| Carbon tetrachloride | Cleaning solvent | 42 | 1,400 |

*CFC use is being phased out, but it will take 50–100 years for the ozone layer to recover.

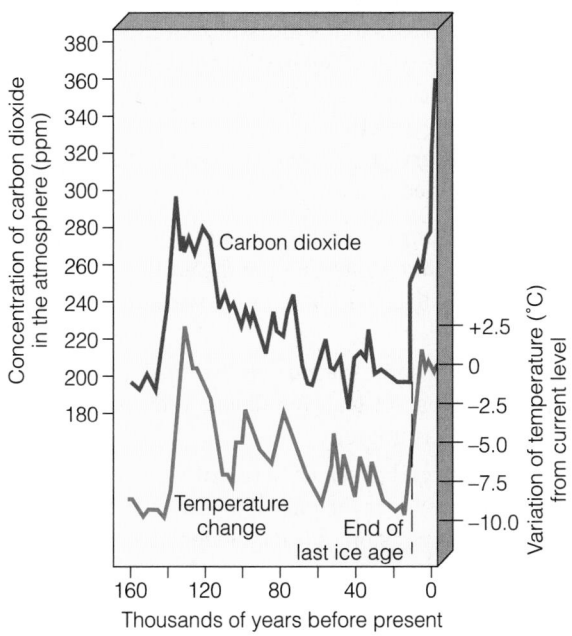

**Figure 18-3** Estimated long-term variations in average global temperature of the atmosphere near the earth's surface and average tropospheric $CO_2$ levels over the past 160,000 years. These $CO_2$ levels were obtained by inserting metal tubes deep into Antarctic glaciers, removing the ice, and analyzing bubbles of ancient air trapped in ice at various depths throughout the past. The rough correlation between $CO_2$ levels in the troposphere and temperature shown in these estimates based on ice core data suggests a connection between these two variables, although no definitive causal link has been established. In 1999, the world's deepest ice core sample revealed a similar correlation between air temperatures and the greenhouse gases $CO_2$ and $CH_4$ going back for 460,000 years. (Data from Intergovernmental Panel on Climate Change and National Center for Atmospheric Research)

release $CO_2$ and $N_2O$ into the atmosphere, and **(3)** cultivation of rice in paddies and use of inorganic fertilizers, which release $N_2O$ into the troposphere.

Figure 18-4 (p. 450) shows that since 1860, the concentrations of the greenhouse gases $CO_2$, $CH_4$, and $N_2O$ in the troposphere have risen sharply, especially since 1950. Figure 18-5 (p. 451) shows the top ten nations in terms of total (left) and per capita (right) emissions of $CO_2$ in 1999.

The two largest contributors to current $CO_2$ emissions are the world's thousands of coal-burning power and industrial plants and more than 700 million gasoline-burning motor vehicles (555 million of them cars). Emissions of $CO_2$ from U.S. coal-burning power and industrial plants alone exceed the combined $CO_2$ emissions of 146 nations, which contain 75% of the world's people.

Based on evidence about past changes in atmospheric $CO_2$ concentrations and atmospheric temperatures (Figure 18-3), most climate scientists believe that increased inputs of $CO_2$ and other greenhouse gases

**Carbon dioxide (CO₂)**

**Methane (CH₄)**

**Nitrous oxide (N₂O)**

**Figure 18-4** Increases in average concentrations of the greenhouse gases $CO_2$, methane, and nitrous oxide in the troposphere between 1860 and 2000. (Data from Intergovernmental Panel on Climate Change, National Center for Atmospheric Research, and World Resources Institute)

from human activities (Figure 18-4) will **(1)** enhance the earth's natural greenhouse effect and **(2)** raise the average global temperature of the atmosphere near the earth's surface. This *enhanced greenhouse effect* is called **global warming** and should not be confused with the different atmospheric problem of ozone depletion (Table 18-2 and Section 18-8, p. 472).

**Are We Experiencing Global Warming?** Considerable evidence suggests that some global warming is occurring. Analysis of ice core samples, temperature measurements at different levels in several hundred boreholes in the earth's surface, and atmospheric temperature measurements show that

- The concentration of $CO_2$ in the troposphere is higher than it has been in the past 420,000 years, and probably during the last 20 million years.

- About 75% of the human-caused emissions of $CO_2$ since 1980 are due to fossil fuel burning and the remainder is the result of deforestation, agriculture, and other human changes in land use.

- The 20th century was the hottest century in the past 1,000 years (Figure 18-2, bottom middle).

- Since 1861 (when direct atmospheric temperature measurements began), the average global temperature of the troposphere near the earth's surface has risen $0.6 \pm 0.2°C$ ($1.1 \pm 0.4°F$), with most of this increase taking place since 1946 (Figure 18-2, bottom).

- Since 1861 nine of the ten warmest years have occurred since 1990, with the two hottest years in 1998 and 2001.

Figure 18-6 (p. 452) shows an apparent correlation between increases in **(1)** fossil fuel use, **(2)** atmospheric concentrations of $CO_2$, and **(3)** global temperature between 1970 and 2000. Climate scientists project significant increases in the emissions of $CO_2$, $CH_4$, and $N_2O$ during the 21st century (Figure 18-7, p. 452) and believe such increases will further enhance the earth's natural greenhouse effect.

Other observed signs of a warmer troposphere during recent decades include

- Increased temperatures and some melting of land-based ice caps and floating ice at the earth's poles and Greenland, as discussed in the two case studies that follow.

- Shrinking of some glaciers on the tops of mountains in the Alps, Andes, Himalayas, and northern Cascades of Washington.

- An average global sea level rise of 10–20 centimeters (4–8 inches) over the past 100 years from a combination of **(1)** expansion of ocean waters from their increased average temperature and **(2)** an increased input of water from the melting of land-based glaciers.

- Northward migration of some fish, tree, and other species to find more optimum temperatures (Figure 4-14, p. 73). For example, over the past 100 years, 34 butterfly species have shifted their range by 35–240 kilometers (22–149 miles) northward.

- Earlier spring arrival and later autumn frosts in many parts of the world (which affects patterns of crop growth and animal migrations).

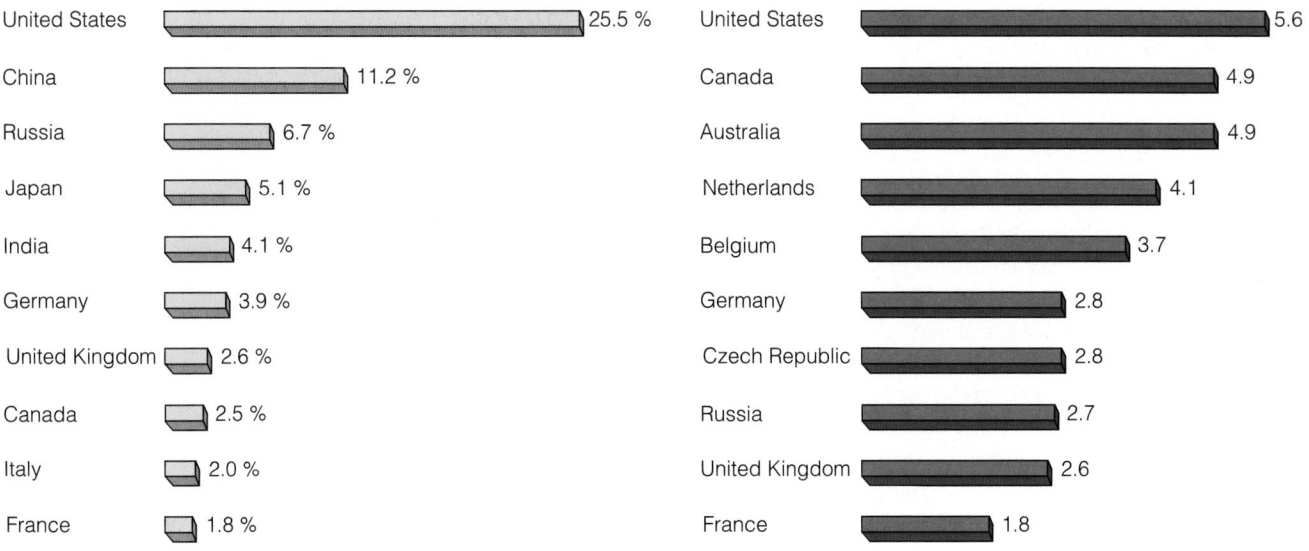

**Contribution to Global Total (%)**

| Nation | % |
|---|---|
| United States | 25.5 % |
| China | 11.2 % |
| Russia | 6.7 % |
| Japan | 5.1 % |
| India | 4.1 % |
| Germany | 3.9 % |
| United Kingdom | 2.6 % |
| Canada | 2.5 % |
| Italy | 2.0 % |
| France | 1.8 % |

**Per Capita Emissions (metric tons)**

| Nation | metric tons |
|---|---|
| United States | 5.6 |
| Canada | 4.9 |
| Australia | 4.9 |
| Netherlands | 4.1 |
| Belgium | 3.7 |
| Germany | 2.8 |
| Czech Republic | 2.8 |
| Russia | 2.7 |
| United Kingdom | 2.6 |
| France | 1.8 |

**Figure 18-5** The top ten nations in terms of total (left) and per capita (right) emissions of $CO_2$ in 1999. (Data from World Resources Institute)

**Table 18-2 Major Characteristics of Global Warming and Ozone Depletion**

| Characteristic | Global Warming | Ozone Depletion |
|---|---|---|
| **Region of atmosphere involved** | Troposphere. | Stratosphere. |
| **Major substances involved** | $CO_2$, $CH_4$, $N_2O$ (greenhouse gases). | $O_3$, $O_2$, chlorofluorocarbons (CFCs). |
| **Interaction with radiation** | Molecules of greenhouse gases absorb infared (IR) radiation from the earth's surface, vibrate, and release longer-wavelength IR radiation (heat) into the lower troposphere. This natural greenhouse effect helps warm the lower troposphere. | About 95% of incoming ultraviolet (UV) radiation from the sun is absorbed by $O_3$ molecules in the stratosphere and does not reach the earth's surface (Figure 4.8, p. 69). |
| **Nature of problem** | There is a high probability that increasing concentrations of greenhouse gases in the troposphere from burning fossil fuels, deforestation, and agriculture are enhancing the natural greenhouse effect and raising the earth's average surface temperature (Figure 18-2, bottom, and Figure 18-6, p. 452). | CFCs and other ozone-depleting chemicals released into the troposphere by human activities have made their way to the stratosphere, where they decrease $O_3$ concentration. This can allow more harmful UV radiation to reach the earth's surface. |
| **Possible consequences** | Changes in climate, agricultural productivity, water supplies, and sea level. | Increased incidence of skin cancer, eye cataracts, and immune system suppression and damage to crops and phytoplankton. |
| **Possible responses** | Decrease fossil fuel use and deforestation; prepare for climate change. | Eliminate CFCs and other ozone-depleting chemicals and find acceptable substitutes. |

Figure 18-6 Apparent connections between increases in **(1)** fossil fuel use, **(2)** atmospheric concentrations of $CO_2$, and **(3)** global temperature between 1970 and 2001. (Data from BP Amoco, U.S. Department of Energy, Goddard Institute for Space Studies, and Worldwatch Institute)

The changes just listed could be the result of **(1)** natural climate fluctuations, **(2)** changes in climate from human activities, or **(3)** a combination of both factors. Regardless of the cause, significant climate change caused by atmospheric warming or cooling over several decades to 100 years has important implications for human life, wildlife, and the world's economies. Such rapid climate change can **(1)** affect the availability of water resources by altering rates of evaporation and precipitation, **(2)** shift areas where crops can be grown, **(3)** change average sea levels, and **(4)** alter the structure and location of the world's biomes (Figure 6-20, p. 123).

**Case Study: Some Early Warnings from the Arctic** As the atmosphere warms, it causes more convection that transfers surplus heat from equatorial to polar areas (Figure 6-11, p. 118). Thus temperature increases tend to be greater at and near the earth's poles than at the middle latitudes. This explains why the earth's frigid poles and Greenland are regarded as *early warning sentinels* of global warming.

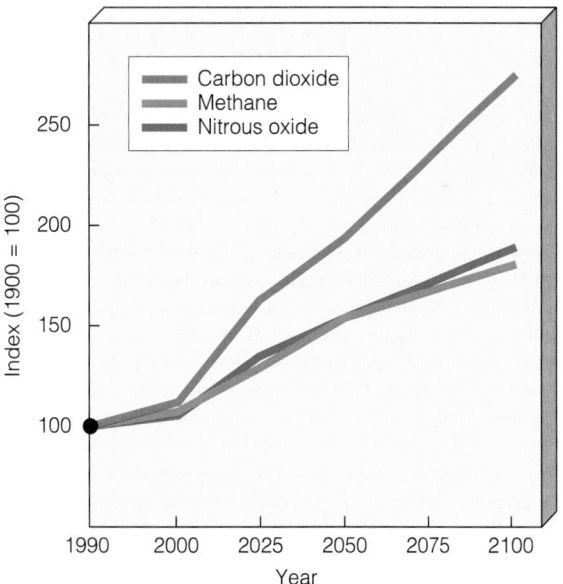

**Figure 18-7** Projected emissions of three important greenhouse gases as a result of human activities, 1990–2100. (Data from United Nations Food and Agriculture Organization, 1997)

The Arctic Sea covers the North Pole. The ice floating in this sea is large enough to cover the United States and is highly sensitive to changes in the air above and the ocean below.

News from the Arctic is alarming. Since 1980, surface temperatures at nine stations north of the Arctic circle have risen much more than the average global temperature and are projected by climate models to rise much more sharply by 2050 (Figure 18-8, top).

The light color of the floating sea ice in the Arctic Ocean helps cool the earth by reflecting 80% of the sunlight it receives back into space. If this ice melted, the darker Arctic Ocean water would absorb 80% of its input of sunlight and drastically affect global and regional climate, especially in the northern hemisphere.

Satellite data and measurements by surface boats and submarines indicate that since the 1950s, the volume of floating sea ice during summer and spring in the Arctic Ocean has been shrinking and is projected by models to continue shrinking (Figure 18-8, bottom). It is not known whether this shrinkage and thinning of sea ice floating in the Arctic Ocean is the result of **(1)** natural polar climate fluctuations, **(2)** global warming caused by increases in greenhouse gases, or **(3)** a combination of both factors.

Because it is floating, large-scale melting of Arctic Ocean ice will not raise global sea levels (just as an ice cube in a glass of water does not raise the water level when it melts). But widespread melting would greatly amplify warming of the Arctic region. This could **(1)** reroute warm ocean currents (Figure 6-7, p. 116, and Figure 6-12, p. 118) and weather patterns further south and **(2)** cause significant cooling in parts of the northern hemisphere, especially in Europe and eastern North America.

According to climate researchers at San Diego State University (California), since 1982 the Arctic's tundra soil has warmed so much that it has been giv-

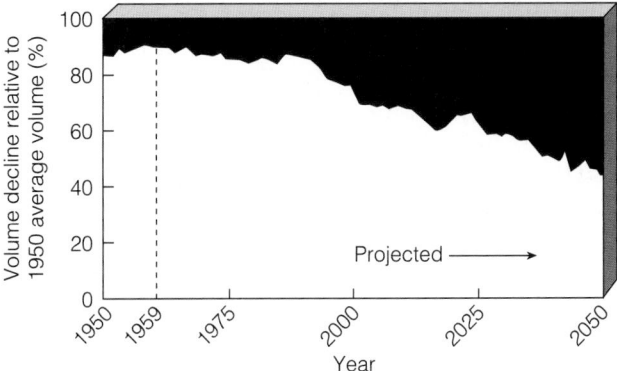

**Figure 18-8** Past and projected temperature changes in the Arctic, 1950–2050 (left). Such changes are expected to decrease the volume of ice floating in the Arctic Sea relative to the average volume in the 1950s (right). (Data from Keith Dixon, NOAA Geophysics Fluid Dynamics Laboratory)

ing off more $CO_2$ than it absorbs. This *positive feedback loop* could speed up the rate of increase of $CO_2$ in the atmosphere and amplify global warming.

**Case Study: News from Antarctica and Greenland** The South Pole is covered by the continent of Antarctica, roughly the size of the continental United States (Figure 18-9). This Antarctic ice cap contains 70% of the world's fresh water and 90% of its reflective ice, which helps cool the earth.

The long-term climate dynamic of Antarctica is complex and poorly understood and varies with different areas of this huge continent. Since 1947, the average temperature of the Antarctic Peninsula (Figure 18-9, top left) has risen by about 2.5°C (4.5°F) in summer and 5.6°C (10°F) in winter. As a result, huge pieces of ice shelf—some as large as the state of Delaware—have begun breaking off (calving) the peninsula's eastern shore into the Weddell Sea. A 2002 study by scientists Eric Rignot and Stanley Jacobs found that floating ice on the edges of 23 surveyed glaciers was melting and breaking away twice as fast as earlier predicted.

This loss of ice does not raise global sea levels because the shelf was already floating in the water. But the shelves do hold back ice sheets on the continent. Thus their large-scale collapse could allow ice on the ground to move slowly to the sea and over time raise sea levels. Scientists do not know whether the increased rate of disintegration of this ice shelf is due to natural processes, global warming, or a combination of both factors.

Antarctica's western ice sheet—the size of Texas and Colorado combined—near the Ross Sea (Figure 18-9, bottom left) has been melting slowly for about 11,000 years since the end of the last glacial period, when average sea levels began a huge rise (Figure 18-10, p. 454).

Climate experts say there is no credible evidence that global warming is responsible for the melting of this ice sheet and that the breakup of this ice sheet is

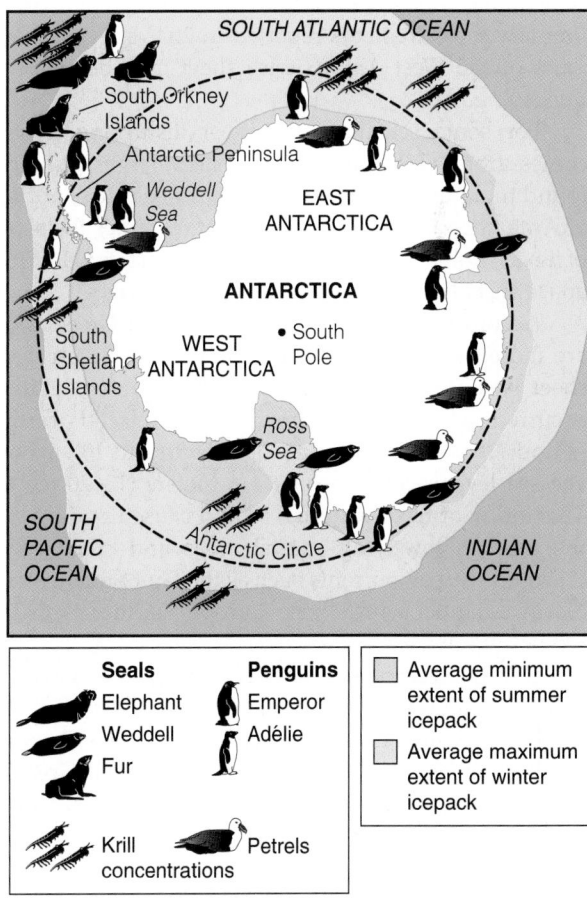

**Figure 18-9** The ice-covered continent of Antarctica makes up 10% of the earth's land mass and is the world's last great wilderness. The ice—up to 3 kilometers (1.9 miles) thick—that covers 98% of the continent contains 90% of the earth's ice and 70% of its fresh water. Antarctica helps regulate the global climate and sea level. In winter, parts of the sea freeze, and the continent doubles in size. In summer, it shrinks when some of the ice pack melts and huge icebergs break off the edges of the ice shelf.

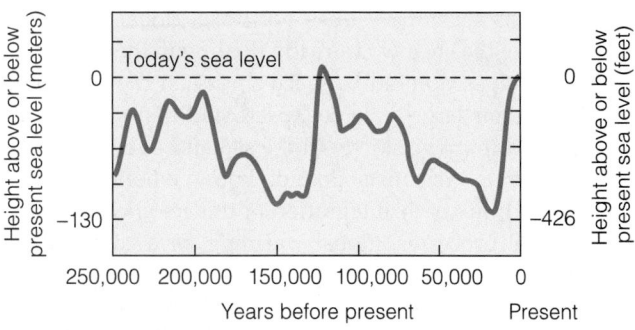

**Figure 18-10** Changes in *average sea level* over the past 250,000 years based on data from cores removed from the ocean. The coming and going of glacial periods (ice ages) largely determine the rise and fall of sea level. As glaciers melted and retreated since the peak of the last glacial period about 18,000 years ago, the earth's average sea level has risen about 125 meters (410 feet) and changed the earth's coastal zones significantly. (Adapted from Tom Garrison, *Oceanography: An Invitation to Marine Science*, 3/E, © 1998. Brooks/Cole.

very unlikely during this century. Moreover, some preliminary measurements reported in 2002 suggest that parts of the West Antarctic ice sheet may be slowly thickening.

For some scientists, the most disturbing news comes from Greenland, the world's largest island found more than 14,500 kilometers (9,000 miles) north of Antarctica. Greenland, which is three times the size of Texas, holds about 6% of the world's fresh water in an ice sheet that covers about 85% of its surface.

According to scientists, the glaciers of Greenland are more likely to melt than Antarctica's western ice sheet because they are closer to the equator. If this occurred, as it did in a previous interglacial warm period 110,000–130,000 years ago (Figure 18-10), average sea levels would rise by 4–6 meters (13–20 feet). This influx of fresh water **(1)** would cause flooding in the world's low-lying coastal areas and cities and **(2)** could shut off currents such as the Gulf Stream and North Atlantic, which keep Europe warmer than it would otherwise be.

In 2000, researchers reported that the vast Greenland ice sheet is starting to melt. Some *good news* is that ice is increasing at high elevations in Greenland's northern areas. However, the *bad news* is that Greenland is losing much more ice at lower elevations, especially along its eastern and southern coasts.

## 18-3 PROJECTING FUTURE CHANGES IN THE EARTH'S CLIMATE

**How Do Scientists Model Climate Changes? Computer Models as Crystal Balls**   To project the effects of increases in greenhouse gases (Figure 18-7)

on average global temperature and the earth's climate, scientists develop *mathematical models* of the global air circulation system (Figure 6-9, p. 117) and run them on supercomputers (Spotlight, p. 456).

These *general circulation models* (*GCMs*) attempt to provide a three-dimensional representation of how energy, air masses, and moisture flow through the atmosphere, based on the laws of physics and general air circulation patterns between the earth's warm equator and cold poles (Figure 6-9, p. 117). The latest atmospheric climate models also include **(1)** ocean circulation models (Figure 6-7, p. 116), **(2)** interactions between the atmosphere and the ocean, **(3)** changes in solar output, **(4)** inputs of aerosols (tiny particles and droplets) into the atmosphere by volcanoes and pollution from human activities, and **(5)** an improved but still limited estimate of the effect of clouds on climate.

Greatly improved climate models and measurements have increased the ability of scientists to **(1)** account for past changes (Figure 18-11) and **(2)** use various model scenarios to project future changes in the earth's average surface temperature (Figure 18-12). But there are still significant scientific uncertainties, as discussed in Section 18-4.

**What Is the Scientific Consensus About Future Climate Change and Its Effects?**   The United Nations and the World Meteorological Organization established the Intergovernmental Panel on Climate

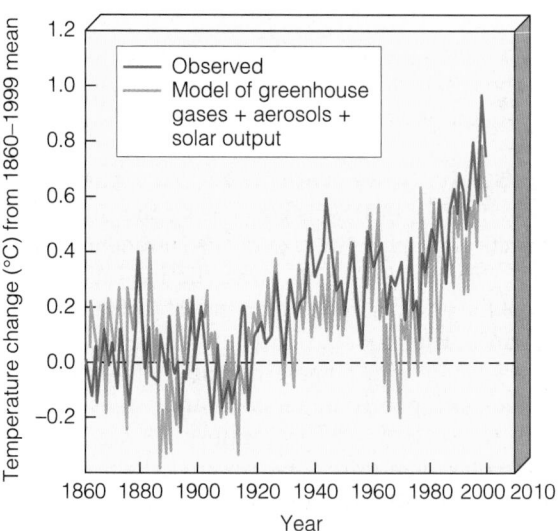

**Figure 18-11** Comparison of measured changes in the average atmospheric temperature near the earth's surface (blue line) with those projected by the latest climate models between 1860 and 2000 (orange line). The latest models have been able to reproduce the climate of the past 100 years or so with increasing accuracy. (Data from Tom L. Wigley, Pew Center on Global Climate Change and Intergovernmental Panel on Climate Change)

**Figure 18-12** Comparison of measured changes in the average temperature of the atmosphere at the earth's surface between 1860 and 2001 and the projected range of temperature increase during this century. Current models indicate that the average global temperature at the earth's surface will rise by 1.4–5.8°C (2.5–10.4°F) sometime during the 21st century. Because of the uncertainty involved in current climate models, the projected warming shown here could be *overestimated* or *underestimated* by a factor of two. (Data from U.S. National Academy of Sciences, National Center for Atmospheric Research, and Intergovernmental Panel on Climate Change)

Change (IPCC) to study climate change. The IPCC is a network of about 2,000 of the world's leading climate experts from 70 nations. In 1990, 1995, and 2001, the IPCC published reports evaluating the available evidence about **(1)** past changes in global temperatures (Figure 18-2) and **(2)** climate models projecting future changes in average global temperatures and climate. The U.S. National Academy of Sciences and the American Geophysical Union have also evaluated possible future climate changes.

According to the 2001 IPCC report,

■ "There is new and stronger evidence that most of the warming observed over the last 50 years is attributable to human activities."

■ There is a 90–95% chance that the earth's mean surface temperature will increase 1.4–5.8°C (2.5–10.4°F) between 2000 and 2100 (Figure 18-12). This projected rate of warming is much higher than that during the 20th century—with a temperature change projected between 2000 and 2030 equal to that for the entire 20th century.

In addition to the IPCC findings,

■ According to a 2001 report by the National Academy of Sciences, "Greenhouse gases are accumulating in the Earth's atmosphere as a result of human activities, causing surface air temperatures and subsurface ocean temperatures and surface ocean temperatures to rise. . . . The changes observed over the last several decades are likely mostly due to human activities. . . . Global warming could have serious societal and ecological impacts by the end of this century."

■ In May 2000, 63 national academies of science issued a joint statement that said, "The balance of scientific evidence demands effective steps now to avert damaging changes to the Earth's climate."

■ At the 1998 World Economic Forum, the CEOs of the world's 1,000 largest corporations voted climate change as the most critical problem facing humanity.

■ A 2002 Bush administration report, prepared by various U.S. government agencies for the United Nations, says recent climate changes "are likely mostly due to human activities" and by 2100 the **(1)** average global temperature is likely to rise by about 3°C (5.4°F) and **(2)** the average seal level will rise by 9–88 centimeters (35 inches).

However, a very small minority of atmospheric and other scientists inside and outside the IPCC contends that

■ There is still insufficient knowledge about natural climate variables that could change the assessment (up or down), as discussed in Section 18-4.

■ Computer models used to predict climate changes are improving but still are not very reliable.

■ Global warming may be a lot less damaging than many people think and not necessarily caused by human activities. For example, **(1)** while many glaciers are shrinking, others are growing, and **(2)** glaciers shrink and grow naturally over long periods of time (Figure 18-8, top).

■ Global warming can be beneficial for some regions. For example, some countries may be able to increase crop productivity because of more rainfall and longer growing seasons.

IPCC and other climate scientists holding the consensus view

■ Agree we need to **(1)** support greatly increased research on how the earth's climate system works and distinguish more clearly between natural and human-induced climate changes and **(2)** improve climate models to help narrow the range of uncertainty in projected temperature changes (Figure 18-12).

**SPOTLIGHT**

# How Do Climate Models Work?

Here is a crude representation of how current three-dimensional general circulation models (GCMs) of global climate are built:

- Simulate the earth's atmosphere mathematically by covering the earth's surface with 9–64 stacked layers of gigantic cells or boxes, each several hundred kilometers on a side and about 3 kilometers (2 miles) high (see figure).

- Assign an *initial condition* (starting value) for each variable to each box in the stacked layers. These variables include **(1)** temperature, **(2)** air pressure, **(3)** wind speed and direction, and **(4)** concentrations of key chemicals such as $H_2O$ and $CO_2$.

- Develop a set of equations describing the expected flow of various types of energy and matter in and out of the box-filled atmosphere. These inputs, called *boundary conditions,* include variables such as **(1)** solar radiation, **(2)** precipitation, **(3)** heat radiated by the earth, **(4)** cloudiness, **(5)** interactions between the atmosphere and oceans, **(6)** greenhouse gases, and **(7)** air pollutants (especially aerosols).

- Develop an elaborate set of mathematical equations that connect the cells so when the value of any of these input variables changes in one cell, the values of variables in surrounding cells change in a realistic way.

- Run the model on a supercomputer to **(1)** simulate changes in average global temperature and climate in the past (to verify the model) and **(2)** project future changes.

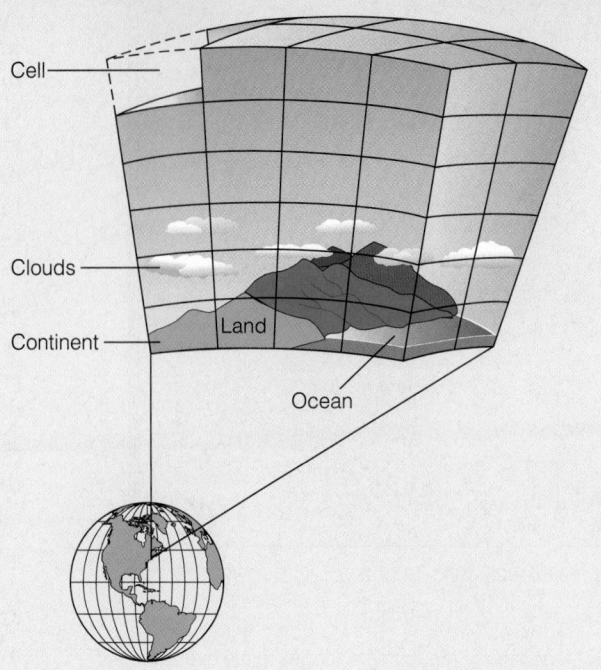

A global circulation model (GCM) of climate (and weather) divides the earth's atmosphere into large numbers of gigantic boxes or cells stacked many layers high. The laws of physics and our understanding of global air circulation patterns (Figure 6-9, p. 117) are used to describe numerically what happens to major variables affecting climate in each cell and from one cell to another.

Such models can provide us with scenarios of what *could* happen based on various assumptions and data fed into each model. How well the results correspond to the real world depends on **(1)** the assumptions of the model based on current knowledge about the systems making up the earth, oceans, and atmosphere, **(2)** the accuracy of the data used, **(3)** magnification of tiny errors over time, **(4)** factors in the earth's climate system that amplify (positive feedback) or dampen (negative feedback) changes in average global temperatures (Section 18-4), and **(5)** the effects of totally unexpected or unpredictable events (chaos).

Current models reproduce fairly accurately the changes in the earth's average global temperature that have taken since 1865 (Figure 18-11). The models can also help us evaluate the possible effects of various ways of slowing or even halting any global warming projected by the models.

## Critical Thinking

How much should we rely on mathematical climate models to help us evaluate the possible effects of human activities on the earth's climate and make decisions about how to prevent the global warming the models project? What are the alternatives?

- Point out that the biggest concern is not just a temperature change but how rapidly it occurs, regardless of its cause. They warn that warming or cooling of the earth's surface by even 1°C (1.8°F) per century as a result of natural or human-caused factors **(1)** would be faster than any temperature change occurring in the last 10,000 years, since the beginning of agriculture (Figure 18-2, top middle) and **(2)** could seriously disrupt the earth's ecosystems and human societies (Section 18-5).

## 18-4 FACTORS AFFECTING CHANGES IN THE EARTH'S AVERAGE TEMPERATURE

**Will the Earth Continue to Get Warmer?** The average temperature at the earth's surface has increased during the past 20 years (Figure 18-11). Will this trend continue?

The answer is *that this is highly likely, but we do not know for sure*. Scientists have identified a number of natural and human-influenced factors that might *amplify* (positive feedback) or *dampen* (negative feedback) changes in the earth's average surface temperature. These factors could influence **(1)** how much and how fast temperatures might climb or drop and **(2)** what the effects might be in various areas.

According to current models, the projected temperature rises will not be distributed evenly over the earth's surface. For example, temperature increases will be **(1)** higher over land than over oceans, **(2)** greater in the high latitudes near the earth's poles than in low-latitude equatorial regions, and **(3)** especially higher in many inland regions in the northern latitudes.

**How Might Changes in Solar Output Affect the Earth's Temperatures?** Solar output varies by about 0.1% over the 18-year and 22-year sunspot cycles and over 80-year and other much longer cycles. These up-and-down changes in solar output can temporarily warm or cool the earth and thus affect the projections of climate models.

Atmospheric scientists have not been able to identify a mechanism related to changes in solar output that could account for more than 50% of the atmospheric warming between 1900 and 2000 (Figure 18-11).

However, according to a hypothesis by climate scientists Paul Beckke and Henrik Svensmark, changes in the sun's exterior magnetic field could affect the atmospheric temperature by altering the amount of cosmic rays (Figure 3-9, p. 52) striking the earth. These rays can convert some electrically neutral molecules of gases in the atmosphere into charged ions that can affect cloud formation. They hypothesize that

■ An increase in cosmic rays caused by a decrease in the sun's exterior magnetic field may help cool the earth's surface by forming more thick, umbrella-like low clouds.

■ A decrease in cosmic rays caused by an increase in the sun's exterior magnetic field (as has been observed since 1901) may help warm the earth's surface by forming more high, thin clouds.

However, according to Kevan Treberth of the U.S. National Center for Atmospheric Research,

■ Very good evidence indicates that the amount of cooling low cloud cover has increased throughout

much of the world in recent decades. This is the opposite of what would be expected according to the cosmic ray hypothesis with an increase in the sun's exterior magnetic field.

■ The effects of aerosol pollutants in the atmosphere on cloud formation and properties probably are at least 10 times greater than such effects from cosmic rays.

**How Might Changes in the Earth's Reflectivity Affect Atmospheric Temperatures? The Ice Albedo Feedback System** Different parts of the earth's surface vary in their **albedo,** or ability to reflect light (Figure 18-13). White or shiny surfaces such as snow, ice, and sand reflect most of the sunlight that hits them. For example, sea ice reflects about 80% of incoming solar radiation, whereas water absorbs about 80% of such radiation.

Albedo increases when polar ice caps expand during glacial periods and decreases when they melt and expose less reflective land and ocean surfaces. Satellite measurements of how albedo varies throughout the world and projections of how this might change have been incorporated into current climate models used to make the projections in Figure 18-12.

A *positive ice albedo feedback* system could accelerate global warming. As the atmosphere warms, the proportion of the earth's surface covered with highly reflective (high albedo) ice will shrink as it is replaced by less reflective (lower albedo) water or land. Then the earth's surface will absorb more heat and cause more warming.

**How Might the Oceans Affect Climate?** Currently, the oceans help moderate the earth's average surface temperature by removing about 29% of the excess $CO_2$ we pump into the atmosphere as part of the

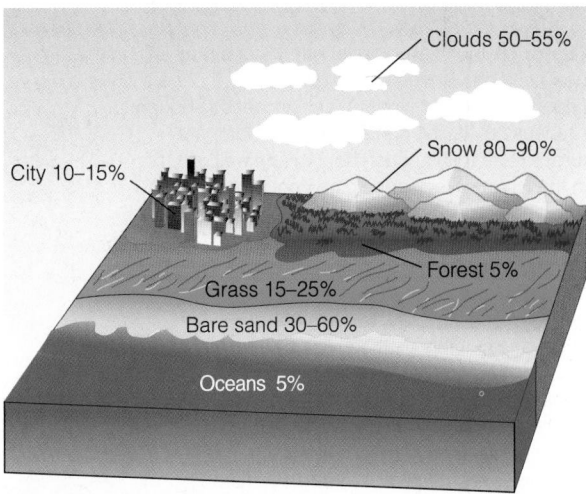

**Figure 18-13** The *albedo*, or reflectivity of incoming solar energy, of different parts of the earth's surface varies greatly (Data from NOAA).

global carbon cycle (Figure 4-28, p. 84). The solubility of $CO_2$ in ocean water decreases with increasing temperature. Thus if the oceans heat up, some of its dissolved $CO_2$ could be released into the atmosphere—like $CO_2$ bubbling out of a warm carbonated soft drink. This could amplify global warming through a positive feedback loop.

The oceans also affect global climate by absorbing heat from the atmosphere and transferring some of it to the deep ocean, where it is stored temporarily. Climate modelers hypothesize that **(1)** this deep-ocean absorption of heat has delayed part of the warming of the earth's atmosphere, and **(2)** some of this stored heat probably will be released back to the atmosphere and could amplify global warming.

In 2001, separate oceanographic research teams led by Sydney Levitus and Tim Barnett developed climate models to simulate how ocean temperatures would respond to current greenhouse levels and other modern-day atmospheric conditions. Both models predicted an amount of warming in the upper 3 kilometers (1.9 miles) of the ocean that was very close to levels actually measured. According to these scientists, their results provide a "95% confidence level" that human-produced greenhouse gases caused most of the observed warming of the ocean between 1955 and 1996.

Global warming could disrupt ocean currents (Figure 6-7, p. 116, and Figure 6-12, p. 118), which are driven largely by differences in water density and winds. Connected deep and surface currents act like a gigantic conveyor belt to transfer heat from one place to another and store $CO_2$ and heat in the deep sea (Figure 18-14). Scientists are concerned that an influx of fresh water from thawing ice in the Arctic (Figure 18-8, bottom) and the Antarctic (Figure 18-9) might slow or disrupt this conveyer belt and decrease the amount of heat it brings to the North Atlantic region. Evidence

suggests the flow of water by this conveyor belt halted suddenly about 12,000 years ago and caused an 8°C (15°F) drop in the temperature of Europe over only a few decades.

Changes in average sea level affect **(1)** the amount of heat and $CO_2$ that can be stored in the ocean and **(2)** changes in the earth's biomes (Figure 6-21, p. 124). According to the 2001 IPCC report, the rate of sea level rise is now faster than at any other time during the past 1,000 years.

**How Do Water Vapor Content and Clouds Affect Climate? The Cloud Feedback System**
Warmer temperatures increase evaporation of surface water and create more clouds. These additional clouds could have **(1)** a warming effect (positive feedback) by absorbing and releasing heat into the troposphere or **(2)** a cooling effect (negative feedback) by reflecting sunlight back into space.

The net result of these two opposing effects depends on **(1)** whether it is day or night, **(2)** the type (thin or thick), coverage (continuous or discontinuous), and altitude of clouds, and **(3)** the size and number of water droplets formed in clouds.

For example, **(1)** an increase in thick and continuous clouds at low altitudes can decrease surface warming by blocking more sunlight (negative feedback), and **(2)** an increase in thin and discontinuous cirrus clouds at high altitudes can warm the lower atmosphere and increase surface warming (positive feedback).

Scientists do not know **(1)** which of these various factors might predominate or **(2)** how cloud types, cover, heights, and chemical content might vary in different parts of the world. What they do know about the effects of clouds has been included in recent climate models, but much uncertainty about these effects remains.

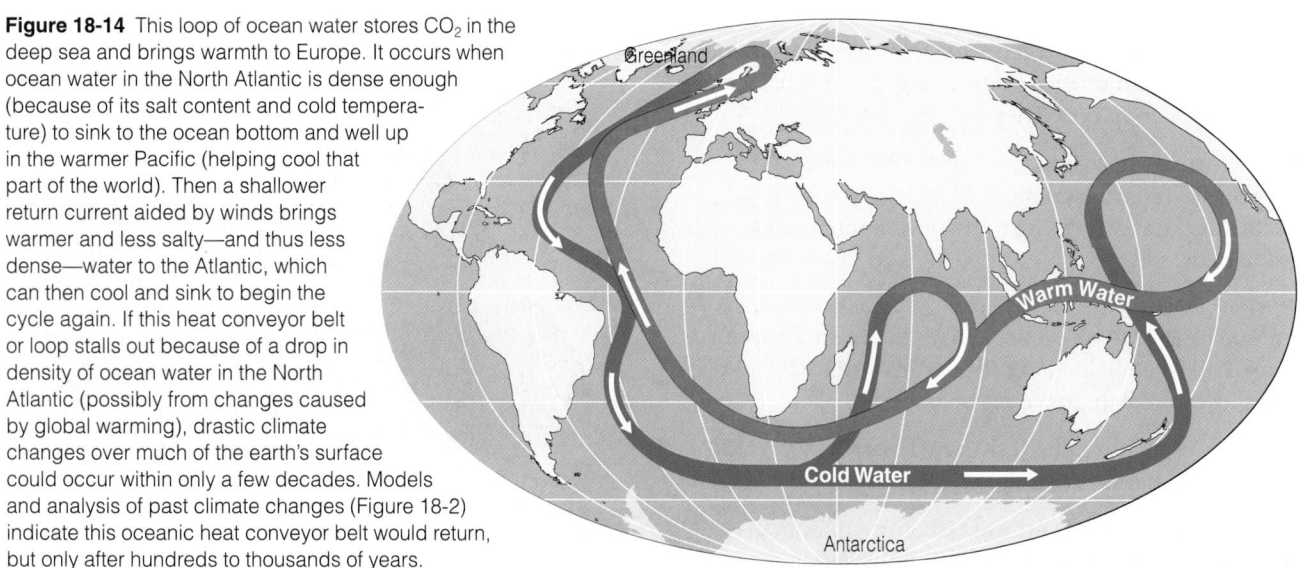

**Figure 18-14** This loop of ocean water stores $CO_2$ in the deep sea and brings warmth to Europe. It occurs when ocean water in the North Atlantic is dense enough (because of its salt content and cold temperature) to sink to the ocean bottom and well up in the warmer Pacific (helping cool that part of the world). Then a shallower return current aided by winds brings warmer and less salty—and thus less dense—water to the Atlantic, which can then cool and sink to begin the cycle again. If this heat conveyor belt or loop stalls out because of a drop in density of ocean water in the North Atlantic (possibly from changes caused by global warming), drastic climate changes over much of the earth's surface could occur within only a few decades. Models and analysis of past climate changes (Figure 18-2) indicate this oceanic heat conveyor belt would return, but only after hundreds to thousands of years.

In 1999, researchers at the University of Colorado reported that the wispy condensation trails (contrails) left behind by jet planes might have a greater impact on the earth's climate than scientists had thought. Using infrared satellite images, they found that jet contrails expand and turn into large cirrus clouds that tend to release heat into the upper atmosphere. If these preliminary results are confirmed, emissions from jet planes could be responsible for as much as half of the atmospheric warming in the northern hemisphere.

**How Might Air Pollution Affect Climate?**  Projected global warming might be partially offset by *aerosols* (tiny droplets and solid particles, Figure 17-8, p. 426) of various air pollutants released or formed in the atmosphere by volcanic eruptions and human activities. Climate scientists hypothesize that higher levels of aerosols attract enough water molecules to form condensation nuclei, leading to increased cloud formation.

Some of the resulting clouds have a high albedo and reflect more incoming sunlight back into space during the day. This could help counteract the heating effects of increased greenhouse gases.

Nights would be warmer because the clouds would still be there and prevent some of the heat stored in the earth's surface (land and water) during the day from being radiated into space. These pollutants may explain why most of the recent warming in the northern hemisphere occurs at night.

However, these interactions are complex. Pollutants in the lower troposphere can either warm or cool the air, depending on the reflectivity of the underlying surface (Figure 18-13) and their ability to limit the size of water droplets. Stanford University professor Mark Jacobson published a study in 2001 indicating that tiny particles of *soot,* produced mainly from burning coal and diesel fuel, may be responsible for 15–30% of the observed global warming over the past 50 years. If this preliminary research is correct, soot would be the second biggest contributor to global warming, just behind the greenhouse gas $CO_2$.

Climate scientists do not expect air pollutants to counteract projected global warming very much in the next 50 years because

- Aerosols fall back to the earth or are washed out of the atmosphere within weeks or months, whereas $CO_2$ and other greenhouse gases remain in the atmosphere for decades to several hundred years (Table 18-1).

- Aerosol inputs into the atmosphere are being reduced (Section 17-7, p. 439) because they (1) kill or sicken large numbers of people each year and (2) damage food crops, trees, and other forms of vegetation (Section 17-6, p. 437).

**How Might Increased $CO_2$ Levels Affect Photosynthesis?**  Some studies suggest that more $CO_2$ in the atmosphere could increase the rate of photosynthesis in areas with adequate amounts of water and other soil nutrients. This would remove more $CO_2$ from the atmosphere and help slow atmospheric warming. However, according to several recent studies, **(1)** this effect would slow as the plants reach maturity and take up less $CO_2$ and **(2)** when the plants die and are decomposed or are burned, the carbon they stored is returned to the atmosphere as $CO_2$.

Other studies suggest that this effect varies with different types of plants and in different climate zones, and much of any increased plant growth could be offset by plant-eating insects that would breed more rapidly and year round in warmer temperatures.

In 2002, a laboratory study of wheat seedlings by Arnold Bloom and his colleagues at the University of California, Davis found that elevated levels of $CO_2$ inhibited the uptake of nitrate fertilizer. If this preliminary study is verified for wheat and other major crops, the decreased uptake of nitrate fertilizer could offset increased plant growth from higher $CO_2$ levels.

**How Might a Warmer Atmosphere Affect Methane Emissions?**  Atmospheric warming can increase the release of methane (a potent greenhouse gas; Table 18-1) from

- Bogs and other wetlands.

- Icelike compounds called *methane hydrates* trapped beneath the Arctic permafrost and sediments on the floor of the Arctic Ocean. Large amounts of methane would be released into the troposphere if **(1)** the blanket of permafrost in tundra soils melts and the Arctic continues to warm (Figure 18-8, top), or **(2)** methane hydrates on the ocean floor are extracted to increase natural gas supplies (a possibility now under study in the United States).

Large releases of this powerful greenhouse gas (Table 18-1) could increase global warming (positive feedback).

**Can Soils Absorb More $CO_2$?**  When a plant dies and is decomposed, some of its carbon returns to the atmosphere as $CO_2$ and some is released into the soil. Some scientists suggest we may be able to slow global warming by increasing the amount of carbon stored in soils by planting more trees, improving forest management, and reducing soil erosion (Section 10-7, p. 222).

A 2001 study of the soil around loblolly pines exposed to elevated levels of $CO_2$ found that the soil accumulated carbon, but much of the carbon was released back into the air as $CO_2$ when organic material in the soil decomposed. The researchers, John Lichter and William H. Schlesinger, suggest that their preliminary findings "call into question the role of soils as long-term carbon sinks." Other experiments with a young sweetgum forest and a mature forest in Tennessee support these findings.

**How Rapidly Could Climate Shift?** If moderate climate change takes place gradually over several hundred years, people in areas with unfavorable climate changes may be able to adapt to the new conditions. However, if the global temperature change takes place over several decades, we may not have enough time (and money) to **(1)** switch food-growing regions, **(2)** relocate millions of people from low-lying coastal areas, and **(3)** build systems of dikes and levees to help protect the large portion of the world's population living near coastal areas. Such rapid changes in temperature could lead to large numbers of premature deaths from lack of food and social and economic chaos, especially in developing countries, and reduce the earth's biodiversity because many species could not move or adapt.

Recent data from analyses of ice cores and deep-sea sediments suggest that during the warm interglacial period that began about 125,000 years ago (Figure 18-2, top), average temperatures varied as much as 10°C (18°F) in only a decade or two and that such warming and cooling periods each lasted 1,000 years or more. If these findings are correct and also apply to the current interglacial period, fairly small rises in greenhouse gas concentrations could trigger rapid up-and-down shifts in the earth's average surface temperatures.

As a result of the factors discussed in this section, climate scientists agree that there are many uncertainties in their climate models. A 2002 model run by Thomas F. Stocker estimates that there is a 40% probability that the global temperature change during this century will exceed that projected by the IPCC (Figure 18-12) and only a 5% chance it will fall below this range.

## 18-5 SOME POSSIBLE EFFECTS OF A WARMER WORLD

**Why Should We Worry If the Earth's Temperature Rises a Few Degrees?** So what is the big deal? Why should we worry about a possible rise of only a few degrees in the earth's average surface temperature? We often have that much change between May and July, or even between yesterday and today.

The key point is that we are not talking about normal swings in *local weather* but a projected *global* change in *climate*—weather averaged over decades, centuries, and millennia.

**What Are Some Possible Effects of Atmospheric Warming? Winners and Losers** A warmer global climate could have a number of beneficial and harmful

- Less severe winters

- More precipitation in some dry areas

- Less precipitation in some wet areas

- Increased food production in some areas

- Expanded population and range for some plant and animal species adapted to higher temperatures

**Figure 18-15** Some possible *beneficial effects* of a warmer atmosphere for some countries and people.

effects (Figures 18-15 and 18-16) for humans, other species, and ecosystems depending mostly on location and how rapidly the climate changes.

Here are some of the projected effects based on current climate models:

### Water Distribution

■ Some areas are expected to get more precipitation and other areas less (Figure 18-17, p. 462).

■ Deserts will expand and droughts will grow more severe in some areas, especially in parts of Africa and Asia.

### Plant and Animal Distribution and Biodiversity

■ For each 1°C (1.8°F) rise in the earth's average temperature, climate belts in middle latitude regions would shift toward the earth's poles by 100–150 kilometers (60–90 miles) or upward 150 meters (500 feet) in altitude. Such shifts could change areas where crops could be grown and affect the makeup and location of at least one-third of today's forests.

■ Ranges of some plant and animal species adapted to warmer temperatures will spread.

■ Tree species whose seeds are spread by wind may not be able to migrate fast enough to keep up with climate shifts and would die out in the affected regions (Figure 18-18, p. 462).

■ Changes in the structure and location of wildlife habitats could cause extinction of plant and animal species that could not migrate to new areas and threaten species with specialized niches (Connections, p. 463).

■ Shifts in regional climate would threaten many parks, wildlife reserves, wilderness areas, wetlands, and coral reefs, wiping out many current efforts to stem the loss of biodiversity.

### Ocean Currents and Sea Levels

■ Some ocean currents may shift and change (Figure 18-14). This could cause sharp temperature

**Agriculture**
- Shifts in food-growing areas
- Changes in crop yields
- Increased irrigation demands
- Increased pests, crop diseases, and weeds in warmer areas

**Water Resources**
- Changes in water supply
- Decreased water quality
- Increased drought
- Increased flooding

**Forests**
- Changes in forest composition and locations
- Disappearance of some forests
- Increased fires from drying
- Loss of wildlife habitat and species

**Biodiversity**
- Extinction of some plant and animal species
- Loss of habitats
- Disruption of aquatic life

**Sea Level and Coastal Areas**
- Rising sea levels
- Flooding of low-lying islands and coastal cities
- Flooding of coastal estuaries, wetlands, and coral reefs
- Beach erosion
- Disruption of coastal fisheries
- Contamination of coastal aquifers with salt water

**Weather Extremes**
- Prolonged heat waves and droughts
- Increased flooding from more frequent, intense, and heavy rainfall in some areas.

**Human Population**
- Increased deaths
- More environmental refugees
- Increased migration

**Human Health**
- Increased deaths from heat and disease
- Disruption of food and water supplies
- Spread of tropical diseases to temperate areas
- Increased respiratory disease and pollen allergies
- Increased water pollution from coastal flooding

**Figure 18-16** Some possible effects of a warmer atmosphere. Most of these effects could be harmful or beneficial depending on where we live. Current models of the earth's climate cannot make reliable projections about where such effects might take place and how long they might last. (Photo from NASA)

drops in areas such as northern Europe and Japan, where climates are more temperate because of warm-water currents (such as the Gulf Stream and Kuroshio; Figure 6-7, p. 116).

■ Global sea levels will rise, mainly because water expands slightly when heated. In their 2001 IPCC report, climate scientists projected a rise of 9–88 centimeters (4–35 inches) during the 21st century.

■ The high projected rise in sea level of about 88 centimeters (35 inches) would **(1)** threaten half of the world's coastal estuaries, wetlands (one-third of those in the United States), and coral reefs and disrupt marine fisheries, **(2)** cause sea level coastlines (especially along the U.S. East Coast) to retreat inland by about 1.3 kilometers (0.8 mile), **(3)** flood low-lying coastal regions and put an estimated 200 million people living in 30 of the world's largest coastal cities

directly at risk (Figure 18-19, p. 463), **(4)** flood agricultural lowlands and deltas in parts of Bangladesh, India, and China, where much of the world's rice is grown, **(5)** contaminate freshwater coastal aquifers with saltwater (Figure 14-17, p. 328), and **(6)** submerge some low-lying islands in the Pacific and Caribbean (Figure 18-19, p. 463). One comedian jokes that he plans to buy land in Kansas because it will probably become valuable beachfront property. Another boasts that she is not worried because she lives in a houseboat—the "Noah strategy."

■ Some analysts (mostly economists) believe that the threats from sea level rise are overblown or can largely be averted. They contend that **(1)** developed countries will be able to build dikes and levees and move populations to help prevent flooding from projected sea level rise, **(2)** developing countries will also

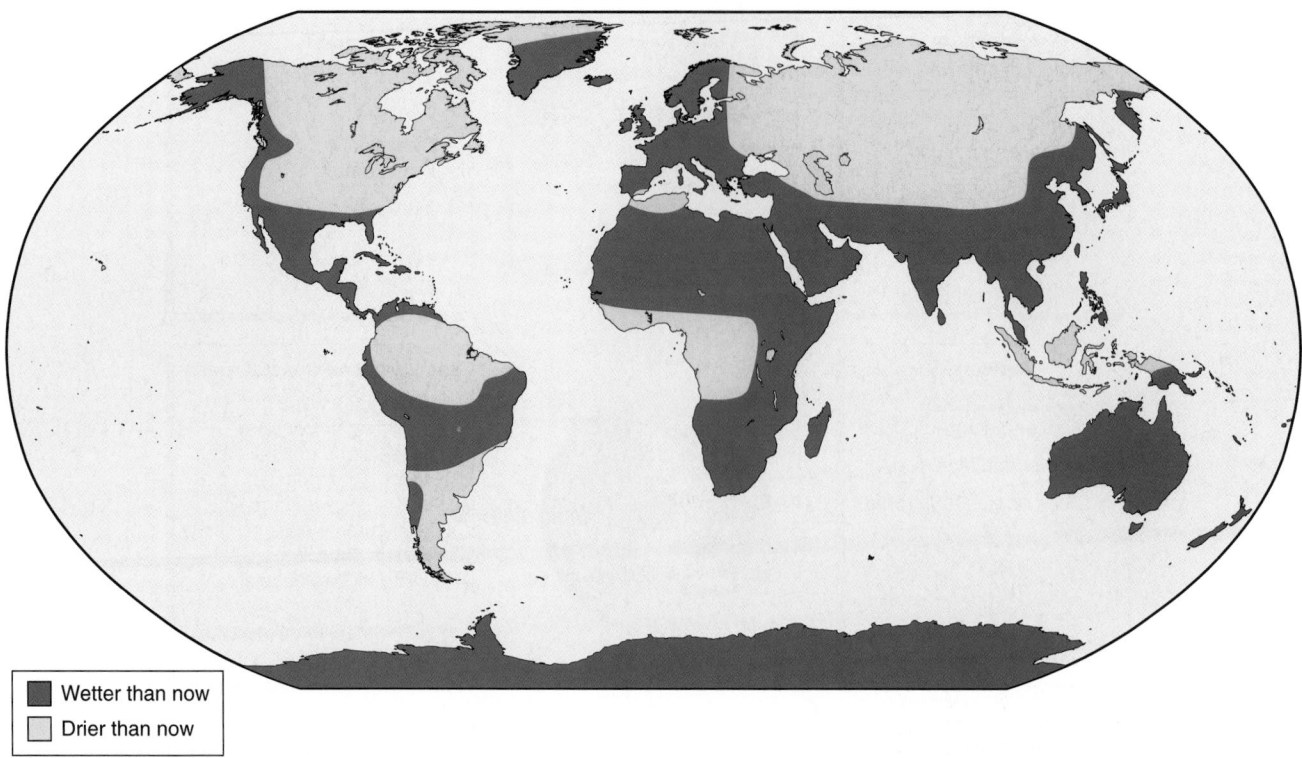

Wetter than now

Drier than now

**Figure 18-17** Projected changes in precipitation patterns in this century as a result of global warming. These preliminary results should not be taken as precise predictions but can be used as a crude guideline for how precipitation patterns may shift in different regions by 2100. (Data from Intergovernmental Panel on Climate Change)

be able to afford such protection because of their projected economic growth, and **(3)** the estimated cost of such protection is only about 0.1% of the GDP for most nations, although this could rise to several percent for low-lying island states.

Present range

Future range

Overlap

- If warming at the poles causes increased melting of land-based ice sheets in Antarctica (Figure 18-9) or Greenland (pp. 453–454), sea levels would rise much more, although the IPCC considers such event very unlikely during this century.

*Extreme Weather*

- According to the IPCC, some places will suffer from **(1)** prolonged heat waves and droughts and **(2)** increased flooding from heavy and prolonged precipitation.

- There has been much speculation that global warming will result in more frequent, more intense, and more destructive hurricanes, typhoons, tornadoes, and violent storms. According to the IPCC 2001 report, there is no credible evidence that projected

**Figure 18-18** Possible effects of global warming on the geographic range of beech trees based on archeological evidence and computer models. According to one projection, if $CO_2$ emissions doubled between 1990 and 2050, beech trees (now common throughout the eastern United States) would survive only in a greatly reduced range in northern Maine and southeastern Canada. This is only one of a number of tree species whose geographic ranges could be changed drastically by increased atmospheric warming. For example, the ranges of some tree species adapted to a warm climate would spread. (Data from Margaret B. Davis and Catherine Zabinski, University of Minnesota)

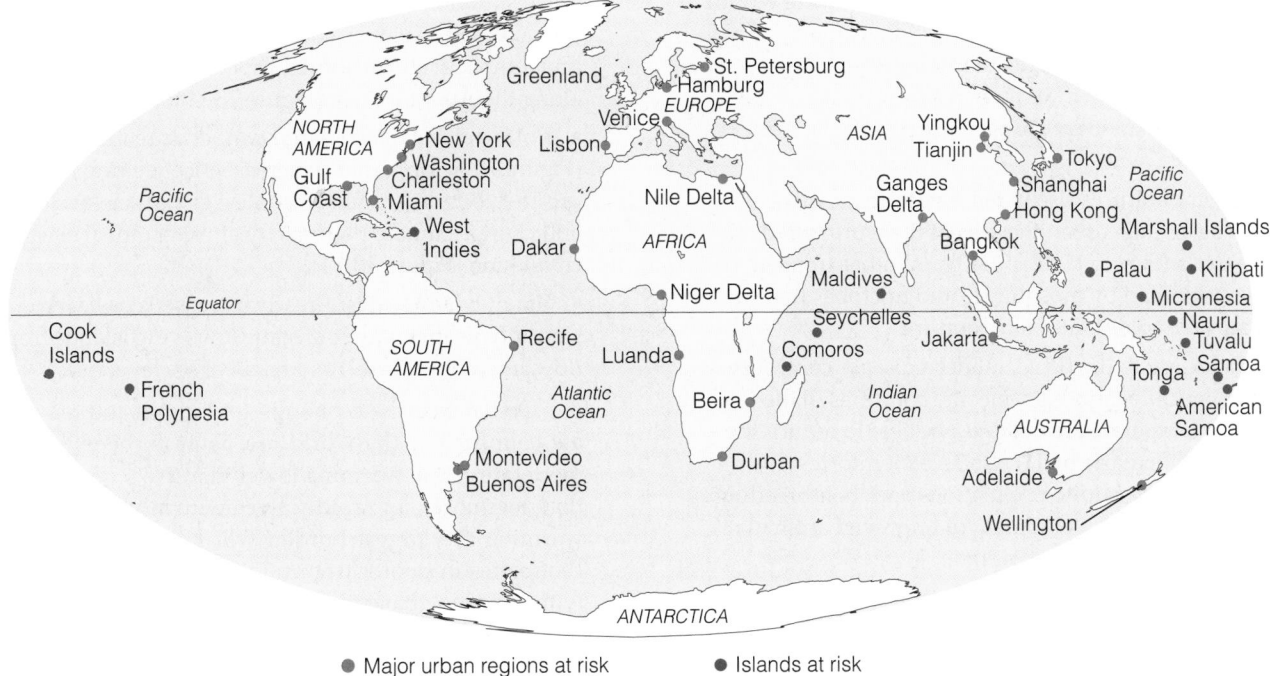

● Major urban regions at risk          ● Islands at risk

**Figure 18-19** The highest projected sea level rise by 2100 could cause severe flooding of many of the world's major cities and low-lying islands. (Data from Intergovernmental Panel on Climate Change, 2001)

global warming will result in such effects—although the possibility cannot be completely ruled out. According to Munich Re and Swiss Re, the world's two largest re-insurer companies, the dramatic increase in damages from hurricanes and other natural disasters in the 1990s resulted primarily from **(1)** increased population and population densities in cities located in high-risk zones and **(2)** the greatly increased economic value of homes, buildings, and businesses located in such areas.

### *Human Health*

■ According to the IPCC, higher temperatures will cause an increase in death and illness, especially among the older people, those with poor health, and the urban poor who cannot afford air conditioning.

## Global Warming, Kirtland's Warblers, and Adélie Penguins

**CONNECTIONS**

Global warming may sharply reduce populations of some species, especially those with specialized niches. For example, Kirtland's warbler, an endangered bird that nests exclusively under young jack pines in northern Michigan, probably would become extinct. The reason is that if northern Michigan ends up with less rain and more heat, jack pines there probably will die off in the next 30–90 years.

Another example involves Adélie penguins (Figure 4-19, p. 78) that live in the western Antarctic (Figure 18-9), which has warmed up by several degrees since 1947 (p. 453). During the past 22 years, University of Montana ecologist William Fraser has observed a 40% drop in the population of this penguin species.

He suggests that sea ice melted by warmer temperatures has reduced populations of shrimplike krill (Figure 4-19, p. 78) that are the Adélie's favorite food. Apparently populations of marine plankton that the krill eat have been dropping, perhaps because of **(1)** melting of the sea ice and **(2)** increased ultraviolet radiation because of drastic drops in concentrations of protective ozone in the stratosphere above Antarctica for several months each year (p. 474). In addition, the penguins' ability to produce young may be decreased by increased spring snowfall (caused by warmer, moisture-laden air) that buries the Adélie's eggs under snowbanks.

Fraser and other scientists believe the plight of Adélie penguins is an early warning of changes other parts of the earth could experience on a much larger scale if projected global warming takes place.

### Critical Thinking

Identify another species with a specialized niche whose population size could be sharply reduced because of projected global warming.

- On the other hand, the IPCC notes that there would also be fewer people dying from cold weather. According to the IPCC, death rates are typically 15–20% higher in winter than in summer and in the United States about twice as many people die from cold as from heat.

- As temperatures rise in temperate areas, there could be an increase in the area of the world affected by malaria (Figure 11-12, p. 243) and other tropical diseases spread by mosquitoes and microbes that cannot survive cold winter temperatures.

- According to the IPCC, modern disease control systems in middle- and high-income countries in the affected temperate areas should be able to reduce the threat from malaria by (1) effective monitoring and reduction of mosquito populations and their breeding grounds and (2) development of improved antimalarial drugs (Case Study, p. 243).

**How Might the Effects of Atmospheric Warming Vary in Different Regions?** In 2001, a report by the IPCC projected the following major changes in different regions of the world during this century:

- **Africa: (1)** Decreased grain yields, **(2)** less water available, **(3)** much higher temperatures in some countries, **(4)** increased desertification (Figure 10-20, p. 220), and **(5)** rising sea levels in Egypt and along the southeastern African coast (Figure 18-19).

- **Asia: (1)** Much higher temperatures in the interior of the continent, **(2)** increased drought in some areas, **(3)** increased floods in some areas (Figure 18-19), **(4)** soil degradation, **(5)** decreased food production, and **(6)** rises in sea level and more intense tropical cyclones in coastal areas that will displace tens of millions of people (Connections, p. 335).

- **Europe: (1)** Increased agricultural productivity with moderate temperature increases, **(2)** increased drought in southern Europe, **(3)** increased flooding in some coastal areas (Figure 18-19), and **(4)** disappearance of half of Alpine glaciers.

- **Latin America: (1)** Increased drought in some areas, **(2)** increased floods in some areas (Figure 18-19), and **(3)** lower yields of key crops in many areas (such as Mexico and northeastern Brazil).

- **North America: (1)** Much higher temperatures in Canada , **(2)** lower winter heating bills but much higher costs for summer cooling in warmer areas, **(3)** increased food production in more northern areas of the United States from moderate warming, **(4)** decreased crop yields in the U.S. Great Plains and Canada's prairies, **(5)** increased forest productivity as more productive southern tree species migrate northward, **(6)** faster and earlier snowmelt in the Rocky Mountains, which would increase spring flooding,

make summers drier, and increase wildfires, and **(7)** increased sea level, coastal erosion, flooding, and greater risk of storm surges, especially in Florida and along the Atlantic coast (Figure 18-19).

- **Polar areas: (1)** Very large temperature increases (Figure 18-8, top) and **(2)** increased ice melting (Figure 18-8, bottom), which can raise global sea levels and change climate patterns by altering global ocean circulation (Figure 18-14).

- **Small island states:** Greatly increased coastal erosion and disappearance of some low-lying islands from flooding (Figure 18-19) as a result of sea level rises.

On balance, the economies of the rich and temperate countries of the world are likely to benefit from moderate global warming lower than 2–3°C (3.6–5.4°F) that does not occur rapidly. Even with moderate global warming the largest burden will fall on people and economies in poorer tropical and subtropical nations, which do not have the economic and technological resources needed to adapt to the harmful impacts of climate change. Many scientists and other analysts call for us to act now to help slow the projected rate and degree of global warming to moderate changes in temperature during this century.

## 18-6 SOLUTIONS: DEALING WITH THE THREAT OF CLIMATE CHANGE

**What Are Our Options?** There are four schools of thought concerning global warming:

- *Do nothing.* A dozen or so scientists contend that climate change from human activities is not a threat, and a few popular press commentators and writers claim that global warming is a hoax.

- *Do more research before acting.* A second group of scientists and economists point to the considerable uncertainty about climate change and its effects. They call for more research before making far-reaching economic and political decisions like phasing out fossil fuels and sharply reducing deforestation.

- *Act now to reduce the risks from climate change.* A third group of scientists and economists urge us to adopt a *precautionary strategy.* When dealing with risky and far-reaching environmental problems such as climate change, they believe the safest course is to take informed preventive action *before* overwhelming scientific evidence justifies acting. In 1997, over 2,500 scientists from a variety of disciplines signed a Scientists' Statement on Global Climate Disruption and concluded, "We endorse those [IPCC] reports and observe that the further accumulation of greenhouse gases commits the earth irreversibly to further global climatic change and consequent ecological, economic, and social disruption. The risks associated with such changes justify preventive action through reductions in emissions of greenhouse gases." Also in 1997, 2,700 economists led by 8 Nobel laureates declared, "As economists, we believe that global climate change carries with it significant environmental, economic, social, and geopolitical risks and that preventive steps are justified."

■ *Act now as part of a no-regrets strategy.* Scientists and economists supporting this approach say we should take the key actions needed to slow projected atmospheric warming even if it is not a serious threat because such actions lead to other important environmental, health, and economic benefits (Solutions, below). For example, a reduction in the combustion of fossil fuels, especially coal, will lead to sharp reductions in air pollution that (1) harms and prematurely kills large numbers of people, (2) lowers food and timber productivity, and (3) decreases biodiversity.

Those who favor doing nothing or waiting before acting point to the 50% chance that we are *overestimating* the impact of rising greenhouse gases. But those urging action remind us also of the 50% chance we are *underestimating* such effects.

**How Can We Reduce the Threat of Climate Change from Human Activities?** Figure 18-20 (p. 466) presents a variety of prevention and cleanup solutions that analysts have suggested for slowing the

rate and intensity of climate change from increased greenhouse gas emissions. Basically it boils down to (1) wasting less energy by improving energy efficiency (Section 16-2, p. 383), (2) using less oil and coal, which produce $CO_2$ (Figure 15-25, p. 358) and other greenhouse gases, (3) relying more on cleaner energy sources such as natural gas (p. 362), solar (p. 393), wind (p. 401), and hydrogen (p. 405), and (4) shifting to organic farming and other more sustainable forms of agriculture (Solutions, p. 468, and Figure 13-36, p. 308). Gradually implementing such solutions over the next 20–30 years could simultaneously reduce the threats from global warming, air pollution, deforestation, and biodiversity loss.

Governments could promote the solutions to slowing global warming listed in Figure 18-20 by

■ Phasing in (1) output-based *carbon taxes* on each unit of $CO_2$ emitted by fossil fuels (especially coal and gasoline) or (2) input-based *energy taxes* on each unit of fossil fuel (especially coal and gasoline) that is burned. Costa Rica has enacted a 15% carbon tax and uses a third of the revenues to finance tree-planting projects by farmers.

■ Decreasing taxes on income, labor, and profits to match any increases in consumption taxes on carbon emissions or fossil fuel use.

■ Greatly increasing government subsidies for energy-efficiency and renewable-energy technologies

## Energy Efficiency to the Rescue

**SOLUTIONS**

According to energy expert Amory Lovins (Guest Essay, p. 384), *the major remedies for slowing possible global warming are things we should be doing even if there were no threat of global warming.* Lovins argues we should (1) waste less energy, (2) reduce air pollution by cutting down on our use of fossil fuels (especially coal and oil) and switching to renewable forms of energy, and (3) harvest trees more sustainably.

According to Lovins, improving energy efficiency (Section 16-2, p. 383) would be the fastest, cheapest, and surest way to slash emissions of $CO_2$ and most other air pollutants within two decades, using existing technology. Lovins estimates that increased energy efficiency would also save (1) the

world $1 trillion per year in reduced energy costs (as much as the annual global military budget) and (2) $300 billion per year in the United States.

Lovins also warns that using fossil fuels such as natural gas ($CH_4$) as a source of hydrogen to power fuel cells (Figure 16-10, p. 387) instead of using solar energy (produced mostly from wind turbines and solar cells) to produce electricity for decomposing (electrolyzing) $H_2O$ to produce hydrogen (Figure 16-34, p. 407) could increase the threat of global warming. The reason is that stripping hydrogen from carbon-based fossil fuels leaves behind $CO_2$ (Figure 16-11, p. 388), which would probably be vented into the atmosphere.

Using energy more efficiently would also (1) reduce pollution, (2) help protect biodiversity, (3) help prevent arguments between gov-

ernments about how $CO_2$ reductions should be divided up and enforced, (4) make the world's supplies of fossil fuel last longer, (5) reduce international tensions over who gets the world's oil supplies, and (6) allow more time to phase in renewable energy sources. A growing number of companies have gotten the message and are saving money and energy while reducing their $CO_2$ emissions and selling their emission reductions in the global marketplace.

### Critical Thinking

1. Do you agree that improving energy efficiency should be done regardless of its impact on the threat of global warming? Explain.

2. Why do you think there has been little emphasis on improving energy efficiency?

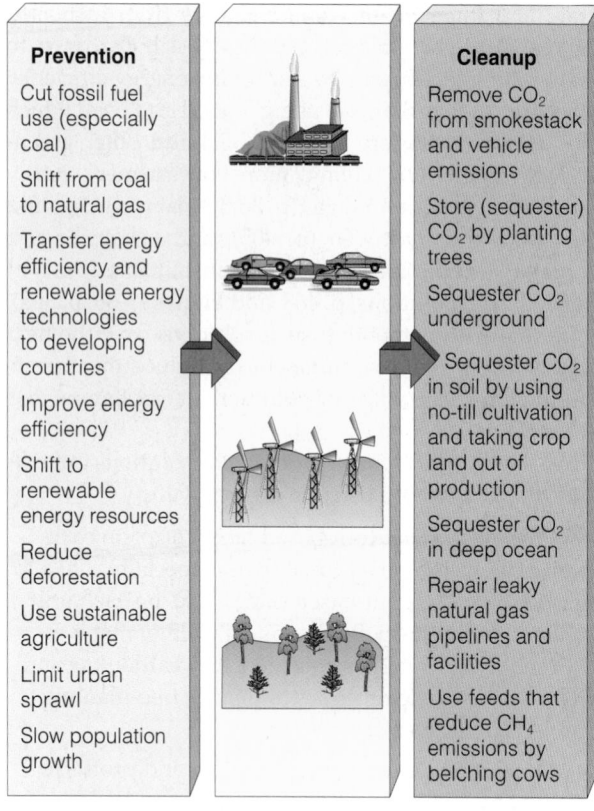

| Prevention | | Cleanup |
|---|---|---|
| Cut fossil fuel use (especially coal) | | Remove $CO_2$ from smokestack and vehicle emissions |
| Shift from coal to natural gas | | Store (sequester) $CO_2$ by planting trees |
| Transfer energy efficiency and renewable energy technologies to developing countries | | Sequester $CO_2$ underground |
| Improve energy efficiency | | Sequester $CO_2$ in soil by using no-till cultivation and taking crop land out of production |
| Shift to renewable energy resources | | Sequester $CO_2$ in deep ocean |
| Reduce deforestation | | Repair leaky natural gas pipelines and facilities |
| Use sustainable agriculture | | Use feeds that reduce $CH_4$ emissions by belching cows |
| Limit urban sprawl | | |
| Slow population growth | | |

**Figure 18-20** *Solutions:* methods for slowing atmospheric warming during the 21st century.

and more sustainable agriculture (Figure 13-36, p. 308) to level the economic playing field and help speed up the shift to these alternatives (Figure 16-44, p. 414).

▪ Funding the transfer of energy-efficiency and renewable-energy technologies from developed countries to developing countries. Increasing the current tax on each international currency transaction by a quarter of a penny could finance this technology transfer, which would then generate wealth for developing countries. This would generate revenues of $200–300 billion a year for projects such as fuel-cell factories in South Africa, wind farms in India and China, and vast solar-powered hydrogen farms in the sunny Middle East.

**What Are the Economic Consequences of Reducing the Threat of Climate Change?** According to a 2001 study by the United Nations Environment Program (UNEP), projected climate change will cost the world's economy more than $300 billion annually by 2050 ($30 billion per year in the United States) unless nations make strong efforts to curb greenhouse gas emissions.

According to some widely publicized economic models developed by economist William Nordhaus and others, however, reducing $CO_2$ emissions will be too costly with the projected costs exceeding the projected benefits. Other economists criticize these models as being unrealistic and too gloomy because they **(1)** do not include the huge cost savings from implementing many of the strategies listed in Figure 18-20 and Solutions, p. 465, and **(2)** underestimate the ability of the marketplace to act rapidly when money is to be made from reducing greenhouse gas emissions.

According to a number of economic studies, implementing the strategies listed in Figure 18-20 would **(1)** boost the global economy, **(2)** provide much needed jobs (especially in developing countries with large numbers of unemployed and underemployed people), and **(3)** cost much less than trying to deal with the harmful effects of these problems.

A 1999 study by the Tellus Institute in Cambridge, Massachusetts, found that if the United States adopted aggressive policies to boost energy efficiency, increase use of renewable energy, and reduce $CO_2$ emissions, within ten years these changes would

▪ Save $43 billion per year in energy costs.

▪ Decrease jobs in the fossil fuel industry but result in a net increase of 870,000 new jobs.

▪ Reduce U.S. energy use by 18% and electricity use by 30%.

▪ Cut $SO_2$ emissions by 50% and emissions of nitrogen oxides by 25%.

▪ Reduce U.S. $CO_2$ emissions by 14% below 1990 levels.

**How Can We Use the Marketplace to Reduce or Prevent Greenhouse Gas Emissions?** An economic approach to helping slow global warming is to **(1)** agree to global and national limits (caps) on greenhouse gas emissions and **(2)** encourage industries and countries to meet these limits by selling and trading greenhouse gas emission permits in the marketplace. This approach also stimulates companies to develop new technologies that reduce emissions of greenhouse gases and increase their profits. In the United States, this market approach has been used to reduce $SO_2$ emissions ahead of target goals at a small fraction of the projected cost (p. 441).

Ways to earn such emission credits include **(1)** improving energy efficiency (Section 16-2, p. 383), **(2)** adopting certain farming, ranching, and soil-building and conservation practices that emit less $CO_2$, $N_2O$, and $CH_4$ (Solutions, p. 468), **(3)** switching from coal to natural gas, **(4)** switching from coal and other fossil fuels to forms of renewable energy such as solar, wind, hydrogen, and geothermal (Chapter 16), and **(5)** sequestering (removing) $CO_2$ from the atmosphere by reforestation or injecting it into the deep ocean or secure underground reservoirs. For example, a coal-burning power plant in Ohio could earn credits to allow some $CO_2$ emissions by financing a $CO_2$-removing tree-planting project in Oregon or Costa Rica.

Some analysts believe this market-based approach is more politically and economically feasible than relying primarily on government regulation to impose taxes on carbon emissions or each unit of fossil fuel used. According to these analysts, government regulation is needed to establish clear guidelines, goals, and quotas, but companies should be free to meet these goals in any way that works and makes money. They agree with the advice given 2000 years ago by Lao-tzu: "Govern a country as you would fry a small fish: Don't poke at it too much."

Other analysts oppose this approach because

- Carbon fuels are burned in so many homes, vehicles, factories, and crop fields that it is almost impossible to monitor such a system to see if trading partners are living up to their agreements.

- It is politically difficult for the world's countries to agree on how to divide up greenhouse gas emission credits and what things should be counted as credits. For example, developed countries and developing countries disagree about allowing developed countries to gain credits toward their $CO_2$ reduction goals by planting trees instead of adopting measures to reduce fossil fuel use, improve energy efficiency, and shift to noncarbon renewable energy resources.

**Can We Remove and Store (Sequester) Enough $CO_2$ To Slow Global Warming?** Scientists are evaluating several ways to remove $CO_2$ from the atmosphere or from smokestacks and store (sequester) it in (1) immature trees, (2) plants that store it in the soil, (3) deep underground reservoirs, and (4) the deep ocean (Figure 18-21).

One way to remove $CO_2$ from the atmosphere temporarily would be to *plant trees* over an area equivalent to the size of Australia in a huge global reforestation program. Such a program would also help restore degraded lands. However, the rate of removal of $CO_2$ from the atmosphere by photosynthesis decreases as trees mature and grow at a slower pace. In addition, trees release their stored $CO_2$ back into the atmosphere when they die and decompose or if they catch fire.

Studies suggest that a global reforestation program (requiring each person in the world to plant and tend to an average of 1,000 trees every year) would offset only about 3 years of our current $CO_2$ emissions from burning fossil fuels. In addition, recent scientific studies call into question the effectiveness of trees (p. 459) and soils (p. 459) as long-term carbon sinks.

**Figure 18-21** Possible methods for removing carbon dioxide from the atmosphere or from smokestacks and storing (sequestering) it in plants, deep underground reservoirs, and the deep ocean.

## Organic Farming and No-Till Cultivation to the Rescue

**SOLUTIONS**

Recent studies by the Rodale Institute in Pennsylvania and other scientists suggest that a wholesale switch to organic farming could help slow global warming. They have shown that crops grown with organic fertilizer produce equivalent yields but much less $CO_2$ through respiration than crops grown with commercial fertilizer. $CO_2$ outputs also are reduced because most organic farming uses 50% less energy than conventional farming methods.

Farmers can also reduce greenhouse emissions by adopting well-known soil conservation methods such as **(1)** using conservation tillage (p. 222) to reduce or eliminate plowing (Figure 18-22), **(2)** retiring former cropland and leaving farmland untouched for at least 10 years (Case Study, p. 223), **(3)** using cover crops in winter, and **(3)** preserving buffer strips of trees along riverbanks.

### Critical Thinking

List three things governments could do to encourage farmers to switch to more sustainable organic farming and soil conservation methods.

There are also ecological concerns. To get a short-term increase in carbon uptake, managers of carbon sequestration projects might be tempted to replace naturally diverse forest areas with tree plantations and thus reduce more of the earth's biodiversity.

Agricultural scientists are investigating the use of plants such as switchgrass that could remove $CO_2$ from the air and deposit it in the soil. Farmers could make money by receiving sequestering payments from power companies to grow such plants on land that is not suitable for ordinary crops. This would also reduce soil erosion and water pollution. The mature crops could be harvested and sold to power companies as a biomass fuel, and the field could be replanted. Research also indicates that using no-till cultivation (Figure 10-25, p. 223) and retiring depleted cropfields and leaving them untouched for ten years as conservation reserves (Case Study, p. 223) can reduce greenhouse gas emissions (Figure 18-22).

Other sequestering approaches include collecting $CO_2$ from smokestacks (and natural gas wells) and **(1)** *pumping it deep underground* into unminable coal seams and abandoned oil fields (as has been done for decades to push up more oil) or **(2)** *injecting it into the*

*deep ocean* (Figure 18-21). In one type of ocean sequestering suggested by oceanographer Peter Brewer, the collected $CO_2$ would be injected deep enough into the sea that it would form heavy $CO_2$ icebergs that could presumably sit on the ocean floor undisturbed for centuries.

In another approach, $CO_2$ emitted by power plants would be dissolved in seawater to form a solution of carbonic acid ($CO_2 + H_2O \longrightarrow H_2CO_3$). This solution would then be reacted with a solution of pulverized carbonate minerals such as limestone ($CaCO_3$) to produce a solution containing bicarbonate ions ($HCO_3^-$) that could be released into the ocean. This would mimic the removal of $CO_2$ as bicarbonates in ocean sediments by the natural carbon cycle (Figure 4-28, p. 84). This approach would cost an estimated one-fourth as much as direct injection of $CO_2$ into the deep sea.

However, any method of underground or deep-sea sequestration would take a costly investment in materials and transportation of the $CO_2$ (presumably by pipeline) to storage sites. In addition, injecting large quantities of $CO_2$ into the ocean could upset the global carbon cycle, seawater acidity, and some forms of deep-sea life in unpredictable ways. Another problem is that current methods can remove only about 30% of the $CO_2$ from smokestack emissions, and using them would double to triple the cost of producing electricity by burning coal.

As part of a *no-regrets* strategy, scientists call for greatly increased research on evaluating various ways

**Figure 18-22** Gross warming potential (GWP) for three types of fields measured by their greenhouse gas emissions. Fields with negative GWPs reduce emissions of these gases. (Data from Michigan State University Kellogg Biological Station)

to sequester carbon as possible ways to help slow projected global warming.

**Can Technofixes Save Us?** Some scientists have suggested various technofixes for reducing the threat of global warming, including **(1)** adding iron to the oceans to stimulate the growth of marine algae (which could remove more $CO_2$ through photosynthesis but would return it to the atmosphere a short time later unless the carbon was somehow deposited in the deep ocean), **(2)** unfurling gigantic foil-surfaced sun mirrors in space or placing such mirrors on about 50,000 orbiting satellites to reduce solar input, **(3)** releasing trillions of reflective balloons filled with helium into the atmosphere, and **(4)** injecting sunlight-reflecting sulfate particulates or firing sulfur dioxide cannonballs into the stratosphere to cool the earth's surface (this would turn the sky white and increase depletion of stratospheric ozone).

Many of these costly schemes might not work, and most probably would produce unpredictable short- and long-term harmful environmental effects. Moreover, once started, those that work could never be stopped without a renewed rise in $CO_2$ levels. Instead of spending huge sums of money on such schemes, many scientists believe it would be more effective and less expensive to improve energy efficiency (Solutions, p. 465) and shift to renewable forms of energy that do not produce $CO_2$ (Chapter 16).

## 18-7 WHAT IS BEING DONE TO REDUCE GREENHOUSE GAS EMISSIONS?

**What Is the Kyoto Treaty?** At the 1992 Earth Summit in Rio de Janeiro, Brazil, 106 nations approved a *UN Framework Convention on Climate Change*. This convention established two basic principles for dealing with climate change:

- Scientific uncertainty must not be used to avoid precautionary action.

- Industrial nations, with the greatest historical contribution to climate change, must take the lead in slowing down the projected *rate and degree of global warming* so that its effects can be managed without disrupting economies, societies, and the earth's biodiversity.

Under this convention developed countries committed themselves to reducing their emissions of $CO_2$ and other greenhouse gases to 1990 levels by the year 2000. However, the convention did not *require* countries to reach this goal, and most countries did not achieve it.

In December 1997, more than 2,200 delegates from 161 nations met in Kyoto, Japan, to negotiate a new treaty to help slow global warming. The resulting treaty would **(1)** require 38 developed countries to cut greenhouse emissions to an average of about 5.2% below 1990 levels by 2012, **(2)** not require developing countries to make any cuts in their greenhouse gas emissions until a later version of the treaty, and **(3)** allow emissions trading among participating countries.

**Should the United States Ratify the Kyoto Treaty?** The U.S. Congress has not ratified the treaty, mostly because of **(1)** its failure to require emission reductions from developing countries, which contain 81% of the world's population, and **(2)** intensive lobbying by a coalition of coal, oil, steel, chemical, and automobile companies that contend it would have a devastating impact on the U.S. economy and workers.

In 2001, President George W. Bush withdrew U.S. participation in the Kyoto treaty because it did not require emissions reductions by developing countries such as China and would hurt the U.S. economy.

This decision set off strong protests by many scientists, citizens, and leaders throughout much of the world. Here are some of the issues raised by opponents and supporters of the treaty.

CHARGE: The treaty does little to help slow global warming. According to computer models, the 5.2% reduction goal of the Kyoto Protocol would shave only about 0.06°C (0.1°F) off the 0.7–1.7°C (1–3°F) temperature rise projected by 2060.

RESPONSE: The treaty is not a 50 or 100 year strategy. Instead it is a first step designed to have industrialized countries producing large amounts of greenhouse gases (Figure 18-5) agree to make modest reductions by 2012.

CHARGE: The treaty does not require reductions by developing countries that make up 81% of the world's population.

RESPONSE: Although developed countries contain only 19% of the world's population they produce 63% of the world's $CO_2$ emissions and should take the lead in reducing their emissions. Then the goal is to bring about required cuts by developing nations and deeper cuts by developed nations at later negotiating sessions. The United States should take the lead because **(1)** it has the highest total and per capita $CO_2$ emissions of any country (Figure 18-5) and **(2)** its population is growing at a rapid rate (Figure 12-14, p. 260).

CHARGE: Reducing emissions of $CO_2$ and other greenhouse gases will hurt the U.S. economy.

RESPONSE: Some economic models indicate that the projected costs of the Kyoto treaty for the United States will exceed the projected benefits. But a number of other economic studies show that reducing greenhouse gases will benefit the U.S. economy in the short and long run as discussed on p. 466. A 2000 study by the

Department of Energy estimated that by 2012 the United States could meet most of its reductions in greenhouse gases under the Kyoto treaty at *no net cost*. This could be done primarily by sharply increasing government subsidies and tax breaks for energy-efficiency and renewable energy technologies and decreasing such subsidies and tax breaks for fossil fuels.

**What Progress Is Being Made?** Here is some *good news:*

- Despite U.S. refusal to support the Kyoto treaty, 178 other countries are going ahead with it and have adopted goals and strategies to reduce their greenhouse gas emissions.

- A 2001 addition to the Kyoto treaty allows developed countries to help meet their greenhouse gas emissions targets by buying and selling emission credits. According to economist Richard Sandor, trading in greenhouse gas emissions allowances will ultimately become "the biggest commodities market in the world."

- A number of developing countries, including China (the world's third largest emitter of $CO_2$, after the United States and the European Union), are voluntarily improving energy efficiency and installing wind, solar, and small hydropower projects even though they are exempt from cuts under the first round of the Kyoto treaty. For example, a Natural Resources Defense Council report in 2001 found that China reduced its $CO_2$ emissions by 17% between 1997 and 2000, while its economy grew by 36%. By comparison, $CO_2$ emissions in the United States rose by 14% between 1997 and 2000. China accomplished the reduction by **(1)** switching from coal to cleaner energy resources by phasing out all coal subsidies, closing coal mines, and shutting down inefficient coal-fired electric plants, **(2)** stepping up its 20-year commitment to promoting energy efficiency, and **(3)** restructuring its economy to reduce dependence on fossil fuels and increase use of renewable energy resources.

- Since 2000 some of the major oil and automobile companies have dropped out of the Global Climate Coalition that opposed the Kyoto treaty and most other action on reducing possible climate change from global warming. Their CEOs **(1)** indicated global warming was a potential risk that should be addressed and **(2)** agreed with most economists that dealing with this problem should stimulate the U.S. economy and create many new jobs.

- Leaders of a number of U.S. companies are concerned that failure of the United States to participate in the treaty will hurt the U.S. economy by **(1)** giving competitors in other countries (especially the European

Union and Japan) a headstart in developing and selling innovative technologies that reduce greenhouse gas emissions and **(2)** hindering U.S. companies from entering into the very lucrative global market in greenhouse emissions trading—projected to reach $100 billion per year by 2010.

- Major companies such as Alcoa, Du Pont, IBM, Toyota, BP, and Shell have established targets to reduce their greenhouse gas emissions by 10–65% from 1990 levels by 2004–2010.

- Major automobile companies are investing billions in developing more efficient motor vehicles powered by *hybrid gas–electric* (Figure 16-9, p. 387) and *fuel cell* (Figure 16-10, p. 387) engines.

- Since 1990, local governments in a number of cities have established programs to reduce their greenhouse gas emissions. For example, Toronto, Canada, has pledged to cut its $CO_2$ emissions 20% below its 1998 level by 2005. By 2002, more than 500 cities around the world (including 110 in the United States) had joined Toronto in pledging to reduce their greenhouse gas emissions.

- In 2002, California became the first state to require a reduction in $CO_2$ emissions from motor vehicles beginning in 2009. Because California's Air Resources Board was established before passage of the Clean Air Act of 1970, it is the only state that can establish its own air quality stands independent of federal regulation. Environmentalists call this measure one of the most significant climate change bills ever passed in the United States.

Environmental, political, and business leaders supporting the Kyoto treaty were encouraged that the Bush administration's 2002 report to the United Nations acknowledged that **(1)** human activities are likely to be changing the climate and **(2)** agreed with most of the 2001 IPCC projections for global warming and sea level rise for this century.

However, they were disappointed that the Bush administration

- Declared to the United Nations that it would not pursue a policy of reducing emissions of $CO_2$ and other greenhouse gases to help slow down the projected rate of warming. In effect, the report said that the world should get used to global warming and adapt to it instead of trying to reduce its impact.

- Rejected having U.S. industries report their annual $CO_2$ emissions. Lack of such data, will **(1)** make it difficult to know what progress the U.S. is making in reducing such emissions on a voluntary basis and **(2)** hurt the economy by not providing adequate data to allow many U.S. companies to participate in the lucrative global $CO_2$ emissions trading market should

**Figure 18-23** *Solutions:* ways to prepare for the possible long-term effects of climate change caused by increased atmospheric temperatures.

the country at some later time decide to participate in the Kyoto treaty.

**How Can We Prepare for Global Warming?**
Politicians in developed countries continue to argue over how to decrease $CO_2$ emissions by about 5.2% over 1990 levels by 2012. However, *according to the latest global climate models, the world needs to reduce current emissions of greenhouse gases (not just $CO_2$) by at least 50% by 2018 to stabilize concentrations of such gases in the air at their present levels.*

Such a large reduction in emissions is extremely unlikely for political and economic reasons because it would take rapid, widespread changes in **(1)** industrial processes, **(2)** energy sources, **(3)** transportation options, and **(4)** individual lifestyles.

Without a much greater sense of urgency and bold leadership by the United States (the world's largest producer of greenhouse gases), many (perhaps most) of the actions that climate experts have recommended for slowing atmospheric warming (Figure 18-20) either will not be done or will be done too slowly. As a result, a growing number of analysts suggest we should also begin to prepare for the possible effects of long-term atmospheric warming and climate change (Figure 18-16). Figure 18-23 shows some ways to do this.

**What Can Individuals Do?** At the individual level, our transportation choices are important factors

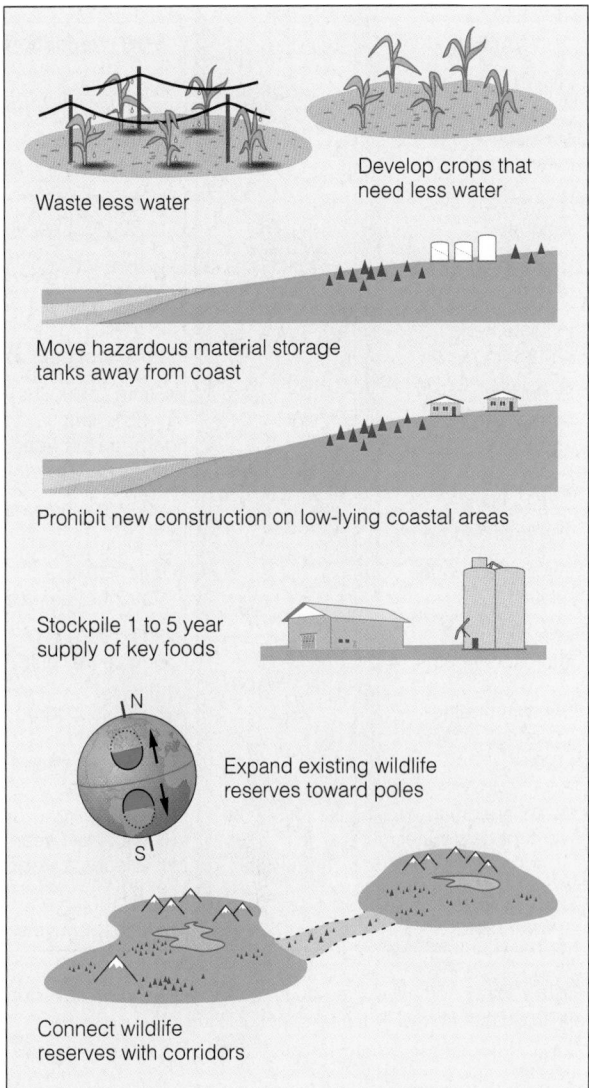

Waste less water

Develop crops that need less water

Move hazardous material storage tanks away from coast

Prohibit new construction on low-lying coastal areas

Stockpile 1 to 5 year supply of key foods

Expand existing wildlife reserves toward poles

Connect wildlife reserves with corridors

| Type of Transportation | $CO_2$ emissions per mile (pounds per passenger) |
|---|---|
| Sport utility vehicle (1 person, 15 mpg) | 1.6 (0.45 kilograms per kilometer) |
| Average car (1 person, 21.5 mpg) | 1.1 (0.31 kilograms per kilometer) |
| Jet (U.S. average occupancy) | 0.97 (0.27 kilograms per kilometer) |
| Mass transit (1/4 full) | 0.75 (0.21 kilograms per kilometer) |
| Economy car (1 person, 40 mpg) | 0.59 (0.17 kilograms per kilometer) |
| Intercity train (U.S. average occupancy) | 0.45 (0.13 kilograms per kilometer) |
| Carpool (3 people, 21.5 mpg) | 0.37 (0.10 kilograms per kilometer) |
| Mass transit (3/4 full) | 0.26 (0.07 kilograms per kilometer) |
| Bike or walk | 0 |

**Figure 18-24** Comparison of $CO_2$ emissions per kilometer using different types of transportation. (Data from U.S. Department of Energy)

| Action | | $CO_2$ Reduction |
| --- | --- | --- |
| Drive fuel-efficient car, walk, bike, car pool, and use mass transit | | 9 kg (20 lbs) per gallon of gasoline saved |
| Use energy-efficient windows | | Up to 4,500 kg (10,000 lbs) per year |
| Use energy-efficient refrigerator | | Up to 1,400 kg (3,000 lbs) per year |
| Insulate walls and ceilings | | Up to 900 kg (2,000 lbs) per year |
| Reduce garbage by recycling and reuse | | 450 kg (1,000 lbs) for 25% less garbage per year |
| Caulk and weatherstrip windows and doors | | Up to 450 kg (1,000 lbs) per year |
| Insulate hot water heater | | Up to 450 kg (1,000 lbs) per year |
| Use compact fluorescent bulbs | | 230 kg (500 lbs) per year per bulb |
| Set water heater at no higher than (120° F) | | 230 kg (500 lbs) for each 6° C (10° F) reduction |
| Wash laundry in warm or cold water | | Up to 230 kg (500 lbs) per year for 2 loads a week |
| Use low-flow shower head | | Up to 140 kg (300 lbs) per year |

**Figure 18-25** What you can do to reduce your annual emissions of $CO_2$. (Data from U.S. Department of Energy)

in the amount of $CO_2$ we emit (Figure 18-24). Figure 18-25 (p. 472) shows a variety of ways we can cut our annual $CO_2$ emissions. See the website material for this chapter for other things you can do to reduce the threat of global warming.

## 18-8 OZONE DEPLETION IN THE STRATOSPHERE

**What Is the Threat from Ozone Depletion?**  A layer of ozone in the lower stratosphere (Figure 17-2, p. 419, and Figure 17-3, p. 420) keeps about 95% of the sun's harmful ultraviolet (UV) radiation from reaching the earth's surface. Measuring instruments on balloons, aircraft, and satellites clearly show seasonal depletion (thinning) of ozone concentrations in the stratosphere above Antarctica and the Arctic. Similar measurements reveal a lower overall thinning of stratospheric ozone everywhere except over the tropics.

Based on these measurements and chemical models, the overwhelming consensus of researchers in this field is that ozone depletion (thinning) in the stratosphere is a serious long-term threat to **(1)** humans, **(2)** many other animals, and **(3)** the sunlight-driven primary producers (mostly plants) that support the earth's food chains and webs.

**What Causes Ozone Depletion? From Dream Chemicals to Nightmare Chemicals** This situation started when Thomas Midgley Jr., a General Motors chemist, discovered the first **chlorofluorocarbon (CFC)** in 1930, and chemists made similar compounds to create a family of highly useful CFCs. The two most widely used are CFC-11 (trichlorofluoromethane, $CCl_3F$) and CFC-12 (dichlorodifluoromethane, $CCl_2F_2$), known by their trade name as Freons.

These chemically stable (nonreactive), odorless, nonflammable, nontoxic, and noncorrosive compounds seemed to be dream chemicals. Cheap to make, they became popular as **(1)** coolants in air conditioners and refrigerators (replacing toxic sulfur dioxide and ammonia), **(2)** propellants in aerosol spray cans, **(3)** cleaners for electronic parts such as computer chips, **(4)** sterilants for hospital instruments, **(5)** fumigants for granaries and ship cargo holds, and **(6)** bubbles in plastic foam used for insulation and packaging. Between 1960 and the early 1990s, CFC production rose sharply.

But CFCs were too good to be true. In 1974, calculations by chemists Sherwood Rowland and Mario Molina at the University of California at Irvine, indicated that CFCs were lowering the average concentration of ozone in the stratosphere. They shocked both the scientific community and the $28-billion-per-year CFC industry by calling for an immediate ban of CFCs in spray cans (for which substitutes were available).

According to Rowland and Molina,

- Large quantities of CFCs were being released into the troposphere mostly from **(1)** the use of CFCs as propellants in spray cans, **(2)** leaks from refrigeration and air conditioning equipment, and **(3)** the production and burning of plastic foam products.

- CFCs remain in the troposphere because they are insoluble in water and are chemically unreactive.

- Over 11–20 years they rise into the stratosphere mostly through convection, random drift, and the turbulent mixing of air in the troposphere.

- In the stratosphere, the CFC molecules break down under the influence of high-energy UV radiation. This releases highly reactive chlorine atoms, which speed up the breakdown of very reactive ozone ($O_3$) into $O_2$ and O in a cyclic chain of chemical reactions (Fig-

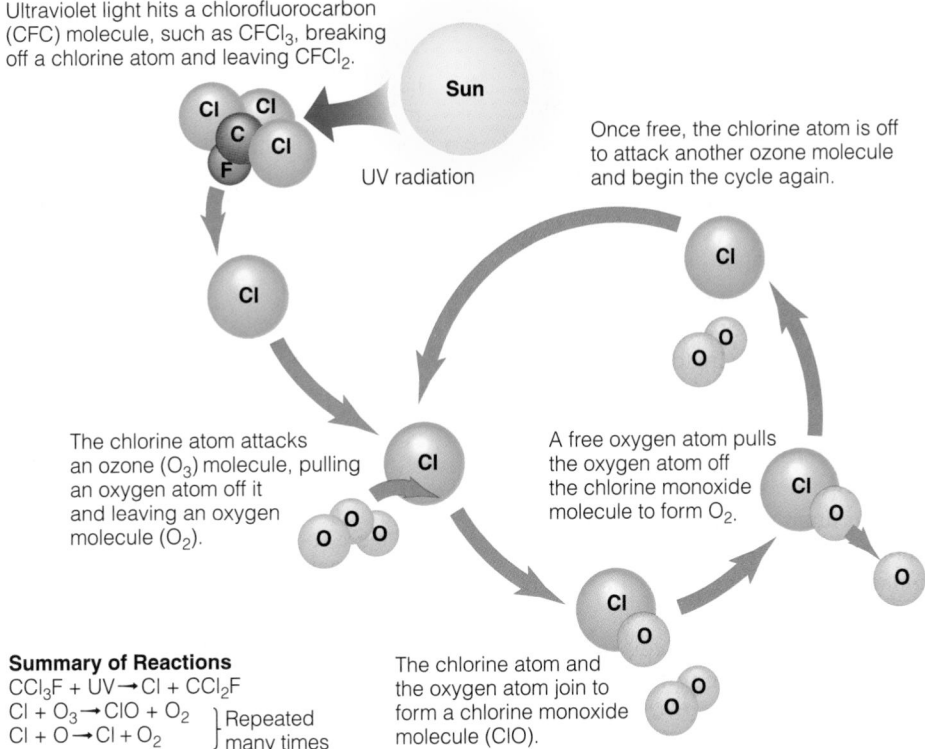

Ultraviolet light hits a chlorofluorocarbon (CFC) molecule, such as $CFCl_3$, breaking off a chlorine atom and leaving $CFCl_2$.

**Sun**

UV radiation

Once free, the chlorine atom is off to attack another ozone molecule and begin the cycle again.

The chlorine atom attacks an ozone ($O_3$) molecule, pulling an oxygen atom off it and leaving an oxygen molecule ($O_2$).

A free oxygen atom pulls the oxygen atom off the chlorine monoxide molecule to form $O_2$.

**Summary of Reactions**
$CCl_3F + UV \rightarrow Cl + CCl_2F$
$Cl + O_3 \rightarrow ClO + O_2$ $\left.\right\}$ Repeated
$Cl + O \rightarrow Cl + O_2$ $\left.\right\}$ many times

The chlorine atom and the oxygen atom join to form a chlorine monoxide molecule (ClO).

**Figure 18-26** A simplified summary of how chlorofluorocarbons (CFCs) and other chlorine-containing compounds destroy ozone in the stratosphere. Note that chlorine atoms are continuously regenerated as they react with ozone. Thus they act as *catalysts*, chemicals that speed up chemical reactions without being used up by the reaction. Bromine atoms released from bromine-containing compounds that reach the stratosphere also destroy ozone by a similar mechanism.

ure 18-26). This causes ozone in various parts of the stratosphere to be destroyed faster than it is formed.

- Each CFC molecule can last in the stratosphere for 65–385 years (depending on its type), with the most widely used CFCs lasting 75–111 years. During that time, each chlorine atom released from these molecules can convert up to 100,000 molecules of $O_3$ to $O_2$.

According to Rowland and Molina's calculations and later models and atmospheric measurements of CFCs in the stratosphere, these dream molecules turned into a nightmare of global ozone destroyers.

The CFC industry (led by the Du Pont Company), a powerful, well-funded adversary with a lot of profits and jobs at stake, attacked Rowland and Molina's calculations and conclusions. However, they held their ground, expanded their research, and explained the meaning of their calculations to other scientists, elected officials, and the media. It was not until 1988—14 years after Rowland and Molina's study—that Du Pont officials acknowledged that CFCs were depleting the ozone layer and agreed to stop producing them once they found substitutes. In 1995, Rowland and Molina received the Nobel Prize in chemistry for their work.

**What Other Chemicals Deplete Stratospheric Ozone?** Other ozone-depleting compounds (ODCs) include

- *Halons* and *HBFCs*, used in fire extinguishers.
- *Methyl bromide* ($CH_3Br$), a widely used fumigant.
- *Carbon tetrachloride* ($CCl_4$), a cheap, highly toxic solvent.
- *Methyl chloroform*, or 1,1,1-trichloroethane ($C_2H_3Cl_3$), used as a cleaning solvent for clothes and metals and as a propellant in more than 160 consumer products such as correction fluid, dry-cleaning sprays, spray adhesives, and other aerosols.
- *N-propyl bromide*, increasingly used as a solvent for degreasing and cleaning metal parts.
- *Hexachlorobutadiene*, also increasingly used as a cleaning solvent.
- *Hydrogen chloride* (HCl), emitted into the stratosphere by U.S. space shuttles.

The oceans and occasional volcanic eruptions also release chlorine compounds into the troposphere. However, most of these chlorine compounds do not make it to the stratosphere because they easily dissolve in water and are washed out of the troposphere in rain. Bromine compounds may be less likely to be washed out of the troposphere, but further study is needed to confirm this possibility. Measurements and models indicate that 75–85% of the observed ozone losses in the stratosphere since 1976 are the result of ODCs released into the atmosphere by human activities beginning in the 1950s.

**Why Is There Seasonal Thinning of Ozone over the Poles?** In 1984, researchers analyzing satellite data discovered that 40–50% of the ozone in the upper stratosphere over Antarctica was being destroyed during the Antarctic spring and early summer (September–December), especially since 1976 (Figure 18-27).

Figure 18-28 shows the seasonal variation of ozone with altitude over Antarctica during 2001. The observed seasonal loss during the summer above Antarctica has been incorrectly called an *ozone hole*. A more accurate term is *ozone thinning* because the ozone depletion varies with altitude (Figure 18-28) and location.

The total area of the atmosphere above Antarctica that suffers from ozone thinning during the peak season varies from year to year (Figure 18-29). In 2000, seasonal ozone thinning above Antarctica was the largest ever and covered an area three times the size of the continental United States.

Measurements indicate that CFCs are the primary culprits. Each sunless winter, steady winds blow in a circular pattern over the earth's poles. This creates a *polar vortex:* a huge swirling mass of very cold air that is isolated from the rest of the atmosphere until the sun returns a few months later.

When water droplets in clouds enter this circling stream of extremely frigid air, they form tiny ice crystals. The surfaces of these ice crystals **(1)** collect CFCs and other ODCs in the stratosphere and **(2)** speed up (catalyze) the chemical reactions that release Cl atoms and ClO. Instead of entering a chain reaction of ozone destruction (Figure 18-26), the ClO atoms combine with one another to form $Cl_2O_2$ molecules. In the dark

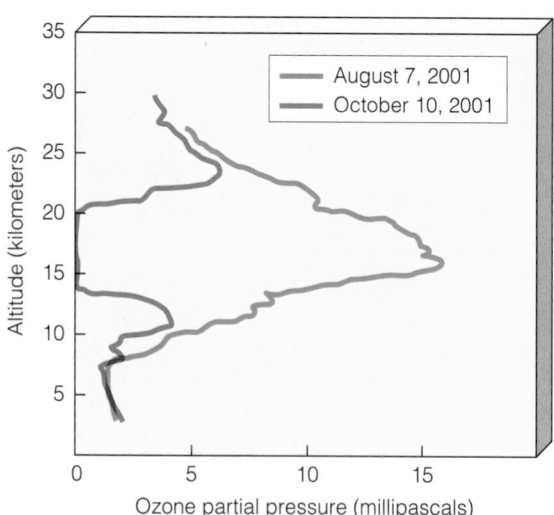

**Figure 18-28** Seasonal variation of ozone level with altitude over Antarctica during 2001. Note the severe depletion of ozone during October (during the Antarctic summer, red line) and its return to more normal levels in August (during the Antarctic winter, green line). (Data from National Oceanic and Atmospheric Administration)

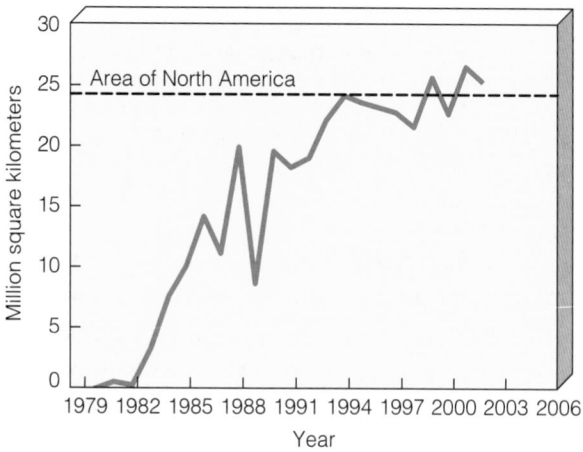

**Figure 18-29** Variation in the average area of ozone thinning above Antarctica between September 7 and October 10 from 1979 to 2001. (Data from National Oceanic and Atmospheric Administration)

of winter, the $Cl_2O_2$ molecules cannot react with ozone, so they accumulate in the polar vortex.

When sunlight and the spring return to Antarctica 2–3 months later (in October), the sunlight breaks up the stored $Cl_2O_2$ molecules, releasing large numbers of Cl atoms and initiating the catalyzed chlorine cycle (Figure 18-26). Within weeks, this typically destroys 40–50% of the ozone above Antarctica (and 100% in some places). The returning sunlight **(1)** gradually melts the ice crystals, **(2)** breaks up the vortex of trapped polar air, and **(3)** allows it to begin mixing again with the rest of the atmosphere. Then new ozone forms over Antarctica until the next dark winter (Figure 18-28).

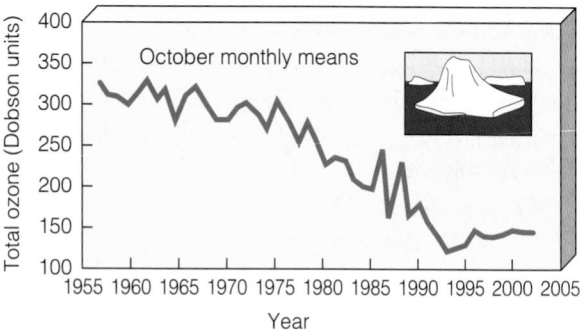

**Figure 18-27** Mean total level of ozone for October over the Halley Bay measuring station in Antarctica, 1956–2001. (Data from British Antarctic Survey and World Meteorological Organization)

When the vortex breaks up, huge masses of ozone-depleted air above Antarctica flow northward and linger for a few weeks over parts of Australia, New Zealand, South America, and South Africa. This raises biologically damaging UV-B levels in these areas by 3–10%, and in some years by as much as 20%.

In 1988, scientists discovered that similar but usually less severe ozone thinning occurs over the Arctic during the arctic spring and early summer (February–June), with a seasonal ozone loss of 11–38% (compared to a typical 50% loss above Antarctica). However, in 1997 and 1999, the average seasonal loss over the Arctic was about 60%. When this mass of air above the Arctic breaks up each spring, large masses of ozone-depleted air flow south to linger over parts of Europe, North America, and Asia. According to a 1998 model developed by scientists at NASA's Goddard Institute for Space Studies, ozone depletion over the Antarctic and Arctic will be at its worst between 2010 and 2019 (Figure 18-30).

**Antarctic**

**Arctic**

**Figure 18-30** Projected total ozone loss, averaged over 2010–2019, during September for the Antarctic (top) and during March for the Arctic (bottom). According to the model used to make these projections, during this period the severity of ozone loss over the Arctic may approach that over the Antarctic. Dark red represents ozone depletion of 54% or more; light blue, 18–30%; and dark blue, 6–12%. (Data from NASA Goddard Institute for Space Studies)

**Human Health**

• Worse sunburn

• More eye cataracts

• More skin cancers

• Immune system suppression

**Food and Forests**

• Reduced yields for some crops

• Reduced seafood supplies from reduced phytoplankton

• Decreased forest productivity for UV-sensitive tree species

**Wildlife**

• Increased eye cataracts in some species

• Decreased population of aquatic species sensitive to UV radiation

• Reduced population of surface phytoplankton

• Disrupted aquatic food webs from reduced phytoplankton

**Air Pollution and Materials**

• Increased acid deposition

• Increased photochemical smog

• Degradation of outdoor paints and plastics

**Global Warming**

• Accelerated warming because of decreased ocean uptake of $CO_2$ from atmosphere by phytoplankton and CFCs acting as greenhouse gases

**Figure 18-31** Expected effects of decreased levels of ozone in the stratosphere.

**Why Should We Be Worried About Ozone Depletion? Life in the Ultraviolet Zone** Why should we care about ozone loss? Figure 18-31 lists some of the expected effects of decreased levels of ozone in the stratosphere. From a human standpoint the answer is that with less ozone in the stratosphere, more biologically damaging UV-A and UV-B radiation will reach the earth's surface. This will give humans **(1)** worse sunburns, **(2)** more eye cataracts (a clouding of the eye's lens that reduces vision and can cause blindness if not corrected), and **(3)** more skin cancers (Figure 18-32, p. 476, and Connections, p. 478).

Humans can make cultural adaptations to increased UV-B radiation by **(1)** staying out of the sun,

Thin long-wavelength (low-energy) form of UV radiation causes aging of the skin, tanning, and sometimes sunburn. It penetrates deeply and may contribute to skin cancer.

Thin shorter-wavelength (high-energy) form of UV radiation causes sunburn, premature aging, and wrinkling. It is largely responsible for basal and squamous cell carcinomas and plays a role in malignant melanoma.

Ultraviolet A

Ultraviolet B

Thin Layer of dead cells

Squamous cells

Basal layer

Melanocyte cells

Basal

Blood vessels

Hair

Epidermis

Sweat gland

Dermis

**Squamous Cell Carcinoma**

Arising from cells in the upper layer of the epidermis, this cancer is also caused by exposure to sunlight or tanning lamps. It is usually curable if treated early. It grows faster than basal cell carcinoma and can metastasize.

**Basal Cell Carcinoma**

The most common skin malignancy usually is caused by excessive exposure to sunlight or tanning lamps. It develops slowly, rarely metastasizes and is nearly 100% curable if diagnosed early and treated properly.

**Melanoma**

This deadliest of skin cancers involves melanocyte cells, which produce pigment. It can develop from a mole or on blemished skin, grows quickly, and can spread to other parts of the body (metastasize).

**Figure 18-32** Structure of the human skin and the relationships between ultraviolet (UV-A and UV-B) radiation and the three types of skin cancer. The incidence of these types of cancer is rising, mostly because more fair-skinned people have increased their exposure to sunlight by moving to areas with sunnier climates and spending more of their leisure time exposed to sunlight. If ozone-destroying chemicals continue to reduce stratospheric ozone levels, incidence of these types of cancers is expected to rise. (The Skin Cancer Foundation)

(2) protecting their skin with clothing, and (3) applying sunscreens (Connections, p. 478). However, UV-sensitive plants and animals that help support us and other forms of life cannot make such changes except through the long process of biological evolution.

## 18-9 SOLUTIONS: PROTECTING THE OZONE LAYER

**How Can We Protect the Ozone Layer?** *The scientific consensus of researchers in this field is that we should immediately stop producing all ozone-depleting chemicals* (ODCs). Even with immediate action, the models indicate it will take about 50 years for the ozone layer to return to 1980 levels and about 100 years for recovery to pre-1950 levels.

Some *good news* is that substitutes are available for most uses of CFCs (Table 18-3), and others are being developed (Individuals Matter, p. 479).

To a growing number of scientists, hydrocarbons (HCs) such as propane and butane are a better way to reduce ozone depletion while doing little to increase global warming. Developing countries could use HC refrigerator technology to leapfrog ahead of industrialized countries without having to invest in costly HFC and HCFC technologies that will have to be phased out within a few decades because they are sources of potent greenhouse gases (Table 18-3). This approach is also less costly because HCs cannot be patented and can be manufactured locally, reducing the need to import expensive HFCs and HCFCs.

**Can Technofixes Save Us?** What about a quick fix from technology, so that we can keep on using CFCs? One proposed scheme for removing ozone from the atmosphere is to launch a fleet of 20–30 radio-controlled blimps the length of football fields into the stratosphere above Antarctica. A huge curtain of electrical wires hanging from the blimps would inject negatively charged electrons into the stratosphere to react with and remove ozone-destroying chlorine atoms (Cl). However, atmospheric chemist Ralph Ciecerone believes this plan will not work because other chemical species in the stratosphere snatch electrons more readily than does chlorine. This scheme could also have unpredictable side effects on atmospheric chemistry.

Others have suggested using tens of thousands of lasers to blast CFCs out of the atmosphere before they can reach the stratosphere. However, both enormous amounts of energy and decades of research would be required to perfect the types of lasers needed. Moreover, we cannot predict the possible effects of such powerful laser blasts on climate, birds, or planes.

**What Is Being Done to Reduce Ozone Depletion? Some Hopeful Progress** In 1987, 36 nations meeting in Montreal, Canada, developed a treaty, commonly known as the *Montreal Protocol,* to cut

---

**Table 18-3 CFC Substitutes**

| Types | Pros | Cons |
|---|---|---|
| **Hydrochlorofluorocarbons** (HCFCs) | Break down faster (2–20 years). Pose about 90% less danger to ozone layer. Can be used in aerosol sprays, refrigeration, air conditioning, foam, and cleaning agents. | Are potent greenhouse gases (Table 18-1). Will still deplete ozone, especially if used in large quantities. Health effects largely unknown. Expensive. May lower energy efficiency of appliances. Can be degraded to trifluoroacetate (TFA), which can inhibit plant growth in wetlands. |
| **Hydrofluorocarbons** (HFCs) | Break down faster (2–20 years). Do not contain ozone-destroying chlorine. Can be used in aerosol sprays, refrigeration, air conditioning, and insulating foam. | Are potent greenhouse gases (Table 18-1). Expensive. Safety questions about flammability and toxicity still unresolved. Can be degraded to TFA, which can inhibit plant growth in wetlands. May lower energy efficiency of appliances. Production of HFC-134a, a refrigerant substitute, yields an equal amount of methyl chloroform, a serious ozone depleter. |
| **Hydrocarbons (HCs)** (such as propane and butane) | Cheap and readily available. Can be used in aerosol sprays, refrigeration, foam, and cleaning agents. Not patentable. Can be made locally in developing countries. | Can be flammable and poisonous if released. Some increase in ground-level air pollution from photochemical smog (Figure 17-6, p. 424). |
| **Ammonia** | Simple alternative for refrigerators; widely used before CFCs. | Toxic if inhaled. Must be handled carefully. |
| **Water and steam** | Effective for some cleaning operations and for sterilizing medical instruments. | Creates polluted water that must be treated. Wastes water unless the used water is cleaned up and reused. |
| **Terpenes** (from the rinds of lemons and other citrus fruits) | Effective for cleaning electronic parts. | None. |
| **Helium** | Effective coolant for refrigerators, freezers, and air conditioners. | This rare gas may become scarce if use is widespread, but very little coolant is needed per appliance. |

## The Cancer You Are Most Likely to Get

Research indicates that years of exposure to UV-B ionizing radiation in sunlight is the primary cause of *squamous cell* (Figure 18-32, left) and *basal cell* (Figure 18-32, center) *skin cancers*. Together these two types make up 95% of all skin cancers. Typically there is a 15- to 40-year lag between excessive exposure to UV-B (which is blocked by window glass) and development of these cancers.

Caucasian children and adolescents who get only a single severe sunburn double their chances of getting these two types of cancers. Some 90–95% of these types of skin cancer can be cured if detected early enough, although their removal may leave disfiguring scars. These cancers kill only 1–2% of their victims, but this still amounts to about 2,200 deaths in the United States each year.

A third type of skin cancer, *malignant melanoma* (Figure 18-32, right), occurs in pigmented areas such as moles anywhere on the body. Within a few months, this type of cancer can spread to other organs. It kills about one-fourth of its victims (most under age 40) within 5 years, despite surgery, chemotherapy, and radiation treatments. Each year it kills about 100,000 people (including more than 7,400 Americans), mostly Caucasians. It can be cured if detected early enough, but recent studies show that some melanoma survivors have a recurrence more than 15 years later.

Recent evidence suggests that about 90% of sunlight's melanoma-causing effect may come from exposure to UV-A (which is not blocked by window glass) and 10% from UV-B. Some sunscreens do not protect from UV-A, and tanning booth lights and sun lamps emit mostly UV-A.

Evidence indicates that people (especially Caucasians) who get three or more blistering sunburns before age 20 are five times more likely to develop malignant melanoma than those who have never had severe sunburns. About 10% of those who get malignant melanoma have an inherited gene that makes them especially susceptible to the disease.

The truth is that there is no known safe way to tan. A suntan is your skin's response to an injury (by producing melanin) when ultraviolet rays penetrate your skin's inner layer.

To protect yourself, the safest course is to (1) stay out of the sun (especially between 10 A.M. and 3 P.M., when UV levels are highest) and (2) not use tanning parlors or sun lamps. When you are in the sun, wear (1) tightly woven protective clothing, (2) a wide-brimmed hat, and (3) sunglasses that protect against UV-A and UV-B radiation (ordinary sunglasses may actually harm your eyes by dilating your pupils so more UV radiation strikes the retina).

Because UV rays can penetrate clouds, overcast skies do not protect you; neither does shade, because UV rays can reflect off sand, snow, water, or patio floors. People who take antibiotics and women who take birth control pills are more susceptible to UV damage.

Use a sunscreen that offers protection against both UV-A and UV-B and has a protection factor of 15 or more (25 if you have light skin).

Apply to all exposed skin (including lips) and reapply sunscreens about every 2 hours or immediately after swimming or excessive perspiration. Most people do not realize that the protection factors for sunscreens are based on using one full ounce of the product—about enough to fill a shot glass. Some people also increase their risk of skin cancer by falsely assuming that sunscreens allow them to spend more time in the sun.

Children who use a sunscreen with a protection factor of 15 every time they are in the sun from age 1 to age 18 decrease their chance of getting skin cancer by 80%. Babies under a year old should not be exposed to the sun at all and should not have sunscreens applied until they are at least 6 months old.

Become familiar with your moles and thoroughly examine your skin and scalp at least once a month. Warning signs of skin cancer are (1) a change in the size, shape, or color of a mole or wart (the major sign of malignant melanoma, which must be treated quickly), (2) sudden appearance of dark spots on the skin, or (3) a sore that keeps oozing, bleeding, and crusting over but does not heal. Be alert for precancerous growths (reddish-brown spots with a scaly crust). If you observe any of these signs, consult a doctor immediately.

### Critical Thinking

What precautions, if any, do you take to reduce your chances of getting skin cancer from exposure to sunlight? Explain why you do or do not take such precautions.

---

emissions of CFCs (but not other ozone depleters) into the atmosphere by about 35% between 1989 and 2000. After hearing more bad news about seasonal ozone thinning above Antarctica in 1989, representatives of 93 countries met in London in 1990 and in Copenhagen, Denmark, in 1992 and adopted a new protocol ac-

celerating the phasing out of key ozone-depleting chemicals.

These landmark international agreements now signed by 177 countries, are important examples of global cooperation in response to a serious global environmental problem. However, according to a 1998

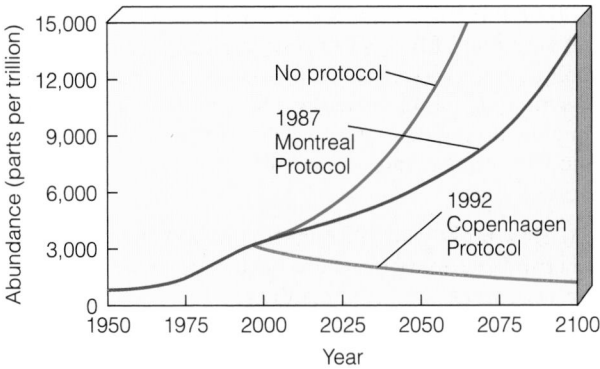

**Figure 18-33** Projected concentrations of ozone-depleting chemicals (ODCs) in the stratosphere under three scenarios: **(1)** no action, **(2)** the 1987 Montreal Protocol, and **(3)** the 1992 Copenhagen Protocol. Projections based on the 1992 Copenhagen Protocol assume **(1)** the conditions of the protocol will be carried out by the signing nations and **(2)** any new chemicals found to be depleting stratospheric ozone will also be phased out. (Adapted from Chiras, *Environmental Science*, 5/E fig. 21.5. Copyright © 1998 by Wadsworth)

World Meteorological Organization (WMO) study by 350 scientists, the ozone layer will

- Continue to be depleted for several decades because of **(1)** the 11- to 20-year time lag between when ODCs are released into the stratosphere and when they reach the stratosphere and **(2)** their persistence for decades in the stratosphere.

- Return to 1980 levels by about 2050 and to 1950 levels by about 2100 (Figure 18-33), assuming **(1)** the international agreements are followed and **(2)** any new chemicals found to be depleting stratospheric ozone will also be phased out.

Without the 1992 international agreement, ozone depletion would be a much more serious threat (Figure 18-33). However, there is a need to **(1)** include and phase out new ozone-depleting chemicals—such as n-propyl bromide, hexachlorobutadiene, and halon-1201—not included in the current treaty and **(2)** continue evaluating and monitoring the ozone reduction potential of new chemicals added to the marketplace.

One piece of *disturbing news* in the 1998 WMO study is that ozone depletion in the stratosphere has been cooling the troposphere and has helped offset or disguise as much as 30% of the global warming from our emissions of greenhouse gases. Thus restoring the ozone layer could lead to an increase in global warming.

The ozone treaty set an important precedent for global cooperation and action to avert potential global disaster. Nations and companies agreed to work together to solve this problem because

- There was convincing and dramatic scientific evidence of a serious problem.

- CFCs were produced by a small number of international companies.

- The certainty that CFC sales would decline unleashed the economic and creative resources of the private sector to find even more profitable substitute chemicals.

International cooperation in dealing with projected atmospheric warming is much more difficult because

- We lack clear-cut and dramatic evidence that a serious problem exists.

- Greenhouse gas emissions result from the actions of hundreds of different large and politically powerful industries (such as coal, oil, chemicals, automobiles, and steel) and billions of consumers.

- Reducing greenhouse gas emissions will take far-reaching and politically controversial changes within most industries and lifestyle changes for billions of consumers.

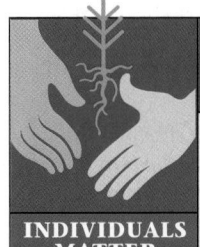

**INDIVIDUALS MATTER**

### Ray Turner and His Refrigerator

Ray Turner, an aerospace manager at Hughes Aircraft in California, made an important low-tech ozone-saving discovery by using his head—and his refrigerator. His concern for the environment led him to look for a cheap and simple substitute for the CFCs used as cleaning agents to remove films of oxidation from the electronic circuit boards manufactured at his plant.

He started by looking in his refrigerator. He decided to put drops of various substances on a corroded penny to see whether any of them removed the film of oxidation. Then he used his soldering gun to see whether solder would stick to the surface of the penny, indicating the film had been cleaned off.

First, he tried vinegar. No luck. Then he tried some ground-up lemon peel, also a failure. Next he tried a drop of lemon juice and watched as the solder took hold. The rest, as they say, is history.

Today, Hughes Aircraft uses inexpensive citrus-based solvents that are CFC-free to clean circuit boards. This new cleaning technique has reduced circuit board defects by about 75% at Hughes. And Turner got a hefty bonus. Now other companies, such as AT&T, clean computer boards and chips using acidic chemicals extracted from cantaloupes, peaches, and plums. Maybe you can find a solution to an environmental problem in your refrigerator, grocery, drugstore, or backyard.

Thus reducing and adapting to the threat of global warming is a difficult political, economic, and scientific challenge. However, it can be done over the next few decades (Figures 18-20 and 18-23). Moreover, numerous economic studies show that meeting this challenge will **(1)** save huge amounts of money, **(2)** create many jobs, and **(3)** be much more profitable for many of the world's major businesses than doing nothing or waiting to act.

*The atmosphere is the key symbol of global interdependence. If we can't solve some of our problems in the face of threats to this global commons, then I can't be very optimistic about the future of the world.*

MARGARET MEAD

## REVIEW QUESTIONS

1. Define the boldfaced terms in this chapter.

2. Summarize briefly how the earth's average temperature has changed over the past 900,000 years and over the past 130 years. Distinguish between *glacial* and *interglacial* periods.

3. List eight ways that scientists get information about past changes in the earth's climate.

4. What is the earth's *natural greenhouse effect?* How widely is this theory accepted? What are the two major greenhouse gases? Describe the *natural cooling process* that takes place near the earth's surface.

5. What is *global warming?* List three human activities that increase the input of greenhouse gases into the troposphere and could enhance the earth's natural greenhouse effect.

6. List five measurements that suggest increases in atmospheric emissions of greenhouse gas are warming the atmosphere. List five other signs that the troposphere is getting warmer.

7. Describe changes at the earth's poles and in Greenland that indicate the troposphere has warmed in recent decades. Describe the significance of these changes for humans and many forms of wildlife.

8. Describe how scientists develop mathematical models to make projections about future climate change.

9. According to the latest models, between 2000 and 2100 about how much increase is projected for **(a)** the global average temperature and **(b)** global sea levels? What is the scientific consensus about how these projected changes are related to human activities such as fossil fuel burning and deforestation? Why does rapid climate change over a few decades to 100 years, whether it is caused by natural or human-related factors, pose a serious threat to human life, wildlife, and the world's economies?

10. Explain how each of the following factors might enhance or dampen global warming: **(a)** changes in solar output, **(b)** changes in the earth's reflectivity (albedo), **(c)** the oceans, **(d)** water vapor content and clouds, **(e)** air pollution, and **(f)** effects of increased $CO_2$ levels on photosynthesis, and **(g)** increased methane emissions. How might planting more trees and conserving soils affect global warming, and what are the limitations of this approach?

11. How rapidly might climates shift? What is the range of error in current projections of changes in the earth's average atmospheric temperature?

12. Why should we worry about a possible rise of only one to a few degrees in the average temperature at the earth's surface?

13. List some beneficial effects of atmospheric warming. Explain how atmospheric warming might affect each of the following: **(a)** food production, **(b)** water supplies, **(c)** forests, **(d)** biodiversity, **(e)** sea levels, **(f)** weather extremes, **(g)** human health, **(h)** developing countries, and **(i)** species such as Kirtland's warblers and Adélie penguins.

14. What are the four schools of thought about what we should do about global warming?

15. According to climate scientists, by how much will we need to reduce the current level of fossil fuel use to stabilize $CO_2$ emissions at their current level?

16. List nine prevention methods and seven cleanup methods for slowing climate change from increased greenhouse gas emissions.

17. Explain how improving energy efficiency and relying more on organic farming could help reduce greenhouse gas emissions.

18. Describe the potential economic consequences of reducing the threat of global warming for **(a)** the world and **(b)** the United States.

19. Describe the pros and cons of selling and trading greenhouse gas emission permits in national and global markets as a way to reduce greenhouse gas emissions.

20. Describe the pros and cons of removing $CO_2$ from the atmosphere or smokestacks and storing it in **(a)** immature trees, **(b)** plants that store it in the soil, **(c)** deep underground reservoirs, and **(d)** the deep ocean.

21. Summarize progress made in developing an international treaty to help reduce greenhouse gas emissions and other actions to reduce such emission by various government and corporations. List the pros and cons of the Kyoto treaty.

22. List seven ways in which we might prepare for and adjust to the harmful effects of global warming.

23. List the five most important ways you could reduce your emissions of greenhouse gases.

24. What is stratospheric *ozone depletion,* and how serious is this problem? What types of chemicals cause ozone depletion? How do these chemicals cause such depletion?

**25.** Explain how seasonal ozone thinning occurs each year over the earth's poles.

**26.** What are the major harmful effects of ozone depletion on **(a)** human health, **(b)** crop yields, **(c)** forest productivity, **(d)** materials such as plastics and paints, and **(e)** plankton productivity?

**27.** Distinguish among *squamous cell skin cancer, basal cell skin cancer,* and *malignant melanoma.* List ways in which you can reduce your chances of getting skin cancer.

**28.** If all ozone-depleting chemicals were banned now, about how long would it take for average concentrations of ozone in the stratosphere to return to levels in **(a)** 1980 and **(b)** 1950?

**29.** Summarize the progress that has been made in reducing the threat of ozone depletion and explain the importance of such efforts.

**30.** List three factors that helped countries agree to an international treaty to phase out ozone-depleting chemicals. List three reasons why getting countries to develop an international treaty and engage in other unified actions to reduce greenhouse gas emissions is much more difficult.

## CRITICAL THINKING

**1.** In preparation for the 1992 UN Conference on the Human Environment in Rio de Janeiro, President George Bush's top economic adviser gave an address in Williamsburg, Virginia, to representatives of governments from a number of countries. He told his audience not to worry about global warming because the average temperature increases scientists are predicting were much less than the temperature increase he experienced in coming from Washington, D.C., to Williamsburg, Virginia. What is the fundamental flaw in this reasoning?

**2.** What changes might occur in the **(a)** global hydrologic cycle (Figure 4-27, p. 83) and **(b)** global carbon cycle (Figure 4-28, p. 84) if the atmosphere experienced significant warming? Explain.

**3.** What effect should clearing forests and converting them to grasslands and crops have on the earth's **(a)** reflectivity (albedo) and **(b)** average surface temperature? Explain.

**4.** Explain how global warming could lead to a much cooler climate in Europe and eastern North America.

**5.** What difference might it make in your life and in that of any child you might have if human activities play an important role in continued warming of the earth's polar regions and Greenland?

**6.** Which of the four schools of thought about what should be done about possible global warming (pp. 464–465) do you favor? Explain.

**7.** Explain why you agree or disagree with each of the proposals listed in **(a)** Figure 18-20 (p. 466) for slowing down emissions of greenhouse gases into the atmosphere and **(b)** Figure 18-23 (p. 471) for preparing for the effects of global warming. What might be the harmful effects on your life of *not* taking these actions?

**8.** Do you agree or disagree with the argument by developing countries that developed countries should bear the brunt of reducing $CO_2$ emissions because they produce much more of these emissions than developing countries? Explain.

**9.** Explain why developed nations are able to adapt to problems caused by increased global warming more easily than developing countries. Should developed countries provide significant aid to help developing countries adapt to the harmful effects of global warming? Explain.

**10.** What consumption patterns and other features of your lifestyle directly add greenhouse gases to the atmosphere? Which, if any, of these things would you be willing to give up to slow global warming and reduce other forms of air pollution?

**11.** You have been diagnosed with a treatable basal cell skin cancer (Figure 18-32, middle). Explain why you could increase your chances of getting more of such cancers within 15–40 years by moving to Australia or Florida.

**12.** Congratulations! You are in charge of the world. List your three most important actions for dealing with the problems of **(a)** global warming and **(b)** depletion of ozone in the stratosphere.

## PROJECTS

**1.** As a class, conduct a poll of students at your school to determine **(a)** whether they understand the difference between global warming of the troposphere and ozone depletion in the stratosphere (Table 18-2, p. 451) and **(b)** whether they believe global warming from an enhanced greenhouse effect is a very serious problem, a moderately serious problem, or of little concern. Tally the results to see whether there are differences related to year in school, political leaning (liberal, conservative, independent), or sex of poll participants.

**2.** As a class, conduct a poll of students at your school to determine whether they believe stratospheric ozone depletion is a very serious problem, a moderately serious problem, or of little concern. Tally the results to see whether there are differences related to year in school, political leaning (liberal, conservative, independent), or sex of poll participants.

**3.** Use the library or the Internet to determine how the current government policy on global warming in the country where you live compares with the policy suggestions made by various analysts and listed in Figures 18-20 and 18-23.

**4.** Write a 1- to 2-page scenario of what your life could be like by 2060 if nations, companies, and individuals do not take steps to reduce projected global warming caused at least partly by human activities. Contrast your scenario with the positive scenario at the opening of this chapter. Compare and critique scenarios written by different members of your class.

**5.** Use the library or the Internet to find bibliographic information about *Paul A. Colinvaux* and *Margaret Mead*, whose quotes appear at the beginning and end of this chapter.

**6.** Make a concept map of this chapter's major ideas, using the section heads and subheads and the key terms (in boldface). Look on the website for this book for information about making concept maps.

## INTERNET STUDY RESOURCES AND RESOURCES FOR FURTHER READING AND RESEARCH

The website for this book contains helpful study aids and many ideas for further reading and research. Log on to

www.info.brookscole.com/miller13

and click on the Chapter-by-Chapter area. Choose Chapter 18 and select a resource:

■ Flash Cards allows you to test your mastery of the Terms and Concepts to Remember for this chapter.

■ Tutorial Quizzes provides a multiple-choice practice quiz.

■ Student Guide to InfoTrac will lead you to Critical Thinking Projects that use InfoTrac College Edition as a research tool.

■ References lists the major books and articles consulted in writing this chapter.

■ Hypercontents takes you to an extensive list of sites with news, research, and images related to individual sections of the chapter.

## INFOTRAC COLLEGE EDITION

Improve your skills with InfoTrac College Edition, a searchable online database of articles from more than 700 periodicals. Log on to

http://www.infotrac-college.com

or access InfoTrac through the website for this book. Try to find the following articles:

**1.** Global Environmental Change Report. 2001. Amphibian deaths traced to climate changes. *Global Environmental Change Report* 13: 6. *Keywords:* "amphibian" and "climate change." Declines in amphibian populations have been well documented over the last several years. Much of the blame has been placed on water pollution, but there is new evidence that global climate change may significantly contribute to these declines.

**2.** Lal, R. 2000. A modest proposal for the year 2001: We can control greenhouse gases and feed the world . . . with proper soil management. *Journal of Soil and Water Conservation* 55: 429. *Keywords:* "greenhouse gases" and "soil management." Much of the debate about global warming centers around vehicle and power plant $CO_2$ emissions, but a substantial amount of $CO_2$ is generated by the world agricultural industry. At a time when there is greater need for food production, can we have both food and a stable climate?

# 19 WATER POLLUTION

## Learning Nature's Ways to Purify Sewage

Some communities and individuals are seeking better ways to purify sewage by working with nature. Ecologist John Todd designs, builds, and operates innovative ecological wastewater treatment systems called *living machines* (Figure 19-1). They look like aquatic botanical gardens and are powered by the sun in greenhouses or outdoors, depending on the climate.

This ecological purification process begins when sewage flows into a passive solar greenhouse or outdoor site containing rows of large open tanks populated by an increasingly complex series of organisms. In the first set of tanks, aquatic plants such as water hyacinths, cattails, and bulrushes take up nutrients produced when algae and microorganisms decompose organic wastes. Sunlight speeds up this decomposition process.

Ocean Arks International

After flowing though several of these natural purification tanks, the water passes through an artificial marsh of sand, gravel, and bulrush plants to filter out algae and remaining organic waste. Some of the plants also absorb (sequester) toxic metals such as lead and mercury and secrete natural antibiotic compounds that kill pathogens.

Next, the water flows into engineered ecosystems in aquarium tanks, where snails and zooplankton consume microorganisms and are in turn consumed by crayfish, tilapia, and other fish that can be eaten or sold as bait. After 10 days, the clear water flows into a second artificial marsh for final filtering and cleansing.

The water can be made pure enough to drink by using ultraviolet light or passing the water through an ozone generator, usually immersed out of sight in an attractive pond or wetland habitat. Selling the ornamental plants, trees, and baitfish produced as by-products of such living machines helps reduce costs. Operating costs are about the same as for a conventional sewage treatment plant.

This technology is sold by Living Technologies, which has installed 30 living machine purification systems in the United States and six other countries, including the system for the innovative environmental science building at Oberlin College in Ohio (Figure 16-24, p. 399). Some communities and industries are working with nature by using natural and artificial wetlands to purify wastewater, as discussed later in this chapter.

Water pollution is related to (1) air pollution, (2) land-use practices, (3) climate change, (4) energy use, (5) solid and hazardous waste, and (6) the number of people, farms, and industries producing sewage and other wastes. These connections explain the need to solve water pollution problems by integrating them with policies for the problems just listed. Otherwise, environmentalists warn that we will continue to shift environmental problems from one part of the environment to another.

**Figure 19-1** Ecological wastewater purification by a *living machine*. At the Providence, Rhode Island, Solar Sewage Treatment Plant, biologist John Todd demonstrates how ecological waste engineering in a greenhouse can be used to purify wastewater in an ecological process he invented. Todd and others are conducting research to perfect solar–aquatic sewage treatment systems based on working with nature.

*Today everybody is downwind or downstream from somebody else.*

WILLIAM RUCKELSHAUS

This chapter addresses the following questions:

- What pollutes water, where do the pollutants come from, and what effects do they have?
- What are the major water pollution problems of streams and lakes?
- What causes groundwater pollution, and how can it be prevented?
- What are the water pollution problems of oceans?
- How can we prevent and reduce surface water pollution?
- How safe is drinking water, and how can it be made safer?

## 19-1 TYPES, EFFECTS, AND SOURCES OF WATER POLLUTION

**What Are the Major Types and Effects of Water Pollutants?** Water pollution is any chemical, biological, or physical change in water quality that has a harmful effect on living organisms or makes water unsuitable for desired uses. Table 19-1 lists the major classes of water pollutants along with their major human sources and harmful effects.

Table 19-2 lists some common diseases that can be transmitted to humans through drinking water contaminated with infectious agents. According to the World Health Organization (WHO), an estimated 3.4 million people worldwide die prematurely each year from water-related diseases. Diarrhea alone kills about 2.1 million people each year.

---

**Table 19-1  Major Categories of Water Pollutants**

**INFECTIOUS AGENTS**

**Examples:** Bacteria, viruses, protozoa, and parasitic worms
**Major Human Sources:** Human and animal wastes
**Harmful Effects:** Disease (Table 19-2)

**OXYGEN-DEMANDING WASTES**

**Examples:** Organic waste such as animal manure and plant debris that can be decomposed by aerobic (oxygen-requiring) bacteria
**Major Human Sources:** Sewage, animal feedlots, paper mills, and food processing facilities
**Harmful Effects:** Large populations of bacteria decomposing these wastes can degrade water quality by depleting water of dissolved oxygen. This causes fish and other forms of oxygen-consuming aquatic life to die.

**INORGANIC CHEMICALS**

**Examples:** Water-soluble (1) acids, (2) compounds of toxic metals such as lead (Pb), arsenic (As), and selenium (Se), and (3) salts such as NaCl in ocean water and fluorides (F⁻) found in some soils

**Major Human Sources:** Surface runoff, industrial effluents, and household cleansers
**Harmful Effects:** Can (1) make freshwater unusable for drinking or irrigation, (2) cause skin cancers and crippling spinal and neck damage (F⁻), (3) damage the nervous system, liver, and kidneys (Pb and As), (4) harm fish and other aquatic life, (5) lower crop yields, and (6) accelerate corrosion of metals exposed to such water.

**ORGANIC CHEMICALS**

**Examples:** Oil, gasoline, plastics, pesticides, cleaning solvents, detergents
**Major Human Sources:** Industrial effluents, household cleansers, surface runoff from farms and yards
**Harmful Effects:** Can (1) threaten human health by causing nervous system damage (some pesticides), reproductive disorders (some solvents), and some cancers (gasoline, oil, and some solvents) and (2) harm fish and wildlife

**PLANT NUTRIENTS**

**Examples:** Water-soluble compounds containing nitrate ($NO_3^-$), phosphate ($PO_4^{3-}$), and ammonium ($NH_4^+$) ions
**Major Human Sources:** Sewage, manure, and runoff of agricultural and urban fertilizers
**Harmful Effects:** Can cause excessive growth of algae and other aquatic plants, which die, decay, deplete water of dissolved oxygen, and kill fish. Drinking water with excessive levels of nitrates lowers the oxygen-carrying capacity of the blood and can kill unborn children and infants ("blue-baby syndrome").

**SEDIMENT**

**Examples:** Soil, silt
**Major Human Sources:** Land erosion
**Harmful Effects:** Can (1) cloud water and reduce photosynthesis, (2) disrupt aquatic food webs, (3) carry pesticides, bacteria, and other harmful substances, (4) settle out and destroy feeding and spawning grounds of fish, and (5) clog and fill lakes, artificial reservoirs, stream channels, and harbors.

**RADIOACTIVE MATERIALS**

**Examples:** Radioactive isotopes of iodine, radon, uranium, cesium, and thorium
**Major Human Sources:** Nuclear power plants, mining and processing of uranium and other ores, nuclear weapons production, natural sources
**Harmful Effects:** Genetic mutations, miscarriages, birth defects, and certain cancers

**HEAT (THERMAL POLLUTION)**

**Examples:** Excessive heat
**Major Human Sources:** Water cooling of electric power plants (Figure 15–35, p. 366) and some types of industrial plants. Almost half of all water withdrawn in the United States each year is for cooling electric power plants.
**Harmful Effects:** Lowers dissolved oxygen levels and makes aquatic organisms more vulnerable to disease, parasites, and toxic chemicals. When a power plant first opens or shuts down for repair, fish and other organisms adapted to a particular temperature range can be killed by the abrupt change in water temperature—known as *thermal shock*.

---

| Table 19-2  Common Diseases Transmitted to Humans Through Contaminated Drinking Water | | |
| --- | --- | --- |
| **Type of Organism** | **Disease** | **Effects** |
| Bacteria | Typhoid fever | Diarrhea, severe vomiting, enlarged spleen, inflamed intestine; often fatal if untreated |
| | Cholera | Diarrhea, severe vomiting, dehydration; often fatal if untreated |
| | Bacterial dysentery | Diarrhea; rarely fatal except in infants without proper treatment |
| | Enteritis | Severe stomach pain, nausea, vomiting; rarely fatal |
| Viruses | Infectious hepatitis | Fever, severe headache, loss of appetite, abdominal pain, jaundice, enlarged liver; rarely fatal but may cause permanent liver damage |
| Parasitic protozoa | Amoebic dysentery | Severe diarrhea, headache, abdominal pain, chills, fever; if not treated can cause liver abscess, bowel perforation, and death |
| | Giardiasis | Diarrhea, abdominal cramps, flatulence, belching, fatigue |
| Parasitic worms | Schistosomiasis | Abdominal pain, skin rash, anemia, chronic fatigue, and chronic general ill health |

**How Do We Measure Water Quality?**   Scientists measure water quality using a variety of methods:

■ Measuring the number of colonies of *coliform bacteria* present in a 100-milliliter (0.1-quart) sample of water (Figure 19-2). The WHO recommends a coliform bacteria count of 0 colonies per 100 milliliters for drinking water, and the U.S. Environmental Protection Agency (EPA) recommends a maximum level for swimming water of 200 colonies per 100 milliliters.

**Figure 19-3** Water quality and dissolved oxygen (DO) content in parts per million (ppm) at 20°C (68°F). Only a few fish species can survive in water with less than 4 ppm of dissolved oxygen at this temperature.

■ Determining water pollution from oxygen-demanding wastes and plant nutrients by measuring the level of dissolved oxygen (Figure 19-3). The quantity of oxygen-demanding wastes in water can be determined by measuring the **biological oxygen demand (BOD):** the amount of dissolved oxygen needed by aerobic decomposers to break down the organic materials in a certain volume of water over a 5-day incubation period at 20°C (68°F).

■ Using *chemical analysis* to determine the presence and concentrations of most inorganic and organic chemicals that pollute water.

■ Using living organisms as *indicator species* to monitor water pollution. For example, the tissues of *filter-feeding mussels,* harvested from the sediments of coastal waters, can be analyzed for the presence of various industrial chemicals, toxic metals (such as mercury and lead), and pesticides. Scientists can remove aquatic plants such as cattails and analyze them to determine pollution in areas contaminated with fuels, solvents, and other organic chemicals.

**Figure 19-2** *Fecal coliform bacteria* test is used to indicate the likely presence of disease-causing bacteria in water. It is carried out by **(1)** passing a water sample through a filter, **(2)** placing the filter disk on a growth medium that supports coliform bacteria for 24 hours, and **(3)** counting the number of colonies of coliform bacteria (shown as clumps in the figure).

**Figure 19-4** Point and non-point sources of water pollution. It is much easier to identify and control point sources than more dispersed non-point sources.

NONPOINT SOURCES

Rural homes

Cropland

Animal feedlot

Urban streets

Suburban development

POINT SOURCES

Factory

Wastewater treatment plant

**What Are Point and Nonpoint Sources of Water Pollution?** **Point sources** discharge pollutants at specific locations through pipes, ditches, or sewers into bodies of surface water (Figure 19-4). Examples include **(1)** factories, **(2)** sewage treatment plants (which remove some but not all pollutants), **(3)** active and abandoned underground mines (Figure 15-7, p. 344), and **(4)** oil tankers. Because point sources are at specific places, they are easy to identify, monitor, and regulate. Most developed countries control discharges of many harmful chemicals into aquatic systems, whereas there is little control of such discharges in most developing countries.

**Nonpoint sources** cannot be traced to any single site of discharge (Figure 19-4). They are usually large land areas or airsheds that pollute water by runoff, subsurface flow, or deposition from the atmosphere. Examples include **(1)** acid deposition (Figure 17-10, p. 428) and **(2)** runoff of chemicals into surface water from croplands, livestock feedlots, logged forests, urban streets, lawns, golf courses, and parking lots.

Nonpoint pollution from agriculture includes **(1)** sediments, **(2)** inorganic fertilizers, **(3)** manure, **(4)** salts dissolved in irrigation water, and **(5)** pesticides. In the United States, the EPA estimates such pollution is responsible for **(1)** 64% of the total mass of pollutants entering streams and **(2)** 57% of those entering lakes. There has been little progress in controlling nonpoint water pollution because of the difficulty and expense of identifying and controlling discharges from so many diffuse sources.

**Connections: How Might Projected Climate Change Affect Water Pollution?** Because of projected global warming (Figure 18-12, p. 455), **(1)** some areas will get much more precipitation and **(2)** others will get less and experience more prolonged drought (Figure 18-17, p. 462).

A moisture-laden atmosphere generates more intense downpours, which can flush more harmful chemicals, plant nutrients, and microorganisms into waterways. Massive flooding, whether caused by normal weather patterns or human impacts on climate, often spreads disease-carrying pathogens (Table 19-2) by **(1)** contaminating water treatment facilities and wells and **(2)** causing the overflow of animal waste lagoons and combined sewer lines (Case Study, p. 487).

Prolonged drought can **(1)** reduce river flows that dilute wastes, **(2)** increase salinity levels, and **(3)** cause infectious diseases to spread more rapidly because people lack enough water to stay clean. Warmer water temperatures can threaten aquatic life by reducing dissolved oxygen levels (Figure 19-3) and increase the growth rate of populations of harmful bacteria.

## 19-2 POLLUTION OF FRESHWATER STREAMS

**What Are the Pollution Problems of Streams?** Flowing streams, including large ones called *rivers*, can recover rapidly from degradable, oxygen-demanding wastes and excess heat through a combination of dilution and bacterial decay. This natural recovery process works as long as **(1)** pollutants do not overload the streams and **(2)** drought, damming, or diversion for agriculture and industry do not reduce their flow. However, these natural dilution

## Hurricanes, Hog Farms, and Water Pollution in Eastern North Carolina

With 10 million animals statewide, North Carolina is the nation's second largest hog producer, after Iowa. Ninety percent of the state's 2,400 hog farms in this $1.9 billion a year business are located in a portion of eastern North Carolina. The area is also a large producer of poultry.

In 1999, three hurricanes dropped more than 0.9 meter (3 feet) of rain in less than 2 months on eastern North Carolina, with the largest amount coming from Hurricane Floyd in September. The resulting massive flooding

- Knocked out electricity in at least 24 municipal sewage treatment plants, causing large spills of raw sewage into coastal rivers.

- Covered more than 50 hog and poultry waste lagoons, col-

lapsed five lagoons, and released large amounts of animal waste into nearby streams, rivers, residential areas, and water supplies— a danger that biologist JoAnn M. Burkholder (Individuals Matter, p. 489) had warned about in 1991.

- Required hog and poultry farmers to pump large volumes of diluted animal wastes onto nearby fields from hundreds of other lagoons to keep them from overflowing or collapsing.

- Caused structural damage to several of the area's 2,000 other animal waste lagoons that could make them vulnerable to future flooding.

- Polluted houses and wells, broke water mains, and threatened water supplies with bacteria, viruses, and parasites. After Floyd, National Guard helicopters and trucks

averted a health crisis by delivering clean water to several counties.

The storm water became **(1)** mixed with raw human and animal sewage, junkyard waste, leaking underground gasoline tanks and oil drums, and pesticide-laced sediments from farm fields and **(2)** poured down rivers into Pamlico Sound, the nation's second largest estuary. Water and wastes flowing into this estuary remained there for about a year because it only has three small outlets to the Atlantic Ocean.

### Critical Thinking

What three actions could the government of North Carolina take to help reduce water pollution and other harmful effects from flooding caused by future hurricanes and large storms?

and biodegradation processes do not eliminate slowly degradable and nondegradable pollutants.

In a flowing stream, the breakdown of degradable wastes by bacteria depletes dissolved oxygen, which reduces or eliminates populations of organisms with high oxygen requirements until the stream is cleansed of wastes. The depth and width of the resulting *oxygen sag curve* (Figure 19-5, p. 488), and thus the time and distance needed for a stream to recover, depend on the volume of incoming degradable wastes and the stream's **(1)** volume, **(2)** flow rate, **(3)** temperature, and **(4)** pH level (Figure 3-5, p. 49). Similar oxygen sag curves can be plotted when heated water from industrial and power plants is discharged into streams.

Although rivers and streams contain only about 1.3% of the world's nonfrozen fresh water, they provide important ecological services (Figure 14-10, p. 319). Major threats to the ecological services and the biodiversity of rivers are **(1)** pollution, **(2)** disruption of water flows and species composition by dams (Figure 14-9, p. 319), channelization (Figure 14-22, middle, p. 332), and the diversion of water from rivers for irrigation and urban areas, and **(3)** overfishing.

One way to improve water quality dramatically is to require cities to withdraw their drinking water down-

stream rather than upstream (as is done now). Then each city would have to clean up its own waste outputs rather than passing them downstream. However, upstream users, who already have the use of clean water without high cleanup costs, fight this pollution prevention approach.

**What Is the Good News About Stream Pollution?** Here is some *good news* about stream pollution cleanup in parts of the world.

- Water pollution control laws enacted in the 1970s have **(1)** greatly increased the number and quality of wastewater treatment plants in the United States and many other developed countries and **(2)** required industries to reduce or eliminate point-source discharges into surface waters. These efforts have enabled the United States to hold the line against increased pollution of most of its streams by disease-causing agents and oxygen-demanding wastes. This is an impressive accomplishment given the rise in economic activity and population since passage of these laws.

- One success story is the cleanup of Ohio's Cuyahoga River, which was so polluted that in 1959 and again in 1969 it caught fire and burned for several

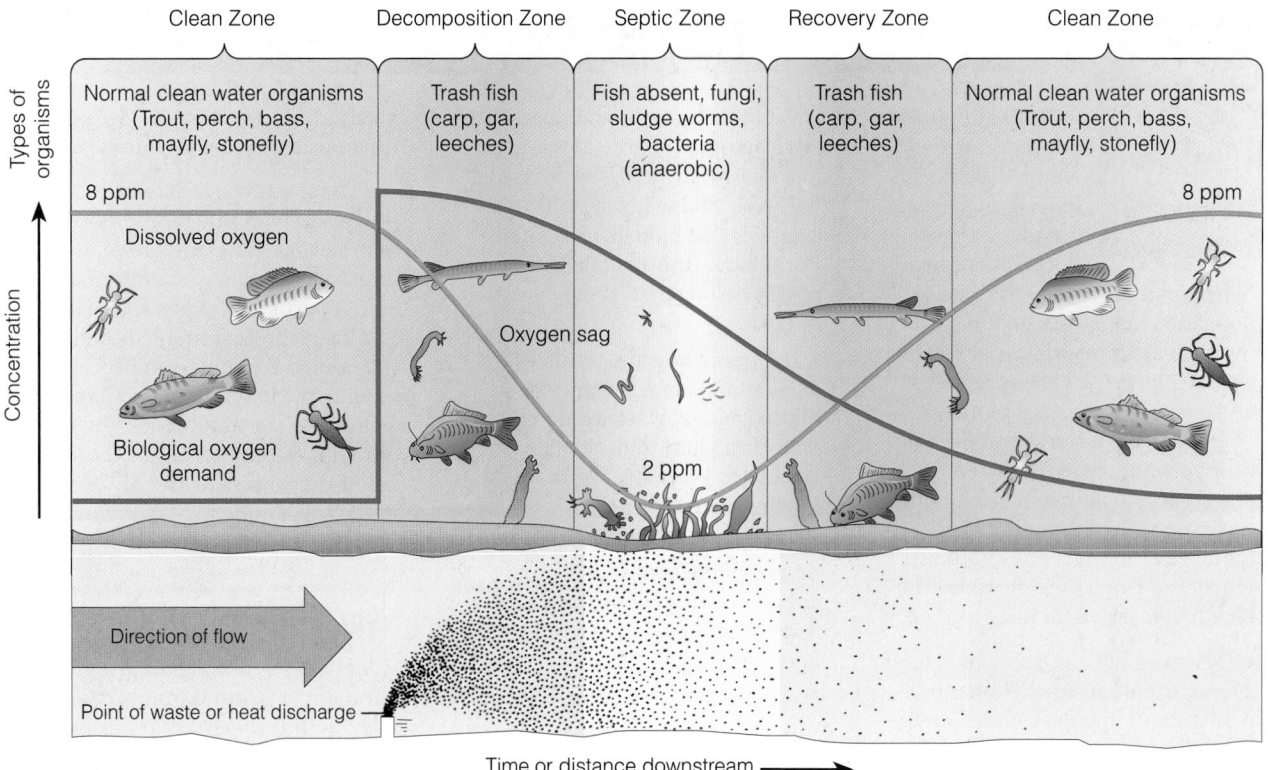

**Figure 19-5** Dilution and decay of degradable, oxygen-demanding wastes and heat, showing the oxygen sag curve (orange) and the curve of oxygen demand (blue). Depending on flow rates and the amount of pollutants, streams recover from oxygen-demanding wastes and heat if they are given enough time and are not overloaded.

days as it flowed through Cleveland, Ohio. The highly publicized image of this burning river prompted city, state, and federal officials to **(1)** enact laws limiting the discharge of industrial wastes into the river and sewage systems and **(2)** appropriate funds to upgrade sewage treatment facilities. Today the river has made a comeback and is widely used by boaters and anglers.

- Fishing, swimming, and wildlife in the harbor waters of New York City have made a comeback because of a sharp drop in untreated river discharges. As a result, dissolved oxygen levels (Figure 19-3) in New York Harbor increased from 3 to 6 ppm between 1970 and 1997.

- Another spectacular cleanup has occurred in Great Britain. In the 1950s, the Thames River was little more than a flowing anaerobic sewer. However, after more than 40 years of effort and hundreds of millions of dollars spent by British taxpayers and private industry, the Thames has made a remarkable recovery. Commercial fishing is thriving, the number of fish species has increased 20-fold since 1964, and many species of waterfowl and wading birds have returned to their former feeding grounds.

- Cleanup of Europe's Rhine River increased dissolved oxygen levels from 2.5 to 7.5 ppm and led to a

sixfold increase in aquatic biodiversity between 1971 and 1997.

**What Is the Bad News About Stream Pollution?**
Despite progress in improving stream quality in most developed countries, large fish kills and drinking water contamination still occur. Most of these disasters are caused by **(1)** accidental or deliberate releases of toxic inorganic and organic chemicals by industries or mines (Case Study, p. 345), **(2)** malfunctioning sewage treatment plants, and **(3)** nonpoint runoff of pesticides and nutrients (eroded soil, fertilizer, and animal waste) from cropland or animal feedlots (Individuals Matter, p. 489).

Available data indicate that stream pollution from discharges of sewage and industrial wastes is a serious and growing problem in most developing countries, where there is little waste treatment. Numerous streams in the former Soviet Union and in eastern European countries suffer from severe pollution. Industrial wastes and sewage pollute more than two-thirds of India's water resources. Untreated sewage and industrial wastes severely pollute 54 of the 78 streams monitored in China. In Latin America and Africa, most streams passing through urban or industrial areas suffer from severe pollution.

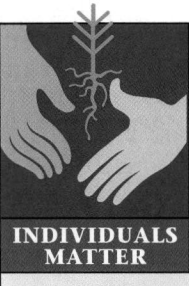

**INDIVIDUALS MATTER**

## Tracking Down the *Pfiesteria* Cell from Hell

JoAnn M. Burkholder is professor of aquatic biology and marine science at North Carolina State University. She knows both what it is like to be sickened by a newly identified fish-killing microbe and to experience the political heat when you go public with your research to alert people about a potentially serious health threat.

In 1986, Burkholder investigated why a colleague's laboratory research fish were dying mysteriously and discovered the culprit was a new microbe so tiny that dozens could fit on the head of a pin. She and her codiscoverer named it *Pfiesteria piscida* (pronounced "fee-STEER-e-ah pis-SEED-uh"), but some biologists call it the cell from hell.

She and her colleagues discovered that this complex microscopic organism could assume at least 24 guises in its lifetime. Without suitable prey, the microbe can masquerade as a plant or lie dormant for years. Then, under certain conditions, these microbes can change from alga eaters into fish-killing dinoflagellates that release neurotoxins that stun fish in rivers and coastal estuaries and usually kill them within 10 minutes to several hours.

The neurotoxin can also form an aerosol above the water. In 1993, Burkholder and her chief research aide breathed toxic fumes released in tanks of fish dying from *Pfiesteria* attacks. They experienced (1) nausea, (2) burning eyes and cramps,

(3) weakness, (4) slow-healing sores, (5) difficulty breathing, and (6) severe loss of memory and mental powers. Eventually they recovered but still suffer from severe shortness of breath after strenuous exercise.

Since then, more than 100 researchers, fishers, and water skiers in North Carolina, Virginia, and Maryland have experienced one or more of these symptoms when exposed to water or air allegedly contaminated by *Pfiesteria* toxins.

In 1995, Burkholder and her colleagues detected a second species of fish-eating *Pfiesteria* in North Carolina's New River after a major spill from a hog-waste lagoon. These two species of single-cell organisms live in waters from the Chesapeake Bay to the Gulf Coast of Florida and Alabama, and each year they cause more than $60 million in losses to U.S. fisheries and tourism.

Through lab and field research, Burkholder and others developed evidence that connected outbreaks or blooms of *Pfiesteria* with excessive levels of nitrogen (as nitrates) and phosphorus (as phosphates) in rivers and estuaries. High levels of such nutrients occur in runoff from fertilized croplands, industrial development, and feedlots (especially those used to raise hogs and chickens) into rivers flowing into coastal estuaries.

In 1991, Burkholder went public with her findings and urged North Carolina state legislators to put curbs on hog farming and enact much tougher laws to reduce the flow of nutrients and other pollutants into the state's rivers. Hog farmers, developers, farming inter-

ests, fishing industry officials (worried about whether it is safe to eat fish and shellfish from affected rivers and estuaries), tourist industry officials (alarmed about a negative image of the state's huge coastal recreational industry), and some state officials reacted negatively to her political activism.

Some challenged her character and competence and accused her of using the results of preliminary research to push for questionable policies. She also received some anonymous death threats.

Burkholder has not backed down, and she continues to criticize state health officials and legislators for not taking her concerns about public health seriously enough. Under the glare of state and national publicity,* the state now supports research on the problem and since 1997 has declared a moratorium on construction of new hog farms and is looking for better ways to deal with hog waste.

Research by other scientists has confirmed the link between *Pfiesteria* outbreaks and nutrient overloading of rivers. Since 1997, a number of federal and state environmental, health, and agricultural agencies have set up a coordinated research effort to learn more about what triggers outbreaks of the organism and how they affect humans and other organisms.

---

*For a popularized description of her research and political battle to alert the public and elected officials to the dangers posed by this microbe, see Rodney Barker's *And the Waters Turned to Blood: The Ultimate Biological Threat* (New York: Simon & Schuster, 1997).

---

## 19-3 POLLUTION OF FRESHWATER LAKES

**What Are the Pollution Problems of Lakes?** In lakes, reservoirs, and ponds, dilution of pollutants often is less effective than in streams because

- Lakes and reservoirs often contain stratified layers (Figure 7-20, p. 158) that undergo little vertical mixing.

- They have little flow. For example, the flushing and changing of water in lakes and large artificial reservoirs can take from 1 to 100 years, compared with several days to several weeks for streams.

- Ponds contain small volumes of water.

Consequently, lakes, reservoirs, and ponds are more vulnerable than streams to contamination by (1) plant nutrients, (2) oil, (3) pesticides, and (4) toxic substances such as lead, mercury, and selenium. These

**Figure 19-6** *Biological magnification* of PCBs (polychlorinated biphenyls) in an aquatic food chain in the Great Lakes. Most of the 209 different PCBs are **(1)** insoluble in water, **(2)** soluble in fats, and **(3)** resistant to biological and chemical degradation—properties that result in their accumulation in the tissues of organisms and their biological amplification in food chains and webs. Although the long-term health effects on people exposed to low levels of PCBs are unknown, high doses of PCBs in laboratory animals produce **(1)** liver and kidney damage, **(2)** gastric disorders, **(3)** birth defects, **(4)** skin lesions, **(5)** hormonal changes, **(6)** smaller penis size, and **(7)** tumors. Boys in Taiwan exposed to PCBs while in their mothers' wombs developed abnormally small penises. In the United States, manufacture and use of PCBs have been banned since 1976; before then, millions of metric tons of these long-lived chemicals were released into the environment, many of them still found in bottom sediments of lakes, streams, and oceans.

Water
0.000002 ppm

Phytoplankton
0.0025 ppm

Herring gull
124 ppm

Herring gull eggs
124 ppm

Zooplankton
0.123 ppm

Lake trout
4.83 ppm

Rainbow smelt
1.04 ppm

contaminants can kill bottom life and fish and birds that feed on contaminated aquatic organisms.

Many toxic chemicals and acids (Figure 17-10, p. 428) also enter lakes and reservoirs from the atmosphere. As they pass through food webs in lakes, the concentrations of some chemicals can be biologically magnified. Examples include **(1)** DDT (Figure 11-4, p. 231), **(2)** PCBs (Figure 19-6), **(3)** some radioactive isotopes, and **(4)** some mercury compounds.

**What Is Cultural Eutrophication?** Lakes receive inputs of nutrients and silt eroded and running off from the surrounding land basin. **Eutrophication** is the name given to this natural nutrient enrichment of lakes. Over time, some lakes become more eutrophic (Figure 7-21, right, p. 158), but others do not because of differences in the surrounding drainage basin.

Near urban or agricultural areas, human activities can greatly accelerate the input of plant nutrients to a lake, which results in a process known as **cultural eutrophication.** Such a change is caused mostly by nitrate- and phosphate-containing effluents from various sources (Figure 19-7).

During hot weather or drought, this nutrient overload produces dense growths of organisms such as algae, cyanobacteria, water hyacinths, and duckweed. When algae die, decomposition by aerobic bacteria depletes dissolved oxygen in the surface layer of water near the shore and in the bottom layer. This oxygen depletion can kill fish and other aerobic aquatic animals. If excess nutrients continue to flow into a lake, anaerobic bacteria take over and produce gaseous decomposition products such as smelly, highly toxic hydrogen sulfide and flammable methane.

According to the EPA, about one-third of the 100,000 medium to large lakes and about 85% of the large lakes near major population centers in the United States have some degree of cultural eutrophication. One-fourth of the lakes in China suffer from cultural eutrophication.

**Solutions: How Can Cultural Eutrophication Be Prevented or Reduced?** Ways to *prevent* or reduce cultural eutrophication include **(1)** advanced waste treatment to remove nitrates and phosphates (Section 19-5), **(2)** bans or limits on phosphates in

**Figure 19-7** Principal sources of nutrient overload causing *cultural eutrophication* in lakes and coastal areas. The amount of nutrients from each source varies according to the types and amounts of human activities occurring in each airshed and watershed. The enlarged populations of algae and plants (stimulated by increased nutrient input) die. Then their decomposition by aerobic bacteria lowers levels of dissolved oxygen (Figure 19-3). This can **(1)** kill fish and other aquatic life and **(2)** reduce biodiversity and the aesthetic and recreational value of the lake.

household detergents and other cleaning agents, and **(3)** soil conservation and land-use control to reduce nutrient runoff. Some *good news* is that in 2001 Japan's Sanyo Electric Company began selling a new type of washing machine that cleans clothes without using a detergent. Instead of liquids and powders, the machine uses ultrasonic waves and electrolysis to clean clothes.

Major *cleanup methods* are **(1)** removing excess weeds, **(2)** controlling undesirable plant growth with herbicides and algicides, and **(3)** pumping air through lakes and reservoirs to avoid oxygen depletion (an expensive and energy-intensive method).

As usual, pollution prevention is more effective and usually cheaper in the long run than cleanup. If excessive inputs of limiting plant nutrients stop, a lake usually can return to its previous state.

**Case Study: Pollution in the Great Lakes**  The five interconnected Great Lakes (Figure 19-8, p. 492) contain at least 95% of the fresh surface water in the

United States and 20% of the world's fresh surface water. The Great Lakes basin is home for about 38 million people—about 30% of the Canadian population and 14% of the U.S. population. Its huge drainage basin receives inputs of water and pollutants from seven states and much of Ontario in Canada (Figure 19-8).

Despite their enormous size, these lakes are vulnerable to pollution from point and nonpoint sources because less than 1% of the water entering the Great Lakes flows out to the St. Lawrence River each year. In addition to land runoff, these lakes receive large quantities of acids, pesticides, and other toxic chemicals by deposition from the atmosphere (often blown in from hundreds or thousands of kilometers away).

By the 1960s, many areas of the Great Lakes were suffering from severe **(1)** cultural eutrophication, **(2)** huge fish kills, and **(3)** contamination from bacteria and a variety of toxic industrial wastes. The impact on Lake Erie was particularly intense because it is the shallowest of the Great Lakes and has the highest

**Figure 19-8** The *Great Lakes basin* and the locations of some of its water quality problems. The Great Lakes region is dotted with several hundred abandoned toxic waste sites listed by the EPA as Superfund sites to receive cleanup priority. (Data from Environmental Protection Agency)

concentrations of people and industrial activity along its shores. Many bathing beaches had to be closed, and by 1970 the lake had lost nearly all its native fish (Figure 19-9, left).

Here is some *good news.* Since 1972, a $20-billion Great Lakes pollution control program has been carried out jointly by Canada and the United States. This joint program has **(1)** significantly decreased levels of phosphates, coliform bacteria, and many toxic industrial chemicals, **(2)** decreased algae blooms, **(3)** increased dissolved oxygen levels and sport and commercial fishing catches (Figure 19-9, right), and **(4)** allowed most swimming beaches to reopen.

These improvements occurred mainly because of **(1)** new or upgraded sewage treatment plants, **(2)** better treatment of industrial wastes, and **(3)** a ban on use of phosphate detergents, household cleaners, and water conditioners.

Here is some *bad news:*

■ Less than 3% of the shoreline of the Great Lakes is clean enough for swimming or for supplying drinking water.

■ Nonpoint land runoff of pesticides and fertilizers from agriculture and urban sprawl now surpasses industrial pollution as the greatest threat to the lakes.

■ Sediments in 26 toxic hot spots (Figure 19-8) remain heavily polluted.

■ About half of the input of toxic compounds comes from **(1)** atmospheric deposition of pesticides, **(2)** mercury from coal-burning plants, and **(3)** other toxic chemicals from as far away as Mexico and Russia.

■ Toxic chemicals such as PCBs have **(1)** built up in food chains and webs (Figure 19-6), **(2)** contaminated many types of sport fish, and **(3)** depleted populations of birds, river otters, and other animals feeding on contaminated fish.

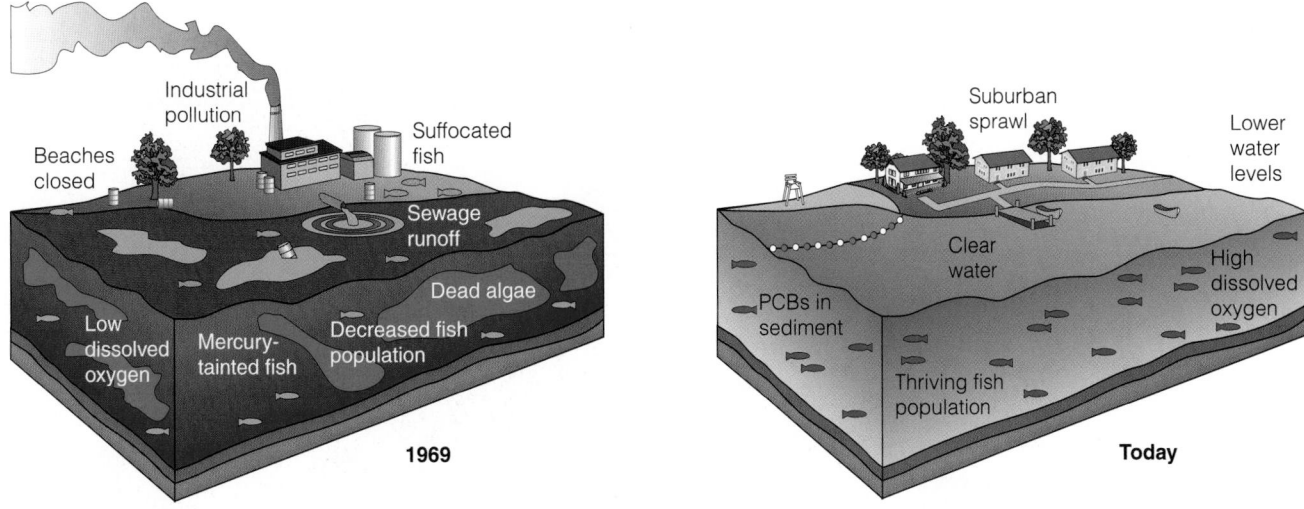

**Figure 19-9** Generalized view of progress in cleaning up Lake Erie since 1969.

■ A survey by Wisconsin biologists revealed that one fish in four taken from the Great Lakes is unsafe for human consumption. Things could be worse. Monitoring by the U.S. Geological Survey shows that levels of DDE (a breakdown product of DDT), dieldrin (a pesticide), and PCBs in freshwater fish in the Great Lakes have dropped sharply since 1979, mostly because of bans on the use of these persistent chemicals. Pollution prevention works.

■ Annual EPA funding for Great Lakes cleanup declined from $9 million in 1992 to $2 million in 2001, and EPA staff charged with coordinating the Great Lakes cleanup dropped from 21 people in 1999 to one person in 2001.

Some environmentalists call for a ban on **(1)** the use of chlorine as a bleach in the pulp and paper industry around the Great Lakes, **(2)** all new incinerators in the area, and **(3)** discharge into the lakes of 70 toxic chemicals that threaten human health and wildlife. Officials of these industries strongly oppose such bans.

## 19-4 GROUNDWATER POLLUTION AND ITS PREVENTION

**Why Is Groundwater Pollution Such a Serious Problem?** According to many scientists, a serious threat to human health is the out-of-sight pollution of groundwater, a prime source of water for drinking and irrigation. Groundwater supplies about **(1)** 75% of the drinking water in Europe, **(2)** 51% in the United States, **(3)** 32% in Asia, and **(4)** 29% in Latin America.

Studies indicate that groundwater pollution comes from numerous sources as we dump more of our wastes into **(1)** storage lagoons, **(2)** septic tanks, **(3)** landfills, **(4)** hazardous waste dumps, and **(5)** deep injection wells (Figure 19-10). We also store gasoline, oil, solvents, and hazardous wastes in metal underground tanks that after 20–40 years can corrode and leak (Figure 19-10). People who dump or spill gasoline, oil, and paint thinners and other organic solvents onto the ground also contaminate groundwater.

Although experts rate groundwater pollution as a low-risk ecological problem, they consider pollutants in drinking water (much of it from groundwater) a high-risk health problem (Figure 11-15, left, p. 246). Human health risks come mostly from groundwater contaminated with **(1)** petrochemicals (such as gasoline and oil), **(2)** organic solvents (such as trichloroethylene, or TCE), **(3)** pesticides, **(4)** arsenic (As), **(5)** lead (Pb), and **(6)** fluoride (F⁻).

When groundwater becomes contaminated, it cannot cleanse itself of *degradable wastes* as flowing surface water does (Figure 19-5). This happens because groundwater **(1)** flows so slowly (usually less than 0.3 meters or 1 foot per day) that contaminants are not diluted and dispersed effectively, **(2)** has much smaller populations of decomposing bacteria, and **(3)** has cold temperatures that slow down the chemical reactions that decompose wastes.

Thus it can take hundreds to thousands of years for contaminated groundwater to cleanse itself of *degradable* wastes. On a human time scale, *nondegradable wastes* (such as toxic lead, arsenic, and fluoride) are there permanently.

**What Is the Extent of Groundwater Pollution?** The answer is that *we do not know* because few countries go to the great expense of locating, tracking, and testing aquifers. However, scientific studies in scattered parts of the world indicate the following:

■ Up to 25% of usable groundwater in the United States is contaminated (and in some areas as much as

**Figure 19-10** Principal sources of groundwater contamination in the United States.

75%). In New Jersey, for example, every major aquifer is contaminated.

■ The EPA has documented groundwater contamination by 74 pesticides in 38 states, mostly in farming regions. In California, pesticides contaminate the drinking water of more than 1 million people.

■ According to the EPA and the U.S. Geological Survey, one or more organic chemicals contaminate about 45% of *municipal* groundwater supplies in the United States.

■ An EPA survey found that **(1)** one-third of 26,000 industrial waste ponds and lagoons in the United States have no liners to prevent toxic liquid wastes from seeping into aquifers, and **(2)** one-third of these sites are within 1.6 kilometers (1 mile) of a drinking water well.

■ The General Accounting Office estimated in 2002 that at least 76,000 underground tanks storing gasoline, diesel fuel, home heating oil, and toxic solvents are leaking their contents into groundwater in the

United States (Figure 19-10). During this century, scientists expect many of the millions of such tanks installed around the world in recent decades to corrode, leak, contaminate groundwater, and become a major global health problem.

■ A 2000 U.S. Geological Survey study found that about 42 million Americans use groundwater subject to contamination by volatile organic compounds (VOCs; Figure 19-11).

■ Determining the extent of a leak from an underground tank can cost $25,000–250,000, and cleanup costs range from $10,000 to more than $250,000. If the chemical reaches an aquifer, effective cleanup is rarely possible. Replacing a leaking tank costs an additional $10,000–60,000. In California's Silicon Valley, where electronics industries use underground tanks to store a variety of waste solvents, local authorities found leaks from 85% of the tanks they inspected.

■ About 60% of the liquid hazardous waste in the United States is injected into deep underground wells

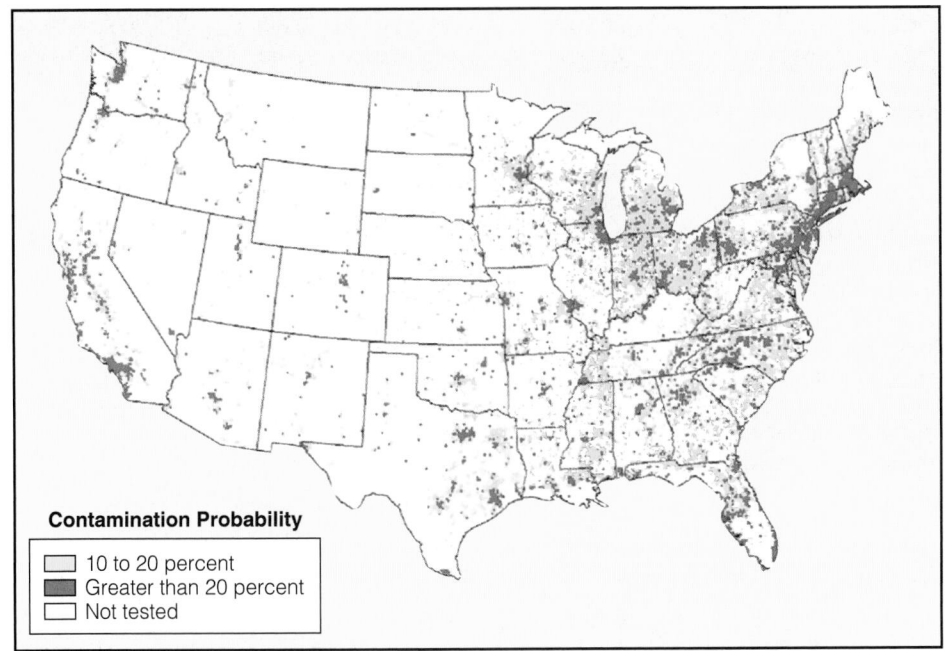

**Figure 19-11** Probability of drinking water contamination by volatile organic compounds (VOCs) in the 48 contiguous states. John Zorgoski, who headed the study, urges people who live in areas with red or yellow dots to have their well and municipal water tested for VOCs. (Data from the U.S. Geological Survey)

**Contamination Probability**
- 10 to 20 percent
- Greater than 20 percent
- Not tested

(Figure 19-10). Although these wastes are injected below the deepest sources of drinking water, **(1)** some of the injection pipes can leak, and **(2)** some of the wastes have entered aquifers used for drinking water in parts of Texas, Florida, Oklahoma, and Ohio.

■ Toxic *arsenic (As)* contaminates drinking water through the drilling of tubewells into aquifers where soils and rock are naturally rich in arsenic. In India's state of West Bengal and parts of Bangladesh, 28–57 million people are drinking water with arsenic levels 5–100 times the WHO limit. According to estimates by the WHO, arsenic in drinking water will cause 200,000–270,00 premature deaths from cancer in Bangladesh alone. In the United States, standards for arsenic in drinking water are controversial (Spotlight, p. 496).

■ According to the WHO, an estimated 70 million people in northern China and 30 million in northwestern India drink groundwater contaminated with high levels of naturally occurring *fluoride* ($F^-$). This can cause crippling backbone and neck damage and a variety of dental problems.

■ Groundwater used a source of drinking water can also be contaminated with nitrate ions ($NO_3^-$), especially in agricultural areas where nitrates in fertilizer can be leached into groundwater. Nitrite ions ($NO_2^-$) in the stomach, colon, and bladder can convert some of the nitrate ions in drinking water to N-nitroso compounds, which can cause cancer in various organs in more than 40 test animal species. The conversion of nitrates in tap water to nitrites in infants under 6 months old can cause a potentially fatal condition known as "blue baby syndrome," in which blood

lacks the ability to carry sufficient oxygen to body cells. A 2001 study by Peter Weyer and his colleagues found that nitrates in drinking water at a level of 2.5 milligrams per liter (one-fourth the EPA standard of 10 milligrams per liter) increases the risk of bladder cancer. Nitrate is difficult to remove from drinking water and requires expensive filtration by distillation, ion exchange, or reverse osmosis. Boiling water and using conventional home water treatment do not remove nitrates. Because of concern about nitrate pollution of groundwater, Iowa has levied a tax on fertilizer to discourage its excessive use.

■ In coastal areas, excessive pumping of water from aquifers can lead to contamination of drinking water by saltwater intrusion (Figure 14-17, p. 328).

**Solutions: How Can We Protect Groundwater?**
Contaminated aquifers are almost impossible to clean because of their **(1)** enormous volume, **(2)** inaccessibility, and **(3)** slow movement. Pumping polluted groundwater to the surface, cleaning it up, and returning it to the aquifer is extremely expensive. Thus *preventing contamination is the only effective way to protect groundwater resources.* Ways to do this include

■ *Monitoring aquifers near landfills and underground tanks.*

■ *Requiring leak detection systems for underground tanks used to store hazardous liquids.*

■ *Banning or more strictly regulating disposal of hazardous wastes in deep injection wells and landfills.*

■ *Storing hazardous liquids above ground in tanks with systems that detect and collect leaking liquids.*

## How Much Arsenic Should We Allow in Drinking Water?

**SPOTLIGHT**

Arsenic is a naturally occurring element in various rocks and can be released into groundwater and surface water from the natural weathering of minerals in deep soils and rocks. In addition, arsenic can be released into the air and water from (1) coal burning, (2) copper and lead smelting, (3) municipal trash incinerators, (4) wood-preserving treatments, (5) leaching from landfills containing arsenic-laden ash produced by coal-burning power plants, and (6) use of certain arsenic-containing pesticides.

According to a 1999 report by the U.S. National Academy of Sciences, long-term exposure to arsenic in drinking water can (1) cause cancer of the skin, bladder, and lungs, (2) possibly cause kidney and liver cancer, (3) cause skin lesions and hardening of the skin (keratosis), and (4) has been linked to adult-onset diabetes, cardiovascular disease, anemia, and disorders of the immune, nervous, and reproductive systems. In 2001, researchers at the Dartmouth Medical School reported that arsenic is also a potent endocrine disrupter (Connections, p. 235).

The acceptable level of arsenic in U.S. drinking water has been 50 parts per billion (50 ppb) since 1942. This is five times the international standard of 10 ppb adopted in 1993 by the WHO and in 1998 by the 15-member European Union.

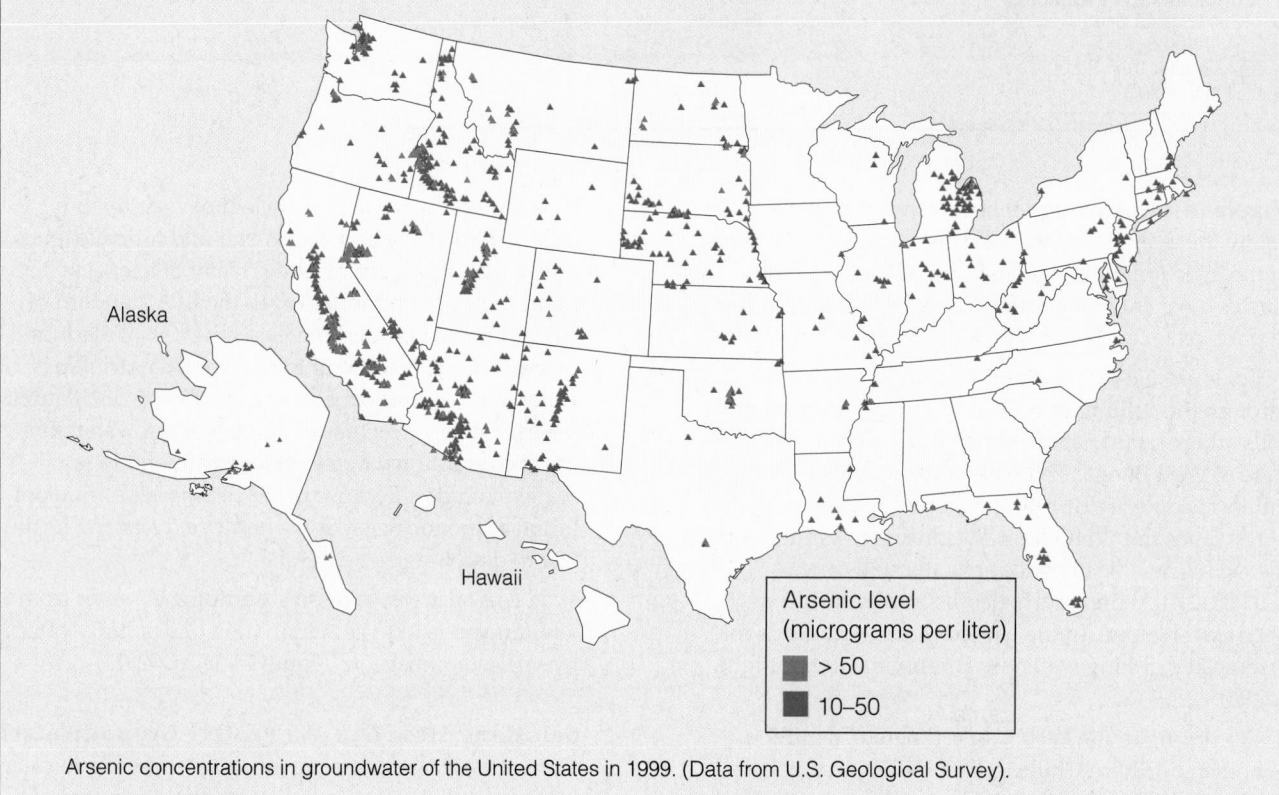

Alaska

Hawaii

Arsenic level
(micrograms per liter)
■ > 50
■ 10–50

Arsenic concentrations in groundwater of the United States in 1999. (Data from U.S. Geological Survey).

## 19-5   OCEAN POLLUTION

**How Much Pollution Can the Oceans Tolerate?**
The oceans are the ultimate sinks for much of the waste matter we produce. Oceans can dilute, disperse, and degrade large amounts of raw sewage, sewage sludge, oil, and some types of degradable industrial waste, especially in deep-water areas. Some forms of marine life have been more resilient than originally expected. Consequently, some scientists suggest it is safer to dump sewage sludge and most other haz-

ardous wastes into the deep ocean than to bury them on land or burn them in incinerators.

Other scientists disagree, pointing out that we know less about the deep ocean than we do about outer space. They add that dumping waste in the ocean would (1) delay urgently needed pollution prevention and (2) promote further degradation of this vital part of the earth's life-support system.

**How Do Pollutants Affect Coastal Areas?**
Coastal areas—especially wetlands and estuaries,

In 1962, the U.S. Public Health Service proposed lowering the U.S. drinking water standard for arsenic from 50 ppb to 10 ppb. After more than 30 years of scientific reviews, including a 1999 study by the National Academy of Sciences, the EPA proposed that the U.S. drinking water standard for arsenic be reduced to the international standard of 10 ppb.

According to the WHO scientists, even the 10 ppb standard is not safe. Based on health concerns, many scientists call for lowering the standard to 3–5 ppb. A 2001 study by the U.S. National Academy of Sciences found that routinely drinking water with arsenic levels of even 3 ppb poses a 1 in 1,000 risk of developing bladder or lung cancer.

Running drinking water through activated aluminia can absorb arsenic. Reverse osmosis also removes arsenic, but is an expensive process.

According to the EPA, implementing the 10 ppb standard would (1) require about 3,000 communities with high levels of arsenic in groundwater (see figure) to improve their drinking water treatment at an average annual cost of about $12 per person, (2) cost about $181 million per year, (3) make drinking water safer for at least 11 million Americans (see figure), and (4) provide annual benefits of $140–198 million from reduction of arsenic-related bladder and liver cancers. Reductions in the incidence of other arsenic-related health problems would provide larger financial benefits, which so far have not been estimated by the EPA.

Mining, coal, and lumber products and other arsenic-producing companies (that could face tougher regulations) oppose the 10 ppb standard and say the estimated costs are too low. In addition, some small communities contend that they cannot afford to implement the new standard. For example, for affected communities with 500 or fewer homes, the annual water bill could increase by $162–327 per household communities. However, the federal government could subsidize some or all treatment costs for small systems.

In March 2001, President George W. Bush (under lobbying pressure from mining interests, coal companies, the wood products industry, and other arsenic producers) withdrew implementation of the new EPA standard, arguing it would cost too much to implement. Health scientists and environmentalists were outraged and accused the Bush administration of caving to the demands of industries whose activities release toxic levels of arsenic into drinking water supplies. That same month, the EPA reversed its controversial earlier decision and lowered the acceptable concentration of arsenic from 50 ppb to 10 ppb, to take effect in 2006.

About 90% of lumber used to build decks, playgrounds, decks, telephone poles, guard rails, and other outdoor uses in the United States is treated with chromated copper arsenate (CCA) to protect the wood from insects. Some *good news* is that the pressure-treated lumber industry in the United States entered into an agreement with the EPA in 2002 to phase out residential uses of wood treated with CCA. Industrial uses of CCA-treated wood such as utility poles and guardrails will still be permitted.

The EPA advises consumers with CCA-treated decks, play sets, and other structures to (1) use paints and sealers to reduce arsenic leaching, (2) cover the lumber with plastic and vinyl covers, (3) replace the treated wood with wood treated with other nontoxic chemicals or with wood substitutes made from recycled plastic and rubber, and (4) use home test kits to check arsenic levels in pressure-treated structures.*

## Critical Thinking

Do you believe the drinking standard for arsenic in U.S. drinking water should be lowered from 50 ppb to (a) 10 ppb or (b) less than 3 ppb? Explain. If you lived in a community affected by such a standard, how much more per year would you be willing to pay on your water bill to implement the standard?

---

*Kits are available, at cost, from the Environmental Working Group, a non-profit research organization, through its website (www.ewg.org).

coral reefs, and mangrove swamps—bear the brunt of our enormous inputs of wastes into the ocean (Figure 19-12, p. 498). This is not surprising because (1) about 40% of the world's population lives on or within 100 kilometers (62 miles) of the coast, (2) 14 of the world's 15 largest metropolitan areas, each with 10 million people or more, are near coastal waters, and (3) coastal populations are growing more rapidly than the global population.

In most coastal developing countries (and in some coastal developed countries), municipal sewage and industrial wastes are dumped into the sea without treatment. The most polluted seas lie off the densely populated coasts of Bangladesh, India, Pakistan, Indonesia, Malaysia, Thailand, and the Philippines. About 85% of the sewage from large cities along the Mediterranean Sea, which has a coastal population of 200 million people during tourist season, is discharged into the sea untreated. This causes widespread beach pollution and shellfish contamination. The Baltic Sea receives water pollutants from nine countries (Case Study, p. 499).

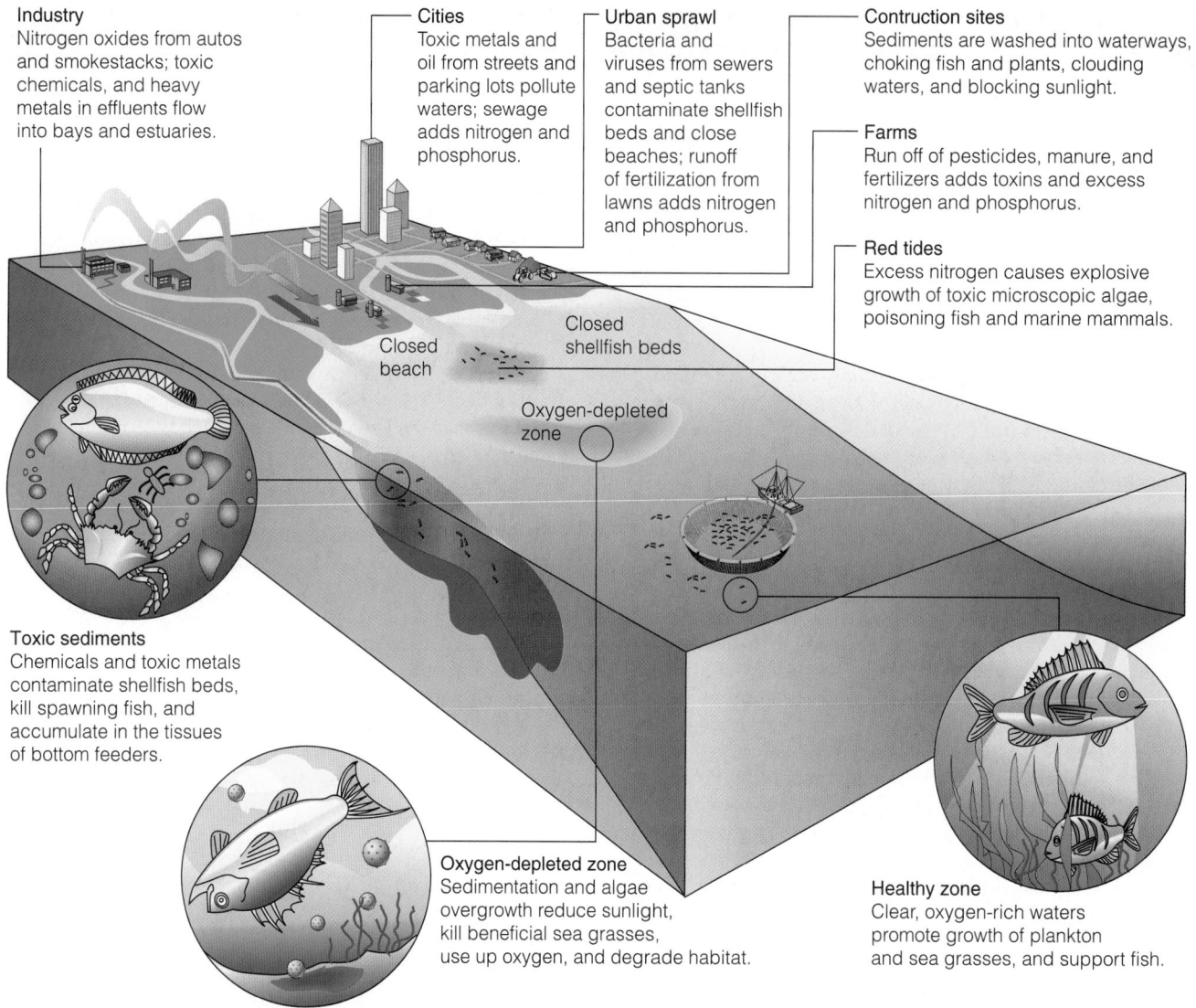

**Industry**
Nitrogen oxides from autos and smokestacks; toxic chemicals, and heavy metals in effluents flow into bays and estuaries.

**Cities**
Toxic metals and oil from streets and parking lots pollute waters; sewage adds nitrogen and phosphorus.

**Urban sprawl**
Bacteria and viruses from sewers and septic tanks contaminate shellfish beds and close beaches; runoff of fertilization from lawns adds nitrogen and phosphorus.

**Contruction sites**
Sediments are washed into waterways, choking fish and plants, clouding waters, and blocking sunlight.

**Farms**
Run off of pesticides, manure, and fertilizers adds toxins and excess nitrogen and phosphorus.

**Red tides**
Excess nitrogen causes explosive growth of toxic microscopic algae, poisoning fish and marine mammals.

Closed beach

Closed shellfish beds

Oxygen-depleted zone

**Toxic sediments**
Chemicals and toxic metals contaminate shellfish beds, kill spawning fish, and accumulate in the tissues of bottom feeders.

**Oxygen-depleted zone**
Sedimentation and algae overgrowth reduce sunlight, kill beneficial sea grasses, use up oxygen, and degrade habitat.

**Healthy zone**
Clear, oxygen-rich waters promote growth of plankton and sea grasses, and support fish.

**Figure 19-12** How residential areas, factories, and farms contribute to the pollution of coastal waters and bays.

Some *good news* is that the percentage of polluted beaches in the European Union dropped from 21% to 5% between 1992 and 1999. Similar figures for U.S. beaches are not available because monitoring and standards are set at the local level and vary widely. In addition, local coastal communities are under pressure from tourism businesses to not carefully monitor or close beaches because of the harmful effects on local economies.

Recent studies of some U.S. coastal waters have found vast colonies of human viruses from raw sewage, effluents from sewage treatment plants (which do not remove viruses), and leaking septic tanks. One study found that about one-fourth of the people using coastal beaches in the United States develop ear infections, sore throats and eyes, respiratory disease, or gastrointestinal disease.

Runoff of sewage and agricultural wastes into coastal waters and acid deposition from the atmo-sphere (Figure 17-10, p. 428) introduce large quantities of nitrate ($NO_3^-$) and phosphate ($PO_4^{3-}$) plant nutri-ents, which can cause explosive growth of harmful algae. These *harmful alga blooms* (HABs) are called red, brown, or green tides, depending on their color. They can **(1)** release waterborne and airborne toxins that damage fisheries, **(2)** kill some fish-eating birds, **(3)** reduce tourism, and **(4)** poison seafood.

Death and decomposition of the alga deplete dis-solved oxygen in coastal waters and cause the deaths of a variety of marine species. Each year some 61 large *oxygen-depleted zones* (sometimes inaccurately called dead zones) form in the world's coastal waters and in landlocked seas such as the Baltic (Case Study, p. 499) and Black Seas because of excessive nonpoint inputs of fertilizers and animal wastes from land runoff and deposition of nitrogen compounds from the atmo-sphere (Figure 19-7). In these zones, much of the aquatic life dies or moves elsewhere. The biggest such

## The Baltic Sea

Nine northern European countries surround the Baltic Sea (see figure). Before the 1960s, the Baltic Sea was fairly clean. Now it is highly polluted because it receives runoff and air pollutants from a huge area with more than 70 million people and 15% of the world's industrial production.

This sea is especially vulnerable to buildup of water pollutants because

- It takes about 50 years for the sea to exchange all of its water because the water must flow to the North Sea through a narrow channel (see figure).

- Its water tends to stratify and thus reduce the exchange of oxygen between its top and bottom layers. This leads to very low levels of dis-

solved oxygen in its bottom layer in deep water.

The Baltic's four major water pollution problems are **(1)** biological magnification of toxic chemicals such as PCBs (Figure 19-6), **(2)** cultural eutrophication from nutrient overload (Figure 19-7), **(3)** accidental releases of hazardous chemicals by industries and mines, and **(4)** oil pollution by the many tankers using its waters.

In 1980, the countries surrounding the Baltic Sea signed the *Helsinki Convention*—the world's first international agreement to reduce marine pollution. It calls for all countries signing the agreement to take all appropriate actions to reduce and prevent pollution of the sea and to protect its wildlife. The participating countries established the Baltic Marine Protection Commission—known as the Helsinki Commis-

sion—to monitor and set priorities for this cooperative program.

However, the agreement has several loopholes. It **(1)** does not cover offshore waters of the nations bordering the sea, **(2)** does not address the deposition of air pollutants, and **(3)** excludes regulation of military aircraft and vessels.

Despite its limitations, the Helsinki Convention has led to progress in controlling water pollution in the Baltic Sea and serves as an example of how countries can work together to help solve common pollution problems.

### Critical Thinking

Use the Internet and library to determine the major successes and failures of the Helsinki Convention. Use this information to suggest the three most important ways to improve its success.

The Baltic Sea receives pollutants from a number of countries.

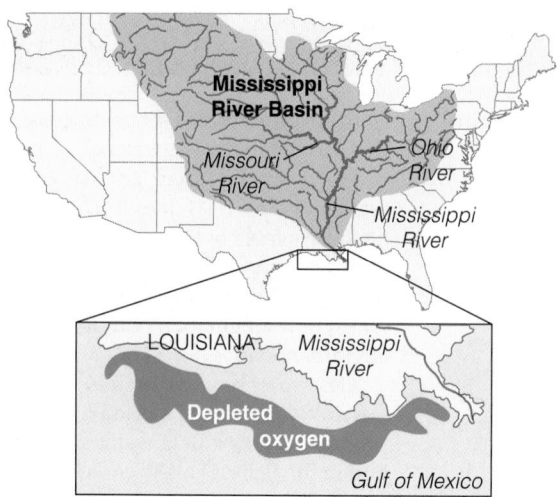

**Figure 19-13** A large zone of oxygen-depleted water forms for half of the year in the Gulf of Mexico as a result of oxygen-depleting alga blooms. It is created mostly by huge inputs of nitrate ($NO_3^-$) and phosphate ($PO_4^{3-}$) plant nutrients from the massive Mississippi River Basin.

zone in U.S. waters and the third largest in the world forms every summer in a narrow stretch of the Gulf of Mexico (Figure 19-13).

**Case Study: The Chesapeake Bay** The Chesapeake Bay, the largest estuary in the United States, is in trouble because of human activities. Between 1940 and 2001, the number of people living in the Chesapeake Bay area grew from 3.7 million to 17 million, and within a few years its population may reach 18 million.

The estuary receives wastes from point and nonpoint sources scattered throughout a huge drainage basin that includes 9 large rivers and 141 smaller streams and creeks in parts of six states (Figure 19-14). The bay has become a huge pollution sink because it is quite shallow and only 1% of the waste entering it is flushed into the Atlantic Ocean.

Phosphate and nitrate levels have risen sharply in many parts of the bay, causing algae blooms and oxygen depletion (Figure 19-14). Studies have shown that point sources, primarily sewage treatment plants, account for about 60% by weight of the phosphates. Nonpoint sources—mostly runoff from urban, suburban, and agricultural land and deposition from the atmosphere—account for about 60% by weight of the nitrates.

Large quantities of pesticides run off cropland and urban lawns, and industries discharge large amounts of toxic wastes (often in violation of their discharge permits). Commercial harvests of oysters (Solutions, p. 501), crabs, and several important fish have fallen sharply since 1960 because of a combination of overfishing, pollution, and disease.

In 1983, the Chesapeake Bay Program, the country's most ambitious attempt at *integrated coastal management*, was implemented. Results have been impressive. Between 1985 and 2000, phosphorus levels declined 27% and nitrogen levels dropped 16%, a significant achievement given the increasing population in the watershed and the fact that nearly 40% of the nitrogen inputs come from the atmosphere. In addition, grasses growing on the floor of the bay are making a slow comeback.

Reaching the declared goal of a 40% reduction in nutrient levels and a significant improvement in habitat water quality throughout the bay will be difficult because of projected population growth. According to the Chesapeake Bay Foundation—a private organization founded in 1968 to press governments to help restore the bay—the current cleanup plan will cost $8.5 billion over 10 years. This is four times the level of current spending. In its *2001 State of the Bay Report*, this private foundation (with 90,000 members) found that despite improvements in some indicators, the overall health of the bay fell for the first time in recent years.

Some *good news* is that since 1998, Maryland, Virginia, and Delaware have enacted laws requiring mandatory management of agricultural nutrients. There is still a long way to go, but the Chesapeake Bay Program shows what can be done when diverse interested parties work together to achieve goals that benefit both wildlife and people.

**What Pollutants Do We Dump into the Ocean?** Industrial waste dumping off U.S. coasts has stopped, although it still occurs in a number of other developed countries and some developing countries. However, barges and ships still legally dump large quantities of

**Figure 19-14** *Chesapeake Bay,* the largest estuary in the United States, is severely degraded as a result of water pollution from point and nonpoint sources in six states and from deposition of air pollutants.

A number of scientists and environmentalists are looking for ways to rebuild the Chesapeake Bay's once huge population of the eastern oyster as a way to help clean up the water. Oysters are filter feeders that vacuum up the algae and nutrient-laden suspended silt that cause many of the Chesapeake's water pollution problems.

According to aquatic biologist Roger Newell, the bay's oyster population served as a natural water purifier by filtering the bay's entire volume of water every 3 or 4 days. But overharvesting and two parasitic oyster diseases have reduced the oyster population to about 1% of its historic high. Consequently, today's oyster population needs about a year to filter the water of the bay.

Computer models project that increasing the oyster population to only 10% of its historic high would improve water quality and spur the growth of underwater sea grass. Methods for restoring the bay's oyster population include (1) introducing disease-resistant Asian oysters, (2) seeding protected oyster beds with large, older oysters presumed to have some disease resistance, (3) dumping hundreds of millions of oyster shells on dozens of historic reef areas with the goal of resurrecting some of the old oyster-breeding reefs, (4) trying to find a reef-building substitute to hasten reef reconstruction, (5) setting aside 20–25% of the bay's oyster beds as sanctuaries to protect stocks from overfishing, and (6) greatly increasing funds for research and implementation of such a program.

### Critical Thinking

Should more of the scarce funds for reducing pollution and degradation of the Chesapeake Bay be used to increase the oyster population? Explain. Use the Internet and library to find out what has been done to help restore the oyster population of the bay.

---

dredge spoils (materials, often laden with toxic metals, scraped from the bottoms of harbors and rivers to maintain shipping channels) at 110 sites off the Atlantic, Pacific, and Gulf coasts.

In addition, many countries dump into the ocean large quantities of sewage sludge, a gooey mixture of toxic chemicals, infectious agents, and settled solids removed from wastewater at sewage treatment plants. Since 1992, the United States has banned this practice.

Fifty countries with at least 80% of the world's merchant fleet have agreed not to dump sewage and garbage at sea, but this agreement is difficult to enforce and violations are common. Most shipowners save money by dumping wastes at sea and if caught risk only small fines. Each year as many as 2 million seabirds and more than 100,000 marine mammals (including whales, seals, dolphins, and sea lions) die when they ingest or become entangled in fishing nets, ropes, and other debris dumped into the sea or discarded on beaches.

Under the London Dumping Convention of 1972, 100 countries agreed not to dump highly toxic pollutants and high-level radioactive wastes in the open sea beyond the boundaries of their national jurisdictions. Since 1983, these same nations have observed a moratorium on the dumping of low-level radioactive wastes at sea, which in 1994 became a permanent ban. France, Great Britain, Russia, China, and Belgium, however, may legally exempt themselves from this ban. In 1992, it was learned that for decades the former Soviet Union had been dumping large quantities of high- and low-level radioactive wastes into the Arctic Ocean and its tributaries.

**What Are the Effects of Oil on Ocean Ecosystems?** *Crude petroleum* (oil as it comes out of the ground) and *refined petroleum* (fuel oil, gasoline, and other processed petroleum products; Figure 15-18, p. 355) are accidentally or deliberately released into the environment from a number of sources.

Tanker accidents and blowouts at offshore drilling rigs (when oil escapes under high pressure from a borehole in the ocean floor) get most of the publicity because of their high visibility. However, more oil is released into the ocean (1) during normal operation of offshore wells, (2) from washing tankers and releasing the oily water, and (3) from pipeline and storage tank leaks.

Natural oil seeps also release large amounts of oil into the ocean at some sites, but most ocean oil pollution comes from activities on land. Almost half (some experts estimate 90%) of the oil reaching the oceans is waste oil dumped, spilled, or leaked onto the land or into sewers by cities, industries, and people changing their own motor oil. Worldwide, about 10% of the oil that reaches the ocean comes from the atmosphere, mostly from smoke emitted by oil fires.

The effects of oil on ocean ecosystems depend on a number of factors: (1) type of oil (crude or refined), (2) amount released, (3) distance of release from shore, (4) time of year, (5) weather conditions, (6) average water temperature, and (7) ocean currents.

Volatile organic hydrocarbons in oil immediately kill a number of aquatic organisms, especially in their vulnerable larval forms. Some other chemicals form tarlike globs that float on the surface and coat the feathers of birds (especially diving birds) and the fur of marine mammals. This oil coating destroys their natural insulation and buoyancy, causing many of them to drown or die of exposure from loss of body heat. Heavy oil components that sink to the ocean floor or wash into estuaries can (1) smother bottom-dwelling organisms such as crabs, oysters, mussels, and clams or (2) make them unfit for human consumption. Some oil spills have killed reef corals.

Research shows that most (but not all) forms of marine life recover from exposure to large amounts of *crude oil* within 3 years. But recovery from exposure to *refined oil*, especially in estuaries, can take 10 years or longer. The effects of spills in cold waters and in shallow enclosed gulfs and bays generally last longer.

Oil slicks that wash onto beaches can have a serious economic impact on coastal residents, who lose income from fishing and tourist activities. Oil-polluted beaches washed by strong waves or currents become clean after about a year, but beaches in sheltered areas remain contaminated for several years. Estuaries and salt marshes suffer the most and longest lasting damage. Despite their localized harmful effects, experts rate oil spills as a low-risk ecological problem (Figure 11-15, left, p. 246).

**How Well Can We Clean Up Oil Spills?** If they are not too large, oils spills can be partially cleaned up by mechanical, chemical, fire, and natural methods. *Mechanical methods* include using (1) floating booms to contain the oil spill or keep it from reaching sensitive areas, (2) skimmer boats to vacuum up some of the oil into collection barges, and (3) absorbent pads or large mesh pillows filled with feathers or hair to soak up oil on beaches or in waters too shallow for skimmer boats.

*Chemical methods* include using (1) coagulating agents to cause floating oil to clump together for easier pickup or to sink to the bottom, where it usually does less harm, and (2) dispersing agents to break up oil slicks. However, these agents can damage some types of organisms. Fire can burn off floating oil, but crude oil is hard to ignite, and this approach produces air pollution. In time, the natural action of wind and waves mixes or emulsifies oil with water (like emulsified salad dressing), and bacteria biodegrade some of the oil.

These methods remove only part of the oil, and none work well on a large spill. Scientists estimate that current methods can recover no more than 12–15% of the oil from a major spill. This explains why preventing oil pollution is the most effective and in the long run the least costly approach, as revealed by the large 1989 spill from the *Exxon Valdez* oil tanker in Alaska's Prince William Sound (Figure 15-20, p. 356).

**Solutions: How Can We Protect Coastal Waters?** Analysts have suggested various ways to prevent and reduce excessive pollution of coastal waters (Figure 19-15). The key to protecting oceans is to reduce the flow of pollution from the land and from

| Prevention | Cleanup |
| --- | --- |
| Reduce input of toxic pollutants | Improve oil-spill cleanup capabilities |
| Separate sewage and storm lines | Require at least secondary treatment of coastal sewage or use wetlands, solar-aquatic, or other sewage treatment methods |
| Ban ocean dumping of sludge and hazardous dredged material | Require improved air pollution cleanup to reduce input from the atmosphere |
| Protect sensitive areas from development, oil drilling, and oil shipping | |
| Regulate coastal development | |
| Recycle used oil | |
| Require double hulls for oil tankers | |

**Figure 19-15** Methods for preventing and cleaning up excessive pollution of coastal waters.

streams emptying into the ocean. Scientists call for integrating such efforts with those to prevent and control air pollution because an estimated 33% of all pollutants entering the ocean worldwide comes from air emissions from land-based sources.

## 19-6 SOLUTIONS: PREVENTING AND REDUCING SURFACE WATER POLLUTION

**What Can We Do About Water Pollution from Nonpoint Sources?** Ways to help control nonpoint water pollution, most of it from agriculture, include the following:

- Reduce fertilizer runoff into surface waters and leaching into aquifers by using slow-release fertilizer and using none on steeply sloped land.

- Reduce the need for fertilizer by alternating plantings between row crops and soybeans or other nitrogen-fixing plants.

- Plant buffer zones of vegetation between cultivated fields and nearby surface water.

- Reduce pesticide runoff by applying pesticides only when needed and using biological control or integrated pest management.

- Control runoff and infiltration of manure from animal feedlots by (1) improving manure control, (2) planting buffers, and (3) not locating feedlots and animal waste on steeply sloped land near surface water and in flood zones (Case Study, p. 487).

- Preserve existing riparian zones (Spotlight, p. 300) and wetlands and create new ones to allow nitrate and phosphate compounds to flow through and be absorbed or decomposed by such areas.
- Reduce soil erosion and flooding by reforesting critical watersheds.

**What Can We Do About Water Pollution from Point Sources? The Legal Approach** According to Sandra Postel, director of the Global Water Policy Project, most cities in developing countries discharge 80–90% of their untreated sewage directly into rivers, streams, and lakes, which are used for drinking water, bathing, and washing clothes.

Developed countries purify most wastes from point sources to some degree. The Federal Water Pollution Control Act of 1972 (renamed the Clean Water Act when it was amended in 1977) and the 1987 Water Quality Act form the basis of U.S. efforts to control pollution of the country's surface waters.

In 1995, the EPA proposed a *discharge trading policy* to use market forces to reduce water pollution (as has been done with sulfur dioxide for air pollution control, p. 441). The policy, put into effect in pilot areas in 2002, would allow water pollution sources to pollute at higher levels than allowed in their permits by buying credits from permit holders with pollution levels below their allowed levels. Environmentalists warn that such a system **(1)** is no better than the caps set in total pollution levels in various areas and **(2)** would allow pollutants to build up to dangerous levels in areas where credits are bought.

Here is some *good news*. The Clean Water Act of 1972 led to the following improvements in U.S. water quality between 1972 and 1998: **(1)** The percentage of U.S. rivers and lakes tested that are fishable and swimmable increased from 36% to 62%, **(2)** the amount of topsoil lost through agricultural runoff was cut by about 1.1 billion metric tons (1 billion tons) annually, **(3)** the proportion of the U.S. population served by sewage treatment plants increased from 32% to 74%, and **(4)** annual wetland losses decreased by 83%.

Here is some *bad news:* **(1)** About 44% of lakes, 38% of rivers (up from 26% in 1984), and 32% of tested estuaries in the United States are still unsafe for fishing, swimming, and other recreational uses, **(2)** hog, poultry, and cattle farm runoff pollutes 70% of U.S. rivers, **(3)** large quantities of toxic industrial wastes are illegally dumped into U.S. rivers each year, **(4)** fish caught in more than 1,400 different waterways and 28% of the nation's lakes are unsafe to eat because of high levels of pesticides and other toxic substances, **(5)** less than 2% of the country's 5.8 million kilometers (3.6 million miles) of tested streams are healthy enough to be considered high quality, **(6)** the number of polluted streams could be 10–20 times higher because as many as 400,000 streams have not been

tested for water quality, **(7)** 40% of the country's surface and groundwater is unsafe for human use, and **(8)** a 2001 study by the National Academy of Sciences found that the area of wetlands in the United States is continuing to fall, despite a government goal of "no net loss" in the area and function of wetlands.

**Should We Strengthen or Weaken the U.S. Clean Water Act?** Some environmentalists and a 2001 report by the EPA's inspector general call for the Clean Water Act to be strengthened by **(1)** increasing funding and authority to control nonpoint sources of pollution, **(2)** increasing monitoring of state programs to see that pollution permits are not allowed to expire, **(3)** strengthening programs to prevent and control toxic water pollution, **(4)** providing more funding and authority for integrated watershed and airshed planning to protect groundwater and surface water from contamination, **(5)** requiring states to do a better job of monitoring and enforcing water pollution laws, and **(6)** expanding the rights of citizens to bring lawsuits to ensure that water pollution laws are enforced. The National Academy of Sciences also calls for **(1)** halting the loss of wetlands, **(2)** higher standards for restoration, and **(3)** creating new wetlands before filling any natural wetlands.

Many people oppose these proposals, contending that the Clean Water Act's regulations and government wetlands regulations are already too restrictive and costly. Farmers and developers **(1)** see the law as a curb on their rights as property owners to fill in wetlands and **(2)** believe they should be compensated for property value losses because of federal wetland protection regulations. State and local officials want more discretion in testing for and meeting water quality standards. They argue that in many communities it is unnecessary and too expensive to test for all the water pollutants required by federal law.

**What Can We Do About Water Pollution from Point Sources? The Technological Approach** As population, urbanization, and industrialization grow, the volume of wastewater needing treatment will increase rapidly. In rural and suburban areas with suitable soils, sewage from each house usually is discharged into a **septic tank** (Figure 19-16, p. 504). About 25% of all homes in the United States are served by septic tanks, which should be cleaned out every 3–5 years by a reputable contractor so they will not contribute to groundwater pollution.

In U.S. urban areas, most waterborne wastes from homes, businesses, factories, and storm runoff flow through a network of sewer pipes to wastewater treatment plants. Some cities have separate lines for runoff of storm water. However, 1,200 U.S. cities have combined the lines for these two systems because it is cheaper. When rains cause combined sewer systems to

Figure 19-16 *Septic tank system* used for disposal of domestic sewage and wastewater in rural and suburban areas. This system traps greases and large solids and discharges the remaining wastes over a large drainage field. As these wastes percolate downward, the soil filters out some potential pollutants, and soil bacteria decompose biodegradable materials. To be effective, septic tank systems must be **(1)** properly installed in soils with adequate drainage, **(2)** not placed too close together or too near well sites, and **(3)** pumped out when the settling tank becomes full.

overflow, they discharge untreated sewage directly into surface waters.

When sewage reaches a treatment plant, it can undergo up to three levels of purification. **Primary sewage treatment** is a *mechanical* process that uses screens to filter out debris such as sticks, stones, and rags and allows suspended solids to settle out as sludge in a settling tank (Figure 19-17). Improved primary treatment uses chemically treated polymers to remove suspended solids more thoroughly. By itself, primary treatment removes about 60% of the suspended solids and 30% of the oxygen-demanding organic wastes from sewage but removes no phosphates, nitrates, salts, radioisotopes, or pesticides.

**Secondary sewage treatment** is a *biological* process in which aerobic bacteria remove up to 90% of biodegradable, oxygen-demanding organic wastes (Figure 19-17). Some treatment plants use *trickling filters*, in which aerobic bacteria degrade sewage as it seeps through a bed of crushed stones covered with bacteria and protozoa. Others use an *activated sludge process*. This involves pumping the sewage into a large tank and mixing it for several hours with bacteria-rich sludge and air bubbles to spur degradation by microorganisms. The water then goes to a sedimentation tank, where most of the suspended solids and microorganisms settle out as sludge. The sludge produced by primary or secondary treatment is broken down in an anaerobic digester and **(1)** incinerated, **(2)** dumped into the ocean or a landfill, or **(3)** applied to land as fertilizer.

A combination of primary and secondary treatment (Figure 19-17) removes about **(1)** 97% by weight of the suspended solids, **(2)** 95–97% of the oxygen-demanding organic wastes, **(3)** 70% of most toxic metal

Figure 19-17 Primary and secondary sewage treatment.

compounds and nonpersistent synthetic organic chemicals, **(4)** 70% of the phosphorus (mostly as phosphates), **(5)** 50% of the nitrogen (mostly as nitrates), and **(6)** 5% of dissolved salts. This process removes only a tiny fraction of long-lived radioactive isotopes and persistent organic substances such as some pesticides.

Because of the Clean Water Act, most U.S. cities have combined primary and secondary sewage treatment plants (Figure 19-17). However, government studies have found that **(1)** at least two-thirds of these plants have violated water pollution regulations, **(2)** 500 cities have failed to meet federal standards for sewage treatment plants, and **(3)** 34 East Coast cities simply screen out large floating objects from their sewage before discharging it into coastal waters.

**Advanced sewage treatment** is a series of specialized chemical and physical processes that remove specific pollutants left in the water after primary and secondary treatment (Figure 19-18). Advanced treatment is rarely used because such plants typically cost twice as much to build and four times as much to operate as secondary plants.

There is growing interest in using membrane-based technologies such as *reverse osmosis, microfiltration, ultrafiltration,* and *nanofiltration* to purify salt water

(p. 328), brackish water, surface water, and wastewater. Currently the costs are high and the membranes can become fouled, but scientists are working on these problems.

Before discharge, water from primary, secondary, or advanced treatment undergoes **(1)** bleaching to remove water coloration and **(2)** disinfection to kill disease-carrying bacteria and some but not all viruses. The usual method for doing this is *chlorination.* However, chlorine can react with organic materials in water to form small amounts of chlorinated hydrocarbons, some of which cause cancers in test animals and may damage the human nervous, immune, and endocrine systems (Connections, p. 235).

Use of other disinfectants, such as ozone and ultraviolet light, is increasing. But they cost more and their effects do not last as long as chlorination.

**What Should We Do with Sewage Sludge?** Sewage treatment produces a toxic, gooey *sludge.* In the United States, about **(1)** 9% by weight is converted to compost for use as a soil conditioner and **(2)** 36% is applied to farmland, forests, golf courses, cemeteries, parkland, highway medians, and degraded land as fertilizer. The remaining 55% is dumped in conventional

**Figure 19-18** *Advanced sewage treatment.* Often only one (or two) of these processes is used to remove specific pollutants in a particular area. This expensive method is not widely used.

landfills (where it can contaminate groundwater) or incinerated (which can pollute the air with toxic chemicals and produces a toxic ash usually buried in landfills that the EPA says will leak eventually).

From an environmental standpoint, it is desirable to recycle the plant nutrients in sewage sludge to the soil on land not used to grow food crops. As long as harmful bacteria and toxic chemicals are not present, sludge can also fertilize land used for food crops or livestock. However, removing bacteria (usually by heating), toxic metals, and organic chemicals is expensive and rarely done in the United States. According to a 2002 report by the National Academy of Sciences, the EPA is using outdated science to set standards for using sewage sludge as a fertilizer in the United States.

A growing number of health problems and lawsuits have resulted from use of sludge to fertilize crops in the United States. To protect consumers and avoid lawsuits, some food packers such as DelMonte and Heinz have banned produce grown on farms using sludge as a fertilizer.

Environmental scientist Peter Montague calls for redesigning the sewage treatment system to prevent toxic and hazardous waste from reaching sewage treatment plants. Ways to do this include the following:

- Requiring industries and businesses to remove all toxic and hazardous wastes from water sent to municipal sewage treatment plants.

- Encouraging or requiring industries to reduce or eliminate toxic chemical use and waste.

- Encouraging the use of less harmful household chemicals and having harmful chemicals picked up and disposed of safely on a regular basis as part of garbage collection services.

- Having households, apartment buildings, and offices eliminate sewage outputs by switching to modern composting toilet systems that are installed, maintained, and managed by professionals. Such systems would be cheaper than current sewage systems because they (1) do not require vast systems of underground pipes connected to centralized sewage treatment plants and (2) conserve large amounts of water.

**How Can We Treat Sewage by Working with Nature?** Some communities and individuals are seeking better ways to purify contaminated water by working with nature (p. 483 and Solutions, p. 507). Mark Nelson has developed a small, low-tech, and inexpensive artificial wetland system to treat raw sewage from hotels, restaurants, and homes in developing countries (Figure 19-19). This *wastewater garden* system removes 99.9% of fecal coliform bacteria and more than 80% of the nitrates and phosphates from incoming sewage that in most developing countries is often dumped untreated into the ocean or into shallow holes in the ground. The water flowing out of such

**(1)** Raw sewage drains by gravity into the first pool and flows through a long perforated PVC pipe into a bed of limestone gravel.

**(3)** Wastewater flows through another perforated pipe into a second pool, where the same process is repeated.

Sewage

Wetland type plants

Treated water

Wetland type plants

**First concrete pool**

45 centimeter layer of limestone gravel coated with decomposing bacteria

**Second concrete pool**

**(2)** Microbes in the limestone gravel break down the sewage into chemicals, that can be absorbed by the plant roots, and the gravel absorbs phosphorus.

**(4)** Treated water flowing from the second pool is nearly free of bacteria and plant nutrients. Treated water can be recycled for irrigation and flushing toilets.

**Figure 19-19** *Wastewater garden.* Hotels, restaurants, and homes in developing countries can use this small gravity-fed artificial wetland system to treat sewage. It uses only 1.9–3.8 square meters (20–30 square feet) of space per person.

## Using Wetlands to Treat Sewage

**SOLUTIONS**

Waste treatment is one of the important ecological services provided by wetlands. More than 150 cities and towns in the United States now use natural and artificial wetlands to treat sewage as a low-tech, low-cost alternative to expensive waste treatment plants.

Some communities have created artificial wetlands to treat their water, as the residents of Arcata, California, did, under the leadership of Humboldt State University professors Robert Gearheart and George Allen.

The people of this coastal town of 17,000 created some 63 hectares (155 acres) of wetlands between the town and the adjacent Humboldt Bay. The marshes, developed on land that was once a dump, act as an inexpensive and natural waste treatment plant. The project cost less than half the estimated cost of a conventional treatment plant.

Here is how it works. First, sewage goes to sedimentation tanks, where the solids settle out as sludge that is removed and processed for use as fertilizer. The liquid is pumped into oxidation ponds, where remaining wastes are broken down by bacteria. After a month or so, the water is released into the artificial marshes, where plants and bacteria carry out further filtration and cleansing.

Although the water is clean enough for direct discharge into the bay, state law requires that it first be chlorinated. The town chlorinates the water and then dechlorinates it before sending it into the bay, where oyster beds thrive.

The marshes and lagoons also serve as an Audubon Society bird sanctuary and provide habitats for thousands of otters, seabirds, and marine animals. The town even celebrates its natural sewage treatment system with an annual "Flush with Pride" festival.

### Critical Thinking

List some possible drawbacks to creating artificial wetlands to treat sewage. Do these drawbacks outweigh the benefits? Explain.

---

systems can be used to **(1)** irrigate gardens or fields or **(2)** flush toilets and thus help save water.

In addition to *living machine* systems (p. 483), scientists at Living Technologies have developed neighborhood *sewage walls* that would run along the length of a residential block. This system channels sewage through a series of four terraced planters that progressively filter and purify the waste. Each planter would be capped with glass to allow use of sunlight and contain the bacteria and plants best suited for the various stages of treatment. Local gardens can use the resulting effluent as fertilizer.

Another approach is to use wastewater to grow forests. While the trees are growing, this approach can also remove carbon dioxide from the atmosphere and help slow global warming.

### 19-7 DRINKING WATER QUALITY

**Is the Water Safe to Drink?** Some *good news* is that according to the WHO the percentage of people in developing countries with access to clean drinking water increased from 30% in 1970 to 68% in 2000. The *bad news* is that one-fifth of the people in developing countries do not have access to clean drinking water.

In China, an estimated 700 million people drink contaminated water, and only 6 of China's 27 largest cities provide drinking water that meets government standards. In India, an estimated 300 million people lack access to safe water. In Russia, half of all tap water is unfit to drink. About 290 million Africans—about equal to the entire U.S. population—do not have access to safe drinking water.

In many poor villages in developing countries, people get their water from **(1)** shallow groundwater wells that are easily contaminated, **(2)** nearby polluted river water, or **(3)** mudholes used by both animals and humans.

In most urban slums in developing countries, officials do not pump in drinking water or the poor there cannot afford a house connection. Such poor urban dwellers must either **(1)** drink contaminated water from rivers or other sources or **(2)** buy it from street vendors at an average cost of 12 times more per liter than middle-class families pay for water piped to their houses. A 1999 study by the World Commission on Water for the 21st Century found that urban street vendors draw much of the water they sell from polluted rivers or other contaminated sources.

The United Nations estimates it would cost about $23 billion a year over 8–10 years to bring low-cost safe water and sanitation to the 1.1 billion people who do not have access to clean drinking water. These expenditures could prevent many of the **(1)** 3.4 million deaths (including 2 million children under age 5) and **(2)** 3.4 billion cases of illness caused each year by unsafe water. Currently, the world is spending only about $16 billion a year on clean water efforts. The $7 billion shortfall is about equal to what the world spends every 4 days for military purposes. Researchers are trying to find cheap and simple ways to purify drinking water in developing nations (Individuals Matter, p. 508).

## Using UV Light, Horseradish, and Slimes to Purify Water

Ashok J. Gadgil, a physicist at California's Lawrence Berkeley National Laboratory, and his colleagues have developed a simple device that uses ultraviolet light to kill disease-causing organisms in drinking water. As water from a well or hand pump (in a village or household in a developing country) passes through this tabletop system, UV radiation from a mercury vapor lamp zaps germs in the water.

This $300 device weighs only 7 kilograms (15 pounds) and can disinfect 57 liters (15 gallons) of water per minute at a very low cost. It draws only 40 watts of power, supplied by solar cells, and can run unsupervised in remote areas of developing countries.

In addition, a $200 handheld device that runs on two AA batteries uses ultraviolet light to kill about 99.99% of the bacteria and viruses found in water. The device can decontaminate 0.5 liter (1 pint) of water in about a minute. It is useful for (1) people traveling abroad, (2) campers and backpackers, and (3) home owners when storms or other disasters shut down water supply systems.

Recently, Pennsylvania State soil biochemists discovered that chopped horseradish mixed with hydrogen peroxide ($H_2O_2$) helps rid contaminated water of organic pollutants called *phenols*. The horseradish contains an enzyme that speeds up the breakdown of the phenols.

Judith Bender and Peter Phillips at Clark Atlanta University in Georgia have found a way to use slime produced by cyanobacteria to decompose chlorinated hydrocarbons that contaminate drinking water. Within 3 weeks, a slimy floating bacterial mat can surround and decompose a glob of toxic chlordane (a pesticide banned in the United States as a suspected carcinogen). Such slime mats can also remove lead, copper, chromium, cadmium, selenium, and other toxic metals from water.

**How Is Drinking Water Purified?** Treatment of water for drinking by city dwellers is much like wastewater treatment. Areas that depend on surface water usually store it in a reservoir for several days. This improves taste and clarity by increasing dissolved oxygen content and allowing suspended matter to settle. Next the water is pumped to a purification plant and treated to meet government drinking water standards. Before disinfection, the water is usually run through sand filters and activated charcoal. In areas with very pure groundwater sources, little treatment is necessary.

Ways to purify drinking water can be simple.

■ In tropical countries without centralized water treatment systems, the WHO is urging people to purify their own drinking water by exposing a plastic bottle filled with contaminated water to the sun (Solutions, p. 244).

■ In Bangladesh, women receive strips of cloth for filtering cholera-producing bacteria from drinking water. Villages where women use such strips to strain water have reduced cholera cases by 50%.

**How Is the Quality of Drinking Water Protected?** About 54 countries, most of them in North America and Europe, have safe drinking water standards. The U.S. Safe Drinking Water Act of 1974 requires the EPA to establish national drinking water standards, called *maximum contaminant levels,* for any pollutants that may have adverse effects on human health.

Privately owned wells are not required to meet federal drinking water standards, primarily because of (1) the costs of testing each well regularly (at least $1,000) and (2) some home owners' opposition to mandatory testing and compliance.

Figuring how many people in the United States get sick or die each year from drinking contaminated water is difficult. Estimates vary and include (1) 7 million illnesses and 1,200 deaths per year according to a 1994 study by the Natural Resources Defense Council, (2) 1 million illnesses and about 900 deaths according to a 1997 report by the Centers for Disease Control and Prevention, and (3) 239,000 illnesses and 50 deaths according to a 1999 EPA study.

In April 1993, residents of Milwaukee, Wisconsin, found out that water from their taps was unsafe to drink. Before this health crisis was over, 111 people had died and 403,000 people had become sick from exposure to *Cryptosporidium,* a parasitic organism. Milwaukee spent an estimated $54 million to deal with this outbreak. In May 1994, another outbreak of this parasite killed 19 and sickened more than 100 people in Las Vegas, Nevada. After these incidents, the EPA stepped up efforts to require public water systems to detect and prevent contamination by disease-causing pathogens such as *E. coli* and *Cryptosporidium* in drinking water obtained from surface sources such as lakes and rivers.

**Should the U.S. Safe Drinking Water Act Be Strengthened or Weakened?** Environmentalists call for the U.S. Safe Drinking Water Act to be strengthened by (1) improving treatment by combining at least half of the 50,000 water systems that serve fewer than

3,300 people each with larger ones nearby, **(2)** strengthening and enforcing public notification requirements about violations of drinking water standards, and **(3)** banning all lead in new plumbing pipes, faucets, and fixtures (current law allows fixtures with up to 10% lead to be sold as lead free). According to the Natural Resources Defense Council (NRDC), such improvements would cost about $30 a year per U.S. household.

However, Congress is being pressured by water-polluting industries to weaken the Safe Drinking Water Act by **(1)** eliminating national tests of drinking water, **(2)** suspending the requirement that the media be advised of emergency water health violations and water system officials notify their customers of such violations, **(3)** allowing states to give drinking water systems a permanent right to violate the standard for a given contaminant if the provider claims it cannot afford to comply, and **(4)** eliminating the requirement that water systems use affordable, feasible technology to remove cancer-causing contaminants. The Bush administration proposed a 41% cut in the 2003 EPA budget for clean and safe water over 2002 levels.

**Is Bottled Water the Answer?** Despite some problems, experts say the United States has some of the world's cleanest drinking water. Yet about half of all Americans worry about getting sick from tap water contaminants, and many drink bottled water or install expensive water purification systems. Studies indicate that many of these consumers are being cheated and in some cases may end up drinking water dirtier than water they can get from their taps.

Bacteria contaminate an estimated one-third of the bottled water purchased in the United States. To be safe, consumers purchasing bottled water should determine whether the bottling company belongs to the International Bottled Water Association (IBWA) and adheres to its testing requirements.* Some companies pay $2,500 annually to obtain more stringent certification by the National Sanitation Foundation, an independent agency that tests for 200 chemical and biological contaminants.

Before drinking expensive bottled water and buying costly home water purifiers, health officials suggest that consumers have their water tested by local health authorities or private labs (not companies trying to sell water purification equipment) to **(1)** identify what contaminants, if any, must be removed and **(2)** recommend the type of purification needed to remove such contaminants. Independent experts contend that unless tests

show otherwise, for most urban and suburban Americans served by large municipal drinking water systems, home water treatment systems are not worth the expense and maintenance hassles.

Some consumers pay up to 1,000 times more for bottled water that may be no safer or cleaner than water from the tap. Use of bottled water also causes some environmental problems. It increases **(1)** the 1.4 million metric tons (1.5 million tons) of plastic bottles thrown away globally each year, **(2)** toxic gases and liquids released during the manufacture of plastic water bottles, and **(3)** greenhouse gases emitted during the shipping and delivery of bottled water.

Buyers should check out companies selling water purification equipment and be wary of claims that the EPA has approved a treatment device. Although the EPA does *register* such devices, it neither tests nor approves them.

**What Is the Next Step? Individuals Matter** As with air pollution, it is encouraging that since 1970 most of the world's developed countries have enacted laws and regulations that have significantly reduced point sources of water pollution—mostly because of political pressure by individuals and organized groups of individuals on elected officials.

However, little has been done to reduce water pollution in most developing countries. In other words, progress has been made in developed countries but much more needs to be done in such countries and especially in developing countries.

To environmentalists the next step is to increase efforts to *reduce and prevent water pollution* by asking the question:. *"How can we not produce water pollutants in the first place?"*

Preventing water pollution over the next several decades involves the following priorities:

- *Greatly reducing poverty.*

- *Putting much greater emphasis on keeping groundwater from being contaminated.*

- *Putting much more emphasis on preventing nonpoint pollution from the runoff of fertilizers, pesticides, and other pollutants from farms, animal feedlots, lawns, and urban developments* (Figure 19-4).

- *Reducing the toxicity or volume of pollutants.* For example, organic solvent-based inks and paints can be replaced with water-based materials).

- *Reusing wastewater instead of discharging it.* An example is reusing treated wastewater for irrigation, which also reduces water use.

- *Recycling pollutants.* An example is cleaning up and recycling contaminated solvents for reuse instead of discharging them.

---

*Check for the IBWA seal of approval on the bottle or contact the International Bottled Water Association (1700 Diagonal Road, Suite 650 , Alexandria, VA 22314; telephone: 703-683-5213; information hotline: 1-800-WATER-11; website: www.bottledwater. org) for a member list.

- *Working with nature to treat sewage* (pp. 483 and 506) and

- *Integrating government policies for water pollution with policies for air pollution, agriculture, energy, solid and hazardous wastes, climate change, land use, and population.*

Like the shift to *controlling water pollution* between 1970 and 2000, this new shift to *preventing water pollution* will not take place without political pressure on elected officials by individual citizens and groups of such citizens. See the website material for this chapter for some actions you can take to help reduce water pollution.

*It is a hard truth to swallow, but nature does not care if we live or die. We cannot survive without the oceans, for example, but they can do just fine without us.*

ROGER ROSENBLATT

## REVIEW QUESTIONS

**1.** Define the boldfaced terms in this chapter.

**2.** Describe John Todd's *living machines* used to purify sewage.

**3.** What is *water pollution?* Describe how a *coliform bacteria count*, measurement of *biological oxygen demand*, and *biological indicators* can be used to determine water quality. What are eight types of water pollutants, and what are the major sources and effects of each type?

**4.** Distinguish between *point* and *nonpoint sources of water pollution*, and give two examples of each type. Which type is easier to control? Why?

**5.** What are the major water pollution problems of streams? Explain how streams can handle some loads of biodegradable wastes, and explain the limitations of this approach.

**6.** Summarize the good and bad news about attempts to prevent or control stream pollution.

**7.** What are the major water pollution problems of lakes? List three reasons why dilution of pollution often is less effective in lakes than in streams.

**8.** Distinguish between *eutrophication* and *cultural eutrophication*. What are the major causes of cultural eutrophication? List three methods for preventing cultural eutrophication and three methods for cleaning up cultural eutrophication.

**9.** Summarize the good and bad news about attempts to reduce water pollution in the Great Lakes.

**10.** Explain how climate change from projected global warming can decrease the quality of surface water.

**11.** List five major sources of groundwater contamination. List three reasons why groundwater pollution is such a serious problem.

**12.** Discuss the problem of reducing levels of arsenic found in drinking water.

**13.** List three examples indicating the seriousness of groundwater pollution. List four ways to prevent groundwater contamination.

**14.** List the major pollution problems of the oceans. Why are most of these problems found in coastal areas?

**15.** Describe the ocean pollution problems caused by large inputs of plant nutrients from river systems.

**16.** Summarize **(a)** the major pollution problems of the Chesapeake Bay in the United States and **(b)** the progress made in dealing with these problems.

**17.** Distinguish between ocean pollution from *dredge spoils* and from *sewage sludge*.

**18.** Distinguish between *crude petroleum* and *refined petroleum*, and summarize the major water pollution problems caused by oil. What are the three major sources of oil pollution in the world's oceans? Discuss the limitations of cleaning up oil pollution.

**19.** List seven ways to prevent and two ways to reduce pollution of coastal waters.

**20.** List seven ways to help prevent water pollution from nonpoint sources. Why has there been so little emphasis on dealing with this problem?

**21.** Explain how the United States and most developed countries have reduced water pollution from point sources by enacting laws, and summarize the good and bad news about such efforts. List **(a)** six ways in which environmentalists believe water pollution control laws in the United States should be strengthened, and **(b)** two reasons why there is opposition to such changes.

**22.** Distinguish among *septic tanks, primary sewage treatment, secondary sewage treatment,* and *advanced sewage treatment* as ways to reduce water pollution. List ways to deal with the sludge produced by waste treatment methods. What are the pros and cons of each approach?

**23.** Describe three ways to treat sewage based on working with nature.

**24.** What percentage of the people in developing countries do not have access to clean drinking water? About how many children under age 5 die each year from infectious diseases caused by drinking contaminated water?

**25.** How can we purify drinking water? How is the quality of drinking water protected in the United States? How successful have these efforts been? List **(a)** three suggestions made by environmentalists for strengthening the U.S. Safe Drinking Water Act and **(b)** four suggestions made by opponents for weakening the act. List the pros and cons of drinking bottled water.

**26.** List three ways to shift the emphasis from cleanup to prevention of water pollution.

## CRITICAL THINKING

**1.** Why is dilution not always the solution to water pollution? Give examples and conditions for which this solution is or is not applicable.

**2.** How can a stream cleanse itself of oxygen-demanding wastes? Under what conditions will this natural cleansing system fail?

**3.** Is each of the eight categories of pollutants listed in Table 19-1 most likely to originate from **(a)** point sources or **(b)** nonpoint sources?

**4.** A large number of fish are found floating dead on a lake during the summer. You are called to determine the cause of the fish kill. What reason would you suggest for the kill? What measurements would you make to verify your hypothesis?

**5.** Explain why a number of communities around the Great Lakes have banned the use of phosphate-containing detergents in recent years.

**6.** Are you for or against banning injection of liquid hazardous wastes into deep wells below drinking water aquifers (Figure 19-10, p. 494)? Explain. What are the alternatives?

**7.** Are you for or against banning all dumping of wastes and untreated sewage into the ocean? Explain. If so, where would you put the wastes instead? What exceptions would you permit, and why? How would you enforce such regulations?

**8.** Your town (Town B) is located on a river between Towns A and C. What are the rights and responsibilities of upstream communities to downstream communities? Should sewage and industrial wastes be dumped at the upstream end of a community that generates them?

**9.** Congratulations! You are in charge of sharply reducing nonpoint water pollution throughout the world. What are the three most important things you would do?

**10.** Congratulations! You are in charge of sharply reducing groundwater pollution throughout the world. What are the three most important things you would do?

## PROJECTS

**1.** In your community,
- **a.** What are the principal nonpoint sources of contamination of surface water and groundwater?
- **b.** What is the source of drinking water?
- **c.** How is drinking water treated?
- **d.** How many times during each of the past 5 years have levels of tested contaminants violated federal standards? Were violations reported to the public?
- **e.** Has pollution led to bans on fishing in or warnings not to eat fish from any lakes or rivers in your region?
- **f.** Is groundwater contamination a problem? If so, where, and what has been done about the problem?
- **g.** Is there a vulnerable aquifer or critical recharge zone that needs protection to ensure the quality of groundwater? Is your local government aware of this? What action (if any) has it taken?

**2.** Are storm drains and sanitary sewers combined or separate in your area? Are there plans to reduce pollution from runoff of storm water? If not, make an economic evaluation of the costs and benefits of developing separate storm drains and sanitary sewers, and present your findings to local officials.

**3.** Arrange a class or individual tour of a sewage treatment plant in your community. Compare the processes it uses with those shown in Figure 19-17. What happens to the sludge produced by this plant? What improvements, if any, would you suggest for this plant?

**4.** Use library research, the Internet, and user interviews to evaluate the relative effectiveness and costs of home water purification devices. Determine the type or types of water pollutants each device removes and the effectiveness of this process.

**5.** Use the library or the Internet to find bibliographic information about *William Ruckelshaus* and *Roger Rosenblatt,* whose quotes appear at the beginning and end of this chapter.

**6.** Make a concept map of this chapter's major ideas, using the section heads and subheads and the key terms (in boldface). See material on the website for this book about how to prepare concept maps.

## INTERNET STUDY RESOURCES AND RESOURCES FOR FURTHER READING AND RESEARCH

The website for this book contains helpful study aids and many ideas for further reading and research. Log on to

www.info.brookscole.com/miller13

and click on the Chapter-by-Chapter area. Choose Chapter 19 and select a resource:

- Flash Cards allows you to test your mastery of the Terms and Concepts to Remember for this chapter.

- Tutorial Quizzes provides a multiple-choice practice quiz.

- Student Guide to InfoTrac will lead you to Critical Thinking Projects that use InfoTrac College Edition as a research tool.

- References lists the major books and articles consulted in writing this chapter.

- Hypercontents takes you to an extensive list of sites with news, research, and images related to individual sections of the chapter.

## INFOTRAC COLLEGE EDITION

Improve your skills with InfoTrac College Edition, a searchable online database of articles from more than 700 periodicals. Log on to

http://www.infotrac-college.com

or access InfoTrac through the website for this book. Try to find the following articles:

**1.** Peipins, L. A., K. A. Highfill, E. Barrett, M. M. Monti, R. Hackler, P. Huang, and X. Jiang. 2002. A Norwalk-like virus outbreak on the Appalachian Trail. *Journal of Environmental Health* 64: 18. *Keywords:* "Appalachian Trail" and "virus outbreak." Long-distance hikers on the Appalachian Trail suddenly develop severe gastrointestinal problems along a specific stretch of the trail. Could it be something in the water?

**2.** Rabalais, N. N., R. E. Turner, and D. Scavia. 2002. Beyond science into policy: Gulf of Mexico hypoxia and the Mississippi River. *BioScience* 52: 129. *Keywords:* "Gulf of Mexico" and "hypoxia." Hypoxia (reduced oxygen levels) and cultural eutrophication are a serious problem in the northern Gulf of Mexico. Is there a solution?

# 20 PESTICIDES AND PEST CONTROL

## *Along Came a Spider*

Since agriculture began about 10,000 years ago, we have been competing with insect pests for the food we grow. Today we are not much closer to winning this competition than we were then. The reasons are the astounding ability of insect pests to **(1)** multiply and **(2)** rapidly develop genetic resistance to poisons we throw at them through directional natural selection (Figure 5-6, left, p. 102).

Some Chinese farmers have switched from a chemical to a biological strategy to help control insect pests. Instead of spraying their rice and cotton fields with poisons, they build little straw huts around the fields in the fall.

These farmers are encouraging insects' worst enemy, one that has hunted them for millions of years: *spiders* (Figure 20-1). The little huts are for hibernating spiders. Protected from the winter cold by the huts, far more of the hibernating spiders become active in the spring. Ravenous after their winter fast, they scuttle off into the fields to stalk their insect prey.

Even without human help, the world's 30,000 known species of spiders kill far more insects every year than insecticides do. A typical acre of meadow or woods contains an estimated 50,000–2 million spiders, each devouring hundreds of insects per year.

Entomologist Willard H. Whitcomb found that leaving strips of weeds around cotton and soybean fields provides the kind of undergrowth favored by insect-eating wolf spiders (Figure 20-1, left). He also sings the praises of a type of banana spider, which lives in warm climates and can keep a house clear of cockroaches (Spotlight, p. 105).

In Maine, Daniel Jennings of the U.S. Forest Service uses spiders to help control the spruce budworm, which devastates the Northeast's spruce and fir forests. Spiders also attack the much feared gypsy moth, which destroys tree foliage.

The idea of encouraging populations of spiders in fields, forests, and even houses scares some people because spiders have bad reputations. From a human standpoint, however, spiders are helpful and mostly harmless creatures.

A few spider species, such as the black widow, the brown recluse, and eastern Australia's Sydney funnel web, are dangerous to people. However, most spider species, including the ferocious-looking wolf spider (Figure 20-1, left), do not harm humans. Even the giant tarantula rarely bites people, and its venom is too weak to harm us or other large mammals. As we seek new ways to coexist with the insect rulers of the planet (p. 64), we would do well to be sure that spiders are on our side.

This chapter looks first at the pros and cons of the conventional chemical approach to pest control based on using synthetic chemical pesticides. Then it discusses the pros and cons of a variety of biological and ecological alternatives for controlling pest populations.

**Figure 20-1** Spiders are insects' worst enemies. Most spiders, such as the wolf spider (left) and the crab spider (right), found in many parts of the world, are harmless to humans.

*A weed is a plant whose virtues have not yet been discovered.*
RALPH WALDO EMERSON

This chapter addresses the following questions:

- What are pesticides, and what types are used?

- What are the pros and cons of using chemicals to kill insects and weeds?

- How well is pesticide use regulated in the United States?

- What are the alternatives to using conventional pesticides, and what are the advantages and disadvantages of each alternative?

## 20-1 PESTICIDES: TYPES AND USES

**How Does Nature Keep Pest Populations Under Control?** A **pest** is any species that (1) competes with us for food, (2) invades lawns and gardens, (3) destroys wood in houses, (4) spreads disease, or (5) is simply a nuisance. In natural ecosystems and many polyculture agroecosystems (p. 284), *natural enemies* (predators, parasites, and disease organisms) (1) control the populations of 50–90% of pest species as part of the earth's ecological services (Figure 4-34, p. 92) and (2) help keep any one species from taking over for very long.

When we replace polyculture agriculture with monoculture agriculture (Figure 6-31, p. 132) and spray fields with huge amounts of pesticides, we upset many of these natural population checks and balances. Then we must devise ways to protect our monoculture crops, tree plantations, and lawns from insects and other pests that nature once controlled at no charge.

**What Are Pesticides?** To help control pest organisms, we have developed a variety of **pesticides** (or *biocides*): chemicals to kill organisms we consider undesirable. Common types of pesticides include (1) *insecticides* (insect killers), (2) *herbicides* (weed killers), (3) *fungicides* (fungus killers), (4) *nematocides* (roundworm killers), and (5) *rodenticides* (rat and mouse killers).

We did not invent the use of chemicals to repel or kill other species; plants have been producing chemicals to ward off or poison herbivores that feed on them for about 225 million years. This is a never-ending, ever-changing process: Herbivores overcome various plant defenses through natural selection; then the plants use natural selection to develop new defenses. The result of these dynamic interactions between predator and prey species is what biologists call *coevolution* (p. 103).

**What Was the First Generation of Pesticides and Repellents?** As the human population grew and agriculture spread, people began looking for ways to protect their crops, mostly by using chemicals to kill or repel insect pests. Sulfur was used as an insecticide well before 500 B.C.; by the 1400s, people were applying toxic compounds of arsenic, lead, and mercury to crops as insecticides. Farmers abandoned this approach in the late 1920s when the increasing number of human poisonings and fatalities prompted a search for less toxic substitutes. However, traces of these nondegradable toxic metal compounds are still being taken up by tobacco, vegetables, and other crops grown on soil dosed with them long ago.

In the 1600s, nicotine sulfate, extracted from tobacco leaves, came into use as an insecticide. In the mid-1800s, two more natural pesticides were introduced: (1) *pyrethrum*, obtained from the heads of chrysanthemum flowers, and (2) *rotenone*, from the roots of various tropical forest legumes. These *first-generation pesticides* were mainly natural substances, chemicals borrowed from plants that had been defending themselves from insects for eons.

In addition to protecting crops, people have used chemicals (produced by plants) to (1) repel or kill insects in their households, yards, and gardens, (2) save money, and (3) reduce potential health hazards associated with using some commercial insecticides. See the website for this chapter to find out about natural chemicals and methods that can be used to (1) repel or kill common pests such as ants, mosquitoes, cockroaches, flies, and fleas and (2) control weeds.

**What Is the Second Generation of Pesticides?** A major pest control revolution began in 1939, when entomologist Paul Müller discovered that DDT (dichlorodiphenyltrichloroethane), a chemical known since 1874, was a potent insecticide. DDT, the first of so-called *second-generation pesticides*, soon became the world's most used pesticide, and Müller received the Nobel Prize in 1948 for his discovery. Since then, chemists have made hundreds of other pesticides.

Since 1950, pesticide use has risen more than 50-fold, and most of today's pesticides are more than 10 times as toxic as those used in the 1950s. Worldwide, about 2.3 million metric tons (2.5 million tons) of these second-generation pesticides—worth about $44 billion—are used yearly. About 75% of these chemicals are used in developed countries, but use in developing countries is soaring.

In the United States, about 630 different biologically active (pest-killing) ingredients and about 1,820 inert (inactive) ingredients are mixed to make some 25,000 different pesticide products. About 25% of pesticide use in the United States is for ridding houses, gardens, lawns, parks, playing fields, swimming pools, and golf courses of pests. According to the U.S. Environmental Protection Agency (EPA), the average lawn in the United States is doused with 10 times more synthetic pesticides per hectare than U.S. cropland.

## Table 20-1 Major Types of Pesticides

| Type | Examples | Persistence | Biologically Magnified? |
|------|----------|-------------|-------------------------|
| **Insecticides** | | | |
| Chlorinated hydrocarbons | DDT, aldrin, dieldrin, toxaphene, lindane, chlordane, methoxychlor, mirex | High (2–15 years) | Yes |
| Organophosphates | Malathion, parathion, diazinon, TEPP, DDVP, mevingphos | Low to moderate (1–2 weeks), but some can last several years | No |
| Carbamates | Aldicarb, carbaryl (Sevin), propoxur, maneb, zineb | Low (days to weeks) | No |
| Botanicals | Rotenone, pyrethrum, and camphor extracted from plants, synthetic pyrethroids (variations of pyrethrum), and rotenoids (variations of rotenone) | Low (days to weeks) | No |
| Microbotanicals | Various bacteria, fungi, protozoa | Low (days to weeks) | No |
| **Herbicides** | | | |
| Contact chemicals | Atrazine, simazine, paraquat | Low (days to weeks) | No |
| Systemic chemicals | 2,4-D, 2,4,5-T, Silvex, diruon, daminozide (Alar), alachlor (Lasso), glyphosate (Roundup) | Mostly low (days to weeks) | No |
| Soil sterilants | Tribualin, diphenamid, dalapon, butylate | Low (days) | No |
| **Fungicides** | | | |
| Various chemicals | Captan, pentachlorphenol, zeneb, methyl bromide, carbon bisulfide | Most low (days) | No |
| **Fumigants** | | | |
| Various chemicals | Carbon tetrachloride, ethylene dibromide, methyl bromide | Mostly high | Yes (for most) |

The EPA estimates that 84% of U.S. homes use pesticide products such as bait boxes, pest strips, bug bombs, flea collars, and pesticide pet shampoos and weed killers for lawns and gardens. Each year, more than 250,000 people in the United States become ill because of household pesticide use, and such pesticides are a major source of accidental poisonings and deaths for children under age 5.

Sending someone roses, carnations, or other cut flowers is a romantic thing to do. According to the U.S. Department of Agriculture about 70% of cut flowers in the United States are imported with 59% of these flowers coming from Columbia and 15% from Ecuador. According to a 1995 report by the World Resources Institute, flowers from these countries are heavily dosed with fungicides, insecticides, and herbicides. Environmentalists urge us to buy organic flowers.*

---

*You can search for local farms, farmers' markets, and community groups that supply fresh and dried organic flowers at www.localharvest.org. There are not a large number of organic flower growers in the United States, but this could change if the demand increased.

Some pesticides, called *broad-spectrum agents,* are toxic to many species; others, called *selective* or *narrow-spectrum agents,* are effective against a narrowly defined group of organisms. Pesticides vary in their *persistence,* the length of time they remain deadly in the environment (Table 20-1). In 1962, biologist Rachel Carson warned against relying on synthetic organic chemicals to kill insects and other species we deem pests (Individuals Matter, p. 33).

## 20-2  THE CASE FOR PESTICIDES

Proponents of conventional chemical pesticides contend that their benefits outweigh their harmful effects. Here are some of the major benefits of conventional pesticides:

- *They save human lives.* Since 1945, DDT and other chlorinated hydrocarbon and organophosphate insecticides probably have prevented the premature deaths of at least 7 million people from insect-transmitted diseases such as **(1)** malaria (carried by the *Anopheles* mosquito; Figure 11-13, p. 243), **(2)** bubonic plague (rat fleas), **(3)** typhus (body lice and fleas), and **(4)** sleeping sickness (tsetse fly).

- *They increase food supplies and lower food costs.* According to the UN Food and Agriculture Organization about 55% of the world's potential human food supply is lost to pests before (35%) or after (20%) harvest. Pests before and after harvest destroy an estimated 37% of the potential U.S. food supply; insects cause 13% of these losses, plant pathogens 12%, and weeds 12%. As a result, food production for humans and livestock worth at least $65 million a year is lost to pests. Without pesticides, these losses would be worse, and food prices would rise. Figure 20-2 shows five of the most common insect pests in the United States and their ranges.

- *They increase profits for farmers.* Pesticide companies estimate that every $1 spent on pesticides leads to an increase in U.S. crop yields worth approximately $4 (but studies have shown that this benefit drops to about $2 if the harmful effects of pesticides are included).

- *They work faster and better than alternatives.* Pesticides **(1)** control most pests quickly at a reasonable cost, **(2)** have a long shelf life, **(3)** are easily shipped and applied, and **(4)** are safe when handled properly. When genetic resistance occurs, farmers can use stronger doses or switch to other pesticides.

- *When used properly, their health risks are insignificant compared with their benefits.* According to Elizabeth Whelan, director of the American Council on Science and Health (ACSH), which presents the position of the pesticide industry, "The reality is that pesticides, when used in the approved regulatory manner, pose no risk to either farm workers or consumers." A 1981 study by cancer researchers Richard Doll and Richard Peto, found that almost no one dies of cancer caused by exposure to synthetic pesticides in food and water. According to the EPA the worst-case scenario is that synthetic pesticides in food cause 0.5–1% of all cancer-related deaths in the United States—or 3,000–6,000 premature deaths per year—far less than the estimated number of lives saved each year by pesticides. According to studies by microbiologist Bruce Ames, we **(1)** consume far more natural pesticides produced by plants than synthetic ones produced by humans, **(2)** about half of all

synthetic and natural pesticides that have been tested are carcinogenic for test animals, **(3)** the risk of getting cancer from exposure to natural or synthetic pesticides in foods we eat is extremely small, and **(4)** exposure to natural pesticides in food causes more cancers than exposure to synthetic pesticides—although neither exposure poses much risk.

- *Newer pesticides are safer and more effective than many older pesticides.* Greater use is being made of botanicals and microbotanicals (Table 20-1), derived originally from plants, that are safer to users and less damaging to the environment. Genetic engineering is

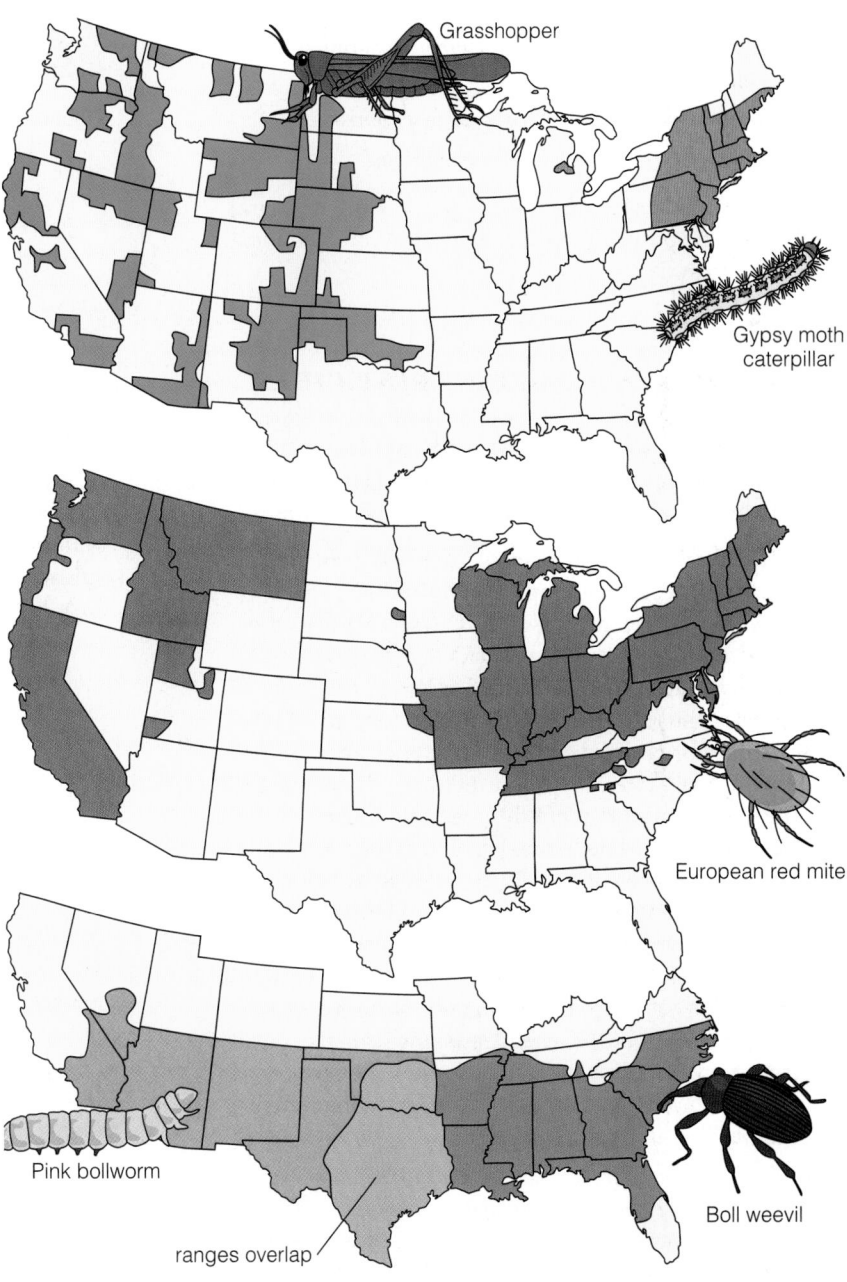

**Figure 20-2** Geographic range of five major pests in the lower 48 states of the United States. (Data from U.S. Department of Agriculture)

also being used to develop pest-resistant crop strains and genetically altered crops that produce pesticides (Figure 13-16, p. 291, and Figure 13-17, p. 292).

■ *Many new pesticides are used at very low rates per unit area compared with those of older products.* For example, application amounts per hectare for many new herbicides are 1/100 the rates for older ones, and genetically engineered crops could reduce the use of toxic insecticides.

Scientists continue to search for the ideal pest-killing chemical, which would have these qualities:

■ *Kill only the target pest.*

■ *Harm no other species.*

■ *Disappear or break down into something harmless after doing its job.*

■ *Not cause genetic resistance in target organisms.*

■ *Be more cost effective than doing nothing.*

The search continues, but so far no known natural or synthetic pesticide chemical meets all or even most of these criteria.

## 20-3   THE CASE AGAINST PESTICIDES

Opponents of widespread pesticide use believe their harmful effects outweigh their benefits. Here are some of the major problems with conventional pesticides:

■ *They accelerate the development of genetic resistance to pesticides.* Insects breed rapidly (Figure 20-3), and within 5–10 years (much sooner in tropical areas) they can develop immunity to pesticides through directional natural selection (Figure 5-6, left, p. 102) and come back stronger than before. Weeds and plant disease organisms also develop genetic resistance, but more slowly. Since 1945, about 1,000 species of insects, mites, weed species, plant diseases, and rodents (mostly rats) have developed genetic resistance to one or more pesticides (Figure 20-4). Because of genetic resistance, many insecticides (such as DDT) no longer protect people from insect-transmitted diseases, such as malaria (Figure 11-13, p. 243), in some parts of the world. This has led to the resurgence of such diseases (Figure 11-12, p. 243). Genetic resistance can also put farmers on a *pesticide treadmill*, whereby they pay more and more for a pest control program that often becomes less and less effective.

■ *Broad-spectrum insecticides kill natural predators and parasites that help control the populations of pest species.* Wiping out natural predators can also unleash new pests whose populations its predators had previously held in check, causing other unexpected effects (Con-

**Figure 20-3** A boll weevil, just one example of an insect capable of rapid breeding. In the cotton fields of the southern United States, these insects lay thousands of eggs, producing a new generation every 21 days and as many as six generations in a single growing season. Attempts to control the cotton boll weevil account for at least 25% of insecticide use in the United States. For example, it typically takes about 114 grams (one-quarter pound) of pesticides to make one cotton T-shirt. Some farmers are increasing their use of natural predators and other biological methods to control this major pest.

nections, p. 200). Currently 100 of the 300 most destructive insect pests in the United States were secondary pests that became major pests after widespread use of insecticides. With wolf spiders (Figure 20-1, left), wasps, predatory beetles, and other natural

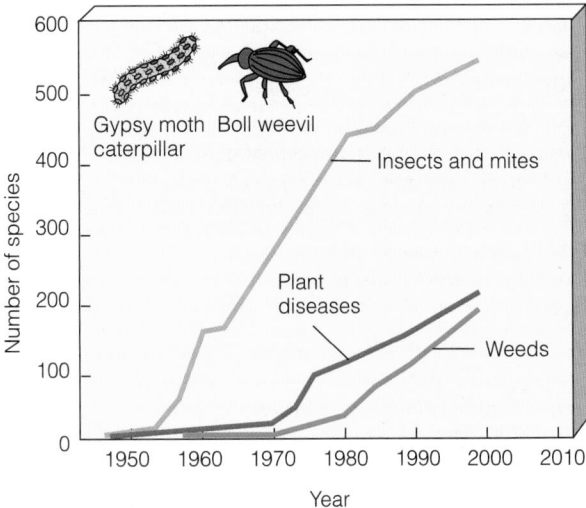

**Figure 20-4** Rise of *genetic resistance to pesticides*, 1945–98. (Data from U.S. Department of Agriculture and the Worldwatch Institute)

## How Effective Have Synthetic Pesticides Been in Reducing Crop Losses?

**SPOTLIGHT**

Studies indicate that pesticides have not been as effective in reducing crop losses in the United States as agricultural experts had hoped. David Pimentel an expert in insect ecology, has evaluated data from more than 300 agricultural scientists and economists and come to the following conclusions:

- Although the use of synthetic pesticides has increased 33-fold since 1942, more of the U.S. food supply is lost to pests today (an estimated 37%) than in the 1940s (31%). Losses attributed to insects almost doubled (from 7% to 13%) despite a 10-fold increase in the use of synthetic insecticides.

- The estimated environmental, health, and social costs of pesticide use in the United States range from $4 to $10 billion per year. The International Food Policy Research Institute puts the estimate much higher, at $100–200 billion per year, or $5–10 in damages for every dollar spent on pesticides.

- Alternative pest control practices (Section 20-5, p. 520) could halve the use of chemical pesticides on 40 major U.S. crops without reducing crop yields.

Numerous studies and experience show that pesticide use can be reduced sharply without reducing yields, and in some cases yields even increase. Sweden has cut pesticide use in half with almost no decrease in crop yields. Campbell Soup uses no pesticides on tomatoes it grows in Mexico, and yields have not dropped. After a 65% cut in pesticide use on rice in Indonesia, yields increased by 15%.

### Critical Thinking

Pesticide proponents argue that although crop losses to pests are higher today than in the past, without the widespread use of pesticides losses would be even higher. Explain why you agree or disagree with this argument.

---

enemies out of the way, the population of a rapidly reproducing insect pest species can rebound and even get larger within days or weeks after initially being controlled. Mostly because of genetic resistance and reduction of natural predators, pesticide use has not reduced crop losses to pests in the United States (Spotlight, above).

- *Pesticides do not stay put.* According to the U.S. Department of Agriculture (USDA), **(1)** no more than 2% (and often less than 0.1%) of the insecticide applied to crops by aerial spraying (Figure 20-5) or ground spraying reaches the target pests, and **(2)** less than 5% of herbicide applied to crops reaches the target weeds. Pesticides that miss their target pests can end up in the **(1)** air, **(2)** surface water, **(3)** groundwater, **(4)** bottom sediments, **(5)** food, and **(6)** nontarget organisms, including humans and wildlife. Crops that have been genetically altered to release small amounts of pesticides directly to pests can help overcome this problem, but can also promote genetic resistance to such pesticides (Figure 13-17, p. 292).

- *Some pesticides harm wildlife.* According to the USDA and the U.S. Fish and Wildlife Service, each year pesticides applied to cropland in the United States **(1)** wipe about 20% of U.S. honeybee colonies and damage another 15%, costing farmers at least $200 million per year from reduced pollination of vital crops, **(2)** kill more than 67 million birds and 6–14 million fish, and **(3)** menace about 20% of the endangered and threatened species in the United States.

National Archives/EPA Documerica

**Figure 20-5** A crop duster spraying an insecticide on grapevines south of Fresno, California. Aircraft apply about 25% of the pesticides used on U.S. cropland, but only 0.1–2% of these insecticides actually reach the target pests. To compensate for the drift of pesticides from target to nontarget areas, aircraft apply up to 30% more pesticide than ground-based application does.

■ *They can threaten human health.* According to the WHO and the UN Environment Programme (UNEP), an estimated 3 million agricultural workers in developing countries (at least 300,000 in the United States) are seriously poisoned by pesticides each year. The result is an estimated 18,000 deaths (about 25 in the United States)—an average of 490 premature deaths each day. Health officials believe the actual number of pesticide-related illnesses and deaths among the world's farm workers probably is greatly underestimated because of **(1)** poor records, **(2)** lack of doctors and disease reporting in rural areas, and **(3)** inaccurate diagnoses. Each year 110,000 Americans, mostly children, get sick from misuse or unsafe storage of pesticides in the home, and about 20 die. According to the EPA, approximately 165 of the active ingredients approved for use in U.S. pesticide products are known or suspected human carcinogens. According to studies by the National Academy of Sciences, exposure to pesticide residues in food causes 4,000–20,000 cases of cancer per year in the United States. Because roughly 50% of people with cancer die prematurely, this amounts to about 2,000–10,000 premature deaths per year in the United States from exposure to legally allowed pesticide residues in foods. This is higher than the EPA estimate of 3,000–6,000 premature deaths per year. Some scientists are becoming increasingly concerned about possible **(1)** genetic mutations, **(2)** birth defects, **(3)** nervous system disorders (especially behavioral disorders), and **(4)** effects on the immune and endocrine systems from long-term exposure to low levels of various pesticides (Connections, p. 235).

## 20-4 PESTICIDE REGULATION IN THE UNITED STATES

**How Are Pesticides Regulated in the United States?** The Federal Insecticide, Fungicide, and Rodenticide Act (FIFRA), established by Congress in 1947 and amended in 1972, requires EPA approval for use of all commercial pesticides. Pesticide companies must evaluate the biologically active ingredients in their products for toxicity to animals (and, by extrapolation, to humans, p. 232). Then, EPA officials review these data before a pesticide can be registered for use. When a pesticide is legally approved for use on fruits or vegetables, the EPA sets a *tolerance level* specifying the amount of toxic pesticide residue that can legally remain on the crop when the consumer eats it.

Some *good news* is that between 1972 and 2001, the EPA banned or severely restricted the use of 56 active pesticide ingredients. The banned chemicals include **(1)** most chlorinated hydrocarbon insecticides, **(2)** several carbamates and organophosphates, and **(3)** the

systemic herbicides 2,4,5-T and Silvex (Table 20-1). However, banned or unregistered pesticides may be manufactured in the United States and exported to other countries (Connections, below).

FIFRA required the EPA to reevaluate the more than 600 active ingredients approved for use in pre-1972 pesticide products to determine whether any of them caused cancer, birth defects, or other health risks. Some *bad news* is that **(1)** in the late 1970s, the EPA discovered that a now defunct laboratory falsified data used to support registrations for more than 200 pesticide active ingredients, which still have not been fully

## What Goes Around Can Come Around

**CONNECTIONS**

U.S. pesticide companies can make and export to other countries pesticides that have been banned or severely restricted—or never even approved—in the United States. Between 1997 and 2000, U.S. exports of such pesticides (most to developing countries) averaged more than 24 metric tons (26 tons) per day—or 1 metric ton (1.1 ton) per hour. Other industrial countries also export banned and unapproved pesticides.

But what goes around can come around. In what environmentalists call a *circle of poison*, residues of some of these banned or unapproved chemicals exported to other countries can return to the exporting countries on imported food. Persistent pesticides such as DDT can also be carried by winds from other countries to the United States.

Environmentalists have urged Congress—without success—to ban such exports. Supporters of pesticide exports argue that **(1)** such sales increase economic growth and provide jobs, **(2)** if the United States did not export pesticides, other countries would, and **(3)** banned pesticides are exported only with the consent of the importing countries.

In 1998, more than 50 countries met to finalize an international treaty that requires exporting countries to have informed consent from importing countries for exports of 22 pesticides and 5 industrial chemicals. In 2000, more than 100 countries developed an international agreement to ban or phase out the use of 12 especially hazardous persistent organic pollutants (POPs)—9 of them persistent chlorinated hydrocarbon pesticides.

**Critical Thinking**

Should U.S. companies be allowed to export pesticides that have been banned, severely restricted, or not approved for use in the United States? Explain.

reevaluated and (2) by 2002, 30 years after Congress ordered the EPA to review these chemicals, less than 10% of these 600 active ingredients had been evaluated fully. The EPA claims it has not been able to complete this evaluation because of the difficulty and expense of determining the health effects of chemicals (Section 11-2, p. 229).

Here is some *disturbing news* according to scientific literature reviewed by the EPA,

- Approximately 165 of the active ingredients approved for use in U.S. pesticide products are known or suspected human carcinogens. By 2001, use of only 41 of these chemicals had been banned by the EPA or discontinued voluntarily by manufacturers.

- A study of Missouri children revealed a statistically significant correlation between childhood brain cancer and use of various pesticides in the home, including (1) flea and tick collars, (2) no-pest strips, and (3) chemicals used to control pests such as roaches, ants, spiders, mosquitoes, and termites.

- Children whose homes contained pest strips (with dichlorovos) faced 2.5–3 times the risk of leukemia as children whose homes did not contain such strips.

- In 2000, EPA scientists published a report indicating that atrazine (widely used as a weed killer by farmers growing corn, sorghum, citrus fruits, and other crops) could cause uterine, prostate, and breast cancer in humans and disrupt reproductive development.

- Recently, Swedish medical researchers found that exposure to glyphosate (the active ingredient in the widely used weed killer Roundup) nearly tripled a person's chances of developing a type of cancer known as non-Hodgkin's lymphoma.

- Children whose yards were treated with pesticides (mostly herbicides) were four times more likely to suffer from cancers of muscle and connective tissues than children whose yards were not treated.

Here is some more *disturbing news*. According to studies by the National Academy of Sciences,

- Federal laws regulating pesticide use in the United States are inadequate and poorly enforced by the EPA, Food and Drug Administration (FDA), and USDA.

- Up to 98% of the potential risk of developing cancer from pesticide residues on food grown in the United States would be eliminated if EPA standards were as strict for pre-1972 pesticides as they are for later ones.

Representatives from pesticide companies dispute these findings. Indeed, the food industry denies that eating food grown using pesticides for the past 50 years has ever harmed anyone in the United States.

## How Can Pesticide Regulation Be Improved?

The U.S. National Academy of Sciences and environmentalists point out that FIFRA

- Allows the EPA to leave inadequately tested pesticides on the market.

- Allows the EPA to license new chemicals without full health and safety data.

- Gives the EPA unlimited time to remove a chemical, even when its health and environmental risks are shown to outweigh its economic benefits.

- Has built-in appeals and other procedures that often keep a dangerous chemical on the market for up to 10 years.

- Is the only major environmental statute that does not allow citizens to sue the EPA for not enforcing the law.

A 1993 study of pesticide safety by the U.S. National Academy of Sciences urged the government to do the following:

- Make human health the primary consideration for setting limits on pesticide levels allowed in food.

- Collect more and better data on pesticide exposure for different groups, including farm workers, adults, and children.

- Develop new and better test procedures for evaluating the toxicity of pesticides, especially for children.

- Consider cumulative exposures of all pesticides in food and water, especially for children, instead of basing regulations on exposure to a single pesticide.

Some *good news* is that progress has been made with the passage of the 1996 Food Quality Protection Act (FQPA), which

- Requires new standards for pesticide tolerance levels in foods, based on a reasonable certainty of no harm to human health (defined for cancer as producing no more than one additional cancer per million people exposed to a certain pesticide over a lifetime).

- Requires manufacturers to demonstrate that the active ingredients in new pesticide products are safe for infants and children.

- Allows the EPA to apply an additional 10-fold safety factor to pesticide tolerance levels to protect infants and children.

- Requires the EPA to consider exposure to more than one pesticide when setting pesticide tolerance levels.

- Requires the EPA to develop rules for a program to screen all active and inactive ingredients for their estrogenic and endocrine effects by 1999 (which had not been achieved by the end of 2002).

Environmentalists believe this law should be strengthened further to **(1)** help prevent contamination of groundwater by pesticides (Section 19-4, p. 493), **(2)** improve the safety of farm workers who are exposed to high levels of pesticides, and **(3)** allow citizens to sue the EPA for not enforcing the law. Pesticide companies oppose such changes and have been able to convince elected officials not to make such improvements.

Pesticide control laws in the United States may have some weaknesses, but most other countries (especially developing countries) have not made nearly as much progress as the United States in regulating pesticides.

## 20-5 OTHER WAYS TO CONTROL PESTS

**What Should Be the Primary Goal of Pest Control?** In most cases, the primary goal of spraying with conventional pesticides is to eradicate pests in the area affected. However, critics say the primary goal of any pest control strategy should be to reduce crop damage to an economically tolerable level (Figure 20-6). The point at which the economic losses caused by pest damage outweigh the cost of applying a pesticide is called the **economic threshold** (Figure 20-6). Because of the risk of increased genetic resistance and other problems, continuing to spray beyond the economic threshold can make matters worse and can cost more than it is worth.

The problem is determining when the economic threshold has been reached. This involves careful monitoring of crop fields to assess crop damage and determine pest populations (often by using traps baited with chemicals that attract the key pests).

Many farmers do not want to bother doing this and instead are likely to use additional *insurance spraying* to be on the safe side. One method used to reduce

unnecessary insurance spraying is the purchase of *pest-loss insurance*. It pays farmers for losses caused by pests and is usually cheaper than using excess pesticides.

Another source of increased pesticide use is *cosmetic spraying*. Extra pesticides are used because consumers often buy only the best-looking fruits and vegetables even though nothing wrong is with blemished ones. The only solution to this problem is consumer education.

**What Are Other Ways to Control Pests?** Many scientists believe we should greatly increase the use of biological, ecological, and other alternative methods for controlling pests and diseases that affect crops and human health. Such methods include using

- *Cultivation practices* such as **(1)** rotating the types of crops planted in a field each year, **(2)** adjusting planting times so major insect pests either starve or get eaten by their natural predators, **(3)** growing crops in areas where their major pests do not exist, **(4)** planting trap crops to lure pests away from the main crop, **(5)** planting rows of hedges or trees around fields to hinder insect invasions and provide habitats for their natural enemies (with the added benefit of reduced soil erosion; Figure 10-26d, p. 224), and **(6)** increasing the use of polyculture (p. 284), which uses plant diversity to reduce losses to pests.

- *Genetic engineering* (Figure 13-16, p. 291) *to speed up the development of pest- and disease-resistant crop strains* (Figure 20-7). However, there is controversy over whether the projected advantages of the increasing use of genetically modified plants and foods outweigh their projected disadvantages (Figure 13-17, p. 292).

- *Biological pest control, in which natural predators* (Figures 20-1 and 20-8), *parasites, and disease-causing bacteria and viruses can be imported to regulate pest populations.* This approach **(1)** focuses on selected target

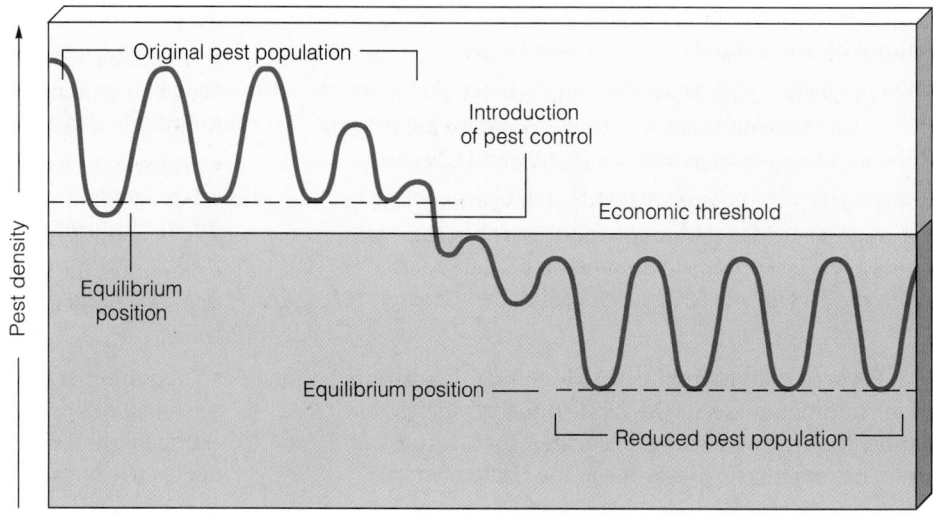

**Figure 20-6** According to environmentalists and many economists, the primary goal of any pest management strategy should be to keep each pest population just below the size at which it causes economic loss.

**Figure 20-7** The results of one example of using *genetic engineering* to reduce pest damage. Both tomato plants were exposed to destructive caterpillars. The normal plant's leaves are almost gone (left), whereas the genetically altered plant (right) shows little damage.

**Figure 20-9** Infestation of a steer by screwworm fly larvae in Texas. An adult steer can be killed in 10 days by thousands of maggots feeding on a single wound.

species, **(2)** is nontoxic to other species, **(3)** can save large amounts of money ($25 for every $1 invested in controlling 70 pests in the United States and $178 for each $1 invested by Nigerian farmers in using parasitic wasps to fight the cassava mealybug), and **(4)** minimizes genetic resistance. However, biological control agents **(1)** cannot always be mass produced, **(2)** often are slower acting and more difficult to apply than conventional pesticides, **(3)** must be protected from pesticides sprayed in nearby fields, and **(4)** can sometimes multiply and become pests themselves.

- *Insect birth control,* in which laboratory-raised males of insect pests are sterilized by radiation or chemicals and released into an infested area to mate unsuccessfully with fertile wild females. This has been used to control **(1)** the screwworm fly, a major livestock pest from the southeastern United States (Figure 20-9), and **(2)** the Mediterranean fruit fly (medfly) during a 1990 outbreak in California. Problems include **(1)** high

**Figure 20-10**
*Pheromones* can help control populations of pests, such as the red scale mites that have infested this lemon grown in Florida.

costs, **(2)** difficulties in knowing the mating times and behaviors of each target insect, **(3)** the large number of sterile males needed, **(4)** the few species for which this strategy works, and **(5)** the need to release sterile males continually to prevent pest resurgence.

- *Sex attractants.* Sex attractants (called *pheromones*) can lure pests into traps or attract their natural predators into crop fields (usually the more effective approach). These chemicals **(1)** attract only one species, **(2)** work in trace amounts, **(3)** have little chance of causing genetic resistance, and **(4)** are not harmful to nontarget species. However, it is costly and time consuming to identify, isolate, and produce the specific sex attractant for each pest or predator. More than 50 companies worldwide sell about 250 pheromones to control pests (Figure 20-10).

- *Hormones that disrupt an insect's normal life cycle* (Figure 20-11, p. 522), *causing the insect to fail to reach maturity and reproduce* (Figure 20-12, p. 522). Insect hormones have the same advantages as sex attractants. However, they **(1)** take weeks to kill an insect,

**Figure 20-8** *Biological pest control:* An adult convergent ladybug (right) is consuming an aphid (left).

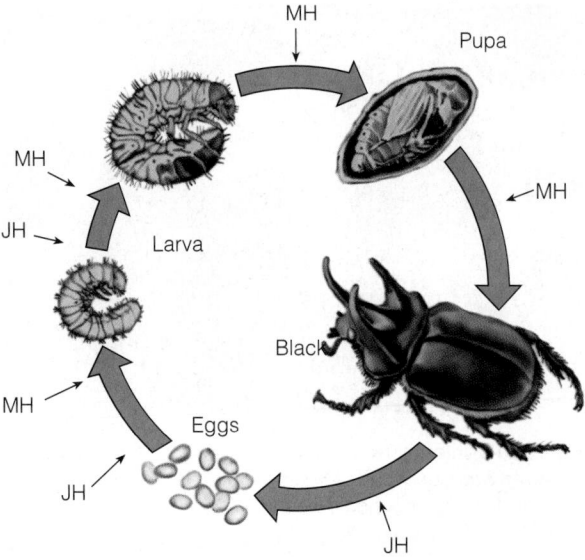

MH

Pupa

MH

MH

Larva

JH

MH

Black

MH

Eggs

JH

JH

**Figure 20-11** For normal insect growth, development, and reproduction to occur, certain juvenile hormones (JH) and molting hormones (MH) must be present at genetically determined stages in the insect's life cycle. If applied at the proper time, synthetic hormones disrupt the life cycles of insect pests and help control their populations.

**Figure 20-12** A use of hormones to prevent insects from maturing completely, making it impossible for them to reproduce. The stunted tobacco hornworm (left) was fed a compound that prevents production of molting hormones; a normal hornworm is shown on the right.

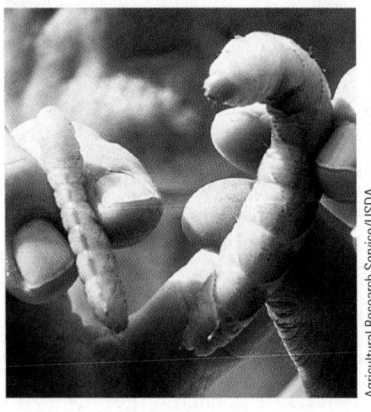

Agricultural Research Service/USDA

**(2)** often are ineffective with large infestations of insects, **(3)** sometimes break down before they can act, **(4)** must be applied at exactly the right time in the target insect's life cycle, **(5)** can sometimes affect the target's predators and other nonpest species, and **(6)** are difficult and costly to produce.

■ *Spraying insects with hot water.* This has worked well on cotton, alfalfa, and potato fields and in citrus groves in Florida. The cost is roughly equal to that of using chemical pesticides.

■ *Exposing foods to high-energy gamma radiation.* Such *food irradiation* extends food shelf life and kills **(1)** insects, **(2)** parasitic worms (such as trichinae in pork), and **(3)** bacteria (such as salmonella, which infects at least 51,000 Americans and kills 2,000 each year, and *E. coli*, which infects more than 20,000 Americans and kills about 250 each year). According

to the U.S. FDA and the WHO, more than 2,000 studies show that foods exposed to low doses of gamma radiation are safe for human consumption. Critics of food irradiation argue that **(1)** irradiating food forms trace amounts of certain chemicals called free radicals, some of which have caused cancer in laboratory animals, **(2)** we do not know the long-term health effects of eating irradiated food, **(3)** current levels of irradiation do not destroy botulinum spores, but they do destroy the bacteria that give off the rotten odor warning us of their presence, **(4)** consumers want fresh, wholesome food, not old, possibly less nutritious food made to appear fresh and healthy by irradiation, and they want clear labels on all irradiated food in order to make informed choices, and **(5)** food irradiation plants contain radioactive isotopes terrorists could steal and use to make dirty nuclear weapons (p. 373), and these plants are poorly protected.

### Is Integrated Pest Management the Answer?

An increasing number of pest control experts and farmers believe the best way to control crop pests is a carefully designed **integrated pest management (IPM)** program. In this approach, each crop and its pests are evaluated as parts of an ecological system. Then a control program is developed that includes cultivation, biological, and chemical methods applied in proper sequence and with the proper timing.

The overall aim of IPM is not to eradicate pest populations but to reduce crop damage to an economically tolerable level (Figure 20-6). Fields are monitored carefully, and when an economically damaging level of pests is reached, farmers first use biological methods (natural predators, parasites, and disease organisms) and cultivation controls, including vacuuming up harmful bugs. Small amounts of insecticides (mostly botanicals or microbotanicals; Table 20-1) **(1)** are applied only as a last resort and **(2)** different chemicals are used to slow development of genetic resistance and to avoid killing predators of pest species.

In 1986, the Indonesian government **(1)** banned the use of 57 of the 66 pesticides used on rice, **(2)** phased out pesticide subsidies over a 2-year period, and **(3)** used some of the money to help launch a nationwide program to switch to IPM, including a major farmer education program. The results were dramatic: Between 1987 and 1992, **(1)** pesticide use dropped by 65%, **(2)** rice production rose by 15%, and **(3)** more than 250,000 farmers were trained in IPM techniques. Norway and Sweden have imposed substantial taxes on pesticides, with the goal of cutting current pesticide use by 25–50%.

The experiences of countries such as China, Brazil, Indonesia, Australia, Bangladesh, the Philippines, Mexico, and the United States show that a well-designed IPM program can **(1)** reduce pesticide use and pest control costs by 50–90%, **(2)** reduce preharvest pest-induced crop losses by 50%, **(3)** improve crop yields, **(4)** reduce inputs of fertilizer and irrigation water, and **(5)** slow the development of genetic resistance because pests are assaulted less often and with lower doses of pesticides.

Thus IPM is an important form of *pollution prevention* that reduces risks to wildlife and human health. Consumers Union estimates that if all U.S. farmers practiced IPM by 2020, public health risks from pesticides would drop by 75%.

Despite its promise, IPM, like any other form of pest control, has some disadvantages: **(1)** It requires expert knowledge about each pest situation, **(2)** is slower acting than conventional pesticides, **(3)** methods developed for a crop in one area might not apply to areas with even slightly different growing conditions, and **(4)** initial costs may be higher, although long-term costs typically are lower than those of using conventional pesticides.

Another problem is that some IPM programs are not integrated. Instead, they use pesticide consultants to monitor crops only to determine when conventional pesticides should be used, without integrating the use of cultural and biological control programs. Critics say that these monitored pesticide management programs should not be called IPM programs.

Widespread use of IPM is hindered by **(1)** government subsidies of conventional chemical pesticides and **(2)** opposition from agricultural chemical companies, whose pesticide sales would drop sharply. In addition, farmers get most of their information about pest control from pesticide salespeople (and in the United States from USDA county farm agents). Most of these advisers do not have adequate training in IPM.

A 1996 study by the National Academy of Sciences recommended that the United States shift from chemically based approaches to ecologically based pest management approaches. A growing number of scientists urge the USDA to promote IPM in the United States by **(1)** adding a 2% sales tax on pesticides and using the revenue to fund IPM research and education, **(2)** setting up a federally supported IPM demonstration project on at least one farm in every county, **(3)** training USDA field personnel and county farm agents in IPM so they can help farmers use this alternative, **(4)** providing federal and state subsidies, and perhaps government-backed crop insurance, to farmers who use IPM or other approved alternatives to pesticides, and **(5)** gradually phasing out subsidies to farmers who depend almost entirely on pesticides as effective IPM methods are developed for major pest species. So far, pesticide company officials have been able to persuade elected officials not to enact such reforms. See the website material for this chapter for some actions you can take to reduce your use of and exposure to pesticides.

*We need to recognize that pest control is basically an ecological, not a chemical problem.*
ROBERT L. RUDD

## REVIEW QUESTIONS

**1.** Define the boldfaced terms in this chapter.

**2.** How can spiders help control insect pests?

**3.** What is a *pest*? How are species we consider pests controlled in nature? What happens to this natural pest control service when we simplify ecosystems? How have plants evolved to protect themselves from herbivores?

**4.** Distinguish among *insecticides, herbicides, fungicides, nematocides,* and *rodenticides.* Distinguish between *first-generation pesticides* and *second-generation pesticides* used by people to combat pests, and give two examples of each type. Distinguish between *broad-spectrum* and *narrow-spectrum* pesticides.

**5.** List seven benefits of relying on chemical pesticides. List five traits of the ideal pest-killing chemical.

**6.** Summarize the harmful effects of pesticides in terms of **(a)** development of genetic resistance among pests, **(b)** killing of natural predators and parasites that help control pest species, **(c)** creation of new pest species, **(d)** migration of pesticides into the environment, **(e)** effects on wildlife, and **(f)** effects on the health of pesticide and farm workers and the general public.

**7.** With respect to pesticides, what is the circle of poison? How might it affect you?

**8.** How are pesticides regulated in the United States? List major strengths and weaknesses in pesticide control laws. According to the U.S. National Academy of Sciences, what four things should be done to minimize the harmful effects of pesticides?

**9.** List six cultivation practices that can be used to help control pests. List the pros and cons of using the following pest control methods: **(a)** genetic engineering to speed up the development of pest- and disease-resistant crop strains, **(b)** biological control, **(c)** insect birth control through sterilization, **(d)** insect sex attractants, **(e)** insect hormones (pheromones), **(f)** food irradiation, and **(g)** integrated pest management (IPM).

## CRITICAL THINKING

**1.** Overall, do you think the benefits of chemical pesticides outweigh their disadvantages? Explain your position.

**2.** Should DDT and other pesticides be banned from use in malaria control efforts throughout the world? Explain. What are the alternatives?

**3.** Do you agree or disagree that because DDT and the other banned chlorinated hydrocarbon pesticides pose no demonstrable threat to human health and have saved millions of lives, they should again be approved for use in the United States? Explain.

**4.** If increased mosquito populations threatened you with malaria, would you spray DDT in your yard and inside your home to reduce the risk? Explain. What are the alternatives?

**5.** Explain how widespread use of a pesticide can **(a)** increase the damage done by a particular pest and **(b)** create new pest organisms.

**6.** Explain why biological pest control often is more successful on a small island than on a continent.

**7.** Do you believe farmers should be given economic incentives for switching to integrated pest management (IPM)? Explain your position.

**8.** Should certain types of foods be irradiated to help control disease organisms and increase shelf life? Explain. If so, should such foods be required to carry a clear label stating that they have been irradiated? Explain.

**9.** What changes, if any, do you believe should be made in the Federal Insecticide, Fungicide, and Rodenticide Act and the Food Quality Protection Act that regulate pesticide use in the United States?

**10.** Congratulations! You have been placed in charge of pest control for the entire world. What are the three most important components of your global pest control strategy?

## PROJECTS

**1.** How are bugs and weeds controlled in **(a)** your yard and garden, **(b)** the grounds of your school, and **(c)** public school grounds, parks, and playgrounds in your community?

**2.** Make a survey of all pesticides used in or around your home. Compare the results for your entire class.

**3.** Some research shows that although many people agree we need to make greater use of alternatives to conventional pesticides for controlling pests, when they are faced with an actual infestation from insects or rodents the first thing they do is spray with pesticides. Survey members of your class and other groups to help determine the validity of these research findings.

**4.** Use the library or the Internet to find bibliographic information about *Ralph Waldo Emerson* and *Robert L. Rudd,* whose quotes appear at the beginning and end of this chapter.

**5.** Make a concept map of this chapter's major ideas, using the section heads and subheads and the key terms (in boldface). Look at the website for this book for information about making concept maps.

## INTERNET STUDY RESOURCES AND RESOURCES FOR FURTHER READING AND RESEARCH

The website for this book contains helpful study aids and many ideas for further reading and research. Log on to

www.info.brookscole.com/miller13

and click on the Chapter-by-Chapter area. Choose Chapter 20 and select a resource:

- Flash Cards allows you to test your mastery of the Terms and Concepts to Remember for this chapter.
- Tutorial Quizzes provides a multiple-choice practice quiz.
- Student Guide to InfoTrac will lead you to Critical Thinking Projects that use InfoTrac College Edition as a research tool.
- References lists the major books and articles consulted in writing this chapter.
- Hypercontents takes you to an extensive list of sites with news, research, and images related to individual sections of the chapter.

## INFOTRAC COLLEGE EDITION

Improve your skills with InfoTrac College Edition, a searchable online database of articles from more than 700 periodicals. Log on to

http://www.infotrac-college.com

or access InfoTrac through the website for this book. Try to find the following articles:

**1.** Davis, S. 2002. Insect communication discovery could lead to new pesticides. (Brief article) *Pesticide and Toxic Chemical News* 30: 9. *Keywords:* "insect communication" and "pesticides." A new generation of pheromone-blocking pesticides may mean more and environmentally safer target-specific insecticides.

**2.** Brown, V. J. 2001. Old pesticides pose new problems for developing world. *Environmental Health Perspectives* 109: 578. *Keyword:* "old pesticides." Developed nations have at least some control over banned and controlled stockpiles of pesticides. But in developing countries where these materials have been exported and used, dealing with old stocks of pesticides is much more difficult.

# 21 SOLID AND HAZARDOUS WASTE

## There Is No "Away": Love Canal

Between 1942 and 1953, Hooker Chemicals and Plastics (owned by OxyChem since 1968) **(1)** sealed chemical wastes containing at least 200 different chemicals into steel drums and **(2)** dumped them into an old canal excavation (called Love Canal after its builder, William Love) near Niagara Falls, New York.

In 1953, Hooker Chemicals filled the canal, covered it with clay and topsoil, and sold it to the Niagara Falls school board for $1. In the deed the company inserted a disclaimer denying legal liability for any injury caused by the wastes. In 1957, Hooker warned the school board not to disturb the clay cap because of the possible danger from toxic wastes.

By 1959, an elementary school, playing fields, and 949 homes had been built in the 10-square-block Love Canal area (Figure 21-1). Some of the roads and sewer lines crisscrossing the dump site disrupted the clay cap covering the wastes. In the 1960s, an expressway was built at one end of the dump. It blocked groundwater from migrating to the Niagara River and allowed contaminated groundwater and rainwater to build up and overflow the disrupted cap.

Residents began complaining to city officials in 1976 about chemical smells and chemical burns their children received playing in the canal area, but their concerns were ignored. In 1977, chemicals began leaking from the badly corroded steel drums into storm sewers, gardens, basements of homes next to the canal, and the school playground.

In 1978, after media publicity and pressure from residents led by Lois Gibbs (a mother galvanized into action as she watched her children come down with one illness after another; Guest Essay, p. 530), the state acted. It closed the school and arranged for the 239 homes closest to the dump to be evacuated, purchased, and destroyed.

Two years later, after protests from families still living fairly close to the landfill, President Jimmy Carter **(1)** declared Love Canal a federal disaster area, **(2)** had the remaining families relocated, and **(3)** offered federal funds to buy 564 more homes. Residents of all but 72 of the homes moved out. Some residents who remained claim that the other residents, environmentalists, and the media exaggerated the problem.

After more than 15 years of court cases, OxyChem agreed in 1994 to **(1)** pay a $98 million settlement to New York State and **(2)** take responsibility for all future treatment of wastes and wastewater at the Love Canal site. In 1999, the company also agreed to reimburse the federal government and New York State $7.1 million for the Love Canal cleanup.

Because of the difficulty in linking exposure to a variety of chemicals to specific health effects (Section 11-2, p. 229), the long-term health effects of exposure to hazardous chemicals on Love Canal residents remain unknown and controversial. However, for the rest of their lives the evacuated families will worry about the possible effects of the chemicals on themselves and their children and grandchildren.

The dump site has been covered with a new clay cap and surrounded by a drainage system that pumps leaking wastes to a new treatment plant. In June 1990, the U.S. Environmental Protection Agency (EPA) allowed state officials to begin selling 234 of the remaining houses in the area (renamed Black Creek Village) at 10–20% below market value. Most of the houses have been sold. Buyers must sign an agreement stating that New York State and the federal government make no guarantees or representations about the safety of living in these homes.

The Love Canal incident is a vivid reminder that **(1)** we can never really throw anything away, **(2)** wastes often do not stay put, and **(3)** preventing pollution is much safer and cheaper than trying to clean it up.

New York State Department of Environmental Conservation

**Figure 21-1** The Love Canal housing development near Niagara Falls, New York, was built near a hazardous waste dump site. The photo shows the area when it was abandoned in 1980. In 1990, the EPA allowed people to buy some of the remaining houses and move back into the area.

*Solid wastes are only raw materials we're too stupid to use.*
ARTHUR C. CLARKE

This chapter addresses the following questions:

- What are solid waste and hazardous waste, and how much of each type do we produce?
- What can we do to reduce, reuse, and recycle solid waste and hazardous waste?
- What are we doing to recycle aluminum, paper, and plastics?
- What are the advantages and disadvantages of burning or burying wastes?
- What can we do to reduce exposure to lead, mercury, hazardous chlorine compounds, and dioxins?
- How is hazardous waste regulated in the United States?
- How can we make the transition to a more sustainable low-waste society?

## 21-1 WASTING RESOURCES

**What Is Solid Waste, and How Much Is Produced?** The United States, with only 4.6% of the world's population, produces about 33% of the world's **solid waste:** any unwanted or discarded material that is not a liquid or a gas. About 98.5% of this solid waste comes from mining (Case Study, p. 527), oil and natural gas production, agriculture, sewage sludge, and industrial activities (Figure 21-2).

The remaining 1.5% of solid waste produced in the United States is **municipal solid waste (MSW)** from homes and businesses in or near urban areas. The amount of MSW, often called *garbage*, produced in the United States each year comes to about 200 million metric tons (506 billion pounds)—almost twice as

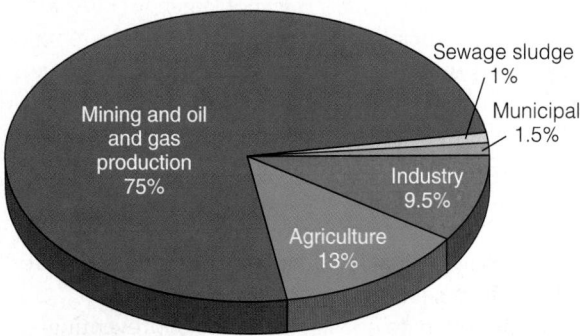

**Figure 21-2** Sources of the estimated 11 billion metric tons (12 billion tons) of solid waste produced each year in the United States. Mining, oil and gas production, agricultural, and industrial activities produce 55 times as much solid waste as household activities. (Data from U.S. Environmental Protection Agency and U.S. Bureau of Mines)

much as in 1970. Each year this is enough waste to fill a bumper-to-bumper convoy of garbage trucks encircling the globe almost eight times.

The annual MSW amounts to an average of 770 kilograms (1,700 pounds) per person in the United States, the world's highest per capita solid waste production. About 54% of this MSW is dumped in landfills, 30% is recycled or composted, and 16% is burned in incinerators.

**What Does It Mean to Live in a High-Waste Society?** Here are a few of the solid wastes U.S. consumers throw away:

- Enough aluminum to rebuild the country's entire commercial airline fleet every 3 months
- Enough tires each year to encircle the planet almost three times
- About 18 billion disposable diapers per year, which if linked end to end would reach to the moon and back seven times
- About 2 billion disposable razors, 30 million cell phones, 18 million computers, and 8 million television sets each year
- Some 8.6 million metric tons (17 billion pounds) per year of polystyrene peanuts used to protect shipped items
- Used carpet each year that would cover 7,800 square kilometers (3,000 square miles)—more than enough to carpet the state of Delaware
- About 1.7 billion metric tons (3.7 trillion pounds) per year of construction waste per year—an average of 6 metric tons (13,200 pounds) per American
- About 2.5 million nonreturnable plastic bottles every hour
- About 670,000 metric tons (1.5 billion pounds) of edible food per year
- Enough office paper each year to build a 3.5-meter (11-foot) high wall from New York City to San Francisco, California
- Some 186 billion pieces of junk mail (an average of 646 per American) each year, about 45% of which are thrown in the trash unopened

According to the EPA, *electronic waste (e-waste)*—primarily cell phones, computers, and TV sets—is the fastest growing solid waste problem in the United States and the world. E-waste is also a source of toxic and hazardous wastes (such as lead-, mercury-, cadmium-, and bromine-containing compounds that can contaminate the air, surface water, groundwater, and soil.

**What Is Hazardous Waste, and How Much Is Produced?** In the United States, **hazardous waste**

## Mining and Smelting Waste in Montana

Environmental laws passed since the 1970s require mining companies and metal smelters operating in the United States to **(1)** reduce their inputs of air and water into the environment and **(2)** stabilize the mining wastes they produce. These changes have helped, but mining still produces large quantities of solid waste and pollutants (p. 341 and Case Study, p. 345).

Mining and smelting operations before these laws were enacted produced a legacy of toxic waste sites. The largest complex of such sites consists of a huge copper mine near Butte, Montana, and a large copper smelter in Anaconda, Montana. Mining began in Butte in the 1800s and continued at a high rate until the early 1900s.

Typically, the ore extracted contained as little as 0.3% by weight

copper. The remaining 99.7% of the rock that was waste was left in piles near the mine mouths and smelters. Today, the Butte-Anaconda area has about 25 square kilometers (10 square miles) of mine spoils and smelter wastes in piles averaging about 15 meters (49 feet) high—about as tall as a five-story building.

Acid wastes (Figure 15-7, p. 344) and toxic metals from these piles have polluted the area's soils, groundwater, and streams and killed aquatic life and stunted plant growth. Wind-blown dust from these spoils and smelter wastes has contaminated entire counties with toxic metal dust.

In the 1980s, arsenic levels in wells in Miltown, a small town on the Clark Fork River about 200 kilometers (120 miles) downstream from Butte, were so high that town officials closed all wells

and had to build an expensive alternative drinking water system. A partial cleanup costing hundreds of millions of dollars is under way. According to the Clark Fork Foundation, a local environmental organization, it will take about $1 billion to fully clean up the Butte mine site, the Anaconda smelter site, and the Clark Fork drainage basin.

Similar toxic legacies from mining are being created in many of the world's developing countries where there are few or poorly enforced environmental regulations.

### Critical Thinking

Should mining and smelting companies or U.S. taxpayers be responsible for cleaning up wastes from mines and smelters that were operating before stricter environmental laws were enacted in the 1970s? Explain.

---

is legally defined as any discarded solid or liquid material that **(1)** contains one or more of 39 toxic, carcinogenic, mutagenic, or teratogenic compounds (Section 11-3, p. 233) at levels that exceed established limits (including many solvents, pesticides, and paint strippers), **(2)** catches fire easily (gasoline, paints, and solvents), **(3)** is reactive or unstable enough to explode or release toxic fumes (acids, bases, ammonia, chlorine bleach), or **(4)** is capable of corroding metal containers such as tanks, drums, and barrels (industrial cleaning agents and oven and drain cleaners).

This official definition of hazardous wastes (mandated by Congress) does *not* include the following materials: **(1)** radioactive wastes (p. 370), **(2)** hazardous and toxic materials discarded by households (Table 21-1), **(3)** mining wastes (Case Study, above),

| Table 21-1 Common Household Toxic and Hazardous Materials | |
|---|---|
| **Cleaning Products** | **Automotive Products** |
| Disinfectants | Gasoline |
| Drain, toilet, and window cleaners | Used motor oil |
| Oven cleaners | Antifreeze |
| Bleach and ammonia | Battery acid |
| Cleaning solvents and spot removers | Solvents |
| Septic tank cleaners | Brake and transmission fluid |
| **Paint and Building Products** | Rust inhibitor and rust remover |
| Latex and oil-based paints | **General Products** |
| Paint thinners, solvents, and strippers | Dry cell batteries (mercury and cadmium) |
| Stains, varnishes, and lacquers | Artists' paints and inks |
| Wood preservatives | Glues and cements |
| Acids for etching and rust removal | Computers and TV sets (cadmium, lead, mercury, and chlorinated and bromiated chemicals) |
| Asphalt and roof tar | |
| **Gardening and Pest Control Products** | Printer toner cartridges (mercury, cobalt, and nickel) |
| Pesticide sprays and dusts | |
| Weed killers | |
| Ant and rodent killers | |
| Flea powder | |

## A Black Day in Bhopal

December 2, 1984, will long be a black day for India because on that date the world's worst industrial accident occurred at a Union Carbide pesticide plant in Bhopal, India.

Some 36 metric tons (40 tons) of highly toxic methyl isocyanate (MIC) gas, used to produce carbamate pesticides, erupted from an underground storage tank after water leaked in through faulty valves and corroded pipes and caused an explosive chemical reaction. Once in the atmosphere, some of the toxic MIC was converted to even more deadly hydrogen cyanide gas.

The toxic cloud of gas settled over about 78 square kilometers (30 square miles), exposing up to 600,000 people. Many of these people were illegal squatters living near the plant because they had no other place to go. Since the safety sirens at the plant had been turned off, the deadly cloud spread through Bhopal without warning.

Eyes, mouths, and lungs burned. Some victims tried to flee through the narrow streets but many were trampled. Others drowned in their own bodily fluids from exposure to the toxic gas. Many of the old, infirm, and very young died in their sleep.

According to Indian officials, at least 6,000 people (some say 7,000–16,000, based on the sales of shrouds and cremation wood) were killed. An international team of medical specialists (the International Medical Commission on Bhopal) estimated in 1996 that 50,000–60,000 people sustained permanent injuries such as blindness, lung damage, and neurological problems.

The economic damage from the accident was estimated at $4.1 billion. Indian officials claim that Union Carbide probably could have prevented the tragedy by spending no more than $1 million to upgrade plant equipment and improve safety. According to Indian officials the already substandard plant was in the middle of a cost-cutting campaign. Management was reducing the number of workers, reducing training time for machine operators, and skimping on safety measures.

On the night of the disaster, six safety measures designed to prevent a leak of toxic materials were inadequate, shut down, or malfunctioning. However, Union Carbide officials contend that the accident was not caused by faulty equipment but was the result of sabotage by a disgruntled Indian employee.

After the accident, Union Carbide reduced the corporation's liability risks for compensating victims by selling off a portion of its assets and giving much of the profits to its shareholders in the form of special dividends. In 1994, Union Carbide sold its holdings in India.

In 1989, Union Carbide agreed to pay an out-of-court settlement of $470 million to compensate the victims without admitting any guilt or negligence concerning the accident. The company also spent $100 million to build a hospital for the victims. By 2000, most victims with injuries had received $600 in compensation, and families of victims who died had received less than $3,000.

On December 2, 1999—the 15th anniversary of the disaster—survivors and families of people killed by the accident filed a lawsuit in a New York U.S. district court charging the Union Carbide Company and its former chief executive officer with violating international law and the fundamental human rights of the victims and survivors of the Bhopal plant accident.

The lawsuit alleges (1) that Union Carbide "demonstrated a reckless and depraved indifference to human life in the design, operation, and maintenance" of the Union Carbide facility in Bhopal and (2) "that the defendants are liable for fraud and civil contempt for their total failure to comply with the lawful orders of the courts of both the United States and India."

### Critical Thinking

Why do you think Union Carbide's stock price rose after the company agreed to pay a $470 million out-of-court settlement to compensate the victims of the Bhopal accident?

---

(4) oil- and gas-drilling wastes (routinely discharged into surface waters or dumped into unlined pits and landfills), (5) liquid waste containing organic hydrocarbon compounds (80% of all liquid hazardous waste), (6) cement kiln dust, produced when liquid hazardous wastes are burned in a cement kiln, and (7) wastes from the thousands of small businesses and factories that generate less than 100 kilograms (220 pounds) of hazardous waste per month.

As a result, *hazardous waste laws do not regulate 95% of the country's hazardous waste.* In most other countries, especially developing countries, even less, if any, of the hazardous waste is regulated.

Including all categories, the EPA estimates that at least 5.5 billion metric tons (12 trillion pounds) of hazardous waste are produced each year in the United States—an average of 19 metric tons (42,000 pounds) per person. This amounts to about 75% of the world's hazardous waste.

**What Is the Threat from Release of Toxic Chemicals from Industrial Plants Because of Acci-**

**dents or Terrorism?** Plants that manufacture and use chemicals are complex facilities that need constant monitoring and maintenance to prevent accidental release of toxic or hazardous chemicals. Managers of industrial facilities work hard to prevent accidental release of chemicals that can harm workers or nearby residents. But accidents can happen, as thousands of people living near a pesticide manufacturing plant in Bhopal, India, learned in 1984 (Case Study, left).

Since the 2001 act of terrorism on New York City's World Trade Center Towers there has been heightened concern about acts of terrorism against industrial plants containing large quantities of hazardous chemicals. Analysts view such plants as easy targets for bombing or acts of sabotage by terrorists.

The more than 20,000 such plants in the United States are not nearly as secure as nuclear power plants, which could also be targets for terrorists (p. 368). A 1999 government study found that chemical plant security ranged from "fair to very poor." Several hundred chemical plants have filed risk-management plans indicating that a worst-case terrorist act at their sites could spread toxic chemicals as far away as 23 kilometers (14 miles) or more.

## 21-2 PRODUCING LESS WASTE AND POLLUTION

**What Are Our Options?** Here are two ways to deal with the solid and hazardous waste we create:

■ *Waste management:* a *high-waste approach* (Figure 3-20, p. 60) that views waste production as an unavoidable product of economic growth. It attempts to manage the resulting wastes in ways that reduce environmental harm, mostly by **(1)** burying them, **(2)** burning them, or **(3)** shipping them off to another state or country. In effect, it transfers solid and hazardous waste from one part of the environment to another.

■ *Waste and pollution prevention:* a *low-waste approach* that recognizes there is no "away" and views most solid and hazardous waste either **(1)** as potential resources (that we should be recycling, composting, or reusing) or **(2)** as harmful substances that we should not be using in the first place (Figure 3-21, p. 61, and Figures 21-3 and 21-4, p. 530). This approach focuses on discouraging waste production and encouraging waste reduction and prevention (Guest Essay, p. 530).

Scientists estimate that in a low-waste society, 60–80% of the solid and hazardous waste produced could be eliminated through *reduction, reuse, recycling* (including composting), and *redesign* of manufacturing processes and buildings. Currently, the order of priorities shown in Figures 21-3 and 21-4 for dealing with solid and hazardous wastes is reversed in the United States (and in most other countries).

**Solutions: How Can We Reduce Waste and Pollution?** Here are some ways to reduce resource use, waste, and pollution:

■ *Consume less.* Before buying anything, ask questions such as **(1)** Do I really need this? **(2)** Can I buy it secondhand? and **(3)** Can I borrow or lease it?

■ *Redesign manufacturing processes and products to use less material and energy* (Solutions, p. 533).

**1st Priority**

**Primary Pollution and Waste Prevention**
• Change industrial process to eliminate use of harmful chemicals
• Purchase different products
• Use less of a harmful product
• Reduce packaging and materials in products
• Make products that last longer and are recyclable, reusable, or easy to repair

**2nd Priority**

**Secondary Pollution and Waste Prevention**
• Reuse products
• Repair products
• Recycle
• Compost
• Buy reusable and recyclable products

**Last Priority**

**Waste Management**
• Treat waste to reduce toxicity
• Incinerate waste
• Bury waste in landfills
• Release waste into environment for dispersal or dilution

**Figure 21-3** *Solutions:* priorities suggested by prominent scientists for dealing with material use and solid waste. To date, these waste-reduction priorities have not been followed in the United States (and in most other countries). Instead, most efforts are devoted to waste management (bury it or burn it). (U.S. Environmental Protection Agency and U.S. National Academy of Sciences)

## We Have Been Asking the Wrong Questions About Wastes

**GUEST ESSAY**

*Lois Marie Gibbs*

*In 1977, Lois Marie Gibbs was a young housewife with two children living near the Love Canal toxic dump site. She had never engaged in any sort of political action until her children began experiencing unexplained illnesses and she learned that toxic chemicals were oozing from the dump site into many of the area's yards and basements. Then she organized her neighborhood and became the president and major strategist for the Love Canal Homeowners Association. This grassroots political action brought hazardous waste issues to national prominence and spurred passage of the federal Superfund legislation to help clean up abandoned hazardous waste sites. Lois Gibbs then moved to Washington, D.C., and formed Citizens' Clearinghouse for Hazardous Wastes (renamed the Center for Health, Environment, and Justice), an organization that has helped more than 7,000 community organizations protect themselves from hazardous wastes. Her story is told in her autobiography,* Love Canal: My Story *(SUNY Press, 1982). She was also the subject of a CBS movie,* Lois Gibbs: The Love Canal, *which aired in 1982. Her latest book is* Dying from Dioxin *(Boston: South End Press, 1995).*

Just about everyone knows our environment is in danger. One of the most serious threats is the massive amount of waste we put into the air, water, and ground every year. All across the United States and around the world are thousands of places that have been, and continue to be, polluted by toxic chemicals, radioactive waste, and just plain garbage.

For generations, the main question people have asked is, "Where do we put all this waste? It's got to go somewhere." That is the wrong question, as has been shown by a series of experiments in waste disposal and by the simple fact that there is no "away" in "throwaway."

We tried dumping our waste in the oceans. That does not work. We tried injecting it into deep, underground wells. That does not work. We've been trying to build landfills that do not leak, but according to the EPA all landfills eventually leak. We've been trying to get rid of waste by burning it in high-tech incinerators; that only produces different types of pollution, such as air pollution and toxic ash. Even recycling, which is a very good thing to do, suffers from the same problem as all the other methods: It addresses waste *after* it has been produced.

For many years, people have been assuming, "It's got to go somewhere," but now many people, especially young people, are starting to ask why. Why do we produce so much waste? Why do we need products and services that have so many toxic by-products? Why can't industry change the way it makes things so that it stops producing so much waste?

When you start asking these questions, you start getting answers that lead to *pollution prevention* and *waste reduction* instead of *pollution control* and *waste management.* People, young and old, who care about pollution prevention are challenging companies to stop making products with gases that reduce ozone in the ozone layer [Section 18-8, p. 472] and contribute to the threatening possibility of global warming [Section 18-5, p. 460]. They are asking why so many goods are wrapped in excessive, throwaway packaging. They are challenging com-

■ *Redesign manufacturing processes to produce less waste and pollution.* Most toxic organic solvents can be recycled within plants or replaced with water-based or citrus-based solvents (Individuals Matter, p. 479). Hydrogen peroxide can be used instead of toxic chlorine to bleach paper and other materials. A $CO_2$-based process can replace dry cleaning with toxic organic solvents such as perchloroethylene (PERC).

■ *Develop products that are easy to repair, reuse, remanufacture, compost, or recycle.* Xerox's latest

**Produce Less Waste**

- Manipulate processes to eliminate or reduce production
- Recycle and reuse

**Convert to Less Hazardous or Nonhazardous Substances**

- Land treatment
- Incineration
- Thermal treatment
- Chemical, physical, and biological treatment
- Ocean and atmospheric assimilation

**Put in Perpetual Storage**

- Landfill
- Underground injection
- Waste piles
- Surface impoundments
- Salt formations
- Arid region unsaturated zone

**Figure 21-4** Solutions: priorities suggested by prominent scientists for dealing with hazardous waste. To date, these priorities have not been followed in the United States (and in most other countries). (U.S. National Academy of Sciences) panies that sell pesticides, cleaning fluids, batteries, and other hazardous products to either remove the toxins from those products or take them back for recovery or recycling rather than disposing of them in the environment. They are demanding alternatives to throwaway materials in general.

Since 1988, hundreds of student groups have contacted my organization to get help and advice in taking these effective types of actions. Oregon students took legal action to get rid of cups and plates made from bleached paper because the paper contains the deadly poison dioxin. As a result the school systems switched to reusable cups, plates, and utensils.

Dozens of student groups have joined with local grassroots organizations to get toxic-waste sites cleaned up or to stop construction of new toxic-waste sites, radioactive-waste sites, or waste incinerators.

Waste issues are not simply environmental issues; they are also tied up with our economy, which is geared to producing and then disposing of waste. *Somebody* is making money from every scrap of waste and has a vested interest in keeping things the way they are.

Waste issues are also issues of *justice* and *fairness.* There is a lot of debate between industry officials and environmentalists, especially those in federal and state environmental agencies, about so-called acceptable risk [Section 11-5, p. 245]. These industry officials and environmentalists decide the degree of people's exposure to toxic chemicals but do not ask the people who will actually be exposed how they feel about it.

Risk analysts often say, "There's only a one in a million chance of increased death from this toxic chemical." That may be true, but suppose I took a pistol and went to the edge of your neighborhood and began shooting into it. There's probably only a one in a million chance that I'd hit somebody, but would you issue me a license to do that?

As long as we do not stand up for our rights and demand that "bullets" in the form of hazardous chemicals not be "fired" in our neighborhoods, we are giving environmental regulators and waste producers a license to kill a certain number of us without our even being consulted.

From my personal experience, I know that decisions made to dump wastes at Love Canal [p. 525] and in thousands of other places were not made purely on the basis of the best available scientific knowledge. The same holds true for decisions about how to manage the wastes we produce today and how to produce less waste.

We live in a world that is shaped by decisions based on money and power. If you really want to understand what's behind any given environmental issue, the first question you should ask is, "Who stands to profit from this?" Then ask, "Who is going to pay the price?" You can then identify both sides of the issue and decide whether you want to be part of the problem or part of the solution.

### Critical Thinking

**1.** Do you believe we should put primary emphasis on pollution prevention and waste reduction? Explain.

**2.** What changes would you be willing to make in your own lifestyle to prevent pollution and reduce waste?

photocopier, with every part reusable or recyclable for easy remanufacturing, should eventually save the company $1 billion in manufacturing costs. In the United States, remanufacturing is a rapidly growing $53 billion per year business with 73,000 different firms employing some 480,000 people—double the number of jobs in the U.S. steel industry.

■ *Design products to last longer.* Today's tires have an average life of 97,000 kilometers (60,000 miles), but researchers believe this use could be extended to at least 160,000 kilometers (100,000 miles).

■ *Eliminate or reduce unnecessary packaging.* Here are some key questions designers, manufacturers, and consumers should ask about packaging: **(1)** Is it necessary? **(2)** Can it use fewer materials? **(3)** Can it be reused? **(4)** Are the resources that went into it nonrenewable or renewable? **(5)** Does it contain the highest feasible amount of consumer-discarded (post-consumer) recycled material? **(6)** Is it designed to be recycled easily? **(7)** Can it be incinerated without producing harmful air pollutants or a toxic ash? **(8)** Can it

be buried and decomposed in a landfill without producing chemicals that can contaminate groundwater?

■ *Use trash taxes* to reduce waste, and use the revenues to reduce taxes on income and wealth as a number of European countries have done. A related *pay-as-you-throw* system reduces solid waste and encourages recycling by basing garbage collection charges on the amount of waste a household or business generates for disposal.

## 21-3 SOLUTIONS: CLEANER PRODUCTION AND SELLING SERVICES INSTEAD OF THINGS

**What Is the Ecoindustrial Revolution, and What Are Its Benefits?** Some analysts urge us to bring about an *ecoindustrial revolution* over the next 50 years as a way to help achieve industrial, economic, and environmental sustainability. This transition would be built around the emerging concept of *cleaner production*

(Guest Essay, p. 536), or *industrial ecology.* In this approach, all industrial manufacturing processes would be designed as **(1)** essentially closed systems of cyclical material flows (Figure 3-21, p. 61) or **(2)** networks in which the wastes of one manufacturer become raw materials for another.

In effect, companies producing goods would **(1)** mimic natural chemical cycles (Section 4-6, p. 82) and **(2)** interact in complex *resource exchange webs* similar to food webs in natural ecosystems. A prototype of this industrial ecosystem concept exists in Kalundborg, Denmark, where an electric power plant and a number of nearby industries, farms, and homes are working together to save money by exchanging and converting their wastes into resources for one another (Figure 21-5). Today more than 25 eco-industrial parks similar to the one in Kalundborg are being developed around the world.

In addition to eliminating most waste and pollution, these industrial forms of *biomimicry* provide economic benefits to businesses by

- Reducing the costs of controlling pollution and complying with pollution regulations.

- Improving the health and safety of workers by reducing exposure to toxic and hazardous material (and thus reducing company health-care insurance costs).

- Reducing future legal liability for toxic and hazardous wastes.

- Stimulating companies to come up with new, environmentally beneficial chemicals, processes, and products that can be sold worldwide.

- Giving companies a better image among consumers based on results rather than on public relations campaigns.

In 1975, the Minnesota Mining and Manufacturing Company (3M), which makes 60,000 different products in 100 manufacturing plants, began a Pollution Prevention Pays (3P) program. It **(1)** redesigned equipment and processes, **(2)** used fewer hazardous raw materials, **(3)** identified hazardous chemical outputs (and recycled or sold them as raw materials to other companies), and **(4)** began making more nonpolluting products.

By 1998, **(1)** 3M's overall waste production was down by one-third, **(2)** its air pollutant emissions per

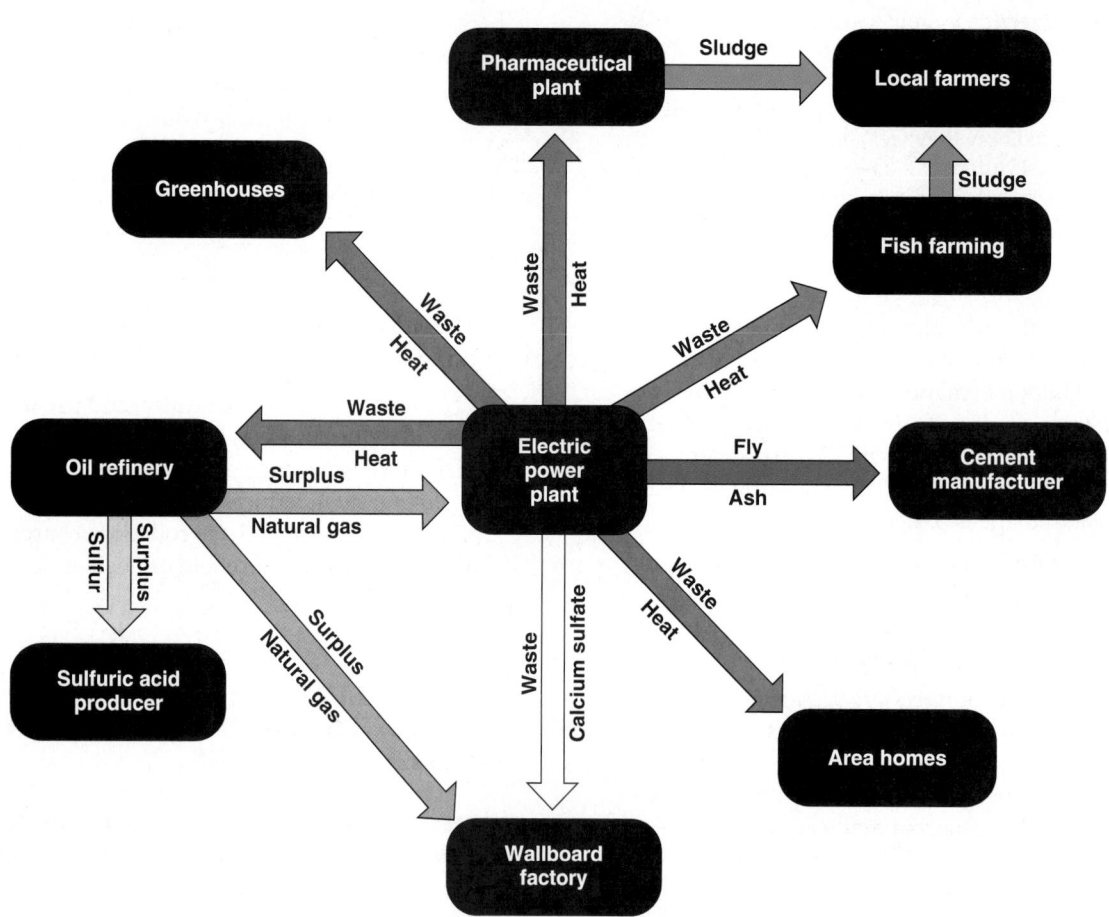

**Figure 21-5** *Industrial ecosystem* in Kalundborg, Denmark, reduces waste production by mimicking a natural food web by having the wastes of one business become the raw materials for another business.

# Doing More with Less: Increasing Resource Productivity

During the last few decades, a *design revolution* has allowed businesses to use less material and energy per unit of goods and services. This has been done mostly by **(1)** finding substitutes for products that use less material and **(2)** redesigning or improving products so they take less material and energy to produce.

Paper documents such as product catalogs, phone directories, technical reference manuals, and parts directories can be accessed on CD-ROMs, DVD-ROMs, or at various Internet sites, saving millions of dollars and tons of paper. All the phone books in the United States can be put on about three CD-ROMs, and a single DVD-ROM could hold all the world's phone numbers.

A skyscraper built today includes about 35% less steel than the same building built in the 1960s because of the use of lighter-weight but higher-strength steel. Use of such steel and replacement of many steel parts with lightweight plastics and composite materials has **(1)** reduced the weight of cars by about 25% without compromising performance and safety, **(2)** increased fuel efficiency, and **(3)** reduced the average weight per unit of appliances such as stoves, washers, dryers, air conditioners, TV sets, and computers.

Since the mid-1970s, **(1)** the thickness of plastic grocery bags has been reduced by 70% without sacrificing strength, **(2)** plastic milk jugs weigh 40% less, **(3)** aluminum drink cans contain one-third less aluminum, **(4)** steel cans are 60% lighter, **(5)** disposable diapers contain 50% less paper pulp, and **(6)** plastic frozen food bags weigh 89% less.

These improvements in resource productivity are important, but according to some analysts they can be greatly increased through a new *resource productivity revolution*. In their 1999 book *Natural Capitalism,* Paul Hawken (Guest Essay, p. 16), Amory Lovins (Guest Essay, p. 384), and Hunter Lovins contend we have the knowledge and technology to greatly increase *resource productivity* by getting 75–90% more work or service from each unit of material resources we use.

To these analysts, the only major impediments to such an economic and ecological revolution are laws, policies, taxes, and subsidies that **(1)** continue to reward inefficient resource use and **(2)** fail to reward efficient resource use.

## Critical Thinking

Do you believe it is possible to decrease resource waste by 75–90% within the next 20 years? Explain. What might be some disadvantages of making such a shift? Do you believe such disadvantages outweigh the advantages? Explain.

---

unit of production were reduced by 70%, and **(3)** the company had saved more than $750 million in waste disposal and material costs. Since 1990, a growing number of companies have adopted similar pollution prevention programs. For example, between 1992 and 2002 Xerox saved $2 billion through reuse, recycling, and elimination of hazardous materials from its products.

**What Is a Service Flow Economy, and What Are Its Advantages?** In the mid-1980s, German chemist Michael Braungart and Swiss industry analyst Walter Stahel independently proposed a new economic model that would provide profits while greatly reducing resource use and waste. Their idea involves shifting from our current *material flow economy* (Figure 3-20, p. 60) to a *service flow economy* over the next few decades. Instead of buying most goods outright, customers would lease or rent the *services* such goods provide.

With such a service flow or product stewardship economy, a product produced by a manufacturer remains as an asset that yields more profit if it **(1)** uses the minimum amount of materials, **(2)** lasts as long as possible, **(3)** is easy to maintain, repair, remanufacture, reuse, or recycle, and **(4)** provides customers with the services they want instead of trying to keep selling them newer models of outmoded products.

This economic shift is under way:

- Since 1992, the Xerox Corporation has been leasing most of its copy machines as part of its mission to provide *document services* instead of selling photocopiers. When the service contract expires, Xerox takes the machine back for reuse or remanufacture and has a goal of sending no material to landfills or incinerators. To save money, machines are designed to **(1)** use recycled paper, **(2)** have few parts, **(3)** be energy efficient, and **(4)** emit as little noise, heat, ozone, and copier chemicals as possible.

- Ray Anderson, CEO of a large carpet tile company, plans to lease rather than sell carpet (Individuals Matter, p. 534).

- For years, 160 firms, called *chauffagistes,* have been providing 10 million buildings in metropolitan France with heat. These firms provide *warmth services* by contracting to keep a client's space within a specified temperature during certain hours at a designated cost.

- Carrier, the world's leading maker of air conditioning equipment, now sells leases to provide its customers with *cooling services*. Carrier also teams up with other service providers to install super-efficient windows and more efficient lighting and make other energy-efficiency upgrades that reduce the cooling needs of its customers. Carrier makes money by

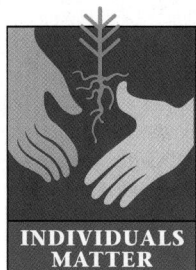
## Ray Anderson

Ray Anderson (see figure) is CEO of Interface, a company based in in Atlanta, Georgia, that makes carpet tiles. The company is the world's largest commercial carpet manufacturer with 26 factories in 6 countries, customers in 110 countries, and more than $1 billion in annual sales.

Anderson changed the way he viewed the world and his business after reading Paul Hawken's book *The Ecology of Commerce* (Guest Essay, p. 16). In 1994, he announced plans to develop the nation's first totally sustainable green corporation.

He has implemented hundreds of projects with the goals of **(1)** zero waste, **(2)** greatly reduced energy use, and **(3)** eventually zero use of fossil fuels by relying on renewable solar energy. By 1999, the company had reduced resource waste by almost 30% and reduced energy waste enough to save $100 million. One of Interface's factories in California runs on solar cells to produce the world's first solar-made carpet.

To achieve the goal of zero waste, Anderson plans to stop selling carpet and lease it as a way to control recycling. For a monthly fee, the company will **(1)** install, clean, and inspect the carpet on a monthly basis, **(2)** repair worn carpet tiles overnight, and **(3)** recycle worn-out tiles into new carpeting. As Anderson puts it, "We want to harvest yesterday's carpets and recycle

Ray Anderson, CEO of Interface, Inc.

them with zero scrap going to the landfill and zero emissions into the ecosystem—and run the whole thing on sunlight."

Du Pont and several other chemical companies have developed processes to remove the nylon and plastic PVC fibers in carpet and recycle it into other lower-quality use products (downcycling).

Interface has gone further and developed a new polymer material, called Solenium, that **(1)** when worn out can be completely recycled back into new carpet tiles (more desirable closed-loop recycling), **(2)** does not mildew, **(3)** is highly stain resistant, and **(4)** is easily cleaned with water. Making this material takes fewer steps, uses up to 40% less raw material and energy, and produces 99.7% less waste than making normal carpet, and the material lasts about four times longer than conventional carpet.

The company also has plans to install and lease a raised-floor system that goes beneath its carpet tiles and integrate this with cooling and heating services provided by other service companies.

Anderson is one of a growing number of business leaders committed to finding a more economically and ecologically sustainable way to do business while still making a profit for stockholders. Between 1993 and 1998, the company's revenues doubled and profits tripled, mostly because the company saved $130 million in material costs with an investment of less than $40 million. Andersen says he is having a blast.

---

having to install less or even no air conditioning equipment to provide cooling services for its customers.

▪ Dow and several other chemical companies are doing a booming business in leasing organic solvents (mostly used to remove grease from surfaces), photographic developing chemicals, and dyes and pigments. In this *chemical service* business, the company **(1)** delivers the chemicals, **(2)** helps the client set up a recovery system, **(3)** takes away the recovered chemicals, and **(4)** delivers new chemicals as needed.

## 21-4 REUSE

**What Are the Advantages of Refillable Containers?** The *good news* is that reuse is a form of waste reduction that **(1)** extends resource supplies, **(2)** keeps high-quality matter resources from being reduced to low-quality matter waste (Figure 3-21, p. 61), and **(3)** reduces energy use (Figure 21-6) and pollution even more than recycling.

The *bad news* is we have increasingly substituted **(1)** throwaway tissues for reusable handkerchiefs, **(2)** disposable paper towels and napkins for reusable cloth ones, **(3)** throwaway paper plates and cups and plastic utensils for reusable plates, cups, and silverware, and **(4)** throwaway beverage containers for refillable ones.

Two examples of reuse are refillable glass beverage bottles and refillable soft drink bottles made of polyethylene terephthalate (PET) plastic. Unlike throwaway and recyclable cans and bottles, refillable beverage bottles create local jobs related to their collection and refilling. Moreover, studies by Coca-Cola and PepsiCo of Canada show that their soft drinks in 0.5-liter (16-ounce) bottles cost one-third less in refillable bottles than in throwaway bottles.

Figure 21-6 Energy consumption for different types of 35-milli-liter (12-fluid-ounce) beverage containers. (Data from Argonne National Laboratory)

Denmark and Canada's Prince Edward Island have led the way by banning all beverage containers that cannot be reused. To encourage use of refillable glass bottles, Ecuador has a refundable beverage container deposit fee that is 50% of the cost of the drink. In Finland, 95% of the soft drink, beer, wine, and spirits containers are refillable, and in Germany, 73% are refillable.

Here are other examples of reusable items:

■ Metal or plastic lunch boxes.

■ Plastic containers for storing lunch box items and refrigerator leftovers instead of using throwaway plastic wrap and aluminum foil.

■ Cloth shopping bags (Solutions, at right).

■ Shipping pallets made of recycled plastic waste instead of throwaway wood pallets. In 1991, Toyota shifted entirely to reusable shipping containers. A similar move by the Xerox Corporation saves the company $2–5 million per year.

■ *Tool libraries* (such as those in Berkeley, California, and Takoma Park, Maryland) where people can check out a variety of power and hand tools.

■ *e-paper,* a flexible and cordless computer screen being developed by Xerox that (1) looks like a sheet of paper, (2) uses no energy for storing or viewing writing or images, and (3) can be electronically written and rewritten at least a million times, making it equivalent to more than a million sheets of paper.

## 21-5 RECYCLING

**What Are the Two Types of Recycling?** Recycling has a number of benefits to people and the environment (Figure 21-7, p. 536). There are two types of recycling for materials:

### What Kind of Grocery Bags Should We Use?

SOLUTIONS

When you are offered a choice between plastic or paper bags for your groceries, which should you choose? The answer is *neither.* Both are environmentally harmful, and the question of which is the more damaging has no clear-cut answer.

On the one hand, plastic bags degrade slowly in landfills and can harm wildlife if swallowed, and producing them pollutes the environment. On the other hand, producing the brown paper bags used in most supermarkets uses trees and pollutes the air and water. Overall, white or clear polyethylene plastic bags take less energy for manufacture and cause less damage to the environment than do paper bags not made mostly from recycled paper.

Instead of having to choose between paper and plastic bags, you can (1) bring your own *reusable* canvas or string containers to the store or (2) save and reuse any paper or plastic bags you get. Reusing a paper or plastic bag just five times displaces the pollution caused by the manufacture of the bag. To encourage people to bring their own reusable bags, stores in the Netherlands charge for paper or plastic bags.

**Critical Thinking**

**1.** Apply similar reasoning to determine what kind of cup (plastic, paper, or reusable) you should use whenever possible. How could you solve the problem of getting coffee or other beverages at fast-food places and at workplaces?

**2.** Do you believe grocery stores should charge for paper or plastic bags and sell reusable bags to encourage reuse? Explain. How would you implement such a policy in all major grocery stores to provide an even economic playing field for all consumers?

■ *Primary,* or *closed-loop, recycling,* in which wastes discarded by consumers (*postconsumer wastes*) are recycled to produce new products of the same type (such as newspaper into newspaper and aluminum cans into aluminum cans). This reduces pollution and use of virgin resources and saves energy (Figure 21-6).

■ *Secondary,* or *downcycling,* in which waste materials are converted into different and usually lower-quality products.

Environmentalists urge us not to be misled by labels claiming that paper and plastic bags or other items are recyclable. Just about anything is recyclable. What counts is whether (1) an item is actually recycled (ideally by primary recycling), (2) it is designed for

**GUEST ESSAY**

# Cleaner Production: A New Environmentalism for the 21st Century

*Peter Montague*

*Peter Montague is director of the Environmental Research Foundation in Washington, D.C., which studies and informs the public about environmental problems and the technologies and policies that might help solve them. He has served as project administrator of a hazardous waste research program at Princeton University and has taught courses in environmental impact analysis at the University of New Mexico. He is the coauthor of two books on toxic heavy metals in the natural environment and editor of* Rachel's Environment and Health Biweekly, *an informative newsletter on environmental problems and solutions.*

Environmentalism as we have known it for the last 33 years is dead. The environmentalism of the 1970s advocated strict numerical controls on releases into the environment of *dangerous wastes* (any unwanted or uncontrolled materials that can harm living things or disrupt ecosystems).

However, after several decades of effort by government regulatory agencies and concerned citizens (the environmental movement), most dangerous chemicals are not regulated in any way. Even the few that are covered by regulations have not been adequately controlled.

In short, the *pollution management* approach to environmental protection has failed; *pollution prevention* is our

only hope. An ounce of prevention really is worth a pound of cure.

Here is the situation facing environmentalists today:

■ *All waste disposal—landfilling, incineration, deep-well injection—is polluting because "disposal" means dispersal into the environment.* Once wastes are created, they cannot be contained or controlled because of the scientific laws of matter conservation [p. 55] and energy conservation [p. 59]. The old environmentalism failed to recognize this important truth and thus squandered enormous resources trying to achieve the impossible.

■ *The inevitable result of our reliance on waste treatment and disposal systems has been an unrelenting buildup of toxic synthetic materials in humans and other forms of life worldwide.* For example, breast milk of women in industrialized countries is so contaminated with pesticides and industrial hydrocarbons that if human milk were bottled and sold commercially, it could be banned by the U.S. Food and Drug Administration as unsafe for human consumption. If a whale beaches itself on U.S. shores and dies, its body must be treated as "hazardous waste" because whales contain concentrations of PCBs [polychlorinated biphenyls; Figure 19-6, p. 490], legally defined as hazardous.

■ *The ability of humans and other life forms to adapt to changes in their environment is strictly limited by the genetic code each form of life inherits.* Continued contamination at a rate hundreds of times faster than we can adapt will sub-

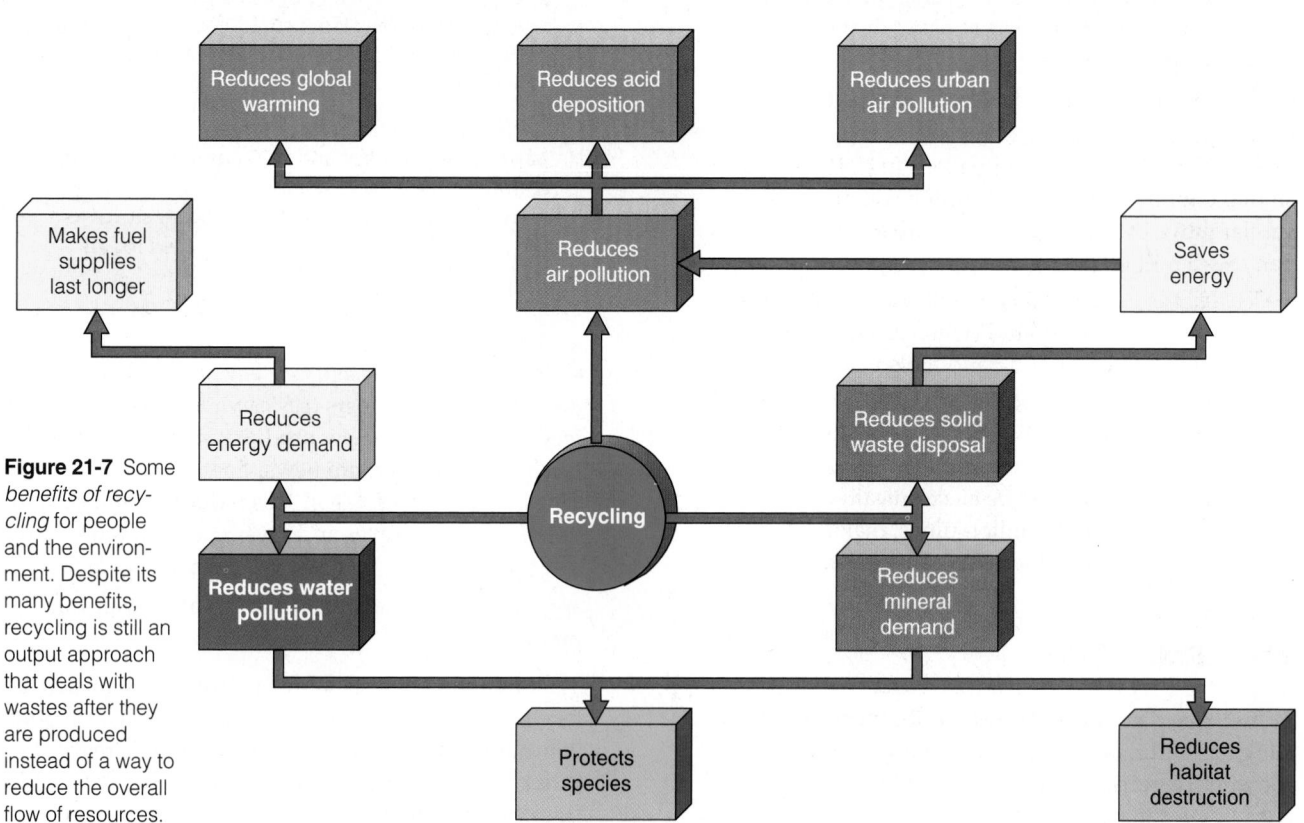

**Figure 21-7** Some benefits of recycling for people and the environment. Despite its many benefits, recycling is still an output approach that deals with wastes after they are produced instead of a way to reduce the overall flow of resources.

ject humans to increasingly widespread sickness and degradation of the species and could ultimately lead to extinction.

- *Damage to humans (and other life forms) is abundantly documented.* Birds, fish, and humans in industrialized countries are enduring steadily rising levels of cancer, genetic mutations, and damage to their nervous, immune, and hormonal systems [Connections, p. 235] as a result of pollution.

If we will but look, the handwriting is on the wall everywhere.

To deal with these problems, industrial societies must abandon their reliance **(1)** on waste treatment and disposal and **(2)** on the regulatory system of numerical standards created to manage the damage that results from relying on waste disposal instead of waste prevention. We must quickly move the industrialized and industrializing countries to new technical approaches accompanied by new industrial goals: *clean production* or zero-discharge systems.

The concept of clean production involves industrial systems that avoid or eliminate dangerous wastes and dangerous products and minimize the use and waste of raw materials, water, and energy. Goods manufactured in a clean production process must not damage natural ecosystems throughout their entire life cycle, including **(1)** raw material selection, extraction, and processing, **(2)** product conceptualization, design, manufacture, and assembly, **(3)** material transport during all phases, **(4)** industrial and household usage, and **(5)** reintroduction of the product into industrial systems or into the environment when it no longer serves a useful function.

Clean production does not rely on *end-of-pipe* pollution controls such as filters or scrubbers [Figure 17-23, p. 442] or chemical, physical, or biological treatment [Figure 19-17, p. 504]. Measures that **(1)** pretend to reduce the volume of waste by incineration or concentration, **(2)** mask the hazard by dilution, or **(3)** transfer pollutants from one environmental medium to another are also excluded from the concept of clean production.

A new industrial pattern, and thus a new environmentalism, is emerging. Human survival and life quality depend on our willingness to make and pay for the changes needed to shift to this cleaner form of industrial production.

## Critical Thinking

**1.** Some environmentalists point to the successes of the *pollution management* approach to environmental protection practiced during the past 33 years and do not agree it has failed. What is your position? Explain.

**2.** List three undesirable economic, health, consumption, and lifestyle changes you might experience as a consequence of putting much greater emphasis on pollution prevention.

---

recycling by not containing mixtures of materials that are difficult and expensive to recycle, and **(3)** we complete the recycling loop by buying products using the maximum feasible content of postconsumer recycled materials.

### Case Study: Recycling Municipal Solid Waste in the United States
In 2000, about 30% of U.S. MSW was recycled or composted (Solutions, p. 539)—the highest rate of any industrialized country. These programs recycle **(1)** 98% of the steel used in cars, **(2)** 96% of car batteries, **(3)** 70% of lead, **(4)** 55% of aluminum cans (down from 68% in 1992), **(5)** 49% of wastepaper and paperboard, **(6)** 40% of yard waste, and **(7)** 27% of glass containers. Pilot studies in several U.S. communities show that 60–80% of all MSW could be recycled and composted.

### Is Centralized Recycling of Mixed Solid Waste the Answer?
Large-scale recycling can be accomplished by collecting mixed urban waste and transporting it to centralized *materials-recovery facilities (MRFs)*. There, machines shred and automatically separate the mixed waste to recover valuable materials for sale to manufacturers as raw materials (Figure 21-8, p. 538). The remaining paper, plastics, and other combustible wastes are recycled or burned to produce steam or electricity to run the recovery plant or to sell to nearby industries or homes. Ash from the incinerator is buried in a landfill.

More than 225 MRFs operate in the United States. However, such plants **(1)** are expensive to build, operate, and maintain (which is why some have been shut down), **(2)** can emit toxic air pollutants if not operated properly, and **(3)** produce a toxic ash that must be disposed of safely. MRFs also must have a large input of garbage to make them financially successful. Thus their owners have a vested interest in increasing *throughput* of matter and energy resources to produce more trash, the reverse of what prominent scientists believe we should be doing (Figure 21-3).

### Is Separating Solid Wastes for Recycling the Answer?
Many solid waste experts argue that it makes more sense economically and environmentally for households and businesses to keep trash separate in recyclable and reusable categories (such as glass, paper, metals, certain types of plastics, and compostable materials). Then compartmentalized city collection trucks, private haulers, or volunteer recycling organizations

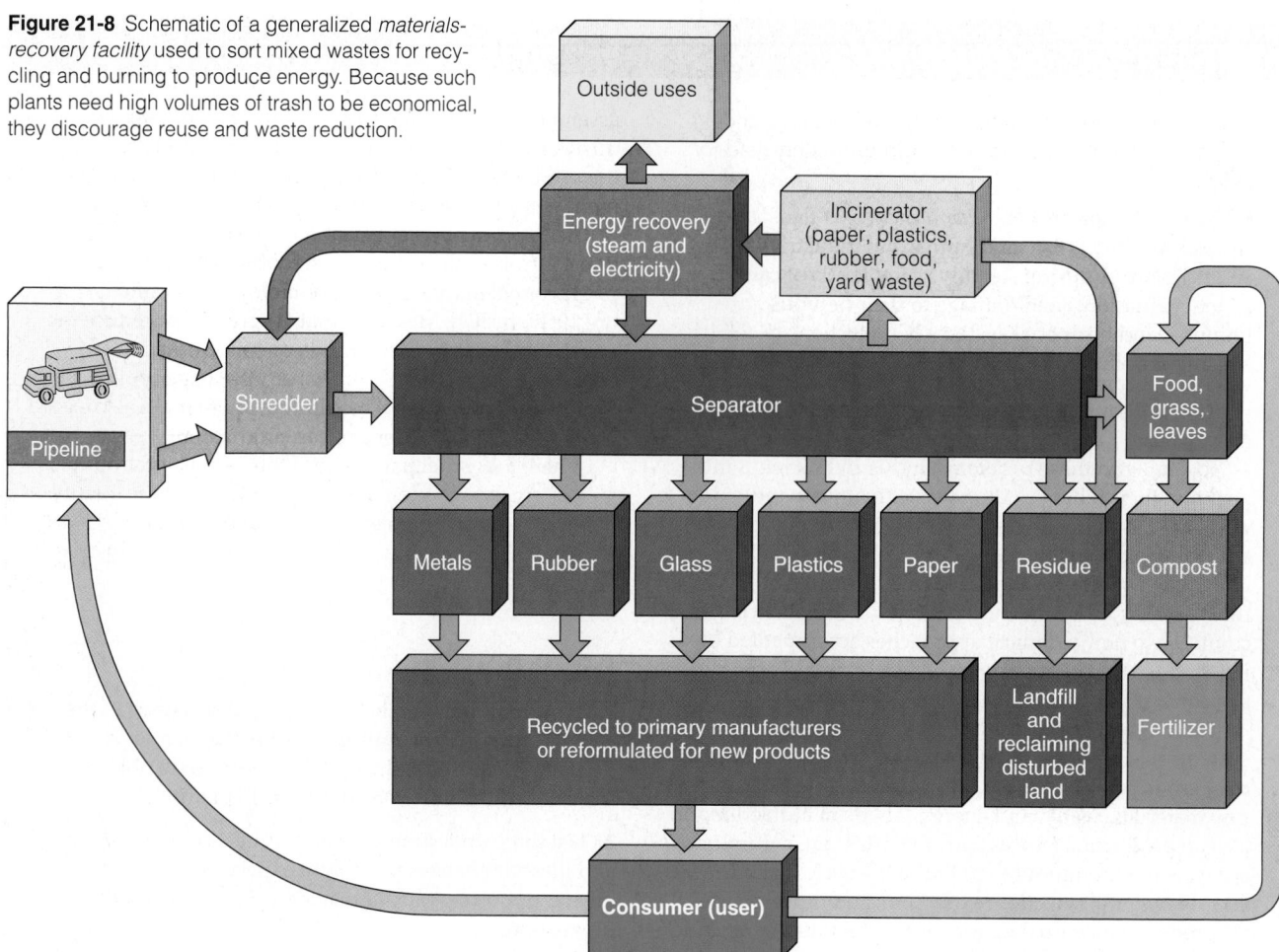

**Figure 21-8** Schematic of a generalized *materials-recovery facility* used to sort mixed wastes for recycling and burning to produce energy. Because such plants need high volumes of trash to be economical, they discourage reuse and waste reduction.

pick up the segregated wastes and sell them to scrap dealers, compost plants, and manufacturers. Another alternative (especially in less populated areas) is to establish a network of drop-off centers, buyback centers, and deposit-refund programs in which people deliver and sell or donate separated recyclable materials.

This *source separation* approach **(1)** produces little air and water pollution, **(2)** has low startup costs and moderate operating costs, **(3)** saves more energy and provides more jobs per unit of material than MRFs, landfills, and incinerators, **(4)** yields cleaner and usually more valuable recyclables, and **(5)** educates people about the need for waste reduction, reuse, and recycling.

Aluminum and paper separated out for recycling are worth a lot of money. As a result, in a growing number of cities people steal these materials—from curbside containers set out by residents and from unprotected recycling drop-off centers—and sell them. This undermines municipal recycling programs by lowering the income available from selling these materials.

**Does Recycling Make Economic Sense?** The answer is yes and no, depending on different ways of looking at the economic and environmental benefits and costs of recycling. Critics contend that recycling

- Has become almost a religion that is above criticism regardless of how much it costs communities.

- Does not make sense if it costs more to recycle materials than to send them to a landfill or incinerator.

- Often is not needed to save landfill space because many areas in the United States are not running out of landfill space.

- May make economic sense for valuable and easy-to-recycle materials (such as aluminum, paper, and steel) but not for cheap or plentiful resources (such as glass from silica) and most plastics (which are expensive to recycle). For example, in 2002, New York City continued recycling paper and metals but stopped recycling plastics and glass.

However, recycling proponents argue that

- Recycling programs should not be judged on whether they pay for themselves any more than are conventional garbage disposal systems based on land burial or incineration.

## Using Composting to Recycle Biodegradable Wastes

**SOLUTIONS**

Composting biodegradable organic waste such as paper, food scraps, and lawn waste is a way to produce plant nutrients that can be recycled into the soil. Biodegradable wastes make up about 35% by weight of the MSW output in the United States and could be converted to compost (p. 225).

However, only about 5% of the MSW in the United States is composted (compared to 17% in France and 10% in Switzerland). Some cities in Austria, Belgium, Denmark, Germany, Luxembourg, and Switzerland recover and compost more than 85% of their biodegradable wastes.

According to a 2001 study by U.S. Department of Agriculture scientists, composting chicken manure essentially rids it of hormones and hormone-mimic compounds

(Connections, p. 235) that may harm crops and wildlife when farmers use the manure directly as fertilizer.

Individuals can compost biodegradable wastes in backyard bins or indoor containers. They can also be collected and composted in centralized community facilities, as is done in many western European countries.

The resulting compost can be used as **(1)** an organic soil fertilizer or conditioner, **(2)** topsoil, or **(3)** landfill cover. Compost also can be used to help restore eroded soil on hillsides and along highways, strip-mined land, overgrazed areas, and eroded cropland.

To be successful, a large-scale composting program must **(1)** overcome siting problems (few people want to live near a giant compost pile or plant), **(2)** control odors, and **(3)** exclude toxic materials that can contaminate the compost and make

it unsuitable for use as a fertilizer on crops and lawns.

Three ways to control or reduce odors for large-scale composting operations are **(1)** enclosing the facilities and filtering the air inside (but residents near large composting plants still complain of unacceptable odors), **(2)** creating municipal compost operations near existing landfills or at other isolated sites, and **(3)** decomposing biodegradable wastes in a closed metal container in which air is recirculated to give precise control of available oxygen and temperature (a technique that has been used successfully in the Netherlands for 20 years).

### Critical Thinking

How would you increase the rate of composting of biodegradable wastes in your community?

---

- The primary benefit of recycling is not reducing the use of landfills and incinerators but the other important benefits it provides for people and the environment (Figure 21-7).

- Studies show the net economic, health, and environmental benefits of recycling (Figure 21-7) far outweigh the costs.

- The recycling industry is an important part of the U.S. economy that employs about 1.1 million people and has $236 billion in annual sales—much larger than either the mining or waste management and disposal industries.

- Programs like **(1)** a single pickup system (for both materials to be recycled and garbage that cannot be recycled) instead of a more expensive dual collection system and **(2)** a pay-as-you-throw system tend to make money and have higher recycling rates.

**Why Don't We Have More Reuse and Recycling?** The following three factors hinder recycling (and reuse):

- Failure to include the harmful environmental and health costs of raw materials in the market prices of consumer items.

- More government tax breaks and subsidies for resource-extracting industries than for recycling and reuse industries.

- Lack of large steady markets for recycled materials.

Analysts suggest overcoming these obstacles by

- Taxing virgin resources and phasing out subsidies for extracting virgin resources.

- Lowering or eliminating taxes on recycled materials based on postconsumer waste content.

- Providing subsidies for reuse and postconsumer waste recycling.

- Greatly increasing use of the *pay-as-you-throw* system.

- Encouraging or requiring government purchases of recycled products to help increase demand and lower prices.

- Viewing landfilling and incineration of solid wastes as last resorts to be used only for wastes that cannot be reused, composted, or recycled (Figure 21-3).

- Passing laws requiring companies to take back and recycle or reuse packaging discarded by consumers. Globally, at least 29 countries (including Japan and 20

## Recycling, Reuse, and Waste Reduction in Germany

**CASE STUDY**

In 1991, Germany enacted the world's toughest packaging law, which was designed to **(1)** reduce the amount of waste being landfilled or incinerated, **(2)** reduce waste production, and **(3)** recycle or reuse 65% of the nation's packaging by 1995. Product distributors must take back their boxes and other containers for reuse or recycling, and incineration of packaging is not allowed.

To implement the system, more than 600 German manufacturers and distributors pay fees to a nonprofit service company they formed to collect, sort, and reprocess the packaging discards (coded with a green dot) of member firms.

The system has been so successful that since 1997, **(1)** at least 86% of all packaging in Germany has been recycled (up from 12% in 1992), **(2)** plastic packaging has lost one-third of its market share to glass and cardboard, **(3)** four out of five German manufacturers have reduced their use of packaging by 17%, and **(4)** about 75% of all produce shipped through Germany is boxed in leased, reusable shipping crates.

Inspired by the German system, **(1)** more than 28 countries have enacted *take-back* laws for packaging materials, **(2)** 16 have done so for batteries, and **(3)** 12 are considering such legislation for electronic items. In 1998, Taiwan started a take-back program for computers, televisions, and large home appliances. In the Netherlands, all packaging waste is banned from landfills.

### Critical Thinking

What might be some long-term disadvantages of Germany's program? Do you believe a similar program should be put into place in the country where you live? Explain.

European nations) have such "take-back" laws, which also encourage reduction of packaging (Case Study, above).

- Requiring manufacturers to take back and recycle or reuse appliances and motor vehicles at the end of their useful lives. This is required for car manufacturers and appliance makers in European Union countries and for major appliances in Japan. Such laws are expected to be expanded to require manufacturers to take back used computers and other electronic devices for recycling, reuse, or remanufacture.

- Requiring labels on all products listing preconsumer and postconsumer recycled content.

## 21-6 CASE STUDIES: RECYCLING WASTEPAPER AND PLASTICS

**How Is Paper Made, and How Much Is Being Recycled?** To make paper, trees are stripped of their bark and chipped into small pieces. A chemical such as caustic soda (sodium hydroxide) or a mechanical grinder is then used to separate or pulp the wood in the chips to a soft mush or pulp of cellulose fibers. The brownish pulp is **(1)** rinsed and washed several times (which yields large volumes of pulping liquor that are either treated or in many developing countries dumped directly into waterways), **(2)** often bleached to make it white (typically using toxic chlorine or chlorine compounds), and **(3)** pressed into a thin sheet and dried.

Paper (especially newspaper and cardboard) is one of the easiest materials to recycle. Recycling paper involves **(1)** removing its ink, glue, and coating and **(2)** reconverting it to pulp that is pressed again into new paper. The perception that recycled paper is weak, coarse, flecked, and too expensive is no longer true. A variety of high-quality recycled papers are available to meet all types of printing demands at competitive prices (including the paper used in this book).

In 2000, the United States recycled about 49% of its wastepaper (up from 25% in 1989) and 70% of its corrugated cardboard containers. At least ten other countries recycle 50–97% of their wastepaper and paperboard, with a global recycling rate of 43%. Despite a 49% recycling rate, the amount of paper thrown away each year in the United States is more than all of the paper consumed in China (where the recycling rate is only 27%).

Recycling paper **(1)** does not involve cutting new trees, **(2)** saves energy because it takes 30–64% less energy to produce the same weight of recycled paper as to make the paper from trees, **(3)** reduces air pollution from pulp mills by 74–95%, **(4)** lowers water pollution by 35%, **(5)** helps prevent groundwater contamination by toxic ink left after paper rots in landfills over a 30- to 60-year period, **(6)** conserves large quantities of water, **(7)** takes little or no bleaching because the fibers recycled from white paper have already been bleached, **(8)** can save landfill space, **(9)** creates five times more jobs than harvesting trees for pulp, and **(10)** can save money.

Chlorine ($Cl_2$) and chlorine compounds (such as chlorine dioxide, $ClO_2$) used to bleach about 40% of the world's pulp for making paper are **(1)** corrosive to processing equipment, **(2)** hazardous for workers,

(3) hard to recover and reuse, and (4) extremely harmful when released to the environment. A growing number of paper mills (mostly in Europe) are replacing chlorine-based bleaching chemicals with oxygen-based chemicals such as hydrogen peroxide ($H_2O_2$) or ozone ($O_3$). Such processes (1) nearly eliminate the release of air pollutants (including highly toxic chlorine-containing dioxins, p. 551), (2) use less water and energy, (3) allow reuse of the water many times, (4) reduce the treatment needed for water that is discharged, and (5) save money.

Buying recycled paper products can save trees and energy and reduce pollution, but it does not necessarily reduce solid waste. Only paper products made from *postconsumer waste*—waste intercepted on its way from consumer to the landfill or incinerator—does that.

Most recycled paper is made from *preconsumer waste:* scraps and cuttings recovered from paper and printing plants. Because paper manufacturers have always recycled this waste, it has never contributed to landfill problems. Now this paper is labeled "recycled" as a marketing ploy, giving the false impression that people who buy such products (often at higher prices) are helping reduce solid waste. Most so-called "recycled" paper has no more than 50% recycled fibers, with only 10% from postconsumer waste. Environmentalists propose that governments require companies to use labels (1) giving postconsumer recycled content and (2) indicating whether the paper was bleached with chlorine or by a chlorine-free process.

**Is It Feasible to Recycle Plastics?** Plastics are various types of polymer molecules made by chemically linking monomer molecules (petrochemicals) produced mostly from oil and natural gas (Figure 21-9).

Currently, only about 7% by weight of all plastic wastes and 10% of plastic containers in the United States are recycled, for the following reasons:

- Plastics are very difficult to isolate from other wastes because they (1) occur in so many different and often difficult-to-identify forms of resins, (2) sometimes consist of composites or laminated layers of different plastics, and (3) contain stabilizers and other chemicals that must be removed before recycling.

- Recovering individual plastic resins does not yield much material because only small amounts of any given resin are used per product.

- The price of oil is so low (Figure 15-22, p. 357) that the cost of virgin plastic resins (except for PET, used mostly in plastic drink bottles) is about 40% lower than that of recycled resins.

Thus mandating that plastic products contain a certain amount of recycled plastic resins is (1) unlikely

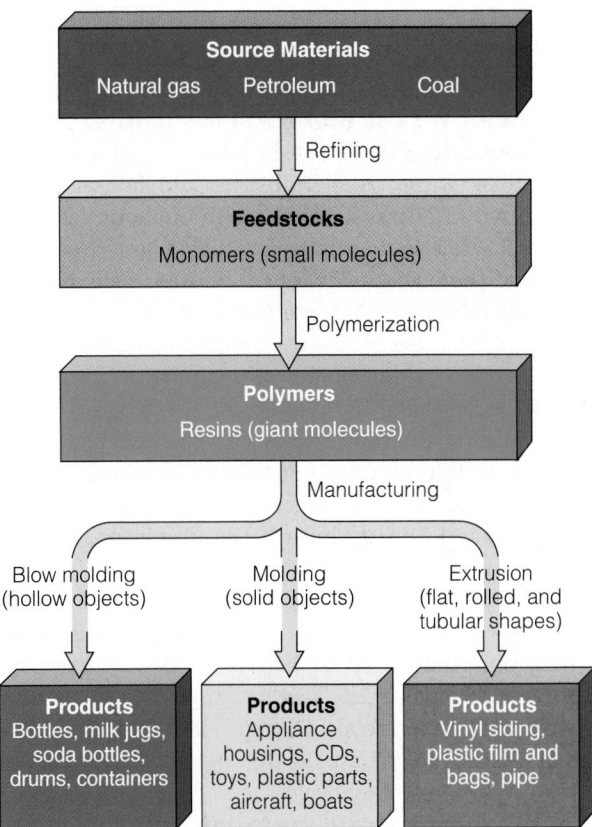

**Figure 21-9** How plastics are made. (Adapted from the Society of the Plastics Industry)

to work and (2) could hinder the use of plastics in reducing the resource content and weight (Solutions, p. 533) of many widely used items such as plastic bags, bottles, and other containers.

Environmentalists recognize the beneficial qualities of plastics: (1) durability (in products such as car and machine parts, carpeting, toys, furniture, reusable tubs and containers, and refillable bottles), (2) light weight, (3) unbreakability (compared to glass), and (4) in some cases reusability as containers.

On the other side of the argument,

- The plastics industry is one of the leading producers of hazardous waste.

- In landfills, toxic cadmium and lead compounds used as binders, colorants, and heat stabilizers can leach out of plastics into groundwater and surface water.

- Most plastics are nondegradable or take 200–400 years to degrade.

- Some widespread uses of plastics—especially excessive and often unnecessary single-use packaging and throwaway beverage and food containers—could be sharply reduced and replaced with less harmful and less wasteful alternatives.

## 21-7 DETOXIFYING, BURNING, BURYING, AND EXPORTING WASTES

**How Can We Use Biological Methods to Detoxify Hazardous Waste?**   In Denmark, all hazardous and toxic waste from industries and households is delivered to 21 transfer stations throughout the country. All waste is then transferred to a large treatment facility. There about 75% of the waste is detoxified by biological and chemical methods and the rest is buried in a carefully designed and monitored landfill.

Some consider biological treatment of hazardous waste, or *bioremediation,* to be the wave of the future for cleaning up some types of toxic and hazardous waste. In this process, microorganisms (usually natural or genetically engineered bacteria) and enzymes help convert toxic or hazardous substances to harmless compounds.

Bioremediation is effective for a number of organic wastes, including pesticides, gasoline, diesel fuel, polychlorinated biphenyls (PCBs), and organic solvents. However, it does not appear to work very well for **(1)** toxic metals, **(2)** highly concentrated chemical wastes, or **(3)** complete digestion of some complex mixtures of toxic chemicals.

Another biological way to treat hazardous wastes is *phytoremediation,* which involves using natural or genetically engineered plants to filter and remove contaminants. Selected plants have been identified as potential "pollution sponges" to help clean up soil and water contaminated with chemicals such as pesticides, organic solvents, radioactive metals, and toxic metals such as lead and mercury. Such plants include poplar, sunflower, clover, mustard, and some ferns. Analysis of small samples of bark from poplar trees can be used for *phytomonitoring* contaminants in soil and groundwater. This is much faster and cheaper than drilling wells to monitor groundwater contamination.

Phytoremediation **(1)** is inexpensive, **(2)** does not involve heavy machinery that produces air pollution, and **(3)** can reduce the amount of material dumped in landfills. But **(1)** it is often slow (it can take several growing seasons to clean a site), **(2)** it is effective only at depths that plant roots can reach, **(3)** some toxic chemicals may evaporate from plant leaves, and **(4)** the plants can become so toxic that they must be kept away from animals, insects (which are eaten by other animals), and people.

**How Can We Use Chemical Methods to Detoxify Hazardous Waste?**   Scientists are testing the use of *cyclodextrin*—a type of sugar made from corn starch—to remove toxic materials such as solvents, pesticides, and polycyclic hydrocarbons from contaminated soil and groundwater. To clean up a site, a solution of cyclodextrin is injected. After this molecular-sponge material moves through the soil or groundwater and attracts various toxic chemicals it is pumped out of the ground, stripped of its contaminants, and reused.

In 2002, the Idaho National Engineering and Environmental Laboratory began testing a new technology, called "Silver II", that chemically oxidizes most organic wastes and eliminates the need for their incineration. Compared to incineration, this technology is easy to control, operates at low temperatures, and emits no toxic aromatic hydrocarbons or dioxins.

**Is Detoxifying Hazardous Waste With a Plasma Torch the Answer?**   Some forms of hazardous waste can be detoxified by using a *plasma arc torch* to expose the wastes to temperatures of 10,000°C (18,000°F) or higher. High temperatures from the torch can **(1)** decompose liquid or solid hazardous organic material into ions and atoms (pyrolysis) that can be converted into simple molecules, cleaned up, and released as a gas and **(2)** convert hazardous inorganic matter into a molten glassy material (vitrification) that encapsulates toxic metals and keeps them from leaching into groundwater.

**Plasma**—known as a fourth state of matter—is an ionized gas consisting of electrically conductive ions and electrons. In a *plasma torch* a sustained electric arc is created by passage of electrical current through a gas to generate very high temperatures. Such devices can be small and consist of a plasma torch, reaction chamber (or furnace), and scrubber or other air pollution control devices to remove unwanted byproducts. Heat is recovered to produce electricity. The system can be mounted on a mobile platform and moved from one waste site to another.

One approach is to feed solid or liquid waste material into the reaction chamber where the intense heat of the plasma breaks down organic molecules (such as oil, solvents, and paint) into their basic atoms. These atoms then recombine into gases such as **(1)** water vapor, $CO_2$ and CO and **(2)** $H_2$ and $CH_4$ (which can be recovered and used as fuels for energy production). Unlike incineration, the plasma process produces no toxic ash that must be disposed of safely.

Another approach is to drill a small hole into a contaminated site (such as an old landfill), insert the torch, and turn it on. The process is repeated over a grid pattern to decontaminate an entire area.

There are some drawbacks. The process produces $CO_2$ (a greenhouse gas) and CO. It can produce particulates and vaporize toxic metals (such as lead, mercury, and copper), chlorine, and radioactive materials (such as americum-241 used in smoke detectors, p. 373). These pollutants are released into the atmosphere unless various air pollution control devices (Figure 17-23, p. 442) remove them. Another problem is high costs. Various companies are developing and testing ways to improve this emerging technology and bring its costs down.

**Is Burning Solid and Hazardous Waste the Answer?** In the United States, about 16% of the mixed trash in municipal solid waste is combusted in about 170 *mass-burn incinerators* (Figure 21-10). About 80% of the hazardous waste is burned in 172 commercial incinerators, cement kilns, and lightweight aggregate kilns. The other 20% is combusted in industrial boilers and other types of industrial furnaces. Figure 21-11 lists the pros and cons of using incinerators to burn solid and hazardous waste.

Since 1985, using incineration for treating wastes in some parts of the world has decreased because of **(1)** high costs, **(2)** health threats from air pollution, and **(3)** intense citizen opposition. For example, **(1)** Sweden banned the construction of new incinerators in 1985, **(2)** Rhode Island and West Virginia banned solid waste incineration in 1992, **(3)** several solid waste incinerators in the United States have been shut down because of excessive costs and pollution and by 2006 an estimated 125 incinerators will be closed because of their inability to meet new and stricter air pollution standards, **(4)** more than 280 new incinerator projects have

**Figure 21-11** Advantages and disadvantages of incinerating solid and hazardous waste.

been blocked, delayed, or canceled in the United States since 1985, **(5)** in 1999, the Philippines became the first country to ban all waste incineration, followed by Costa Rica, and **(6)** a growing number of hospitals are destroying infectious material by using steam heat and

**Figure 21-10** Schematic of a *waste-to-energy incinerator* with pollution controls that burns mixed solid waste and recovers some of the energy to produce steam used for heating or producing electricity. (Adapted from EPA, *Let's Reduce and Recycle*)

pressure in autoclaves (which are cheaper to run than incinerators) and other nonincinerator methods for treating medical wastes.

**Is Land Disposal of Solid Waste the Answer?**
About 54% by weight of the MSW in the United States is buried in sanitary landfills (compared to 90% in the United Kingdom, 80% in Canada, 15% in Japan, and 12% in Switzerland). In a **sanitary landfill,** solid wastes are **(1)** spread out in thin layers, **(2)** compacted, and **(3)** covered daily with a fresh layer of clay or plastic foam.

Modern state-of-the-art landfills on geologically suitable sites are lined with clay and plastic before being filled with garbage (Figure 21-12). The bottom is covered with a second impermeable liner, usually made of several layers of clay, thick plastic, and sand. This liner collects *leachate* (rainwater contaminated as

it percolates through the solid waste) and is intended to prevent its leakage into groundwater. Collected leachate is **(1)** pumped from the bottom of the landfill, **(2)** stored in tanks, and **(3)** sent to a regular sewage treatment plant or an on-site treatment plant. When full, the landfill is covered with clay, sand, gravel, and topsoil to prevent water from seeping in. Several wells are drilled around the landfill to monitor any leakage of leachate into nearby groundwater. Figure 21-13 lists the pros and cons of using sanitary landfills for solid waste disposal.

Since 1997, only state-of-the-art landfills (Figure 21-12) are allowed to operate in the United States. As a result, many older and small landfills have been closed and replaced with larger local and regional modern landfills. Some cities in the eastern United States, notably Philadelphia and New York, are having trouble finding nearby landfills. However, there is no

**Figure 21-12** State-of-the-art *sanitary landfills* are designed to eliminate or minimize environmental problems that plague older landfills. Even such state-of-the-art landfills are expected to leak eventually, passing both the effects of contamination and cleanup costs on to future generations.

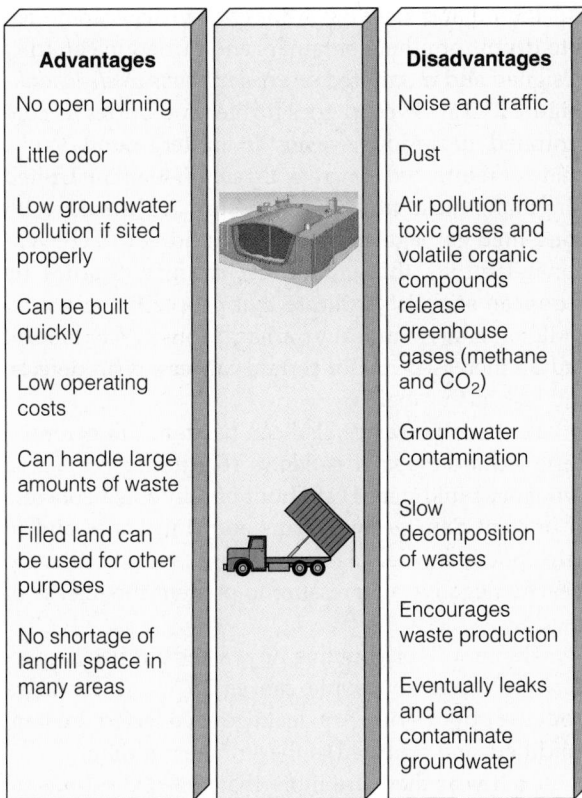

| Advantages | Disadvantages |
|---|---|
| No open burning | Noise and traffic |
| Little odor | Dust |
| Low groundwater pollution if sited properly | Air pollution from toxic gases and volatile organic compounds release greenhouse gases (methane and $CO_2$) |
| Can be built quickly | |
| Low operating costs | Groundwater contamination |
| Can handle large amounts of waste | Slow decomposition of wastes |
| Filled land can be used for other purposes | Encourages waste production |
| No shortage of landfill space in many areas | Eventually leaks and can contaminate groundwater |

**Figure 21-13** Advantages and disadvantages of using sanitary landfills to dispose of solid waste.

shortage of landfill space in most parts of the United States.

These new landfills are equipped with a connected network of vent pipes to collect landfill gas (consisting mostly of two greenhouse gases, methane and carbon dioxide; Table 18-1, p. 449) released by the underground (anaerobic) decomposition of wastes. The methane is filtered out and burned in small gas turbines to produce steam or electricity (Figure 21-12) for nearby facilities (Individuals Matter, p. 549) or sold to utilities.

However, thousands of older and abandoned landfills do not have such systems and will emit methane and carbon dioxide, both potent greenhouse gases, for decades. A 2001 study by Steve Linberg and his associates found very high levels of highly toxic methyl mercury in gases emitted by landfills. Apparently bacteria in the landfill waste converted inorganic mercury into organic methyl mercury, a dangerous nerve poison. This toxin can get into water supplies and be biologically magnified to dangerous levels in fish (p. 549).

Contamination of groundwater and nearby surface water by leachate from unlined and lined older landfills is a serious problem. Some 86% of older U.S. landfills studied have contaminated groundwater, and

a fifth of all Superfund hazardous waste sites (p. 552) are former municipal landfills that will cost billions of dollars to clean up.

According to G. Fred Lee (an experienced landfill consultant) and Ann Christy (a researcher at Ohio State University), the best solution to the leachate problem is to (1) apply clean water to landfills continuously and (2) collect and treat the resulting leachate in carefully designed and monitored facilities. They contend that after 10–20 years of such washing, little potential for groundwater pollution should remain. This wetting would also (1) hasten the breakdown of many wastes to 5–10 years instead of 100 years or longer, (2) provide more room for more trash in the same landfill, and (3) allow old landfills to be dug out and used again.

**Is Land Disposal of Hazardous Waste the Answer?** Hazardous waste in the United States is disposed of on land in (1) deep underground wells, (2) surface impoundments such as ponds, pits, or lagoons, (3) state-of-the-art landfills, and (4) above-ground storage facilities.

In *deep-well disposal*, liquid hazardous wastes (such as cleaning solutions, metals, cyanides, and corrosive solutions) are pumped under pressure through a pipe into dry, porous geologic formations or zones of rock far beneath aquifers tapped for drinking and irrigation water (Figure 19-10, p. 494). In theory, these liquids soak into the porous rock material and are isolated from overlying groundwater by essentially impermeable layers of rock.

Figure 21-14 lists the pros and cons of deep-well disposal of liquid hazardous wastes. Many scientists believe current regulations for deep-well disposal are inadequate and should be improved.

| Advantages | Disadvantages |
|---|---|
| Simple technology | Leaks or spills at surface |
| Safe method if sites are chosen carefully | Leaks from corrosion of well casing |
| Wastes can be retrieved if problems develop | Existing fractures or earthquakes can allow wastes to escape into groundwater |
| Easy to do | |
| Low cost | Encourages waste production |

**Figure 21-14** Advantages and disadvantages of injecting liquid hazardous wastes into deep underground wells.

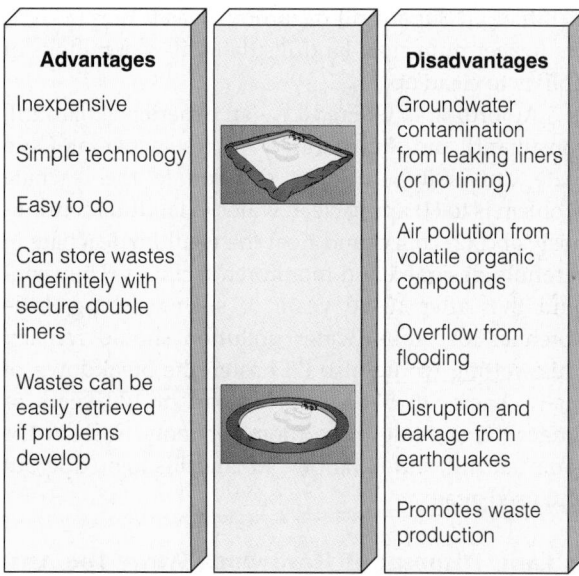

| Advantages | Disadvantages |
|---|---|
| Inexpensive | Groundwater contamination from leaking liners (or no lining) |
| Simple technology | |
| Easy to do | Air pollution from volatile organic compounds |
| Can store wastes indefinitely with secure double liners | Overflow from flooding |
| Wastes can be easily retrieved if problems develop | Disruption and leakage from earthquakes |
| | Promotes waste production |

**Figure 21-15** Advantages and disadvantages of storing liquid hazardous wastes in surface impoundments.

*Surface impoundments* are excavated depressions such as ponds, pits, or lagoons into which liquid hazardous wastes are drained and stored (Figure 19-10, p. 494). As water evaporates, the waste settles and becomes more concentrated. Figure 21-15 lists the pros and cons of this method. EPA studies found that 70% of these storage basins in the United States have no liners, and as many as 90% may threaten groundwater. According to the EPA, all liners are likely to leak eventually and can contaminate groundwater.

Liquid and solid hazardous waste also can be put into drums or other containers and buried in carefully designed and monitored *secure hazardous waste landfills* (Figure 21-16). Sweden goes further and buries its concentrated hazardous wastes in underground vaults made of reinforced concrete. By contrast, in the United Kingdom, most hazardous wastes are mixed with household garbage and stored in hundreds of conventional landfills throughout the country. Studies by European scientists indicate that people living within 3 kilometers (1.9 miles) of a hazardous waste landfill had an increased risk of certain cancers, birth defects, and low birth weights.

Hazardous wastes also can be stored in carefully designed *aboveground buildings* (Figure 21-17). These two-story buildings **(1)** are built of reinforced concrete to prevent damage by storms and hurricanes and to help contain any leakage and **(2)** use fans and filters to create a negative air pressure to prevent the release of toxic gases.

The first floor contains no wastes but has inspection walkways so people can easily check for leaks from the upper story. Any leakage is collected, treated, solidified, and returned to the storage building.

Each year there are more than 500,000 shipments of hazardous wastes (mostly to landfills and incinerators in trucks or by train) in the United States. On average, trucks and trains carrying hazardous materials are involved in about 13,000 accidents per year in the United States. In a typical year, these accidents **(1)** kill about 100 people, **(2)** cause more than 10,000 injuries, and **(3)** necessitate evacuation of more than 500,000 people. Most communities do not have the

**Figure 21-16** Secure hazardous waste landfill.

**Figure 21-17** Aboveground hazardous waste storage facilities can help keep wastes from contaminating groundwater. So far, there has been little use and evaluation of this method. Some scientists and engineers believe with careful design this would be a safer way to deal with hazardous wastes than incinerators, deep wells, surface impoundments, and secure landfills.

equipment and trained personnel to deal with hazardous waste spills.

**Is Exporting Hazardous Waste the Answer?**
Some hazardous waste producers in the United States and several other industrialized countries have been getting rid of some of these wastes by legally (or illegally) shipping them to other countries, especially developing countries.

In 2001, about 10% of the world's hazardous waste moved across an international border. For example, because of its less restrictive regulations, Canada is a major receiver of U.S. hazardous wastes. In 1998, an estimated 89% of the world's exported hazardous wastes was recycled and the other 11% was burned, landfilled, or otherwise disposed of.

Waste disposal firms can charge high prices for picking up hazardous wastes. If they can then dispose of them (legally or illegally) at low costs, they pocket huge profits.

According to a 2001 study by the UN Food and Agriculture Organization, more than 450,000 metric tons (500,000 tons) of banned or expired pesticides are seriously threatening the health of millions of people and the environment in nearly all developing countries.

In 1989, countries met and drew up the *Basel Convention on Hazardous Waste*. It requires exporters to get approval from the recipient nation before a shipment of hazardous wastes can be sent. In 1995, the Basel Convention was strengthened to ban all hazardous waste exports from developed countries to developing countries.

If enforced, this ban on hazardous waste exports will help. However, it would not end illegal trade in these wastes because the potential profits are much too great. To most environmental scientists, the only solution to the hazardous waste problem is to produce as little as possible in the first place (Figure 21-4).

## 21-8   CASE STUDIES: LEAD, MERCURY, CHLORINE, AND DIOXINS

**What Is the Threat From Lead?**   Lead is a potent neurotoxin that can harm the nervous system, especially in young children. Each year, 12,000–16,000 American children under age 9 are treated for acute lead poisoning, and about 200 die. About 30% of the survivors suffer from palsy, partial paralysis, blindness, and mental retardation. Lead can also cause damage at levels far below those that cause acute lead poisoning, especially in children and unborn fetuses. Research indicates that children under age 6 and unborn fetuses with fairly low blood levels of lead are especially vulnerable to **(1)** nervous system impairment, **(2)** a lowered IQ (by 4–7 points), **(3)** a shortened attention span, **(4)** hyperactivity, **(5)** hearing damage, and **(6)** various behavior disorders.

**Figure 21-18** Sources of *lead exposure* for children and fetuses.

It is *good news* that between 1976 and 1999 the percentage of U.S. children ages 1–5 with lead levels above the current blood level standard of 5 micrograms per deciliter (5 µg/dl) dropped from 85% to 4%, preventing at least 9 million childhood lead poisonings. The primary reason is that government regulations banned **(1)** leaded gasoline in 1976 (with phaseout to be completed by 1986) and **(2)** lead-based paints in 1970 (but illegal use continued until about 1978).

The *bad news* is that even with the encouraging drop in average blood levels of lead, the U.S. Centers for Disease Control and Prevention estimate that at least 800,000 U.S. children still have unsafe levels of lead, caused by exposure to a number of sources (Figure 21-18). Moreover, a 1993 study by the National Academy of Sciences and numerous other studies indicate there is no safe level of lead in children's blood. This means several million children in the United States (and an estimated 130–200 million children throughout the world) may be suffering from reduced mental capacity and other harmful effects of lead poisoning.

**How Can We Reduce Exposure to Lead?** Health scientists have proposed a number of ways to help protect children from lead poisoning:

▪ *Testing all children for blood levels of lead by age 1.*

▪ *Banning incineration of solid and hazardous waste or greatly increasing current pollution control standards for old and new incinerators.*

▪ *Phasing out leaded gasoline worldwide over the next decade.*

▪ *Testing older housing and buildings for leaded paints and lead dust and removing this hazard.* According to government estimates, 83% of U.S. homes (and 86% of public housing units) built between 1950 and 1978 contain lead-based paint.

▪ *Banning all lead solder in plumbing pipes and fixtures and in food cans.*

▪ *Removing lead from piping and other parts of municipal drinking water systems within 10 years.*

▪ *Banning incineration or landfill disposal of TV sets and computer monitors and requiring removal and reuse of the lead they contain.* Each picture tube in a TV set or computer monitor contains 1.8–3.2 kilograms (4–7 pounds) of lead, which can enter the air during incineration or leach from landfills into soil and groundwater.

- *Washing fresh fruits and vegetables and hands thoroughly to remove particles of lead dust.*
- *Testing ceramicware used to serve food for lead glazing.*
- *Banning imports of lead-laden polyvinyl chloride (PVC) miniblinds and candles with lead cores.*

Taking most of these actions will cost an estimated $50 billion in the United States. However, health officials say the alternative is to keep poisoning and mentally handicapping millions of children.

Although the threat from lead has been reduced in the United States, this is not the case in many developing countries. The World Health Organization (WHO) estimates that **(1)** 130–200 million children around the world are at risk from lead, and **(2)** 15–18 million children in developing countries suffer permanent brain damage because of lead poisoning, with 90% of the lead coming from leaded gasoline.

**What Is the Threat From Mercury?**  Mercury, like lead, is a potent neurotoxin that can harm the brain and spinal cord, particularly in the developing nervous system of a fetus or young child. Humans are exposed to mercury in two ways:

- Inhaling vaporized elemental mercury (Hg) or particulates of inorganic mercury ($Hg^{2+}$) salts (such as $HgS$ and $HgCl_2$).
- Eating fish contaminated with methyl mercury ($CH_3Hg$), a highly toxic form of organic mercury that is easily absorbed in the tissues of fish, birds, and people and generally remains in the bodies of organisms longer than inorganic forms of mercury. The greatest risk is brain damage from exposure to low levels of methyl mercury by fetuses and young children whose nervous systems are still developing.

Natural inputs of mercury into the environment include volcanoes, weathering of natural mercury deposits, and volatilization from the ocean. The three major human-based sources of mercury are **(1)** coal burning, **(2)** waste incineration (including hazardous and municipal waste and medical waste incinerators), and **(3)** electric arc furnaces used to melt and recycle steel from cans. Studies indicate that human activities have doubled or tripled the amount of mercury in the atmosphere.

These human-related sources emit elemental mercury (Hg) vapor and particles of inorganic mercury ($Hg^{2+}$) salts into the atmosphere. These nondegradable pollutants can be carried long distances by winds and deposited onto land and aquatic systems, mostly by rainfall.

### Using Landfill Methane to Heat a School

In January 1997, Pattonville High School in Maryland Heights, Missouri (near St. Louis), became the first public school to use methane gas produced by a nearby landfill as a source of heat for the school's 117 classrooms and 2 gymnasiums.

Most students at the high school looked at the nearby landfill and saw garbage. In 1993, however, members of the school's Ecology Club saw it as an environmental opportunity.

After doing their homework, they convinced school officials to **(1)** build a pipeline to transfer waste methane gas from the landfill to the school and **(2)** rebuild two basement heating system boilers to burn the methane to heat the school. The school has recouped its investment and is now saving money. In addition, students at the school are getting a lesson in applied environmental science by studying the operation and design of the system.

#### Critical Thinking

This project may not have wide application because most schools are not near landfills. Are there any renewable energy resources (Chapter 16, p. 380) available at your school site that could be used to provide all or part of the school's heat or electricity? If so, consider evaluating such resources and presenting a plan to school officials.

Once in an aquatic system, mercury enters into a complex cycle in which one form is converted to another (Figure 21-19, p. 550). Bacteria commonly found in polluted waters can convert moderately harmful inorganic mercury ions ($Hg^{2+}$) to highly toxic methyl mercury, which can be absorbed in the tissues of aquatic organisms and biologically magnified as it passes through food chains and webs. Levels of methyl mercury in lakes and lake organisms appear to be connected to acid deposition (Figure 17-10, p. 428) because the conversion rate of inorganic mercury to methyl mercury is higher in acidified lakes.

According to the EPA, most Americans are not at risk from mercury exposure. Exceptions are **(1)** pregnant women and children less than six years who eat certain types of fish and **(2)** people who consume unusually large quantities of certain types of fish. According to a 2000 report by the National Academy of Sciences Report, 60,000 pregnant women a year in the United States are putting their fetuses at risk of brain damage because of methyl mercury in the fish they eat.

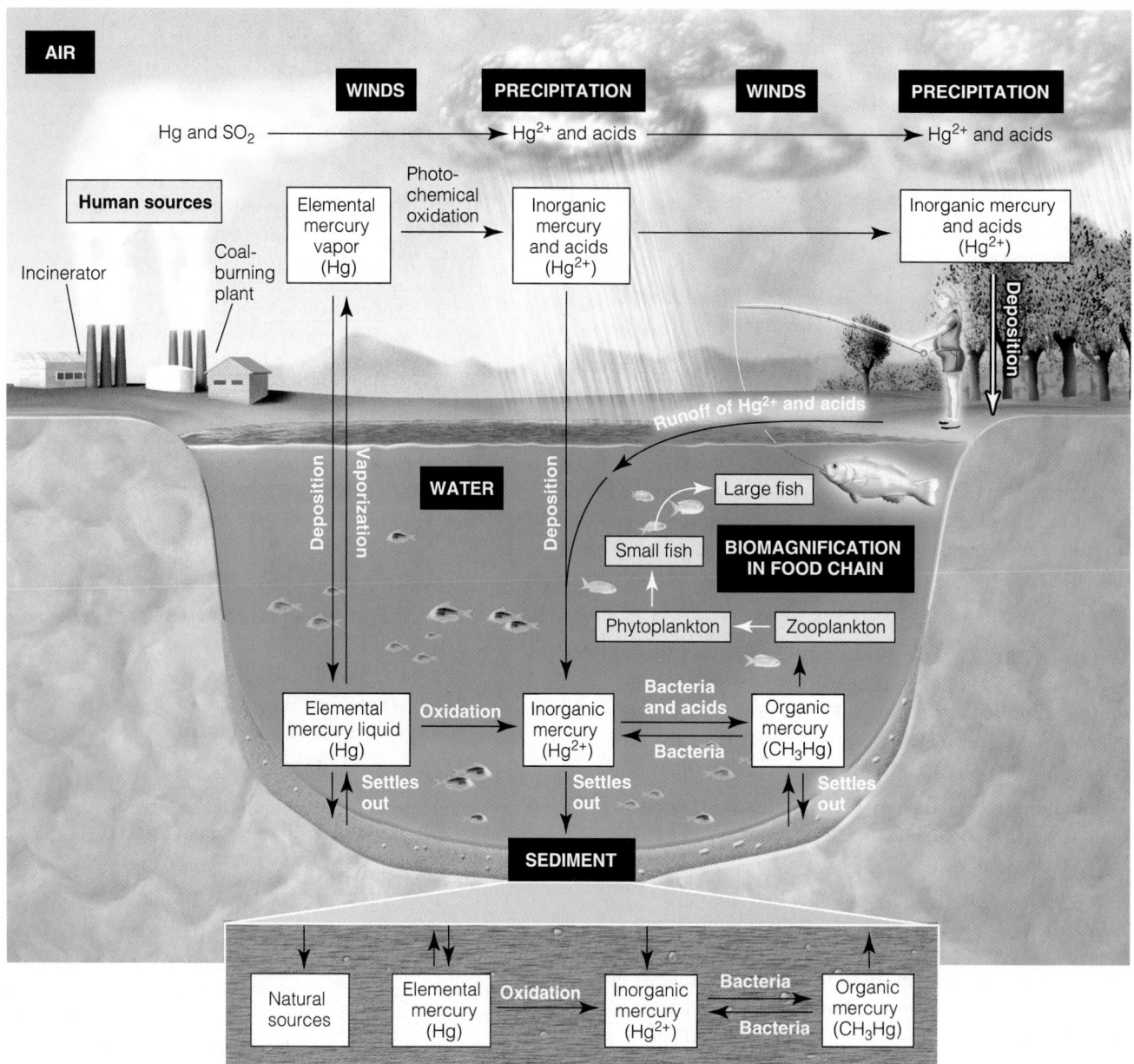

**Figure 21-19** Cycling of mercury in aquatic environments in which various forms are converted from one form to another. The most toxic form to humans is methyl mercury (CH₃Hg), which can be biologically magnified in aquatic food chains. Some mercury is also released back into the atmosphere as mercury vapor.

In 2001, the U.S. Food and Drug Administration warned pregnant women and young children not to eat swordfish, shark, king mackerel, and tilefish. The Environmental Working Group added sea bass, Gulf Coast oysters, tuna steaks, marlin, halibut, pike, walleye, white croaker, and largemouth bass to this list.

According to a 2001 study by the Centers for Disease Control and Prevention, one in ten American women of childbearing age risks having a baby born with neurological problems because of exposure of fetuses to mercury. Statistically, this means 375,000 babies are at risk each year.

People in South America's Amazon, southern Africa, the Philippines, and other areas who work in or live near gold mines where mercury is used to extract gold ore are also at high risk from mercury poisoning (Case Study, p. 345).

**How Can We Reduce Exposure to Mercury?**
Here are ways to control or reduce human exposure to mercury:

*Emissions Control*

■ Lower the allowed emissions of mercury for coal burning plants and all types of incinerators.

■ Tax each unit of mercury emitted by coal burning plants and incinerators.

- Remove mercury from emissions produced by coal burning plants and waste incinerators (removes 4–44% of mercury depending on type of device used).

### Prevention

- Remove mercury from coal before it is burned (can reduce mercury emissions by 20–40% depending on coal type).

- Convert coal to a liquid or gaseous fuel (Figure 15-33, p. 365, and Figure 15-34, p. 365).

- Phase out coal burning and shift to natural gas (Figure 15-29, p. 362) and renewable sources of energy, especially wind (Section 16-5, p. 401) and hydrogen (Section 16-7, p. 405).

- Phase out incineration of wastes.

- Phase out use of mercury in electrical switches and relays, as Xerox and several automakers have done.

- Ban use of mercury in dry-cell batteries (as has been done in Michigan) and thermometers (as has been done by several major drugstore chains).

- Ban disposal of fluorescent bulbs (which contain mercury) and require that they be collected and sent to licensed recycling facilities.

- Prohibit use of mercury in inks, dyes, pigments, paints, fungicides, and packaging products.

- Require labels on all products containing mercury.

**What Should We Do About Chlorine?** Modern society depends heavily on chlorine ($Cl_2$) and chlorine-containing compounds. However, some of the around 11,000 chlorine-containing organic compounds we produce **(1)** are persistent, **(2)** accumulate in body fat, and **(3)** are harmful to human health (according to animal and other toxicity studies; Section 11-2, p. 229).

The three largest uses of chlorine are **(1)** plastics (mostly polyvinyl chloride or PVC), **(2)** solvents, and **(3)** paper and pulp bleaching. Together, they account for about 80% of all chlorine use. Most of these uses have substitutes and could be phased out.

The production of PVC generated many toxic by-products, including dioxins and furans (at right). At the end of its life, most PVC waste is either landfilled or incinerated (which also produces dioxins). Nonchlorine plastics and other materials could replace most uses of PVCs, and PVC incineration could be prohibited. Denmark has imposed a tax on all PVC products. A number of companies, including manufacturers of automobiles and medical products, are phasing out PVC in response to growing concern over its harmful environmental and health impacts.

Studies estimate that 60% of the chlorinated organic solvents currently used could be phased out over a decade and replaced with less harmful, affordable substitutes such as **(1)** soap and water, **(2)** steam cleaning, **(3)** citrus-based solvents (Individuals Matter, p. 479), and **(4)** physical cleaning (including elbow grease and blasting with plastic beads and a pressurized solution of water and baking soda). Such a phaseout has already begun, not just for environmental reasons but also to **(1)** reduce legal liability for possible effects of such chemicals on workers and consumers and **(2)** save money needed to dispose of such chemicals).

Using chlorine to bleach wood pulp and paper could be replaced with less harmful processes that rely on oxygen, ozone, and hydrogen peroxide, as several paper companies are doing. By the early 1990s, the German paper industry had achieved totally chlorine-free paper production (which is 30% cheaper than processes using chlorine); the rest of Europe is following Germany's lead. The United States lags far behind in production of chlorine-free paper.

About 5% of the chlorine produced in the United States is used to purify drinking water (1%) and wastewater from sewage treatment plants (4%). Much of this could be replaced gradually with ozone and other nonchlorine purification processes. However, drinking water may still need to be purified by chlorination because it kills harmful microorganisms in water lines.

The remaining 35% of chlorine is used to manufacture a variety of organic and inorganic chemicals, many of them for small and specialized uses. Each of these chemicals could be evaluated to determine which are essential (many pharmaceuticals) and which might be replaced by affordable and environmentally acceptable substitutes.

If given proper financial incentives and 10–20 years to develop and phase in substitutes, chemical producers could **(1)** profit from sales of chlorine substitutes and **(2)** protect themselves from adverse publicity, lawsuits, and cleanup costs.

**How Dangerous Are Dioxins?** *Dioxins* are a family of more than 75 different chlorinated hydrocarbon compounds formed (along with toxic furans) as unwanted by-products in high-temperature chemical reactions involving chlorine and hydrocarbons. Exposing chlorine-containing compounds to high temperatures creates conditions that can produce dioxins and related compounds called furans.

Dioxins are mainly unwanted by-products of a wide range of industrial processes but can also result from natural processes, such as forest fires and volcanic eruptions. Worldwide, incineration of municipal and medical wastes accounts for about 70% of dioxin and furan releases to the atmosphere. Other sources include **(1)** residential wood-burning fireplaces, **(2)** coal-fired power plants, **(3)** metal smelting and refining facilities, **(4)** wood pulp and paper mills, and **(5)** sludge from municipal wastewater treatment plants.

About 30 dioxin compounds are considered to have significant toxicity. One dioxin compound, TCDD, is the most toxic (Table 11-1, p. 232) and the most widely studied. Dioxins such as TCDD are persistent chemicals that linger in the environment for decades, especially in soil and human fat tissue.

About 90% of the human exposure to dioxins is through the food supply. Concern about the harmful health effects of exposure to low levels of dioxins on humans and wildlife is growing.

A 2001 draft report of a comprehensive, EPA-sponsored, 6-year, $4 million review by more than 100 scientists around the world concluded that

- TCDD should be classified as a definite human carcinogen, and other dioxin compounds should be classified as likely human carcinogens, especially for people who eat large amounts of fatty meats and dairy products. In 2000, the National Toxicology Program of the U.S. Department of Health and Human Services recommended that TCDD be classified as a known human carcinogen.

- The most powerful effect of exposure to low levels of dioxin by the general public is disruption of the reproductive, endocrine, and immune systems (Connections, p. 235) and their harmful effects on developing fetuses.

- Very small levels of dioxin released into the environment can cause serious damage to certain wildlife species.

Industries producing dioxins say the dangers of long-term exposure to low levels of dioxins are overestimated. They cite a 2000 study by Kyle Steenland, a researcher with the National Institute for Occupational Safety and Health, who found no significant risk of cancer for the general public exposed to low levels of toxic dioxins.

Some environmental scientists argue (1) it will take decades to resolve these issues, and (2) meanwhile we should adopt stricter regulations to reduce dioxin emissions as a *precautionary strategy*. According to these scientists, the best ways to sharply reduce emissions of dioxins in the United States (and elsewhere) would be to (1) eliminate the chlorinated hydrocarbon compounds that produce dioxins from hazardous wastes burned in incinerators, iron ore sintering plants, and cement kilns and (2) use nonchlorine methods to bleach paper (as is done in several European countries).

## 21-9 HAZARDOUS WASTE REGULATION IN THE UNITED STATES

**What Is the Resource Conservation and Recovery Act?** In 1976, the U.S. Congress passed the *Resource Conservation and Recovery Act (RCRA*, pro-

nounced "RICK-ra") and amended it in 1984. This law requires (1) the EPA to identify hazardous wastes and set standards for their management by states, (2) firms that store, treat, or dispose of more than 100 kilograms (220 pounds) of hazardous wastes per month to have a permit stating how such wastes are to be managed, and (3) permit holders to use a cradle-to-grave system to keep track of waste transferred from point of origin to approved off-site disposal facilities.

**What Is the Superfund Act?** In 1980, the U.S. Congress passed the *Comprehensive Environmental Response, Compensation, and Liability Act*, commonly known as the *Superfund* program. Through taxes on chemical raw materials, this law (plus later amendments) has provided a trust fund for (1) identifying abandoned hazardous waste dump sites (p. 525 and Spotlight, p. 553) and underground tanks leaking toxic chemicals, (2) protecting and if necessary cleaning up groundwater near such sites, (3) cleaning up the sites, and, (4) when they can be found, requiring the responsible parties to pay for the cleanup.

Once the EPA identifies a site, the following procedure is used:

- Groundwater around the site is tested for contamination. If these tests reveal no immediate threat to human health, nothing more may be done.

- If a threat to human health is identified, immediate steps are taken to isolate and stabilize the wastes and protect the public. This may include (1) digging a deep trench and installing a concrete containment dike around the site and (2) covering the site with impervious layers of plastic and clay to prevent further infiltration and leaching of wastes into nearby groundwater.

- The worst sites that represent an immediate and severe threat to human health are put on a *National Priorities List (NPL)* and scheduled for total cleanup using the most cost-effective method. Cleanup methods include (1) removing and treating any chemical wastes stored in drums or other containers, (2) excavating contaminated soil and burning it in an on-site incinerator or kiln, and (3) cleaning up contaminated soil by bioremediation or phytoremediation (p. 542).

To keep taxpayers from footing most of the bill, cleanups are based on the *polluter-pays principle*. The EPA is charged with (1) finding the parties responsible for each site, (2) ordering them to pay for the entire cleanup, and (3) suing them if they do not. When the EPA can find no responsible party, it draws money out of the Superfund for cleanup.

To implement the polluter-pays principle, the Superfund legislation considers all polluters of a site to be subject to strict, joint, and several liability. This controversial strategy means that individual polluters (regardless of their contributions) can be held liable for the entire cost of cleaning up a site if the other parties cannot be found or have gone bankrupt.

Since 1981, about 1,900 sites have been placed on a National Priority List for cleanup because they pose a real or potential threat to nearby populations. Emergency cleanup has been carried out at almost all sites, and wastes on more than half the sites have been contained and stabilized to prevent leakage. Between 1981 and 2000, 750 sites had been cleaned up and removed from the list at a cost of more than $300 billion. The almost 1,500 remaining sites are in various stages of cleanup with no cleanup plan for 56% of the sites. Attempts are being made to improve the Superfund Act without seriously weakening it (Solutions, p. 554).

The former U.S. Office of Technology Assessment and the Waste Management Research Institute estimate the Superfund list could eventually include at least 10,000 priority sites, with cleanup costs of up to $1 trillion, not counting legal fees. Other studies project 2,000 sites with estimated cleanup costs of $200–300 billion over the next 30 years.

The Superfund law does not cover numerous other sites containing hazardous and toxic wastes. According to government estimates,

- Cleaning up toxic military dumps will cost $100–200 billion and take at least 30 years. The U.S. military produces about 0.9 metric tons (1 ton) of hazardous wastes *every minute.*

- Cleaning up 113 Department of Energy sites used to make nuclear weapons will cost $168–212 billion and take 70 years.

- Cleaning up 300,000 active and abandoned mine sites, 200,000 sites leased for oil and gas drilling, 3,000 landfills, and 4,200 leaking underground storage tanks on public lands under the Department of Interior will cost at least $100 billion.

The total cleanup bill of roughly $750 billion will cost U.S. taxpayers an average $41 million *per day* or $1.7 million *per hour* without stop for about 50 years. These estimated costs are only for cleanup to prevent future damage and do not include the health and ecological costs associated with such wastes. Some environmentalists and economists cite this as compelling evidence that preventing pollution costs much less than cleaning it up.

**What Are Brownfields?** *Brownfields* are abandoned industrial and commercial sites that in most cases are contaminated. Examples include factories, junkyards, older landfills, and gas stations. Some

## Using Honeybees to Detect Toxic Pollutants

**SPOTLIGHT**

Honeybees are being used to detect the presence of toxic and radioactive chemicals in concentrations as low as several parts per trillion. On their forays from a hive, bees pick up water, nectar, pollen, suspended particulate matter, volatile organic compounds, and radioactive material found in the air near the sites they visit.

The bees then bring these materials back to the hive. There they fan the air vigorously with their wings to regulate the hive's temperature. This action releases and circulates pollutants they picked up into the air inside the hive.

Scientists have put portable hives, each containing 7,000–15,000 bees, near known or suspected hazardous waste sites. A small copper tube attached to the side of each hive pumps air out. Portable equipment is used to analyze the air for toxic and radioactive materials.

To find out where the bees have gone to forage for food, a botanist uses a microscope to examine pollen grains to determine what kinds of plants they come from. These data can be correlated with the plants found in an area up to 1.6 kilometers (1 mile) from each hive. This allows scientists to develop maps of toxicity levels and hot spots on large tracts of land.

This approach is much cheaper than setting up a number of air pollution monitors around mines, hazardous waste dumps, and other sources of toxic and radioactive pollutants. These *biological indicator* species have helped locate and track toxic pollutants and radioactive material at more than 30 sites across the United States.

### Critical Thinking

Because honeybees can pick up toxic pollutants anywhere they go, should honey from all beehives be tested for such pollutants before it is placed on the market? Explain.

450,000–600,000 brownfield sites exist in the United States, many of them in economically distressed inner cities.

Many of these sites could be cleaned up and reborn as parks, nature reserves, athletic fields, and neighborhoods. But first old oil and grease, industrial solvents, toxic metals, and other contaminants must be removed from their soil and groundwater.

Such efforts have been hampered by concerns of urban planners, developers, and lenders about legal liability for past contamination of such sites. However,

Since the Superfund program began, polluters and their insurance companies have been working hard to do away with the *polluter-pays* principle at the heart of the program and make it mostly a *public-pays* approach.

This strategy, which is working, has three components: **(1)** Deny responsibility (stonewall) to tie up the EPA in expensive legal suits for years, **(2)** sue local governments and small businesses to make them responsible for cleanup, both as a delaying tactic and to turn local governments and small businesses into opponents of Superfund's strict liability requirements, and **(3)** mount a public relations campaign declaring that toxic dumps pose little threat, cleanup is too expensive compared to the risks involved, and the Superfund law is unfair, wasteful, and ineffective.

According to the authors of the Superfund law, the strict, joint, and several liability scheme would work better than any other liability scheme. Suppose, for instance, the EPA had been required to identify and bring an enforcement action against every party liable for a dump site. Then **(1)** the agency would be overwhelmed with lawsuits, **(2)** the pace of cleanup would be still slower, and **(3)** administrative costs would rise sharply and cause the program to become more of a *public-pays program* favored by the polluters.

The EPA also points out that the strict polluter-pays principle in the Superfund Act has been effective in making illegal dump sites virtually relics of the past—an important form of pollution prevention for the future. It has also forced waste producers who are fearful of future liability claims to reduce their production of such waste and to recycle or reuse much more of what they generate.

However, the Bush administration supports shifting cleanup costs from industries to taxpayers. In 2002, the President proposed **(1)** shifting the cleanup for 33 Superfund sites in 18 states to the government's general fund (meaning taxpayers would pay) or **(2)** cutting off funding for these sites.

Critics say it has taken 30 years and more than $300 billion to stabilize sites on the list but clean up only about half of them. According to the EPA, the delaying tactics just described have caused much of the delay and high costs.

Suggestions for improving the program include the following:

- Setting up an $8 billion Environmental Insurance Resolution Fund funded by insurers for a 10-year period. Companies found liable for cleanup of wastes they disposed of before 1986 would be able to use money from this fund rather than going to their individual insurance companies.

- Exempting innocent individuals, small businesses, and municipalities from Superfund liability. Congress passed a law that went into effect in 2002 that generally eliminates financial liability for **(1)** companies that contributed only small amounts of hazardous waste to Superfund sites and **(2)** small businesses and residential property owners who deposited only municipal trash at Superfund sites.

- Involving local governments and people living near Superfund sites in cleanup decisions from start to finish.

Some experts argue that sites on the National Priorities List should be ranked in three general categories: **(1)** sites needing immediate full cleanup, **(2)** sites considered to pose a serious hazard but located far from concentrations of people or endangered ecosystems (these sites would receive emergency cleanup and then be isolated by barriers and signs, with more complete cleanup to come later), and **(3)** lower-risk sites needing only stabilization (capping and containment) and monitoring.

**Critical Thinking**

Do you support the *polluter-pays principle* used in the original Superfund legislation? Defend your position. Use the library or Internet to find out whether there have been any recent changes in the Superfund law. If so, evaluate these changes and decide which of them you support. Defend your position.

---

Congress and almost half of the states have passed laws limiting the financial liability for lenders and developers of brownfield sites.

As a result, by 2002, more than 40,000 former brownfield sites had been redeveloped as part of urban revitalization and many other projects are underway. Here are two examples of brownfield projects:

- In Dallas, Texas, a brownfield site consisting of a 100-year-old city dump, abandoned grain silos, an aging coal-burning power plant, and a railroad maintenance building has been cleaned up and converted to a $420 million downtown site for a sports and entertainment arena and a complex of apartments, offices and stores.

- Developers in Philadelphia, Pennsylvania, plan to rehabilitate an 18-kilometer- (11-mile-) long abandoned industrial park along the Delaware River, just north of downtown.

## 21-10 SOLUTIONS: ACHIEVING A LOW-WASTE SOCIETY

**What Is the Role of Grassroots Action? Bottom-Up Change** In the United States, local citizens have worked together to prevent hundreds of incinerators, landfills, or treatment plants for hazardous and radioactive wastes from being built in or near their communities. Opposition has grown as numerous studies have shown that such facilities have traditionally been located in communities populated mostly by African Americans, Asian Americans, Latinos, and poor whites. This practice has been cited as an example of *environmental injustice.*

Most members of such groups recognize that health risks from incinerators and landfills, when averaged over the entire country, are quite low. However, they also know the risks for the people near these facilities are much higher. These people, not the rest of the population, are the ones whose health, lives, and property values are being threatened.

Manufacturers and waste industry officials point out that something must be done with the toxic and hazardous wastes produced to provide people with certain goods and services. They contend that if local citizens adopt a "not in my backyard" (NIMBY) approach, the waste still ends up in someone's backyard.

Many citizens do not accept this argument. To them, the best way to deal with most toxic or hazardous wastes is to produce much less of them, as suggested by the National Academy of Sciences (Figure 21-4 and Guest Essay, p. 530). For such materials, their goal is "not in anyone's backyard" (NIABY) or "not on planet Earth" (NOPE) by emphasizing pollution and waste prevention and use of the precautionary principle.

**What Can Be Done at the International Level? The POPs Treaty** In 2001, the UN Commission On Human Rights declared that being able to live free of pollution is a basic human right. There is a long way to go in converting this ideal into reality, but important progress has been made.

Between 1989 and 1994, an international treaty to limit transfer of hazardous waste from one country to another was developed (p. 547). In 2000, delegates from 122 countries completed a global treaty to control 12 *persistent organic pollutants* (POPs), which will go into effect when ratified by 50 countries.

These widely used toxic chemicals are insoluble in water and soluble in fatty tissues. This allows them to be concentrated in the fatty tissues of humans and other organisms feeding at high trophic levels in food webs to levels hundreds of thousand times higher than in the general environment (Figure 11-4, p. 231, and Figure 19-6, p. 490). These persistent pollutants can also be transported long distances by wind and water.

The list of 12 chemicals, called the *dirty dozen*, includes DDT and 8 other chlorine-containing persistent pesticides, PCBs, dioxins, and furans. The goals of the treaty are to **(1)** ban or phase out use of these chemicals and **(2)** detoxify or isolate stockpiles of such chemicals in warehouses and dumps. About 25 countries can continue using DDT to combat malaria until safer alternatives are available. Developed nations will provide developing nations about $150 million per year to help them switch to safer alternatives for the 12 POPs.

Environmentalists consider the POPs treaty an important milestone in international environmental law because it uses the *precautionary principle* (p. 236) to manage and reduce the risks from toxic chemicals. This list is expected to grow as scientific studies uncover more evidence of toxic and environmental damage from some of the chemicals we use.

In 2000, the Swedish Parliament enacted a law that would ban on all chemicals that are persistent and can bioaccumulate in living tissue by 2020. The Swedish law requires an industry to show that a chemical it uses is safe rather than having the government show it is dangerous.

**How Can We Make the Transition to a Low-Waste Society?** According to physicist Albert Einstein, "A clever person solves a problem, a wise person avoids it." To prevent pollution and reduce waste, many environmental scientists urge us to understand and live by four key principles: **(1)** Everything is connected, **(2)** there is no "away" for the wastes we produce, **(3)** dilution is not always the solution to pollution, and **(4)** the best and cheapest way to deal with waste and pollution is to produce less of them and then reuse and recycle most of the materials we use (Figures 21-3 and 21-4).

Visible signs of **(1)** *cleaner production* (p. 531 and Guest Essay, p. 536), **(2)** increased *resource productivity* (Solutions, p. 533), and **(3)** *service flow* businesses (p. 533) are emerging. Ecoindustrial parks (p. 532 and Figure 21-5) are being built and planned.

In addition, at least 24 countries have *ecolabeling programs* that certify a product or service as having met specified environmental standards. The first national ecolabeling, Germany's *Blue Angel* program, began in 1978. It now awards its seal of approval to more than 3,900 products and services. Other examples are India's *Ecomark*, Singapore's *Green Label*, and the *Green Seal* program in the United States.

Such revolutions start off slowly but can accelerate rapidly as their economic, ecological, and health advantages become more apparent to investors, business leaders, elected officials, and citizens. See the website material for this chapter for some actions you can take to reduce your production of solid waste and hazardous waste.

*The key to addressing the challenge of toxics use and wastes rests on a fairly straightforward principle: harness the innovation and technical ingenuity that has characterized the chemicals industry from its beginning and channel these qualities in a new direction that seeks to detoxify our economy.*

ANNE PLATT MCGINN

## REVIEW QUESTIONS

**1.** Define the boldfaced terms in this chapter.

**2.** Summarize what happened at Love Canal and the lessons learned from this environmental problem.

**3.** Distinguish between *solid waste* and *municipal solid waste*. What are the major sources of solid waste in the United States? What happens to municipal solid waste in the United States? Describe the problem of mining and smelting waste in Montana. Give five examples of solid waste thrown away in the United States.

**4.** What is *hazardous waste*? Hazardous waste laws regulate what percentage of the overall hazardous waste produced in the United States?

**5.** Summarize the threat from release of toxic chemicals from industrial plants because of accidents or terrorism. Describe the 1984 accident at the Dow pesticide plant in Bhopal, India.

**6.** Distinguish between the *high-waste* and *low-waste* approaches to solid and hazardous waste management. According to the U.S. National Academy of Sciences, what should be the five goals of solid and hazardous waste management in order of their importance? According to scientists, what percentage of solid and hazardous waste produced could be eliminated through a combination of waste reduction, reuse, and recycling (including composting)?

**7.** What does Lois Gibbs (p. 530) think we should do with solid and hazardous waste, and what major questions does she believe we should ask about such wastes?

**8.** List seven ways to reduce waste and pollution. What is *resource productivity*? List five ways in which resource productivity has been improved. By how much do some experts think we can improve resource productivity? List four advantages of greatly increasing resource productivity.

**9.** What is *cleaner production*? Describe the resource exchange system used in Denmark and the pollution prevention program implemented by the Minnesota Mining and Manufacturing (3M) company in the United States. List five economic benefits of cleaner production.

**10.** Explain why Peter Montague (p. 536) believes the regulation and standards approach used to control pollu-

tion during the past 33 years has failed. Describe what he thinks should replace this approach.

**11.** What is a *service flow economy*? What are four economic advantages of such an economy for businesses and consumers? List four examples of how a service economy is being implemented. Describe how Ray Anderson (Individuals Matter, p. 534) is developing a carpet tile service flow business.

**12.** What is *reuse*, and what are three advantages of using this approach for waste reduction? List five examples of reuse.

**13.** Distinguish between *primary (closed-loop)* and *secondary, or downcycling*. What is *compost*, and how is it used as a way to deal with solid waste? About what percentage of the municipal solid waste produced in the United States is recycled and composted, and what percentage do experts believe could be recycled and composted?

**14.** Distinguish between the *centralized recycling* of mixed solid waste and *consumer separation* of solid waste, and list the pros and cons of each approach to recycling.

**15.** List the pros and cons of recycling. What three factors hinder recycling and reuse? List nine ways to encourage more recycling and reuse. Describe Germany's approach to recycling.

**16.** Describe how paper is made and how paper is recycled. List nine benefits from recycling paper. Distinguish between *preconsumer* and *postconsumer paper waste*.

**17.** List three reasons why so few plastics are recycled. List four advantages and four disadvantages of using plastics.

**18.** Describe Denmark's hazardous waste detoxification program. Give the pros and cons of using *bioremediation* and *phytoremediation* for detoxifying hazardous waste. Describe two chemical methods for detoxifying hazardous waste.

**19.** Give the pros and cons of using a *plasma torch* to detoxify hazardous waste.

**20.** Describe the major components of a *mass-burn incinerator* and a *sanitary landfill*. List the pros and cons of dealing with solid and hazardous waste by **(a)** burning it in incinerators and **(b)** burying it in sanitary landfills.

**21.** List the pros and cons of storing hazardous wastes in **(a)** deep underground wells, **(b)** surface impoundments, **(c)** secure landfills, and **(d)** aboveground buildings. Describe what is being done at the international level about the exporting of hazardous wastes from one country to another.

**22.** Describe the hazards of lead exposure, and list ten ways to reduce such exposure.

**23.** Describe the hazards of mercury exposure, and list three ways to reduce mercury emissions and nine ways to reduce inputs of mercury into the environment from human sources.

**24.** What are three major problems with many chlorine-containing compounds? What are the three major uses of chlorine? How can we reduce exposure to harmful chlorine-containing compounds?

**25.** What are *dioxins?* How are they produced, what harm can they cause, and how can we reduce exposure to these hazardous chemicals?

**26.** How is the Resource Conservation and Recovery Act used to deal with the problem of hazardous wastes in the United States?

**27.** What is the Superfund Act, and what are its strengths and weaknesses? List three ways to improve this act.

**28.** What are *brownfields,* and what has been done to help redevelop such sites in the United States? Give an example of a reclaimed brownfield site.

**29.** Describe international efforts to control use of 12 persistent organic pollutants (POPs).

**30.** List four principles that can be used as guidelines for making the transition to a low-waste society.

## CRITICAL THINKING

**1.** Explain why you support or oppose requiring that **(a)** all beverage containers be reusable, **(b)** all households and businesses put recyclable materials into separate containers for curbside pickup, **(c)** garbage-collecting systems implement the pay-as-you-throw approach, and **(d)** consumers pay for plastic or paper bags at grocery and other stores to encourage the use of reusable shopping bags.

**2.** Use the second law of thermodynamics (p. 59) to explain why a *properly designed* source-separation recycling program takes less energy and produces less pollution than a centralized program that collects mixed waste over a large area and hauls it to a centralized facility where workers or machinery separate the wastes for recycling.

**3.** What short- and long-term disadvantages (if any) might an ecoindustrial revolution based on cleaner production (p. 531) bring? Do you believe it will be possible to phase in such a revolution in the country where you live over the next two to three decades? Explain. What are the three most important strategies for doing this?

**4.** Explain why some businesses participating in an exchange and chemical-cycling network (Figure 21-5, p. 532) might produce large amounts of waste for use as resources within the network rather than redesigning their manufacturing processes to reduce waste production.

**5.** What short- and long-term disadvantages (if any) might there be in shifting to a service flow economy (p. 533)? Do you believe it will be possible to phase in such a shift in the country where you live over the next two to three decades? Explain. What are the three most important strategies for doing this?

**6.** Would you oppose having a hazardous waste landfill, waste treatment plant, deep-injection well, or incinerator in your community? Explain. If you oppose these disposal facilities, how do you believe the hazardous waste generated in your community and your state should be managed?

**7.** Give your reasons for agreeing or disagreeing with each of the following proposals for dealing with hazardous waste:
  **a.** Reducing the production of hazardous waste and encouraging recycling and reuse of hazardous materials by charging producers a tax or fee for each unit of waste generated
  **b.** Banning all land disposal and incineration of hazardous waste to encourage recycling, reuse, and treatment and to protect air, water, and soil from contamination
  **c.** Providing low-interest loans, tax breaks, and other financial incentives to encourage industries producing hazardous waste to reduce, recycle, reuse, treat, and decompose such waste
  **d.** Banning the shipment of hazardous waste from one country to another

**8.** Congratulations! You are in charge of bringing about a cleaner production, resource productivity, and service flow economic revolution throughout the world over the next 20 years. List the three most important components of your strategy.

## PROJECTS

**1.** For 1 week, keep a list of the solid waste you throw away. What percentage of this waste consists of materials that could be recycled, reused, or burned for energy? What percentage of the items could you have done without in the first place? Tally and compare the results for your entire class.

**2.** What percentage of the municipal solid waste in your community is **(a)** landfilled, **(b)** incinerated, **(c)** composted, and **(d)** recycled? What technology is used in local landfills and incinerators? What leakage and pollution problems have local landfills or incinerators had? Does your community have a recycling program? Is it voluntary or mandatory? Does it have curbside collection? Drop-off centers? Buyback centers? Hazardous waste collection system?

**3.** What hazardous wastes are produced **(a)** at your school and **(b)** in your community? What happens to these wastes?

**4.** Use the library or the Internet to find bibliographic information about *Arthur C. Clarke* and *Anne Platt McGinn,* whose quotes appear at the beginning and end of this chapter.

**5.** Make a concept map of this chapter's major ideas, using the section heads and subheads and the key terms (in boldface). Look on the website for this book for information about making concept maps.

## INTERNET STUDY RESOURCES AND RESOURCES FOR FURTHER READING AND RESEARCH

The website for this book contains helpful study aids and many ideas for further reading and research. Log on to

www.info.brookscole.com/miller13

and click on the Chapter-by-Chapter area. Choose Chapter 21 and select a resource:

- Flash Cards allows you to test your mastery of the Terms and Concepts to Remember for this chapter.

- Tutorial Quizzes provides a multiple-choice practice quiz.

- Student Guide to InfoTrac will lead you to Critical Thinking Projects that use InfoTrac College Edition as a research tool.

- References lists the major books and articles consulted in writing this chapter.

- Hypercontents takes you to an extensive list of sites with news, research, and images related to individual sections of the chapter.

## INFOTRAC COLLEGE EDITION

Improve your skills with InfoTrac College Edition, a searchable online database of articles from more than 700 periodicals. Log on to

http://www.infotrac-college.com

or access InfoTrac through the website for this book. Try to find the following articles:

**1.** Isaacs, L. 2001. Rounding up household hazardous waste: Local governments have developed several ways to keep household chemicals and poisonous materials from harming the environment. *American City and County* 116: 24. *Keyword:* "phytoremediation." Dealing with hazardous wastes generated in the home is becoming more of a problem than ever. This article looks at some of the ways that household hazardous waste is being managed by a variety of municipalities.

**2.** Evans, L. D. 2002. The dirt on phytoremediation. *Journal of Soil and Water Conservation* 57: 13. *Keyword:* "household hazardous wastes." Using plants to clean up certain hazardous wastes has been done for some time, but studies show that plants can contribute even more to the cleanup effort than previously realized.

# PART V

# SUSTAINING BIODIVERSITY AND CITIES

*Only when the last tree has died and the last river poisoned and the last fish has been caught will we realize that we cannot eat money.*

Nineteenth-Century Cree Indian Saying

# 22 SUSTAINING WILD SPECIES

## The Passenger Pigeon: Gone Forever

In the early 1800s, bird expert Alexander Wilson watched a single migrating flock of an estimated 2 million passenger pigeons darken the sky for more than 4 hours. By 1914, the passenger pigeon (Figure 22-1) had disappeared forever.

How could a species that was once the most common bird in North America become extinct in only a few decades? The answer is *humans*. The main reasons for the extinction of this species were **(1)** uncontrolled commercial hunting and **(2)** loss of the bird's habitat and food supply as forests were cleared to make room for farms and cities.

Passenger pigeons were good to eat, their feathers made good pillows, and their bones were widely used for fertilizer. They were easy to kill because they flew in gigantic flocks and nested in long, narrow colonies.

Commercial hunters would capture one pigeon alive, sew its eyes shut, and tie it to a perch called a stool. Soon a curious flock would land beside this "stool pigeon." Then the birds would be shot or ensnared by nets that might trap more than 1,000 birds at once.

Beginning in 1858, passenger pigeon hunting became a big business. Shotguns, traps, artillery, and even dynamite were used. Burning grass or sulfur below their roosts sometimes suffocated birds. Shooting galleries used live birds as targets. In 1878, one professional pigeon trapper made $60,000 by killing 3 million birds at their nesting grounds near Petoskey, Michigan.

By the early 1880s, only a few thousand birds remained. At that point, recovery of the species was doomed because the females laid only one egg per nest. On March 24, 1900, a young boy in Ohio shot the last known wild passenger pigeon. The last passenger pigeon on earth, a hen named Martha after Martha Washington, died in the Cincinnati Zoo in

1914. Her stuffed body is now on view at the National Museum of Natural History in Washington, D.C.

Eventually, all species become extinct or evolve into new species. However, biologists estimate that every day 2–200 species become *prematurely extinct* primarily because of human activities. Studies indicate that this rate of loss of biodiversity is expected to increase as the human population **(1)** grows, **(2)** consumes more resources, **(3)** disturbs more of the earth's land, and **(4)** uses more of the earth's net plant productivity that supports all species.

**Figure 22-1** Passenger pigeons, extinct in the wild since 1900. The last known passenger pigeon died in the Cincinnati Zoo in 1914.

*The last word in ignorance is the person who says of an animal or plant: "What good is it?" . . . If the land mechanism as a whole is good, then every part of it is good, whether we understand it or not. . . . Harmony with land is like harmony with a friend; you cannot cherish his right hand and chop off his left.*

ALDO LEOPOLD

This chapter addresses the following questions:

- How have human activities affected the earth's biodiversity?
- Are human activities causing an extinction crisis?
- Why should we care about biodiversity and species extinction?
- What human activities endanger wildlife?
- How can we prevent premature extinction of species?
- How can we manage game animals more sustainably?

## 22-1 HUMAN IMPACTS ON BIODIVERSITY

**What Major Factors Affect Biodiversity?** Factors that tend to *increase* biodiversity are (1) a physically diverse habitat, (2) moderate environmental disturbance (Figure 8-17, p. 184), (3) small variations in environmental conditions such as nutrient supply, precipitation, and temperature, (4) the middle stages of succession (Figure 8-14, p. 180, and Figure 8-15, p. 181), and (5) evolution (Section 5-2, p. 100).

Factors that tend to *decrease* biodiversity are (1) environmental stress, (2) a large environmental disturbance (Table 8-2, p. 183), (3) extreme environmental conditions, (4) severe limitation of an essential nutrient, habitat, or other resource, (5) introduction of an nonnative species, and (6) geographic isolation (Figure 5-8, p. 105). Many of these factors are related to human activities.

**How Have Human Activities Affected Global Biodiversity?** Figure 22-2 summarizes the major connections between human activities and the earth's biodiversity. Here are some examples of how human activities have decreased and degraded the earth's biodiversity:

- Humans have taken over, disturbed, or degraded 40–50% of the earth's land surface (Figure 1-5, p. 7), especially by filling in wetlands and converting grasslands and forests to crop fields and urban areas.

- Humans use, waste, or destroy about (1) 27% of the earth's total potential net primary productivity and (2) 40% of the net primary productivity of the planet's terrestrial ecosystems (Figure 4-26, p. 82)

- About half of the world's wetlands were lost during the last century.

- Logging and land conversion have reduced global forest cover by at least 20%, and possibly as much as 50%.

- An estimated 27% of the world's incredibly diverse coral reefs (Figure 7-2, p. 145, and Figure 7-16, p. 154) have been severely damaged, and by 2050 another 70% may be severely damaged or eliminated.

- Biologists estimate that the current global extinction rate of species is at least 100 and probably close to 1,000 to 10,000

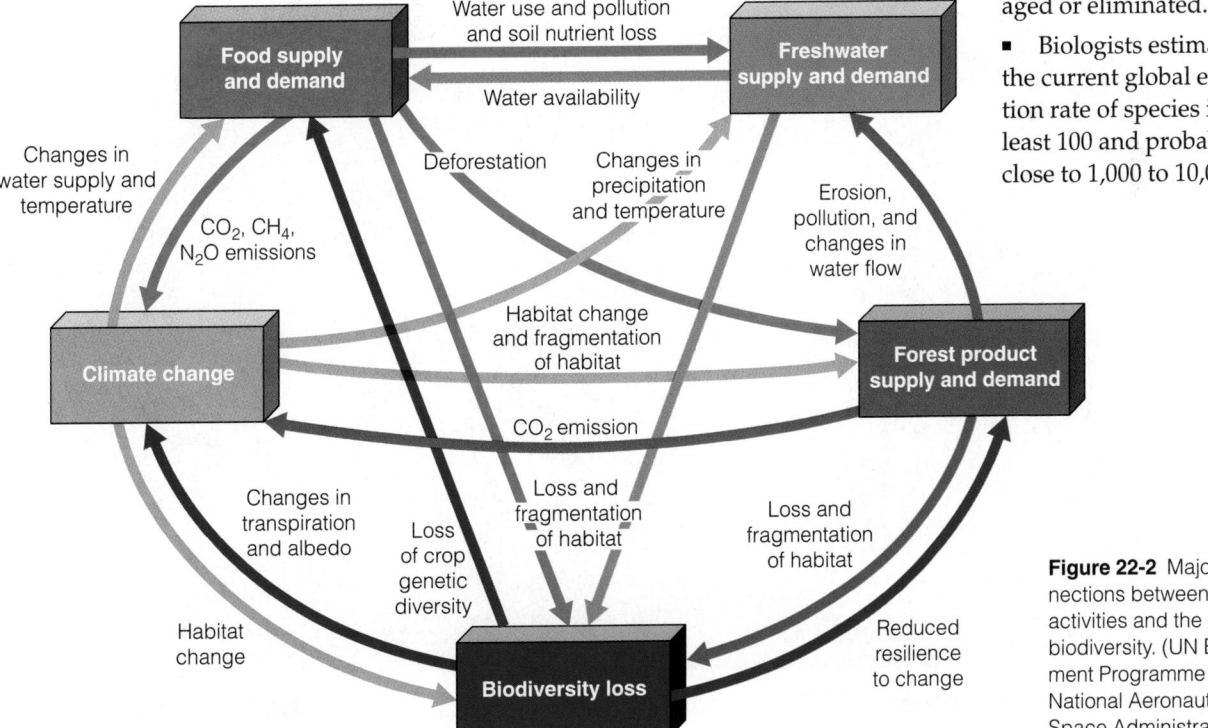

**Figure 22-2** Major connections between human activities and the earth's biodiversity. (UN Environment Programme and U.S. National Aeronautics and Space Administration)

times what it was before humans existed. The rate of premature extinction is expected to increase during this century as more people use more of the world's resources.

- A 2000 joint study by World Conservation Union and Conservation International and a 1999 study by the World Wildlife Fund found that **(1)** 34% of the world's fish species (51% of freshwater species), **(2)** 25% of amphibians (Connections, p. 170), **(3)** 24% of mammals, **(4)** 20% of reptiles, **(5)** 14% of plants, and **(6)** 12% of bird species are threatened with premature extinction.

- According to a 2000 survey by the Nature Conservancy and Association for Biodiversity Information, about 33% of 21,000 animal and plant species in the United States are vulnerable to premature extinction (Figure 22-3).

- A 1999 study by the U.S. Geological Survey found that in the United States **(1)** 95–98% of the virgin forests in the lower 48 states have been destroyed since 1620, **(2)** 98% of tallgrass prairie in the Midwest and Great Plains has disappeared, **(3)** 99% of California's native grassland, 91% of its wetlands, and 85% of its redwood forests are gone, **(4)** 90% of Hawaii's dry forests has disappeared, **(5)** 81% of the nation's fish communities have been disturbed by human activities, and **(6)** more than half of the country's original wetlands have been destroyed.

**Figure 22-4** Projected status of the earth's biodiversity between 1998 and 2018. (Data from World Resources Institute, World Conservation Monitoring Center, and Conservation International)

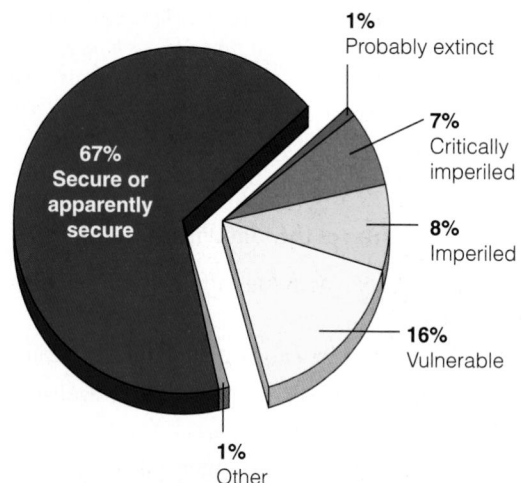

**Figure 22-3** The state of U.S. species. Recently scientists surveyed the status of plant and animal species in the United States. The *good news* is that about two-thirds of the species surveyed apparently are not in danger of extinction. The *bad news* is that about one-third of these species are in trouble. Species with the highest levels of risk are flowering plants and freshwater aquatic species such as mussels (70% of species in danger), crayfishes (more than half of species in danger), amphibians (Connections, p. 170), and fishes. (Data from the Nature Conservancy)

- According to biodiversity expert Edward O. Wilson, "The natural world in 2001 is everywhere disappearing before our eyes—cut to pieces, mowed down, plowed under, gobbled up, replaced by human artifacts."

These threats to the world's biodiversity are projected to increase sharply by 2018 (Figure 22-4).

**Projected Status of Biodiversity 1998–2018**

Critical and endangered   Threatened   Stable or intact

**The Species Approach**

**Goal**

Protect species from premature extinction

↓

**Strategies**

- Identify endangered species
- Protect their critical habitats

↓

**Tactics**

- Legally protect endangered species
- Manage habitat
- Propagate endangered species in captivity
- Reintroduce species into suitable habitats

**The Ecosystem Approach**

**Goal**

Protect populations of species in their natural habitats

↓

**Strategy**

Preserve sufficient areas of habitats in different biomes and aquatic systems

↓

**Tactics**

- Protect habitat areas through private purchase or government action
- Eliminate or reduce populations of nonnative species from protected areas
- Manage protected areas to sustain native species
- Restore degraded ecosystems

**Figure 22-5** Goals, strategies, and tactics for protecting biodiversity.

**How Can We Reduce Biodiversity Loss?** Some *good news* is that we know how to slow down this biological impoverishment by reducing these threats to the earth's biodiversity. Figure 22-5 outlines the goals, strategies, and tactics for **(1)** preventing the premature extinction of species, as discussed in this chapter, and **(2)** preserving and restoring the ecosystems and aquatic systems that provide habitats and resources for

the world's species and serve as centers for new speciation, as discussed in Chapter 23 for terrestrial species and Chapter 24 for aquatic species.

## 22-2 SPECIES EXTINCTION

**What Are Three Types of Species Extinction?** Biologists distinguish among three levels of species extinction:

- *Local extinction,* occurs when a species is no longer found in an area it once inhabited but is still found elsewhere in the world. Most local extinctions involve losses of one or more populations of species.
- *Ecological extinction,* when so few members of a species are left that it can no longer play its ecological roles in the biological communities where it is found.
- *Biological extinction,* when a species is no longer found anywhere on the earth (Figures 22-1 and 22-6). Biological extinction is forever.

**What Are Endangered and Threatened Species?** Biologists classify species heading toward biological extinction as either *endangered* or *threatened* (Figure 22-7, pp. 564–565). An **endangered species** has so few individual survivors that the species could soon become extinct over all or most of its natural range. Unless it is protected, an endangered species makes the transition to critically endangered, then to the living dead, and finally to oblivion.

A **threatened,** or **vulnerable, species** is still abundant in its natural range but because of declining numbers is likely to become endangered in the near future. Endangered and threatened species are ecological smoke alarms.

Some species have characteristics that make them more vulnerable than others to ecological and biological extinction (Figure 22-8, p. 566, and Case Study, p. 567).

**How Do Biologists Estimate Extinction Rates?** Recall that the number and diversity of the earth's species at any given time is determined by the interplay

Passenger pigeon     Great Auk     Dodo     Dusky seaside sparrow     Aepyornis (Madagascar)

**Figure 22-6** Some animal species that have become prematurely extinct largely because of human activities, mostly habitat destruction and overhunting.

Florida manatee

Northern spotted owl
(threatened)

Gray wolf

Florida panther

Bannerman's turaco
(Africa)

Devil's hole pupfish

Snow leopard
(Central Asia)

Symphonia
(Madagascar)

Black-footed ferret

Utah prairie dog

Ghost bat
(Australia)

California condor

Black lace cactus

Black rhinoceros
(Africa)

Oahu tree snail

**Figure 22-7** Species that are endangered or threatened with premature extinction largely because of human activities. Almost 30,000 of the world's species and 1,200 of those in the United States are officially listed as being in danger of becoming extinct. Most biologists believe the actual number of species at risk is much larger.

between extinction and speciation (Section 5-4, p. 104). Evolutionary biologists estimate that 99.9% of all the species that have ever existed are now extinct because of a combination of background extinction, mass extinctions, and mass depletions taking place over thousands to several million years, as discussed on p. 105. Biologists also talk of an *extinction spasm,* where

large numbers of species are lost over a period of a few centuries or at most 1,000 years.

Mass extinctions, mass depletions, and extinction spasms temporarily reduce biodiversity. But they also create opportunities for the evolution of new species to fill new or vacated ecological niches under the changed environmental conditions. According to fossil

Grizzly bear
(threatened)

Kirkland's warbler

White top pitcher plant

Arabian oryx
(Middle East)

African elephant
(Africa)

Mojave desert tortoise
(threatened)

Swallowtail butterfly

Humpback chub

Golden lion tamarin
(Brazil)

Siberian tiger
(Siberia)

West Virginia spring
salamander

Giant panda
(China)

Whooping crane

Knowlton cactus

Blue whale

Mountain gorilla
(Africa)

Pine barrens
tree frog (male)

Swamp pink

Hawksbill sea turtle

El Segunda blue butterfly

| Characteristic | Examples |
|---|---|
| Low reproductive rate (K-strategist) | Blue whale, giant panda, rhinoceros |
| Specialized niche | Blue whale, giant panda, Everglades kite |
| Narrow distribution | Many island species, elephant seal, desert pupfish |
| Feeds at high trophic level | Bengal tiger, bald eagle, grizzly bear |
| Fixed migratory patterns | Blue whale, whooping crane, sea turtles |
| Rare | Many island species, African violet, some orchids |
| Commercially valuable | Snow leopard, tiger, elephant, rhinoceros, rare plants and birds |
| Large territories | California condor, grizzly bear, Florida panther |

**Figure 22-8** Characteristics of species that are prone to ecological and biological extinction.

evidence, it takes at least 5 million years for such *adaptive radiations* to rebuild biological diversity after a large loss of species.

Two critical questions are: **(1)** How have human activities affected natural extinction rates? and **(2)** How are we likely to affect such rates in the near future (50–100 years)? Answering these questions is a difficult and controversial process because

- The extinction of a species typically takes a long time and is very difficult to document. For example, **(1)** we have regular population counts of only a few species, **(2)** members of endangered species are rare and hard to find, and **(3)** we can never be certain that one or a few individuals exist somewhere.

- We have identified only about 1.4–1.8 million of the world's estimated 5–100 million species (with a best guess of 12–14 million species) and know little about most of the species we have identified. Thus many unknown and unobserved species have become extinct

**Figure 22-9** A *species–area curve* showing how the number of species increases with habitat size. The slope of such curves varies from one habitat to another. However, the basic pattern of an initial rapid rise in the number of species followed by a leveling off in the number of species has been found to occur regardless of habitat. This *species–area relationship* suggests that, on average, a 90% loss of habitat causes the extinction of about 50% of the species living in that habitat. For example, if we assume **(1)** about 50% of the world's existing terrestrial species live in tropical forests and **(2)** about one-third of the remaining tropical forests will be cut or burned during the next few decades, the species–area relationship suggests about 1 million species in these forests will become extinct during this period.

in the past and will become extinct in future because of our actions and without our direct knowledge.

The only way to deal with this lack of information and the complexity of the earth's biodiversity is **(1)** do statistical sampling and **(2)** develop models for estimating how many species are likely to be threatened with extinction in various parts of the biosphere because of natural and human-related factors.

This is the way scientists and other analysts attempt to understand and make projections about the behavior of most of the earth's complex weather, climate, population, resource, and economic systems.

Estimates of species extinction rates are based on the following:

- Observations of how the number of species present increases with the size of an area (Figure 22-9). This *species–area relationship* suggests that, on average, a 90% loss of habitat causes the extinction of about 50% of the species living in that habitat—although this can vary with different types of habitats and biomes. However, destruction of the last 10% of an area's habitat can wipe out all of the remaining species that cannot move to other suitable habitats.

- Using models such as a **population viability analysis (PVA):** a *risk assessment* using mathematical and statistical methods to predict the probability that a population will persist for a certain number of generations based on factors such as **(1)** current and projected habitat conditions and resource needs, **(2)** genetic variability, **(3)** interactions with other species (Section 8-3, p. 172, and Section 8-4, p. 178), and **(4)** reproductive rates and population dynamics (Section 9-3, p. 195).

- Estimates of **minimum viable population (MVP):** the smallest number of individuals necessary to ensure the survival of a population in a region for a specified time period (typically ranging from decades

## Bats Are Getting a Bad Rap

**CASE STUDY**

Despite their variety (950 known species) and worldwide distribution, bats—the only mammals that can fly—have certain traits that make them vulnerable to extinction: **(1)** they reproduce slowly, and **(2)** many bat species that live in huge colonies in caves and abandoned mines become vulnerable to destruction when people block the passageways or disturb their hibernation.

Bats play important ecological roles. About 70% of all bat species feed on crop-damaging nocturnal insects and other pest species such as mosquitoes, making them the primary control agents for such insects.

In some tropical forests and on many tropical islands, pollen-eating bats pollinate flowers, and fruit-eating bats distribute plants throughout tropical forests by excreting undigested seeds (p. 165).

As *keystone species*, such bats are vital for maintaining plant biodiversity and for regenerating large areas of tropical forest cleared by human activities. If you enjoy bananas, cashews, dates, figs, avocados, or mangos, you can thank bats.

Many people mistakenly view bats as fearsome, filthy, aggressive, rabies-carrying bloodsuckers. However, most bat species are harmless to people, livestock, and crops. In the United States, only 10 people

have died of bat-transmitted disease in four decades of recordkeeping; more Americans die each year from falling coconuts.

Because of unwarranted fears of bats and lack of knowledge about their vital ecological roles, several bat species have been driven to extinction. Currently, 26% of the world's bat species, including the ghost bat (Figure 22-7), are listed as endangered or threatened. Conservation biologists urge us to view bats as valuable allies, not as enemies.

### Critical Thinking

How do you feel about bats? What would you do if you found bats flying around your yard at night?

---

to 100 years). Most population viability analyses indicate that at least a few thousand individuals are needed to ensure the survival of most species for more than a few decades.

- Estimates of **minimum dynamic area (MDA):** the minimum area of suitable habitat needed to maintain the minimum viable population. Studies suggest that maintaining populations of many small animals requires MDAs of 100–1,000 square kilometers (39–390 square miles). However, to sustain a population of 50 grizzly bears (which have a large home range) requires an MDA of about 49,000 square kilometers (18,900 square miles), and a population of 100 bears would need an area of 98,000 square kilometers (37,800 square miles).

- Models such as the theory of island biogeography (Figure 8-6, p. 168, and Figure 8-7, p. 169).

- Changes in species diversity at different latitudes (Figure 8-3, p. 167).

- Differing assumptions about **(1)** the earth's total number of species (5–100 million, with a best estimate of 12–14 million), **(2)** the proportion of these species that are found in tropical forests (50–80%), and **(3)** the rate at which tropical forests are being cleared (0.6–2% per year).

### What Effects Are Human Activities Having on Extinction Rates?
Before we came on the scene the estimated extinction rate was roughly one species per million species. This amounted to an annual extinction rate of about 0.0001% per year.

Using the methods just described, biologists conservatively estimate that the current rate of extinction is at least 100 to 1,000 times the rate before humans existed. This amounts to an extinction rate of 0.01% to 0.1% per year.

The best evidence suggests that the current extinction rate is at least 0.1% per year (1,000 times the rate before we arrived) and perhaps as high as 1% per year (10,000 times the rate before we arrived). This exponential rate of loss may seem small but recall that exponential change carried out over a period of 100 years or more amounts to a huge change in numbers (p. 2)

So how many species are we losing prematurely each year? This depends on how many species there are on the earth. Assuming that the extinction rate is about 0.1%, each year we are losing **(1)** 5,000 species per year if there are 5 million species **(2)** 14,000 if there are 14 million species, and **(3)** 100,000 if there are 100 million species.

Most biologists would consider the premature loss of 1 million species over a 100–200 year period an extinction crisis or spasm that if kept up would lead to a mass depletion or even a mass extinction. At an extinction rate of 0.1% a year we would lose 1 million species in **(1)** 200 years with 5 million species, **(2)** 71 years with 14 million species, and **(3)** 10 years with 100 million species.

Most biologists consider these to be conservative estimates because:

- Both the exponential rate of species loss and extent of biodiversity loss (Figure 22-4) are likely to increase very sharply during the next 50–100 years because of the projected exponential growth of the world's human population (Figure 1-1, p. 2 and Figure 12-11, p. 258) and per capita resource use (Figure 1-8, p. 10).

- Current and projected extinction rates are much higher than the global average in parts of the world that are especially rich in biodiversity and thus contain the majority of the world's species (Figure 22-4). Examples are tropical forests and coral reefs that are under increasing stress from human activities. Conservation biologists estimate that such biologically rich areas could lose 25–50% of their estimated species within a few decades. Thus they urge us to focus our efforts on slowing the much higher rates of extinction in such *hot spots* as the best way to protect much of the earth's biodiversity from being lost prematurely.

- We are eliminating, degrading, and simplifying many biologically diverse environments (such as tropical forests, tropical coral reefs, wetlands, and estuaries) that serve as potential colonization sites for the emergence of new species. Thus, in addition to increasing the rate of extinction, we may also be limiting long-term recovery of biodiversity by reducing the rate of speciation for some types of species—thus also creating a *speciation crisis* (Guest Essay, p. 108).

- Other biologists, such as Philip Levin and Donald Levin, argue that the increasing human fragmentation and disturbance of habitats throughout the world may increase the speciation rate for rapidly reproducing opportunist species such as rodents, cockroaches (Spotlight, p. 105) and other insects, and weeds. This would shift the current mix of types of species with a major decrease in the variety of higher-level taxonomic groups of animal species (primates, for example) and plant species (tree species, for example). Thus, the real long-term threat to biodiversity from current human activities may not be a permanent decline in the number of species but a long-term erosion in the earth's variety of species and habitats.

- According to biologist Jennifer Hughes and her colleagues at Stanford University, the loss of *local populations* of key species may be a better indicator of biodiversity loss than species extinction because these local populations provide most of the ecological services (Figure 4-34, p. 92) of an area. These researchers estimate that the loss of local populations is tens of thousands of times greater than the current estimated rate of species loss.

Because of these factors, many researchers believe the current annual extinction rate is somewhere between 1,000 (0.1% per year) and 10,000 (1% a year) times the rate before humans arrived. If the latter estimate is correct, researchers Edward O. Wilson and Stuart Primm estimate that 20% of the world's current animal and plant species could be gone by 2030 and half by the end of this century. In the words of biodiversity

expert Norman Myers (Guest Essay, p. 108), "Within just a few human generations, we shall—in the absence of greatly expanded conservation efforts—impoverish the biosphere to an extent that will persist for at least 200,000 human generations or twenty times longer than the period since humans emerged as a species."

Some people, most of them not biologists, say the current estimated extinction rates are too high and are based on inadequate data and models. Researchers agree that their estimates of extinction rates are based on inadequate data and sampling, and they are continually striving to get better data and improve the models they use to estimate extinction rates. However, they point out that

- There is clear evidence that human activities have increased the rate of species extinction and that this rate is likely to rise sharply.

- Arguing over the numbers and waiting to get better data and models should not be used as excuses for not implementing a *precautionary strategy* to reduce the ecological and economic threats from a significant decrease in the earth's genetic, species, ecological, and functional diversity.

To these biologists, we are not heeding Aldo Leopold's (Section 2-5, p. 36) warning about preserving biodiversity as we tinker with the earth: "To keep every cog and wheel is the first precaution of intelligent tinkering."

## 22-3 WHY SHOULD WE CARE ABOUT BIODIVERSITY?

**Why Preserve Wild Species and Ecosystems?** So what is all the fuss about? If all species eventually become extinct, why should we worry about losing a few more because of our activities? Does it matter that **(1)** the passenger pigeon (Figure 22-1), **(2)** the great auk (Figure 22-6), **(3)** the green sea turtle (photo on p. 39), **(4)** the 50 or so remaining Florida panthers (photo on p. 559), or **(5)** some unknown plant or insect in a tropical forest becomes prematurely extinct because of human activities?

If new species evolve to take the place of ones lost through extinction spasms, mass depletions, or mass extinctions, why should we care if we speed up the extinction rate over the next 50–100 years? The answer is that it will take at least 5 million years for speciation to rebuild the biodiversity we destroy during this century.

Because ecosystems are constantly changing in response to changing environmental conditions (Section 8-6, p. 184), why should we try to preserve ecosystem diversity? Does it matter that tropical forests, grasslands, wetlands, coral reefs, and others systems making up the earth's ecological diversity are being destroyed or degraded by human activities?

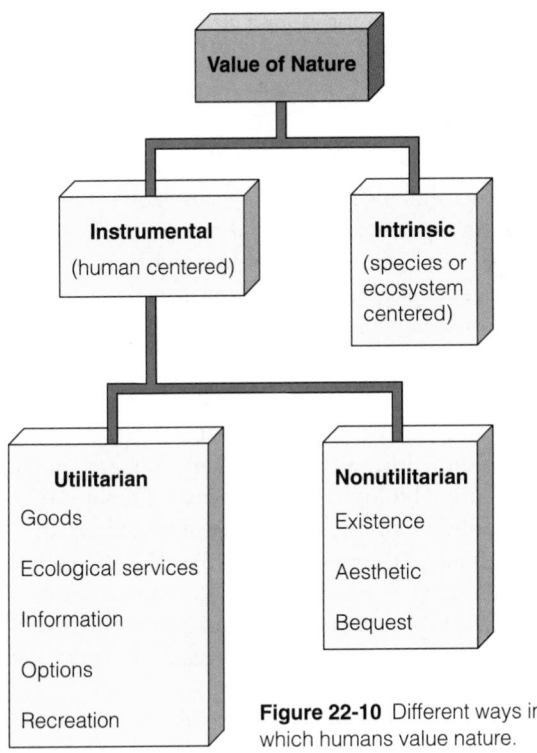

**Value of Nature**

**Instrumental** (human centered)

**Intrinsic** (species or ecosystem centered)

**Utilitarian**
Goods
Ecological services
Information
Options
Recreation

**Nonutilitarian**
Existence
Aesthetic
Bequest

**Figure 22-10** Different ways in which humans value nature.

Conservation biologists and ecologists contend that we should act to preserve the earth's overall biodiversity because the its genes, species, ecosystems, and ecological processes have two types of value (Figure 22-10):

- **Instrumental value** because of their usefulness to us
- **Intrinsic value** because they exist, regardless of whether they have any usefulness to us

**What Are the Instrumental Values of Biodiversity?** The genes, species, ecosystems, and ecological processes that make up the earth's biodiversity have several types of instrumental or human-centered values that can be classified as **(1)** *utilitarian* or *use* and **(2)** *nonutilitarian* or *nonuse* (Figure 22-10).

Examples of utilitarian values involve the following uses of nature:

*Economic Goods*

- Species provide food, fuel, fiber, lumber, paper, medicine, and many other useful products.

- About 90% of today's food crops were domesticated from wild tropical plants (Figure 13-7, p. 282), and scientists need the genetic diversity of existing wild plant species to develop future crop strains.

- At least 40% of all medicines (worth at least $200 billion per year) and 80% of the top 150 prescription drugs used in the United States were originally derived from living organisms. About 74% of these medicines were derived from plants, mostly from tropical developing countries (Figure 22-11).

- The active chemicals in about 85% of the antibiotics in current use were derived from various species of ascomycete fungi. So far we have evaluated only

**Rauvolfia**
*Rauvolfia sepentina*,
Southeast Asia
Tranquilizer, high
blood pressure
medication

**Foxglove**
*Digitalis purpurea*,
Europe
Digitalis for heart failure

**Pacific yew**
*Taxus brevifolia*,
Pacific Northwest
Ovarian cancer

**Cinchona**
*Cinchona ledogeriana*,
South America
Quinine for malaria treatment

**Rosy periwinkle**
*Cathranthus roseus*,
Madagascar
Hodgkin's disease,
lymphocytic leukemia

**Neem tree**
*Azadirachta indica*,
India
Treatment of many
diseases, insecticide,
spermicide

**Figure 22-11** *Nature's pharmacy.* Parts of these and a number of other plants and animals (many of them found in tropical forests) are used to treat a variety of human ailments and diseases. About 70% of the 3,000 plants identified by the National Cancer Institute as sources of cancer-fighting chemicals come from tropical forests. Despite their economic and health potential, fewer than 1% of the estimated 125,000 flowering plant species in tropical forests (and a mere 1,100 of the world's 260,000 known plant species) have been examined for their medicinal properties. Many of these tropical plant species are likely to become extinct before we can study them.

about 2% of the known species of such fungi for their potential to produce new antibiotics.

■ The world's flowering plants have been sources of alkaloids, a class of natural chemicals that have proved to be some of the most potent agents for curing various forms of cancer and other diseases. So far we have evaluated only about 3% of the world's known species of flowering plants for the presence of alkaloids.

■ Evaluating or *bioprospecting* the world's known and yet to be discovered species as sources of (1) pharmaceuticals, (2) genes for increasing and improving food supplies (p. 290), (3) microbes to extract metals from ores (Solutions, p. 349) and (4) microbes and plants to clean up toxic wastes (p. 542) are likely to be some of the world's most profitable and beneficial ventures. Carelessly eliminating many of the species making up the world's vast genetic library is like burning books before we read them.

### Ecological Services

■ The ecological services provided by wild species and ecosystems are key factors in sustaining the earth's biodiversity and ecological functions that support human economies and human health.

■ Such ecological services consist of the flow of materials, energy, and information from the biosphere that support all life and economies. These services include (1) photosynthesis, (2) pollination of crops and other plants, (3) soil formation and maintenance, (4) nutrient recycling, (5) pest control, (6) climate regulation, (7) moderation of weather extremes, (8) flood control, (9) drinking and irrigation water, (10) waste decomposition, (11) absorption and detoxification of pollutants, (12) purification of air and water, and (13) production of lumber, fodder, and biomass fuel (Figure 4-34, p. 92).

### Information

■ The genetic information in species allows them to (1) adapt to changing environmental conditions and (2) form new species.

■ The genetic information in the genes of species is used in genetic engineering to produce new types of crops and foods (Figure 13-16, p. 291 and Figure 13-17, p. 292) and edible vaccines for diseases such as hepatitis B (Solutions, p. 242).

■ We obtain educational or scientific information by studying genes, species, ecosystems, and ecological processes.

### Options

■ People would be willing to pay in advance to preserve the option of directly using a resource such as a tree, an elephant, a forest, or a clean lake or river in the future.

### Recreation

■ We value recreational pleasure provided by wild plants and animals and natural ecosystems. For example, each year Americans spend over three times more to watch wildlife than they do to watch movies or professional sporting events. Examples of such uses that do not consume wildlife include nature photography, nature walks, and bird-watching.

■ Another normally nonconsumptive use of nature is wildlife tourism, or *eco-tourism*. It generates at least $500 billion worldwide, and perhaps twice as much. Conservation biologist Michael Soulé estimates that one male lion living to age 7 generates $515,000 in tourist dollars in Kenya but only $1,000 if killed for its skin. Similarly, over a lifetime of 60 years, a Kenyan elephant is worth about $1 million in ecotourist revenue—many times more than its tusks are worth when sold illegally for their ivory.

Ideally, eco-tourism (1) should not cause ecological damage, (2) should provide income for local people to motivate them to preserve wildlife, and (3) should provide funds for the purchase and maintenance of wildlife preserves and conservation programs. However, much nature tourism does not meet these standards, and excessive and unregulated eco-tourism can destroy or degrade fragile areas and promote premature species extinction. Also, typically less than 1% of the money earned from eco-tours ends up as income for local people or for wildlife conservation. The website for this chapter lists some guidelines for evaluating eco-tours.

### Nonutilitarian (Nonuse) Values

■ *Existence:* We find value in knowing that a redwood forest, wilderness, or an endangered species exists, even if we will never see it or get direct use from it.

■ *Aesthetic:* We find value in a resource such as a tree, forest, wild species, or a vista because of its beauty.

■ *Bequest:* People are willing to pay to protect some forms of natural capital for use by future generations.

**What Is the Total Economic Value of the Earth's Biodiversity?** Recently, ecologists and economists have attempted to place a monetary value on the instrumental ecosystem services provided by earth's natural resources (Spotlight, right). They hope that such estimates of the total instrumental value or wealth of nature will (1) alert people to the value of these free services to our lives and economies and (2) help slow down the unsustainable use and degradation of many of the world's ecosystems and species.

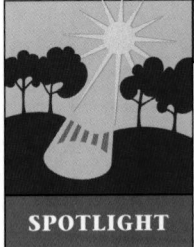

## What Is the Economic Value of the Earth's Ecological Services?

In 1997, a team of 13 ecologists, economists, and geographers attempted to estimate the monetary worth of the earth's natural ecological services (Figure 4-34, p. 92).

According to this crude appraisal led by ecological economist Robert Costanza of the University of Maryland, the economic value of income from the earth's natural capital is at least $36 trillion per year. This is close to the annual gross world product of about $41 trillion. To provide an annual natural income of $36 trillion per year, the world's natural capital would have a value of at least $500 trillion—an average of about $82,000 for each person on earth.

To make these estimates, the researchers divided the earth's surface into 16 biomes (Figure 6-20, p. 123) and aquatic life zones

(they omitted deserts and tundra because of a lack of data). Then they **(1)** agreed on a list of 17 goods and services provided by nature (Figure 4-34, p. 92) and **(2)** sifted through more than 100 studies that attempted to put a dollar value on such services in the 16 different types of ecosystems.

Some analysts believe such estimates are misleading and dangerous because they put a dollar value on ecosystem services that have an infinite value because they are irreplaceable. In the 1970s, economist E. F. Schumacher warned that "to undertake to measure the immeasurable is absurd" and is a "pretense that everything has a price."

The researchers admit their estimates rely on many assumptions and omissions and could easily be too low by a factor of 10 to 1 million or more. For example, their calculations **(1)** included only estimates of the ecosystem services

themselves, not the natural capital that generates them, and **(2)** omitted the value of nonrenewable minerals and fuels. They also recognize that as the supply of ecosystem services declines their value will rise sharply, and such services can be viewed as having an infinite value.

However, they contend their estimates are much more accurate than the *very* low or *zero* value the market usually assigns to these ecosystem services. They hope such estimates will call people's attention to the fact that the earth's ecosystem services (Figure 4-34, p. 92) are essential for all humans and their economies and their economic value is huge.

### Critical Thinking

Should we put a price on nature's services? Explain. What are the alternatives?

### What Is the Intrinsic Value of Biodiversity?
Some people believe all wild species and ecosystems have *intrinsic value.* Each species is said to have an inherent value and a right to exist that is unrelated to their usefulness to humans.

According to this intrinsic view, we have an ethical responsibility to **(1)** protect species from becoming prematurely extinct as a result of human activities and **(2)** prevent the degradation of the world's ecosystems and its overall biodiversity. Biologist Edward O. Wilson believes most people feel obligated to protect other species and the earth's biodiversity because most humans seem to have a natural affinity for nature (Connections, p. 572).

Some people distinguish between the survival rights of plants and those of animals, mostly for practical reasons. Poet Alan Watts once said he was a vegetarian "because cows scream louder than carrots." Other people distinguish among various types of species. For example, they might think little about getting rid of the world's mosquitoes, cockroaches (Spotlight, p. 105), rats, or disease-causing bacteria.

Some proponents go further and assert that each individual organism, not just each species, has a right to survive without human interference. Others apply this to individuals of some species but not to those of

other species. Unless they are strict vegetarians, for example, some people might see no harm in having others kill domesticated animals in slaughterhouses to provide them with meat, leather, and other products. However, these same people might deplore the killing of wild animals such as deer, squirrels, or rabbits.

Others emphasize the importance of preserving the whole spectrum of biodiversity by protecting entire ecosystems rather than individual species or organisms, as discussed in Chapter 23.

Based on practical, aesthetic, and ethical reasons and their decades of research, the basic message biologists are sending us is that *biodiversity matters and should not be depleted or degraded by our activities.* To biologists, preserving biodiversity is a global insurance policy for helping protect life and economies.

They also caution us not to focus conservation efforts primarily on protecting relatively big organisms—the plants and animals we can see and are familiar with. They remind us that the true foundation of the earth's ecosystems and ecological process are the invisible bacteria, singe-celled, algae, fungi and other *microorganisms* that decompose the bodies of larger organisms and recycle the nutrients needed by all life (Figure 4-15, p. 75, and Connections, p. 65).

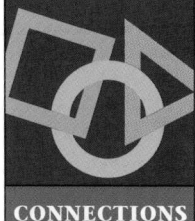

## Biophilia

Biologist Edward O. Wilson contends that because of the billions of years of biological connections leading to the evolution of the human species, we have an inherent affinity for the natural world, a phenomenon he calls *biophilia* (love of life).

Evidence of this natural affinity for life is seen in the preference most people have for almost any natural scene over one from an urban environment. Given a choice, most people prefer to live in an area where they can see water, grassland,

or a forest. More people visit zoos and aquariums than attend all professional sporting events combined.

In the 1970s, I was touring the space center at Cape Canaveral in Florida. During our bus ride the tour guide pointed out each of the abandoned multimillion-dollar launch sites and gave a brief history of each launch. Most of us were utterly bored. Suddenly people started rushing to the front of the bus and staring out the window with great excitement. What they were looking at was a baby alligator—a dramatic example of how *biophilia* can triumph over *technophilia*.

### Critical Thinking

**1.** Do you have an affinity for wildlife and wild ecosystems (biophilia)? If so, how do you display this love of wildlife in your daily actions? What patterns of your consumption help destroy and degrade wildlife?

**2.** Some critics contend there is no verifiable genetic evidence of Wilson's biophilia concept and view this idea as opinion, not science. If you have an affinity for wildlife, do you believe it is inherent in your genes or culturally conditioned? Does it matter? Explain.

## 22-4 EXTINCTION THREATS FROM HABITAT LOSS AND DEGRADATION

**What Is the Role of Habitat Loss and Degradation?** Figure 22-12 shows the underlying and direct causes of the endangerment and premature extinction of wild species. Biologists agree the greatest threat to wild species is habitat loss (Figure 22-13), degradation, and fragmentation. According to biodiversity researchers, tropical deforestation is the greatest eliminator of species, followed by **(1)** destruction of coral reefs (p. 152 and Figure 7-17, p. 155) and wetlands (p. 155 and p. 160), **(2)** plowing of grasslands (Figure 6-31, p. 132), and **(3)** pollution of fresh water streams (Section 19-2, p. 486) and lakes (Section 19-3, p. 489) and marine habitats (Section 19-5, p. 496). Globally, temperate biomes have been affected more by habitat disturbance, degradation, and fragmentation than have tropical biomes because of widespread development in temperate developed countries over the past 200 years (Figure 22-14, p. 574).

According to the Nature Conservancy, the major types of habitat disturbance threatening endangered species in the United States are, in order of importance, **(1)** agriculture, **(2)** commercial development, **(3)** water development, **(4)** outdoor recreation including off-road vehicles, **(5)** livestock grazing, and **(6)** pollution.

Island species, many of them *endemic species* found nowhere else on earth, are especially vulnerable to extinction. Scientists have used the theory of island biogeography (Figure 8-6, p. 168) to project the num-

ber and percentage of species that would become extinct when habitats on islands are destroyed, degraded, or fragmented. They have also applied the model to the protection of national parks, tropical rain forests, lakes, and nature reserves, which often can be

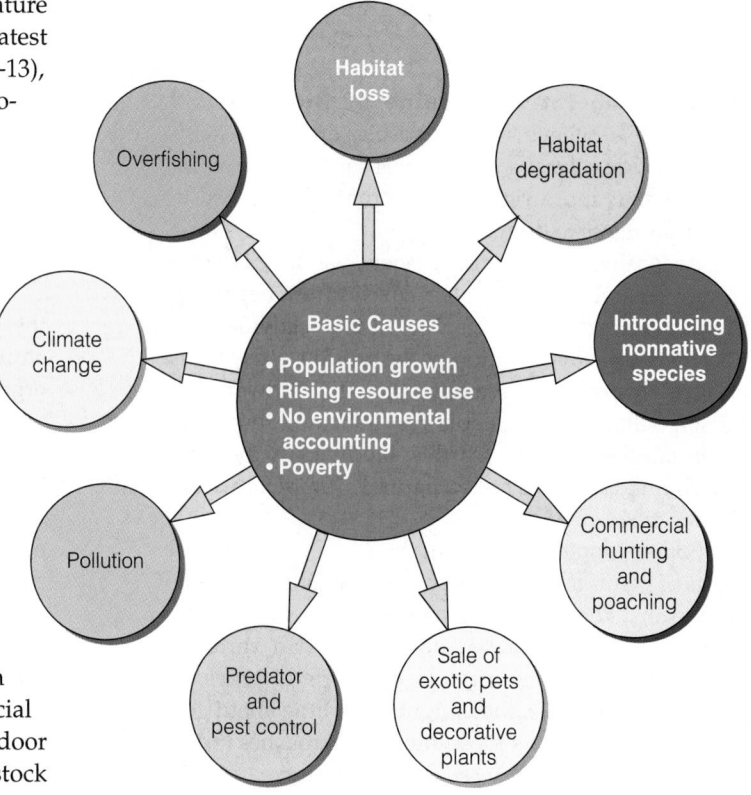

**Figure 22-12** Underlying and direct causes of depletion and premature extinction of wild species. The two biggest direct causes of wildlife depletion and premature extinction are **(1)** habitat loss, fragmentation, and degradation and **(2)** deliberate or accidental introduction of nonnative species into ecosystems.

**Indian Tiger**

Range 100 years ago
Range today
(about 2,300 left)

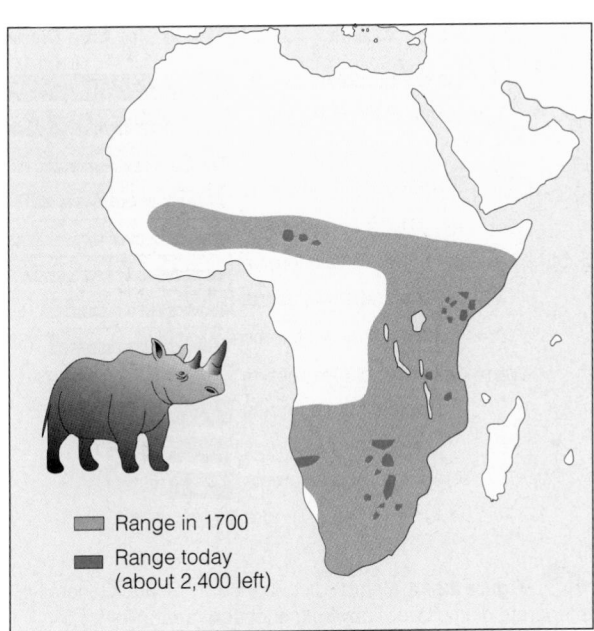

**Black Rhino**

Range in 1700
Range today
(about 2,400 left)

**African Elephant**

Probable range 1600
Range today
(300,000 left)

**Asian or Indian Elephant**

Former range
Range today
(34,000–54,000 left)

**Figure 22-13** Reductions in the ranges of four wildlife species, mostly the result of habitat loss and hunting. What will happen to these and millions of other species when the world's human population doubles and per capita resource consumption rises sharply in the next few decades? (Data from International Union for the Conservation of Nature and World Wildlife Fund)

viewed as *habitat islands* in an inhospitable sea of human-altered habitat.

**What Is the Role of Habitat Fragmentation?**
*Habitat fragmentation* occurs when a large, continuous area of habitat is **(1)** reduced in area and **(2)** divided into a patchwork of isolated areas or fragments. The three main problems caused by habitat fragmentation are

■ A decrease in the sustainable population size for many species when an existing population is divided into two or more isolated subpopulations.

■ Increased surface area or edge, which makes some species more vulnerable to **(1)** predators, **(2)** competition from nonnative and pest species, **(3)** wind, and **(4)** fire.

**Figure 22-14** Habitat disturbance by biome. Generally, temperate biomes (red) have experienced greater levels of habitat disturbance than have tropical biomes (yellow). The least disturbed biomes are boreal forests and arctic biomes, although logging is a growing threat to boreal forests. (Data from the Nature Conservancy)

▪ Creation of barriers that limit the ability of some species to **(1)** disperse and colonize new areas, **(2)** find enough to eat, and **(3)** find mates. Some species of migrating birds face loss, degradation, or fragmenta-

tion of their seasonal habitats (Case Study, right). Figure 22-15 shows the ten most threatened U.S. songbirds according to a 2001 study by the National Audubon Society.

Types of species vulnerable to local and regional extinction because of habitat fragmentation are those that **(1)** are rare, **(2)** need to roam unhindered over a large area, **(3)** cannot rebuild their population because of a low reproductive capacity, **(4)** have specialized niches (habitat or resource needs), and **(5)** are sought by people for furs, food, medicines, or other uses.

## 22-5 EXTINCTION THREATS FROM NONNATIVE SPECIES

**What Harm Do Nonnative Species Cause in the United States?** After habitat loss and degradation, deliberate or accidental introduction of nonnative species into ecosystems is the biggest cause of animal and plant extinctions. The nonnative invaders arrive from other continents as **(1)** stowaways on aircraft, **(2)** in the ballast water of tankers and cargo ships, and **(3)** as hitchhikers on imported products such as wooden packing crates.

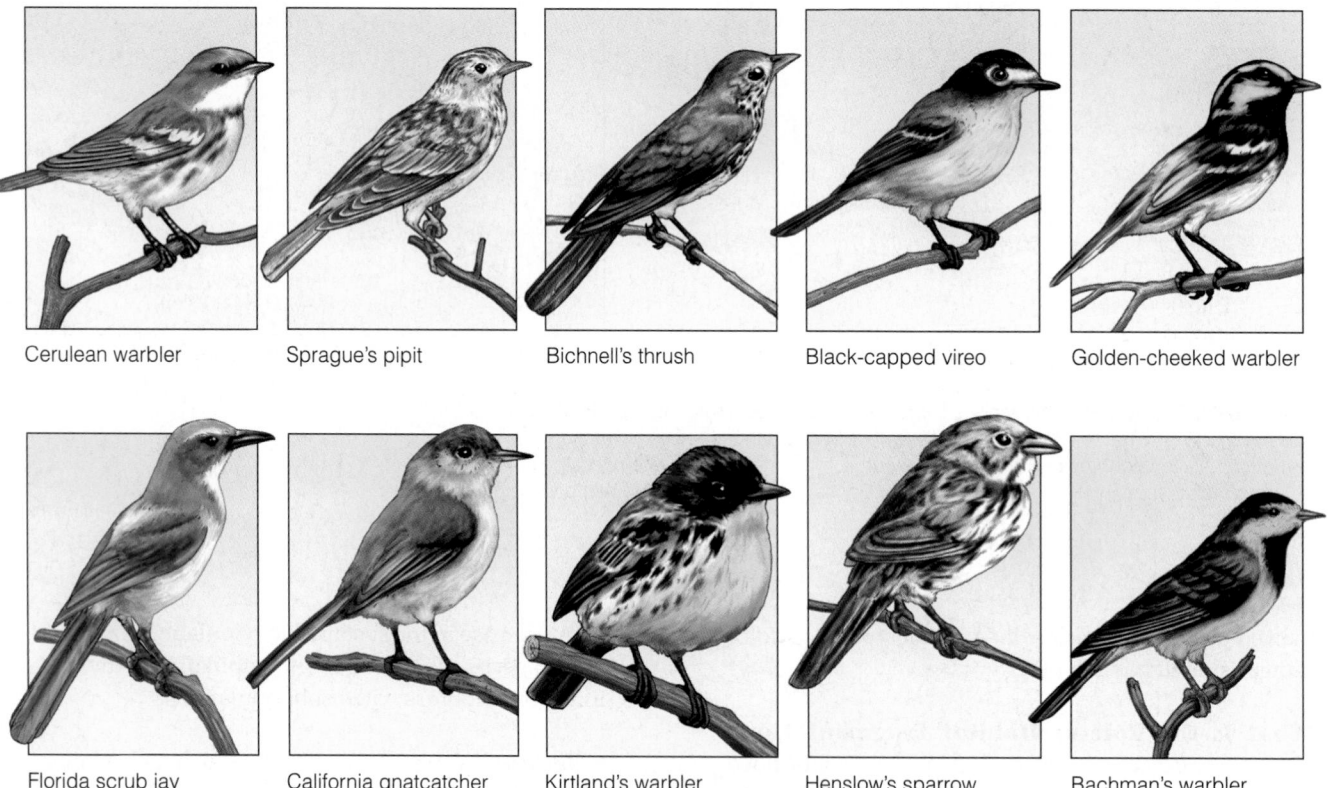

Cerulean warbler | Sprague's pipit | Bichnell's thrush | Black-capped vireo | Golden-cheeked warbler

Florida scrub jay | California gnatcatcher | Kirtland's warbler | Henslow's sparrow | Bachman's warbler

**Figure 22-15** The ten most threatened species of U.S. songbirds according to a 2001 study by the National Audubon Society. Most of these species are threatened because of habitat loss and fragmentation.

## The Plight of Migrating Birds

**CASE STUDY**

Migrating bird species face a double habitat problem. Nearly half of the 700 U.S. bird species spend two-thirds of the year in the tropical forests of Central or South America or on Caribbean islands. During the summer they return to North America to breed.

A USFWS study showed that between 1978 and 1987, populations of 44 of the 62 surveyed species of insect-eating, migratory songbirds in North America declined; 20 species experienced drops of 25–45%.

Researchers have identified several possible culprits:

- Logging of tropical forests that serve as winter habitats for migrating songbirds.

- Fragmentation of their summer forest and grassland habitats in North America. The intrusion of farms, freeways, and suburbs breaks forests into patches. This fragmentation makes it easier for **(1)** predators

to feast on the eggs and the young of migrant songbirds, **(2)** parasitic cowbirds to lay their eggs in the nests of various songbird species and have those birds raise their young for them, and **(3)** invasions of nonnative shrubs to give nesting birds less protection from predators. In Texas, an environmental group is paying ranchers to set traps for parasitic cowbirds to decrease their harmful effects on songbirds.

- Deaths of at least 4 million migrating songbirds each year when they fly into TV, radio, and phone towers.

However, there is no universal trend in North American songbird populations. Evidence indicates that some species are generally declining, whereas populations of other species are declining in some areas and increasing in other areas.

Approximately 70% of the world's 9,600 known bird species are declining in numbers (58%) or are threatened with extinction (12%), mostly because of habitat

loss and fragmentation. Conservation biologists view this decline of bird species as an early warning of the greater loss of biodiversity to come. Birds are excellent environmental indicators because they **(1)** live in every climate and biome, **(2)** respond quickly to environmental changes in their habitats, and **(3)** are easy to track and count.

In addition to serving as indicator species, birds play important ecological roles such as **(1)** helping control populations of insects (including the spruce budworm, gypsy moth, and tent caterpillar, which decimate many tree species) and rodents, **(2)** pollinating a wide variety of flowering plants, and **(3)** spreading plants throughout their habitats by consuming plant seeds and excreting them in their droppings.

### Critical Thinking

What three actions would you take to help prevent the population decline of migrating birds?

---

The estimated 50,000 nonnative species in the United States

- Result in at least $137 billion per year in damages and pest control costs—an average loss of $16 million per hour—according to a 2000 study by David Pimentel (Figure 22-16).

- Threaten 49% of the more than 1,200 endangered and threatened species in the United States (and 95% of those in Hawaii) according to the U.S. Fish and Wildlife Service (USFWS).

- Are blamed for about 68% of fish extinctions in the United States between 1900 and 2000.

Figure 22-17 (p. 576) shows some of the nonnative species that have been deliberately or accidentally introduced into the United States.

**What Is the Role of Deliberately Introduced Species?** Deliberate introduction of nonnative species can be beneficial or harmful depending on the species and where they are introduced. We depend heavily on nonnative organisms for ecosystem services, food, shelter, medicine, and aesthetic enjoyment.

According to a 2000 study by ecologist David Pimentel, introduced species such as corn, wheat, rice,

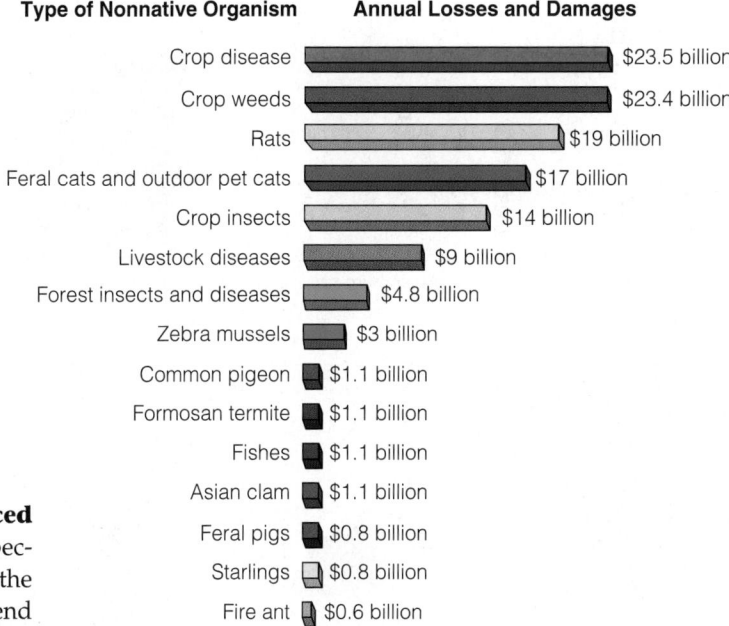

**Figure 22-16** Estimated annual damages from selected types of nonnative species in the United States. Many biologists believe the actual costs are several times higher than the conservative estimates shown here. (Data from David Pimentel)

## Deliberately Introduced Species

Purple looselife

European starling

African honeybee ("Killer bee")

Nutria

Salt cedar (Tamarisk)

Marine toad (Giant toad)

Water hyacinth

Japanese beetle

Hydrilla

European wild boar (Feral pig)

## Accidentally Introduced Species

Sea lamprey (attached to lake trout)

Argentina fire ant

Brown tree snake

Eurasian muffe

Common pigeon (Rock dove)

Formosan termite

Zebra mussel

Asian long-horned beetle

Asian tiger mosquito

Gypsy moth larvae

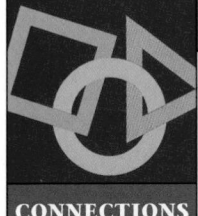

## Deliberate Introduction of the Kudzu Vine

**CONNECTIONS**

In the 1930s, the *kudzu vine* was imported from Japan and planted in the southeastern United States to help control soil erosion. It does control erosion, but it is so prolific and difficult to kill that it engulfs hillsides, trees, abandoned houses and cars, stream banks, patches of forest, and anything else in its path (see figure below).

This vine, sometimes called "the vine that ate the South," **(1)** has spread throughout much of the southern United States (see figure at right) and **(2)** could spread as far north as the Great Lakes by 2040 if projected global warming occurs.

Although kudzu is considered a menace in the United States, Asians

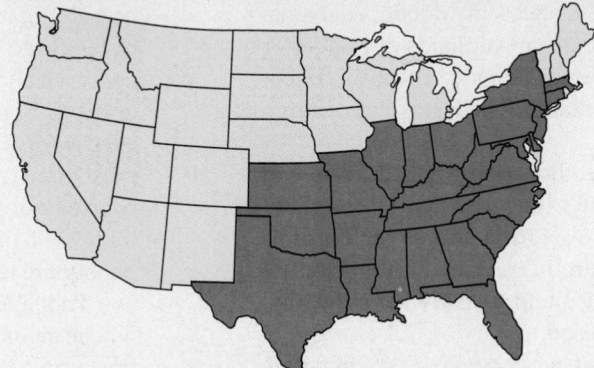

Expansion of kudzu in the United States. It is also found in Hawaii. (U.S. Department of Agriculture).

use a powdered kudzu starch in beverages, gourmet confections, and herbal remedies for a range of diseases. A Japanese firm has built a large kudzu farm and processing plant in Alabama and ships the extracted starch to Japan.

In an ironic twist, kudzu—which can engulf and kill trees— could eventually

help save trees from loggers. Research at Georgia Institute of Technology indicates that kudzu may be used as a source of tree-free paper.

### Critical Thinking

On balance, do you think the potential beneficial uses of the kudzu vine outweigh its harmful ecological effects? Explain.

Kudzu taking over a house and a truck. This vine can grow 0.3 meter (1 foot) per day and is now found from East Texas to Florida and as far north as southeastern Pennsylvania and Illinois. Kudzu was deliberately introduced into the United States for erosion control, but it cannot be stopped by being dug up or burned. Grazing by goats and repeated doses of herbicides can destroy it, but goats and herbicides also destroy other plants, and herbicides can contaminate water supplies. Recently, scientists have found a common fungus (*Myrithecium verrucaria*) that can kill kudzu within a few hours, apparently without harming other plants.

---

other food crops, cattle, poultry, and other livestock supply more than 98% of the U.S. food supply at a value of approximately $800 billion per year. Similarly, about 85% of industrial forestry tree plantations use species nonnative to the areas where they are grown. Some deliberately introduced species have also helped control pests.

However, some introduced species have no natural predators, competitors, parasites, or pathogens to control their numbers in their new habitats. Thus they can reduce or wipe out the populations of many native

species and trigger ecological disruptions. One example of a deliberately introduced plant species is the kudzu ("CUD-zoo") vine, which grows rampant in the southeastern United States (Connections, above). Two examples of deliberately introduced animals are

- The estimated 1 million *European wild (feral) pigs* (Figure 22-17) found in parts of Florida and other states. They **(1)** hog food from endangered animals, **(2)** root up farm fields, and **(3)** cause traffic accidents. Game and wildlife officials have had little success in controlling their numbers with hunting and trapping and say there is no way to stop them.

- The estimated 30 million *feral cats* and 41 million *outdoor pet cats* introduced into the United States kill about 568 million birds per year.

**Figure 22-17** (facing page) Some nonnative species that have been deliberately or accidentally introduced into the United States.

## What Is the Role of Accidentally Introduced Species?

In the late 1930s, the extremely aggressive Argentina fire ant (Figure 22-17) was introduced accidentally into the United States in Mobile, Alabama. They may have arrived **(1)** on shiploads of lumber or coffee imported from South America or **(2)** by hitching a ride in the soil-containing ballast water of cargo ships.

Without natural predators, these ants have spread rapidly by land and water (they can float) throughout the South, from Texas to Florida and as far north as Tennessee and North Carolina (Figure 22-18) They are also found in Puerto Rico and recently have invaded California and New Mexico.

Wherever the fire ant has gone, up to 90% of native ant populations have been sharply reduced or wiped out. Their extremely painful stings have also killed deer fawn, birds, livestock, pets, and at least 80 people allergic to their venom. They have also **(1)** invaded cars and caused accidents by attacking drivers, **(2)** made crop fields unplowable, **(3)** disrupted phone service and electrical power, **(4)** caused some fires by chewing through underground cables, and **(5)** cost the United States an estimated $600 million per year.

Widespread pesticide spraying in the 1950s and 1960s temporarily reduced fire ant populations. In the end, however, this chemical warfare hastened the advance of the rapidly multiplying fire ant by **(1)** reducing populations of many native ant species and **(2)** promoting development of genetic resistance to heavily used pesticides in the rapidly multiplying fire ants through directional natural selection (Figure 5-6, left, p. 102 and p. 516).

Researchers at the U.S. Department of Agriculture are experimenting with use of biological controls such as a tiny parasitic Brazilian fly and a pathogen imported from South America to reduce fire ant plantations. Before widespread use of these biological control agents, however, researchers must be sure they will not cause problems for native ant species or become pests themselves.

About 50 years ago, the *brown tree snake* (Figure 22-17) arrived accidentally on the island of Guam in the cargo of a military plane. Since then, this highly aggressive, nocturnal, climbing snake with no natural enemies has eliminated or decimated bird and lizard species on Guam. It has also snatched chickens and pets from yards, attacked babies asleep in cribs, and shorted out power lines. In some areas of Guam, more than 1,900 of these snakes per square kilometer (5,000 per square mile) have been counted.

This light-sensitive snake can hide in an airplane wheel or outgoing cargo during daylight hours and thus spread to other areas such as Hawaii, which is home for 41% of all endangered bird species in the United States. Hawaii has a lot to lose from an invasion by this snake.

In 1985, *Asian tiger mosquitoes* (Figures 22-17), which breed in scrap tires, arrived in the United States in a Japanese ship carrying tires to a Houston, Texas, recapping plant. Since then, they have spread to 25 states. Aggressive biters, these mosquitoes can transmit 17 potentially fatal tropical viruses, including dengue fever, yellow fever, and forms of encephalitis. University of Kentucky scientists have flown a radar-equipped plane over the Ohio River Valley to find the Asian tiger mosquito. Radar cannot detect the mosquitoes, but it can spot hidden mounds of scrap tires, where the insects breed. Another harmful invader is the Formosan termite (Case Study, right).

Accidentally introduced species can also create trade controversies. In 1998, the United States banned the import of goods from China in untreated wooden packing crates. Such crates were the primary culprits in the recent invasion of the voracious *Asian long-horned beetle* (Figure 22-17), which poses a major threat to U.S. hardwood trees. China has complained the ban is an unfair trade barrier and hopes to get the World Trade Organization to overturn the ban.

## Solutions: What Can Be Done to Reduce the Threat from Nonnative Species?

Once a nonnative species gets established in an ecosystem, its wholesale removal is almost impossible—somewhat like trying to get smoke back into a chimney or trying to unscramble an egg. Thus the best way to limit the harmful impacts of nonnative species is to prevent them from being introduced and becoming established. This can be done by

- Identifying major characteristics that allow species to become successful invaders and the types of ecosystems that are vulnerable to invaders and using this information to screen out potentially harmful invaders (Figure 22-19).

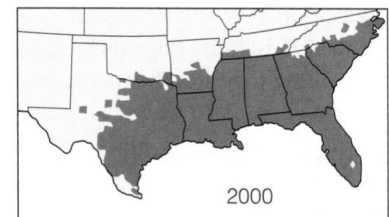

**Figure 22-18**
Expansion of the *Argentina fire ant* in southern states, 1918–2000. This invader is also found in Puerto Rico, New Mexico, and California. (Data from U.S. Department of Agriculture)

Forget killer bees and fire ants. The home owner's nightmare is the Formosan termite (Figure 22-17). It is the most voracious, aggressive, and prolific of more than 2,000 known termite species.

These termites invaded the Hawaiian Islands by 1900. They probably arrived on the U.S. mainland during or soon after World War II in wooden packing materials on military cargo ships that docked in southern ports such as New Orleans, Louisiana, and Houston, Texas.

They can quickly munch through wooden beams and plywood and can even chew through brick. Their huge colonies, which can contain up to 73 million insects (73 times as many as a nest of native termites), can be found under houses or in their attics.

Formosan termites also consume wood nine times faster than domestic termites. Domestic termites have to be in contact with soil, which can be treated around the outside of a building to reduce infestation. However, Formosan termites can establish a colony in an attic. This makes applying pesticides around the perimeter of a building virtually worthless in fighting these pests.

Over the past decade, the Formosan termite has caused more damage in New Orleans than hurricanes, floods, and tornadoes combined. Infestations affect as many as 90% of the houses and one-third of the oak trees in the city. The famous French Quarter has one of the most concentrated infestations in the world.

Once confined to Louisiana, they have invaded at least a dozen other states, including Alabama, Florida, Mississippi, North and South Carolina, Texas, and California. They cause at least $1.1 billion in damage each year.

Most pesticides do not work on these termites. In New Orleans, the U.S. Department of Agriculture is using a variety of techniques all at once in an attempt to control the species in a heavily infested 15-block area of the French Quarter. They hope to develop other techniques for dealing with these invaders elsewhere.

**Critical Thinking**

What important ecological roles do termites play in nature? If the Formosan termite and other termite species could be eradicated (a highly unlikely possibility), would you favor doing this? Explain.

---

- Stepping up inspections of goods coming into a country.

- Identifying major harmful invader species and passing international laws banning their transfer from one country to another (as is now done for endangered species).

| Characteristics of Successful Invader Species | Characteristics of Ecosystems Vulnerable to Invader Species |
|---|---|
| • High reproductive rate, short generation time (r-selected species) | • Similar climate to habitat of invader |
| • Pioneer species | • Absence of predators on invading species |
| • Long lived | • Early successional systems |
| • High dispersal rate | • Low diversity of native species |
| • Release growth-inhibiting chemicals into soil | • Absence of fire |
| • Generalists | • Disturbed by human activities |
| • High genetic variability | |

**Figure 22-19** Some general characteristics of successful invader species and ecosystems vulnerable to invading species.

- Requiring ships to **(1)** discharge their ballast (bilge) water and replace it with salt water at sea before entering ports, **(2)** sterilize such water, or **(3)** pump nitrogen into the water (Individuals Matter, p. 580).

## 22-6 EXTINCTION THREATS FROM HUNTING AND POACHING

**What Is the Role of Commercial Hunting and Poaching?** The international trade in wild plants and animals brings an estimated $20 billion a year. According to a 2002 study by the World Life Conservation Society, illegal international trade in endangered and threatened species or their parts amounts to about $8 billion per year. Organized crime has moved into illegal wildlife smuggling because of the huge profits involved (second only to international drug smuggling).

The demand for illegal wildlife comes mostly from wealthy collectors and other consumers in Asia, the Middle East, North America, and Europe. At least two-thirds of all live animals illegally smuggled around the world die in transit.

Worldwide, some 622 animal and plant species face extinction, mostly because of illegal trade. To poachers, **(1)** a live mountain gorilla is worth $150,000, **(2)** a gyrfalcon $120,000, **(3)** a panda pelt $100,000 (with only about 1,000 pandas thought to remain in the wild),

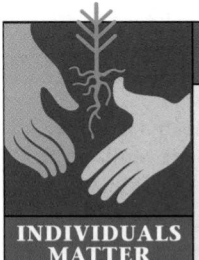

## Killing Invader Species and Saving Shipping Companies Money

A large cargo ship typically has a dozen or more ballast tanks below deck. Each tank is the size of a high school gymnasium and holds millions of gallons of water.

When a ship takes on cargo and leaves a port it sucks water into its ballast tanks to keep it low in the water, submerge its rudder, and help maintain stability. The enormous amount of water sucked into the ship also contains large numbers of fish, crabs, clams, and other species found in the port's local waters.

When the ship's cargo is removed at its destination its ballast water is released until the ship is loaded again. This dumps millions of foreign organisms into rivers and bays. Thus, cargo ships moving about 80% of the goods traded internationally play a major role in the release of nonnative aquatic organisms into various parts of the world.

In 2002, researchers Mario Tamburri and Kerstin Wasson found that pumping nitrogen gas into ballast tanks while at sea virtually eliminates dissolved oxygen in the ballast water. This **(1)** saves the shipping industry money by reduc-

ing corrosion of a ship's steel compartments and **(2)** within three days kills most fish, crabs, clams, and other potential invader species lurking in the ballast tanks.

Including the cost of nitrogen, over the 25-year life of a large cargo ship this process can save a shipping company about $1.7 million, or $70,000 a year, in painting and maintenance costs. This *win-win solution* also kills most of the invader organisms and offers hope for dealing with one of the world's most serious environmental problems. No wonder it has been greeted favorably by environmentalists and ship owners.

---

**(4)** a chimpanzee $50,000, **(5)** an Imperial Amazon macaw $30,000, and **(6)** rhinoceros horn as much as $28,600 per kilogram ($13,000 per pound) mostly because of its use in dagger handles in the Middle East and as a fever reducer and alleged aphrodisiac in China and other parts of Asia. Excessive hunting brought the American bison to near extinction (p. 21).

In much of West and Central Africa, wildlife in the form of *bushmeat* is an important source of protein for many local people (Figure 22-20). The growing bushmeat trade for restaurants—much of it illegal—also

generates revenues of more than $150 million per year. This illegal hunting for the meat of wild animals at an unsustainable rate has threatened **(1)** about 15 primate species, **(2)** the African forest elephant, **(3)** the leopard, **(4)** six species of duikers (a small African antelope; Figure 6-29, p. 130) and several other species of African wildlife. In Africa's Congo Basin, the demand for bushmeat has replaced habitat loss as the biggest threat to the animals whose meat is eaten or sold. The bushmeat trade is also increasing in Asia, the Caribbean, and Central and South America.

In 1950, an estimated 100,000 tigers existed in the world. Despite international protection, today only 5,000–6,500 tigers are left (about 4,000 of them in India), mostly because of habitat loss and poaching for their furs and bones. Bengal tigers are at risk because a tiger fur sells for $100,000 in Tokyo. With the body parts of a single tiger worth $5,000–20,000, it is not surprising that illegal hunting has skyrocketed, especially in India. Without emergency action, few or no tigers may be left in the wild within 20 years.

As commercially valuable species become endangered, the demand for them on the black market soars. This hastens their chances of premature extinction from poaching. Most poachers are not caught, and the money to be made far outweighs the risk of fines and the much smaller risk of imprisonment.

**Figure 22-20** *Bushmeat*, such as this gorilla head, is consumed as a source of protein by local people in parts of West Africa and sold in the national and international marketplace. You can find bushmeat on the menu in Cameroon and the Congo in West Africa as well as in Paris, France, and Brussels, Belgium. Much of this is organized and illegal poaching to supply restaurants.

**Case Study: How Should We Protect Elephants from Extinction?** Habitat loss (Figure 22-13, bottom left) and legal and illegal trade in ivory from elephant tusks (Figure 22-21) have reduced wild African elephant numbers from 2.5 million in 1970 to about 300,000 today (plus about 300 in zoos).

**Figure 22-21** Vultures are feeding on this African elephant carcass. It was killed for its valuable ivory tusks, which have been cut off and sold.

A 1989 international ban on the sale of ivory from African elephants has slowed this decline, but things are not quite that simple. First, the ban on elephant ivory sales has increased the killing of other species with ivory parts such as **(1)** bull walruses (for their ivory tusks, worth $500–1,500 a pair) and **(2)** hippos (for their ivory teeth, worth $70 per kilogram). Second, an increase in elephant populations in areas where their habitat has shrunk has resulted in widespread destruction of vegetation by these animals. This in turn reduces the niches available for other wild species and leads farmers to kill elephants destroying their crops.

In 1997, the *Convention on International Trade in Endangered Species* (*CITES*) voted to give Zimbabwe, Botswana, and Namibia onetime limited permits to sell ivory obtained from culling large elephant herds and from natural deaths to Japan under strict monitoring. The $5 million raised from the sales is being used for wildlife protection and rural development programs. These three countries and South Africa have proposed they be allowed to cull and sell ivory from their elephant herds annually.

Some wildlife conservationists oppose such sales. They believe the best way to protect African elephants from extinction is to continue the ivory ban, which discourages poaching by keeping the price of ivory down.

Instead of increasing the death rate by culling (killing) elephants, the U.S. Humane Society has proposed using birth control to reduce their birth rate in areas where high numbers of elephants are destroying natural vegetation and crops. Critics of this approach are concerned that preventing female elephants from conceiving for long periods of time could disrupt the normal social structure of elephant herds.

## 22-7 OTHER EXTINCTION THREATS

**What Is the Role of Predators and Pest Control?** People try to exterminate species that compete with them for food and game animals. For example, U.S. fruit farmers exterminated the Carolina parakeet around 1914 because it fed on fruit crops. The species was easy prey because when one member of a flock was shot, the rest of the birds hovered over its body, making themselves easy targets.

African farmers kill large numbers of elephants to keep them from trampling and eating food crops. Many ranchers, farmers, and hunters in the United States support the killing of coyotes, wolves, and other species that can prey on livestock and on species prized by game hunters.

Since 1929, U.S. ranchers and government agencies have poisoned 99% of North America's prairie dogs because horses and cattle sometimes step into the burrows and break their legs. This has also nearly wiped out the endangered black-footed ferret (Figure 22-7; about 600 left in the wild), which preyed on the prairie dog.

**What Is the Role of the Market for Exotic Pets and Decorative Plants?** The global legal and illegal trade in wild species for use as pets is a huge and very profitable business. However, for every live animal captured and sold in the pet market, an estimated 50 other animals are killed.

About 25 million U.S. households have exotic birds as pets, 85% of them imported. More than 60 bird species, mostly parrots, are endangered or threatened because of this wild bird trade. According to the USFWS, collectors of exotic birds may pay $10,000 for a threatened hyacinth macaw smuggled out of Brazil; however, during its lifetime, a single macaw left in the wild might yield as much as $165,000 in tourist income. A 1992 study suggested that keeping a pet bird indoors for more than 10 years doubles a person's chances of getting lung cancer from inhaling tiny particles of bird dander.

Other wild species whose populations are depleted because of the pet trade include amphibians, reptiles, mammals, and tropical fish (taken mostly from the coral reefs of Indonesia and the Philippines). Divers catch tropical fish by using plastic squeeze bottles of cyanide to stun them. For each fish caught alive, many more die. In addition, the cyanide solution kills the coral animals that create the reef, which is a center for marine biodiversity (Figure 7-1, bottom, p. 144, and Figure 7-16, p. 154).

Some exotic plants, especially orchids and cacti, are endangered because they are gathered (often illegally) and sold to collectors to decorate houses, offices, and landscapes. A collector may pay $5,000 for a single rare orchid, and a single rare mature crested saguaro cactus can earn cactus rustlers as much as $15,000.

**What Are the Roles of Climate Change and Pollution?** Most natural climate changes in the past have taken place over long periods of time (Figure 18-2, p. 447), which gave species more time to adapt and evolve to these changing environmental conditions. But human activities such as greenhouse gas emissions and deforestation can bring about rapid climate change during this century (Figure 18-12, p. 455). If these projected climate changes take place, **(1)** some wild species may not have enough time to adapt or migrate (Figure 18-18, p. 462), and **(2)** some wildlife in well-protected and well-managed terrestrial reserves and ocean sanctuaries could be depleted within a few decades.

According to a 2000 study by the World Wildlife Fund, global warming could increase extinction by altering one-third of the world's wildlife habitats by 2100. This includes 70% of the habitat in high altitude arctic and boreal biomes. Ten of the world's 17 penguin species are endangered or threatened, mostly because of global warming.

According to the USFWS, each year in the United States pesticides kill about 20% of the country's beneficial honeybee colonies and kill more than 67 million birds and 6–14 million fish. They also threaten about 20% of the country's endangered and threatened species.

## 22-8 PROTECTING WILD SPECIES FROM DEPLETION AND EXTINCTION: THE RESEARCH AND LEGAL APPROACH

**How Can Bioinformatics Help Protect Biodiversity?** To protect biodiversity, we need basic information about the biology and ecology of wild species. In particular, information is needed about **(1)** species names, **(2)** descriptions, **(3)** distributions, **(4)** status of populations, **(5)** habitat requirements, and **(6)** interactions with other species (Section 8-3, p. 172, and Section 8-4, p. 178).

**Bioinformatics** is the applied science of managing, analyzing, and communicating biological information. It involves **(1)** *building computer databases* to organize and store useful biological information, **(2)** *developing computer tools to find, visualize, and analyze* the information, and **(3)** *communicating* the information, especially using the Internet. Bioinformatics is being applied to many aspects of biology, ranging from storing DNA sequences to storing names, descriptions, and locations of collections of biological organisms in museums.

One example is *Species 2000,* an Internet-based global research project with the goal of providing information about all known species of plants, animals, fungi, and microbes on the earth as the baseline data set for studies of global biodiversity. Users worldwide will be able to verify the scientific name, status, and classification of any known species via the Species Locator, which will provide online access to authoritative species data drawn from an array of participating databases.

Another example is the proposed Global Biological Information Facility, which would put more than 350 years of information on biological resources currently housed in the world's museums on the Internet. A website would list each of the world's named species, with links to information about each species, literature references, and which museums house specimens.

**How Can International Treaties Help Protect Endangered Species?** Several international treaties and conventions help protect endangered or threatened wild species. One of the most far reaching is the 1975 *Convention on International Trade in Endangered Species (CITES).* This treaty, now signed by 152 countries, lists **(1)** some 900 species that cannot be commercially traded as live specimens or wildlife products because they are in danger of extinction and **(2)** restricts international trade of 29,000 other species because they are at risk of becoming threatened.

CITES has helped reduce international trade in many threatened animals, including elephants, crocodiles, and chimpanzees. However, the effects of this treaty are limited because **(1)** enforcement is difficult and spotty, **(2)** convicted violators often pay only small fines, **(3)** member countries can exempt themselves from protecting any listed species, and **(4)** much of the highly profitable illegal trade in wildlife and wildlife products goes on in countries that have not signed the treaty.

The *Convention on Biological Diversity (CBD),* ratified by 172 countries, legally binds signatory governments to reversing the global decline of biological diversity. However, its implementation has proceeded slowly because **(1)** some key countries, such as the United States, have not ratified the treaty, and **(2)** it contains no severe penalties or other enforcement mechanisms.

**How Can National Laws Help Protect Endangered Species?** The United States controls imports and exports of endangered wildlife and wildlife products through two laws:

- The *Lacey Act of 1900,* which prohibits transporting live or dead wild animals or their parts across state borders without a federal permit.

- The *Endangered Species Act of 1973* (*ESA*, amended in 1982 and 1988), which makes it illegal for Americans to import or trade in any product made from an endangered or threatened species unless it is used (1) for an approved scientific purpose or (2) to enhance the survival of the species.

The ESA authorizes (1) the National Marine Fisheries Service (NMFS) to identify and list endangered and threatened ocean species and (2) the USFWS to identify and list all other endangered and threatened species. These species cannot be hunted, killed, collected, or injured in the United States.

Any decision by either agency to add or remove a species from the list must be based on biology only, not on economic or political considerations. However, economic factors can be used in (1) deciding whether and how to protect endangered habitat and (2) developing recovery plans for listed species. The act also forbids federal agencies to carry out, fund, or authorize projects that would jeopardize an endangered or threatened species or destroy or modify the critical habitat it needs to survive. On private lands, fines and even jail sentences can be imposed to ensure protection of the habitats of endangered species.

Between 1973 and 2002, the number of U.S. species on the official endangered and threatened list increased from 92 to about 1,250 species (about 59% of them plants and 41% animals). According to a 2000 study by the Nature Conservancy, about 33% of the country's species are at risk of extinction, and 15% of them are at high risk (Figure 22-3). This amounts to about 30,000 species, compared to the roughly 1,250 species currently protected under the ESA. The study found that many of the country's rarest and most imperiled species are concentrated in a few hot spots (Figure 22-22).

The ESA generally requires the secretary of the interior to designate and protect the *critical habitat* needed for the survival and recovery of each listed species. By June 2001, only 124 designated critical habitats had been established.

Getting listed is only half the battle. Next, the USFWS or the NMFS is supposed to prepare a plan to help the species recover. By 2002, final recovery plans had been developed and approved for about 75% of the endangered or threatened U.S. species, but about half of those plans exist only on paper.

The ESA requires all commercial shipments of wildlife and wildlife products to enter or leave the country through one of nine designated ports. Few illegal shipments are confiscated (Figure 22-23, p. 584) because the 60 USFWS inspectors can examine only about one-fourth of at least 90,000 shipments that enter and leave the United States each year. Even if caught, many violators are not prosecuted, and convicted violators often pay only a small fine.

**How Can Private Landowners Be Encouraged to Protect Endangered Species?** One problem is that the ESA has encouraged some developers, timber companies, and other private landowners to avoid

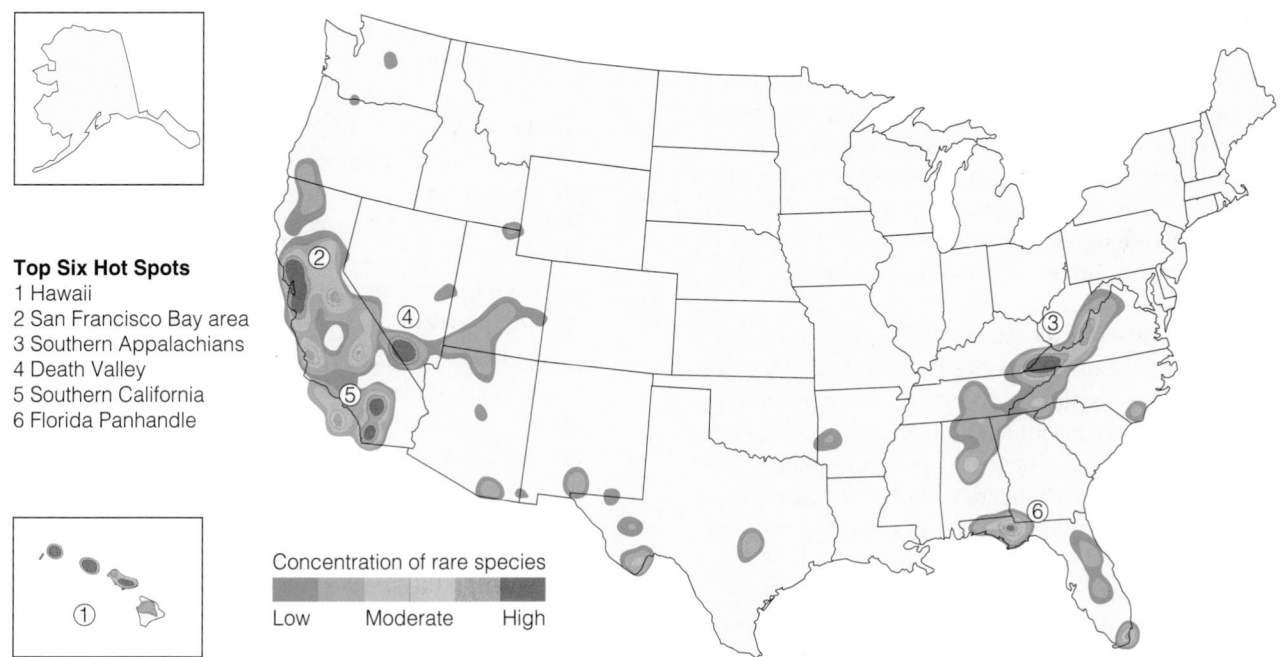

**Top Six Hot Spots**
1 Hawaii
2 San Francisco Bay area
3 Southern Appalachians
4 Death Valley
5 Southern California
6 Florida Panhandle

Concentration of rare species

Low    Moderate    High

**Figure 22-22** *Biodiversity hot spots* in the United States. This map shows areas that contain the largest concentrations of rare and potentially endangered species. (Data from State Natural Heritage Programs, the Nature Conservancy, and Association for Biodiversity Information)

**Figure 22-23** Confiscated products made from endangered species. Because of a scarcity of funds and inspectors, probably no more than one-tenth of the illegal wildlife trade in the United States is discovered. The situation is even worse in most other countries.

government regulation by managing their land to reduce its use by endangered species. The National Association for Homebuilders, for example, has published practical tips for developers and other landowners to avoid ESA issues. Suggestions include (1) planting crops, (2) plowing fields between crops to prevent native vegetation and endangered species from occupying the fields, (3) clearing forests, and (4) burning or managing vegetation to make it unsuitable for local endangered species.

In 1982, Congress amended the ESA to allow the secretary of the interior to use *habitat conservation plans* (*HCPs*) to strike a compromise between the interests of private landowners and the interests of endangered and threatened species without reducing the recovery chances of a protected species. With an HCP, landowners, developers, or loggers are allowed to destroy some critical habitat or kill all or a certain number of endangered or threatened species on private land in exchange for taking steps to protect that species.

Such protective measures might include (1) setting aside a part of the species' habitat as a preserve, (2) paying to relocate the species to another suitable habitat, or (3) paying money to have the government buy suitable habitat elsewhere. Once the plan is approved it cannot be changed, even if new data show that the plan is inadequate to protect a species and help it recover.

Some wildlife conservationists support this approach because it can (1) head off use of evasive techniques and (2) reduce political pressure to seriously weaken or eliminate the ESA. However, there is growing concern that such plans are being developed without enough scientific evaluation of their effects on a

species' recovery. Suggestions for improving HCPs include (1) developing scientific standards for such plans, (2) having plans reviewed by a scientific advisory committee, and (3) requiring more compensating efforts by private landowners as a buffer when important data such as population trends or assessment of the impacts on the affected species are not known.

In 1999, the USFWS approved two new approaches for encouraging private landowners to protect threatened or endangered species:

- *Safe harbor agreements* in which landowners voluntarily agree to take specified steps to restore, improve, or maintain habitat for threatened or endangered species located on their land. In return, landowners get (1) technical help from local conservation agencies, (2) government assurances that the land, water, or other natural resources involved will not face future restrictions once the agreement is over, and (3) assurances that after the agreement has expired landowners can return the property to its original condition without penalty.

- Voluntary *candidate conservation agreements* in which landowners agree to take specific steps to help conserve a species whose population is declining but is not yet listed as endangered or threatened. Participating landowners receive (1) technical help and (2) assurances that no additional resource use restrictions will be imposed on the land covered by the agreement if the species is listed as endangered or threatened in the future.

**Should the Endangered Species Act Be Weakened?** Opponents of the ESA contend it has (1) not worked and (2) caused severe economic losses by hindering development on private land. Since 1995, efforts have been made to weaken the ESA by

- Making protection of endangered species on private land voluntary.

- Having the government compensate landowners if it forces them to stop using part of their land to protect endangered species.

- Making it harder and more expensive to list newly endangered species by requiring government wildlife officials to navigate through a series of hearings and peer review panels.

- Giving the secretary of the interior (1) the power to permit a listed species to become extinct without trying to save it and (2) power over the listing of species.

- Allowing the secretary of the interior to give any state, county, or landowner permanent exemption from the law, with no requirement for public notification or comment.

- Prohibiting the public from commenting on or bringing lawsuits to change poorly designed HCPs.

**Should the Endangered Species Act Be Strengthened?** Most conservation biologists and wildlife scientists contend that the ESA has not been a failure (Spotlight, p. 586). They also refute the charge that the ESA has caused severe economic losses.

- Since 1979, only about 0.05% of the almost 200,000 projects evaluated by the USFWS have been blocked or canceled as a result of the ESA.

- The act allows for economic concerns. By law, a decision to list a species must be based solely on science. However, once a species is listed, economic considerations can be weighed against species protection in protecting critical habitat and designing and implementing recovery plans.

- The act allows a special cabinet-level panel, called the "God Squad," to exempt any federal project from having to comply with the act if the economic costs are too high.

- The act allows the government to (1) issue permits and exemptions to landowners with listed species living on their property and (2) use habitat conservation plans, safe harbor agreements, and candidate conservation agreements to bargain with private landowners.

A study by the U.S. National Academy of Sciences recommended changes to make the ESA more scientifically sound and effective by (1) greatly increasing the meager funding for implementing the act, (2) developing recovery plans more quickly, (3) developing guidelines to avoid provisions that are scientifically or economically unsound and spell out which actions are likely to harm recovery, and (4) establishing a core of

"survival habitat" as a temporary emergency measure when a species is first listed that could support the species for 25–50 years. According to conservation biologists, recovery success would improve significantly if a greater share of the budget was used for recovery of plants and invertebrates, which make up 68% of the listed species.

Most biologists and wildlife conservationists believe the United States should develop a new system to protect and sustain biological diversity and ecosystem function based on three principles:

- Find out what species and ecosystems the country has.

- Locate and protect the most endangered ecosystems (Figure 22-22) and species.

- Give private landowners who agree to help protect specific endangered species and ecosystems (1) financial incentives (tax breaks and write-offs), (2) technical help, and (3) assurances of no additional requirements in the future (safe harbor and candidate conservation agreements).

**Should We Try to Protect All Endangered and Threatened Species?** Because of limited funds, information, and trained personnel, only a few endangered and threatened species can be saved. Some analysts suggest concentrating the limited funds available for preserving threatened and endangered wildlife on species that (1) have the best chance for survival, (2) have the most ecological value to an ecosystem, and (3) are potentially useful for agriculture, medicine, or industry.

Recent research suggests judging the health of an ecosystem not on the basis of sheer numbers of species but on which species (1) play keystone roles and (2) are tolerant to environmental change such as acid deposition, climate change, and toxins. Researchers say preserving 10 key and adaptable species in an ecosystem is likely to be better than preserving 10,000 weak ones. In addition to protecting keystone species, biologists call for protection of *keystone resources* such as (1) salt licks and mineral pools that provide essential minerals for wildlife, (2) deep pools in streams and springs that serve as refuges for fish and other aquatic species during dry periods, and (3) hollow tree trunks used as breeding sites and homes for many bird and mammal species.

Others oppose selective protection of species on ethical grounds or contend we do not have enough biological information to make such evaluations. Proponents argue that (1) in effect we are already deciding by default which species to save and (2) despite limited knowledge, the selective approach is more effective and a better use of limited funds than the current one. What do you think?

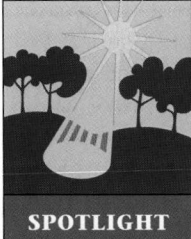
## Accomplishments of the Endangered Species Act

Critics of the ESA call it an expensive failure because only a few species have been removed from the endangered list. Most biologists strongly disagree that the act has been a failure, for several reasons:

- Species are listed only when they are already in serious danger of extinction. This is like setting up a poorly funded hospital emergency room that takes only the most desperate cases, often with little hope for recovery, and then saying it should be shut down because it has not saved enough patients.

- It takes decades for most species to become endangered or threatened. Thus it usually takes decades to bring a species in critical condition back to the point where it can be removed from the list. Expecting the ESA (which has been in existence only since 1973) to quickly repair the biological depletion of many decades is unrealistic.

- The most important measure of the law's success is that the conditions of almost 40% of the listed species are stable or improving. A hospital emergency room taking only the most desperate cases and then stabilizing or improving the condition of 40% of its patients would be considered an astounding success.

- The federal endangered species budget was only $126 million in 2002 (up from $23 million in 1993)—about one-third the cost of one C-17 transport plane. The amount spent by the federal government to help protect endangered species amounts to only about 44¢ a year per U.S. citizen.

To most biologists, it is amazing that so much has been accomplished in stabilizing or improving the condition of almost 40% of the listed species on a shoestring budget.

### Critical Thinking

Explain why you agree or disagree with each of the proposals made on p. 585 to **(a)** weaken the ESA and **(b)** strengthen the act.

## 22-9 PROTECTING WILD SPECIES FROM DEPLETION AND EXTINCTION: THE SANCTUARY APPROACH

**How Can Wildlife Refuges and Other Protected Areas Help Protect Endangered Species?** Since 1903, when President Theodore Roosevelt established the first U.S. federal wildlife refuge at Pelican Island,

Florida, the National Wildlife Refuge System has grown to 524 refuges. Some 34 million Americans visit these refuges each year to hunt, fish, hike, or watch birds and other wildlife.

More than three-fourths of the refuges are wetlands for protecting migratory waterfowl. About 20% of the U.S. endangered and threatened species have habitats in the refuge system, and some refuges have been set aside for specific endangered species. These have helped Florida's key deer, the brown pelican, and the trumpeter swan to recover.

Conservation biologists urge the establishment of more refuges for endangered plants. They also call for Congress and state legislatures to allow abandoned military lands that contain significant wildlife habitat to become national or state wildlife refuges.

According to a General Accounting Office study, activities considered harmful to wildlife occur in nearly 60% of the nation's wildlife refuges. There is much controversy over whether to allow oil and gas development in Alaska's Arctic National Wildlife Refuge (Pro/Con, p. 360). According to a 2001 study by the Audubon Society, the U.S. Refuge System is in a state of crisis. Pollutants and invasive species are degrading many refuges, and the system has a $1.6 billion backlog of unmet operations and maintenance needs.

**Can Gene Banks, Botanical Gardens, and Farms Help Save Most Endangered Species?** Gene or seed banks preserve genetic information and endangered plant species by storing their seeds in refrigerated, low-humidity environments (Spotlight, p. 295). Most of the world's 50 seed banks have focused on storing seeds of the approximately 100 plant species that provide about 90% of the food consumed by humans. However, some banks are devoting more attention to storing seeds for a wider range of species that may be threatened with extinction or a loss of genetic diversity.

Scientists urge the establishment of many more such banks, especially in developing countries. However, some species cannot be preserved in gene banks, and maintaining the banks is very expensive.

The world's 1,600 botanical gardens and arboreta contain about 4 million living plants, representing about 80,000 species or approximately 30% of the world's known plant species. The world's largest botanical garden is the Royal Botanical Gardens of England at Kew. It contains an estimated 25,000 species of living plants, or about 10% of the world's total. About 2,700 of these species are listed as threatened.

Botanical gardens are increasingly focusing on cultivation of rare and endangered plant species. In the United States, the Center for Plant Conservation coordinates efforts by 28 botanical gardens to **(1)** store nearly 600 endangered U.S. plant species and (2) propagate and reintroduce some of them into the wild. In addition, botanical gardens help educate an estimated 150 million visitors a year about the need for plant conservation. However, these sanctuaries have too little storage capacity and too little funding to preserve most of the world's rare and threatened plants.

We can take pressure off some endangered or threatened species by raising individuals on farms for commercial sale. Two examples are the use of farms in Florida to raise alligators for their meat and hides, and butterfly farms in Papua New Guinea, where many butterfly species are threatened by habitat destruction and fragmentation, commercial overexploitation, and environmental degradation.

**Can Zoos and Aquariums Help Protect Most Endangered Species?** Zoos, aquariums, game parks, and animal research centers are being used to preserve some individuals of critically endangered animal species, with the long-term goal of reintroducing the species into protected wild habitats.

Two techniques for preserving endangered terrestrial species are egg pulling and captive breeding. *Egg pulling* involves collecting wild eggs laid by critically endangered bird species and then hatching them in zoos or research centers. In *captive breeding,* some or all of the wild individuals of a critically endangered species are captured for breeding in captivity, with the aim of reintroducing the offspring into the wild.

Other techniques for increasing the populations of captive species include (1) artificial insemination, (2) surgical implantation of eggs of one species into a surrogate mother of another species (embryo transfer), (3) use of incubators, (4) cross-fostering, in which the young of a rare species are raised by parents of a similar species, (5) using computer databases of the family lineages of species in zoos and DNA analysis to match individuals for mating and prevent genetic erosion through inbreeding, and (6) genetic cloning.

The increased use of *cloning* to help revive endangered species is controversial. Proponents urge zoos and wildlife managers to collect and freeze cells of endangered species for cloning. However, several conservation groups fear this could divert attention and very limited funds from what endangered species need most: *protected habitats* and in some cases *protection from poaching.*

Captive breeding programs at zoos in Phoenix, Arizona, and San Diego and Los Angeles, California, temporarily saved the nearly extinct Arabian oryx (Figure 22-7), a large antelope that once lived throughout the Middle East. By 1960, it had been hunted nearly to extinction in the wild (with only about 48 left) by people riding in jeeps and helicopters and wielding rifles and machine guns. Between 1980 and 1996, the return of oryx bred in captivity to protected habitats in the Middle East allowed the population to reach about 400. However, since 1996, poachers have been capturing these animals for sale to private zoos. As a result, the wild population has been reduced to about 100, and the species is again facing extinction.

Before release, many captive-raised animals and birds need extensive training to help them learn how to find food and shelter, avoid predators, and interact in social groups. Because released populations often are small and thus vulnerable, scientists often try to estimate the *minimum viable population* (p. 566) needed for an introduced species to survive.

After more than two decades of captive breeding efforts, only a handful of endangered species have been returned to the wild. Examples shown in Figure 22-7 include the black-footed ferret, California condor, Arabian oryx, and golden lion tamarin. However, most reintroductions fail because of (1) lack of suitable habitat, (2) inability of individuals bred in captivity to survive in the wild, or (3) renewed overhunting or capture of some returned species (such as the Arabian oryx).

When the money is available, scientists can gain information about the numbers, movement, and behavior of natural or released populations of animals by using radio transmitters and satellite tracking or setting up video cameras throughout the habitat of a species.

Ways to establish new populations of rare and endangered plants at suitable sites include (1) promoting seed dispersal by wind, animals, water, and manual seeding, (2) planting wild-collected or greenhouse-grown seedlings or adult plants, and (3) controlling competing plant species and herbivore populations until the new populations become established.

Lack of space and money limit efforts to maintain populations of endangered species in zoos and research centers. The captive population of each species must number 100–500 individuals to avoid extinction through accident, disease, or loss of genetic diversity through inbreeding. Recent genetic research indicates that 10,000 or more individuals are needed for an endangered species to maintain its capacity for biological evolution.

Today's zoos and research centers have space to preserve healthy and sustainable populations of only about 925 of the 2,000 large vertebrate species that could vanish from the planet. According to one estimate, using all the space in the 201 accredited U.S. zoos for captive breeding could sustain only about 100 large animal species on a long-term basis.

Public aquariums that exhibit unusual and attractive fish and some marine animals such as seals and dolphins help educate the public about the need to protect such species. In the United States, more than

35 million people visit aquariums each year. However, unlike some zoos, public aquariums have not served as effective gene banks for endangered marine species, especially marine mammals that need large volumes of water.

Instead of seeing zoos and aquariums as Noah's Arks, some critics see them as prisons for once wild animals. They also contend that zoos and aquariums foster the notion that we do not need to preserve large numbers of wild species in their natural habitats.

Some zoos display many of their animals in natural settings and use this to educate visitors about the need to preserve natural habitats for wildlife throughout the world. For example, New York's Bronx Zoo has a display capable of exposing visitors to the sounds and sights of an African rainforest. Such displays, however, are not real rainforests. Many of the trees are made of plastic and the real trees shock gorillas to keep them from eating the leaves. In some zoos elephants and other animals that roam free in habitat areas during the day are chained up in a barn at night.

Some people criticize zoos and aquariums for putting on shows that show animals wearing clothes, riding bicycles, or performing tricks. Instead of educating people about the true nature of such animals, they contend that fosters the idea that the animals are there primarily to entertain us by doing things people do and in the process raise money for their keepers.

Regardless of their benefits and drawbacks, conservation biologists point out that zoos, aquariums, and botanical gardens are not a biologically or economically feasible solution for (1) most of the world's current endangered species and (2) the much larger number expected to become endangered over the next few decades.

## 22-10  WILDLIFE MANAGEMENT

**How Can Wildlife Populations Be Managed?**
**Wildlife management** involves manipulating wildlife populations (especially game species) and their habitats for their welfare and for human benefit. The *wildlife management approach* manages game species for sustained yield by (1) using laws to regulate hunting and fishing, (2) establishing harvest quotas, (3) developing population management plans, (4) improving wildlife habitat, and (5) using international treaties to protect migrating game species such as waterfowl.

In the United States, funds for state game management programs come from the sale of hunting and fishing licenses and from federal taxes on hunting and fishing equipment. Two-thirds of the states also have provisions on state income tax returns that allow individuals to contribute money to state wildlife programs.

The first step in wildlife management is to decide which species are to be managed in a particular area. Ecologists and conservation biologists emphasize preserving biodiversity, wildlife conservationists are concerned about endangered species, bird-watchers want the greatest diversity of bird species, and hunters want large populations of game species.

In the United States and other developed countries, most wildlife management is devoted to producing surpluses of game animals and birds for hunters. Since the passage of the Wildlife Restoration Act in 1937, there has been a large increase in the number of game animals (such as white-tailed deer, wild turkeys, Rocky Mountain elk, and pronghorn antelope) sought by many sport hunters.

After goals have been set, the wildlife manager must develop a management plan. Ideally, this plan is based on the principles of (1) ecological succession (Figure 8-14, p. 180, and Figure 8-15, p. 181), (2) wildlife population dynamics (Figure 9-3, p. 192, and Figure 9-7, p. 194), (3) an understanding of the cover, food, water, space, and other habitat needs of each species to be managed, and (4) the *maximum sustained yield (MSY)* of a population, in which harvested individuals are not removed faster than they can be replaced through reproduction. The manager must also consider (1) the number of potential hunters, (2) their likely success rates, and (3) the regulations for preventing excessive hunting.

This information is difficult, expensive, and time consuming to obtain. It involves much educated guesswork and trial and error, which is why wildlife management is as much an art as a science. Management plans must also be sensitive to political pressures from conflicting groups and to budget constraints.

Estimating maximum sustained yields is difficult because (1) the necessary data on population size and breeding potential often are not available, (2) the estimated yields vary with environmental factors such as climate change, drought, and availability of sufficient habitat and other resources, and (3) estimates must take into account how particular harvesting levels affect other species or ecosystem properties.

**How Can Vegetation and Water Supplies Be Manipulated to Manage Wildlife?**  Wildlife managers can encourage the growth of plant species that are the preferred food and cover for a particular animal species by controlling the ecological succession (Figure 8-15, p. 181) of the vegetation in an area.

Wildlife species can be classified into four types, according to the stage of ecological succession at which they are most likely to be found: early successional, midsuccessional, late successional, and wilderness (Figure 8-16, p. 182):

- *Early successional species* find food and cover in weedy pioneer plants that invade an area that has been disturbed, whether by human activities or natural phenomena (fires, volcanic activity, or glaciation).

- *Midsuccessional species* are found around abandoned croplands and partially open areas created by (1) logging of small timber stands, (2) controlled burning, and (3) clearing of vegetation for roads, houses, firebreaks, oil and gas pipelines, and electrical transmission lines. Such openings of the forest canopy (1) promote the growth of vegetation favored by midsuccessional mammal and bird species and (2) increase the amount of edge habitat, where two communities such as a forest and a field come together. This transition zone allows animals such as deer to feed on vegetation in clearings and then quickly escape to cover in the nearby forest.

- *Late successional species* rely on old-growth and mature forests to produce the food and cover on which they depend. These animals need the protection of moderate-sized, old-growth forest refuges.

- *Wilderness species* flourish only in undisturbed, mature vegetation communities such as large areas of old-growth forests, tundra, grasslands, and deserts. They can survive only in large wilderness areas and wildlife refuges.

Various types of habitat management can be used to attract a desired species and encourage its population growth. Examples are (1) planting seeds, (2) transplanting certain types of vegetation, (3) building artificial nests, and (4) deliberately setting controlled, low-level ground fires to help control vegetation. Wildlife managers often create or improve ponds and lakes in wildlife refuges to provide water, food, and habitat for waterfowl and other wild animals.

**How Useful Is Sport Hunting in Managing Wildlife Populations?** Most developed countries use sport hunting laws to manage populations of game animals. Licensed hunters are allowed to hunt only during certain portions of the year to protect animals during their mating season. Limits are set on the size, number, and sex of animals that can be killed, and on the number of hunters allowed in a given area.

Close control of sport hunting is difficult. Accurate data on game populations may not exist and may cost too much to get. People in communities near hunting areas, who benefit from money spent by hunters, may seek to have hunting quotas raised.

Sport hunting is controversial. Proponents argue that without carefully regulated sport hunting, deer and other large game animals exceed the carrying capacity of their habitats and destroy vegetation they and other species need. For example, between 1900 and 2001, the estimated population of white-tailed deer in the United States increased from 500,000 to 25–30 million. Many of these deer (1) invade subdivisions and eat shrubs and home gardens, (2) raid farmers' fields and orchards, (3) threaten rare plants and animals in some areas, (4) help spread Lyme disease, carried by deer ticks to humans, and (5) are involved in more than 500,000 vehicle collisions each year that kill more Americans than any other wild animal, injure thousands, and cost at least $1.1 billion. Wildlife biologist William Porter estimates that without hunting, the U.S. deer population would be five times its current level and cause extensive ecological damage.

Some communities have hired sharpshooters to reduce the deer population. Others have trapped and relocated deer or are experimenting with using contraceptives to reduce the deer birth rate.

Deer are not the only problem. Other wild species whose populations have grown because of hunting and trapping restrictions and lack of natural predators include (1) *bear* populations in 20 states, (2) *beavers*, which can chop down trees around waterways and threaten drinking water supplies, (3) *elk* herds in Colorado, (4) *golden eagles*, which can prey on sheep in the West, (5) *cormorant* birds, which consume large numbers of catfish grown in aquaculture ponds in Alabama, Mississippi, and Louisiana, (6) protected *sea lions* in the Northwest, which consume large numbers of endangered salmon and steelhead fish, (7) *moose* in parts of the Northeast, which are destroying vegetation along some riverbanks, (8) nonmigratory *Canada geese*, which have become pests in many areas, and (9) *mountain lions* in parts of the West. As wildlife populations increase and more people move into areas inhabited by wildlife, the ethical dilemma over increased use of sport hunting and trapping will become more acute.

According to its proponents, sport hunting also (1) provides recreational pleasure for millions of people (15 million in the United States), (2) stimulates local economies, and (3) provides money through sales of hunting licenses and taxes on firearms and ammunition (more than $1.7 billion since 1937) that is used to buy, restore, and maintain wildlife habitats and to support wildlife research in the United States. Environmental groups such as the Sierra Club and Defenders of Wildlife support carefully controlled sport hunting as a way to preserve biological diversity by helping prevent depletion of native species of plants and animals.

Some individuals and groups, however, including the Humane Society, oppose sport hunting. They argue that (1) it inflicts unnecessary pain and suffering on wild animals (most of which are not killed to supply food that humans need for survival), and (2) game managers create a surplus of game animals by deliberately eliminating their natural predators (such as wolves) and then claim the surplus must be harvested by hunters to prevent habitat degradation or starvation of the game. Instead of eliminating natural predators, say opponents, wildlife managers should reintroduce them in some areas to reduce the need for sport hunting.

Supporters of hunting point out that **(1)** populations of many game species (such as deer) are so large that predators such as wolves cannot control them, and **(2)** because most wildlife habitats are fragmented, introducing predators can lead to the loss of nearby livestock. However, critics of hunting contend that deer (which make up only 2% of the 200 million animals that hunters kill in the United States each year) are being used as a smoke screen argument to allow killing of many other game species that do not threaten vegetation. What do you think?

**How Can Populations of Migratory Waterfowl Be Managed?** Migratory birds—including ducks, geese, swans, and many songbirds (Case Study, p. 575)—make north-to-south journeys from one habitat to another each year, usually to find food, suitable climate, and other conditions necessary for reproduction. Such bird species use many different routes called **flyways,** but only about 15 are considered major routes (Figure 22-24).

Some countries along such flyways have entered into agreements and treaties to protect crucial habitats needed by such species, both along their migration routes and at each end of their journeys. However, the populations of migrating snow geese have risen to the point where they are causing serious ecological damage (Connections, right).

Wildlife officials manage waterfowl by **(1)** regulating hunting, **(2)** protecting existing habitats, and **(3)** developing new habitats, including artificial nesting sites, ponds, and nesting islands. More than 75% of the federal wildlife refuges in the United States are wetlands used by migratory birds. Local and state agencies and private conservation groups such as Ducks Unlimited, the Audubon Society, and the Nature Conservancy have also established waterfowl refuges.

Since 1934, the *Migratory Bird Hunting and Conservation Stamp Act* has required waterfowl hunters to buy a duck stamp each season they hunt. Revenue from these sales goes into a fund to buy land and easements for the benefit of waterfowl.

In this chapter, we have seen that protecting the terrestrial species that make up part of the earth's biodiversity from premature extinction is a difficult, controversial, and challenging responsibility. See the website for this chapter for some actions you can take to help protect wildlife and preserve biodiversity.

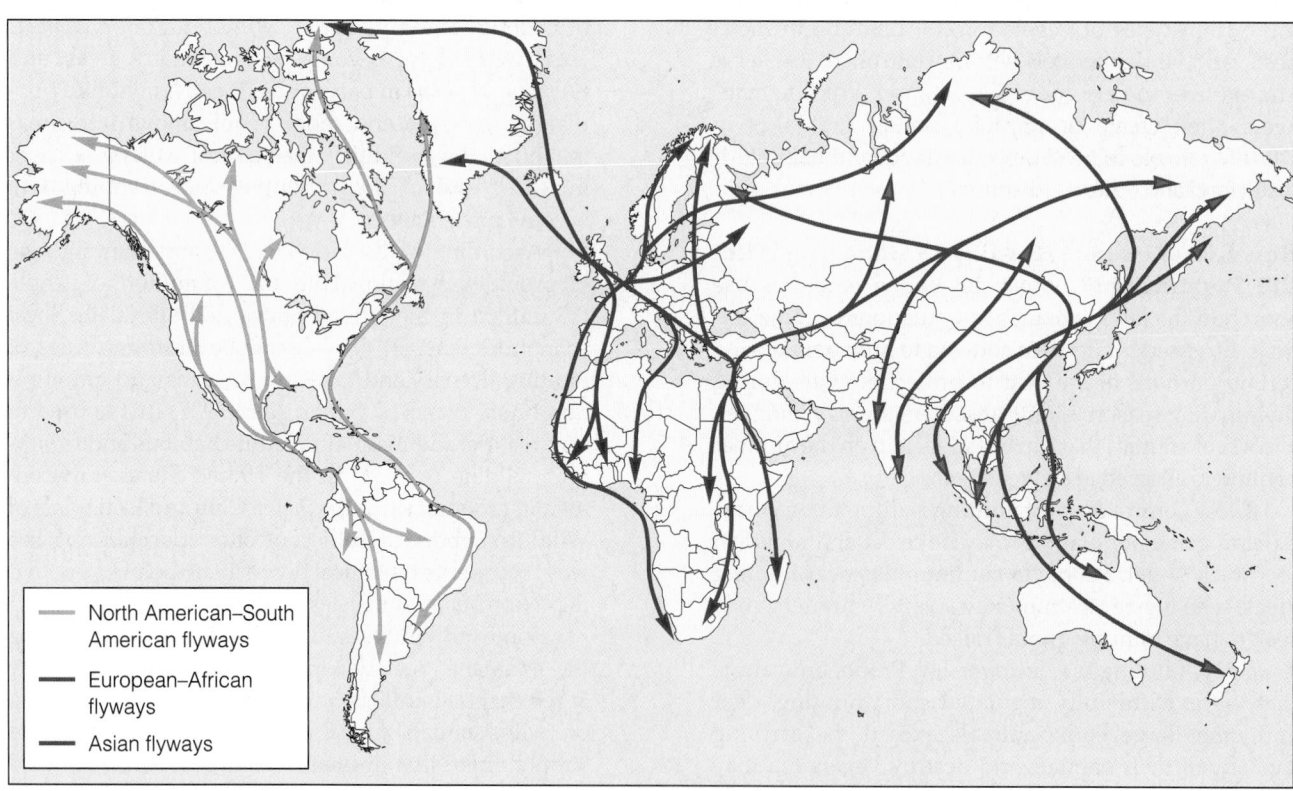

North American–South American flyways

European–African flyways

Asian flyways

**Figure 22-24** Major *flyways* used by migratory birds, mostly waterfowl. Each route has a number of subroutes.

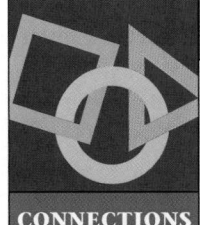

## What Should Be Done About Snow Geese?

**CONNECTIONS**

The populations of the lesser snow goose and Ross's goose have grown so large that they threaten their arctic tundra and wetlands habitats. According to the USFWS, the populations of these species rose from about 800,000 in the 1960s to about 5 billion by 2000. Hunters kill about 500,000 of these birds annually, but their population is still growing at a rate of about 250,000 birds per year.

Their massive numbers have converted vast tracts of arctic tundra in Canada and Alaska to highly saline, almost bare soil, creating what has been called a *botanical desert*. These geese have also destroyed about one-third of the salt marshes along the Hudson and

James Bays and have heavily damaged another third of these marshes.

The geese have thrived because each year they can gorge themselves on the abundant grains in the U.S. agricultural heartland from the Great Plains to the Gulf Coast. Thus they arrive at their winter breeding grounds in better condition, leading to higher rates of reproduction.

Two options have been suggested for dealing with this problem:

- Let nature takes its course. Eventually the geese will destroy their winter breeding ground and their population will crash. However, this may take decades and lead to widespread ecosystem degradation.
- Encourage hunters to kill more of these birds each year. In 1999, the USFWS announced plans to allow

24 states to ease hunting restrictions on the species, hoping to at least double the number killed. Although endorsed by many conservation and hunting groups, this plan was denounced by the Humane Society of the United States, which has filed a lawsuit saying the expanded hunt violates laws protecting migratory birds.

This problem, which connects high agricultural productivity with overpopulation of a species and ecosystem degradation, is another reminder we can never do one thing in nature.

**Critical Thinking**

What do you think should be done about snow goose overpopulation? Explain.

---

*We know what to do. Perhaps we will act in time.*
EDWARD O. WILSON

## REVIEW QUESTIONS

**1.** Define the boldfaced terms in this chapter.

**2.** What factors led to the extinction of the passenger pigeon in the United States?

**3.** Describe ways in which human activities have reduced the biodiversity of **(a)** the world and **(b)** the United States.

**4.** List the major goals, strategies, and tactics for **(a)** preventing the premature extinction of species and **(b)** preserving and restoring ecosystems and aquatic systems.

**5.** Distinguish among *local*, *ecological*, and *biological* extinction of a species.

**6.** Distinguish between *endangered* and *threatened* species. List eight characteristics that make species vulnerable to biological extinction.

**7.** Give two reason why it is so difficult to estimate how human activities are affecting extinction rates.

**8.** List seven methods scientists use to estimate how human activities are affecting extinction rates. What is the estimated range of annual extinction rates caused by human activities based on using these methods? How do these rates compare with the estimated annual extinction rate before humans appeared.

**9.** List five reasons why most biologists believe their current estimates of extinction rates from human activities are probably too low.

**10.** Distinguish between *instrumental* and *intrinsic* values of wildlife. Give examples of instrumental values of wildlife as sources of **(a)** economic goods, **(b)** ecological services, **(c)** information, and **(d)** psychological and aesthetic benefits. Distinguish between the following types of instrumental values: **(a)** *direct use*, **(b)** *option*, **(c)** *indirect use*, **(d)** *existence*, **(e)** *aesthetic*, **(f)** *educational*, and **(g)** *bequest*. List some *consumptive* and *nonconsumptive* values of wildlife.

**11.** What is the estimated total economic value of the earth's biodiversity?

**12.** What is the *intrinsic value* of biodiversity? What is *biophilia*?

**13.** What are four underlying causes of the population reduction and extinction of wild species? Describe how each of the following factors contributes to the premature extinction of species, and give an example of a species affected by each factor: **(a)** habitat loss and degradation, **(b)** habitat fragmentation, **(c)** deliberately introduced nonnative species, **(d)** accidentally introduced nonnative species, **(e)** commercial hunting and illegal hunting (poaching), **(f)** predator and pest control, **(g)** the legal and illegal market for exotic pets and decorative plants, and **(h)** climate change and pollution.

**14.** Give two examples of **(a)** deliberately introduced harmful species and **(b)** accidentally introduced harmful species.

**15.** What are major characteristics of **(a)** successful invader species and **(b)** ecosystems vulnerable to invader species?

**16.** List four ways to reduce the threat from nonnative species. Explain how pumping nitrogen into the ballast water of cargo ships may help reduce the transfer of non-native species into aquatic systems throughout much of the world.

**17.** Why are many island species especially vulnerable to extinction? Why are some migrating birds vulnerable to premature extinction? What are some important ecological roles of bats, and why are they vulnerable to extinction?

**18.** What is *bioinformatics*, and how can it be used to help protect biodiversity?

**19.** List the benefits and limitations of protecting species using **(a)** the Convention on International Trade in Endangered Species (CITES) and **(b)** the Endangered Species Act (ESA) in the United States.

**20.** Give reasons why you believe the ESA has been a failure or a success. List measures that would strengthen and weaken the ESA in the United States.

**21.** Distinguish among *habitat conservation plans, safe harbor agreements,* and *candidate conservation plan*s used as ways to help implement the ESA.

**22.** What are the pros and cons of trying to protect all endangered and threatened species? List three guidelines that could be used to decide which species to protect.

**23.** Summarize the pros and cons of using the following to help protect endangered species: **(a)** wildlife refuges, **(b)** gene banks and botanical gardens, **(c)** zoos and animal research centers, and **(d)** aquariums. Distinguish between *egg pulling* and *captive breeding*.

**24.** What is *wildlife management,* and what are the major steps in managing wildlife? What are the major limitations of wildlife management?

**25.** Describe how each of the following methods can be used to help manage wildlife, and list the limitations of each approach: **(a)** manipulating vegetation and water supplies, **(b)** sport hunting, and **(c)** controlling populations of migratory waterfowl. List the pros and cons of sport hunting.

## CRITICAL THINKING

**1.** How do **(a)** population growth, **(b)** poverty, and **(c)** climate change affect biodiversity?

**2.** Discuss your gut-level reaction to the following statement: "Eventually all species become extinct. Thus it does not really matter that the passenger pigeon is extinct and that the blue whale, the whooping crane, the California condor, and the world's remaining rhinoceros and tiger species are endangered mostly because of human activities." Be honest about your reaction, and give arguments for your position.

**3.** **(a)** Do you accept the ethical position that each *species* has the inherent right to survive without human interference, regardless of whether it serves any useful purpose for humans? Explain. Would you extend this right to the *Anopheles* mosquito, which transmits malaria and to infectious bacteria? **(b)** Do you believe each *individual* of an animal species has an inherent right to survive? Explain. Would you extend such rights to **(a)** individual plants and microorganisms and **(b)** tigers that kill people? Explain.

**4.** Explain why you agree or disagree with **(a)** using animals for research, **(b)** keeping animals captive in a zoo, and **(c)** killing surplus animals produced by a captive-breeding program in a zoo when no suitable habitat is available for their release.

**5.** Is the current mass depletion that scientists believe is taking place necessarily bad? Explain.

**6.** Your lawn and house are invaded by fire ants, which can cause painful bites. What would you do?

**7.** Which of the following statements best describes your feelings toward wildlife: **(a)** As long as it stays in its space, wildlife is OK, **(b)** as long as I do not need its space, wildlife is OK, **(c)** I have the right to use wildlife habitat to meet my own needs, **(d)** when you have seen one redwood tree, fox, elephant, or some other form of wildlife you have seen them all, so lock up a few of each species in a zoo or wildlife park and do not worry about protecting the rest, and **(e)** wildlife should be protected.

**8.** List your three favorite wild species. Examine why they are your favorites. Are they cute and cuddly looking, like the giant panda and the koala? Do they have humanlike qualities, like apes or penguins that walk upright? Are they large, like elephants or blue whales? Are they beautiful, like tigers and monarch butterflies? Are any of them plants? Are any of them species such as bats, sharks, snakes, or spiders that most people are afraid of? Are any of them microorganisms that help keep you alive? Reflect on what your choice of favorite species tells you about your attitudes toward most wildlife.

**9.** Environmental groups in a heavily forested state want to restrict logging in some areas to save the habitat of an endangered squirrel. Timber company officials argue that the well-being of one type of squirrel is not as important as the well-being of the many families affected if the restriction causes them to lay off hundreds of workers. If you had the power to decide this issue, what would you do and why? Can you come up with a compromise?

**10.** Explain why some developers and extractors of resources on public land oppose the development of databases such as Species 2000 and national databases of the species found in a particular country.

**11.** If you moved to the suburbs and deer invaded your yard and ate your shrubs and vegetables, what would you do?

**12.** Recently scientists have begun using gene-transfer techniques to clone some endangered species as a way to help prevent their extinction. However, some conservationists are concerned this could divert money and attention from what endangered species need most: protected habitats and protection from poaching. What is your opinion on this issue? Explain.

**13.** Congratulations! You are in charge of preventing the premature extinction of the world's existing species from human activities. What would be the three major components of your program to accomplish this goal?

## PROJECTS

**1.** Make a log of your own consumption of all products for a single day. Relate your level and types of consumption to the **(a)** decline of wildlife species and **(b)** increased destruction, degradation, and fragmentation of wildlife habitats in the United States (or the country where you live) and in tropical forests.

**2.** Identify examples of habitat destruction or degradation in your community that have had harmful effects on the populations of various wild plant and animal species. Develop a management plan for rehabilitating these habitats and species.

**3.** Choose a particular endangered animal or plant species and use the library or the Internet to find out what is being done to protect it from extinction. Develop a protection plan for this species.

**4.** Use the library or the Internet to find bibliographic information about *Aldo Leopold* and *Edward O. Wilson*, whose quotes appear at the beginning and end of this chapter.

**5.** Make a concept map of this chapter's major ideas, using the section heads and subheads and the key terms (in boldface). Look on the website for this book for information about making concept maps.

## INTERNET STUDY RESOURCES AND RESOURCES FOR FURTHER READING AND RESEARCH

The website for this book contains helpful study aids and many ideas for further reading and research. Log on to

www.info.brookscole.com/miller13

and click on the Chapter-by-Chapter area. Choose Chapter 22 and select a resource:

■ Flash Cards allows you to test your mastery of the Terms and Concepts to Remember for this chapter.

■ Tutorial Quizzes provides a multiple-choice practice quiz.

■ Student Guide to InfoTrac will lead you to Critical Thinking Projects that use InfoTrac College Edition as a research tool.

■ References lists the major books and articles consulted in writing this chapter.

■ Hypercontents takes you to an extensive list of sites with news, research, and images related to individual sections of the chapter.

## INFOTRAC COLLEGE EDITION

Improve your skills with InfoTrac College Edition, a searchable online database of articles from more than 700 periodicals. Log on to

http://www.infotrac-college.com

or access InfoTrac through the website for this book. Try to find the following articles:

**1.** Levin, D. A. 2002. Hybridization and extinction: In protecting rare species, conservationists should consider the dangers of interbreeding, which compound the more well-known threats to wildlife. *American Scientist* 90: 254. *Keywords:* "hybridization" and "extinction." An excellent introduction to the science of population genetics and species conservation.

**2.** Seneen, S. 2002. Going, going . . . exotic species are decimating America's native wildlife. *E* 13: 34. *Keywords:* "exotic species" and "native wildlife." Human aesthetics when it comes to wildlife may be having profound effects on populations of native species.

# 23 SUSTAINING TERRESTRIAL BIODIVERSITY: THE ECOSYSTEM APPROACH

## Who Is Afraid of the Big Gray Wolf?

At one time, the gray wolf (Figure 23-1) ranged over most of North America. Between 1850 and 1900, however, an estimated 2 million wolves were shot, trapped, and poisoned by ranchers, hunters, and government employees. The idea was to make the West and the Great Plains safe for livestock and for big game animals prized by hunters.

It worked. When Congress passed the U.S. Endangered Species Act (p. 583) in 1973, only about 400–500 gray wolves remained in the lower 48 states, primarily in Minnesota and Michigan. In 1974, the U.S. Fish and Wildlife Service (USFWS) listed the gray wolf as endangered in all 48 lower states except Minnesota. Alaska was not included because it had 6,000–8,000 gray wolves.

With such protection, the gray wolf population increased to about 3,000 in eight states (Arizona, Idaho, Michigan, Minnesota, Montana, New Mexico, Wisconsin, and Wyoming). Therefore, in 2000, the USFWS proposed moving the gray wolf from the endangered to the threatened category in these states.

Ecologists recognize the important role this keystone predator species once played in parts of the West and the Great Plains. These wolves **(1)** culled herds of bison, elk, caribou, and mule deer, **(2)** kept down coyote populations, and **(3)** provided uneaten meat for scavengers such as ravens, bald eagles, ermines, and foxes.

In recent years, herds of elk, moose, and antelope have expanded. Their larger numbers have **(1)** devastated some of the area's vegetation, **(2)** increased erosion, and **(3)** threatened the niches of other wildlife species. Reintroducing a keystone species such as the gray wolf into a terrestrial ecosystem is one way to help sustain its biodiversity and prevent environmental degradation.

In 1987, the USFWS proposed reintroducing gray wolves into the Yellowstone ecosystem. This idea brought vehement protests. Some objections came from ranchers who feared the wolves would attack their cattle and sheep; one enraged rancher said that the idea was "like reintroducing smallpox." Other protests came from **(1)** hunters who feared the wolves would kill too many big game animals and **(2)** miners and loggers who worried the government would halt their operations on wolf-populated federal lands.

Since 1995, federal wildlife officials have caught gray wolves in Canada and relocated them in Yellowstone National Park and northern Idaho. By 2002, the population of these wolves had grown by natural reproduction to around 270.

National Park Service (NPS) officials have trapped or shot wolves that kill livestock outside park areas. In addition, the Defenders of Wildlife set up a private fund to reimburse ranchers who establish that gray wolves wandering out of the Yellowstone ecosystem killed any of their sheep or cattle.

Some ranchers and hunters say they will take care of the wolves in their own way—what they call the "shoot, shovel, and shut up" solution. Meanwhile, efforts continue in Congress to eliminate the program and its funding. In 2001, ranchers and hunters succeeded in having the secretary of interior block USFWS plans to reintroduce an experimental population of grizzly bears into a large protected wilderness area in Idaho.

Population growth, economic development, and poverty are exerting increasing pressure on the world's forests, grasslands, parks, wilderness, and other storehouses of terrestrial biodiversity. Biodiversity researchers and protectors urge us to use these renewable natural resources more sustainably, as discussed in this chapter.

**Figure 23-1** The gray wolf is a threatened species in the lower 48 states. Ranchers, hunters, miners, and loggers have vigorously opposed efforts to return this keystone species to its former habitat in the Yellowstone National Park area. However, wolves were reintroduced beginning in 1995 and now number around 270.

*Forests precede civilizations, deserts follow them.*
François-Auguste-René de Chateaubriand

This chapter addresses the following questions:

- How is land used in the world and in the United States?

- What are the major types of public lands in the United States, and how are they used?

- Why are forest resources important, and how are they used and managed in the world and in the United States?

- Are tropical deforestation and fuelwood shortages serious problems? If so, what can we do about them?

- What problems do parks face, and how should we manage them?

- How should we establish, design, protect, and manage terrestrial nature reserves?

- What is ecological restoration, and why is it important?

## 23-1  LAND USE IN THE WORLD AND THE UNITED STATES

**How Is Land Used?**  Figure 23-2 shows the major categories of land use in the world, and Figure 23-3 shows land use and ownership in the United States. Human activities have disturbed about two-thirds of the earth's inhabitable land area (Figure 1-5, p. 7).

No nation has set aside as much of its land—about 42%—for public use, resource extraction, enjoyment, and wildlife as has the United States (Figure 23-3, top). The federal government manages roughly 35% of the country's land that belongs to every American (Figure 23-3, bottom). About 73% of this federal public land is in Alaska, and another 22% is in the western states (where 60% of all land is public land).

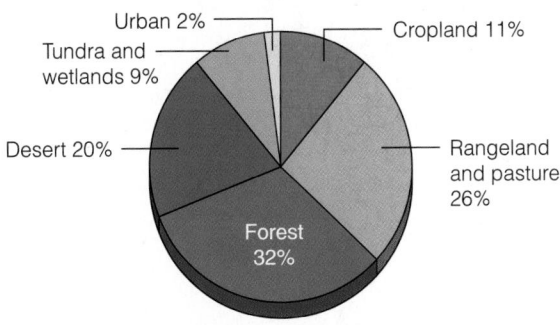

**Figure 23-2** How the world's land is used. Excluding uninhabitable areas of rock, ice, desert, and steep mountain terrain, only about 27% of the planet's land area remains undisturbed by human activities (Figure 1-5, p. 7). (Data from UN Food and Agriculture Organization)

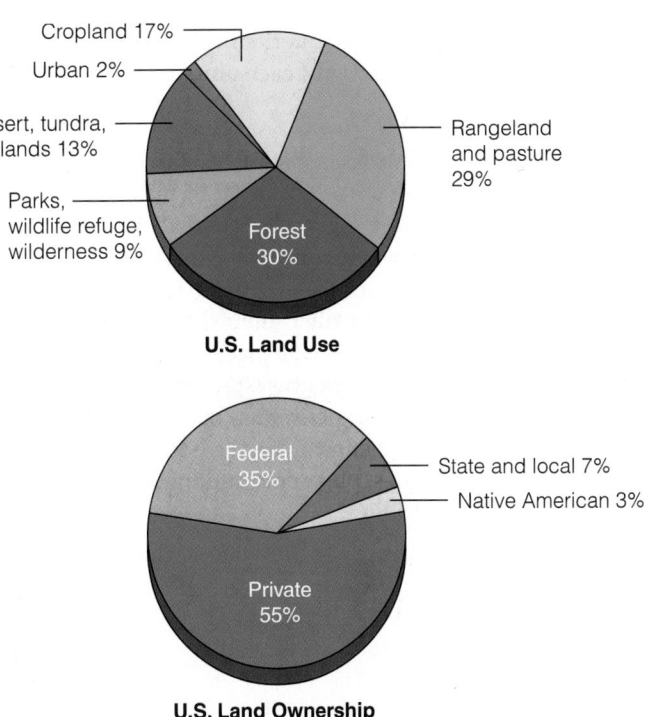

**Figure 23-3** How land is used (top) and owned (bottom) in the United States. (Data from U.S. Department of Agriculture)

**What Are the Major Types of U.S. Public Lands?**
Federal public lands are classified as **(1)** multiple-use lands, **(2)** moderately restricted-use lands, and **(3)** restricted-use lands.

### Multiple-Use Lands

- The *National Forest System*, managed by the U.S. Forest Service, consists of 156 forests (Figure 23-4, p. 596) and 22 grasslands. These forests are used for logging, mining, livestock grazing, farming, oil and gas extraction, recreation, sport hunting, sport and commercial fishing, and conservation of watershed, soil, and wildlife resources. Off-road vehicles usually are restricted to designated routes.

- The Bureau of Land Management (BLM) manages the *National Resource Lands* in the western states and Alaska. It emphasizes **(1)** providing a secure domestic supply of energy and strategic minerals and **(2)** preserving rangelands for livestock grazing under a permit system.

### Moderately Restricted-Use Lands

- The USFWS manages the 524 *National Wildlife Refuges* (Figure 23-4). Most refuges protect habitats and breeding areas for waterfowl and big game to provide a harvestable supply for hunters; a few protect endangered species from extinction. Permitted activities include sport hunting, trapping, sport and commercial fishing, oil and gas development, mining, logging, grazing, some military activities, and farming—as long as the Department of the Interior finds such uses compatible with the purposes of each unit.

### Restricted-Use Lands

- The *National Park System* consists of 385 units managed by the NPS. These units include **(1)** 55 major parks (mostly in the West; Figure 23-4) and **(2)** 324 national recreation areas, monuments, memorials, battlefields, historic sites, parkways, trails, rivers, seashores, and lakeshores. Only camping, hiking, sport fishing, and boating can take place in the national parks. Motor vehicles must stay on park roads, although some parks permit use of off-road vehicles. In national recreation areas, the NPS permits these same activities, plus sport hunting, mining, and oil and gas drilling.

- The 630 roadless areas of the *National Wilderness Preservation System* lie within the national parks, national wildlife refuges, and national forests. Management of these areas is the responsibility of the NPS (42%), Forest Service (33%), USFWS (20%), and BLM (5%). These areas are open only for recreational activities such as hiking, sport fishing, camping, nonmotorized boating, and, in some areas, sport hunting and horseback riding.

Roads, motorized vehicles, logging, livestock grazing, mining, commercial activities, and buildings are banned, except when they predate the wilderness designation.

| | National parks and preserves | | National forests | | (and Xs) National wildlife refuges |

**Figure 23-4** National forests, national parks, and wildlife refuges managed by the U.S. federal government. U.S. citizens jointly own these and other public lands. (Data from U.S. Geological Survey)

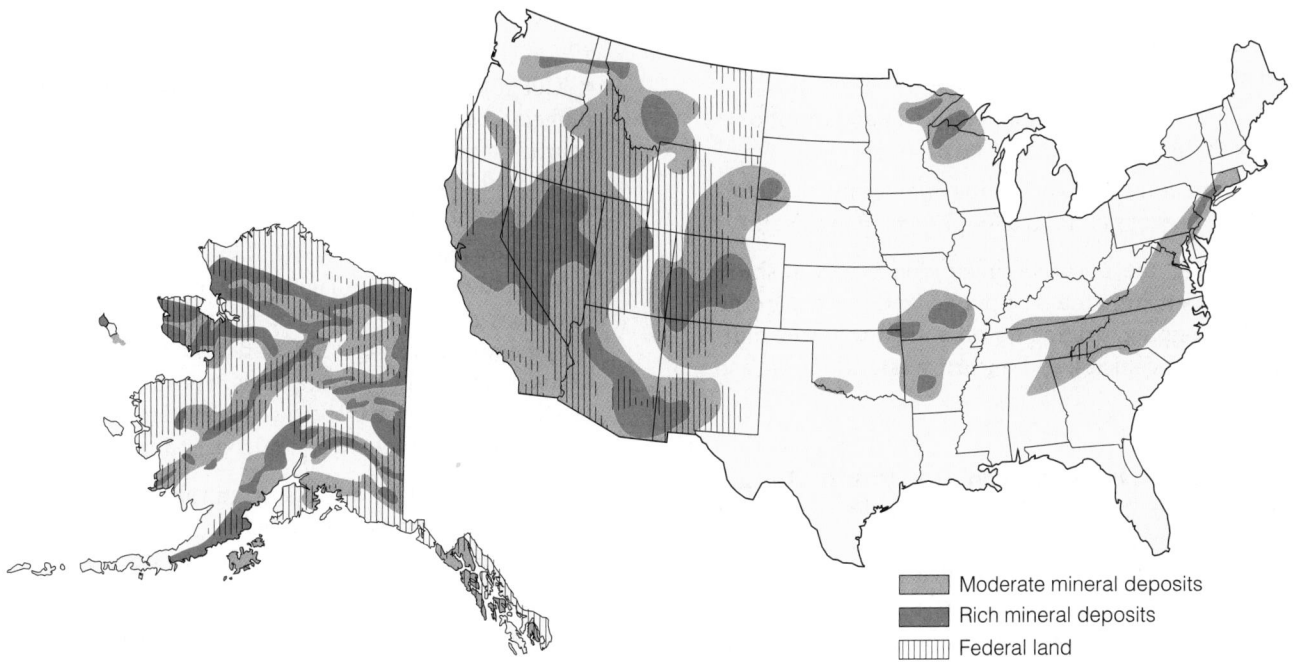

**Figure 23-5** Major mineral deposits on private land and federal public lands in the United States. Minerals found on public lands include **(1)** energy resources such as oil, oil shale, natural gas, coal, and uranium and **(2)** metallic minerals such as copper, cobalt, nickel, titanium, and platinum. Public lands also contain valuable forest and grassland resources. There is much conflict over the use of these publicly owned resources. (Data from U.S. Geological Survey)

## How Should U.S. Public Lands Be Managed?

Federal public lands contain an estimated **(1)** 20% of the country's oil reserves, **(2)** 30% of its natural gas reserves, **(3)** 40% of its coal reserves, **(4)** 40% of its commercial forests, and **(5)** large amounts of hard-rock minerals (Pro/Con, p. 347, and Figure 23-5). Because of the valuable resources they contain, how public lands should be used and managed has been extremely controversial (Spotlight, p. 32, and Pro/Con, p. 347). Most conservation biologists and environmental economists and many free-market economists believe the following four principles should govern use of public land:

- Protecting biodiversity, wildlife habitats, and the ecological functioning of public land ecosystems should be the primary goal.

- No one should receive subsidies or tax breaks for using or extracting resources on public lands.

- The American people deserve fair compensation for the use of their property.

- All users or extractors of resources on public lands should be fully responsible for any environmental damage they cause.

Aldo Leopold's land-use ethic (Section 2-5, p. 36) is the basis for most of these guiding principles.

There is strong and effective opposition to these ideas. Economists, developers, and resource extractors tend to view public lands in terms of their **(1)** usefulness in providing mineral, timber, and other resources

(Figure 23-5) and **(2)** ability to increase short-term economic growth.

They have succeeded in blocking implementation of the four principles just listed. For example, in recent years, the government has given more than $1 billion a year in subsidies to privately owned mining (Pro/Con, p. 347), logging, and grazing interests using U.S. public lands.

Some developers and resource extractors are going further and have mounted a campaign to get the U.S. Congress to pass laws that would

- Sell public lands or their resources to corporations or individuals, usually at less than market value.

- Slash federal funding for regulatory administration of public lands.

- Cut all old-growth forests in the national forests and replace them with tree plantations.

- Open all national parks, national wildlife refuges, and wilderness areas to oil drilling, mining, off-road vehicles, and commercial development.

- Do away with the NPS and launch a 20-year construction program of new concessions and theme parks run by private firms in the national parks.

- Continue mining on public lands under the provisions of the 1872 Mining Law (Pro/Con, p. 347), which allows mining interests to **(1)** pay no royalties to taxpayers for hard-rock minerals they remove and **(2)** not be responsible for any environmental damage they cause.

- Repeal the Endangered Species Act (p. 583) or modify it to allow economic factors to override protection of endangered and threatened species.

- Redefine government-protected wetlands so about half of them would no longer be protected.

- Prevent individuals or groups from legally challenging these uses of public land for private financial gain.

In 2001, the Bush administration began pushing hard to open large tracts of public land (mostly in the West) to logging, drilling for oil and natural gas, mining, off-road vehicles, and nuclear waste storage (Case Study, p. 374).

**Case Study: Livestock and U.S. Public Rangeland** About 25,000 U.S. ranchers hold permits to graze about 2% of the country's cattle and 10% of the sheep on BLM and Forest Service rangelands in 16 western states. Permit holders pay the federal government a grazing fee for this privilege.

Since 1981, Congress has set grazing fees on public rangeland at one-fourth to one-tenth the going rate for comparable private land. This means that taxpayers give the roughly 1% of U.S. ranchers with federal grazing permits subsidies amounting to $100–500 million a year, depending on how the costs of federal rangeland management are calculated.

The public subsidy does not end with low grazing fees. Other government costs include water pipelines, stock ponds, weed control, livestock predator control (with about 96,000 wild animals killed in 1999 by the USDA predator control program), clearing of undesirable vegetation, grass planting, erosion, and biodiversity loss. When these costs are added, taxpayers are giving 25,000 ranchers an annual subsidy of about $1–2 billion (an average of $40,000–80,000 per rancher) to produce 2% of the country's beef and 10% of its mutton (from sheep). It is not surprising that politically influential permit holders have fought hard to block any change in this system.

Ranchers with permits say that grazing fees on public lands should be low because most private rangeland is more productive than public rangeland. Environmentalists contend (1) this varies with the land involved, and (2) even when this is true, current grazing fees on public rangelands are much too low.

Here are three positions on the use of public rangelands (mostly in the West):

- Phase out commercial grazing of livestock on western public lands over the next 10–15 years. Proponents contend that water-poor western rangeland (Figure 14-7, p. 317) is not a good place to raise cattle and sheep, which (1) need a lot of water and can overgraze rangeland (Figure 13-26, left, p. 299), (2) can degrade riparian areas (Figure 13-27, p. 300, and Spotlight,

p. 300), and (3) threaten or endanger at least 175 plant and animal species.

- Get government out of the management of public rangeland and allow it to be (1) managed by grazing boards made up of ranchers exempt from most environmental laws or (2) sold to private ranching or development interests.

- Get progressive ranchers (Individuals Matter, p. 599), federal land managers, and environmentalists to work together to (1) develop more sustainable ways to manage public rangelands and (2) help keep ranchers using public and private lands in business so rangeland is not destroyed by being converted to houses, condos, small "ranchettes," and tourist attractions.

Although their numbers are still small, some coalitions of environmentalists, federal range managers, and ranchers are working together to develop more sustainable ways of using public rangeland such as

- *Banning or strictly limiting grazing on riparian areas* (Figure 13-27, p. 300, and Individuals Matter, p. 599).

- *Banning or strictly limiting grazing on rangeland where it (1) endangers habitats of threatened and endangered species, (2) causes desertification* (Figure 10-20, p. 220, and Figure 10-21, p. 221), *or (3) is otherwise ecologically unsustainable.*

- *Allowing individuals and environmental groups to purchase grazing permits and not use the land for grazing.* In 2000, the U.S. Supreme Court upheld this practice.

- *Encouraging ranchers to establish conservation easements that allow ranching but prevent the land from ever being sold for development in exchange for tax writeoffs.*

So far, western ranchers with grazing permits have had enough political power to prevent government officials and government land management agencies from implementing most of these measures.

## 23-2 MANAGING AND SUSTAINING FORESTS

**What Are the Major Types of Forests?** Forests with 50% or more tree cover (1) occupy about 32% of the earth's land surface (Figure 23-6 and Figure 6-35, p. 136) and (2) provide numerous ecological and economic services (Figure 23-7, p. 600). The four general types of forests are based primarily on climate: *tropical, subtropical, temperate,* and *polar (boreal)* (Figure 6-35, p. 136). About 47% of the world's forests are tropical, 33% boreal, 11% temperate, and 9% subtropical (Figure 23.8).

Forest managers and ecologists also classify forests as

- **Old-growth forests** (sometimes called *frontier forests*): uncut forests or regenerated forests that have

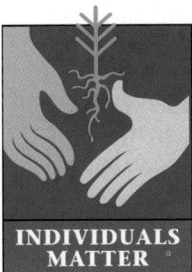

## The Eco-Rancher

Wyoming rancher Jack Turnell (see figure) is one of a new breed of cow-puncher who gets along with environmentalists. He talks about riparian ecology and biodiversity as fluently as he does about cattle: "I guess I have learned how to bridge the gap between the environmentalists, the bureaucracies, and the ranching industry."

Turnell grazes cattle on his 32,000-hectare (80,000-acre) ranch south of Cody, Wyoming, and 16,000 hectares (40,000 acres) of Forest Service land on which he has grazing rights. For the first decade after he took over the ranch, he raised cows the conventional way. Since then, he has made some changes.

Turnell disagrees with the proposals by some environmentalists to raise grazing fees and remove sheep

Jack Turnell is a rancher who is trying to practice more environmentally sustainable ranching.

and cattle from public rangeland. He believes if ranchers are kicked off the public range, ranches like his will be sold to developers and chopped up into vacation sites and homes ("ranchettes"). This will destroy the range for wildlife and livestock alike.

At the same time, he believes there are more ecologically sustain-able ways to operate ranches. To demonstrate this, Turnell **(1)** began rotating his cows away from the riparian areas (Figure 13-27, p. 300, and Spotlight, p. 300), **(2)** gave up most uses of fertilizers and pesticides, and **(3)** crossed his Hereford and Angus cows with a French breed that tends to congregate less around water. He makes most of his ranching decisions in consultation with range and wildlife scientists, and he uses photographs to monitor changes in range condition.

The results have been impressive. Willows and other plant life line riparian areas on the ranch and Forest Service land. This has provided lush habitat for an expanding population of wildlife, including pronghorn antelope, deer, moose, elk, bear, and mountain lions. In addition, this eco-rancher makes more money because the higher-quality grass puts more meat on his cattle.

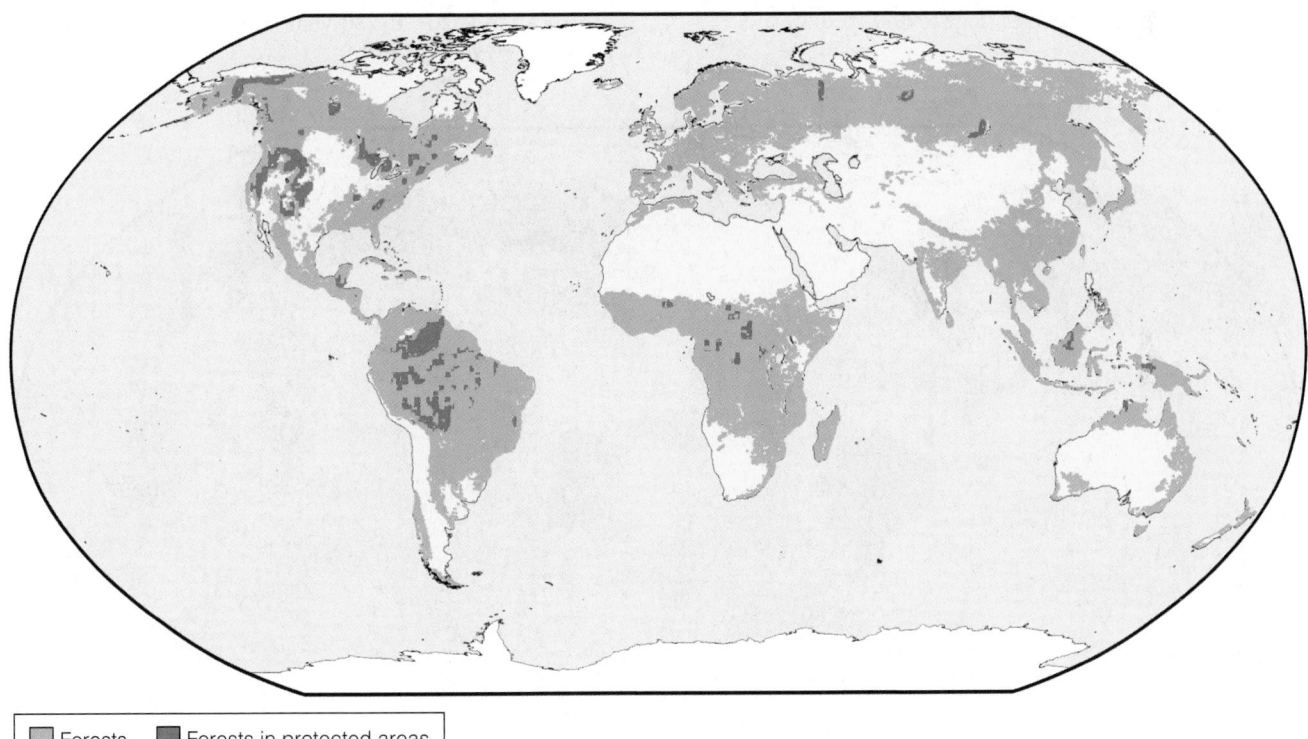

Forests ▮ Forests in protected areas

**Figure 23-6** In 2000, natural forests covered about 32% of the world's land area (green). South America has 24% of the total, the Russian Federation 23%, Africa 17%, North and Central America 14%, and Asia 12%. Only about 12% of these forests are in areas that receive varying degrees of protection (red). Much of this protection is on paper only. (Data from UN Food and Agriculture Organization)

**Figure 23-7** Major ecological and economic services provided by forests.

■ **Second-growth forests:** stands of trees resulting from secondary ecological succession (Figure 8-15, p. 181) after the trees in an area have been removed by **(1)** human activities such as clear-cutting for timber or conversion to cropland or **(2)** natural forces such as fire, hurricanes, or volcanic eruption.

■ **Tree plantations,** also called **tree farms:** managed tracts with uniformly aged trees of one species (Figure 23-10) that are harvested by clear-cutting as soon as they become commercially valuable. Then they are replanted and clear-cut again on regular cycles (Figure 23-11). These plantations, created mostly by clearing old-growth and second-growth forests, now occupy about 5% of the world's tree cover area (62% of them in Asia, mostly in China and India) and produce about 10% of the world's wood.

**What Are the Major Types of Forest Management?** The total volume of wood produced by a particular stand of forest varies as it goes through different stages of growth and ecological succession (Figure 23-12, p. 602). Producing fuelwood or fiber for paper production in the shortest time requires harvesting the trees on a short rotation cycle (Figure 23-11), well before the volume of wood produces peaks (point A in Figure 23-12). Harvesting of pulpwood plantations typically occurs in 6- to 10-year rotations in the tropics and 20- to 30-year rotations in temperate regions (Figure 23-11).

not been seriously disturbed by human activities or natural disasters for at least several hundred years. Old-growth forests provide ecological niches for a multitude of wildlife species (Figure 6-37, p. 137, and Figure 23-9).

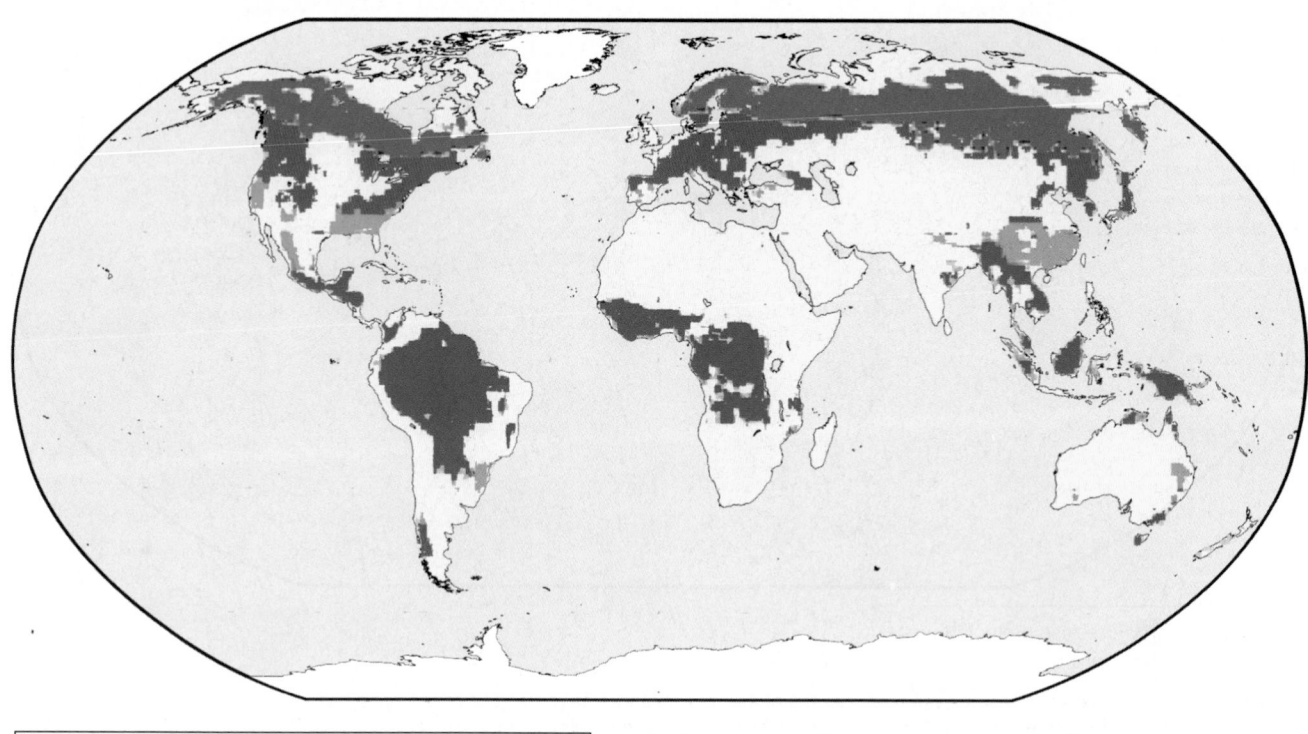

Boreal ■ Temperate ■ Subtropical ■ Tropical

**Figure 23-8** Distribution of the world's forest by major ecological zone. (Data from UN Food and Agriculture Organization)

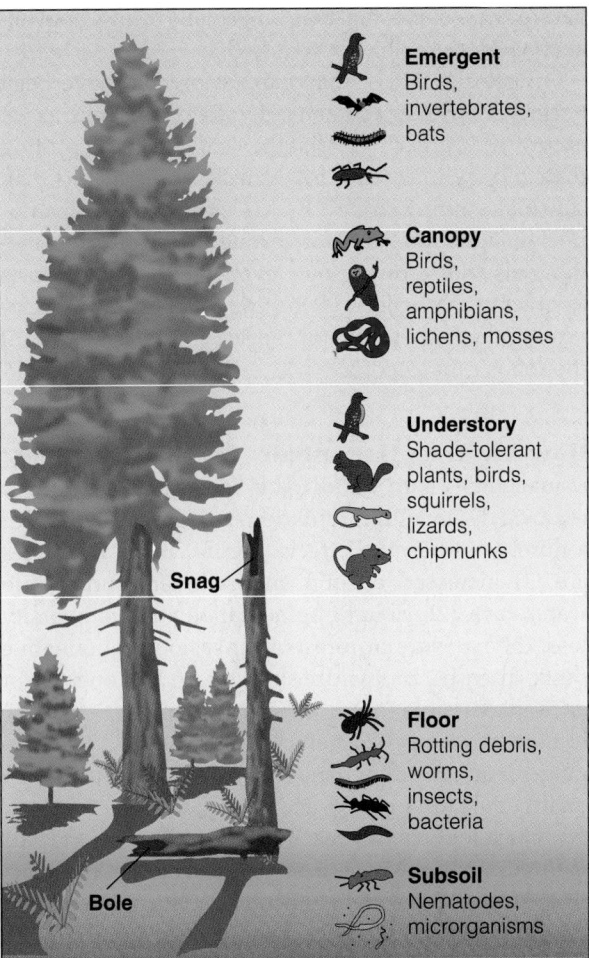

**Figure 23-9** Layers of biodiversity in an old-growth Douglas fir forest in the Pacific Northwest. There is much controversy over whether to **(1)** clear-cut such forests on public lands in the United States and Canada for their valuable timber or **(2)** preserve them for their biodiversity and important ecosystem services.

**Emergent**
Birds, invertebrates, bats

**Canopy**
Birds, reptiles, amphibians, lichens, mosses

**Understory**
Shade-tolerant plants, birds, squirrels, lizards, chipmunks

Snag

**Floor**
Rotting debris, worms, insects, bacteria

Bole

**Subsoil**
Nematodes, microrganisms

Courtesy of Dennis Gonsalves and Stephen Ferreira/Cornell University

**Figure 23-10** *Tree plantation* in Puna, Hawaii. Such managed tracts consist of uniformly aged trees that are harvested by clear-cutting when they are large enough to be commercially valuable. Tree plantations account for about 5% of the world's tree cover.

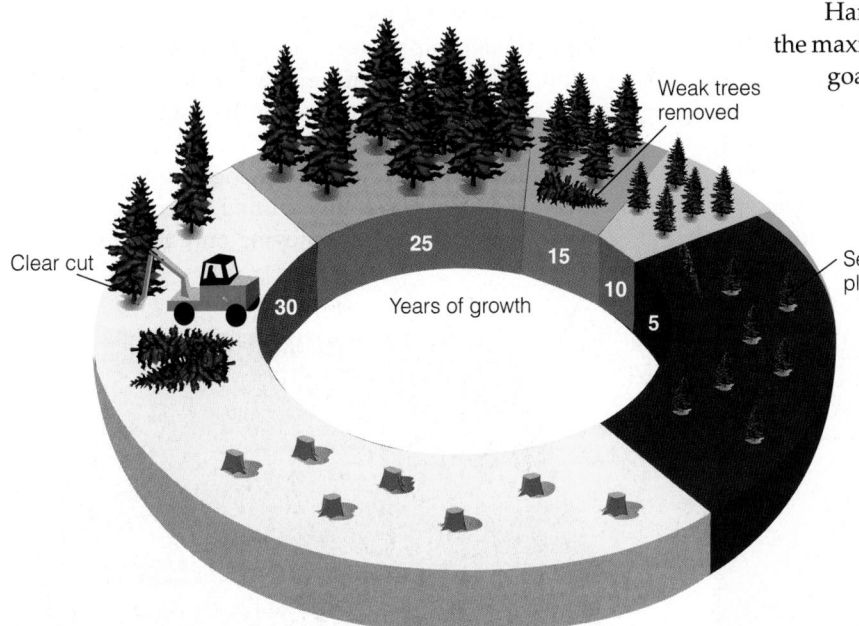

Weak trees removed

Clear cut

Years of growth

Seedlings planted

**Figure 23-11** Short (25- to 30-year) rotation cycle of cutting and regrowth of a monoculture tree plantation in modern industrial forestry. In tropical countries, where trees can grow more rapidly year round, the rotation cycle can be 6–10 years.

Harvesting at point B in Figure 23-12 gives the maximum yield of wood per unit of time. If the goal is high-quality wood for fine furniture or veneer, managers use longer rotations. This allows the development of larger older-growth trees whose rate of growth has leveled off (point C in Figure 23-12, p. 602).

There are two forest management systems:

- **Even-aged management,** which involves maintaining trees in a given stand at about the same age and size. In this approach, sometimes called *industrial forestry,* a simplified *tree plantation* (Figure 23-10) replaces a biologically diverse old-growth or second-growth forest. The plantation consists of one or two fast-growing and economically desirable species that can be harvested every 6–100 years, depending on the species.

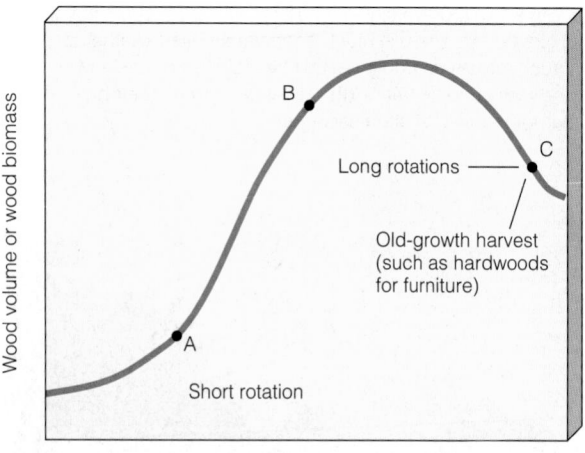

**Figure 23-12** Changes in wood volume over various growth and harvest cycles in forest management. Forest management occurs over a cycle of decisions and events called a *rotation* (Figure 23-11). The most important steps in a rotation include **(1)** taking an inventory of the site, **(2)** developing a forest management plan, **(3)** building roads into the site, **(4)** preparing the site for harvest, **(5)** harvesting timber, and **(6)** regenerating and managing the site until the next harvest.

■ **Uneven-aged management,** which involves maintaining a variety of tree species in a stand at many ages and sizes to foster natural regeneration. Here the goals are **(1)** biological diversity, **(2)** long-term sustainable production of high-quality timber (Figure 23-12, point C), **(3)** selective cutting of individual mature or intermediate-aged trees, and **(4)** multiple use of the forest for timber, wildlife, watershed protection, and recreation.

The rate of economic return plays a major role in determining whether forest owners will use short-term, even-aged management or longer-term, uneven-aged management. Before the 1960s, forest owners figured a rate of return on their investment of 2–3%. Because the trees grew about as fast as the money invested in them, owners could afford to wait decades

before they harvested them, normally using uneven-aged management.

Since the 1960s, many forest owners have been basing their management decisions on returns of almost 10%, reflecting what they could earn by putting their money into other investments. This means they can make more money by **(1)** clear-cutting diverse, uneven-aged forests, **(2)** investing the profits in something else, **(3)** growing new even-aged stands of trees as quickly as possible, **(4)** cutting them down, **(5)** reinvesting the money, and **(6)** repeating this process until the soil is exhausted.

**How Are Trees Harvested?** The first step in forest management is to build roads for access and timber removal. Even with careful design, logging roads have a number of harmful effects (Figure 23-13). Examples are **(1)** increased erosion and sediment runoff into waterways, **(2)** habitat fragmentation and biodiversity loss, **(3)** exposure of forests to invasion by nonnative pests, diseases, and wildlife species, and **(4)** opening of once-inaccessible forests to farmers, miners, ranchers, hunters, and off-road vehicle users. In addition, logging roads on public lands in the United States disqualify the land for protection as wilderness.

Once loggers can reach a forest, they use various methods to harvest the trees (Figure 23-14). With **selective cutting,** intermediate-aged or mature trees in an uneven-aged forest are cut singly or in small groups (Figure 23-14a). Selective cutting **(1)** reduces crowding, **(2)** encourages growth of younger trees, **(3)** maintains an uneven-aged stand of trees of different species, **(4)** allows natural regeneration from the surrounding trees, **(5)** can help protect the site from soil erosion and wind damage, **(6)** can be used to remove diseased trees, and **(7)** allows a forest to be used for multiple purposes.

However, much of the logging in tropical forests involves a form of selective cutting called *high grading.* It involves cutting and removing only the largest and

**Figure 23-13** Building roads into previously inaccessible forests paves the way to fragmentation, destruction, and degradation.

**a.** Selective Cutting

**b.** Shelterwood Cutting

Cut 1

Cut 2

**c.** Seed-Tree Cutting

**d.** Clear-Cutting

**e.** Strip Cutting

Uncut

Cut

6–10 years ago

Cut

3–5 years ago

Cut

1 year ago

Uncut

**Figure 23-14** Tree harvesting methods.

best specimens of the most desirable species. Studies have shown that for every large tree felled, 16 or 17 other trees are damaged or pulled down because a network of vines usually connects the trees in tropical forest canopies. This reduction of the forest canopy (Figure 6-37, p. 137) **(1)** causes the forest floor to become warmer, drier, and more flammable and **(2)** increases erosion of the forest's thin and usually nutrient-poor soil (Figure 10-15, bottom left, p. 215).

Some tree species grow best in full or moderate sunlight in medium- to large-size clearings. Methods for harvesting such species include

- **Shelterwood cutting,** which removes all mature trees in two or three cuttings over a period of about 10 years (Figure 23-14b).
- **Seed-tree cutting,** which harvests nearly all a stand's trees in one cutting, leaving a few uniformly distributed seed-producing trees to regenerate the stand (Figure 23-14c).
- **Clear-cutting,** which removes of all trees from an area in a single cutting (Figure 23-14d).

According to timber companies, clear-cutting **(1)** increases timber yield per hectare, **(2)** permits reforesting with genetically improved stocks of fast-growing trees, **(3)** shortens the time needed to establish a new stand of trees (Figure 23-11), **(4)** takes less skill and planning than other harvesting methods, **(5)** usually provides the maximum economic return in the shortest time, and, **(6)** if done carefully and responsibly, often is the best way to harvest tree plantations and stands of some tree species that need full or moderate sunlight for growth.

On the negative side, clear-cutting **(1)** leaves moderate to large forest openings, **(2)** eliminates most recreational value for several decades, **(3)** reduces biodiversity, disrupts ecosystem processes, and destroys and fragments some wildlife habitats, **(4)** makes nearby trees more vulnerable to being blown down by windstorms, and **(5)** leads to severe soil erosion, sediment water pollution, and flooding when done on steep slopes (Figure 14-23, p. 333).

A clear-cutting variation that can allow a sustainable timber yield without widespread destruction is **strip cutting** (Figure 23-14e). It involves clear-cutting a strip of trees along the contour of the land, with the corridor narrow enough to allow natural regeneration within a few years. After regeneration, loggers cut another strip above the first, and so on. This allows clear-cutting of a forest in narrow strips over several decades with minimal damage.

**What Is Happening to the World's Forests?**
Forests are renewable resources as long as the rate of cutting and degradation does not exceed the rate of regrowth. Here is some *bad news:*

- According to the World Resources Institute (WRI), human activities have reduced the earth's original forest cover by almost 50% over the past 8,000 years (much of it lost since 1970) and another 30% degraded or fragmented. Some sources put the loss at about 20% but provide little data to back up such a claim and cover periods of only 140–300 years.

- In recent years, forests have been cut or fragmented and degraded faster than they can regenerate in many parts of the world, especially in tropical areas of Latin America, Africa, and Asia (Figure 23-15, red areas). About 61% of the world's recorded wood harvest now comes from developing countries.

- A 2000 study by the UN Food and Agriculture Organization estimated that worldwide, the average loss of forests during the 1990s was about 16.1 million hectares (40 million acres) per year. About 95% of these losses took place in the tropics (Figure 23-15, red area). During the 1990s, 18 nations (most in Africa) lost 20% or more of their forest cover, and another 16 nations lost 10–19%. However, because of reforestation, natural regrowth, and establishment of tree plantations (Figure 23-15, green areas) the net forest loss in the 1990s was over 9 million hectares (22 million acres).

- According to researchers at the World Resources Institute, the forest loss is about 17% higher than the FAO estimate. They point out that in its most recent analysis the FAO **(1)** counted clear-cuts as forest as long as there were plans for them to be reforested, **(2)** included tree plantations as natural forest, and **(3)** decreased the minimum tree coverage an area needed to be counted as a forest from 20% to 10%.

- According to the UN Food and Agriculture Organization, only about 12% of the world's forest area is protected legally from logging, and much of this protection exists on paper only (Figure 23-6).

Here is some *good news:*

- The area of many temperate forests in North America and Europe has increased slightly because of reforestation from secondary ecological succession (Figure 8-15, p. 181) on cleared forest areas and abandoned croplands.

- Some of the cut areas of tropical forest have increased tree cover from regrowth and planting of tree plantations (Figure 23-15, green areas), although ecologists do not believe that tree plantations (with their much lower biodiversity) should be counted as forest anymore than croplands should be counted as grassland.

Clearing forests can provide land for crops, livestock, or urban growth. However, it also **(1)** decreases the overall net primary productivity (Figure 4-25, p. 81) of the cleared area, **(2)** reduces the stock of nutrients

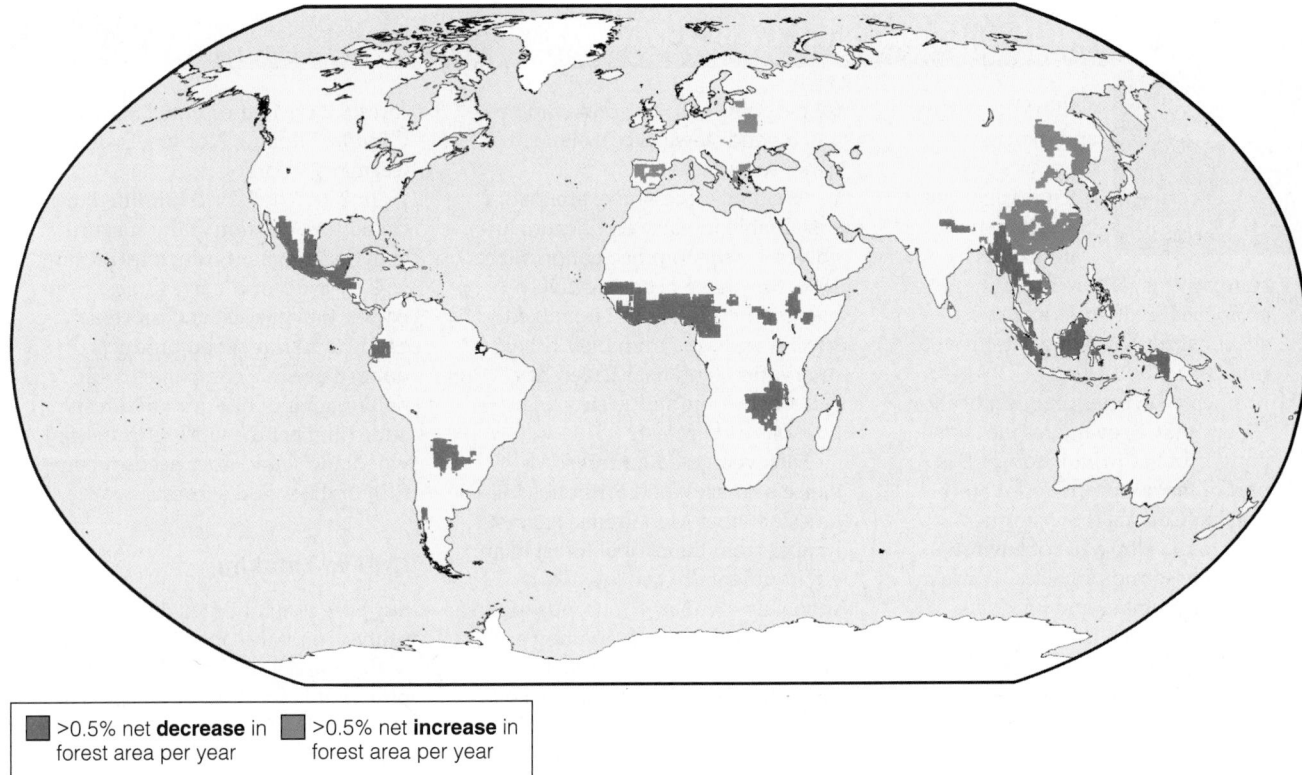

**Figure 23-15** Net change of the world's forest area during the 1990s. Forested areas are colored **(1)** red where deforestation caused more than a 0.5% net *decrease* in forest area per year and **(2)** green where reforestation from regrowth and planting of tree plantations caused more than a 0.5% net increase in forest area per year. (Data from UN Food and Agriculture Organization)

once stored in the trees and leaf litter, **(3)** diminishes biodiversity, **(4)** makes the soil more prone to erosion and drying, **(5)** increases the rate of runoff of water and soil nutrients from the land (Case Study, p. 90, and Figure 14-23, p. 333), **(6)** reduces the uptake of the greenhouse gas $CO_2$ from the atmosphere, and **(7)** adds $CO_2$ to the atmosphere if cleared trees are burned or allowed to decay. According to a 2001 study by the World Resources Institute, over the past 140 years deforestation has contributed an estimated 30% of the atmospheric buildup of $CO_2$ (Figure 18-4, top, p. 450).

**How Can Forests Be Managed More Sustainably?** Instead of increased use of conventional short-rotation industrial forestry (Figure 23-11), biodiversity researchers and a growing number of foresters call for more sustainable forest management that

■ *Grows more timber on long rotations*, generally about 100–200 years (point C, Figure 23-12), depending on the species and soil quality.

■ *Emphasizes* **(a)** *selective cutting of individual trees or small groups of most tree species* (Figure 23-14a), **(b)** *strip cutting* (Figure 23-14e) *instead of conventional clear-cutting, and* **(c)** *not clear-cutting (including seed-tree and shelterwood cutting) on land that slopes more than 15°.*

■ *Minimizes fragmentation of remaining large blocks of forest.*

■ *Stops or sharply reduces road building into uncut forested areas.*

■ *Uses road-building and logging methods that minimize soil erosion and compaction.*

■ *Leaves most standing dead trees (snags) and fallen timber (boles) to maintain diverse wildlife habitats and to be recycled as nutrients* (Figure 23-9 and Figure 4-15, p. 75).

■ *Has timber grown by sustainable methods certified and labeled by outside certifying groups* (Solutions, p. 606).

■ *Includes the estimated ecological services provided by trees and a forest* (Spotlight, p. 571) *in estimates of their economic value.*

Some foresters have suggested the United States and the world meet most of its demand for wood and wood products by growing genetically improved trees on carefully managed tree plantations (Figure 23-10). According to one estimate, *tree plantations* occupying less than 10% of the world's forested land could supply the entire world demand for forest products (except fuelwood). This would **(1)** reduce pressures to cut timber in old-growth and second-growth forests and **(2)** help protect wildlife habitats.

## Certifying Sustainably Grown Timber

Collins Pine owns and manages a large area of productive timberland in northeastern California. The company's goals are to maintain ecological, economic, and social sustainability by using selective cutting (since the 1940s).

Each year, Scientific Certification Systems (SCS) evaluates the company's timber production. SCS is part of the nonprofit Forest Stewardship Council (FSC), formed in 1993 to develop a list of environmentally sound practices for use in certifying timber and products made from such timber.

Each year, SCS evaluates all of Collins's landholdings to ensure that **(1)** cutting has not exceeded long-term forest regeneration, **(2)** roads and harvesting systems have not caused unreasonable ecological damage, **(3)** management of soils, downed wood, and standing snags provides adequate nutrient cycling and wildlife habitat, and

**(4)** the company is a good employer and a good steward of its land and water resources.

Another successful example of sustainable forestry certification involves the Menominee nation. Since 1890, they have been selectively harvesting (Figure 23-14a) mixed species and ages from their tribal reservation land near Green Bay, Wisconsin—the state's single largest tract of virgin forest.

Each year, the Rainforest Alliance's Smart Wood Program evaluates whether Menominee harvest lumber from their tribal forest in an environmentally and socially responsible manner. Thousands of people flock to the reservation each year to look at a sustainable forest operation that honors wildlife and biodiversity while providing jobs and income for the local economy.

According to a 2001 report by the UN Food and Agriculture Organization, in 2000 certified forests made up about 2% of the world's total forest area. Worldwide, 92% of the world's certified

forests were in the United States, Canada, Finland, Norway, Sweden, Germany, and Poland.

In 2001, the World Wildlife Fund called for adoption of the sustainable management principles of the FSC by the world's five largest companies that harvest and process timber and buy wood products. If done, these five companies could halt logging of old-growth forests and still meet the world's industrial wood and wood fiber needs on one-fifth of the world's forests.

### Critical Thinking

Suppose you inherited a sustainable timber company operation similar to the one described at the beginning of this box. If you switched to clear-cutting most of the land, you could **(1)** make millions in a short time, **(2)** sell the clear-cut land, and **(3)** invest the money elsewhere at a much higher rate of return than long-term sustainable timber harvesting. What would you do with your inheritance? Explain.

---

Conservation biologists and environmentalists support using this approach only with implementation of the following policies:

- Banning or sharply reducing the harvesting of the world's remaining old-growth forests

- Phasing out the harvesting of second-growth forests over a 10- to 20-year period as tree plantations are phased in

- Establishing tree plantations only on truly degraded land, not on any newly cleared land or existing cropland

- Phasing out government subsidies and tax breaks for harvesting timber from old-growth and second-growth forests and phasing in government subsidies and tax breaks for establishing tree plantations on truly degraded areas

Some *good news* is that the World Bank by 2005 has the goals of **(1)** having 200 million hectares (49 million acres) of forestland in its client countries under sustainable management and **(2)** protecting 50 million hectares (120 million acres) of natural forest with a high level of biodiversity in its client countries.

**How Can Pathogens and Insects Affect Forests?**
Insects and tree diseases can damage and kill trees in natural forests and tree plantations. Three deadly tree diseases caused by parasitic fungi that were accidentally introduced into the United States from other countries are **(1)** chestnut blight (from China), **(2)** Dutch elm disease (from Asia via Europe), and **(3)** white pine blister rust (from Europe).

Examples of insects that can have caused serious damage to certain tree species in the United States include

- *Bark beetles* such as the bronze birch borer and Asian longhorned beetle (Figure 22-17, p. 576). They bore channels through the layer beneath the bark of spruce, fir, birch, and pine trees.

- *Spruce budworm* and *gypsy moth* larvae (Figure 22-17, p. 576; accidentally introduced from Europe in 1869 and now established in 16 states; Figure 23-16). They can kill trees by eliminating the foliage they need to carry out photosynthesis and produce food.

- The *hemlock woolly adelgid,* which was accidentally introduced into the United States from Asia in 1924. During the 1990s, this insect pest destroyed large areas of hemlock forest throughout the eastern United States. In 1996, scientists began trying to control this invader by introducing a tiny beetle from Japan that is a natural enemy of the woolly adelgid.

Ways to reduce the impact of tree diseases and of insects on forests include **(1)** preserving biodiversity, **(2)** banning imported timber that might introduce harmful new pathogens or insect pests, **(3)** removing infected and infested trees or clear-cutting infected and infested areas and burning all debris, **(4)** treating diseased trees with antibiotics, **(5)** developing tree species that are disease-resistant, **(6)** applying pesticides (Section 20-2, p. 514), and **(7)** using integrated pest management (p. 522).

**How Do Fires Affect Forest Ecosystems?** Intermittent natural fires set by lightning are an important part of the ecological cycle of some types of forests and grasslands. Such fires maintain the vegetation of many ecosystems at a certain stage of ecological succession (Figure 8-15, p. 181). Examples of fire-maintained communities include **(1)** savanna, **(2)** temperate grasslands (Figure 6-30, p. 131), **(3)** chaparral, **(4)** southern pine forests, **(5)** western forests containing giant sequoia trees, and **(6)** evergreen coniferous forest (Figure 6-40, p. 140). In such ecosystems, occasional fires burn away much of the low-lying vegetation and small trees. A burst of new vegetation follows.

Several types of fires can affect forest ecosystems. Some, called *surface fires* (Figure 23-17, left), usually burn only undergrowth and leaf litter on the forest floor. These fires can kill seedlings and small trees but spare most mature trees and allow most wild animals to escape.

Occasional surface fires **(1)** burn away flammable ground material and help prevent more destructive fires, **(2)** release valuable mineral nutrients tied up in slowly decomposing litter and undergrowth, **(3)** increase the activity of underground nitrogen-fixing bacteria, **(4)** stimulate the germination of certain tree seeds (such as those of the giant sequoia, lodgepole pine, and jack pine), and **(5)** help control pathogens and insects. In addition, some wildlife species such as deer, moose, elk, muskrat, woodcock, and quail depend on occasional surface fires to **(1)** maintain their habitats and **(2)** provide food in the form of vegetation that sprouts after fires.

Some extremely hot fires, called *crown fires* (Figure 23-17, right), may start on the ground but eventually burn whole trees and leap from treetop to treetop. They usually occur in forests in which no surface fires have occurred for several decades. This allows dead wood, leaves, and

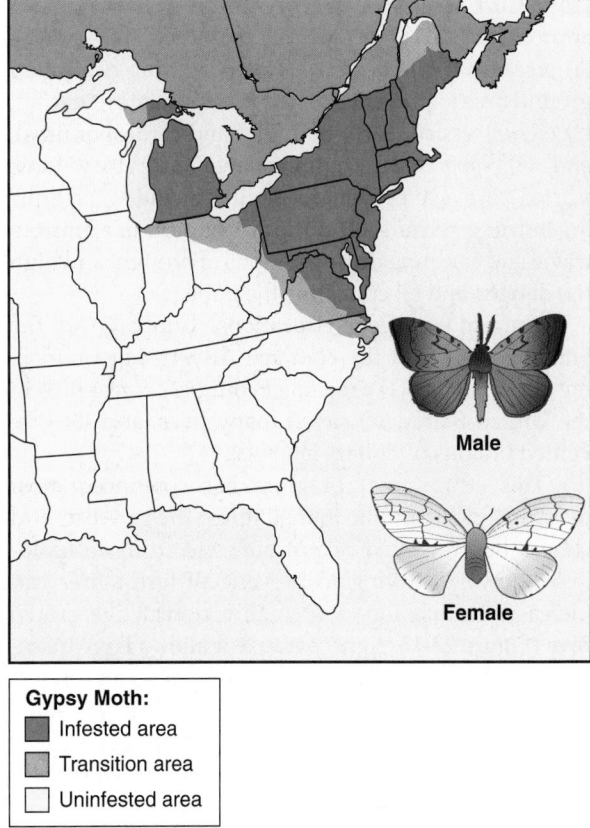

**Figure 23-16** Extent of gypsy moth infestation in the eastern United States. (U.S. Forest Service)

other flammable ground litter to build up. These rapidly burning fires can **(1)** destroy most vegetation, **(2)** kill wildlife, and **(3)** increase soil erosion.

Sometimes surface fires go underground and burn partially decayed leaves or peat. Such *ground fires* are most common in northern peat bogs. They may smolder for days or weeks and are difficult to detect and extinguish.

**Surface fire**          **Crown fire**

**Figure 23-17** Surface fires (left) usually burn undergrowth and leaf litter on a forest floor and can help prevent more destructive crown fires (right) by removing flammable ground material. Sometimes carefully controlled surface fires are deliberately set to prevent buildup of flammable ground material in forests.

**How Can We Protect Forests from Fire?** Four approaches used to protect forest resources from fire are (1) *prevention,* (2) *prescribed burning* (setting controlled ground fires to prevent buildup of flammable material), (3) *presuppression* (early detection and control of fires), and (4) *suppression* (fighting fires once they have started). Ways to prevent forest fires include (1) requiring burning permits, (2) closing all or parts of a forest to travel and camping during periods of drought and high fire danger, and (3) educating the public.

The Smokey Bear educational campaign of the Forest Service and the National Advertising Council, for example, has (1) prevented countless forest fires in the United States, (2) saved many lives, and (3) prevented billions of dollars in losses.

This educational program has convinced most members of the public that all forest fires are bad and should be prevented or put out. According to ecologists, however, trying to prevent all forest fires can increase the likelihood of highly destructive crown fires (Figure 23-17, right) because it allows large quantities of highly flammable underbrush and undergrowth and smaller trees to accumulate in some forests. This can convert normally harmless surface fires into fires intense enough to destroy the larger fire-resistant species needed for forest regeneration.

Ecologists propose two principles for the fire management of forests:

- Set carefully controlled prescribed ground fires to keep down flammable ground litter in fire-adapted forests as part of the natural ecological cycle of succession and regeneration (Figure 8-15, p. 181).
- Allow many fires in national parks, national forests, and wilderness areas to burn as long as they do not threaten human structures and life.

Government officials have heeded this advice. To help prevent crown fires, the U.S. Park Service and the Forest Service have set controlled *prescribed fires* in forests in which ecologists consider occasional fires to be beneficial to trees and various forms of forest life.

However, such fires require careful planning and monitoring to keep them from getting out of control. For example, during the spring of 2000, a poorly planned prescribed fire got out of hand in an area managed by the Park Service near Los Alamos, New Mexico. The result was a 33-day fire that (1) burned 19,000 hectares (47,000 acres), (2) destroyed or damaged 280 homes, (3) damaged 40 structures at the Los Alamos National Laboratory, and (4) caused an estimated $1 billion in damages.

Since 1972, government policy has been to allow most lightning-caused fires in national parks and national forests to burn themselves out as long as they do not threaten human lives, park or forest service facilities, private property, or endangered wildlife.

During the summers of 1988, 1994, and 2000, fires broke out in parts of Yellowstone National Park and a number of national forests in the West. This led some timber company lobbyists and politicians to call for a reversal of the federal let-it-burn policy.

However, biologists contend that the Yellowstone and some of the other fires caused more damage than they should have because a lack of natural and prescribed fires had allowed the buildup of flammable ground litter and small plants. Moreover, the fire in Yellowstone was ecologically beneficial. Today, its meadows and forests have (1) lush growths of regenerating trees and wildflowers and (2) more diverse habitats and better food supplies for many of its natural species because of secondary ecological succession after the fires.

Logging companies say they can help prevent crown fires if Congress allows them to clear-cut more trees or selectively remove large trees in national forests and parks. Biologists point out that this would increase the chances of severe fires because

- The most dangerous fuel of all is the unwanted waste material or "slash" left behind after a forest is cut. Indeed, many of the worst fires in U.S. history (including some of those during the 1990s) burned through cleared forest areas.
- Allowing logging companies to selectively cut or thin larger trees will not reduce the fire hazard because larger trees are difficult to ignite. The smaller trees, shrubs, and slash fuel most fires.

Environmentalists oppose such *salvage logging* in protected areas of national forests, parks, and wilderness. They call it a thinly disguised ploy to allow logging companies to increase road building and commercial logging in national forests and in roadless areas eligible for inclusion in the national wilderness system.

**How Do Air Pollution and Climate Change Threaten Forests?** Forests at high elevations and those downwind from urban and industrial centers are exposed to a variety of air pollutants that can harm trees (especially conifers) and make them more vulnerable to drought, diseases, and insects (Figure 17-15, p. 432). The solution is to reduce emissions of the offending pollutants from coal-burning power plants, industrial plants, and motor vehicles (Section 17-7, p. 439).

In coming decades, an even greater threat to forests (especially temperate and boreal forests) may come from regional climate changes brought about by global warming. This can (1) increase the threat of forest fires in areas that may get less precipitation (Figure 18-17, p. 462) and (2) cause some types of tree species to die out in some areas (Figure 18-18, p. 462). Ways to deal with projected global warming are discussed in Section 18-6, p. 464.

## 23-3 FOREST RESOURCES AND MANAGEMENT IN THE UNITED STATES

**What Is the Status of Forests in the United States?** Forests **(1)** cover about 30% of U.S. land area (Figure 23-3, top), **(2)** provide habitats for more than 80% of the country's wildlife species, and **(3)** supply about two-thirds of the nation's total water runoff. Forests in the United States are among the most diverse in the world—ranging from tropical forest in Hawaii to boreal forest in Alaska.

Some *good news* is that

- Forests (including tree plantations) in the United States now cover more area than they did in 1920, when the country's population was around 100 million. Many of the old-growth forests that were cleared or partially cleared between 1620 (Figure 23-18, left) and 1960 have grown back naturally through secondary ecological succession as fairly diverse second-growth (and in some cases third-growth) forest.

- The United States was the world's first country to set aside large areas of forest in protected areas. By 2000, protected forest made up about 40% of the country's total forest area (most in the National Forests).

However, some *bad news* is that

- Between 1620 and 1998, most of the existing old-growth forests in the lower 48 states were cut (Figure 23-18).

- Since the mid-1960s, an increasing area of the nation's remaining old-growth and fairly diverse second-growth forests has been clear-cut and replaced with biologically simplified tree plantations.

According to biodiversity researchers, replacing diverse forest with tree plantations **(1)** reduces overall forest biodiversity and **(2)** disrupts ecosystem processes such as energy flow and chemical cycling.

However, proponents argue that tree plantations help preserve overall forest biodiversity by reducing the pressure to clear-cut more diverse old-growth and second-growth forests.

**Why Should We Care About National Forests?**
The 156 national forests (Figure 23-4) managed by the U.S. Forest Service provide the following economic, ecological, and recreational benefits:

### Economic

- Contain about 19% of the country's forest area and supply about 3% of the nation's softwood timber (down from 15% in the 1980s).

- Serve as grazing lands for more than 3 million cattle and sheep each year.

- Provide about $4 billion worth of minerals, oil, and natural gas per year.

- Contain a network of more than 612,000 kilometers (380,000 miles) of roads, equal in area to the country's entire interstate highway system. Taxpayers pay for building and maintaining these mostly narrow dirt roads that give private logging companies access to timber stands.

### Ecological

- Provide habitats for almost 200 threatened and endangered species and hundreds of other wild species and fish.

- Are the principal habitats for thousands of pollinator species that contribute $4–7 billion per year to U.S. agriculture.

- Provide some of the country's cleanest drinking water (worth about $3.7 billion per year) for more than 60 million Americans in more than 3,400 communities. This single ecological service is worth more than the annual value of the timber harvested from these lands.

**Virgin forests, 1620**

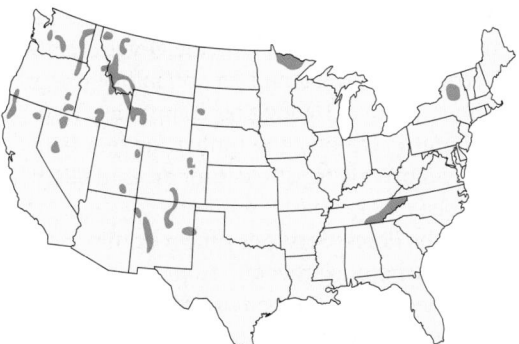

**Virgin forests, 1998**

**Figure 23-18** Vanishing old-growth forests in the United States between 1620 and 1998. Since 1960, second-growth forests and tree plantations have replaced some of these forests but this represents a net loss of biodiversity. (Data from the Wilderness Society and the U.S. Forest Service)

- Contain about one-third of the country's protected wilderness area.

### Recreational

- Receive more visits for recreation, hunting, and fishing than any other federal public lands, with recreational use rising sharply since 1930.

**Case Study: How Should U.S. National Forests Be Managed?** The Forest Service is required by law to manage national forests according to the principles of **(1)** *sustained yield* (which states that potentially renewable tree resources should not be harvested or used faster than they are replenished) and **(2)** *multiple use* (which says that each of these forests should be managed for a variety of simultaneous uses such as sustainable timber harvesting, recreation, livestock grazing, watershed protection, and wildlife).

The use of forest resources in the national forests is very controversial. Timber companies push to cut as much of this timber as possible at low prices. Biodiversity experts and environmentalists call for **(1)** sharply reducing or eliminating tree harvesting in public forests, **(2)** using more sustainable forest management practices (p. 605) for timber cutting in national forests, **(3)** having timber companies pay more for trees they harvest from national forests, and **(4)** managing national forests primarily to provide recreation and to sustain their biodiversity, water resources, and other ecological services.

Between 1930 and 1988, overall timber harvesting from national forests increased sharply, mostly because of **(1)** intense lobbying of Congress by timber company interests, **(2)** a law that allows the Forest Service to keep most of the money it makes on timber sales (and thus increase its budget), and **(3)** a 1908 law that gives counties within the boundaries of national forests 25% of the gross receipts from timber sales.

By law, the Forest Service must sell timber for no less than the cost of reforesting the cleared land. However, this price does not include the government-subsidized cost of building and maintaining access roads for timber removal by logging companies. Usually, the companies also buy the timber for less than they would pay a private landowner for an equivalent amount of timber.

As a result, the Forest Service's timber-cutting program loses money because revenue from timber sales does not cover the costs of **(1)** road building, **(2)** timber sale preparation, **(3)** administration, and **(4)** other overhead costs. Because of such government subsidies, timber sales from U.S. federal lands have turned a profit for taxpayers in only 3 of the last 100 years.

In addition, a 2000 study by the National Forest Protection Alliance found that logging in national forests **(1)** causes more economic harm than good to local communities near such forests, **(2)** costs the nation's taxpayers about $1.2 billion per year in logging subsidies (an estimate confirmed by the U.S. Congressional Research Service), and **(3)** costs taxpayers and nearby communities many billions of dollars more each year from rivers polluted and fisheries damaged by sediments from logged lands, increased flooding, lost recreational opportunities, and degraded scenery.

Timber company officials argue that logging in national forests

- Helps satisfy the country's demand for wood.

- Provides cheap timber that benefits consumers by keeping lumber and paper prices down.

- Improves forest health by removing diseased trees and helping prevent forest fires.

- Provides jobs and stimulates economic growth in nearby communities.

Environmentalists respond that

- Timber cutting in national forests provides only about 3% of the country's wood.

- Ample private forestland is available to meet the country's demand for wood.

- Below-cost timber prices in national forests **(1)** increase pressure for timber cutting in national and state forests and **(2)** have little effect on the consumer costs of lumber and paper.

- Communities relying heavily on 25% of the proceeds from national forest timber sales experience severe economic slumps as timber companies deplete the timber and move to other areas.

- Recreation in national forests provides many more jobs and much more income for local communities than does logging. According to a 2000 study by the accounting firm Econorthwest, recreation, hunting, and fishing in national forests generate about 2.9 million jobs and add about $234 billion to the national economy each year. By contrast, logging, mining, grazing, and other extractive uses in the national forests add about 407,000 jobs and $23 billion to the economy per year.

- According to the Congressional Budget Office, eliminating losses from timber sales in the national forest would save taxpayers about $1.6 billion over the next 10 years.

In 2001, timber company officials were pleased that the Bush administration

- Proposed increasing the sale of timber in the national forests by about 40%.

- Moved to reverse decisions by the Clinton administration to block road construction in roadless areas of national forests (which makes them ineligible for protection in the National Wilderness System).

- Called for eliminating the long-standing requirement that the Forest Service manage national forests to protect the viability of wildlife.

- Dropped a requirement imposed by the Clinton administration that "ecological sustainability of resources be the overall goal of forest management."

In 2002, the Bush administration proposed that Congress create a new category of national forests called *charter forest* that would be managed locally instead of by the Forest Service. This idea is similar to charter schools, which typically operate outside of state education bureaucracies. According to Mark Rey, a former timber industry lobbyist who now oversees the Forest Service, the goal is not to increase any particular activity, such as logging or recreation, but to reduce management costs such as preparing complex environmental assessment documents. Conservationists and some elected officials worry that this is a attempt to circumvent environmental regulations governing use of national forests and make increased timber cutting the primary focus. They also point out that local officials are often more easily influenced by timber company interests.

**How Can We Cut Fewer Trees By Using Wood More Efficiently?** One way to reduce the pressure to harvest trees on public and private land is to improve the efficiency of wood use. According to the Worldwatch Institute and forestry analysts, up to 60% of the wood consumed in the United States is wasted unnecessarily through (1) inefficient use of construction materials, (2) excess packaging, (3) overuse of junk mail, (4) inadequate paper recycling (p. 540), and (5) failure to reuse wooden shipping containers.

Only 3% of the total U.S. production of softwood timber comes from the national forests. Thus reducing the waste of wood and paper products by only 3% could (1) eliminate the need to remove any timber from the national forests and (2) allow these lands to be used primarily for recreation and biodiversity protection.

Some analysts have suggested we can save wood by switching to nonwood home-building and remodeling materials such as (1) steel framing and floor joists, (2) aluminum framing, (3) concrete slabs instead of wooden floor joists, and (4) carpet instead of finished wood floors. However, this involves shifting from a potentially renewable resource (wood) to nonrenewable resources such as limestone, iron and other mineral products, and crude oil used to make these products.

Analyses show that switching to these nonrenewable resources usually takes more energy for transportation and manufacture and produces more pollution than using wood and wood products. For example, (1) steel framing takes 13 times more energy than wood framing, (2) aluminum framing for walls takes 20 times more energy than wood framing, (3) steel floor joists take 50 times more energy than those made of wood, and (4) wall-to-wall carpeting takes four times more energy than wood floors.

**How Can We Cut Fewer Trees By Making Paper from Tree-Free Fibers?** Producing paper is the world's fastest growing use of wood. According to the Worldwatch Society, packaging accounts for nearly half of the paper produced each year. This is followed by paper used for (1) writing and printing (30%), (2) newsprint (12%), and (3) paper tissue and towels (about 8%).

Another way to reduce the pressure to harvest trees is to make paper by using fiber that does not come from trees. *Tree-free fibers* for making paper come from two sources: (1) agricultural residues left over from crops such as wheat, rice, and sugar and (2) fast-growing crops such as kenaf and industrial hemp.

Currently, tree-free paper fibers account for about 7% of the world's fiber supply for paper, with 97% of it used in developing countries and less than 1% in the United States. China uses tree-free pulp, such as rice straw and other agricultural wastes left after harvest, to make 60% of its paper.

Most of the small amount of tree-free paper produced in the United States is made from the fibers of a rapidly growing woody annual plant called *kenaf* (pronounced "kuh-NAHF"; Figure 23-19). Compared to pulpwood, kenaf (1) needs less herbicide because it grows faster than most weeds, (2) needs less insecticide because its outer fibrous covering is nearly insect proof, (3) does not deplete soil nitrogen because it is a nitrogen fixer, (4) takes fewer chemicals and less energy to break down its fibers, and (5) produces less toxic wastewater.

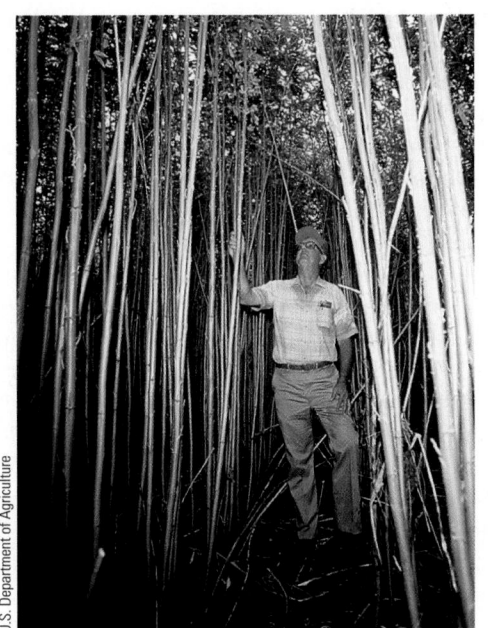

U.S. Department of Agriculture

**Figure 23-19** *Kenaf* growing in a field in south Texas. This fast-growing plant can be harvested annually and its fibers used to make paper. Its widespread use could reduce the need to grow and harvest trees to make paper.

Kenaf paper currently costs three to five times more than virgin or recycled paper stock. However, prices probably will come down if demand increases and greater demand allows lower production costs. Biologists urge caution against the widespread planting of kenaf or industrial hemp because (1) they fear such rapidly growing plants could take over ecosystems, crowd out other plant species, and disrupt food webs, and (2) large plantations of such plants could compete with increasingly scarce land needed to provide food for the world's growing population.

## 23-4 TROPICAL DEFORESTATION AND THE FUELWOOD CRISIS

**How Fast Are Tropical Forests Being Cleared and Degraded?** Tropical forests (1) cover about 6% of the earth's land area (roughly the area of the lower 48 states of the United States) and 47% of the world's forest cover (Figure 23-6) and (2) grow in equatorial Latin America, Africa, and Asia (Figure 23-8). Tropical forests come in several varieties, including (1) rain forests (which receive rainfall almost daily), (2) deciduous forests with one or two dry seasons each year, (3) dry deciduous forests, and (4) forests on hills and mountains.

Climatic and biological data suggest that mature tropical forests once covered at least twice as much area as they do today, with most of the destruction occurring since 1950. Satellite scans and ground-level surveys used to estimate forest destruction indicate that large areas of tropical forests are being clear-cut (reducing local forest areas to 10% or less of the area they originally covered) rapidly in parts of South America (especially Brazil), Africa, and Asia (Figure 23-15). Haiti has lost 99% of its original forest cover, the Philippines 97%, and Madagascar 84%.

Brazil has about half the world's remaining tropical rain forest in the vast Amazon basin, which is half the size of the continental United States. This important center of biodiversity is home for up to 30% of the world's plant and animal species.

In 1970, deforestation affected only 1% of the area of the Amazon basin. By 2000, almost 15% had been deforested. According to a 2001 study by Penn State researcher James Alcock, without immediate and aggressive action to change current forest destruction and degradation practices, Brazil's original Amazon rain forests will largely disappear within 40–50 years.

Current rates of tropical deforestation and degradation are debatable because of (1) difficulties in interpreting satellite images, (2) different ways of defining forest, deforestation, and forest degradation, and (3) political and economic factors that cause countries to hide or exaggerate deforestation. Consequently, estimates of total global tropical forest loss per year vary from 50,000 square kilometers (19,300 square miles) to 170,000 square kilometers (65,600 square miles). This amounts to a loss of 0.3–1% per year—with forestry researchers at the World Resources Institute putting the estimated annual loss at 0.9–1.0%. Scientists estimate that each year serious degradation and fragmentation affect an equivalent area of these forests. Thus tropical forests are being cut and degraded at a rate of 0.6–2% per year—high enough to lose or degrade half of the world's remaining tropical forests in 25–83 years.

However, critics such as biogeographer Philip Stott claim that (1) tropical forest losses are exaggerated, (2) many deforested areas are regenerating as second-growth forests, (3) the loss of tropical forests is no more ecologically important than the clearing of the old-growth forests that once covered Europe and parts of eastern North America (Figure 23-18), and (4) excessive concern over loss of tropical forests diverts attention from more important ecological threats to the world's oceans.

**Why Should We Care About Tropical Forests?** Most biologists disagree with Stott's assessment. They believe cutting and degrading most remaining old-growth tropical forests is a serious global environmental problem because of (1) the important ecological and economic services they provide (Figure 23-7) and (2) their instrumental values (Figure 23-20). For example, (1) chemicals from plants in tropical forests are used as blueprints for making most of the world's prescription drugs (Figure 22-11, p. 569), and (2) some tropical tree species can be used for many purposes (Solutions, p. 614).

**Case Study: Madagascar: A Threatened Jewel of Biodiversity** Madagascar, the world's fourth largest island, lies in the Indian Ocean off the East African coast (Figure 23-21, right). Because of its astounding biological diversity, scientists view this Texas-size island as a crown jewel of biodiversity among the earth's ecosystems.

Most of its species have evolved in near isolation for at least 40 million years. This occurred because the continental drift of the plates found in the earth's lithosphere (Figure 5-9, p. 106) moved the island far enough from Africa's mainland to prevent migrations of species to and from Africa.

The result is that about 85% of all plant and animal species found on the island are *endemic species* unique to this island. Most live in its vanishing eastern rain forests (Figure 23-21).

Madagascar's plant and animal species are among the world's most endangered, mostly because of loss of habitat from slash-and-burn agriculture (Figure 2-2, p. 23) on poor soils, fueled by rapid population growth.

## Instrumental Values of Tropical Forest Ecosystems

### Use Values

#### Direct Use Values

Timber and other building materials

Fuelwood

Medicinal plants

Edible wild fruits and plants

Fiber

#### Indirect Use Values

Soil fertility

Flood control

Water purification

Pollution control

Recreation and tourism

Education

Ecological services (pest control, pollination)

Genetic information

#### Option Values

Future products:

Medicines

Genetic resources

Biological insights

Food sources

Building supplies

Future ecological services

### Nonuse Values

#### Existence Values

Protection of biological diversity

Maintaining cultures of local people

Continuing ecological and evolutionary processes

**Figure 23-20** Some of the many *instrumental values* of tropical forests. These show the importance of preserving the rich diversity of these forests instead of cutting them down or degrading them for short-term economic gain. Some people also believe tropical forests have *intrinsic value* and thus have an inherent right to exist regardless of their usefulness to people.

For example, **(1)** 16 of the island's 31 primate species face extinction, and **(2)** officials have not succeeded in curbing the illegal smuggling of endangered species—especially frogs, chameleons, and lizards—to Europe and Asia.

Since humans arrived about 1,500 years ago, **(1)** 84% of the island's tropical seasonal forests and more than 66% of its rain forests have been cut for cropland, fuel, and lumber, and **(2)** what is left is being cleared or burned rapidly. The resulting erosion from fields and hillsides make Madagascar the world's most eroded country. Evidence for this comes from the huge quantities of eroded sediment flowing in its rivers and emptying into its coastal areas (Figure 7-8, p. 148).

Since 1984, the government, conservation organizations, and scientists worldwide have united to slow the island's ecological degradation. For such efforts to succeed, the country's population growth, projected to almost double from 17 million to 31 million between 2002 and 2025, will have to slow drastically. Even with full implementation of this internationally funded effort, Madagascar probably will lose half of its remaining plant and animal species.

**Case Study: Cultural Extinction in Tropical Forests** An estimated 250 million people belong to indigenous cultures found in about 70 countries. Many of these peoples—such as the Kuana of Panama, the Kenyah in Indonesia, the Yaneshé in Peru, and the Yanomami in Brazil—have been living in and using tropical and other forests sustainably for centuries. They get most of their food from hunting and gathering, trapping, and sustainable slash-and-burn and shifting cultivation (Figure 2-2, p. 23).

**Figure 23-21** Some biomes in Madagascar, a large island off the eastern coast of Africa. A combination of population growth, poverty, and deforestation seriously threaten the rich biodiversity and numerous endemic species of plants and animals found only on this island.

MADAGASCAR

INDIAN OCEAN

Existing rain forest

Former rain forest

Southern spiny desert

Western tropical deciduous forest

## The Incredible Neem Tree

Suppose a single plant existed that could **(1)** quickly reforest bare land, **(2)** supply fuelwood and lumber in dry areas, **(3)** provide alternatives to toxic pesticides, **(4)** be used to treat numerous diseases, and **(5)** help control population growth? There is: the *neem tree*, a broadleaf evergreen member of the mahogany family.

This remarkable tropical species, native to India and Burma, is ideal for reforestation because it can grow to maturity in only 5–7 years. It grows well in poor soil in semiarid lands such as those in Africa, providing abundant fuelwood, lumber, and lamp oil.

It also contains various natural pesticides. Chemicals from its leaves and seeds can repel or kill more than 200 insect species, including termites, gypsy moths (Figure 23-16), locusts, boll weevils, and cockroaches.

Extracts from neem seeds and leaves (Figure 22-11, p. 569) can fight bacterial, viral, and fungal infections. Villagers call the tree a "village pharmacy" because its chemicals can relieve so many different health problems. People also use the tree's twigs as an antiseptic toothbrush and the oil from its seeds to make toothpaste and soap.

That is not all. Neem-seed oil evidently acts as a strong spermicide and may help in the development of a much-needed male birth control pill. According to a study by the U.S. National Academy of Sciences, the neem tree "may eventually benefit every person on the planet."

Despite its numerous advantages, ecologists caution against widespread planting of neem trees outside its native range. As a nonnative species, it could take over and displace native species because of its rapid growth and resistance to pests.

### Critical Thinking

Assume you are an elected county official. Someone proposes widespread planting of neem trees on abandoned cropland in the area where you live. Would you favor this proposal? Explain. What tests might you want to run before approving this project?

---

Many of the earth's remaining tribal peoples, representing 5,000 cultures, are vanishing as the lands they have lived on for centuries are taken over for economic development. To ecologists and cultural anthropologists, this results in an irreplaceable loss of ecological knowledge and cultural diversity. People in these cultures have important knowledge about **(1)** how to live sustainably in tropical forests (and in other biomes) and **(2)** which plants are useful as food and medicines.

Many analysts urge governments to protect the rights of the earth's remaining indigenous cultures by **(1)** giving them full ownership of the land they have occupied for centuries and **(2)** protecting their lands from intrusion and illegal resource extraction.

Other people, mostly resource extractors, strongly disagree. They believe road building, resource extraction, crop raising, livestock grazing, and other forms of development in tropical forests (and other undeveloped biomes) should not be held back by granting legal rights to land and resources to small numbers of primitive tribal peoples. What do you think?

### What Causes Tropical Deforestation and Degradation?

Tropical deforestation results from a number of interconnected causes (Figure 23-22). All these factors are related to increasing use of the net primary productivity (Figure 4-26, p. 82) and mineral resources of the earth's forests for human use as a result of **(1)** population growth, **(2)** poverty, and **(3)** government policies that encourage deforestation. Population growth and poverty combine to drive subsistence farmers and the landless poor to tropical forests, where they try to grow enough food to survive.

Government subsidies can accelerate deforestation by **(1)** making timber or other tropical forest resources cheap relative to their full ecological value and **(2)** encouraging the poor to colonize tropical forests by giving them title to land they clear, as is done in Indonesia, Mexico, and Brazil. In addition, international lending agencies encourage developing countries to borrow huge sums of money from developed countries to finance projects such as roads, mines, logging operations, oil drilling, and dams in tropical forests.

The process of degrading a tropical forest usually begins by cutting a logging road deep into a once inaccessible area (Figure 23-13). This typically sets into motion a downward spiral of biodiversity loss and soil depletion (Connections, p. 616)

The original roads open once inaccessible forest areas to a number of factors that can cause forest depletion and degradation. These factors include the following:

- *Commercial logging.* The largest importers of tropical timber are Japan, Europe, the United States, and China. After depleting tropical timber in much of Asia, cutting is now shifting to Latin America and Africa (Figure 23-15). Timber exports to developed countries contribute significantly to tropical forest depletion and degradation. However, domestic use accounts for more than 80% of the trees cut in developing countries.

- *Cattle ranching.* Ranchers, sometimes supported by government subsidies, often establish cattle ranches on exhausted or abandoned cropland. Torrential rains and overgrazing turn the usually thin and nutrient-poor tropical forest soils (Figure 10-15, bottom left, p. 215) into eroded wastelands. Ranchers often sell their land to new settlers, move to another area, and repeat this destructive grazing process.

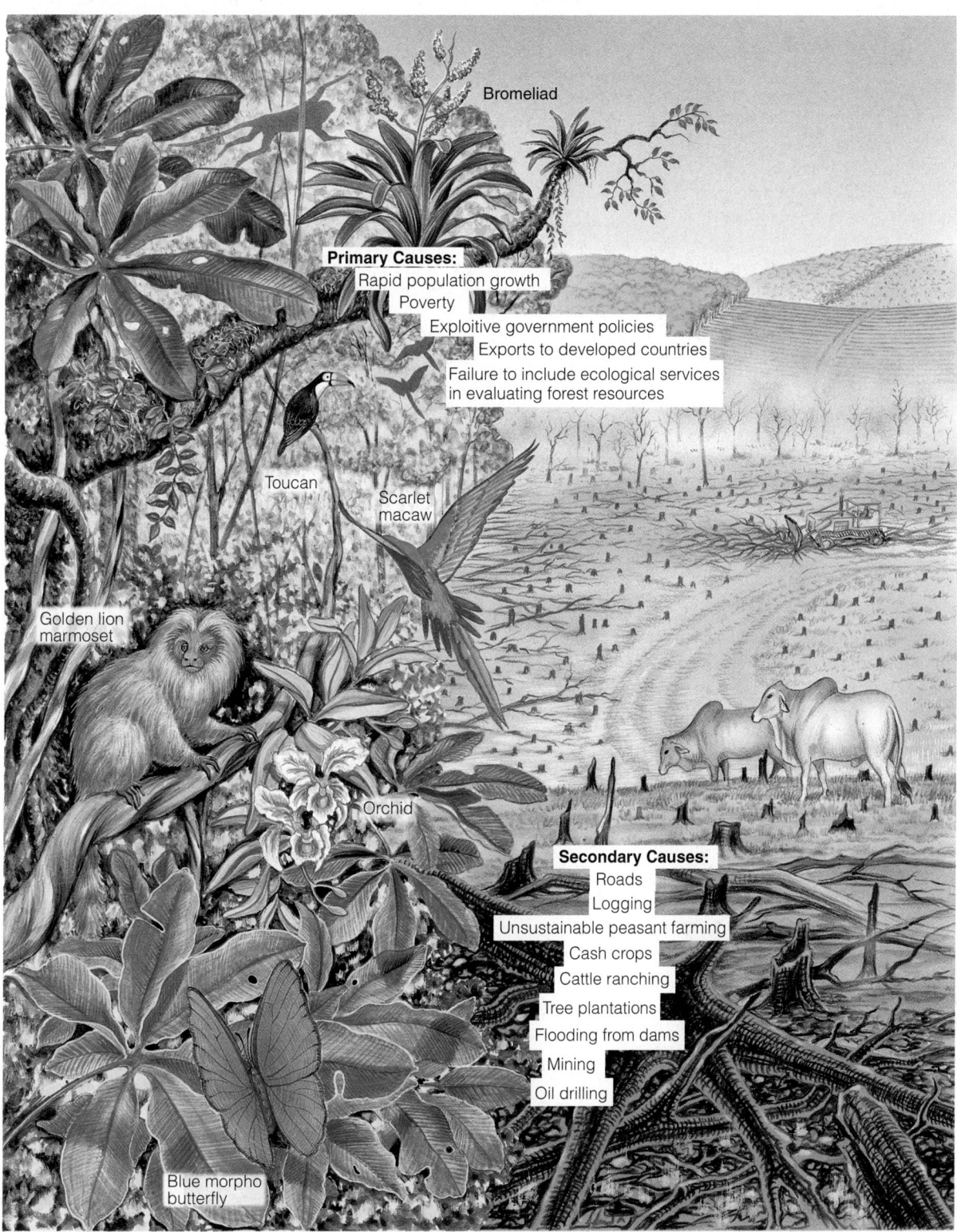

Bromeliad

Primary Causes:
Rapid population growth
Poverty
Exploitive government policies
Exports to developed countries
Failure to include ecological services in evaluating forest resources

Toucan

Scarlet macaw

Golden lion marmoset

Orchid

Secondary Causes:
Roads
Logging
Unsustainable peasant farming
Cash crops
Cattle ranching
Tree plantations
Flooding from dams
Mining
Oil drilling

Blue morpho butterfly

**Figure 23-22** Major interconnected causes of the destruction and degradation of tropical forests. These factors ultimately are related to **(1)** population growth, **(2)** poverty, and **(3)** government policies that encourage deforestation.

The depletion and degradation of a tropical forest follows a typical sequence:

- Cut a road deep into the forest interior for logging and settlement (Figure 23-13).

- Build trails and camps for the work crews and have hunters provide them with bushmeat (Figure 22-20, p. 580).

- Use selective cutting to remove the best timber (high-grading). This topples many other trees because of their shallow roots and the network of vines connecting trees in the forest's canopy (Figure 6-37, p. 137).

- Sell the land to ranchers who typically overgraze it, sell it settlers who have migrated to the forest hoping to grow enough food to survive, and move their destructive ranching operations to another area of the forest.

- The settlers cut most of the remaining trees, burn the debris after it has dried for about a year, and plant crops using slash-and-burn agriculture (Figure 2-2, p. 23). They can also endanger species by hunting them for bushmeat.

- After a few years of crop growing and rainfall, the nutrient-poor tropical soil (Figure 10-15, bottom left, p. 215) is depleted of nutrients and the settlers move on hoping to repeat the process.

- Healthy rain forests do not burn. But increased logging, settlements, grazing, and farming along roads built in these forests (Figure 23-13) fragment and dry out areas of forests to the point where they are easily ignited by lightning or deliberate burning by farmers and ranchers. The fires also release $CO_2$ into the atmosphere, which can help accelerate global warming.

- If forest destruction occurs over a large enough area, the climate may become so dry that secondary ecological succession will lead to tropical grassland instead of a tropical forest. This occurs because water evaporating and transpiring into the atmosphere from its trees provided about half the heavy rain needed to sustain the original forest.

### Critical Thinking

You are in charge of stopping this downward spiral of tropical forest degradation. What are the three most important things you would do?

---

- *Unsustainable forms of small-scale farming* that deplete soils and destroy large tracts of forests.

- *Clearing large areas of tropical forest for raising cash crops.* Large plantations grow crops such as sugarcane, bananas, pineapples, peppers, strawberries, cotton, tea, and coffee, mostly for export to developed countries.

- *Increasing forest fires.* Between 1997 and 1999, huge areas of forest burned in Indonesia, Malaysia, Brazil, Guatemala, Nicaragua, and Mexico. Farmers using fire to prepare fields for planting or cattle grazing and corporations clearing forests and burning the remaining plant residues to establish pulp, palm oil, and rubber plantations started most of these fires. The resulting highly polluted air (1) sickened tens of millions of people, (2) killed hundreds, (3) caused billions of dollars in damage, and (4) released large amounts of $CO_2$ into the atmosphere.

- *Mining* (Case Study, p. 345) *and oil drilling.*

- *Building dams on rivers that flood large areas of tropical forests.*

Clearing tropical forests can also degrade tropical rivers that carry two-thirds of the world's freshwater runoff. The clearing of tropical forests near rivers causes dramatic increases in soil erosion, often as much as 25-fold. The eroded soil (1) converts normally clear water to muddy water, (2) silts river bottoms and destroys many forms of aquatic life, (3) fills reservoirs, (4) overloads estuaries with nutrients and silt (Figure 7-8, p. 148), and (5) smothers offshore coral reefs with silt.

Tropical deforestation also accelerates flooding and reduces the recharging of aquifers by removing the tree cover that slows rainfall runoff and lets it percolate downward into aquifers. For example, China's Yangtze River basin has lost about 85% of its original tree cover. In 1998, this area experienced some of the worst flooding in its history, mostly because of its lack of water-absorbing tree cover.

Deforestation can also affect patterns of precipitation. As forest area shrinks, the flow of moisture to downwind areas can drop. For example, researchers cite deforestation in the eastern and southern provinces of China as an important factor in the decline of rainfall in northwestern China.

**Solutions: How Can We Reduce Degradation and Deforestation of Tropical Forests?**   A number of analysts have suggested various ways to protect tropical forests and use them more sustainably (Figure 23-23). Some promising methods are as follows:

- Establishing programs to help new settlers in tropical forests learn how to practice small-scale sustainable agriculture and forestry (Solutions, p. 618).

- Using debt-for-nature swaps, conservation easements, and conservation concessions to make it financially profitable for countries to protect tropical forests. In a *debt-for-nature swap*, participating countries act as custodians for protected forest reserves in return for foreign aid or debt relief (Figure 23-24). More than 20 such agreements, totaling $110 million, have been established in 10 countries. In a *conservation easement*, a private organization, country, or group of countries compensates other countries for protecting selected forest areas. With a *conservation concession*, a nongovernmental conservation organization protects land from logging by leasing it from a government. In 2000, Conservation International (CI) purchased the world's first conservation concession from Guyana. Guyana makes at least as much money as it would from leasing the forest area to a logging company and ends up protecting part of its forests. In 2001, CI was negotiating similar leasing agreements with six other countries.

| Prevention | | Restoration |
|---|---|---|
| Protect most diverse and endangered areas | | Reforestation |
| Educate settlers about sustainable agriculture and forestry | | Rehabilitation of degraded areas |
| Phase out subsidies that encourage unsustainable forest use | | Concentrate farming and ranching on already-cleared areas |
| Add subsidies that encourage sustainable forest use | | |
| Protect forests with *debt-for-nature* swaps, *conservation easements*, and *conservation concessions* | | |
| Certify sustainably grown timber | | |
| Reduce illegal cutting | | |
| Reduce poverty | | |
| Slow population growth | | |

**Figure 23-23** *Solutions:* ways to protect tropical forests and use them more sustainably.

- Establishing an international system for evaluating and labeling timber produced by sustainable methods (Solutions, p. 606).

- Using gentler methods for harvesting trees. For example, (1) cutting canopy vines (lianas) before felling a tree can reduce damage to neighboring trees by 20–40% and (2) using the least obstructed paths to remove the logs can halve the damage to other trees.

- Mounting national and global efforts to reforest and rehabilitate degraded tropical forests and watersheds (Individuals Matter, p. 619). In 1998, China's government instituted a 10-year plan to (1) reduce timber harvests in natural forests, (2) restore natural forests in ecologically sensitive areas, (3) convert marginal farmland to forestland, (4) regenerate natural forests in degraded forest areas, and (5) increase timber production in tree plantations.

- Reducing the waste and overconsumption of industrial timber, paper, and other resources by consumers, especially in developed countries (p. 611).

**How Serious Is the Fuelwood Crisis in Developing Countries?** Wood provides about 7% of the world's annual energy supply. In developing countries, wood accounts for 15% of the supply, compared to 3% in developed countries. Burning wood for heat and cooking ac-

counts for about 80% of the wood harvested in developing countries.

According to the UN Food and Agriculture Organization, in 2000 about 2.7 billion people in 77 developing countries (1) did not get enough fuelwood to meet their basic needs (800 million people) or (2) were forced to meet their needs by using wood faster than it is replenished (Figure 23-25, p. 618).

**Figure 23-24** Blending economic development and conservation in a 1.5-million-hectare (3.7-million-acre) tract in Bolivia. A U.S. conservation organization arranged a *debt-for-nature swap* to help protect this land from destructive development.

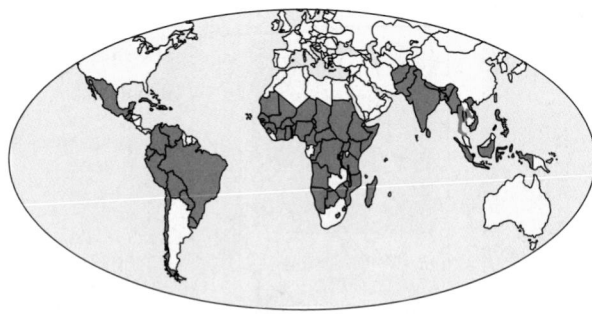

**Figure 23-25** Scarcity of fuelwood, 2000. (Data from UN Food and Agriculture Organization)

City dwellers in many developing countries burn *charcoal* because it is much lighter than fuelwood and thus much cheaper to transport. However, burning wood in traditional earthen pits to produce charcoal consumes more than half the wood's energy. Thus each city dweller burning charcoal uses twice as much wood for a given amount of energy as a rural dweller who burns firewood. This helps explain the expanding rings of deforested land that surround many cities in developing countries where charcoal is the major fuel source.

Besides local deforestation and accelerated soil erosion, fuelwood scarcity has other harmful effects:

- It places a burden on the rural poor, especially women and children, who often must walk long distances searching for firewood.

- Buying fuelwood or charcoal can take 40% of a poor family's income.

- Waterborne infectious diseases and deaths can occur as prices rise and burning wood or charcoal to boil water becomes an unaffordable luxury.

- An estimated 800 million poor people who cannot get enough fuelwood burn dried animal dung and crop residues for cooking and heating (Figure 23-26). Not returning these natural fertilizers to the soil reduces cropland productivity and can increase hunger and malnutrition.

**Figure 23-26** Making fuel briquettes from cow dung in India. Increased fuelwood scarcity causes people to collect and burn more dung. This deprives the soil of an important source of plant nutrients.

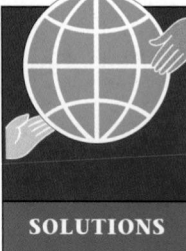

## Sustainable Agriculture and Forestry in Tropical Forests

**SOLUTIONS**

A combination of the knowledge of indigenous peoples, ecological research, and modern technology can show people how to grow crops and harvest timber in tropical forests more sustainably.

One approach is to show people migrating to forests how to grow crops using forms of more sustainable agroforestry developed by indigenous peoples throughout the world. The Lacandon Maya Indians of Chiapas, Mexico, for example, use a multilayered system of agroforestry to cultivate as many as 75 crop species on 1-hectare (2.5-acre) plots for up to 7 years. After that, they plant a new plot to allow regeneration of the soil in the original plot.

In the lush rain forests of Peru's Palcazú Valley, Yaneshé Indians use strip cutting (Figure 23-14e) to harvest tropical trees for lumber. They **(1)** harvest widely spaced thin strips in an alternating pattern (for example, strips 1, 3, 5, and then 2, 4, and 6) and **(2)** allow any given strip to regenerate 30–40 years before being harvested again. This type of harvesting reduces environmental degradation and promotes rapid natural regeneration of native tree species from stumps or from seeds of nearby trees. Tribe members also act as consultants to help other forest dwellers set up similar systems.

Another way to maintain biodiversity is to grow coffee in shade tree plantations under a diverse canopy of trees instead of in unshaded plantations. However, in the tropics there is increasing conver-

sion of shade tree coffee plantations to higher-yield unshaded coffee plantations that need more pesticides and fertilizers.

Some coffee drinkers are fighting this loss of biodiversity by buying only coffee certified (by organizations such as the Rainforest Alliance) as grown under shade trees. In the United States, such coffee is available through a number of coffee distributors and mail-order retailers. Such organic coffee should also be labeled as *fair trade*—meaning that it was bought directly from its growers.

### Critical Thinking

What applications (if any) might these practices have for growing food and harvesting timber in the United States and other developed countries?

**Solutions: What Can We Do About the Fuelwood Crisis?** Developing countries can reduce the severity of the fuelwood crisis by **(1)** planting more fast-growing fuelwood trees or shrubs, **(2)** burning wood more efficiently, and **(3)** switching to other fuels.

However, to prevent harm to local ecosystems, ecologists urge careful selection of fast-growing tree and shrub species used to establish fuelwood plantations. The planting of fuelwood plantations with eucalyptus trees is an example.

Because these species grow fast even on poor soils, planting them might seem like a good idea. However, ecologists and local villagers see it as an ecological disaster.

In their native Australia, these trees thrive in areas with good rainfall. However, when planted in arid areas the trees suck up so much of the scarce soil water that most other plants cannot grow. This **(1)** reduces the amount of fodder farmers have to feed their livestock and **(2)** hinders replenishment of groundwater.

Eucalyptus trees also **(1)** deplete the soil of nutrients, **(2)** produce toxic compounds that accumulate in the soil (because of low rainfall), and **(3)** inhibit nitrogen uptake. In Karnata, India, villagers became so enraged over a government-sponsored project to plant eucalyptus trees that they uprooted the saplings.

Experience shows that the most successful fuelwood planting projects **(1)** involve local people in their planning and implementation, **(2)** give village farmers incentives, such as ownership of the land or ownership of any trees they grow on village land, **(3)** grow the trees on community woodlots, which are easy to tend and harvest, rather than on large fuelwood plantations located far from where the wood is needed.

Another promising method is to encourage villagers to use the sun-dried roots of various gourds and squashes as cooking fuel. These *root-fuel plants* **(1)** regenerate themselves each year, **(2)** produce large quantities of burnable biomass per unit area on dry, deforested lands, **(3)** help reduce soil erosion, and **(4)** produce an edible seed with a high protein content.

Using a traditional three-stone fire to burn wood typically wastes about 94% of the wood's energy content. New, cheap, more efficient, and less polluting stoves can provide both heat and light while reducing indoor air pollution. The stoves must be easy and cheap to build, and the materials used to make them must be easily accessible locally (Individuals Matter, p. 620).

Cheap and easily made solar ovens (Figure 16-21d, p. 397) that capture sunlight to provide heat can reduce wood use and air pollution in sunny and warm areas. However, people in cultures that use fires for light and heat at night and as centers for social interaction often do not accept these stoves.

There have been some encouraging successes in reducing fuelwood shortages in countries such as

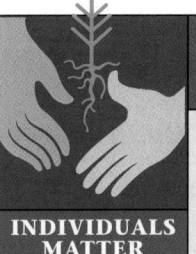

**INDIVIDUALS MATTER**

### Kenya's Green Belt Movement

In Kenya, Wangari Maathai (see figure) started the Green Belt Movement. The goals of this highly regarded women's self-help group are to **(1)** establish tree nurseries, **(2)** raise seedlings, and **(3)** plant and protect a tree for each of Kenya's 30 million people. By 2002, the 100,000 members of this grassroots group had planted and protected more than 12 million trees.

This project's success has sparked the creation of similar programs in more than 30 other African countries. This inspiring leader has said,

*I don't really know why I care so much. I just have something inside me that tells me that there is a problem and I have to do something about it. And I'm sure it's the same voice that is speaking to everyone on this planet, at least everybody who seems to be concerned about the fate of the world, the fate of this planet.*

Wangari Maathai, the first Kenyan woman to earn a Ph.D. (in anatomy) and to head an academic department (veterinary medicine) at the University of Nairobi, organized the internationally acclaimed Green Belt Movement in 1977.

China, Nepal, Senegal, and South Korea. However, most developing countries suffering from fuelwood shortages have inadequate forestry policies, budgets, and trained foresters. Such countries are cutting trees for fuelwood and forest products 10–20 times faster than new trees are being planted.

## 23-5 MANAGING AND SUSTAINING NATIONAL PARKS

**How Popular Is the Idea of National Parks?** Today, more than 1,100 national parks larger than 10 square kilometers (4 square miles) are located in more than 120 countries. These parks cover a total area equal to that of Alaska, Texas, and California combined.

The U.S. national park system, established in 1912, has 55 national parks (sometimes called the country's *crown jewels*), most of them in the West (Figure 23-4).

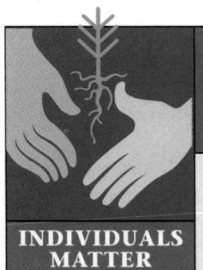
These national parks are supplemented by state, county, and city parks. Most state parks are located near urban areas and have about twice as many visitors per year as the national parks.

**How Are Parks Being Threatened?** Parks everywhere are under pressure from external and internal threats. According to a 1999 study by the World Bank and the World Wildlife Fund, only 1% of the parks and wildlife reserves in developing countries receive protection. The other 99% are mostly *paper parks* that exist in name only and have no protection. Most of these parks are invaded by **(1)** local people who need wood, cropland, game animals, and other natural products for their daily survival and **(2)** loggers, miners, and wildlife poachers (who kill animals to obtain and sell items such as rhino horns, elephant tusks, and furs). Park services in developing countries typically have too little money and too few personnel to fight these invasions, either by force or by education.

In addition, most of the world's national parks are too small to sustain many large animal species, and many suffer from invasions by nonnative species that can reduce the populations of native species and cause ecological disruption.

Popularity is one of the biggest problems of national and state parks in the United States and other developed countries. Because of increased numbers of roads, cars, and affluent people, annual recreational visits to major U.S. national parks increased more than fourfold between 1950 and 2000, and visits to state parks rose sevenfold.

Many parks provide spectacular scenery, solitude, and enjoyable recreational experiences for visitors. However, because of a lack of funds, visitors to some of the most heavily used parks find **(1)** closed campgrounds, **(2)** uncollected garbage, **(3)** debris on trails and beaches, **(4)** dirty toilets, and **(5)** fewer nature lectures and tours by park rangers. During the summer, users of the most popular U.S. national and state parks often face hour-long entrance backups and experience noise, congestion, and stress instead of peaceful solitude.

U.S. Park Service rangers spend an increasing amount of their time on law enforcement instead of conservation, management, and education. Currently, there is 1 ranger for every 84,200 visitors to the major national parks. Many overworked and underpaid rangers are leaving for better paying jobs.

Many parks suffer damage from the migration or deliberate introduction of nonnative species. European wild boars (imported to North Carolina in 1912 for hunting; Figure 22-17, p. 576) threaten vegetation in part of the Great Smoky Mountains National Park. The Brazilian pepper tree has invaded Florida's Everglades National Park. Mountain goats in Washington's Olympic National Park trample native vegetation and accelerate soil erosion. While some nonnative species have moved into parks, some native species of animals and plants (including many threatened or endangered species) are being killed or removed illegally in almost half of U.S. national parks.

Nearby human activities that threaten wildlife and recreational values in many national parks include **(1)** mining, **(2)** logging, **(3)** livestock grazing, **(4)** coal-burning power plants, **(5)** water diversion, and **(6)** urban development. Polluted air, drifting hundreds of kilometers, kills ancient trees in California's Sequoia National Park and often blots out the awesome views at Arizona's Grand Canyon. Car smog damages many plant species in the heavily used Great Smoky Mountains National Park. According to the NPS, air pollution affects scenic views in national parks more than 90% of the time.

That is not all. Mountains of trash wash ashore daily at Padre Island National Seashore in Texas. Water use in Las Vegas (Spotlight, p. 334) threatens to shut down geysers in the Death Valley National Monument. Visitors to Sequoia National Park and Kentucky's Mammoth Cave complain of raw sewage flowing through a parking lot. Worn-out sewage treatment plants in Yellowstone National Park dump untreated waste into Yellowstone Lake and other park waterways. Unless a massive ecological restoration project is successful, Florida's Everglades National Park may dry up because of diversion of water for urban areas and agriculture.

**Solutions: How Can Management of U.S. National Parks Be Improved?** The U.S. NPS uses the principle of *natural regulation* to manage the 55 major U.S. national parks. This means managing the parks as if they were wilderness ecosystems that can adapt and sustain themselves if left alone. Many ecologists consider natural regulation a misguided policy. Most parks are far too small to come close to sustaining themselves. Even the biggest ones, such as Yellowstone, cannot be isolated from **(1)** the harmful effects caused by activities in nearby areas and **(2)** destruction from within by exploding populations of some native plant-eating species such as elk and by invading nonnative species.

The U.S. NPS has two goals that increasingly conflict: **(1)** to preserve nature in parks and **(2)** to make nature more available to the public. In 1988, the Wilderness Society and the National Parks and Conservation Association made a number of suggestions for sustaining and expanding the national park system, including the following:

- *Require integrated management plans for parks and other nearby federal lands.*

- *Increase the budget for* **(1)** *adding new parkland near the most threatened parks and* **(2)** *buying private lands inside parks.*

- *Locate all new and some existing commercial facilities and visitor parking areas outside parks and provide shuttle buses for entering and touring most parks,* as was done in 2000 in Zion National Park, Utah. Shuttle bus systems are also available at the Yosemite, Grand Canyon, and Denali National Parks.

- *Require private concessionaires who provide campgrounds, restaurants, hotels, and other services for park visitors to* **(1)** *compete for contracts,* and **(2)** *pay franchise fees equal to 22% of their gross (not net) receipts.* Private concessionaires in national parks pay the government an average of only about 6–7% of their gross receipts in franchise fees; many large concessionaires with long-term contracts pay as little as 0.75% of their gross receipts.

- *Allow concessionaires to lease but not own facilities inside parks.*

- *Provide more funds for park system maintenance and repairs.* Currently, there is a $4.9 billion backlog of maintenance, repairs, and high-priority construction projects at a time when park usage and external threats to the parks are increasing.

- *Survey the condition and types of wildlife species in parks.*

- *Raise entry fees for park visitors and pour receipts back into parks.*

- *Limit the number of visitors to crowded park areas.*

- *Increase the number and pay of park rangers.*

- *Encourage volunteers to give tours and lectures to visitors.*

- *Encourage individuals and corporations to donate money for park maintenance and repair.*

## 23-6 ESTABLISHING, DESIGNING, AND MANAGING NATURE RESERVES

**How Much of the Earth's Land Should We Protect from Human Exploitation?** Most ecologists and conservation biologists believe the best way to preserve biodiversity is through a worldwide network of protected areas. Currently, more than 17,000 nature reserves, parks, wildlife refuges, wilderness, and other areas provide strict or partial protection for about 10% of the world's land area. However, many existing reserves **(1)** are too small to protect their native wild species and **(2)** receive too little protection to prevent illegal and unsustainable exploitation of their plant and animal resources.

Conservation biologists call for strict protection of at least 20% of the earth's land area in a global system of biodiversity reserves that includes multiple examples of all the earth's biomes. Doing this will take action and funding by **(1)** national governments (Solutions, p. 622), **(2)** private groups (Solutions, p. 623), and **(3)** cooperative ventures involving governments, businesses, and private conservation groups.

In 1997, the Brazilian government proposed establishing 80 parks in the Amazon on government owned lands and asked the World Wildlife fund to help it plan the system. The system would be spread over 10% of the Amazon and occupy a combined area greater than the state of California. Mining and logging would not be permitted in the parks, and hunting and fishing would be allowed only for aboriginal inhabitants. In 2001, the project was launched. It is to be phased in over a decade, with funding from a number of international lending and aid organizations.

Most developers and resource extractors oppose protecting even the current 10% of the earth's remaining undisturbed ecosystems. They contend that most of these areas contain valuable resources that would add to economic growth. Ecologists and conservation biologists disagree and view protected areas as islands of biodiversity that are **(1)** vital parts of the earth's natural resources that sustain all life and economies (Figure 4-34, p. 92) and **(2)** centers of evolution.

**What Principles Should Be Used to Establish and Manage Nature Reserves?** According to most ecologists and conservation biologists, the selection, design, and management of biodiversity reserves

## Parks in Costa Rica

Once tropical forests completely covered Costa Rica, which is smaller in area than West Virginia. Between 1963 and 1983, however, politically powerful ranching families **(1)** cleared much of the country's forests to graze cattle and **(2)** exported most of the beef to the United States and western Europe.

Despite such widespread forest loss (which continues today), tiny Costa Rica is a superpower of biodiversity, with an estimated 500,000 plant and animal species. A single park in Costa Rica is home for more bird species than in all of North America.

In the mid-1970s, Costa Rica established a system of national parks and conservation reserves that by 2001 included 12% of its land (6% of it in reserves for indigenous peoples). Costa Rica now has a larger proportion of land devoted to biodiversity conservation than any other country.

The country's parks and reserves are consolidated into eight *megareserves* designed to sustain about 80% of the country's biodiversity (see figure). Each reserve contains a protected inner core surrounded by buffer zones that local and indigenous people use for sustainable logging, food growing, cattle grazing, hunting, fishing, and eco-tourism.

One reason for this accomplishment in biodiversity protection was the establishment of the Organization of Tropical Studies in 1963. It is a consortium of more than 50 U.S. and Costa Rican universities with the goal of promoting research and education in tropical ecology. The resulting infusion of several thousand scientists **(1)** helped Costa Ricans appreciate their country's great biodiversity and **(2)** led to the establishment in 1989 of the National Biodiversity Institute (INBio), a private non-profit organization set up to survey and catalog the country's biodiversity.

This biodiversity conservation strategy has paid off. Today, the $1 billion a year tourism business (almost two-thirds of it from eco-tourists) is the country's largest source of income.

Some *bad news* is that legal and illegal deforestation threatens this plan because of the country's **(1)** population growth, **(2)** poverty (which affects 10% of its people), and **(3)** lack of government regulations. Currently, this small country still loses roughly 400 square kilometers (150 square miles) of primary forest per year—four times the rate of loss in Brazil.

In addition, without careful government control, the 1 million tourists visiting Costa Rica each year can **(1)** degrade some of the protected areas and **(2)** lead to too many hotels, resorts, and other potentially harmful forms of development.

### Critical Thinking

Why do you think Costa Rica has been able to set aside a much larger percentage of its land for national parks and nature reserves than any other country? Do you support implementing such a plan in the country where you live?

Costa Rica has consolidated its parks and reserves into eight *megareserves* designed to sustain about 80% of the country's rich biodiversity.

---

should be guided by the following three ecological principles:

- Ecosystems are rarely at a stable point (the "balance of nature" concept) and thus cannot be locked up and protected from human disturbances. Instead, they are mostly in an ever-changing *nonequilibrium state* because of disturbances caused by natural processes and human activities.

- Ecosystems and communities that experience fairly frequent but moderate disturbances have the greatest diversity of species, known as the *intermediate disturbance hypothesis* (Figure 8-17, p. 184).

- We should view most reserves as *habitat islands* surrounded by a sea of developed and fragmented land.

Conservation biologists use the theory of island biogeography (Figure 8-6, p. 168) to help them **(1)** locate (and try to protect) areas in greatest danger of losing species diversity, **(2)** estimate the size of a nature reserve needed to prevent it from losing species, **(3)** evaluate how closely a series of small wildlife reserves should be spaced to allow immigration from one preserve to another if a species in one reserve becomes locally extinct, and **(4)** assess the size and number of protected corridors needed to connect various reserves and encourage the spread of protected species between them.

Experience shows that the following two social principles are useful in establishing, managing, and protecting reserves:

- Include local people in the planning and design of a reserve.

- Create user-friendly reserves that allow local people to use parts of a reserve or a buffer zone surrounding a reserve for sustainable timber cutting, livestock grazing, growing crops, hunting, and fishing (Figure 23-24). Also train local people as guides and local wildlife experts and hire them to help restore degraded areas. This turns local people into partners in protecting a reserve from unsustainable uses instead of destroyers.

**How Should Nature Reserves Be Designed?** For years, conservation biologists have engaged in debates and conducted research to answer several key questions about nature reserves:

*Question:* What is the best shape for a nature reserve?

*Answer:* Ideally, a circular reserve is preferable to an elongated reserve because the circular shape allows better protection of the interior area that is further away from the edges of the reserve (Figure 23-27, p. 624). A long, linear reserve has the most edge, and all of its interior area is close to the edge. In practice, most reserves have irregular shapes because they depend on what land is available.

*Question:* Is it better to have a *S*ingle *L*arge *O*r *S*everal *S*mall reserves of an equal total area (known as the SLOSS debate)?

*Answer:* There is general agreement that large reserves **(1)** are the only way to maintain viable populations of large, wide-ranging species such as panthers (photo on p. 559), elephants, and grizzly bears, **(2)** sustain more species based on the species–area curve (Figure 22-9, p. 566), **(3)** minimize the area of outside edges exposed to natural disturbances (such as fires and hurricanes), invading species, and human disturbances from nearby developed areas, and **(4)** provide greater habitat diversity than small reserves.

However, in some locales, several well-placed, medium-sized, isolated reserves **(1)** may have a wider variety of habitats and thus preserve more biodiversity than a single large reserve of the same area, **(2)** may better protect more populations of endemic species with small ranges than a single large reserve, and **(3)** are less likely to be simultaneously devastated by a single event such as a flood, fire, disease, or invasion by a nonnative species than a single large reserve. A mixture of both large and small reserves (Solutions figure, left) may be the best way to protect a variety of species and communities against a number of different threats.

---

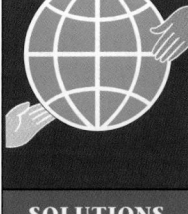

## The Nature Conservancy

**SOLUTIONS**

Private groups play an important role in establishing wildlife refuges and other reserves to protect biological diversity. For example, since 1951, the Nature Conservancy has preserved more than **(1)** 44,500 square kilometers (17,200 square miles) of vital wildlife habitats in the United States and **(2)** 243,000 square kilometers (94,000 square miles) throughout Canada, Latin America, the Caribbean, Asia, and the Pacific Ocean.

The Nature Conservancy has more than 1 million members throughout the world. It has one of the lowest overhead rates of any nonprofit organization, with 85% of all contributions going directly to its conservation programs.

The Nature Conservancy began in 1951 when an association of professional ecologists wanted to use their scientific knowledge to con-serve natural areas. Since then, this science-based organization has used the most sophisticated scientific knowledge available to identify and rank sites that are unique and ecologically significant and whose biodiversity or existence is threatened by development or other human activities (Figure 23-29, p. 625).

After identifying sites, the organization uses **(1)** a variety of techniques to see they receive legal protection and **(2)** science-based management plans to maintain or restore the ecological health of each site and provide long-term stewardship.

This conservation organization uses private and corporate donations to maintain a fund for buying ecologically important pieces of land or wetlands threatened by development. If it cannot buy land for habitat protection, the conservancy helps landowners obtain tax benefits in exchange for accepting legal restrictions or conservation easements preventing development. Other techniques include long-term management agreements and debt-for-nature swaps. Landowners also receive sizable tax deductions by donating their land to the Nature Conservancy in exchange for lifetime occupancy rights.

Through such efforts, this organization has created the world's largest system of private natural areas and wildlife sanctuaries, using the guiding principle of *land conservation through private action.*

### Critical Thinking

Do you favor this private approach to protecting biodiversity over the government approach to protecting public lands and endangered species? Explain. Would you be in favor of selling or giving some public lands to private groups such as the Nature Conservancy? Explain.

**Figure 23-27** A reserve with a generally circular shape offers better protection of species in its core area than a long, linear reserve of the same area. In a linear reserve, all species are fairly close to an edge and are more vulnerable to disturbances such as fire, disease, and predation and invasion by other species.

*Question:* Is it better to have a heterogeneous reserve with a variety of habitats or a homogeneous reserve?

*Answer:* A heterogeneous reserve generally is favored because nature is rarely at an equilibrium state and undergoes continuous change. A heterogeneous reserve **(1)** provides a variety of habitat patches (*patch dynamics*) of different sizes, shapes, and successional stages and **(2)** can allow species in disturbed patches to move to undisturbed patches.

*Question:* Should several small reserves in the same area be isolated from one another or connected by corridors?

*Answer:* Establishing protected habitat corridors between reserves can **(1)** help support more species, **(2)** allow migration of vertebrates that need large ranges, **(3)** permit migration of individuals and populations when environmental conditions in a reserve deteriorate, **(4)** help preserve animals that must make seasonal migrations to obtain food, and **(5)** enable some species to shift their ranges if global warming makes their current ranges uninhabitable. However, corridors can **(1)** threaten once-isolated populations by allowing the movement of pest species, disease, fire, and exotic species between reserves, **(2)** increase exposure of migrating species to natural predators, human hunters, and pollution, and **(3)** be costly to acquire, protect, and manage.

*Question:* What should be the role of buffer zones in establishing nature reserves?

*Answer:* Whenever possible, it is important to use the *buffer zone concept.* This means protecting an inner core of a reserve by two buffer zones in which local people can extract resources in ways that are sustainable and that do not harm the inner core. The United Nations uses this principle in establishing its global network of biosphere reserves (Solutions, p. 626).

**What Is Gap Analysis?** Scientists have developed *gap analysis* to determine whether existing networks of nature reserves provide enough protection for native plant and animal species and natural communities. *Conservation gaps* can occur in parts of reserve networks where species and communities lack adequate protection.

Gap analysis involves several steps:

- Combine existing vegetation data and remote-sensing (satellite) data to produce computerized GIS maps (Figure 4-32, p. 91) of the topography, vegetation, hydrology, land ownership, and existing or proposed nature reserves of a region.

- Use databases of biological information (bioinformatics) and other sources of data to show the known or estimated geographic distribution of the region's plant and animal species.

- Superimpose the species distribution maps onto the GIS maps of existing vegetation and protected areas to determine **(1)** unprotected areas, **(2)** gaps with very high species diversity, or **(3)** unprotected pockets of rare species.

- Use this information to close the gaps by **(1)** establishing new nature reserves, **(2)** expanding the size and shape of existing reserves, **(3)** adding corridors, or **(4)** persuading private landowners or developers to modify their existing or proposed patterns of land use.

The Biological Resources Division of the U.S. Geological Survey has initiated a National Gap Analysis Program (GAP) to provide broad geographic information on the status of biodiversity protection throughout the United States.

**What Areas Should Receive Top Priority for Establishing Reserves?** In reality, few countries are physically, politically, or financially able to set aside and protect large biodiversity reserves. Because there will not be enough money or political support to protect most of the world's terrestrial biodiversity, ecologists suggest using two approaches:

- A *prevention strategy* designed to reduce the future loss of biodiversity. It focuses international efforts on establishing a variety of large and small reserves in the world's most biodiverse countries (Figure 23-28) and threatened species-rich areas within such countries.

- An *emergency action* strategy that identifies and quickly protects *biodiversity hot spots* (Figure 23-29). They are areas especially rich in plant and animal

**Figure 23-28** The earth's 19 most biodiverse countries. Conservation biologists believe efforts to preserve repositories of biodiversity as protected wilderness areas and other nature reserves should be concentrated in these 19 countries, which contain at least 60% of the world's known terrestrial species. Protecting the world's biodiversity will take financial and scientific help from developed countries. (Data from Conservation International and World Wildlife Fund)

species that are found nowhere else and are in great danger of extinction or serious ecological disruption.

The 25 hot spots identified so far (Figure 23-29) **(1)** cover only 1.4% of the land area of the earth, about the same land area as Alaska and Texas combined, **(2)** consist mostly of tropical forests, **(3)** contain about 60% of the earth's terrestrial biodiversity, and **(4)** are the only locations for more than one-third of the planet's known terrestrial plant and animal species

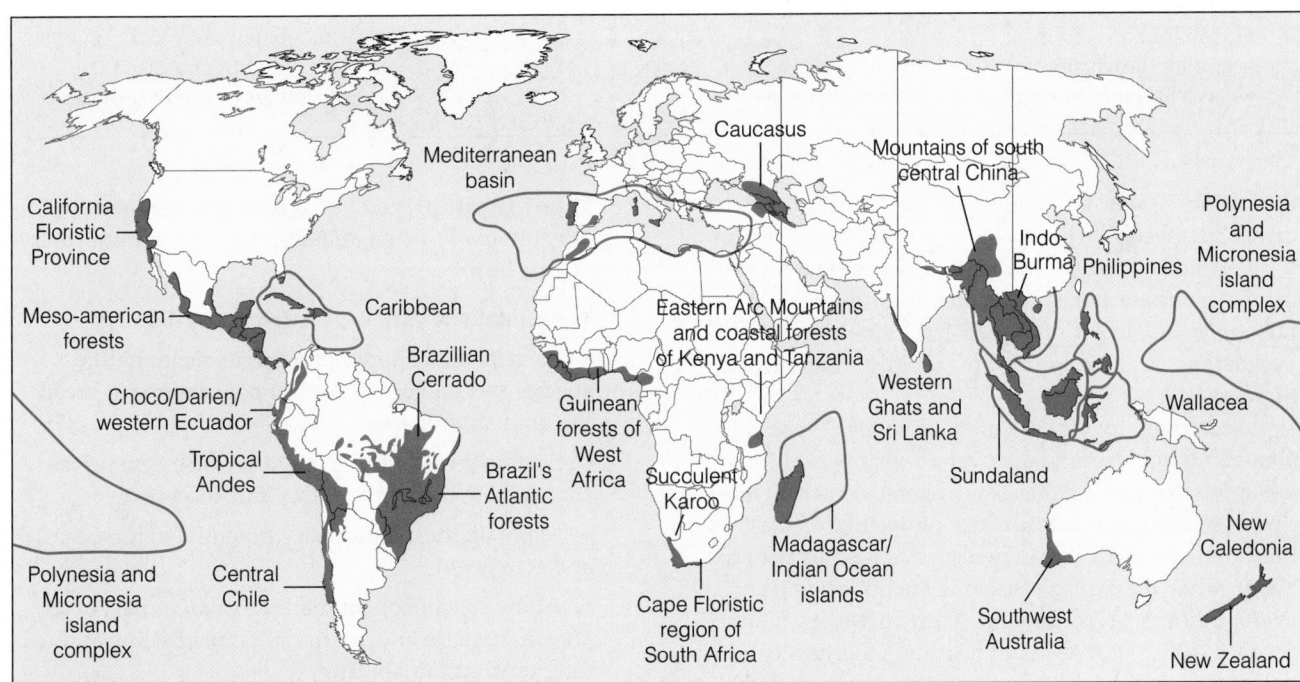

**Figure 23-29** Twenty-five hot spots identified by ecologists as being important but endangered centers of biodiversity that contain a large number of endemic plant and animal species found nowhere else. (Data from Conservation International)

## Biosphere Reserves

In 1971, the UN Educational, Scientific, and Cultural Organization (UNESCO) created the Man and the Biosphere (MAB) Programme to improve the relationship between people and the environment. A major goal of the program is to establish at least one (and ideally five or more) *biosphere reserves* in each of the 193 biogeographical zones of the earth.

Ideally, each reserve should **(1)** be large enough to prevent gradual species loss and **(2)** combine both conservation and sustainable use of natural resources. Today there are more than 350 biosphere reserves in 90 countries.

Each reserve must **(1)** receive a nomination from its national government, **(2)** meet certain size requirements, and **(3)** contain three zones (see figure):

- A *core area* containing an important ecosystem that the government legally protects from all human activities except nondestructive research and monitoring.

- A *buffer zone* that surrounds and protects the core area. In this zone, emphasis is on **(1)** nondestructive research, education, and recreation and **(2)** sustainable logging, agriculture, livestock grazing, hunting, and fishing by local people as long as such activities do not harm the core.

- A second *buffer*, or *transition*, *zone*, that combines conservation and more intensive but sustainable forestry, grazing, hunting, fishing, agriculture, and recreation by local people and eco-tourists.

So far, most biosphere reserves fall short of the ideal (see figure), and receive too little funding for their protection and management. An international fund to help countries protect and manage biosphere reserves would cost about $100 million per year—about what the world's nations spend on weapons every 90 minutes.

**Biosphere Reserve**

Core area

Buffer zone 1

Buffer zone 2

Human settlements

Research station

Tourism and education center

Design of a model *biosphere reserve*. In traditional parks and wildlife reserves, well-defined boundaries keep people out and wildlife in. By contrast, biosphere reserves recognize people's needs for access to sustainable use of various resources in parts of the reserve.

### Critical Thinking

Would you be willing to spend $10 a year to help establish and maintain a global network of biosphere reserves? Can you think of any disadvantages of such a system?

---

(including 55% of all primate species and 22% of all carnivore species).

Currently, many of the 1.1 billion people who live in or near these hot spots suffer from extreme malnutrition, and in 19 of the 25 hot spots the human population is growing more rapidly than world population.

According to conservation biologists, spending about $500 million annually over a 5-year period could go far in safeguarding these endangered centers of biodiversity. This expenditure for protecting at least a third of the world's threatened species is equivalent to about what the world's nations spend on weapons every 8 hours. According to Norman Myers (Guest Essay, p. 108), "I can think of no other biodiversity initiative that could achieve so much at a comparatively small cost, as the hot spots strategy." A coalition of conservation groups has also identified biodiversity hot spots in the United States (Figure 22-22, p. 583).

**What Is Adaptive Ecological Management?** Ideally, the major management goals of a nature reserve should be to

- Maintain its variety of native ecosystem types.

- Sustain viable populations of its major native species and prevent or control populations of invading nonnative species.

- Sustain its essential ecological processes such as energy flow, nutrient cycling, and succession.

- Maintain the evolutionary potential of its species and ecosystems.

- Allow sustainable human use of all or part of its area in ways that do not harm its functioning and long-term sustainability.

In the real world, these goals are difficult to achieve because **(1)** nature reserves are affected by mostly unpredictable biological, cultural, economic, and political changes, and **(2)** their size, shape, and biological makeup often are determined by political, legal, and economic factors that depend on land ownership and conflicting public demands rather than by ecological principles and considerations.

One way to deal with these uncertainties and conflicts is through *adaptive ecosystem management* that

- Integrates ecological, economic, and social principles to help maintain and restore the sustainability and biological diversity of ecosystems while supporting sustainable economies and communities.

- Seeks ways to get government agencies, private conservation organizations, scientists, business interests, and private landowners to reach a consensus on how to achieve common conservation objectives.

- Views all decisions and strategies as scientific and social experiments and uses failures as opportunities for learning and improvement.

- Emphasizes continual information gathering, monitoring, reassessment, flexibility, adaptation, and innovation in the face of uncertainty and usually unpredictable change.

Integrating different perspectives and getting people with diverse and sometimes conflicting interests to cooperate in achieving ecological and economic sustainability is not easy and takes time, effort, and patience. However, experience shows that the human and ecological rewards from such a process are worth the effort.

**What Is Wilderness?** One way to protect undeveloped lands from human exploitation is by legally setting them aside as *wilderness*. According to the U.S. Wilderness Act of 1964, *wilderness* consists of areas "of undeveloped land affected primarily by the forces of nature, where man is a visitor who does not remain." U.S. president Theodore Roosevelt summarized what we should do with wilderness: "Leave it as it is. You cannot improve it."

The U.S. Wilderness Society estimates that a wilderness area should contain at least 4,000 square kilometers (1,500 square miles); otherwise it can be affected by air, water, and noise pollution from nearby human activities.

**Why Preserve Wilderness?** According to wilderness supporters, we need wild places where people can **(1)** experience the beauty of nature and observe natural biological diversity and **(2)** enhance their mental and physical health by getting away from noise, stress, development, and large numbers of people. Wilderness preservationist John Muir advised us,

*Climb the mountains and get their good tidings. Nature's peace will flow into you as the sunshine into the trees. The winds will blow their freshness into you,*

*and the storms their energy, while cares will drop off like autumn leaves.*

According to the renowned conservationist David Brower, "Without wilderness the world is a cage."

Even those who never use wilderness areas may want to know they are there, a feeling expressed by novelist Wallace Stegner:

*Save a piece of country . . . and it does not matter in the slightest that only a few people every year will go into it. This is precisely its value. . . . We simply need that wild country available to us, even if we never do more than drive to its edge and look in. For it can be a means of reassuring ourselves of our sanity as creatures, a part of the geography of hope.*

Some critics oppose protecting wilderness for its scenic and recreational value for a small number of people. They believe this is an outmoded concept that keeps some areas of the planet from being economically useful to humans.

To most biologists, however, *the most important reasons for protecting wilderness and other areas from exploitation and degradation are* **(1)** *to preserve the biodiversity they contribute as a vital part of the earth's natural capital* (Figure 4-34, p. 92) *and* **(2)** *to protect them as centers for evolution in response to mostly unpredictable changes in environmental conditions* (Guest Essay, p. 108).

Wilderness areas **(1)** provide mostly undisturbed habitats for wild plants and animals, especially those that need a large range, **(2)** help protect diverse biomes from damage, and **(3)** provide a natural laboratory in which we can discover more about how nature works in the few remaining areas not seriously disturbed by human activities. In other words, wilderness is a biodiversity and wildness bank and an eco-insurance policy.

Some analysts also believe wilderness should be preserved because the wild species it contains have an ethical right to **(1)** exist (or struggle to exist) and **(2)** play their roles in the earth's ongoing saga of biological evolution and ecological processes, without human interference. In other words, wild species have *intrinsic value*, regardless of their usefulness to us (Figure 22-10, p. 569).

Wilderness advocates call for protecting more wilderness in **(1)** the world's most endangered hot spots (Figure 23-29) in species-rich countries (Figure 23-28) and **(2)** the United States (Case Study, p. 628). They also call for **(1)** emphasis on wilderness protection of grasslands, lowland forests, and wetlands that are largely absent from the current system and **(2)** allowing some degraded areas to return to a more wild state.

**How Should Wilderness Be Managed?** To protect the most popular areas from damage, wilderness managers **(1)** designate sites where camping is allowed,

## The U.S. National Wilderness Preservation System

In the United States, preservationists have been trying to save wild areas from development since 1900. Overall, they have fought a losing battle. Not until 1964 did Congress pass the Wilderness Act, which allowed the government to protect undeveloped tracts of public land from development as part of the National Wilderness Preservation System.

To wilderness supporters, the *good news* is that the area of protected wilderness in the United States increased tenfold between 1970 and 2000. The *bad news* is that (1) only about 4.6% of U.S. land is protected as wilderness, with almost three-fourths of it in Alaska, and (2) only 1.8% of the land area of the lower 48 states is protected, most of it in the West. According to a 1999 study by the World Conservation Union (IUCN), the United States ranks 42nd among nations in terms of terrestrial area protected as wilderness, and Canada is in 36th place.

More *bad news* is that (1) of the 413 wilderness areas in the lower 48 states, only 4 are larger than 4,000 square kilometers (1,500 square miles), (2) the system includes only

81 of the country's 233 distinct ecosystems, and (3) most wilderness areas in the lower 48 states are threatened habitat islands in a sea of development.

Almost 400,000 square kilometers (150,000 square miles) in scattered blocks of public lands could qualify for designation as wilderness, about 60% of it in the national forests. Conservation biologists urge wilderness protection for all of this land. However, officials of timber, mining, and other resource extraction industries lobby elected officials to build roads in these areas to make them ineligible for wilderness protection.

Some wilderness advocates also call for creating *wilderness recovery areas* by (1) closing and obliterating nonessential roads in large areas of public lands, (2) restoring wildlife habitats, (3) allowing natural fires to burn, and (4) reintroducing key species that have been driven from such areas.

Some ecologists and conservation biologists call for development of *The Wildlands Project* (TWP) to establish a network of protected wildlands and ecosystems throughout as much of the United States as possible. This goal of this science-based approach is to reconnect many of the existing fragmented

and threatened pieces of wild nature for use by wildlife and people. Proponents call for doing this by establishing regional networks of protected core wilderness areas, buffer zones, wildlife corridors, wilderness recovery areas, and areas undergoing ecological restoration. Accomplishing this would require cooperative efforts among government agencies, scientists, conservation groups, and private owners and users.

There is strong opposition to expansion of wilderness areas, establishment of wilderness recovery areas, and TWP by timber, mining, ranching, energy, and other interests who want to (1) extract resources from these and most other public lands or (2) convert them to private ownership (p. 597).

### Critical Thinking

1. Should the government reclassify a large portion of U.S. Forest Service and BLM land as wilderness recovery areas, closed off such areas for many uses, and allow them to undergo natural restoration as wildlife habitat? Explain.

2. Do you support or oppose TWP? Explain.

(2) limit the number of people using these sites at any one time, (3) use wilderness rangers to patrol vulnerable areas, and (4) enlist volunteers to pick up trash discarded by thoughtless users who do not follow the *Leave No Trace* (*LNT*) wilderness ethic.

Environmental historian and wilderness expert Roderick Nash suggests dividing wilderness areas into three categories:

- Easily accessible, popular areas that have trails, bridges, hikers' huts, outhouses, assigned campsites, and extensive ranger patrols.

- Large, remote wilderness areas used only by people who get a permit by demonstrating their wilderness skills.

- Undisturbed biologically unique areas with no human entry allowed.

## 23-7 ECOLOGICAL RESTORATION

**How Can We Rehabilitate and Restore Damaged Ecosystems?** The *bad news* is that almost every place on the earth has been degraded to some degree by human activities. The *good news* is that ecological restoration can partially reverse much of the environmental damage we have inflicted on nature.

Farmer and philosopher Wendell Berry says we should try to answer three questions in deciding whether and how to modify or rehabilitate natural ecosystems: (1) What is here? (2) What will nature permit us to do here? (3) What will nature help us do here?

By studying how degraded natural ecosystems recover, scientists have developed the following methods to speed up the natural repair of degraded ecosystems:

- *Restoration,* which involves trying to return a particular degraded habitat or ecosystem to a condition as similar as possible to its predegraded state. Three difficulties are **(1)** lack of knowledge about the previous composition of a system, **(2)** changes in climate, soil, and species composition that may make it impossible to restore an area to an earlier state, and **(3)** the need to deal with a moving target because ecosystems are always undergoing change.

- *Rehabilitation,* which involves any attempt to restore at least some of a degraded system's natural species and ecosystem functions. Examples include **(1)** removing pollutants and **(2)** replanting areas such as mining sites, landfills, and clear-cut forests to reduce soil erosion.

- *Replacement,* which involves replacing a degraded ecosystem with another type of ecosystem. For example, a productive pasture or tree plantation may replace a degraded forest.

- *Creating artificial ecosystems.* Examples are the **(1)** ecological wastewater treatment systems developed by John Todd (p. 483) and **(2)** artificial wetlands developed to treat sewage in Arcata, California (Solutions, p. 507).

**How Can We Restore or Rehabilitate Degraded Ecosystems?** Researchers have suggested the following basic principles for carrying out ecological restoration:

- Mimic nature and natural processes and let nature do most of the work, wherever possible.

- Recreate important ecological niches (Section 5-3, p. 103) that have been lost.

- Rely on pioneer species and natural ecological succession (Figure 8-15, p. 181) to facilitate the restoration process.

- Control or remove harmful nonnative species.

Based on these principles, here are some basic steps used in ecological restoration and rehabilitation:

- Identify what caused the degradation (such as pollution, farming, overgrazing, mining, or invading species).

- Eliminate or sharply reduce these factors. Examples include **(1)** removing toxic soil pollutants, **(2)** adding nutrients to depleted soil, **(3)** adding new topsoil, and **(4)** eliminating disruptive nonnative species.

- If necessary, reintroduce species (especially keystone species, pp. 172 and 594) to restore natural ecological processes.

- Protect the area from further degradation and from the disruptive effects of fires.

- Monitor restoration efforts, assess success, and use adaptive ecosystem management (p. 626) to modify strategies as needed.

Most attempts to restore degraded land involve the use of secondary ecological succession (Figure 8-15, p. 181). They include

- Trying to hold an ecosystem at a particular desirable stage of secondary ecological succession. Examples include **(1)** using controlled burning to eliminate nonnative grass and tree species and **(2)** removing trees to restore grassland to an early successional stage.

- Speeding up natural secondary ecological succession. Examples include **(1)** planting young trees in clear-cut forest areas and **(2)** preventing fires that can set back succession in areas such as degraded tropical seasonal forests (Individuals Matter, p. 630).

- Allowing natural secondary ecological succession to proceed. For example, much of the land set aside in 1935 as the Shenandoah National Park in Virginia in 1935 had suffered from over 200 years of grazing, mining, logging, and burning. Primarily by protection and allowing nature to take its course through secondary ecological succession, most of this area is now a diverse temperate forest dominated by oak and hickory trees (Figure 8-15, p. 181).

Repairing ecosystems requires that a pool of suitable existing plant species and soil organisms be available. For example, recovery of the Shenandoah National Park took place mostly because there were enough seeds (mostly underground) and patches of uncut diverse segments left for natural regeneration to take place. Thus an important step in restoration efforts is to identify the remaining native species found above and below the ground of the site or in nearby areas.

Private enterprise is getting into ecological restoration. In May 2000, the Australian Stock Exchange listed an Australian firm called Earth Sanctuaries, Ltd. This firm buys degraded land, restores it, and earns income from eco-tourism and consulting on ecosystem assessment and ecological restoration.

**Case Study: Tall-Grass Prairie Restoration in Illinois** Prairies are ideal subjects for ecological restoration because **(1)** many residual or transplanted native plant species can be established within a few years, **(2)** the technology involved is similar to that in gardening and agriculture, and **(3)** the process is well suited for volunteer labor needed to plant native species and weed out invading species until the natural species can take over.

The Fermi National Accelerator Laboratory in Batavia, Illinois, is the site for one of the world's largest tall-grass prairie restoration projects. It is the brainchild of scientists Ray Schulenberg and Robert

## Ecological Restoration of a Tropical Dry Forest in Costa Rica

**INDIVIDUALS MATTER**

Costa Rica is the site of one of the world's largest *ecological restoration* projects. In the lowlands of the country's Guanacaste National Park (see figure, Solutions , p. 622), a small tropical dry deciduous forest has been burned, degraded, and fragmented by large-scale conversion to cattle ranches and farms.

Now it is being restored and relinked to the rain forest on adjacent mountain slopes. The goal is to eliminate damaging nonnative grass and cattle and reestablish a tropical dry forest ecosystem over the next 100–300 years.

The keys to restoring the resulting grasslands to tropical dry forest are to (1) exclude fires and cattle grazing from much of the park and (2) enhance seed dispersal from remaining small patches of native woodland.

The strategy seems to be working. Areas of the park covered with monoculture expanses of nonnative grasses 10–15 years ago are now

healthy secondary-growth dry forests of native species. This project illustrates two lessons about restoration: (1) The causes of degradation must be known, and (2) enough remnants of native plant species must be present for seed dispersal and regrowth.

Daniel Janzen, professor of biology at the University of Pennsylvania and a leader in the field of restoration ecology, has helped galvanize international support and has raised more than $10 million for this restoration project.

He recognizes that ecological restoration and protection of the park will fail unless the people in the surrounding area believe they will benefit from such efforts. Janzen's vision is to make the nearly 40,000 people who live near the park an essential part of the restoration of the degraded forest, a concept he calls *biocultural restoration.*

By actively participating in the project, local residents reap educational, economic, and environmental benefits. Local farmers make money by sowing large areas with

tree seeds and planting seedlings started in Janzen's lab. Local grade school, high school, and university students and citizens' groups study the ecology of the park and go on field trips to the park. The park's location near the Pan American Highway makes it an ideal area for ecotourism, which stimulates the local economy.

The project also serves as a training ground in tropical forest restoration for scientists from all over the world. Research scientists working on the project give guest classroom lectures and lead some of the field trips.

Janzen recognizes that in a few decades today's children will be running the park and the local political system. If they understand the importance of their environment, they are more likely to protect and sustain its biological resources. He believes that education, awareness, and involvement—not guards and fences—are the best ways to (1) restore degraded ecosystems and (2) protect largely intact ecosystems from unsustainable use.

---

Betz, who began by locating remnants of virgin Illinois prairie in old cemeteries, on embankments, and on other patches of land. In 1972, they transplanted these remnants by hand to a 4-hectare (10-acre) patch at the Fermi Laboratory site.

Each year since then, volunteers have (1) carefully prepared more land, (2) sowed it with native prairie plants, (3) weeded it by hand, and (4) used controlled burning to maintain established communities. The result is more than 180 hectares (445 acres) of restored prairie. New native species are introduced each year, with the goal of eventually establishing the 150–200 species that once flourished on the site.

### Is Ecological Restoration the Best Approach?

Some analysts worry that environmental restoration could encourage continuing environmental destruction and degradation by suggesting any ecological harm we do can be undone. However, ecologists point out that preventing ecosystem damage in the first place is cheaper and more effective than any form of ecological restoration.

Another concern is government policies that allow developers to destroy one ecosystem or wetland if

they protect, restore, or "create" a similar one of roughly the same size. This trade-off, or *mitigation,* approach is preferable to wanton destruction of ecosystems. However, according to ecological restoration expert John Berger, "The purpose of ecological restoration is to repair previous damage, not legitimize further destruction."

**What Is the Next Step? Individuals Matter** In 2002, Edward O. Wilson, considered to be one of the world's foremost experts on biodiversity, published a book called *The Future of Life* (Knopf, New York). In this book, he proposed the following priorities for protecting most of the world's remaining ecosystems and species:

- *Take immediate action to preserve the world's 25 biological hot spots* (Figure 23-29).

- *Keep intact the world's five remaining frontier forests, which are the earth's last remaining true wilderness areas.* They are the remaining (1) rain forests of the Amazon, central Africa, and New Guinea and (2) temperate coniferous forests of North America, Russia, Finland, and Scandinavia (Figure 6-20, p. 123 and Figure 23-8).

- *Cease all logging of old-growth forests everywhere.*

- *Concentrate on protecting and restoring everywhere the world's lakes and river systems, which are the most threatened ecosystems of all* (as discussed in Chapter 24).

- *Determine precisely the world's marine hot spots, and assign them the same priority for immediate action as for those on land.*

- *Complete the mapping of the world's terrestrial and aquatic biodiversity so we know what we have and can make conservation efforts more precise and cost-effective.*

- *Ensure that the full range of the earth's terrestrial and aquatic ecosystems are included in a global conservation strategy.*

- *Make conservation profitable.* This involves **(1)** finding ways to raise the income of people who live in or near nature reserves so they can become partners in their protection and sustainable use, **(2)** providing financial help from private and government sources to governments that protect their forests and other nature reserves, and **(3)** helping governments understand that ecotourism, bioprospecting, and eventually greenhouse gas (carbon) trading credits for protecting remaining wild land can yield more income than logging or clearing such land for agriculture.

This strategy for protecting the earth's precious biodiversity will not be implemented without political pressure on elected officials by individual citizens and groups of such citizens. See the website material for this chapter for some actions you can take to help sustain the earth's biodiversity.

*We abuse land because we regard it as a commodity belonging to us. When we see land as a community to which we belong, we may begin to use it with love and respect.*

ALDO LEOPOLD

## REVIEW QUESTIONS

**1.** Define the boldfaced terms in this chapter.

**2.** List the pros and cons of reintroducing the gray wolf as a keystone predator species in the Yellowstone ecosystem.

**3.** List the major uses of land in **(a)** the world and **(b)** the United States.

**4.** What percentage of the land in the United States does the federal government own and manage as public lands? Describe the five major types of public lands in the United States and list the major uses allowed on each type.

**5.** List four principles that most biologists and some economists believe should govern the use of public land in the United States. Compare these principles with the views of users of mineral and other resources about the use, ownership, and management of the country's public land.

**6.** List the pros and cons of providing government subsidies to ranchers holding permits to graze livestock on public lands in the United States. Describe three major positions on the use of public rangelands. List three ways suggested by some ranchers, environmentalists, and federal range managers for using public rangeland more sustainably. Describe how Jack Turnell has managed rangeland he uses.

**7.** List **(a)** eight important ecological services provided by forests and **(b)** seven important economic benefits of forests.

**8.** Distinguish among *old-growth forests, second-growth forests,* and *tree plantations.*

**9.** Describe the *rotation cycle* for harvesting and managing a forest. Distinguish between *even-aged* and *uneven-aged management* of a forest, and list the advantages and disadvantages of each type.

**10.** Describe five major ways for harvesting trees. List the advantages and disadvantages of **(a)** selective cutting and **(b)** clear-cutting.

**11.** Summarize the state of forest growth and loss in the world's temperate and tropical forests. What are the pros and cons of deforestation?

**12.** List eight ways to use forests more sustainably. Describe **(a)** how industrial forestry based on tree plantations could lead to more sustainable use of forests, and **(b)** list four conditions ecologists believe are necessary for this approach to work.

**13.** List seven ways to help protect forests from diseases and insects.

**14.** Distinguish among *surface, crown,* and *ground* forest fires. What are the benefits of fire for some plant and animal species? List the pros and cons of reducing the chances of crown fires on public lands by **(a)** setting prescribed fires, **(b)** allowing most natural fires to burn, and **(c)** cutting trees to thin out forests.

**15.** Summarize the threats to forests from **(a)** air pollution and **(b)** global warming.

**16.** Describe two pieces of *good news* and two pieces of *bad news* about the extent and condition of forests in the United States.

**17.** List nine services provided by U.S. national forests. What are the principles of *sustained yield* and *multiple use* that are supposed to guide the use of national forests in the United States?

**18.** What are the pros and cons of giving government subsidies to companies cutting timber in national forests? List the pros and cons of making **(a)** timber cutting and **(b)** recreation the primary use of national forests.

**19.** Describe and list the advantages of the program for certifying that timber has been grown sustainably.

**20.** List three ways to reduce the pressure to harvest trees by reducing wood waste. List the pros and cons of making more paper from tree-free sources such as rice straw and kenaf fibers.

**21.** How rapidly are tropical forests being cleared and degraded?

**22.** List major *direct use, indirect use, option, existence,* and *ethical* values of tropical forests. Describe the many uses of the tropical *neem tree,* and list the pros and cons of widespread planting of neem trees.

**23.** Describe **(a)** the importance of Madagascar's biodiversity and **(b)** what is happening to its biodiversity.

**24.** Why are some people concerned about the cultural extinction of indigenous peoples in tropical forests and in other biomes?

**25.** List three underlying causes and seven direct causes of tropical deforestation and degradation.

**26.** List **(a)** nine ways to prevent or reduce tropical deforestation and degradation and **(b)** three ways to restore degraded tropical forests.

**27.** Describe **(a)** ways to achieve more sustainable farming and logging in tropical forests and **(b)** Kenya's Green Belt Movement.

**28.** What is the *fuelwood crisis?* List three ways to deal with this crisis.

**29.** What are the major threats to national parks in the United States and in other countries? List twelve ways to improve national park management in the United States.

**30.** According to scientists, what is the minimum percentage of the earth's land area that we should strictly protect from harmful human activities?

**31.** Describe **(a)** efforts by Costa Rica to establish reserves to protect its biodiversity and **(b)** the role of the Nature Conservancy in establishing nature reserves in the United States and other parts of the world.

**32.** List three scientific principles and two social principles for guiding the selection, design, and management of nature reserves.

**33.** Explain why a nature reserve system should ideally consist of a mixture of large and small reserves. What is the best shape for a nature reserve? List the pros and cons of establishing large reserves or several small reserves with the same total area. Why is it usually better to have a heterogeneous reserve with a variety of habitats than a homogeneous reserve? List the pros and cons of establishing corridors between nature reserves.

**34.** What is a *biosphere reserve?* What is *gap analysis,* and why is it an important tool for protecting biodiversity?

**35.** Explain the importance of protecting biodiversity in **(a)** the world's centers of biodiversity and **(b)** in biodiversity hot spots.

**36.** List four goals of *adaptive ecosystem management.*

**37.** What is *wilderness,* and why is it important? List the pros and cons of protecting more wilderness. List three ways to manage wilderness.

**38.** Distinguish among ecosystem *restoration, rehabilitation,* and *replacement.* List **(a)** four basic steps in carrying out ecological restoration or rehabilitation and **(b)** five techniques for implementing these steps.

**39.** Describe efforts to restore **(a)** a tall-grass prairie in Illinois and **(b)** a degraded tropical dry forest in Costa Rica. What is *biocultural restoration?*

**40.** What are two concerns some people have about ecological restoration?

## CRITICAL THINKING

**1.** Do you agree or disagree with the program to reintroduce populations of the gray wolf in the Yellowstone ecosystem? Explain. Do you favor reintroducing grizzly bears to the Yellowstone or other public lands in the western United States? Explain.

**2.** Explain why you agree or disagree with **(a)** the four principles that biologists and some economists have suggested for using public land in the United States (p. 597) and **(b)** the nine suggestions made by developers and resource extractors for managing and using U.S. public land (pp. 597–598).

**3.** Explain why you agree or disagree with each of the proposals for providing more sustainable use of **(a)** public rangeland in the United States listed on p. 598 and **(b)** forests throughout the world listed on p. 605.

**4.** Should there be a ban on the use of off-road vehicles and snowmobiles on all public lands? Explain.

**5.** Should the U.S. government continue providing private companies that harvest timber from U.S. national forests with subsidies for reforestation and for building and maintaining access roads? Explain.

**6.** In the early 1990s, Miguel Sanchez, a subsistence farmer in Costa Rica, was offered $600,000 by a hotel developer for a piece of land that he and his family had been using sustainably for many years. The land contained an old-growth rain forest and a black sand beach in an area under rapid development. Sanchez refused the offer. What would you have done if you were a poor subsistence farmer in Miguel Sanchez's position? Explain your decision.

**7.** Should the United States (or the country where you live) meet most of its demand for wood and wood products by growing genetically improved trees on carefully managed tree plantations? Explain. If you agree, what regulations and safeguards would you impose to help ensure that such an approach would be sustainable and have a low environmental impact?

**8.** Explain why you agree or disagree with each of the proposals listed in Figure 23-23 (p. 617) for protecting the world's tropical forests. Should developed countries provide most of the money to preserve remaining tropical forests in developing countries? Explain.

**9.** List five actions you could take to help preserve some of the world's tropical forests. Which, if any, of these actions do you plan to carry out?

**10.** Explain why you agree or disagree with each of the proposals listed on p. 621 concerning the U.S. national park system.

**11.** An ecologist recommends a controlled burn of vegetation in a heavily forested nearby state park to help reduce the chance of serious damage from a major forest fire. Many local citizens oppose the burn. If you were an elected official, would you support the proposed controlled burn? If you approved the burn, what restrictions would you impose for ecological and human health reasons?

**12.** Are you in favor of establishing more wilderness areas in the United States, especially in the lower 48 states (or in the country where you live)? Explain. What might be some drawbacks?

**13.** List ecological, economic, political, and social reasons that might explain why **(a)** there is little protection of natural grasslands in nature reserves, and **(b)** many ecological restoration projects are devoted to restoring degraded grasslands.

**14.** If ecosystems are undergoing constant change, why should we **(a)** establish and protect nature reserves and **(b)** carry out ecological restoration?

**15.** Congratulations! You are in charge of protecting and sustaining the world's terrestrial biodiversity. List the three most important features of your policies for using and managing **(a)** forests, **(b)** parks, and **(c)** wilderness and other protected biodiversity reserves.

## PROJECTS

**1.** Obtain a topographic map of the region where you live and use it to identify local, state, and federally owned lands in the form of parks, rangeland, forests, and wilderness areas. Identify the government agency responsible for managing each of these areas, and evaluate how well these agencies are preserving the natural resources on this land on your behalf.

**2.** If possible, try to visit **(a)** a diverse old-growth forest, **(b)** an area that has been recently clear-cut, and **(c)** an area that was clear-cut 5–10 years ago. Compare the biodiversity, soil erosion, and signs of rapid water runoff in each of the three areas.

**3.** For many decades, New Zealand has had a policy of meeting all its demand for wood and wood products by growing timber on intensively managed tree plantations. Use the library or Internet to evaluate the effectiveness of this approach and its major advantages and disadvantages.

**4.** Evaluate timber harvesting on private and public lands in your local area. What are the most widely used harvesting methods? Try to document any harmful environmental impacts. Have the economic benefits to the community outweighed any harmful environmental effects?

**5.** Use the library and Internet to find one example of a successful ecological restoration project not discussed in this chapter and one that failed. For each example, describe **(a)** the strategy used, **(b)** the ecological principles involved, and **(c)** why the project succeeded or failed.

**6.** Use the library or the Internet to find bibliographic information about *François-Auguste-René de Chateaubriand* and *Aldo Leopold,* whose quotes appear at the beginning and end of this chapter.

**7.** Make a concept map of this chapter's major ideas, using the section heads and subheads and the key terms (in boldface). Look on the website for this book for information about making concept maps.

## INTERNET STUDY RESOURCES AND RESOURCES FOR FURTHER READING AND RESEARCH

The website for this book contains helpful study aids and many ideas for further reading and research. Log on to

www.info.brookscole.com/miller13

and click on the Chapter-by-Chapter area. Choose Chapter 23 and select a resource:

■ Flash Cards allows you to test your mastery of the Terms and Concepts to Remember for this chapter.

■ Tutorial Quizzes provides a multiple-choice practice quiz.

■ Student Guide to InfoTrac will lead you to Critical Thinking Projects that use InfoTrac College Edition as a research tool.

■ References lists the major books and articles consulted in writing this chapter.

■ Hypercontents takes you to an extensive list of sites with news, research, and images related to individual sections of the chapter.

## INFOTRAC COLLEGE EDITION

Improve your skills with InfoTrac College Edition, a searchable online database of articles from more than 700 periodicals. Log on to

http://www.infotrac-college.com

or access InfoTrac through the website for this book. Try to find the following articles:

**1.** Matthews, M. 2002. When fire and forest health came to town: The forest service hopes its national fire plan can restore woodlands while benefiting local economies. *American Forests* 107: 25. *Keyword:* "National Fire Plan." Utilizing forests, maintaining forest health, and minimizing the impact of wildfires are all parts of the new National Fire Plan.

**2.** Helmuth, L. 1999. Can this swamp be saved? *Science News* 155: 252. *Keywords:* "swamp" and "Florida Everglades." The restoration of the Florida Everglades is a huge undertaking. It took a long time to mess it up; will we be able to fix it?

## Connections: Can Lake Victoria Be Saved?

Lake Victoria, shared by Kenya, Tanzania, and Uganda in East Africa, is the world's second largest freshwater lake (Figure 24-1, right). It is also the source of the Nile River, which drains into the Mediterranean Sea. The lake has been in ecological trouble for more than two decades, and the situation is getting worse.

Until the early 1980s, Lake Victoria had more than 350 species of fish found nowhere else. About 80% of them were small algae-eating fishes known as cichlids (pronounced "SIK-lids"), each with a slightly different ecological niche. These fishes were the main source of protein for the more than 30 million people living in the area surrounding the lake and provided a fishing livelihood for many local people.

Currently, only one native minnow species and two introduced fish species dominate the lake. All the remaining fish species are endangered or extinct.

Several factors played a role in this dramatic loss of aquatic biodiversity:

- A large increase in the population of the Nile perch (Figure 24-1, left). This fish was deliberately introduced into the lake in 1960 to stimulate local economies and the fishing industry, despite the protests of some biologists. The population of this large, prolific, and ravenous fish exploded by preying on the cichlids and by 1985 had wiped out most of these species. With the cichlids gone, the Nile perch now feeds on tiny native shrimp and its own young. There is concern that the Nile perch population, which supports a large fishing industry that processes and exports large amounts of the fish to several European countries,

may collapse. The native people who depended on the cichlids for protein cannot afford the perch, and the mechanized fishing industry has put most small-scale fishers and fish vendors out of business. This has increased poverty and protein malnutrition.

- In the 1980s, the lake began experiencing frequent algal blooms and cultural eutrophication (Figure 19-7, p. 491) because of nutrient runoff from surrounding farms, deforested land, untreated sewage, and declines in the populations of the algae-eating cichlids. This **(1)** greatly decreased oxygen levels in the lower depths of the lake and **(2)** drove remaining native cichlids and other fish species to shallower waters, where they are more vulnerable to Nile perch and fishing nets.

- Since 1987, the nutrient-rich lake has been invaded by the water hyacinth (Figure 22-17, p. 576). This rapidly growing plant now carpets large areas of the lake and **(1)** blocks out sunlight, **(2)** deprives fish and plankton of oxygen, **(3)** reduces the diversity of important aquatic plant species, **(4)** hinders the movement of small fishing boats, and **(5)** creates stagnant water that is the breeding ground for malaria-spreading mosquitoes and snails that host bilharzia (a human parasite that attacks the liver, lungs, and eyes). Men are vacating villages in search of jobs, often having to leave behind women and children who face severe poverty, disease, and protein malnutrition.

- To make matters worse, in 2000 the Tanzanian government constructed a large gold mine next to a river that drains into the lake. The mine uses highly toxic sodium cyanide to recover the gold. If the cyanide ends up in the lake, it will devastate aquatic life.

Some of the lake's biological diversity and fish productivity could be restored by **(1)** controlling rapid human population growth (more than 3% a year), nutrient runoff, overfishing, and population of the Nile perch and **(2)** instituting an aggressive reforestation program along the shores of the lake and the three rivers that feed it. However, restoring a eutrophic lake of this size has never been attempted.

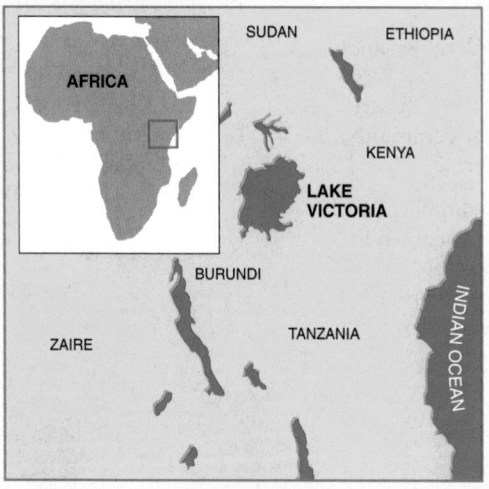

SUDAN
ETHIOPIA
AFRICA
KENYA
LAKE VICTORIA
BURUNDI
INDIAN OCEAN
ZAIRE
TANZANIA

**Figure 24-1** Although the Nile perch (left) is a fine food fish, it has played a key role in a major loss of biodiversity in East Africa's Lake Victoria (right).

*The coastal zone may be the single most important portion of our planet. The loss of its biodiversity may have repercussions far beyond our worst fears.*

G. CARLETON RAY

This chapter addresses the following questions:

- What is aquatic biodiversity, and what is its economic and ecological importance?

- How are human activities affecting aquatic biodiversity?

- How can we protect and sustain marine biodiversity?

- How can we manage and sustain the world's marine fisheries?

- How can we protect, sustain, and restore wetlands?

- How can we protect, sustain, and restore lakes, rivers, and freshwater fisheries?

## 24-1 THE IMPORTANCE OF AQUATIC BIODIVERSITY

**What Do We Know About the Earth's Aquatic Biodiversity?** Although we live on a water planet (Figure 7-5, p. 147), we know fairly little about the earth's aquatic systems. Indeed, less than 5% of the earth's global ocean has been explored and mapped with the same level of detail as the surface of the moon and Mars. According to aquatic scientists, the scientific investigation of poorly understood aquatic systems is a poorly funded *research frontier* whose study could result in immense ecological and economic benefits.

Oceans cover 71% of the planet's surface (p. 1 and Figure 7-5, p. 147), and represent more than 99% of the living space or volume of the earth's biosphere. These oceans consists of a rich mosaic of large and small habitats that support a variety of species at different depths (Figure 7-7, p. 148, and Figure 24-2, p. 636). A large variety of species is found in the coastal zone, with an array of niches for birds (Figure 7-13, p. 152) and other species at the water's edge (Figure 7-12, p. 151). The three most biologically diverse habitats found in the world's oceans are **(1)** *coral reefs* (Figure 7-1, p. 144, and Figure 7-16, p. 154), **(2)** *estuaries* (Figure 7-8, p. 148, and Figure 7-11, p. 150), and **(3)** *the deep-ocean floor.*

Of the roughly 25,000 known fish species, about 63% are found in marine systems (about 50% in coastal waters, 12% in the deep sea, and 1% in the waters of the open ocean), and the remaining 37% live in freshwater systems. However, some scientists believe largely unexplored deep-water marine habitats could harbor at least 10 million species.

Freshwater aquatic systems also contain a variety of visible plant and animal species (Figure 24-3, p. 637) and microscopic species. Many *lakes* contain a variety of species found in different layers (Figure 7-20, p. 158), although this varies with the amount of nutrients added to a lake's waters (Figure 7-21, p. 158) by natural or human causes (Figure 19-7, p. 491). As they flow from their mountain (headwater) stream to the ocean, *river systems* have a variety of ecological habitats that support different aquatic species (Figure 7-23, p. 160). Most people are unaware of the vulnerability of freshwater environments to environmental degradation and depletion.

**What Are Some General Patterns of Marine Biodiversity?** Despite the lack of knowledge about overall marine biodiversity, scientists have established the following general patterns:

- The greatest marine biodiversity occurs in coral reefs (Figure 7-16, p. 154) and on the deep-sea floor (Figure 8-4, p. 167).

- Biodiversity is higher near coasts than in the open sea because of the greater variety of producers, habitats, and nursery areas in coastal areas.

- Biodiversity is higher in the benthic (bottom) region of the ocean than in the pelagic (surface) region because of the greater variety of habitats and food sources on the ocean bottom.

- The lowest marine biodiversity probably is found in the middle depths of the open ocean (Figure 8-4, p. 167).

- Top-level predators, some of which are keystone species (p. 172), often dominate the biodiversity and ecological dynamics of many marine intertidal zones (Figure 7-12, p. 151). When key predators are eliminated or their populations drop sharply, trophic cascades from these *top-down food web dynamics* can reduce system biodiversity.

- The biodiversity of coastal upwelling systems (Figure 6-13, p. 119) generally is governed by *bottom-up food web dynamics* in which variations at lower trophic levels and nutrient levels have effects that *cascade* to higher trophic levels.

**What Is the Ecological and Economic Importance of Aquatic Biodiversity?** Aquatic systems and species, like terrestrial ecosystems and species, have instrumental and intrinsic values (Figure 22-10, p. 569). Marine systems provide a variety of important ecological and economic services (Figure 7-6, p. 147).

For example, on average, people get about 6% of their total protein and 16% of their animal protein from fish and shellfish (Figure 13-29, p. 302), with these sources providing as much nutrition as all the world's

**Figure 24-2** *Marine biodiversity.* Some ocean inhabitants.

Labels in figure: Kelp, Hogfish, Cobia, Carrageen, Pacific sailfish, Batfish, Yellow jack, Moray, Red snapper, Red algae, Striped drum, Angelfish, Bladder kelp, Sea lettuce, Orange roughy, Chinook salmon, Devilfish, Great barracuda, Laminaria, Porcupine fish, Sockeye salmon, Grouper, Dulse, Chilean sea bass

cows and chickens combined. However, fish and shellfish supply about 30% of the protein for nearly 1 billion people, mostly in Asia.

Marine seaweed (Figure 24-2) and other organisms provide chemicals used in cosmetics and pharmaceuticals worth $400 million per year. Examples include

- Chemicals from several types of algae, sea anemones (Figure 8-12b, p. 179), sponges, and mollusks that have antibiotic and anticancer properties.

- Anticancer chemicals from porcupine fish (Figure 24-2), puffer fish, and shark liver.

- Chemicals to treat hypertension extracted from seaweeds and octopuses.

- Bone reconstruction material from coral.

- A binding adhesive for tooth fillings ("nature's superglue") from barnacles.

- Chemicals effective against viral encephalitis and herpes (worth $50–100 million per year) from sponges.

Despite the ecological and economic importance of marine ecosystems, spending on research in the ocean sciences is quite low.

Bulrush

Bluegill

White bass

Brook trout

White waterlily

Water lettuce

Rainbow trout

Muskellunge

Water hyacinth

Rainbow darter

Bladderwort

Bowfish

Black crappie

White sturgeon

Largemouth black bass

Walleyed pike

American smelt

Yellow perch

Velvet cichlid

Duckweed

Eelgrass

Longnose gar

Common piranha

Carp

Channel catfish

Egyptian
white lotus

African lungfish

**Figure 24-3** *Freshwater biodiversity.* Some inhabitants of freshwater rivers and lakes.

Freshwater systems also provide important ecological and economic services (Figure 7-19, p. 157, and Figure 14-10, p. 319). Although lakes, rivers, and wetlands occupy only 1% of the earth's surface, they provide ecological and economic services worth trillions of dollars per year.

## 24-2 HUMAN IMPACTS ON AQUATIC BIODIVERSITY

**What Are the Major Human Impacts on Aquatic Biodiversity?** The indirect and direct causes of the

degradation of aquatic ecosystems and premature extinction of aquatic wildlife species are the same as those for terrestrial ecosystems and species (Figure 22-12, p. 572). They include the following:

### Species Loss and Endangerment

- According to marine biologists, at least 1,200 marine species have become extinct in the past few hundred years, and many thousands of additional species could disappear during this century as a result of human activities such as **(1)** overfishing, **(2)** habitat destruction and degradation, and **(3)** pollution.

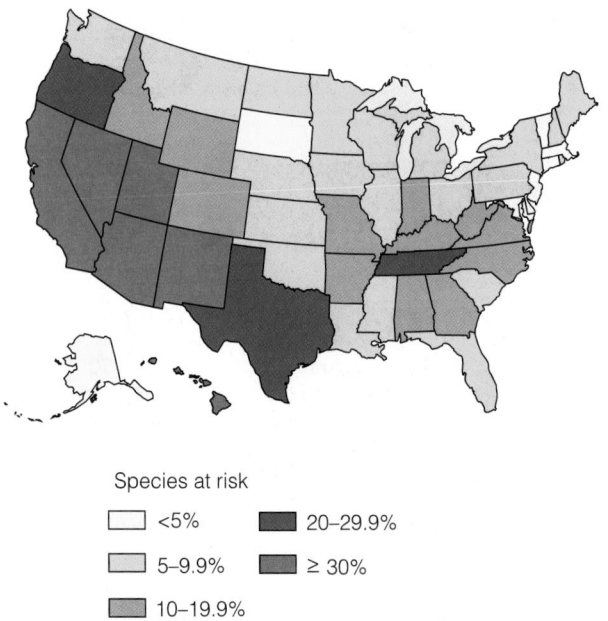

Species at risk

| | <5% | | 20–29.9% |
| | 5–9.9% | | ≥ 30% |
| | 10–19.9% | | |

**Figure 24-4** Distribution of freshwater species at risk in the lower 48 states and Hawaii. (Data from the Nature Conservancy and the Natural Heritage Network)

- As a whole, freshwater species are more at risk of extinction than land-based species. According to the UN Food and Agriculture Organization and the World Wildlife Fund, at least 20% of the world's 10,000 known freshwater fish species are threatened with extinction or have already become extinct.

- A 1997 study by the Nature Conservancy and the Natural Heritage Network found that in the United States, which has the world's highest diversity of known freshwater species, **(1)** 69% of freshwater mussel species, **(2)** 51% of crayfish, **(3)** 36% of amphibians, and **(4)** 37% of freshwater fish are at risk of extinction, with the risk varying widely in the lower 48 states (Figure 24-4).

### Marine Habitat Loss and Degradation

- Scientists estimate that half the world's original coastal wetlands and 53% of those in the lower 48 U.S. states have disappeared since 1800, mostly by being filled in for agriculture and coastal development.

- According to a 1999 study by the World Resources Institute, **(1)** about 58% of the world's coral reefs (Figure 7-2, p. 145, and Figure 7-16, p. 154) are threatened by human activities such as coastal development, over-fishing, pollution, and warmer ocean temperatures (Figure 7-17, p. 155), **(2)** 27% are gone or seriously threatened, and **(3)** 70% could be gone within 50 years. Jamaica has lost 90% of its coral reefs, Costa Rica 75%, and Kenya 70%.

- According to a 2001 report by the Pew Oceans Committee, two-thirds of the surface area of U.S. estu-

aries and bays are at risk from pollution mostly from land runoff.

- At least 35% of the world's original mangroves (Figure 7-2, p. 145, and Figure 7-9, p. 149) have disappeared, mostly because of clearing for coastal development, growing crops, and aquaculture shrimp farms. Such activities threaten many of the world's remaining mangrove systems.

- According to a World Wildlife Fund study, almost 70% of the world's beaches are eroding because of coastal developments and a rising sea level (caused mostly by global warming). Computer models project significant increases in erosion and flooding during this century (Figure 18-19, p. 463).

- Bottom habitats are being degraded and destroyed by dredging operations and trawler boats, which drag huge nets weighted down with chains over ocean bottoms to harvest bottom fish and shellfish (Figure 7-18, p. 156). Each year, thousands of trawlers scrape and disturb an area of ocean bottom equal to the combined size of Brazil and India and about 150 times larger than the area of forests clear-cut each year. Recovery in heavily trawled areas rarely is possible because of repeated scraping.

- Some biologists warn that deep-sea mining (p. 348) could devastate mostly unknown marine biodiversity in the deep ocean by **(1)** destroying or disrupting bottom-dwelling communities and **(2)** possibly burying some bottom habitats with sediment.

### Freshwater Habitat Loss and Degradation

- According to a 2000 study by the World Wildlife Fund, since 1800 the world has lost more than half of its inland wetlands (53% in the lower 48 U.S. states), mostly by being drained and filled in for agriculture and urban development. This loss disrupts many of the important ecological and economic services provided by inland wetlands (p. 160).

- According to a 2000 study by the World Resources Institute, almost 60% of the world's 237 large rivers (Figure 7-2, p. 145) are strongly or moderately fragmented by dams, diversions, or canals. This alters and destroys wildlife habitats along rivers and in coastal deltas and estuaries by reducing water flow (Figure 14-9, p. 319). More than 20% of all freshwater fish are now threatened or endangered because dams and water withdrawals have severely altered the river systems where they live.

- Flood control levees (Figure 14-22, middle, p. 332) and dikes **(1)** alter and destroy aquatic habitats, **(2)** disconnect rivers from their floodplains, and **(3)** eliminate wetlands and backwaters that are important spawning grounds for fish.

### Overfishing

- According to a 2001 report by the UN Food and Agriculture Organization, about 75% of the world's 200 commercially valuable marine fish species are either overfished or fished to the limit (p. 304). The primary cause of this depletion of fish stocks is too many fishing boats pursuing too few fish—another example of the tragedy of the commons (Connections, p. 305).

- In most cases, overfishing leads to *commercial extinction*. This is usually only a temporary depletion of fish stocks, as long as depleted areas and fisheries are allowed to recover. However, by depleting prized species and shifting to harvesting species at lower trophic levels, fishers can **(1)** unravel food webs, **(2)** disrupt marine ecosystems, and **(3)** hinder the recovery of fish feeding at higher trophic levels (Figure 24-5).

- Overfishing can lead to serious depletion and extinction of species such as sea turtles, dolphins, and other marine mammals that are unintentionally caught as bycatch (Figure 24-6, p. 641).

### Nonnative Species

- Hundreds of nonnative species have been deliberately or accidentally introduced into coastal waters, lakes, and wetlands (Spotlight, p. 640, and Figure 22-17, p. 576) throughout the world. These bioinvaders displace or cause the extinction of native species and disrupt ecosystem functions, as happened to Lake Victoria (p. 634).

- An example of an accidental invader is the *Asian swamp eel*, a fish that invaded the waterways of south Florida, probably after escaping from a home aquarium. This prolific eel **(1)** eats almost anything, including bluegill, bass, crayfish, and many other species, by sucking them in like a vacuum cleaner, **(2)** can elude

cold weather, drought, fires, and predators (including humans with nets) by burrowing into mud banks, **(3)** is resistant to waterborne poisons because it can breathe air, **(4)** can wriggle across dry land to invade new waterways, ditches, canals, and marshes, and **(5)** eventually could take over much of the waterways of the southeastern United States as far north as the Chesapeake Bay.

- Bioinvaders are blamed for about 68% of fish extinctions in the United States between 1900 and 2000.

### Pollution and Global Warming

- The major pollution threats to aquatic systems and species are **(1)** oil (p. 501), **(2)** acid deposition (Figure 17-10, p. 428; Figure 17-12, p. 429; and Figure 17-14, p. 431), **(3)** excess plant nutrients and oxygen-demanding wastes (Figure 19-5, p. 488, and Figure 19-7, p. 491), **(4)** toxic chemicals such as cyanide, PCBs (Figure 19-6, p. 490), and DDT (Figure 11-4, p. 231), **(5)** coastal development (Figure 7-15, p. 153 and Figure 19-12, p. 498), and **(6)** sedimentation from soil erosion (Figure 7-8, p. 148).

- An estimated 44% of marine pollution comes from runoff from developed coastal areas and rivers flowing into estuaries. An additional 33% comes from the atmosphere, and the remaining 23% comes from shipping, offshore oil and gas production, and ocean dumping.

- Current and projected global warming (Figure 18-12, p. 455) could **(1)** alter migration and feeding patterns of marine species, **(2)** increase average ocean temperatures, which can destroy many of the world's coral reef systems (Figure 7-2, p. 145), and **(3)** raise average sea levels (Figure 18-19, p. 463), which can flood and destroy coastal wetlands, mangroves, and coral reefs.

**Figure 24-5** Mean trophic levels of the global marine (right) and freshwater (left) fish catch have declined since 1950. (Data from Daniel Pauly)

## Invasion of Wetlands by Purple Loosestrife

Purple loosestrife (Figure 22-17, p. 576) is a perennial plant that grows in wetlands in Eurasia. In the early 1880s, it was imported into the United States as an ornamental plant.

Since then it has spread to temperate and boreal wetlands in 35 states (see figure). This rapidly reproducing nonnative species has no natural enemies in the United States and is spreading at a rate of 300 hectares (700 acres) per day. As it spreads, it reduces wetland biodiversity by displacing native vegetation and reducing habitat for some forms of wetland wildlife.

Mowing and using herbicides to eliminate established stands of this plant generally are ineffective. Some states have recently introduced two natural predators of loosestrife from Europe: a weevil species and a leaf-eating beetle. It will take some time to **(1)** determine the effectiveness of this biological control approach and **(2)** be sure the introduced species themselves do not become pests.

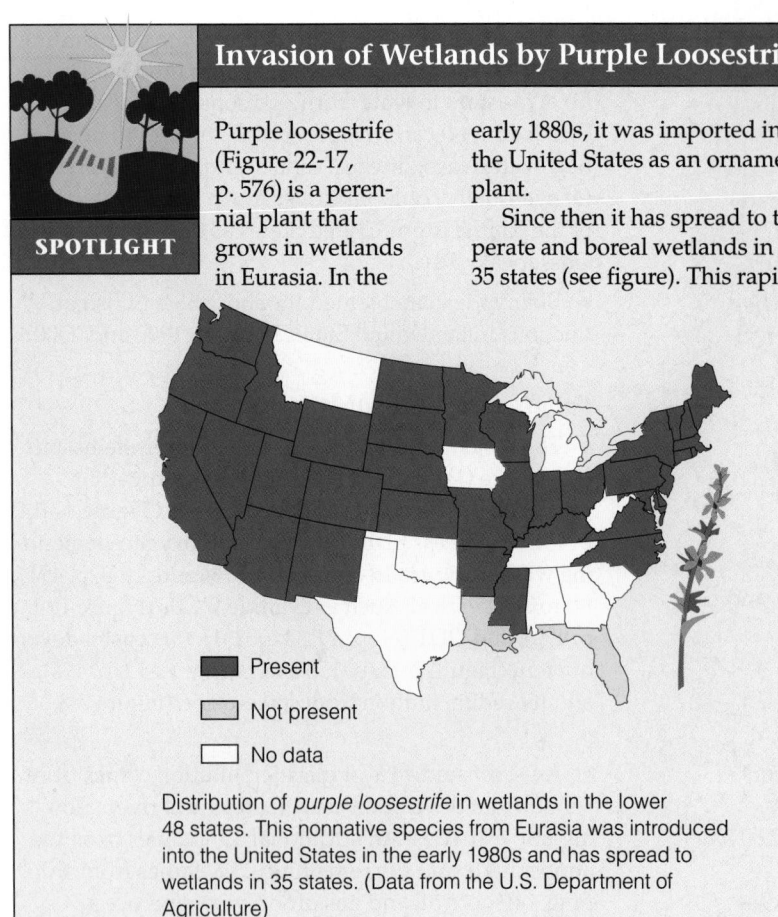

Present

Not present

No data

Distribution of *purple loosestrife* in wetlands in the lower 48 states. This nonnative species from Eurasia was introduced into the United States in the early 1980s and has spread to wetlands in 35 states. (Data from the U.S. Department of Agriculture)

### Critical Thinking

Why should we care if a pleasant-looking species such as loosestrife takes over wetlands?

## 24-3 PROTECTING AND SUSTAINING MARINE BIODIVERSITY

**Why Is It Difficult to Protect Marine Biodiversity?** Protecting marine biodiversity is difficult for several reasons:

- Coastal development and the accompanying massive inputs of sediment and other wastes from land (Figure 7-8, p. 148) **(1)** harm shore-hugging species and **(2)** threaten biologically diverse and highly productive coastal ecosystems such as coral reefs, marshes, and mangrove forest swamps.

- Much of the damage is not visible to most people.

- Many people view the seas as an inexhaustible resource that can absorb an almost infinite amount of waste and pollution.

- Most of the world's ocean area lies outside the legal jurisdiction of any country and is thus an *open-access resource,* subject to overexploitation because of the tragedy of the commons (Connections, p. 11).

- No effective international agreements protect biodiversity in the open seas, mostly because such agreements are difficult to develop, monitor, and enforce.

**How Can We Protect and Sustain Marine Biodiversity?** Ways to protect and sustain marine biodiversity include

- Protecting endangered and threatened species.

- Establishing protected areas.

- Using integrated coastal management.

- Regulating and preventing ocean pollution, as summarized in Figure 19-15, p. 502.

- Sustainably managing marine fisheries.

**How Can We Protect Endangered and Threatened Marine Species?** One widely used method for protecting biodiversity is identifying and protecting endangered, threatened, and rare species, as has been done to help save a number of endangered terrestrial species (Section 22-8, p. 582).

In addition to fish, this strategy has been used to protected a number of endangered and threatened marine reptiles (turtles) and mammals (especially whales, seals, and sea lions; Figures 24-6 and 24-7). Three of eight major sea turtle species (Figure 24-8, p. 642) are endangered (Kemp's ridley, leatherbacks, and hawksbills), and the rest are threatened.

![Figure 24-6 map of endangered marine species]

**Figure 24-6** *Endangered marine mammals* (whales, seals, and sea lions) and reptiles (turtles). Many marine fish, seabirds (Figure 7-13, p. 152), and invertebrate species are also threatened.

The world's sea turtle species are endangered or threatened because of **(1)** loss or degradation of beach habitat (where they come ashore to lay their eggs), **(2)** legal and illegal taking of their eggs, **(3)** their increased use as sources of food, medicinal ingredients, tortoiseshell (for jewelry), and leather from their flippers (with some turtles selling for up to $1,500 in China), and **(4)** unintentional capture and drowning by commercial fishing boats (especially shrimp trawlers).

Until recently, U.S. shrimp trawling boats killed as many as 55,000 sea turtles (mostly endangered loggerheads and Kemp's ridleys) each year. To reduce this slaughter, the U.S. government has required offshore shrimp trawlers to use turtle exclusion devices (TEDs) since 1989 (Figure 24-9, p. 642). Certain governments such as Costa Rica and Mexico have taken a lead in protecting sea turtles, mostly as a result of pressure from environmentalists.

National and international laws and treaties to help protect marine species include **(1)** the 1975 Convention on International Trade in Endangered Species (CITES, p. 582), **(2)** the 1979 Global Treaty on Migratory Species, **(3)** the U.S. Marine Mammal Protection Act of 1972, **(4)** the U.S. Endangered Species Act of 1973 (p. 583), **(5)** the U.S. Whale Conservation and Protection Act of 1976, and **(6)** the 1995 International Convention on Biological Diversity.

Doris Alcorn/U.S. National Marine Fisheries

**Figure 24-7** Before this discarded piece of plastic was removed, this Hawaiian monk seal was slowly starving to death. Each year plastic items dumped from ships and left as litter on beaches threaten the lives of millions of marine mammals, turtles, and seabirds that ingest, become entangled in, choke on, or are poisoned by such debris.

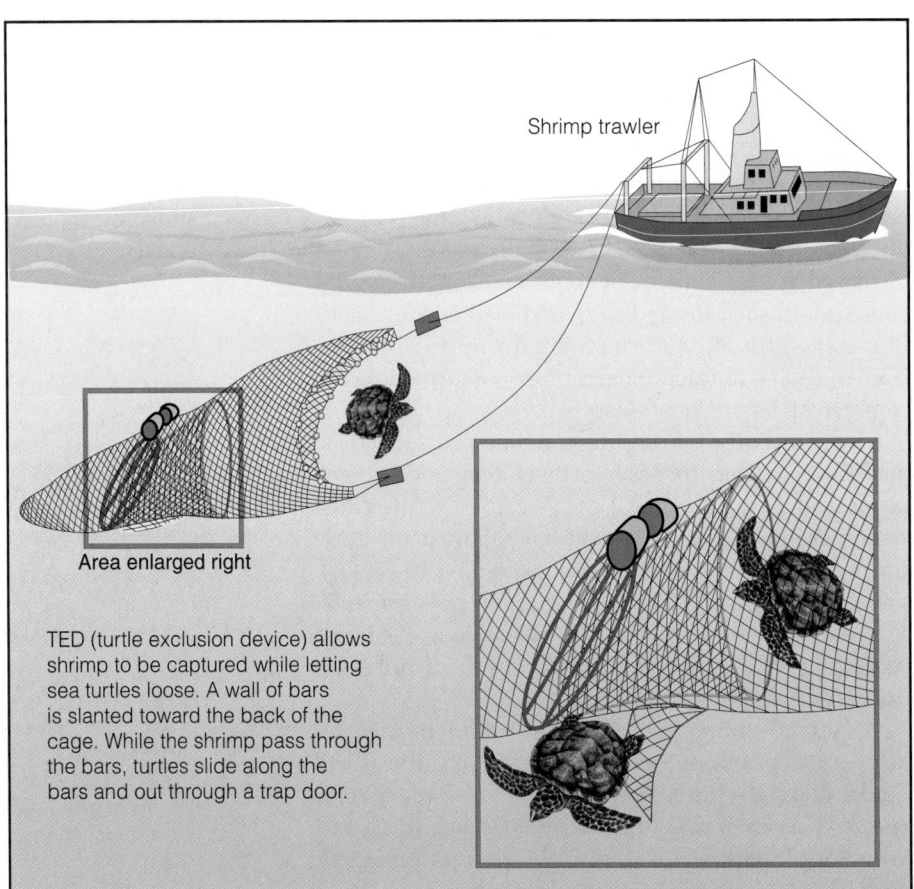

Loggerhead
119 centimeters

Olive ridley
76 centimeters

Leatherback
188 centimeters

Hawksbill
89 centimeters

Australian
flatback
99 centimeters

Black turtle
99 centimeters

Green turtle
124 centimeters

Kemp's ridley
76 centimeters

**Figure 24-8** Major species of sea turtles that have roamed the seas for 150 million years, showing their relative adult sizes. Three of these species (Kemp's ridley, leatherbacks, and hawksbills) are endangered, and the rest are threatened as a result of human activities.

Shrimp trawler

Area enlarged right

TED (turtle exclusion device) allows shrimp to be captured while letting sea turtles loose. A wall of bars is slanted toward the back of the cage. While the shrimp pass through the bars, turtles slide along the bars and out through a trap door.

**Figure 24-9** *Turtle exclusion device* (TED) designed to release turtles caught in shrimp trawling nets. Since 1989, the government has required these devices on the nets of all shrimp boats trawling in U.S. waters.

Public aquariums that exhibit unusual and attractive fish and some marine animals such as seals and dolphins have been successful in educating the public about the need to protect such species. In the United States, more than 35 million people visit aquariums each year. However, unlike zoos, public aquariums have not yet served as effective gene banks for endangered marine species, especially marine mammals that need large volumes of water.

Two major problems with protecting marine biodiversity by protecting endangered species are **(1)** lack of knowledge about marine species and **(2)** difficulty in monitoring and enforcing treaties to protect marine species, especially in the open ocean.

**Case Study: Should Commercial Whaling Be Resumed?** *Cetaceans* are an order of mostly marine mammals ranging in size from the 0.9-meter (3-foot) porpoise to the giant 15- to 30-meter (50- to 100-foot) blue whale. They are divided into two major groups: toothed whales and baleen whales (Figure 24-10, p. 644).

*Toothed whales,* such as the porpoise, sperm whale, and killer whale (orca), bite and chew their food, and they feed mostly on squid, octopus, and other marine animals. *Baleen whales,* such as the blue, gray, hump-

back, and finback, are filter feeders (Spotlight, p. 149). Instead of teeth, they have several hundred horny plates made of baleen, or whalebone, that hang down from the upper jaw. These plates filter plankton from the seawater, especially tiny shrimplike krill (Figure 4-19, p. 78). Baleen whales are the most abundant group of cetaceans.

Whales are fairly easy to kill because of their large size and their need to come to the surface to breathe. Mass slaughter has become very efficient with the use of fast ships, harpoon guns, and inflation lances (which pump dead whales full of air and make them float).

Whale harvesting, mostly in international waters, has followed the classic pattern of a tragedy of the commons, with whalers killing an estimated 1.5 million whales between 1925 and 1975. This overharvesting **(1)** drove the populations of 8 of the 11 major species to commercial extinction, the point at which it no longer paid to hunt and kill them, and **(2)** drove some commercially prized species such as the giant blue whale to the brink of biological extinction (Case Study, below).

In 1946, the International Convention for the Regulation of Whaling established the International Whaling Commission (IWC) to regulate the whaling industry by setting annual quotas to prevent overharvesting and

### Near Extinction of the Blue Whale

**CASE STUDY**

The biologically endangered blue whale (Figure 24-10, p. 644) is the world's largest animal. Fully grown, it is more than 30 meters (100 feet) long—longer than three train boxcars—and weighs more than 25 elephants. The adult has a heart the size of a Volkswagen Beetle car, and some of its arteries are so big that a child could swim through them.

Blue whales spend about 8 months of the year in Antarctic waters. There they find an abundant supply of krill (Figure 4-19, p. 78), which they filter daily by the trillions from seawater. During the winter, they migrate to warmer waters, where their young are born.

Before commercial whaling began, an estimated 200,000 blue whales roamed the Antarctic Ocean. Today, the species has been hunted

to near biological extinction for its oil, meat, and bone.

A combination of prolonged overharvesting and certain natural characteristics of blue whales caused its decline. Their huge size made them easy to spot. They were caught in large numbers because they grouped together in their Antarctic feeding grounds. They also take 25 years to mature sexually and have only one offspring every 2–5 years. This low reproductive rate makes it difficult for the species to recover once its population falls beneath a certain threshold.

Blue whales have not been hunted commercially since 1964 and have been classified as an endangered species since 1975. Despite this protection, some marine biologists fear too few blue whales remain—an estimated 2,000–3,000 from the waters of Oregon south to Costa Rica and another 1,000 around Antarctica (Figure 18-9,

p. 453)—for the species to recover and avoid extinction. Others believe that with continued protection they will make a slow comeback.

Their extinction could also be hastened by melting polar ice (Case Study, p. 453) because of climate change. This melting reduces populations of krill, which are a main food source for blue whales (Figure 4-19, p. 78).

### Critical Thinking

Opponents of commercial whaling contend that resuming commercial whaling for some whale species such as minke, pilot, and gray could lead to illegal harvesting of blue whales. Japan contends that excess population of minkes in Antarctic waters is threatening the blue whale population by consuming much of the krill they eat (Figure 4-19, p. 78). What scientific evidence would you require to resolve this issue?

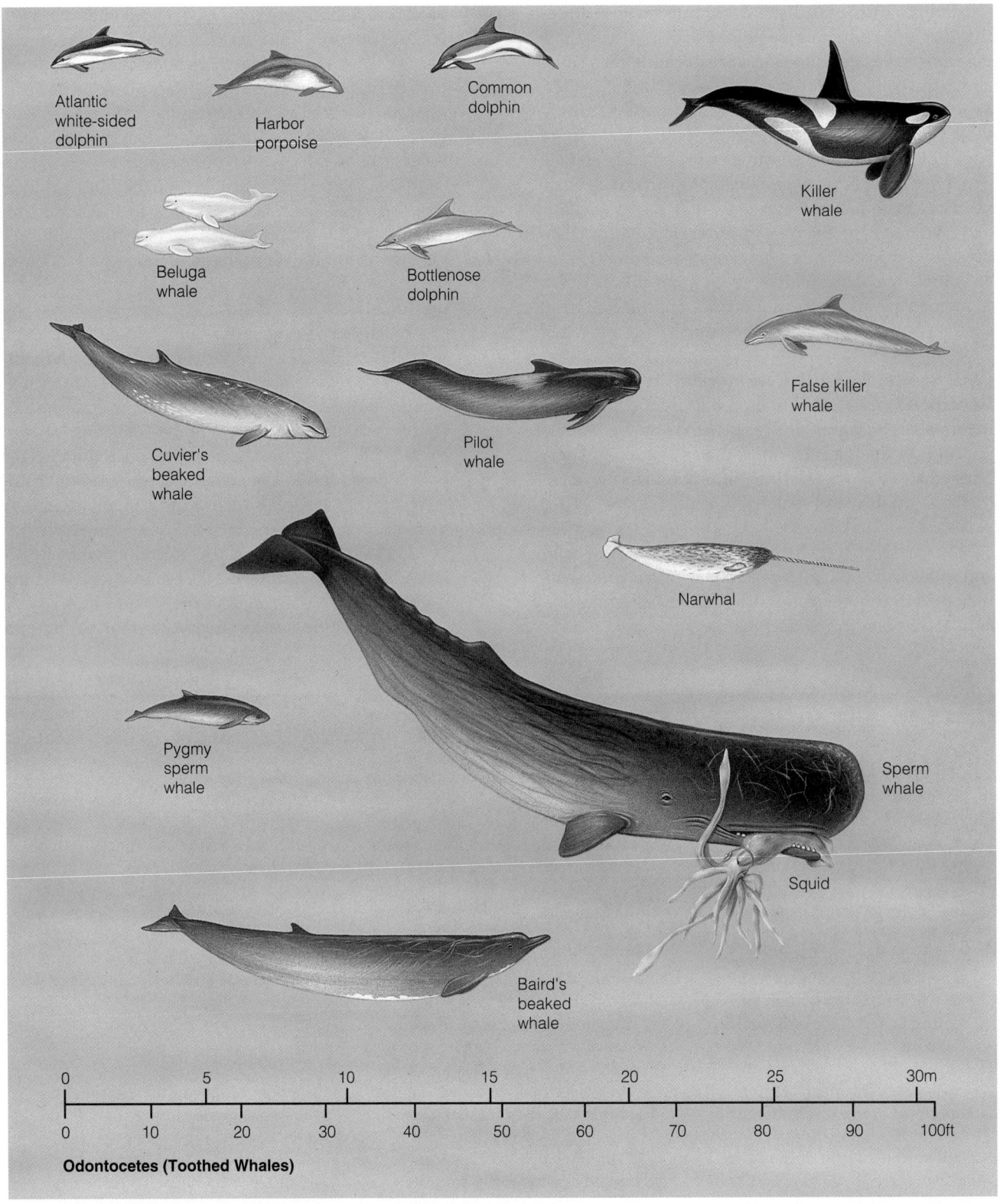

Atlantic white-sided dolphin

Harbor porpoise

Common dolphin

Killer whale

Beluga whale

Bottlenose dolphin

False killer whale

Cuvier's beaked whale

Pilot whale

Narwhal

Pygmy sperm whale

Sperm whale

Squid

Baird's beaked whale

| 0 | 5 | 10 | 15 | 20 | 25 | 30m |

| 0 | 10 | 20 | 30 | 40 | 50 | 60 | 70 | 80 | 90 | 100ft |

**Odontocetes (Toothed Whales)**

**Figure 24-10** Examples of cetaceans, which can be classified as toothed whales and baleen whales.

commercial extinction. However, IWC quotas often were based on inadequate data or ignored by whaling countries. Without any powers of enforcement, the IWC has been unable to stop the decline of most commer-

cially hunted whale species to the point at which they were commercially extinct.

In 1970, the United States stopped all commercial whaling and banned all imports of whale products.

Humpback whale

Bowhead whale

Right whale

Minke whale

Blue whale

Feeding on krill

Fin whale

Sei whale

Gray whale

**Mysticetes (Baleen Whales)**

Under intense pressure from environmentalists, the U.S. government, and governments of many non-whaling countries in the IWC, the IWC has imposed a moratorium on commercial whaling since 1986. As a result, the estimated number of whales killed commercially worldwide dropped from 42,480 in 1970 to about 1,200 in 2002. Despite the ban, IWC members Japan and Norway have continued to hunt certain whale species, and Iceland resumed hunting whales in 2002.

Japan, Norway, Iceland, Russia, and a growing number of small tropical island countries (which Japan has brought into the IWC to support its position) continue working to **(1)** overthrow the IWC ban on commercial whaling and **(2)** reverse the CITES international ban on buying and selling whale products. Unless the CITES designation is overturned, any decision by the IWC to resume some commercial whaling would be mostly useless because whaling countries would have no legal market for whale meat (which sells as a gourmet food in Japan for up to $90 per pound) and other whale products.

These and other whaling nations believe the international ban on commercial whaling of most species and the CITES ban on international trade of whale meat and products should be lifted for several reasons:

- Whaling should be allowed because it has long been a traditional part of the economies and cultures of countries such as Japan, Iceland, and Norway.

- The ban is based on emotion, not updated scientific estimates of whale populations. According to IWC estimates, the population of minke whales (which Japan and Norway continue to hunt) now numbers about 1 million (with an estimated 760,000 in Antarctic waters) and that of pilot whales about 1.4 million. They see no scientific reason for not resuming controlled hunting of these species, along with sperm, Bryde's, and gray whales (in the eastern Pacific).

- DNA testing of whale meat could be used to detect harvesting of species that are still banned.

Environmentalists disagree for several reasons:

- Some argue that whales are peaceful, intelligent, sensitive, and highly social mammals that pose no threat to humans and should be protected for ethical reasons.

- Some question the estimates of minke, Bryde's, gray, and pilot whale populations, noting the inaccuracy of past IWC estimates of whale populations.

- Most fear that opening the door to any commercial whaling may eventually lead to widespread harvests of most whale species by weakening current international disapproval and legal sanctions against commercial whaling by the IWC and CITES.

- DNA tests of all whale meat would be difficult to enforce and monitor because **(1)** much of the meat could be consumed before tests are made and illegal meat can be confiscated, and **(2)** fines would be too small to be effective.

- If the ban were lifted for some species, it would be easier to hide illegal taking of protected species. For example, recent DNA tests have uncovered the sale of whale meat from several banned species in the Japanese marketplace.

**What Is the Role of Protected Marine Sanctuaries?** Individual governments have used several international treaties, agreements, and actions to protect living marine resources in parts of the world. Here is some *good news*:

- Under the United Nations Law of the Sea, all coastal nations have **(1)** sovereignty over the waters and seabed up to 19 kilometers (12 miles) offshore and **(2)** almost total jurisdiction over their Exclusive Economic Zone (EEZ), which extends 320 kilometers (200 miles) offshore. Taken together, the nations of the world have jurisdiction over 36% of the ocean surface and 90% of the world's fish stocks.

- The United Nations Environment Programme has spearheaded efforts to develop 12 regional agreements to protect large marine areas shared by several countries.

- About 90 of the world's 350 biosphere reserves (Solutions, p. 626) include coastal or marine habitats.

- The United States has designated 12 marine sanctuaries.

- Since 1986, the World Conservation Union (also known as the IUCN) has helped establish a global system of *marine protected areas* (MPAs), mostly at the national level. The 1,300 existing MPAs help protect about 0.2% of the earth's total ocean area.

Here is some *bad news*:

- Currently, less than 0.01% of the world's ocean area consists of fully protected marine reserves. In the United States, the total area of fully protected marine habitat is only about 130 square kilometers (50 square miles).

- Most existing MPAs are too small to protect the species within them, and many globally unique marine habits are not protected.

- Many existing marine sanctuaries and MPAs allow extractive activities that are prohibited in marine reserves.

- Stresses from nearby coastal areas can disrupt marine reserves unless they are also protected as part of an integrated coastal management plan.

In 2001, the National Center for Ecological Analysis and Synthesis reported scientific studies showing that within fully protected marine reserves **(1)** fish populations double, **(2)** fish size grows by 30%, **(3)** fish reproduction triples, and **(4)** species diversity is 23% higher. Furthermore, this improvement happens within 2–4 years after protection from fishing and other exploitive activities is implemented and lasts for decades. In 1997, a group of international marine scientists called for governments to increase fully protected marine reserves to 20% of the ocean's surface by 2020.

**What Is the Role of Integrated Coastal Management?** *Integrated coastal management* is a community-based attempt to develop and use coastal resources sustainably. The overall aim is for groups competing for the use of coastal resources to **(1)** identify shared problems and goals and **(2)** agree to workable and cost-effective solutions that preserve biodiversity and environmental quality while meeting economic and social needs.

Ideally, the overall goal is to zone the land and sea portions of an entire coastal area. Such zoning would include **(1)** some protected areas where no exploitive human activities would be allowed and **(2)** other zones where different kinds and levels of human activities are permitted. Australia's huge Great Barrier Reef Marine Park is managed in this way. Currently, more than 100 integrated coastal management programs are being developed throughout the world.

In the United States,

■ Ninety coastal counties are working to establish coastal management systems, but fewer than 20 of these plans have been implemented.

■ Since the early 1980s, people have worked together with some success to develop an integrated coastal management plan for the Chesapeake Bay (Case Study, p. 500, and Figure 19-15, p. 502).

**Case Study: What Can We Do About Beach Erosion?** One problem that affects coastal marine biodiversity and the economic health of increasingly populated coastal areas is *beach erosion*. An estimated 70% of the world's beaches are eroding as a result of natural and human-related causes.

Beach erosion is a serious problem along most of the gently sloping beaches of barrier islands and mainland shores (Figure 7-12, bottom, p.151), with 30% of the U.S. shoreline experiencing significant erosion. The main cause of this problem is that the sea level has been rising gradually for the past 12,000 years or so (Figure 18-10, p. 454), mainly because the warmer climate (Figure 18-2, p. 447) since the most recent ice age has melted much ice and expanded the volume of seawater. Other causes of rising sea levels are **(1)** extracting groundwater, **(2)** redirecting rivers, **(3)** draining wetlands, and **(4)** other human activities that divert more water to the oceans. Computer models project an increase in beach erosion and flooding of coastal areas during this century (Figure 18-19, p. 463).

Engineers have tried several methods to halt or reduce beach erosion (Figure 24-11, p. 648). However, at best these attempts are only temporary solutions. The problem is that beach erosion in one place and beach buildup in another is a natural process that we can do little to control.

Many coastal zone ecologists call for banning or severely limiting the **(1)** construction of seawalls, breakwaters, groins, and jetties (essentially long groins used to protect harbors and inlets) and **(2)** movement of inlets (which can easily be closed again or moved again by storms). In the long run these approaches can cause more damage than they prevent. These analysts also favor prohibiting development on most remaining undeveloped beach areas or allowing such development only behind protective dunes (Figure 7-14, p. 152).

According to a 2000 study by the Federal Emergency Management Agency, about 25% of homes and structures within 150 meters (500 feet) of the U.S. coastline will be damaged or fall into the sea as a result of beach erosion between 2000 and 2060. Especially hard hit will be areas along the Atlantic and Gulf of Mexico coastlines, which are expected to account for 60% of nationwide losses.

Since 1965, governments, developers, and communities in the United States have spent almost $4 billion replenishing beaches that have been eroded and will continue to erode. Under present policy the government (taxpayers) usually pays 65% of the cost of beach replenishment. Some critics have called for **(1)** eliminating this federal subsidy or **(2)** reducing the government's share to no more than 35% of the costs.

A growing number of analysts also believe federal flood insurance subsidies, which greatly reduce the financial risk of building structures at the sea's edge, should be eliminated. They argue that such insurance subsidies encourage **(1)** irresponsible development, **(2)** dune destruction (Figure 7-14, p. 152), and **(3)** beach erosion on barrier beaches and islands (Figure 7-15, p. 153) that are at risk of serious damage from storms, hurricanes, and rising sea levels.

Proponents of federal flood insurance subsidies argue they are necessary to promote urban development, jobs, and economic growth in coastal areas. Opponents believe people who choose to live in risky areas should be responsible for their own insurance payments and the government should take measures such as **(1)** enacting much tougher building codes, **(2)** banning coastal and inland wetland destruction (which reduces flood protection), and **(3)** requiring endangered structures to be elevated, moved inland, or demolished and cleared away to reduce the impact of coastal storms, hurricanes, and rising sea levels on people and marine biodiversity.

**Groin**
Groins are structures that extend from the beach into the water. They help counter erosion by trapping sand from the current. Groins accumulate sand on their updrift side, but erosion is worse on the downdrift side, which is deprived of sand.

Current

**Seawall**
Seawalls protect property temporarily, but they also increase beach erosion by deflecting wave energy onto the sand in front of and beside them. High waves can wash over seawalls and destroy them and property.

**Importing sand**
Importing sand to a beach is considered the best response to erosion. The new sand often is dredged from offshore, can cost tens of millions of dollars, and can disturb aquatic biodiversity. Because it is often finer than beach sand, dredged sand erodes more quickly.

Standpipe

Pump

Discharge pipe

Drain pipe

**Drainage system**
Water rushing onto a beach soaks through the sand and into a perforated drainpipe buried parallel to the shoreline. A pump discharges the water offshore. This expensive process is still in the testing stage.

Water curtain

**Beachsaver module**
Beachsaver modules are made from concrete and a microsilica additive that resists corrosion. Placed offshore, they channel water upward to create a curtain that blocks sand loss. This approach is still in the testing stage.

Sand carried back to shore

Beachsaver module

**Figure 24-11** Building groins or seawalls and importing sand to reduce beach erosion can make matters worse or provide only an expensive temporary fix. Two new techniques for reducing beach erosion shown here—a drainage system and beachsaver modules that act as an artificial reef—are being evaluated for effectiveness and cost.

## 24-4 MANAGING AND SUSTAINING THE WORLD'S MARINE FISHERIES

**How Can We Project Populations of Marine Fisheries?** Overfishing (Figure 13-33, p. 305) is a serious threat to biodiversity in coastal waters and to some marine species in open-ocean waters. Ways to reduce overfishing include (1) developing better measurements and models for projecting fish populations and (2) controlling fishing methods and access to fisheries.

Methods used to project populations of commercially important fish include (1) *maximum sustained yield (MSY)*, (2) *optimum sustained yield (OSY)*, (3) multispecies management, (4) large marine system management, and (5) the precautionary principle.

Until recently, management of commercial fisheries has been based primarily on the maximum sustained yield (MSY). It involves using a mathematical model to project the maximum number of fish that can be harvested annually from a fish stock without driving it into decline.

However, experience has shown that the MSY concept has helped hasten the collapse of most commercially valuable stocks because

- Populations and growth rates of fish stocks are (1) difficult to measure and predict and (2) usually vary because of changes in ocean temperatures, currents, food supplies, predator–prey relationships, and other mostly unpredictable factors.

- Most fish population estimates are based on fishers reporting their catch, and they may be lying or under-reporting their take for financial gain.

- Harvesting a fishery at its estimated maximum sustainable level leaves little margin for error.

- Fishing quotas are difficult to enforce.

- Many groups managing fisheries have ignored projected MSYs for short-term political or economic reasons.

- Maximum sustainable harvesting of one species can affect the populations of other target and non-target fish species and other marine organisms.

In recent years, fishery biologists and managers have begun placing more emphasis on the *optimum sustained yield* (OSY) concept. This approach attempts to take into account interactions with other species and to provide more room for error. This approach can improve the reliability of fish stock estimates but (1) it still depends on the poorly understood biology of fish and changing ocean conditions, and (2) many bodies governing fisheries ignore OSY estimates for short-term political and economic reasons.

Another approach is *multispecies management* of a number of interacting species that takes into account their competitive and predator–prey interactions. Fishery expert Pauly Daniel of the Fisheries Centre at the University of British Columbia has developed several free computer modeling programs used by scientists in 94 countries (including major fishing nations such as Iceland and Norway). These models allow researchers to keep track of up to 2,500 interactions among as many as 50 different species or groups of species involved in a marine food web. However, such models are still in the development and testing stage and are no better than the data fed into them and the validity of the assumptions built into them.

An even more ambitious approach is to develop models for managing multispecies fisheries at the level of *large marine systems.* This approach involves developing even more complex computer models of such systems, and there are political challenges in getting groups of nations to cooperate in their planning and management. Despite the scientific and political difficulties, some limited management of several large marine systems is under way. Examples include (1) the Mediterranean Sea by 17 of the 18 nations involved, (2) the Great Barrier Reef under the exclusive control of Australia, and (3) negotiations between China and South Korea for managing the Yellow Sea.

The basic problem is the uncertainties built into using any of these approaches. As a result, many fishery scientists and environmentalists are increasingly interested in using the *precautionary principle* for managing fisheries and large marine systems to prevent harm to such systems and humans. According to this principle, where significant risk of damage to the environment and scientific evidence is inconclusive, we should take precautionary action to limit the potential risk of damage.

**Should We Use Public Management or Private Ownership to Control Access to Fisheries?** The three major approaches used to control access to fisheries in various parts of the world are (1) international and national laws, (2) community-based comanagement, and (3) *individual transfer quotas* (ITQs) (Spotlight, p. 650).

By international law, a country's offshore fishing zone extends to 370 kilometers (200 nautical miles, or 230 statute miles) from its shores. Foreign fishing vessels can take certain quotas of fish within such zones, called *exclusive economic zones,* but only with a government's permission.

Ocean areas beyond the legal jurisdiction of any country are known as the *high seas.* International maritime law and international treaties set some limits on the use of the living and mineral common-property resources in the high seas. Such laws and treaties are difficult to monitor and enforce.

## Managing Fisheries with Individual Transfer Quotas

With the ITQ system, the government gives each fishing vessel owner a specified percentage of the total allowable catch (TAC) for a fishery in a given year.

Owners are permitted to buy, sell, or lease their quotas like private property. This approach uses a limited form of private ownership of fish stocks to help prevent overfishing by reducing the number of fishers and fishing boats to more sustainable levels.

Currently, about 50 of the world's fisheries are managed by the ITQ system. Since the ITQ system was introduced in New Zealand in 1986 and in Iceland in 1990, there has been (1) some reduction in overfishing and the overall fishing fleet and (2) an end to government fishing subsidies that encourage overfishing.

However, (1) enforcement has been difficult, (2) some fishers illegally exceed their quotas, (3) the wasteful bycatch has not been reduced, and (4) in some cases, TACs have been set at levels that are too high to reduce overfishing.

Some environmentalists generally oppose this free-market environmental approach to commercial fishing or have made suggestions for its improvement. They contend that the ITQ system

- In effect transfers ownership of publicly owned fisheries to the private commercial fishers but still makes the public responsible for the costs of enforcing and managing the system. Reformers suggest that fees (not to exceed 5% of the value of the catch) should be collected from quota holders to pay for the costs of government enforcement and management of the ITQ system.

- Can squeeze out small fishing vessels and companies because they do not have the capital to buy the ITQs from others. For example, 5 years after the ITQ system was implemented in New Zealand, three companies controlled half the ITQs. To help resolve this fairness issue, reformers suggest that no fisher or fishing company should be allowed to accumulate more than 20% of the total quota of a fishery.

- Can increase poaching and sales of illegally caught fish on the black market by (1) small-scale fishers who receive no quota or too small a quota to make a living or (2) larger-scale fishers who deliberately exceed their quotas, as has happened to some degree in New Zealand. Reformers suggest that cheating can be reduced by implementing strict record keeping and having well-trained observers on every fishing vessel.

- May not reduce overall fishery stress by encouraging fishers to move elsewhere and to select only the highest quality species.

- Often sets quotas too high. To eliminate overfishing, reformers suggest that 10–50% of the estimated MSY of an ITQ fishery should be left as a buffer to protect the fishery from unexpected decline.

### Critical Thinking

Are you for or against using ITQs as the major method for managing fisheries? Explain. What are the alternatives?

---

Traditionally, many coastal fishing communities have developed allotment and enforcement systems that have sustained their fisheries, jobs, and communities for hundreds and sometimes thousands of years. However, the influx of large modern fishing boats and fleets has weakened the ability of many coastal communities to regulate and sustain local fisheries.

Many of these community management systems have been replaced by *comanagement*, in which coastal communities and the government work together to manage fisheries. In this approach, a central government typically (1) sets quotas for various species, (2) divides the quotas among different communities, and (3) may limit fishing seasons and regulate the type of fishing gear that can be used to harvest a particular species.

Each community then allocates and enforces its quota among its members based on its own rules. Often communities focus on managing inshore fisheries, and the central government manages an area's offshore fisheries. Comanagement is being used successfully in Kiribati, Japan, in Norway, and for Alaska's salmon fishery but has had mixed success in Canada, Maine, and the United Kingdom. When it works, community-based comanagement illustrates that the tragedy of the commons is not inevitable.

**How Can We Manage Fisheries to Sustain Stocks and Protect Biodiversity?** Analysts suggest the following measures for managing global fisheries more sustainably and protecting marine biodiversity:

*Fishery Regulations*

- *Set, monitor, and enforce fishery catch limits well below their estimated maximum sustained yields.*

- *Divide up fishing quotas based on fairness and inputs from local communities and fishers.*

- *Require selective gear that avoids catching unwanted or undersized fish.*

- *Improve monitoring and enforcement of fishing regulations.* Peru, Australia, and New Zealand use satellite-based systems to monitor their waters to **(1)** prevent overfishing and **(2)** keep vessels from moving into no-fishing zones or areas off limits to foreign vessels.

### Economic Approaches

- *Sharply reduce or eliminate fishing subsidies* (Connections, p. 305).

- *Impose fees for harvesting fish and shellfish from publicly owned and managed offshore waters, and use the money for government fishery management, as Australia does.*

- *Certify sustainable fisheries* (as the Marine Stewardship Council has done for six fisheries).

### Bycatch

- *Reduce bycatch levels* by **(1)** using wider-mesh nets to allow smaller species and smaller individuals of the targeted species to escape, **(2)** outfitting trawling nets with devices to exclude seabirds and sea turtles (Figure 24-9), **(3)** having observers on fishing vessels, **(4)** licensing boats to catch several species instead of only one target species, and **(5)** enacting laws that prohibit throwing edible and marketable fish back to sea (as Nambia and Norway have done).

### Protected Areas

- *Establish no-fishing marine areas, seasonal fishery closures, and marine protected areas to allow depleted fish species to recover.*

- *Start by protecting marine habitats that are in good condition or those most likely to benefit from protection instead of using limited funds to protect potentially hopeless cases.*

- *Strengthen commitment to marine biodiversity protection and integrated coastal management programs that promote both sustainable fishing and the ecological health of marine ecosystems.*

### Nonnative Invasions

- *Reduce invasions by nonnative aquatic species* by **(1)** using heat, disinfectants, or pumping in nitrogen gas (Individuals Matter, p. 580) to kill organisms in ship ballast water, **(2)** developing filters to trap the organisms when ballast water is taken into or discharged from a ship, and **(3)** requiring ships to dump their ballast water at least 320 kilometers (200 miles) from shore and replace it with deep-sea water.

### Consumer Information

- *Use labels that allow consumers to identify fish that have been harvested sustainably.* See the website material for this chapter for lists of seafood species that consumers should consider not buying and those that are safe for now, as compiled by the National Audubon Society and the Monterey Bay Aquarium.

### Aquaculture

- *Restrict location of fish farms to reduce loss of mangrove forests and other threatened coastal environments.*

- *Enact and enforce stricter pollution regulations for aquaculture operations.*

- *Increase production of herbivorous aquaculture fish species (such as carp, tilapia, and shellfish) that need little or no grain or fish meal in their diets.*

## 24-5 PROTECTING, SUSTAINING, AND RESTORING WETLANDS

**How Are Wetlands Protected in the United States?** Coastal wetlands (Figure 7-10, p. 149, and Figure 7-11, p. 150) and inland wetlands (Figure 7-25, p. 162) are important reservoirs of aquatic biodiversity that provide many important ecological and economic services.

In the United States, a federal permit is required to fill or to deposit dredged or fill material into wetlands occupying more than 1.2 hectares (3 acres). Some *good news* is that according to the U.S. Fish and Wildlife Service, this law has helped cut the average annual wetland loss by 80% since 1969.

The *bad news* is that **(1)** attempts to weaken it by using unscientific criteria to classify areas as wetlands have continued, **(2)** only about 8% of remaining inland wetlands are under federal protection, and **(3)** federal, state, and local wetland protection is weak.

The stated goal of current U.S. federal policy is zero net loss in the function and value of coastal and inland wetlands. A policy known as *mitigation banking* allows destruction of existing wetlands as long as an equal area of the same type of wetland is created or restored.

Some wetland restoration projects have been successful (Individuals Matter, p. 652). However, a 2001 study by the National Academy of Sciences found that **(1)** at least half of the attempts to create new wetlands fail to replace lost ones, **(2)** most of the created wetlands do not provide the ecological functions of natural wetlands, and **(3)** when finished, wetland creation projects often fail to meet the standards set for them and are not adequately monitored.

Wetlands are also being created to serve as sewage treatment plants (Solutions, p. 507) and to treat hog wastes, with the goal of eliminating much of the storage of such wastes in open lagoons that can pollute the air, groundwater, and nearby streams.

## Restoring a Wetland

Humans have drained, filled in, or covered over swamps, marshes, and other wetlands for centuries. They have done this to **(1)** create rice fields and other land to grow crops, **(2)** create land for urban development and highways, **(3)** reduce disease such as malaria caused by mosquitoes, and **(4)** extract minerals, oil, and natural gas.

Some have begun to question such practices as we learn more about the ecological and economic importance of coastal wetlands (p. 147) and inland wetlands (p. 160).

Can we turn back the clock to restore or rehabilitate lost marshes?

California rancher Jim Callender decided to try. In 1982, he bought 20 hectares (50 acres) of a Sacramento Valley rice field that had been a marsh until the early 1970s. To grow rice, the previous owner had destroyed the marsh by bulldozing, draining, leveling, uprooting the native plants, and spraying with chemicals to kill the snails and other food of the waterfowl.

Callender and his friends set out to restore the marshland. They **(1)** hollowed out low areas, **(2)** built up islands, **(3)** replanted tules and bulrushes, **(4)** reintroduced smartweed and other plants needed by birds, and **(5)** planted fast-growing Peking willows. After 6 years of care, hand planting, and annual seeding with a mixture of watergrass, smartweed, and rice, the marsh is once again a part of the Pacific flyway used by migratory waterfowl (Figure 22-24, p. 590).

Jim Callender and others have shown that at least part of the continent's degraded or destroyed wetlands can be reclaimed with scientific knowledge and hard work. Such restoration is useful, but to most ecologists the real challenge is to protect remaining wetlands from harm in the first place.

## How Can Wetlands Be Sustained and Restored?

Ecologists and environmentalists call for several strategies to protect and sustain existing wetlands, restore degraded ones, and create new ones. They include

- Enacting and enforcing laws to protect existing wetlands from destruction and degradation.

- Using comprehensive land-use planning to steer developers, farmers, and resource extractors away from existing wetlands.

- Using mitigation banking only as a last resort.

- Requiring creation and evaluation of a new wetland before destroying any existing wetland.

- Restoring degraded wetlands.

- Trying to prevent and control invasions of wetlands by nonnative species (Spotlight, p. 640).

Many developers, farmers, and resource extractors vigorously oppose such wetland protection. In 2002, developers were pleased when the Bush administration eased the rules for protecting wetlands.

**Case Study: Can We Restore the Florida Everglades?** South Florida's Everglades was once a 100-kilometer-wide (60-mile-wide), knee-deep sheet of water flowing slowly south from Lake Okeechobee to Florida Bay (Figure 24-12).

As this shallow body of water trickled south to Florida Bay, it created a vast network of wetlands with a variety of wildlife habitats. Today the Everglades is a haven for 56 endangered or threatened species, including the American alligator (Connections, p. 173) and the highly endangered Florida panther (see photo on p. 559).

Since 1948, much of the southward natural flow of the Everglades has been diverted and disrupted by 2,250 kilometers (1,400 miles) of canals, levees, spillways, and pumping stations. The most devastating blow came in the 1960s, when the U.S. Army Corps of Engineers transformed the meandering 103-mile-long Kissimmee River (Figure 24-12) into a straight 84-kilometer (56-mile) canal. The canal provided flood control by speeding the flow of water. However, it drained water from large wetlands north of Lake Okeechobee, which farmers turned into cow pastures.

Below Lake Okeechobee, farmers planted vast agricultural fields of sugarcane and vegetables. The runoff of phosphorus and other plant nutrients from these fields has stimulated the growth of cattails, which have **(1)** taken over and displaced saw grass, **(2)** choked waterways, and **(3)** disrupted food webs in a vast area of the Everglades. Mostly as a result of these human alterations, the natural Everglades has shrunk to half of its original size and dried out, leaving large areas vulnerable to summer wildfires.

To help preserve the lower end of the system, in 1947 the U.S. government established Everglades National Park, which contains about 20% of the remaining Everglades. However, this did not work because (as environmentalists had predicted) the massive plumbing and land development project to the north cut off much of the water flow needed to sustain the park's wildlife. As a result, **(1)** 90% of the park's wading birds have vanished, **(2)** populations of other vertebrates, from deer to turtles, are down 75–95%,

FLORIDA

Kissimmee River

Channelized (- - - - -)

Unchannelized (∿∿)

Lake Okeechobee

Fort Myers

GULF OF MEXICO

Naples

West Palm Beach

Fort Lauderdale

Miami

**Legend:**
- Agricultural area
- Treatment marsh
- Water conservation area
- Canal

Everglades National Park

ATLANTIC OCEAN

FLORIDA

Area of detail

Florida Bay

Key Largo

| 0 | 20 | 40 | 60 miles |
| 0 | 20 | 40 | 60 kilometers |

**Figure 24-12** The world's largest ecological restoration project is an attempt to undo and redo an engineering project that has been destroying Florida's Everglades and threatening water supplies for south Florida's growing population.

After more than 20 years of political haggling, in 1990 Florida's state government and the federal government agreed on the world's largest ecological restoration project. It is to be carried out by the U.S. Army Corps of Engineers between 2000 and 2038. The projected cost for this massive replumbing of south Florida is at least $7.8 billion, with the cost to be shared equally by Florida and the federal government. In 2000, Congress approved $1.4 billion for the first phase of the project, and Florida has approved contributing $2 billion between 2000 and 2010.

The project's major goals are to **(1)** restore the curving flow of more than half of the Kissimmee River, **(2)** remove 400 kilometers (250 miles) of canals and levees blocking water flow south of Lake Okeechobee, **(3)** buy 240 square kilometers (93 square miles) of farmland and allow it to flood to create artificial marshes to filter agricultural runoff before it reaches the Everglades National Park, **(4)** add land adjacent to Everglades National Park's eastern border, **(5)** create a network of artificial marshes, **(6)** create 18 large reservoirs (including drilling hundreds of holes in the briny Florida aquifer and pumping fresh water into it during the wet season and pumping it out during the dry season) to ensure an adequate water supply for south Florida's current and projected population and the lower Everglades, and **(7)** build new canals, reservoirs, and huge pumping systems to capture 80% of the water currently flowing out to sea and return it to the Everglades (Figure 24-12).

Whether this huge ecological restoration project will work depends not only on the abilities of scientists and engineers but also on prolonged support from citizens and elected state and federal officials.

Critics also point out that the project is primarily designed to provide water for urban and agricultural development with ecological restoration as a secondary goal. The top scientist at Everglades National Park warns that **(1)** the park would receive no benefits from the first 10 years and $4 billion of the scheme, and **(2)** the plan does not specify how much of the water rerouted toward south and central Florida will go to the parched park instead of to increased industrial, agricultural, and urban development.

The need to make expensive efforts to undo some of the damage to the Everglades caused by 120 years of agricultural and urban development is another example of a fundamental lesson from nature: Prevention is the cheapest and best way to go.

and **(3)** the Everglades has become the country's most endangered national park.

Large volumes of fresh water that once flowed through the park into Florida Bay have been diverted for crops and cities, causing the bay to become saltier and warmer. This and increased nutrient input from crop fields and cities have stimulated the growth of large algae blooms in the bay. This large-scale cultural eutrophication (Figure 19-7, p. 491) threatens the coral reefs and the diving and fishing industries of the Florida Keys.

By the 1970s, state and federal officials recognized that this huge plumbing project threatens **(1)** wildlife (a major source of tourism income for Florida) and **(2)** the water supply for the 6 million residents of south Florida and the 6 million more people projected to be living there by 2050.

## Protecting Lake Baikal

Lake Baikal in southern Siberia is the world's oldest and deepest lake and contains the world's largest volume of fresh water.

The lake is famous for its breathtaking scenery and its biodiversity. It contains about 1,500 species of plants and animals, 1,200 of them not found anywhere else on the earth (compared to only 4 such endemic species in Lake Superior). The lake's huge watershed consists almost entirely of boreal forest or taiga (Figure 6-40, p. 140).

By global standards, most of Lake Baikal's waters are still clean. However, its purity and biodiversity are threatened by **(1)** extensive logging of some of its surrounding coniferous forests, which has led to soil erosion and landslides, **(2)** acid deposition from nearby industrial centers, and **(3)** serious air and water pollution from more than 100 factories on the lake's shores.

The most notorious source of pollution is a large pulp and paper mill at Baykalsk on the lake's southern shore. Since it opened in 1966, the plant has been emitting large quantities of air and water pollutants, especially chlorinated hydrocarbon compounds such as dioxins and PCBs, which can be biologically

magnified in food webs (Figure 19-6, p. 490). Since the plant opened in 1966, Russian environmentalists have tried without success to have the plant modernized or converted to a nonpolluting industry.

Because of its biological uniqueness, protecting the lake is a global concern. In 1996, the United Nations Educational, Scientific and Cultural Organization (UNESCO) added Lake Baikal to its World Heritage list as an international treasure. UNESCO recommended that the Russian government **(1)** enact a law to convert Lake Baikal into a protected ecological zone, **(2)** convert the Baykalsk pulp and paper plant to a nonpolluting industry, **(3)** cease logging in the lake's water basin, and **(4)** improve environmental monitoring of the lake.

By 2002, the Russian government had not put any of these recommendations into effect. Currently, Russian environmentalists are trying to protect Lake Baikal by **(1)** bringing court action to force the Baykalsk plant owners to pay for cleaning up environmental damage they inflict, as required under Russian law, **(2)** exerting international pressure on the government by pressuring UNESCO to place Lake Baikal on its list of *endangered* World Heritage Sites, and **(3)** asking the United States and

other developed countries and international environmental organizations to help fund improved environmental monitoring and conversion of the Baykalsk pulp and paper plant to an environmentally safe form of production (at an estimated cost of $100 million).

The plant's 3,000 workers and many people living in nearby Baykalsk, a town of 17,000 near the pulp and paper plant, fear for their jobs, with little opportunity for other work in Russia's troubled economy. Opponents of forcing the plant to modernize contend that **(1)** environmentalists have exaggerated the pollution of Lake Baikal, **(2)** the lake is so vast that the pollution from the plant poses no threat to its biodiversity, and **(3)** a 1998 joint study by Russian and British scientists found no evidence that pollution is harming the lake's biodiversity.

### Critical Thinking

**1.** Should the United States and other developed countries and international environmental organizations provide funds to help protect Lake Baikal? Explain.

**2.** Use the library and the Internet to find information about the latest developments in efforts to protect Lake Baikal.

## 24-6 PROTECTING, SUSTAINING, AND RESTORING LAKES AND RIVERS

**What Are the Greatest Environmental Threats to Lakes?** The major threats to the ecological functioning and biodiversity of lakes are **(1)** pollution, especially from cultural eutrophication (Figure 19-7, p. 491) and toxic wastes (Figure 19-9, p. 493), **(2)** invasion by nonnative species, and **(3)** dropping water levels by diversion of water for irrigation (Case Study, p. 324). Siberia's Lake Baikal, one of the world's largest and most biologically diverse lakes, is under threat mostly from pollution caused by increased forestry and industrial plants around its shores (Case Study, above).

In many cases, cultural eutrophication of lakes can be reversed by reducing the input of plant nutrients (nitrates and phosphates) through **(1)** better sewage treatment or **(2)** diverting polluted water into less sen-

sitive areas. Lake Washington in the Seattle, Washington, metropolitan area is a success story of recovery from severe cultural eutrophication caused by decades of sewage inputs.

Recovery took place within about 4 years after the sewage was diverted into Puget Sound. This worked for three reasons: **(1)** A large body of water (Puget Sound) with a rapid rate of exchange with the Pacific Ocean was available to receive and dilute the sewage wastes, **(2)** the lake had not yet filled with weeds and sediment because of its large size and depth, and **(3)** preventive corrective action was taken before the lake had become a shallow, highly eutrophic lake (Figure 7-21, right, p. 158). Today, the lake's water quality is good, but there is concern about increased urban runoff caused by the area's rapidly growing population.

Since 1972, cultural eutrophication and inputs of toxic chemicals into the Great Lakes have been significantly reduced by an ongoing joint program carried out by the United States and Canada (Case Study, p. 491, and Figure 19-8, p. 492).

**Case Study: Nonnative Invaders in the Great Lakes** Since the 1920s, the Great Lakes have been invaded by at least 145 nonnative species including the sea lamprey, zebra mussel, quagga mussel, round goby, Eurasian ruffe, and hydrilla Figure 22-17, p. 576). In 1986, larvae of the *zebra mussel* (Figure 22-17, p. 576), a nonnative species, arrived in ballast water discharged from a European ship near Detroit, Michigan. The rapidly reproducing mussel, a native of eastern Europe and western Asia, disperses widely, mostly **(1)** through canals, **(2)** in ship ballast water, and **(3)** on the bottoms of recreational boats.

The *bad news* is that with no known natural enemies, these thumbnail-sized mussels have **(1)** displaced other mussel species, **(2)** depleted the food supply for other Great Lakes species, **(3)** clogged irrigation pipes, **(4)** shut down water intake systems for power plants and city water supplies, **(5)** fouled beaches, **(6)** grown in huge masses on boat hulls, piers, pipes, rocks, and almost any exposed aquatic surface, and **(7)** have cost the Great Lakes basin at least $700 million per year. The zebra mussel has spread and is dramatically altering freshwater communities in parts of southern Canada and 18 states in the United States (Figure 24-13).

**Figure 24-13** Since 1986, the nonnative *zebra mussel* has established rapidly growing populations in southern Canada and 18 states in the United States. (Data from U.S. Department of Interior)

In 2001, scientists at Purdue University Calumet in north Indiana reported on the use of an oscillating dipole apparatus to produce what is popularly known as a "zebra mussel death ray." It produces extremely low frequency electromagnetic waves that can kill zebra mussels, apparently without harming the environment or other species. This approach is being evaluated.

However, zebra mussels may be *good news* for a number of aquatic plants. By consuming algae and other microorganisms, the mussels increase water clarity, which permits deeper penetration of sunlight and more photosynthesis. This allows some native plants to thrive and return the plant composition of Lake Erie (and presumably other lakes) closer to what it was 100 years ago. Because the plants provide food and increase dissolved oxygen, their comeback may benefit certain aquatic animals (including the mussels).

There is more *bad news*, however. In 1991, a larger and potentially more destructive species, the *quagga mussel*, invaded the Great Lakes, probably discharged in the ballast water of a Russian freighter. It can survive at greater depths and tolerate more extreme temperatures than the zebra mussel. There is concern that it may eventually colonize areas such as the Chesapeake Bay and waterways in parts of Florida.

By 1999, a European fish, the *round goby*, had invaded all of the Great Lakes. The *good news* is that these tiny predators have a voracious appetite for zebra mussels. The *bad news* is that these bottom-dwelling fish also devour eggs and the young of any fish sharing their habitat. This includes prized recreational fish such as perch, walleye, and smallmouth bass.

A related problem is that zebra mussels pick up and store toxic pollutants from the water. Mussel-eating gobies can then pass these pollutants on to fish preying on the gobies. This process can transfer the poisons further up the food web and contaminate fish that people eat.

Another recent invader from Europe's Black, Caspian, and Azov Seas is the *Eurasian ruffe* (Figure 22-17, p. 576). This small bottom-feeding fish preys on bottom insects, perch and trout eggs, and young fish. Because it reproduces rapidly, it overwhelms native populations.

In 2000, biologist John Maden warned that the *hydrilla* (Figure 22-17, p. 576), an alien plant species that has invaded waterways in Florida and Connecticut, could soon invade the Great Lakes. This thick weed can form a carpet over water surfaces at the rate of 2.4 centimeters (1 inch) per day. Its spread in the Great Lakes could disrupt biodiversity and cause navigation, flood control, and hydroelectric problems.

Some scientists warn that nonnative microorganisms in ship ballast water pose a greater danger than bigger invading species such as mussels and fish. Each liter of ballast carries billions of nonnative viruses and bacteria, including some disease-causing bacterial strains of cholera.

## What Are the Greatest Environmental Threats to Rivers?
Although rivers and streams contain only about 1.3% of the world's nonfrozen fresh water, they provide important ecological services (Figure 14-10, p. 319). Major threats to the ecological services and the biodiversity of rivers are (1) pollution (Figure 19-5, p. 488), (2) disruption of water flows and species composition by dams (Figure 14-9, p. 319), channelization (Figure 14-22, middle, p. 332), (3) the diversion of water from rivers for irrigation and urban areas, and (4) overfishing.

## Case Study: Managing the Columbia River Basin for People and Salmon
The Columbia River, flowing 1,900 kilometers (1,200 miles) through the Pacific Northwest, receives water from a huge basin extending across parts of seven U.S. states and two Canadian provinces (Figure 24-14).

This basin has the world's largest hydroelectric power system, consisting of more than 119 dams, 19 of them large hydroelectric dams. Most of these dams were built fairly cheaply by the U.S. government in the 1930s to (1) furnish jobs, (2) produce cheap electricity (40% below the national average), (3) provide flood control, and (4) help stimulate industrial and agricultural development. The river and its reservoirs are also used for recreation (such as swimming, boating, and windsurfing) and for sport and commercial fishing for salmon, steelhead trout, and other fish.

**Figure 24-14** The Columbia River basin. (Data from Northwest Power Planning Council)

Since the dams were built, the Columbia River's migratory wild Pacific salmon population has dropped by 94%. Nine Pacific Northwest salmon species are listed as endangered or threatened under the Endangered Species Act. Major causes of this decline include (1) dams and reservoirs that hinder or prevent salmon migration during their life cycles (Figure 13-34, left, p. 306), (2) overfishing of salmon in the Pacific Ocean, (3) destruction of salmon spawning grounds in streams by sediment from logging and mining, and (4) withdrawals of water for irrigation and other human uses.

Commercial fishing operations have modified the salmon's natural cycle by using *salmon ranching*, in which salmon eggs and young are raised in a hatchery and then released (Figure 13-34, right, p. 306). However, hatchery-raised salmon can cause problems: (1) their close quarters permit rapid spread of diseases, (2) because of their genetic uniformity, they are more susceptible to diseases and environmental stress after release, and (3) ranch salmon that interbreed with wild ones reduce the genetic diversity of the wild fish and their ability to survive.

In 1980, the U.S. Congress passed the Northwest Power Act. Its main goals were to (1) develop and implement long-range plans to meet the region's electricity needs and (2) rebuild wild and hatchery-raised salmon and other fish populations. The Northwest Power Planning Council (NPPC), which combines federal and state authority, administers this act.

The NPPC began experimenting with ways to restore the Columbia River's wild salmon runs by (1) building hatcheries upstream of the dams and releasing juveniles from these hatcheries to underpopulated streams (so they will return to them as adults to reproduce), (2) building fish ladders to enable some of the adult salmon to bypass dams during their upstream migration, (3) using trucks and barges to transport juvenile wild salmon around dams, (4) turning off dam turbines to allow juveniles to swim safely over dams during periods of heavy downstream migration, (5) releasing extra water from dams to help wash juvenile salmon downstream at a faster rate closer to their natural migration rate, (6) putting more than 64,000 kilometers (40,000 miles) of stream off limits for hydropower development, and (7) obliterating old logging roads and reducing the runoff of silt from existing dirt logging roads above salmon spawning streams.

Environmentalists, Native American tribes, and commercial salmon fishers want the government to remove four small hydroelectric dams on the lower Snake River in Washington to restore salmon spawning habitat. However, farmers, barge operators, and aluminum workers oppose doing this. They argue that removing the dams would devastate local economies by (1) reducing the supply of irrigation water, (2) eliminating cheap transportation of commodities by ship in the affected areas, and (3) reducing the supply of cheap electricity for industries and consumers.

In 2000, the federal government decided against any dam removal for the Columbia River basin. Instead it proposed spending $1 billion to protect salmon by (1) restoring streamside habitat and water quality in rivers and streams in which salmon spawn, (2) releasing more water from Idaho reservoirs to help young salmon migrate to the ocean, (3) limiting salmon harvests for 10 years while maintaining tribal fishing rights, and (4) expanding hatcheries designed specifically to rebuild wild salmon populations.

Will this wild salmon restoration project work? No one knows because it will take decades to see whether the salmon populations can be rebuilt. Despite problems, this program demonstrates that people with diverse and often conflicting economic, political, and environmental interests can work together to (1) try new ideas and (2) develop potentially sustainable solutions to complex resource management issues.

Critics of this expensive salmon restoration program argue that (1) populations of wild salmon are stable in Alaska, so we should not care that wild salmon are declining in the Pacific Northwest, and (2) the economic costs to the hydroelectric power, shipping, and timber industries and to farmers and consumers exceed the value of saving the salmon. What do you think?

**How Can Freshwater Fisheries Be Managed and Sustained?** Managing freshwater fish involves encouraging populations of commercial and sport fish species and reducing or eliminating populations of less desirable species. Ways to do this include regulating (1) the time and length of fishing seasons and (2) the number and size of fish that can be taken.

Other techniques include (1) building reservoirs and farm ponds and stocking them with fish, (2) fertilizing nutrient-poor lakes and ponds, (3) protecting and creating spawning sites, (4) protecting habitats from sediment buildup and other forms of pollution, (5) removing debris, (6) preventing excessive growth of aquatic plants from cultural eutrophication (Figure 19-7, p. 491), and (7) building small dams to control water flow.

Predators, parasites, and diseases can be controlled by (1) improving habitats, (2) breeding genetically resistant fish varieties, and (3) using antibiotics and disinfectants judiciously. Hatcheries can be used to restock ponds, lakes, and streams with prized species such as trout and salmon, and entire river basins can be managed to protect such valued species as salmon (Figure 13-34, p. 306).

**How Can Wild and Scenic Rivers Be Protected and Restored?** In 1968, the U.S. Congress passed the National Wild and Scenic Rivers Act. It established the National Wild and Scenic Rivers System to protect rivers and river segments with outstanding scenic, recreational, geological, wildlife, historical, or cultural values.

These waterways are to be kept free of development and cannot be widened, straightened, dredged, filled, or dammed along the designated lengths. The only activities allowed are camping, swimming, non-motorized boating, sport hunting, and sport and commercial fishing. New mining claims are permitted in some areas, however.

Currently, only 0.2% of the country's 6 million kilometers (3.5 million miles) of waterways along some 150 stretches are protected by the Wild and Scenic Rivers System. In contrast, dams and reservoirs are found on 17% of the country's total river length.

Environmentalists urge Congress to add 1,500 additional river segments to the system, a goal vigorously opposed by some local communities and anti-environmental groups. Achieving this goal would protect about 2% of the country's river systems. There is also a need to focus on improving the condition of the country's most endangered rivers.

In this chapter, we have seen that threats to marine biodiversity are real and growing and are even greater than threats to terrestrial biodiversity (Chapters 22 and 23). Keys to sustaining life in the waters that occupy 71% of the earth's surface include (1) increasing research to learn more about aquatic life, (2) greatly expanding efforts to protect and restore aquatic biodiversity, and (3) promoting integrated ecological management of connected terrestrial and aquatic systems.

*To promote conservation, fishers and officials need to view fish as a part of a larger ecological system, rather than simply as a commodity to extract.*
ANNE PLATT McGINN

## REVIEW QUESTIONS

1. Define the boldfaced terms in this chapter.

2. Describe the ecological and economic problems of Africa's Lake Victoria, and list two ways to reduce these threats.

3. What are the three most biologically diverse habitats found in the world's oceans?

4. List six general patterns of marine biodiversity.

5. List the major human impacts on aquatic biodiversity in terms of (a) species loss and endangerment, (b) marine habitat loss and degradation, (c) freshwater habitat loss and degradation, (d) overfishing, (e) nonnative species, and (f) pollution and global warming.

**6.** Explain how most commercial marine fishing can be viewed as an example of the tragedy of the commons.

**7.** Describe the threat to wetlands from invasion by purple loosestrife.

**8.** List five factors that make it difficult to protect marine biodiversity.

**9.** List five major ways to protect and sustain marine biodiversity.

**10.** List four threats to marine sea turtles.

**11.** Distinguish between *toothed whales* and *baleen whales*. Explain how commercial whaling has been an example of the tragedy of the commons, and list the pros and cons of resuming commercial whaling.

**12.** Describe factors leading to the near extinction of the blue whale.

**13.** List five examples of marine sanctuaries and four limitations of the current international program to establish *marine protected areas.*

**14.** List the advantages and difficulties of *integrated coastal management.*

**15.** Describe methods used to reduce beach erosion, and explain why they usually fail.

**16.** List the pros and cons of federal flood insurance and beach replenishment subsidies in the United States.

**17.** Describe the strengths and weaknesses of projecting fish populations using **(a)** maximum sustained yield (MSY), **(b)** optimum sustained yield (OSY), **(c)** multispecies management, **(d)** large marine system management, and **(e)** the precautionary principle.

**18.** List the advantages and disadvantages of limiting access to marine fisheries by **(a)** international and national laws, **(b)** community-based comanagement, and **(c)** individual transfer quotients (ITQs).

**19.** List ways to prevent overfishing and protect marine biodiversity by **(a)** enacting fishery regulations, **(b)** using economic approaches, **(c)** reducing bycatch, **(d)** setting aside protected areas, **(e)** dealing with nonnative invasions, **(f)** providing consumer information, and **(g)** controlling aquaculture.

**20.** List the pros and cons of the current wetland protection policy in the United States.

**21.** Describe six ways to sustain and restore wetlands.

**22.** Describe the ecological and water supply problems of south Florida's Everglades, and describe efforts to deal with these problems.

**23.** List the three greatest environmental threats to lakes. Describe the recovery of Washington state's Lake Washington.

**24.** Describe the biological importance of Siberia's Lake Baikal and the problems that threaten this lake's biodiversity.

**25.** Describe the threats to the Great Lakes from invasions by nonnative species.

**26.** List four major threats to the world's streams and rivers.

**27.** Describe efforts to manage the Pacific Northwest's Columbia River for people and wild salmon.

**28.** Describe the National Wild and Scenic Rivers System in the United States.

## CRITICAL THINKING

**1.** What three actions would you take to deal with the ecological and economic problems of Africa's Lake Victoria?

**2.** Why is marine biodiversity higher **(a)** near coasts than in the open sea, **(b)** on the ocean's bottom than at its surface, and **(c)** in the open ocean waters of the tropics than in the open waters of the North Pole?

**3.** Why is it more difficult to identify and protect endangered marine species than to protect such species on land?

**4.** Should commercial whaling of selected species with fairly high population levels be resumed? Explain. How would you establish, monitor, and enforce annual commercial whaling quotas?

**5.** Are you for or against federal subsidies in the United States (or the country where you live) for **(a)** beach replenishment and **(b)** flood insurance? Explain.

**6.** List five methods for using the precautionary principle as a way to manage marine fisheries and help protect marine biodiversity.

**7.** Should fishers harvesting fish from a country's publicly owned waters be required to pay the government (taxpayers) fees for the fish they catch? Explain. If your livelihood depended on commercial fishing, would you be for or against such fees?

**8.** Are you for or against using *mitigation banking* to help sustain wetlands? Explain.

**9.** Congratulations! You are in charge of protecting the world's aquatic biodiversity. List the three most important points of your policy to accomplish this goal.

## PROJECTS

**1.** Survey the condition of a nearby wetland, coastal area, river, or stream. Has its condition improved or deteriorated during the last 10 years? What local, state, or national efforts are being used to protect this aquatic system? Develop a plan for protecting this system.

**2.** Use the library or the Internet to find bibliographic information about *G. Carleton Ray* and *Anne Platt McGinn*, whose quotes appear at the beginning and end of this chapter.

**3.** Make a concept map of this chapter's major ideas, using the section heads and subheads and the key terms (in boldface). Look on the website for this book about how to prepare concept maps.

## INTERNET STUDY RESOURCES AND RESOURCES FOR FURTHER READING AND RESEARCH

The website for this book contains helpful study aids and many ideas for further reading and research. Log on to

www.info.brookscole.com/miller13

and click on the Chapter-by-Chapter area. Choose Chapter 24 and select a resource:

- Flash Cards allows you to test your mastery of the Terms and Concepts to Remember for this chapter.

- Tutorial Quizzes provides a multiple-choice practice quiz.

- Student Guide to InfoTrac will lead you to Critical Thinking Projects that use InfoTrac College Edition as a research tool.

- References lists the major books and articles consulted in writing this chapter.

- Hypercontents takes you to an extensive list of sites with news, research, and images related to individual sections of the chapter.

## INFOTRAC COLLEGE EDITION

Improve your skills with InfoTrac College Edition, a searchable online database of articles from more than 700 periodicals. Log on to

http://www.infotrac-college.com

or access InfoTrac through the website for this book. Try to find the following articles:

**1.** Coles, S. L., and L. G. Eldredge. 2002. Nonindigenous species introductions on coral reefs: A need for information. *Pacific Science* 56: 191. *Keywords:* "nonindigenous species" and "coral reefs." The impacts of exotic species are gaining needed exposure, but most of the exposure is on land-based and freshwater ecosystems. This article looks at an ecosystem that has yet to be adequately studied for the impacts of exotic species: coal reefs.

**2.** Dunn, S., R. Friedman, and S. Baish. 2000. Coastal erosion. *Environment* 42: 36. *Keyword:* "coastal erosion." Building a beachfront house is becoming less appealing as erosion of the U.S. coastline begins to have greater economic and environmental impact.

# 25 SUSTAINABLE CITIES: URBAN LAND USE AND MANAGEMENT

## The Ecocity Concept in Davis, California

Few of today's cities are sustainable. They depend on distant sources for their food, water, energy, and materials, and their massive use of resources damages nearby and distant air, water, soil, and wildlife.

Environmental and urban designers envision the development of more sustainable cities, called *ecocities* or *green cities*. The ecocity is not a futuristic dream. The citizens and elected officials of Davis, California, a city of about 54,000 people about 130 kilometers (80 miles) northeast of San Francisco, committed themselves in the early 1970s to making their city more ecologically sustainable.

Davis's Village Homes, America's first solar neighborhood, was developed in the 1970s by Michael and Judy Corbett (Figure 25-1). It has 220 passive solar and energy-efficient houses facing into a common open space reserved for people and bicycles. There are more walking and bicycle paths than roads. Cars are parked around the back on narrow tree-lined streets that provide shade and natural cooling.

The abundant open space has community **(1)** orchards, **(2)** vineyards, **(3)** organic gardens (with some of the vegetables sold to help finance upkeep of the community's open space), **(4)** playgrounds and playing fields, **(5)** natural surface drainage by vegetation-covered swales (instead of costly underground concrete drains) that allow water to soak in and are used as walking and bike paths, and **(6)** a solar-heated community center used for day care, meetings, and

**Figure 25-1** Passive solar home in Village Homes in Davis, California, a neighborhood of 240 passive solar houses that face into a common open space. This community, developed in the 1970s and completed in 1982, is an experiment in urban sustainability. Direct solar gain provides 50–75% of the heating needs in winter. In the hot summers, most residents rarely need air conditioning because carefully sited trees shade the houses and narrow streets.

social gatherings. The development uses xeriscaping (Figure 14-21, p. 332) to cultivate drought-resistant plants to reduce water use. Even though it was built in the 1970s, Village Homes is still one of the city's most desirable subdivisions.

In Davis, where peak temperatures can reach 45°C (113°F), building codes encourage the use of solar energy for water and space heating, and all new homes must meet high energy-efficiency standards. Since 1975, the city has cut its use of energy for heating and cooling in half. It has a solar power plant and has plans to generate all its own electricity using renewable energy.

The city discourages the use of automobiles and encourages the use of bicycles by **(1)** closing some streets to automobiles, **(2)** having bike lanes on major streets, and **(3)** building a network of bicycle paths. As a result, bicycles account for 40% of all in-city transportation, and less land is needed for parking spaces. The city's warm climate and flat terrain aid this heavy dependence on the bicycle.

Davis limits the type and rate of its growth, and it maintains a mix of homes for people with low, medium, and high incomes. City officials restrict development of the fertile farmland surrounding the city for residential or commercial use. The city also limits the size of shopping centers to encourage smaller neighborhood shopping centers, each easily reached by foot or bicycle.

Between 2000 and 2100, the percentage of people living in the world's urban areas is expected to increase from 47% to 80–90%. An exciting challenge for the 21st century will be to reshape existing cities and design new ones like Davis that are more livable and sustainable and have a lower environmental impact.

*The test of the quality of life in an advanced economic society is now largely in the quality of urban life. Romance may still belong to the countryside—but the present reality of life abides in the city.*

JOHN KENNETH GALBRAITH

This chapter addresses the following questions:

- How is the world's population distributed between rural and urban areas, and what factors determine how urban areas develop?

- What are the major resource and environmental problems of urban areas?

- How do transportation systems shape urban areas and growth, and what are the pros and cons of various forms of transportation?

- What methods are used for planning and controlling urban growth?

- How can cities be made more sustainable and more desirable places to live?

## 25-1 URBANIZATION AND URBAN GROWTH

**What Are Urban and Rural Areas?**  For more than 6,000 years, cities have been centers of commerce, education, technological developments, culture, social change, vitality, progress, and political power. They have also suffered from crowding, pollution, disease, poverty, and human misery.

An **urban**, or **metropolitan, area** often is defined as a town or city plus its adjacent suburban fringes with a population of more than 2,500 people (although some countries set the minimum at 10,000–50,000 residents). A **rural area** usually is defined as an area with a population of less than 2,500 people.

A **village** consists of a group of rural households linked together by custom, culture, and family ties, usually surviving by harvesting local natural resources for food, fuel, and other basic needs. By contrast, a **city** is a much larger group of people with a variety of specialized occupations who depend on a flow of resources from other areas to meet most of their needs and wants.

**What Causes Urban Growth?**  A country's **degree of urbanization** is the percentage of its population living in an urban area. **Urban growth** is the rate of increase of urban populations.

Urban areas grow in two ways: **(1)** *natural increase* (more births than deaths) and **(2)** *immigration* (mostly

from rural areas) caused by a combination of *push factors* that force people out of rural areas and *pull factors* that draw them into the city.

People can be *pushed* from rural areas into urban areas by factors such as **(1)** poverty, **(2)** lack of land, **(3)** declining agricultural jobs (because of increased use of mechanized agriculture or government policies that set food prices for urban dwellers so low that rural farmers find it uneconomical to grow crops), **(4)** famine, and **(5)** war.

Rural people are *pulled* to urban areas in search of jobs, food, housing, a better life, entertainment, and freedom. Many are also seeking an escape from social constraints of village cultural life and from religious, racial, and political conflicts. Urban growth in developing countries also is fueled by government policies that **(1)** distribute most income and social services to urban dwellers (especially in capital cities, where a country's leaders live) and **(2)** provide lower-priced food than in rural areas.

**What Patterns of Urbanization and Urban Growth Are Occurring Throughout the World?**  Five trends are important in understanding the problems and challenges of urban growth:

- *The proportion of the global population living in urban areas is increasing.* Between 1850 and 2002, the percentage of people living in urban areas increased from 2% to 47% (Figure 25-2, p. 662). Each day about 160,00 people are added to the world's urban areas. If UN projections are correct, by 2050 about 63% of the world's people will be living in urban areas, with 90% of this urban growth occurring in developing countries (Figure 25-3, p. 662).

- *The number of large cities is mushrooming.* In 1900, only 19 cities had a million or more people, and more than 95% of humanity lived in rural communities. In 2002, **(1)** more than 400 cities had a million or more people (projected to increase to 564 by 2015), and **(2)** there were 19 *megacities* (up from 8 in 1985) with 10 million or more people and **(3)** most of them were in developing countries (Figure 25-2). With 27.7 million people, Tokyo's population approaches that of the 31 million people living in Canada, and Mexico City's population of 18 million nearly equals that of Australia.

- *Urbanization and the urban population are increasing rapidly in developing countries* (Figure 25-3, p. 662). Currently, about 40% of the people in developing countries live in urban areas. However, 79% of the people in South America live in cities, mostly along the coasts (Figure 25-2). By 2025, analysts expect urbanization in developing countries to increase to at least 54%, with

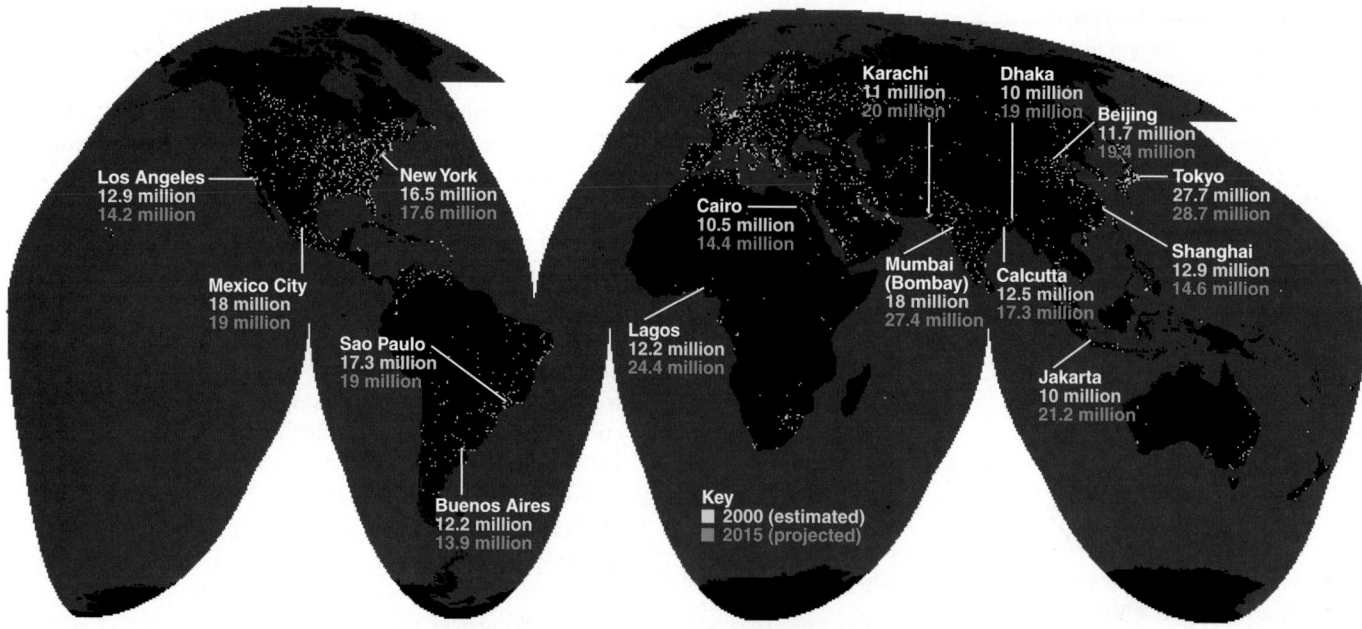

**Figure 25-2** Major urban areas throughout the world based on satellite images of the earth at night that show city lights. Currently, the 47% of the world's people living in urban areas occupy about 2% of the earth's land area. Note that **(1)** most of the world's urban areas are found along the coasts of continents, and **(2)** most of Africa and much of the interior of South America, Asia, and Australia is dark at night. This figure also shows the populations of 16 of the world's *megacities* with 10 or more million people in 2000 and their projected populations in 2015. (National Geophysics Data Center, National Oceanic and Atmospheric Administration, and United Nations)

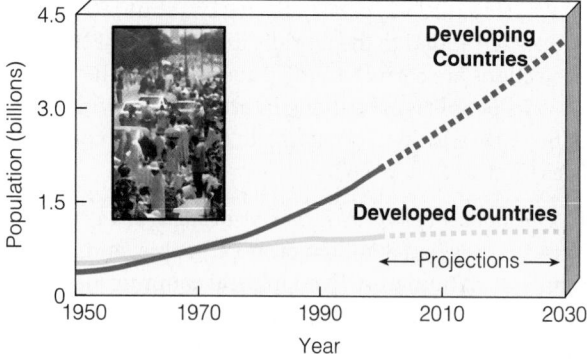

**Figure 25-3** Urban population in developed and developing countries, 1950–2000, with projections to 2030. (United Nations Population Division)

the most rapid urban growth expected to take place in Africa and Asia. Many of these cities will be water short, waste filled, and choked with pollution.

■ *Urban growth is much slower in developed countries* (with 75% urbanization) *than in developing countries* (Figure 25-3). Still, developed countries are projected to reach 84% urbanization by 2025.

■ *Poverty is becoming increasingly urbanized as more poor people migrate from rural to urban areas.* The United Nations estimates that at least 1 billion people live in crowded **(1)** *slums* (tenements and rooming houses where 3–6 people live in a single room) of central cities and **(2)** *squatter settlements* and *shantytowns* (where people build shacks from scavenged building materials) that surround the outskirts of most cities in developing countries (Spotlight, p. 663).

**Case Study: Mexico City** About 18.0 million people—about one of every five Mexicans—live in Mexico City, the world's second most populous city (after Tokyo) (Figure 25-4).

Mexico City suffers from **(1)** severe air pollution, **(2)** high unemployment (close to 50%), **(3)** deafening noise, and **(4)** a soaring crime rate. More than one-third of its residents live in crowded slums (called *barrios*) or squatter settlements, without running water or electricity.

At least 8 million people have no sewer facilities. This means huge amounts of human waste are deposited in gutters and vacant lots every day, attracting armies of rats and swarms of flies. When the winds pick up dried excrement, a *fecal snow* often falls on

## The Urban Poor

Squatter settlements and shantytowns in developing countries usually lack clean water supplies, sewers, electricity, and roads. Often the land on which they are built is not suitable for human habitation because **(1)** they experience severe air and water pollution and hazardous wastes from nearby factories or **(2)** the land is especially subject to landslides, flooding, earthquakes, or volcanic eruptions.

Half of all urban children under age 15 in developing countries live in conditions of extreme poverty, and about one-fifth of them are street children with little or no family support. In Cairo, Egypt, children of kindergarten age can be found digging through clods of ox dung, looking for undigested kernels of corn to eat.

Many cities do not provide squatter settlements and shantytowns with drinking water, sanitation facilities, electricity, food, health care, housing, schools, or jobs. These cities lack the needed money, and their officials fear that improving services will attract even more of the rural poor.

Many city governments regularly bulldoze squatter shacks and send police to drive the illegal settlers out. The people then move back in or develop another shantytown somewhere else.

Despite joblessness, squalor, overcrowding, environmental hazards, and rampant disease, most squatter and slum residents are better off than the rural poor. With better access to family planning programs, they tend to have fewer children, who have better access to schools. Most residents are adaptable and resilient and have hope for a better future. Many squatter settlements provide a sense of community and a vital safety net of neighbors, friends, and relatives for the poor.

### Critical Thinking

Should squatters around cities of developing countries be given title to land they do not own? Explain. What are the alternatives?

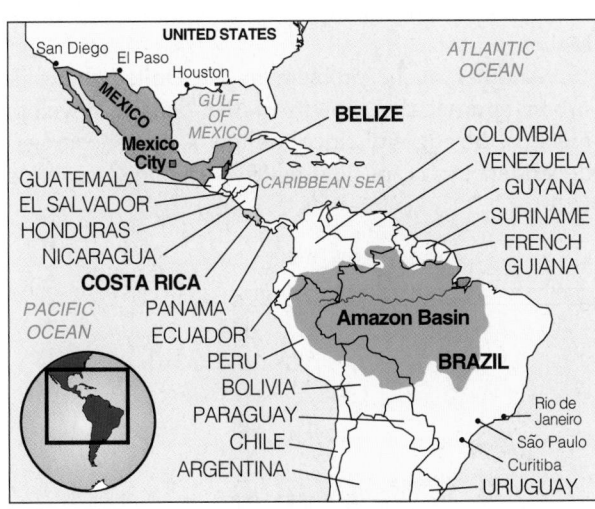

**Figure 25-4** The locations of Mexico, Brazil, Belize, and Costa Rica. Other countries highlighted here are discussed in other chapters.

parts of the city. This bacteria-laden fallout leads to widespread salmonella and hepatitis infections, especially among children.

Some 3.5 million motor vehicles and 30,000 factories spew pollutants into the atmosphere. Air pollution is intensified because the city lies in a basin surrounded by mountains, and frequent thermal inversions trap pollutants at ground level (Figure 17-9, top, p. 427). Since 1982, the amount of contamination in the city's smog-choked air has more than tripled. Breathing the city's air is said to be roughly equivalent to smoking three packs of cigarettes a day.

The city's air and water pollution cause an estimated 100,000 premature deaths per year. Writer Carlos Fuentes has nicknamed this megacity "Makesicko City."

Excessive groundwater withdrawal has caused parts of Mexico City to sink (subside) more than 9 meters (30 feet) since 1900. Some children mark their height on pipes and buildings to see whether they are growing faster than the ground is sinking.

The Mexican government is industrializing other parts of the country in an attempt to slow migration to Mexico City. Other efforts include **(1)** banning cars from a 50-block central zone, **(2)** taking taxis built before 1985 off the streets, **(3)** having buses and trucks run only on liquefied petroleum gas (LPG), **(4)** planting 25 million trees, **(5)** buying some land for green space, **(6)** phasing out use of leaded gasoline, **(7)** barring cars without catalytic converters from city streets one day a week, and **(8)** enforcing stricter emissions standards for industries.

Some progress has been made, but the city still fails to meet minimum air quality standards on an average of 300 days a year. Older Volkswagen taxis and minibuses make up less than one-fourth of the city's vehicles but produce nearly half of all emissions.

If the city's population continues to grow as projected, these problems, already at crisis levels, will become even worse. If you were in charge of Mexico City, what would you do?

**How Urbanized Is the United States?**   Between 1800 and 2002, the percentage of the U.S. population living in urban areas increased from 5% to 75% (Figure 25-5). This rural-to-urban population shift has taken place in four phases.

- *Migration to large central cities.* Currently, **(1)** 75% of Americans live in 271 *metropolitan areas* (cities and towns with at least 50,000 people), and **(2)** nearly half of the country's population lives in consolidated metropolitan areas containing 1 million or more residents (Figure 25-6).

- *Migration from large central cities to suburbs and smaller cities.* Currently, about 51% of the U.S. population live in suburbs.

- *Migration from the North and East to the South and West.* Since 1980, about 80% of the U.S. population increase has occurred in the South and West, particularly near the coasts. For example, California in the West, with 34.5 million people, is the most populous state—followed by Texas in the Southwest with 21.3 million people. This shift is expected to continue.

- *Migration from urban areas back to rural areas* since the 1970s and especially since 1990.

**What Are the Major Urban Problems in the United States?**   Here is some *good news:*

- Since 1920, many of the worst urban environmental problems in the United States have been reduced significantly.

- Most people have better working and housing conditions, and air and water quality have improved.

- Better sanitation, public water supplies, and medical care have slashed death rates and the prevalence of sickness from malnutrition and transmittable diseases such as measles, diphtheria, typhoid fever, pneumonia, and tuberculosis.

- Concentrating most of the population in urban areas has helped protect the country's biodiversity by reducing the destruction and degradation of wildlife habitat.

Here is some *bad news.* A number of cities in the United States (especially older ones) have **(1)** deteriorating services, **(2)** aging infrastructures (streets, schools, bridges, housing, and sewers), **(3)** budget crunches from rising costs as some businesses and people move to the suburbs or rural areas and reduce revenues from property taxes, and **(4)** rising poverty in many central city areas, where unemployment typically is 50% or higher.

Another major problem in the United States is **urban sprawl:** the growth of low-density development on the edges of cities and towns that encourages dependence on cars (Figure 25-7). Factors promoting

**Figure 25-5** Rural-to-urban shift in the United States, 1790–2002. (U.S. Bureau of the Census).

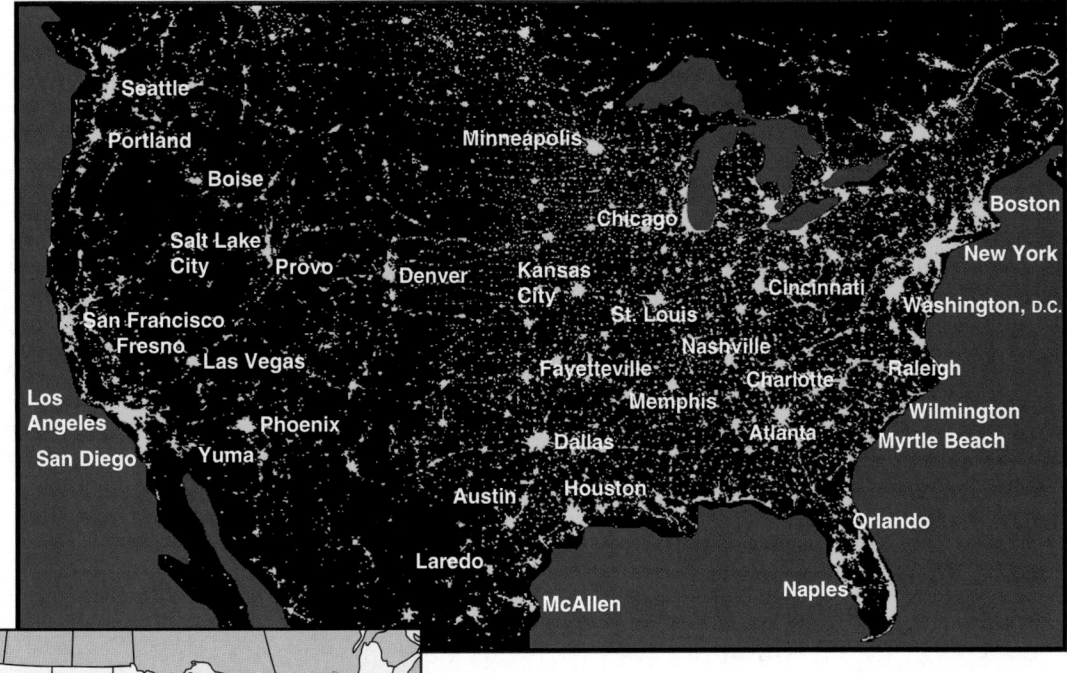

**Figure 25-6** Major urban areas in the United States based on satellite images of the earth at night that show city lights (top). About 75% of Americans live in urban areas occupying about 3% of the country's land area. Areas with names in white are the fastest growing metropolitan areas. Nearly half (48%) of Americans live in *consolidated metropolitan areas* with 1 million or more people (bottom). (Data from National Geophysical Data Center/National Oceanic and Atmospheric Administration, U.S. Census Bureau)

urban sprawl in the United States since 1945 include **(1)** ample land for expansion, **(2)** federal government loan guarantees for new single-family homes for World War II veterans, **(3)** federal and state government funding of highways that encourages the development of once-inaccessible outlying tracts of land, **(4)** low-cost gasoline (Figure 16-8, p. 386), which encourages automobile use, **(5)** greater availability of mortgages for homes in new subdivisions than in older cities and suburbs, and **(6)** state and local zoning laws that require large residential lots and separation of residential and commercial use of land in new communities.

Figure 25-8 (p. 666) shows some of the undesirable consequences of urban sprawl. Some critics say the concern over urban sprawl is overblown because only

| 1952 | 1967 | 1972 | 1995 |

Image provided courtesy of the U.S. Geological Survey

**Figure 25-7** Urban sprawl in and around Las Vegas, Nevada, 1952–1995. Between 1970 and 2000, the population of water-short Las Vegas (Spotlight, p. 334) more than tripled from 463,00 to 1.4 million. Between 1990 and 2001, the city led the nation in urban growth (62%).

about 4% of the land in the United States is developed. However, other analysts point out they fail to note that three out of four Americans live in developed urban areas, and one out of two reside in sprawling suburban areas.

### What Are the Major Spatial Patterns of Urban Development?
Three generalized models of urban structure are shown in Figure 25-9.

A *concentric circle city,* such as New York City, develops outward from its central business district (CBD) in a series of rings as the area grows in population and size. Typically industries and businesses in the CBD and poverty-stricken inner-city housing areas are ringed by housing zones that usually become more affluent toward the suburbs. In many developing countries, affluent residents cluster in the central city, and many of the poor live in squatter settlements that spring up on the outskirts.

A *sector city* grows in pie-shaped wedges or strips when commercial, industrial, and housing districts push outward from the CBD along major transportation routes. An example is the large urban area extending from San Francisco to San Jose in California.

A *multiple-nuclei city* develops around a number of independent centers, or satellite cities, rather than a single center. Metropolitan Los Angeles, California, comes fairly close to this pattern. Some cities develop in various combinations of these three patterns.

As they grow and sprawl outward, separate urban areas may merge to form a *megalopolis.* For example, the

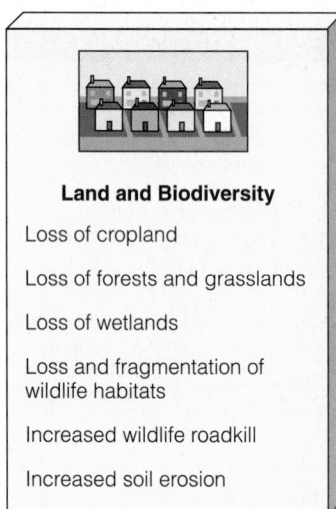

**Land and Biodiversity**

Loss of cropland

Loss of forests and grasslands

Loss of wetlands

Loss and fragmentation of wildlife habitats

Increased wildlife roadkill

Increased soil erosion

**Human Health and Aesthetics**

Contaminated drinking water and air

Noise pollution

Sky illumination at night

Traffic congestion

**Water**

Increased runoff

Increased surface water and groundwater pollution

Increased use of surface water and groundwater

Decreased storage of surface water and groundwater

Increased flooding

Decreased natural sewage treatment

**Energy, Air, and Climate**

Increased energy use and waste

Increased air pollution

Increased greenhouse gas emissions

Enhanced global warming

Warmer microclimate (heat island effect)

**Economic Effects**

Higher taxes

Decline of downtown business districts

Increased unemployment in central city

Loss of tax base in central city

**Figure 25-8** Some of the undesirable impacts of *urban sprawl* or car-dependent development.

**Concentric Circle Model**

1 Central business district (CBD)
2 Deteriorating transition zone
3 Workers' homes
4 Middle-class suburbs
5 Commuters' zone

**Sector Model**

1 High-rent residential
2 Intermediate-rent residential
3 Low-rent residential
4 Education and recreation
5 Transportation
6 Industrial
7 CBD

**Multiple-Nuclei Model**

1 CBD
2 Wholesale, light manufacturing
3 Low-rent residential
4 Intermediate-rent residential
5 High-rent residential
6 Heavy manufacturing
7 Outlying business district
8 Residential suburb
9 Industrial suburb

**Figure 25-9** Three models of *urban spatial structure.* Although no city perfectly matches any of them, these simplified models can be used to identify general patterns of urban development. (Modified with permission from Harm J. de Blij, *Human Geography*, New York: Wiley, 1977)

remaining open space between Boston, Massachusetts, and Washington, D.C., is rapidly urbanizing and coalescing. This 800-kilometer-long (500-mile-long) urban area, sometimes called *Bowash* (Figure 25-10, p. 668), contains almost 60 million people, about twice Canada's entire population.

Megalopolises have developed all over the world. Examples include **(1)** the area between Amsterdam and Paris in Europe, **(2)** the Tokyo–Yokohama–Osaka–Kobe corridor (with nearly 50 million people) in Japan, and **(3)** the Brazilian industrial triangle made up of São Paulo, Rio de Janeiro, and Belo Horizonte.

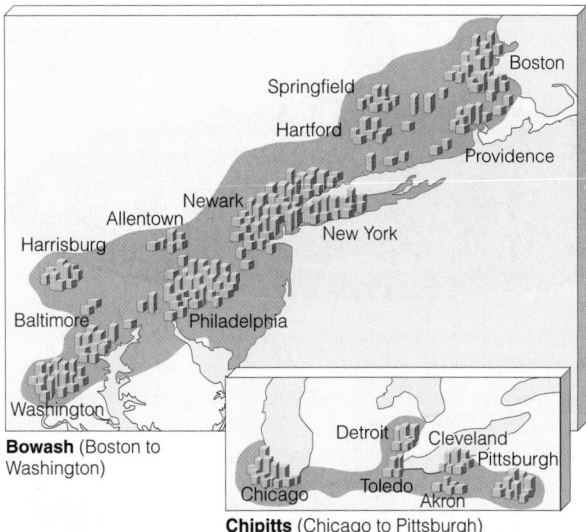

**Bowash** (Boston to Washington)

**Chipitts** (Chicago to Pittsburgh)

**Figure 25-10** Two megalopolises: *Bowash*, consisting of urban sprawl and coalescence between Boston and Washington, D.C., and *Chipitts*, extending from Chicago to Pittsburgh.

## 25-2 URBAN RESOURCE AND ENVIRONMENTAL PROBLEMS

**What Are the Economic and Environmental Advantages of Urbanization?** Historically, cities have **(1)** been the centers of industry, commerce, transportation, and jobs, **(2)** spurred economic development, and **(3)** nurtured innovations in science and technology. The high density of urban populations has also provided governments with significant cost advantages in delivering goods and services.

Urbanization also has some important health and environmental benefits:

- In many parts of the world, urban populations live longer and have lower infant mortality rates than do rural populations.

- Urban dwellers generally have better access to **(1)** medical care, **(2)** family planning, **(3)** education, **(4)** social services, and **(5)** environmental information than do people in rural areas.

- Urban areas have played a crucial role in reducing fertility and thereby slowing population growth.

- Recycling is more economically feasible because of the large concentration of recyclable materials.

- Per capita expenditures on environmental protection are higher in urban areas.

- The 47% of the world's people currently living in urban areas occupy only about 2% of the planet's land area (Figure 25-2).

- Concentrating people in urban areas helps preserve biodiversity by reducing the stress on wildlife habitats.

**What Are the Environmental Disadvantages of Urbanization?** Urbanization also has some harmful environmental effects:

*Sustainability*

- Most of the world's cities are not self-sustaining systems because of their high resource input and high waste output (Figure 25-11).

*Resource Use, Land Use, and Biodiversity*

- Although urban dwellers occupy only about 2% of the earth's land area (Figures 23-2, p. 595, and 25-2), they consume about 75% of the earth's resources.

- Large areas of the earth's land area must be disturbed and degraded (Figure 1-5, p. 7, and Figure 1-8, p. 10) to provide urban dwellers with food, water, energy, minerals, and other resources. This decreases and degrades the earth's biodiversity.

- Rural cropland, fertile soil, forests, wetlands, and wildlife habitats are lost as cities expand. In the United States, the loss of rural land—mostly prime cropland and forestland—is equivalent in area to building a 3.7-kilometer-wide (2.3-mile-wide) highway across the United States from New York City to Los Angeles, California, each year.

*Lack of Trees and Food Production*

- Most cities have few trees, shrubs, or other plants that **(1)** absorb air pollutants, **(2)** give off oxygen, **(3)** help cool the air as water transpires from their leaves and as they provide shade, **(4)** reduce soil erosion, **(5)** muffle noise, **(6)** provide wildlife habitats, and **(7)** give aesthetic pleasure. As one observer remarked, "Most cities are places where they cut down the trees and then name the streets after them."

- Most cities produce little of their own food. However, people can grow their own food by **(1)** planting community gardens in unused lots, **(2)** using window boxes and balcony planters, **(3)** creating gardens or greenhouses on the roofs of apartment buildings and on patios, and **(4)** raising fish in aquaculture tanks and sewage lagoons. According to the United Nations, about 800 million urban farmers provide about 15% of the world's food, and this proportion could be increased.

*Water Resource Problems*

- Many cities have water supply problems. As cities grow and their water demands increase, expensive reservoirs and canals must be built and deeper wells drilled. This can deprive rural and wild areas of surface water and deplete groundwater faster than it is replenished.

| Inputs | | Outputs |
|--------|--|---------|
| Energy | | Solid wastes |
| Food | | Waste heat |
| Water | | Air pollutants |
| Raw materials | | Water pollutants |
| Manufactured goods | | Greenhouse gases |
| Money | | Manufactured goods |
| Information | | Noise |
| | | Wealth |
| | | Ideas |

**Figure 25-11** Urban areas rarely are sustainable systems. The typical city is an open system that depends on other areas for large inputs of matter and energy resources and for large outputs of waste matter and heat. Large areas of nonurban land must be used to supply urban areas with resources. For example, according to an analysis by Mathis Wackernagel and William Rees, 58 times the land area of London is needed to supply its residents with resources. They estimate that meeting the needs of all the world's people at the same rate of resource use as London would take at least three more earths.

- In urban areas of many developing countries, 50–70% of water is lost or wasted because of leaks and poor management of water distribution systems.

- Flooding tends to be greater in cities because **(1)** many cities are built on floodplain areas subject to natural flooding (Figure 14-22, p. 332), and **(2)** covering land with buildings, asphalt, and concrete causes precipitation to run off quickly and overload storm drains.

- Many of the world's largest cities are in coastal areas (Figure 25-2) that could be flooded sometime in this century if sea levels are raised by global warming (Figure 18-19, p. 463).

### Pollution and Health

- Because of their high population densities and high resource consumption (Figure 25-11), urban dwellers produce most of the world's air pollution, water pollution, and solid and hazardous wastes.

- Pollution levels normally are higher in urban areas than in rural areas because pollutants are produced in a small area and cannot be as readily dispersed and diluted as those produced in rural areas.

- According to the World Health Organization, more than 1.1 billion people (most in developing countries) live in urban areas where air pollution levels exceed healthful levels.

- The World Bank estimates that almost two-thirds of urban residents in developing countries do not have adequate sanitation facilities. About 90% of all sewage in developing countries (98% in Latin America) is discharged directly into rivers, lakes, and coastal waters without treatment of any kind.

- According to the World Bank, at least 220 million people in the urban areas of developing countries do not have safe drinking water.

- High population densities in urban areas can increase **(1)** the spread of infectious diseases (especially if adequate drinking water and sewage systems are not available) and **(2)** physical injuries (mostly from industrial and traffic accidents).

### Noise Pollution

- Most urban dwellers are subjected to **noise pollution:** any unwanted, disturbing, or harmful sound

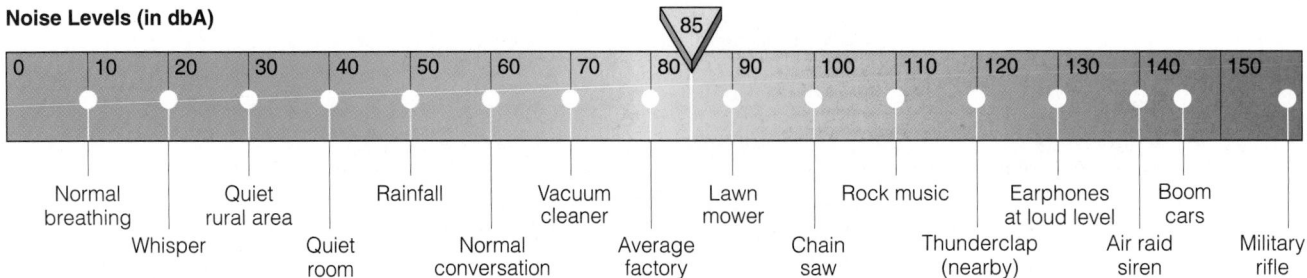

**Permanent damage begins after 8-hour exposure**

**Noise Levels (in dbA)**

85

| 0 | 10 | 20 | 30 | 40 | 50 | 60 | 70 | 80 | 90 | 100 | 110 | 120 | 130 | 140 | 150 |

Normal breathing

Whisper

Quiet rural area

Quiet room

Rainfall

Normal conversation

Vacuum cleaner

Average factory

Lawn mower

Chain saw

Rock music

Thunderclap (nearby)

Earphones at loud level

Air raid siren

Boom cars

Military rifle

**Figure 25-12** *Noise levels* (in decibel-A [dbA] sound pressure units) of some common sounds. Sound pressure becomes damaging at about 75 dbA and painful around 120 dbA. At 180 dbA it can kill. Because the db and dbA scales are logarithmic, sound pressure is multiplied 10-fold with each 10-decibel rise. Thus a rise from 30 dbA (quiet rural area) to 60 dbA (normal restaurant conversation) represents a 1,000-fold increase in sound pressure on the ear.

that **(1)** impairs or interferes with hearing, **(2)** causes stress, **(3)** hampers concentration and work efficiency, or **(4)** causes accidents. Noise levels (Figure 25-12) above 65 dbA are considered unacceptable, and prolonged exposure to levels above 85 dbA can cause permanent hearing damage.

▪ You are being exposed to a sound level high enough to cause permanent hearing damage if **(1)** you need to raise your voice to be heard above the racket, **(2)** a noise causes your ears to ring, or **(3)** nearby speech seems muffled.

▪ Ways to control noise include **(1)** modifying noisy activities and devices to produce less noise, **(2)** shielding noisy devices or processes, **(3)** shielding workers from noise, **(4)** moving noisy operations or

things away from people, and **(5)** using anti-noise, a new technology that cancels out one noise with another.

### Microclimate

▪ Cities generally are warmer, rainier, foggier, and cloudier than suburbs and nearby rural areas. The enormous amounts of heat generated by cars, factories, furnaces, lights, air conditioners, and heat-absorbing dark roofs and roads in cities create an **urban heat island** (Figure 25-13) surrounded by cooler suburban and rural areas. As urban areas grow and merge (Figure 25-10), individual heat islands also merge. This can affect the climate of a large area and keep polluted air from being diluted and cleansed.

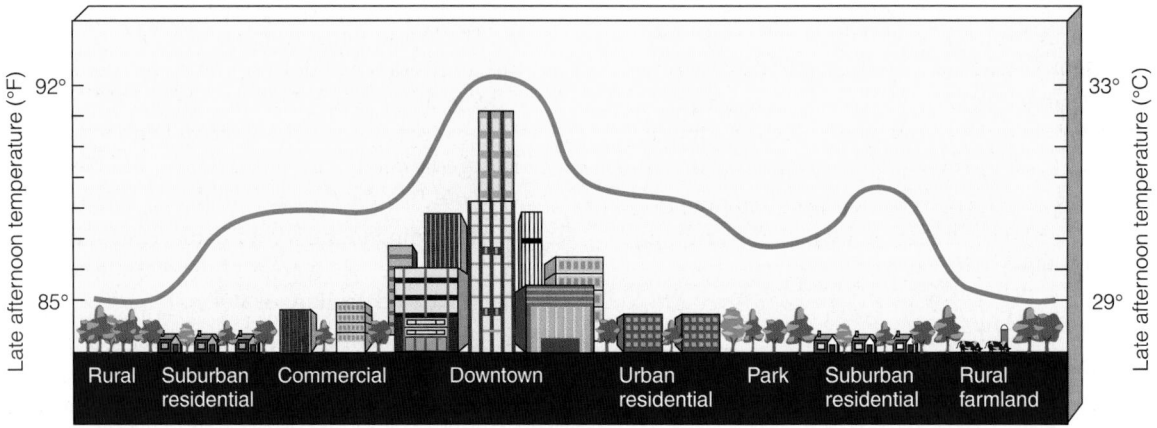

**Figure 25-13** Profile of an urban heat island showing how temperature changes as the density of development and trees changes. Most urban areas have few trees and large areas of heat-absorbing paved streets, roofs, and other dark surfaces that absorb and release heat. Thus urban areas are hotter than surrounding suburban and rural areas with more trees and less heat-absorbing surfaces. At night urban areas are still radiating heat while rural areas are cooling rapidly. (Data from U.S. Department of State)

## How Can Reducing Crime Help the Environment?

Most people do not realize that reducing crime can also help improve environmental quality. For example, crimes such as robbery, assault, and shootings

- Drive people out of cities, which are our most energy-efficient living arrangements. Every brick in an abandoned urban building represents an energy waste equivalent to burning a 100-watt lightbulb for 12 hours. Each new suburb means replacing farmland or reservoirs of natural biodiversity with dispersed, energy- and resource-wasting roads, houses, and shopping centers.

- Make people less willing to use walking, bicycles, and energy-efficient public transit systems.

- Force many people to use more energy to deter burglars by **(1)** leaving lights, TVs, and radios on and **(2)** clearing away trees and bushes near houses that can reduce solar heat gain in the summer and provide windbreaks in the winter.

- Cause overpackaging of many items to deter shoplifting or poisoning of food or drug items.

### Critical Thinking

Can you think of any environmental benefits of certain types of crimes?

---

- Cities can partially counteract the heat island effect by **(1)** planting trees, **(2)** using lighter-colored paving, building surfaces, and rooftops to reflect heat away, **(3)** reducing inputs of waste heat into the atmosphere by establishing high energy-efficiency standards for vehicles, buildings, and appliances, and **(4)** establishing gardens on the roofs of large buildings (as is done in parts of the Netherlands and Germany).

### Poverty and Social Problems

- Rapid urban growth is increasing urban poverty and inequality, which could increase civil unrest and undermine governments.

- High population densities in urban areas can increase *crime rates* (Connections, above).

- The outward expansion of cities creates numerous problems for towns in nearby rural areas: **(1)** Streets become congested with traffic, **(2)** health, school, police, fire, water, sanitation, and other services are overwhelmed, **(3)** taxes must be raised to meet the demand for new public services, and **(4)** some long-time residents are forced out because of rising prices, higher property taxes, decreased environmental quality, and disruption of their way of life.

## 25-3 TRANSPORTATION AND URBAN DEVELOPMENT

**How Do Transportation Systems Affect Urban Development?** Transportation and land-use decisions are linked together and determine **(1)** where people live, **(2)** how far they must go to get to work and buy food and other necessities, **(3)** how much land is paved over, and **(4)** how much air pollution people are exposed to.

If a city cannot spread outward, it must grow vertically—upward and downward (below ground)—so it occupies a small land area with a high population density. Most people living in such *compact cities* walk, ride bicycles, or use energy-efficient mass transit. Many European cities and urban areas such as Hong Kong and Tokyo are compact and tend to be more energy efficient than the dispersed cities in the United States (Figure 25-10), Canada, and Australia, where ample land often is available for outward expansion.

A combination of cheap gasoline, plentiful land, and a network of highways produces sprawling, automobile-oriented cities with low population density that have a number of undesirable effects (Figure 25-8). As cities sprawl, cars become essential, and walking, bicycling, and mass transit become less practical. Most people in such urban areas live in single-family houses with unshared walls that lose and gain heat rapidly unless they are well insulated and airtight. Urban sprawl also **(1)** gobbles up unspoiled forests and natural habitats, **(2)** paves over fertile farmland, **(3)** promotes heavy dependence on the automobile, **(4)** degrades watersheds and air, **(5)** wastes resources, and **(6)** promotes age and economic inequalities.

Dispersed car-centered cities use up to ten times more energy per person for transportation than more compact cities that allow better use of mass transit, bicycles, and walking (Solutions, p. 678). In Europe, for example, walking and bicycling are used for 40–50% of all land-based trips and mass transit for 10%. By contrast, in the United States, 95% of all trips are by car, 3% by mass transit, and 2% by bicycling and walking. In addition, spread-out cities use more building materials, roads, power lines, and water and sewer lines.

Building more highways and freeways and using gasoline taxes to build these roads accelerates urban sprawl in a vicious circle based on positive feedback.

The new roads lead to new suburban developments. This promotes longer commutes to and from work between the suburbs and the city or between far-flung suburban areas. Drivers use more gasoline, with much of the taxes on gasoline used to build more highways. This leads to new, even more distant suburban developments and perpetuates the cycle.

**What Are the Pros and Cons of Motor Vehicles?**
The two main types of ground transportation are *individual* (such as cars, motor scooters, bicycles, and walking) and *mass* (mostly buses and rail systems). Only about 10% of the world's people can afford a car. Thus about 90% of all travel in the world is by foot, bicycle, or motor scooter.

With 4.7% of the world's people, the United States has 32% of the world's 700 million cars and trucks (including 555 million cars and 145 million trucks). About two-thirds of the 225 million passenger motor vehicles in the United States are cars and the remaining third are SUVs, pickup trucks, and vans. In the United States, these passenger vehicles are used for 95% of all urban transportation and 91% of travel to work (with 76% of Americans driving to work alone, 4% commuting to work on public transit, and 1% bicycling to work). Americans drive 4.3 trillion kilometers (2.7 trillion miles) each year—as far as the rest of the world combined and four times the distance in 1955. Despite their many advantages, a number of drawbacks are associated with relying on motor vehicles as the major form of transportation (Pro/Con, right).

However, many governments in developing countries such as China favor developing an automobile-centered transportation system. According to Lester R. Brown, if China succeeded in having one or two cars in every garage and consumed oil at the U.S. rate, it would **(1)** need slightly more oil each year than the world now produces and **(2)** have to pave over an area of land equal to half of the land it now uses to produce food.

**Is It Feasible to Reduce Automobile Use?** Two recent estimates by economists put the harmful costs of driving in the United States at roughly $300 billion to 7 trillion per year. These largely hidden costs include **(1)** deaths and injuries from accidents, **(2)** higher health insurance costs, **(3)** air and water pollution, **(4)** $CO_2$ emissions that increase global warming, **(5)** the value of time wasted in traffic jams, and **(6)** decreased property values near roads because of noise and congestion. All Americans, whether they drive or not, pay these costs but rarely associate them with driving.

There are additional costs. According to a study by the World Resources Institute, federal, state, and local governments provide automobile subsidies in the United States amounting to $300–600 billion a year

(depending on the costs included), an average subsidy of $1,200–2,400 per vehicle.

Environmentalists and a number of economists suggest that one way to reduce the harmful effects of automobile use is to make drivers pay directly for most of the full costs of automobile use—a *user-pays* approach. This could be done by **(1)** including the estimated harmful costs of driving as a tax on gasoline, **(2)** phasing out government subsides for motor vehicle owners, and **(3)** using the gasoline tax revenues and savings from reduced motor vehicle subsidies to lower taxes on income and wages and to help finance mass transit systems, bike paths, and sidewalks.

If U.S. drivers had to pay the hidden costs of driving directly in the form of a gasoline tax (as is done in most European countries and Japan), the tax on each gallon would be about $5–7. Such a tax would face intense political opposition unless taxpayers faced an equivalent drop in taxes on wages and profits to compensate for increases in gasoline taxes. Such taxes would also spur the use of more energy-efficient motor vehicles (p. 385).

Other ways to reduce automobile use and congestion are **(1)** charging tolls on roads, tunnels, and bridges (especially during peak traffic times), **(2)** raising parking fees, **(3)** reducing mortgage charges on federally financed loans for homeowners who do not use a car to get to work, and **(4)** encouraging employers to use staggered hours and have more employees use telecommuting to work at home.

Other countries have had success in reducing car use:

- In Hong Kong, motorists are charged by distance for all car travel, with the highest rates during commuter hours. Electronic sensors record highway travel and time of day, and drivers receive a monthly bill.

- Densely populated Singapore is rarely congested because it **(1)** taxes cars heavily, **(2)** auctions the rights to buy a car, **(3)** charges anyone driving downtown a daily user fee of $3–6 that rises during rush hours, and **(4)** uses the revenue from taxes and fees to fund an excellent mass transit system.

- In the central business district of Amsterdam in the Netherlands, existing streets have been made narrower, and the extra space is being used to widen sidewalks and build bike lanes.

- Scores of cities (including Rome, Stockholm, Vienna, and Prague) have established *car-free areas.*

- More than 300 cities in Germany, Austria, Italy, Switzerland, and the Netherlands have a *car-sharing* network. Each member pays for a card that opens lockers containing keys to cars parked at designated spots around a city. Members reserve a car in advance

## Good and Bad News About Motor Vehicles

**PRO/CON**

The automobile provides convenience and mobility. To many people, cars are also symbols of power, sex, excitement, social status, and success and islands of privacy in an increasingly hectic world. Moreover, much of the world's economy is built on producing motor vehicles and supplying roads, services, and repairs for them. In the United States, **(1)** $1 of every $4 spent and one of every six nonfarm jobs is connected to the automobile, and **(2)** five of the seven largest U.S. industrial firms produce either cars or their fuel.

Despite their important benefits, motor vehicles have many destructive effects on people and the environment. Since 1885, when Karl Benz built the first automobile, almost 18 million people have been killed in motor vehicle accidents. According to the World Health Organization and the World Bank, car accidents throughout the world annually **(1)** kill an estimated 885,000 people (an average of 2,400 deaths per day, equal to eight accidental jumbo jet crashes each day with no survivors) and **(2)** injure or permanently disable another 15 million people.

In the United States alone, 16 million motor vehicle accidents (up from 7 million in 1970) per year **(1)** kill more than 40,000 people and **(2)** injure another 5 million (at least 300,000 of them severely). *More Americans have been killed by cars than have died in all wars in the country's history.* Each week, motor vehicles in the United States also kill a mil-

lion wild animals and tens of thousands of pets.

Motor vehicles also are the largest source of air pollution (including 23% of global $CO_2$ emissions), laying a haze of smog over the world's cities (Figure 17-7, p. 425). Transportation is also the fastest growing source of climate-changing emissions of carbon dioxide.

In the United States, motor vehicles produce at least 50% of the air pollution, even though emission standards are as strict as any in the world. Two-thirds of the oil used in the United States and one-third of the world's total oil consumption are devoted to transportation.

By making long commutes and shopping trips possible, automobiles and highways have helped create urban sprawl and reduced use of more efficient forms of transportation. Worldwide, at least a third of urban land is devoted to roads, parking lots, gasoline stations, and other automobile-related uses.

In the United States, more land is devoted to cars than to housing. Half the land in an average U.S. city is used for cars, prompting urban expert Lewis Mumford to suggest that the U.S. national flower should be the concrete cloverleaf.

The United States spends nearly $200 million *per day* building and rebuilding roads. Such roads have harmful ecological effects including **(1)** increasing the killing of wild animals by vehicles, **(2)** promoting dispersal of nonnative species, **(3)** blocking movements of some species, and **(4)** dividing populations of various species into smaller, less viable subpopulations.

In 1907, the average speed of horse-drawn vehicles through the borough of Manhattan in New York City was 18.5 kilometers (11.5 miles) per hour; today, cars and trucks creep along Manhattan streets at an average speed of 5 kilometers (3 miles) per hour. In 2001, the average resident of the sprawling urban area of Atlanta, Georgia, spent 70 hours in traffic delays, compared with 25 hours in 1992. Atlanta loses more than $6 million *per day* because of traffic delays.

The U.S. General Accounting Office projects that the country's traffic congestion will triple in 15 years. If current trends continue, U.S. motorists will spend an average of 2 years of their lifetimes in traffic jams. According to the International Center for Technology Assessment, the hidden and harmful costs of gasoline-powered cars in the United States is $560 billion–$1.7 trillion a year—an average yearly cost of $1,950–5,920 per person.

Even if the money is available, building more roads is not the answer because, as economist Robert Samuelson put it, "Cars expand to fill available concrete." According to transportation expert Michael Replogle, "Adding highway capacity to solve traffic congestion is like buying larger pants to deal with your weight problem."

### Critical Thinking

If you own a car (or hope to own one), what conditions (if any) would encourage you to rely less on the automobile and travel to school or work by bicycle, on foot, by mass transit, or by a carpool or vanpool?

or call the network and are directed to the closest locker and car. They are billed monthly for the time they use a car and the distance they travel. In Berlin, Germany, car sharing has cut car ownership by 75% and car commuting by nearly 90% without decreasing mobility options.

Including the hidden costs in the market prices of cars, trucks, and gasoline up front may make eco-

nomic and environmental sense and has helped reduce car usage in a number of other countries. However, most analysts say it is not feasible in the United States because

- It faces strong political opposition from the public (mostly because they are unaware of the huge hidden costs they are already paying) and from powerful transportation-related industries (such as oil and tire companies, road builders, carmakers, and many real estate developers). However, taxpayers might accept sharp increases in gasoline taxes if the extra costs were offset by decreases in taxes on wages and income.

▪ Fast, efficient, reliable, and affordable mass transit options and bike paths are not widely available as alternatives to automobile travel.

▪ The dispersed nature of most urban areas makes people dependent on the car.

▪ Most people who can afford cars are virtually addicted to them, and most people who cannot afford a car hope to buy one someday.

**What Are Alternatives to the Car?** Cars are an important form of transportation, but some countries encourage alternatives, each with various advantages and disadvantages. Here are some examples:

### Motor Scooters

▪ They have various advantages and disadvantages (Figure 25-14) and are especially useful for people in developing countries who cannot afford a car. Electric scooters can reduce air pollution (p. 389) and noise.

### Bicycles

▪ Because of their advantages (Figure 25-15), bicycles outsell cars by more than two to one. They are widely used in countries such as China (50% of urban trips) and the Netherlands (30% of urban trips) but make up only about 1% of urban trips in the United States.

▪ In 1996, a California firm developed a simple $15 bicycle that eliminates the chain by attaching the pedals to the front wheel. This inexpensive design could greatly increase bicycle use in developing countries.

▪ In Copenhagen, Denmark, 2,300 bicycles are available for public use at no charge. The system is financed by ads attached to the bicycle frames and wheels. The system is so popular that each bicycle is used on average once every 8 minutes.

▪ Unless efficient and affordable forms of mass transportation are already in place, many urban residents in developing countries abandon bikes and walking as soon as they can afford to buy motor scooters or cars, as is happening in China, India, and Indonesia.

▪ Only about 1% of Americans bicycle to work. However, 20% of Americans say they would bicycle to work if **(1)** safe bike lanes were available and **(2)** their employers provided secure bike storage and showers at work.

| Advantages | | Disadvantages |
|---|---|---|
| Affordable | 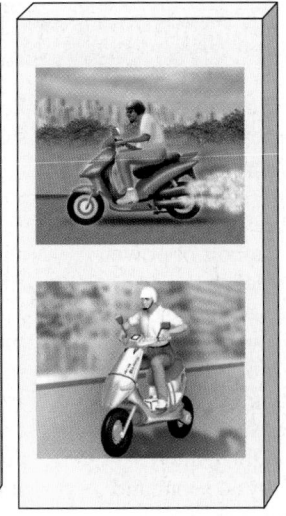 | Little protection in an accident |
| Produce less air pollution than cars | | Does not protect drivers from bad weather |
| Require little parking space | | Gasoline engines are noisy |
| Easy to maneuver in traffic | | Gasoline engines emit large quantities of air pollutants |
| Electric scooters are quiet and produce little pollution | | |

**Figure 25-14** Advantages and disadvantages of *motor scooters*.

| Advantages | | Disadvantages |
|---|---|---|
| Affordable | 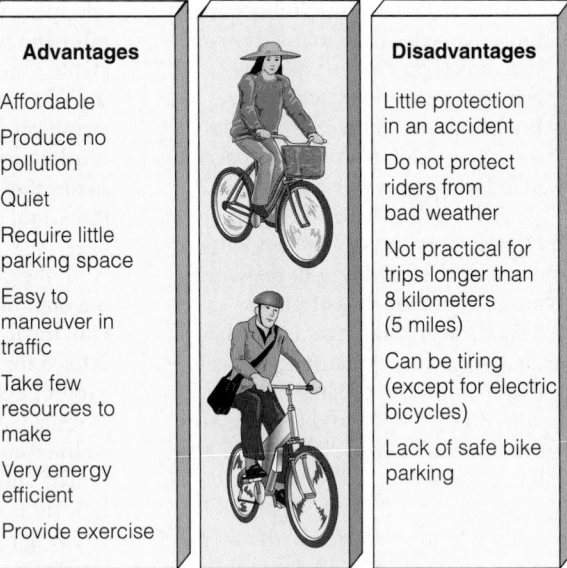 | Little protection in an accident |
| Produce no pollution | | Do not protect riders from bad weather |
| Quiet | | Not practical for trips longer than 8 kilometers (5 miles) |
| Require little parking space | | Can be tiring (except for electric bicycles) |
| Easy to maneuver in traffic | | Lack of safe bike parking |
| Take few resources to make | | |
| Very energy efficient | | |
| Provide exercise | | |

**Figure 25-15** Advantages and disadvantages of *bicycles*.

▪ Using separate bike paths or lanes running along roads, cyclists can make most trips shorter than 8 kilometers (5 miles) faster than drivers can.

▪ For longer trips, secure bike parking spaces can be provided at mass transit stations, and buses and trains can be equipped to carry bicycles. Such *bike-and-ride* systems are widely used in Japan, Germany, the Netherlands, and Denmark.

▪ About 1.5 million *electric bicycles* are on the road (750,000 of them in China), and about 400,000 more are added each year. Existing bikes can easily be converted to electric bikes, and new ones can be bought for $500–1,200 (p. 389).

| Advantages | | Disadvantages |
|---|---|---|
| More energy efficient than cars | 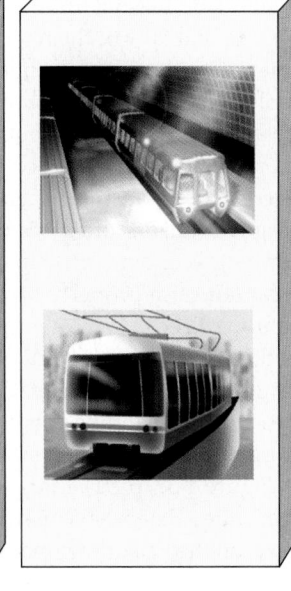 | Expensive to build and maintain |
| Produce less air pollution than cars | | Cost effective only along a densely populated narrow corridor |
| Require less land than roads and parking areas for cars | | Commits riders to transportation schedules |
| Cause fewer injuries and deaths than cars | | Can cause noise and vibration for nearby residents |
| Reduces car congestion in cities | | |

**Figure 25-16** Advantages and disadvantages of *mass transit rail systems* within urban areas.

- Bicycles powered by small fuel cells should be available within a few years.

### Conventional Rail Systems Within Urban Areas

- *Heavy-rail* systems (subways, elevated railways, and metros operating on exclusive right-of-way tracks) and *light-rail* systems (streetcars, trolley cars, and tramways running along tracks that may not be separated from other traffic) have various advantages and disadvantages (Figure 25-16).

- To be cost effective, rail systems must travel along corridors in urban areas with a density of at least 50 people per hectare (2.5 acres) as found in most European cities (compared to a typical urban population density in American cities of about 14 people per hectare).

- A light-rail line **(1)** costs about one-tenth as much to build per kilometer as a highway or a heavy-rail system, **(2)** has lower operating costs than a com-

parable bus system, **(3)** can carry up to 400 people for each driver, compared with 40–50 passengers on a typical bus, and **(4)** is quieter and produces less air pollution than a bus system. At one time the United States had an effective light-rail system, but it was dismantled to promote car and bus use (Case Study, p. 677).

- One of the world's most successful mass transit rail systems is in Hong Kong. Several factors contribute to its success: **(1)** The city is densely populated, making it ideal for a rapid-rail system running through its corridor, **(2)** half the population can walk to a subway station in 5 minutes, and **(3)** a car is an economic liability in this crowded city even for those who can afford one.

### Rapid-Rail Systems Between Urban Areas

- In western Europe and Japan, *bullet trains,* or supertrains, travel between cities on new or upgraded tracks at speeds up to 330 kilometers (200 miles) per hour. Such systems have advantages and disadvantages (Figure 25-17).

- In Europe, 12 countries plan to spend $76 billion to link major cities with nearly 30,000 kilometers (18,600 miles) of high-speed rail lines.

- A high-speed train network could replace airplanes, buses, and private cars for most medium-distance travel between major American cities (Figure 25-18, p. 676). Critics say such a system would cost too much in government subsidies. However, this ignores the fact that motor vehicle transportation receives subsidies of $300–600 billion per year in the United States.

### Buses

- Buses are the most widely used form of mass transit, mainly because they have more advantages than disadvantages (Figure 25-19. p. 676).

- Curitiba, Brazil, has developed one of the world's best bus systems and has led the way in becoming a more sustainable city (Solutions, p. 678).

| Advantages | | Disadvantages |
|---|---|---|
| Can reduce travel by car or plane |  | Expensive to run and maintain |
| Ideal for trips of 200–1,000 kilometers (120–620 miles) | | Must operate along heavily used routes to be profitable |
| Much more energy efficient per rider over the same distance than a car or plane | | Cause noise and vibration for nearby residents |

**Figure 25-17** Advantages and disadvantages of *rapid rail systems* between urban areas.

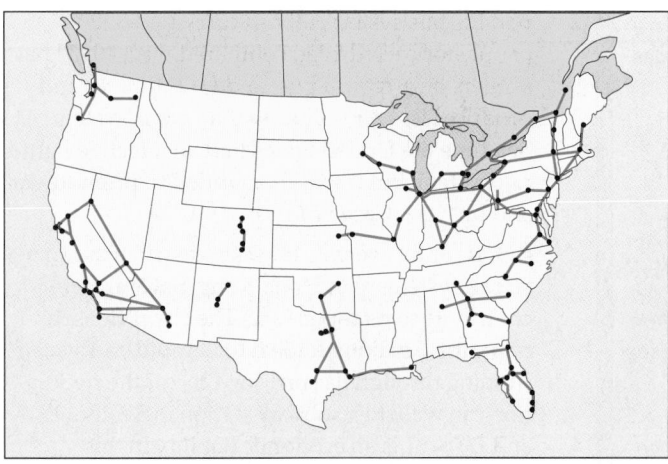

**Figure 25-18** Potential routes for high-speed bullet trains in the United States and parts of Canada. Such a system could allow rapid, comfortable, safe, and affordable travel between major cities in a region. It would greatly reduce dependence on cars, buses, and airplanes for trips between these urban areas. (Data from High Speed Rail Association)

| Advantages | | Disadvantages |
|---|---|---|
| More flexible than rail system | 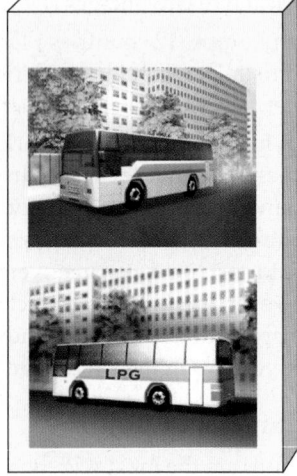 | Can lose money because they need low fares to attract riders |
| Can be rerouted as needed | | Often get caught in traffic unless operating in express lanes |
| Cost less to develop and maintain than heavy-rail system | | Commits riders to transportation schedules |
| Can greatly reduce car use and pollution | | Noisy |

**Figure 25-19** Advantages and disadvantages of *bus systems* for transport within urban areas.

## 25-4 URBAN LAND-USE PLANNING AND CONTROL

**What Is Conventional Land-Use Planning?** Most urban areas and some rural areas use some form of **land-use planning** to determine the best present and future use of each parcel of land in the area.

Much land-use planning is based on the assumption that considerable future population growth and economic development should be encouraged, regardless of the environmental and other consequences. Typically this leads to uncontrolled or poorly controlled urban growth and sprawl (Figures 25-7 and 25-8).

A major reason for this often destructive process is that 90% of the revenue that local governments in the United States use to provide schools, police and fire protection, water and sewer systems, and other public services comes from *property taxes* levied on all buildings and property based on their economic value. Thus local governments often try to raise money by promoting economic growth because they usually cannot raise property taxes enough to meet expanding needs. Typically the long-term result is poorly managed economic growth leading to more environmental degradation.

Land-use planning can be aided by the use of geographic information system (GIS) technology (Figure 4-32, p. 91). Many cities and counties in the United States have used this technology to convert all their planning maps into digital form.

In the 1990s, GIS data from satellite images, historical data, and census data were used to create maps showing snapshots of certain years of urban development in the Baltimore, Maryland, and Washington, D.C., area between 1862 and 1999. These data were presented in an animated video showing how the area had merged into one gigantic urban area by the 1990s (Figure 25-10). The video helped a governor of Maryland win legislative approval for his antisprawl, smart growth program.

**What Is Ecological Land-Use Planning?** Environmentalists urge communities to use comprehensive, regional **ecological land-use planning** to anticipate a region's present and future needs and problems. It is a complex process that takes into account geological, ecological, economic, health, and social factors (Solutions, p. 680).

Ecological land-use planning sounds good on paper, but it is not widely used for several reasons:

■ Local officials seeking reelection every few years **(1)** usually focus on short-term rather than long-term problems and **(2)** often can be influenced by economically powerful developers.

■ Often, officials and the majority of citizens are unwilling to pay for costly ecological land-use planning and implementation, even though a well-designed plan can prevent or ease many urban problems and save money in the long run.

■ It is difficult to get municipalities within a region to cooperate in planning efforts. As a result, an ecologically sound development plan in one area may be undermined by unsound development in nearby areas.

**CASE STUDY**

In 1917, all major U.S. cities had efficient electrical trolley or streetcar (light-rail) systems. Many people think of Los Angeles, California, as the original car-dominated city, but in the early 20th century Los Angeles had the largest electric rail mass transit system in the United States.

General Motors, Firestone Tire, Standard Oil of California, Phillips Petroleum, and Mack Truck (which also made buses) formed a holding company called National City Lines. By 1950, the holding company had purchased privately owned streetcar systems in 83 major cities. It then dismantled these systems to increase sales of cars and buses.

The courts found the companies guilty of conspiracy to eliminate the country's light-rail system, but the damage had already been done. The executives responsible were fined $1 each, and each company paid a fine of $5,000, less than the profit returned by replacing a single streetcar with a bus. Rebuilding these dismantled streetcar (light-rail) systems today would cost at least $300 billion.

During this same period, National City Lines worked to convert electric-powered commuter locomotives to much more expensive and less reliable diesel-powered locomotives. The resulting increased costs contributed significantly to the sharp decline of the nation's railroad system.

In the United States, 80% of federal gasoline tax revenue is used to build and maintain highways, and only 20% is used for mass transit. This encourages states and cities to invest in highways instead of mass transit. According to a 2001 study by the American Public Transit System, between 1988 and 1999 the United States spent six times more on highways than on other forms of public transportation.

The federal tax code also penalizes mass transit users and those who cycle or walk to work. In the United States, only 10% of commuting employees pay for parking, mainly because employers can deduct from their taxes the expense of providing parking for workers (amounting to a government subsidy of $31.5 billion per year). This gives such auto commuters a tax-free fringe benefit worth $200–400 a month in major cities. In contrast, employers can write off only about $15 a month for employees who use public transit and nothing for those who walk or bike.

One remedy would be for the government to provide a general transportation tax deduction to employers for their employees. Instead of getting free parking, all employees would receive a certain amount of money per month that could be used for any type of transportation to work.

**Critical Thinking**

Do you favor splitting funds collected from gasoline taxes in the United States (or country where you live) equally between mass transit and highway building and maintenance? Explain.

---

- In developing countries, most cities do not have the information or funding to carry out ecological land-use planning. Urban maps often are 20–30 years old and lack descriptions of large areas of cities, especially those growing rapidly because of squatter settlements.

**What Are the Pros and Cons of Using Zoning to Control Land Use?**  Once a land-use plan is developed, governments control the uses of various parcels of land by legal and economic methods. The most widely used approach is **zoning,** in which various parcels of land are designated for certain uses.

Zoning can be used to control growth and protect areas from certain types of development. For example, cities such as Portland, Oregon, and Curitiba, Brazil (Solutions, p. 678), have used zoning to encourage high-density development along major mass transit corridors to reduce automobile use and air pollution.

Despite its usefulness, zoning has some drawbacks:

- It can be influenced or modified by developers in ways that cause environmental harm such as destruction of wetlands, prime cropland, forested areas, and open space.

- It often favors high-priced housing and factories, hotels, and other businesses over protecting environmentally sensitive areas and providing low-cost housing because local governments depend on property taxes for revenue.

- Overly strict zoning can discourage innovative approaches to solving urban problems. For example, the pattern in the United States (and in some other countries) has been to prohibit businesses in residential areas, which increases suburban sprawl. There is renewed interest in returning to *mixed-use zoning* to help reduce urban sprawl, but current zoning laws often prohibit this.

**How Is Smart Growth Being Used to Control Growth and Sprawl?**  There is growing use of the concept of **smart growth** to encourage development that requires less dependence on cars. It recognizes that growth will occur but uses zoning laws and an

## Curitiba, Brazil

**SOLUTIONS**

One of the world's showcase ecocities is Curitiba, Brazil, with a population of 2.3 million. The city is one of Latin America's most livable cities and has a worldwide reputation for its innovative urban planning and environmental protection efforts.

Trees are everywhere in Curitiba because city officials have given neighborhoods more than 1.5 million trees to plant and care for. No tree in the city can be cut down without a permit, and two trees must be planted for each one cut down.

The air is clean because (1) the city is not built around the car, and (2) officials have integrated land-use and transportation planning. There are 160 kilometers (100 miles) of bike paths, and more are being built. With the support of shopkeepers, many streets in the downtown shopping district have been converted to pedestrian zones in which no cars are allowed.

Curitiba probably has the world's best bus system. Each weekday a network of clean and efficient buses carries more than 1.9 million passengers—75% of the city's commuters and shoppers—at a low cost (20–40¢ per ride, with unlimited transfers) on express bus lanes. This privately operated system radiates out from the center city along main routes like spokes in a bicycle wheel along express lanes dedicated to buses (see figure).

Since 1974, car traffic has declined by 30% even though the city's population has doubled. Two-thirds of all trips in the city are made by bus. The city's bus stations are linked to the city's network of bike paths. Special buses, taxis, and other services are provided for the handicapped.

Only high-rise apartment buildings are allowed near major bus routes. Each building must devote the bottom two floors to stores, which reduces the need for residents to travel. Extra-large buses run on popular routes, and tube-shaped bus shelters (see figure) where riders pay in advance enhance the system's speed and convenience. As a result, Curitiba has one of Brazil's lowest outdoor air pollution rates. The system has also reduced traffic congestion and saved energy.

The city recycles roughly 70% of its paper and 60% of its metal, glass, and plastic, which is sorted by households for collection three times a week. Recovered materials are sold mostly to the city's more than 500 major industries. Litter and graffiti are almost nonexistent because of the civic pride of Curitiba's residents.

Instead of being torn down, existing buildings and sites are recycled for new uses. A glue factory was converted to a creativity center where children make handicrafts, which the city's tourist shops sell to help fund social programs. A garbage dump was converted to a botanical garden that houses 220,000 species, and a quarry was filled and converted to the Free University of the Environment.

The city (1) bought a plot of land downwind of downtown as an industrial park, (2) put in streets, services, housing, and schools, (3) ran a special workers' bus line to the area, and (4) enacted stiff air and water pollution control laws. This development has attracted national and foreign corporations and 500 nonpolluting industries that provide one-fifth of the city's jobs. Most of these workers can walk or bike to work from their nearby homes.

To give the poor basic technical training skills needed for jobs, the city set up old buses as roving technical training schools. Each bus gives courses, costing the equivalent of two bus tokens (less than a dollar), for 3 months in a particular area and then moves to another area. Other retired buses became (1) classrooms, (2) health clinics, (3) soup kitchens, and (4) some of the city's 200 day-care centers, which are open 11 hours a day and free for low-income parents.

The city provides environmental education for adults and children by (1) using signs along roadways to present environmental information and (2) having all schoolchildren study ecology. Older children are given apprenticeships, job training, and entry-level jobs, often emphasizing environmental skills such as forestry, water pollution control, ecological restoration, and public health.

The city's 700,000 poorest residents can swap sorted trash for locally grown vegetables and fruits or bus tokens and receive free medical, dental, and child care; 40 feeding centers are available for street children. Poor children get free checkups and regular visits from health workers. Preventive health care is emphasized throughout the city's schools, day-care centers, and teen centers. As a result, the infant mortality rate has fallen by more than 60% since 1977.

In Curitiba, (1) 99.5% of households have electricity and drinking water and 98% have trash collection, (2) the literacy rate is 95%, (3) 83% of the adults have at least a high school education, and (4) the average GNP PPP per capita is about $12,600 (compared to $7,300 for Brazil as a whole).

The city has a *build-it-yourself* system that gives each poor family ownership of a plot of land, building materials, two trees, and an hour's consultation with an archi-

array of other tools to (1) discourage urban sprawl, (2) direct growth to certain areas, (3) protect ecologically sensitive and important lands and waterways, and (4) develop urban areas that are more environmentally sustainable and more enjoyable places to live.

It involves a return to some 19th-century town-planning principles such as (1) building grocery stores, pharmacies, other stores, professional offices, and mass transit lines within walking or bicycling distances from residences, (2) encouraging sufficient population

City
center

**Route**

━ Express ━ Interdistrict ━ Direct ━ Feeder ━ Workers

The bus system in Curitiba, Brazil. This systems moves large numbers of passengers around rapidly because **(1)** each of the five major spokes has two express lanes used only by buses, **(2)** double and triple length bus sections are hooked together and used as needed, and **(3)** boarding is speeded up by the use of extra-wide doors and raised tubes that allow passengers to pay before getting on the bus (top right).

tect. A public geographic information system (GIS) gives everyone equal access to information about all the land in the city. The government has an array of telephone- and Internet-based systems that respond quickly to the problems and inquiries of its citizens.

All of these things have been accomplished despite Curitiba's enormous population growth, from 300,000 in 1950 to 2.3 million in 2002, as rural poor people have flocked to the city. By 2020, city planners expect another 1 million residents.

Curitiba has slums, shantytowns, and squatter settlements on its outskirts, and most of the problems of other cities. However, the city designates tracts of land where squatters can settle instead of allowing them to settle wherever they can— often in high-risk areas where it is difficult to provide basic services such as water, sewers, and roads.

Most of Curitiba's citizens **(1)** have a sense of vision, solidarity, pride, and hope, and **(2)** are committed to making their city even better. Polls show that 99% of the city's inhabitants would not want to live anywhere else.

The entire program is the brainchild of architect and former college teacher Jaime Lerner, an energetic and charismatic leader who has served as the city's mayor three times since the 1970s. Under his leadership, the municipal government has dedicated itself to **(1)** finding solutions to problems that are *simple, innovative, fast, cheap,* and *fun* and **(2)** establishing a government that is honest, accountable, and open to public scrutiny. For example, when people pay their property taxes they get to vote for the improvements they would like to see in their neighborhood.

The government innovates and takes risks with the expectation that mistakes will be made and then quickly detected, diagnosed, and corrected (adaptive management). The World Bank cites Curitiba as an example of what can be done to make cities more sustainable and livable through innovative civic leadership and community effort. Curitiba's dependence on a well-planned bus network and bicycle paths are being replicated in Bogotá, Colombia; Lima, Peru; and several other Latin American cities.

### Critical Thinking

**1.** Why do you think Curitiba has been so successful in its efforts to become an ecocity, compared with the generally unsustainable cities found in most developed and developing countries?

**2.** What is the city or area where you live doing to make itself more ecologically and economically sustainable?

density to support use of mass transit to make more distant trips to work or for specialized shopping, and **(3)** allocating more open space for squares, parks, and community gardens (p. 660). Existing car-dependent suburbs can be retrofitted with sidewalks, bicycle paths, and bus lanes. Abandoned or existing nearby shopping centers can be rebuilt as town centers where people can work, shop, and live. Figure 25-20 (p. 681) lists smart growth tools used to prevent and control urban growth and sprawl.

## Ecological Land-Use Planning

Six basic steps are involved in ecological land-use planning:

**1.** *Make an environmental and social inventory.* Experts survey **(a)** geological factors (soil type, floodplains, water availability), **(b)** ecological factors (wildlife habitats, stream quality, pollution), **(c)** economic factors (housing, transportation, and industrial development), and **(d)** health and social factors (disease, crime rates, and poverty). A top priority is to identify and protect areas that are critical for **(a)** preserving water quality, **(b)** supplying drinking water, and **(c)** reducing erosion and identifying areas that are most likely to suffer from toxic wastes and natural hazards such as flooding.

**2.** *Identify and prioritize goals.* For example, goals may be to **(a)** encourage or discourage further economic development (at least some types) and population growth, **(b)** protect prime cropland, forests, and wetlands from development, and **(c)** reduce soil erosion.

**3.** *Develop individual and composite maps.* Data for each factor surveyed in the environmental and social inventory are plotted on separate transparent plastic maps, sometimes using GIS techniques (Figure 4-32, p. 91). The transparencies are then superimposed or combined by computer into three composite maps, one each for geological, ecological, and socioeconomic factors.

**4.** *Develop a master composite.* The three composite maps are combined to form a master composite, which

shows how the variables interact and indicates the suitability of various areas for different types of land use.

**5.** *Develop a master plan.* Experts, public officials, and the public evaluate the master composite (or a series of alternative master composites), and a final master plan is drawn up and approved.

**6.** *Implement the master plan.* The plan is set in motion, monitored, updated, and revised as needed by the appropriate government, legal, environmental, and social agencies.

### Critical Thinking

Would you be willing to pay slightly higher local taxes to support ecological land-use planning where you live? Explain.

---

Some developers, real estate firms, and business interests strongly oppose many of the measures listed in Figure 25-20, arguing that they **(1)** hinder economic growth, **(2)** restrict what private landowners can do with their land, and **(3)** involve too much regulation by local, state, and federal agencies. However, several studies have shown that most forms of smart growth provide more jobs and spur more economic renewal than conventional economic growth.

There is a growing focus on smart growth in the United States as many people in sprawling urban areas are becoming fed up with traffic jams and strip malls. Between 1997 and 2000, 22 states enacted some type of law to help control urban sprawl.

Some critics say concern over sprawl is often is a matter of perception. They point out that although people are fed up with the problems it creates, they also like what it usually provides (such as good schools, safe neighborhoods, and for some more affordable housing), and most prefer it to the alternative of living in a more crowded and expensive urban environment. One problem is agreeing on what dumb growth is and getting municipalities to plan better to reduce the undesirable effects of urban development.

China has taken the strongest stand of any country against sprawl. The government has designated 80% of the country's arable land as *fundamental land*. Building on such land requires approval from local

and provincial governments and the State Council—somewhat like having to get congressional approval for a new subdivision in the United States. Developers violating these rules face the death penalty. National land-use planning also is used in Japan and much of western Europe, and state land-use planning is used in Oregon in the United States (Solutions, p. 683).

Most European countries have been successful in discouraging urban sprawl and encouraging compact cities by **(1)** keeping a tight grip on development at the national level, **(2)** imposing high gasoline taxes to encourage people to live closer to work and shops and to discourage car use, **(3)** using high taxes on heating fuel to encourage living in apartments and small houses, and **(4)** using gasoline and heating fuel tax revenues to develop efficient train and other mass transit systems within and between cities.

**How Can Urban Open Space Be Preserved?** Some U.S. cities have had the foresight to preserve significant blocks of open space in the form of municipal parks. Central Park in New York City, Golden Gate Park in San Francisco, Fairmont Park in Philadelphia, and Grant Park in Chicago are examples of large urban parks in the United States.

In 1883, Minneapolis, Minnesota, officials vowed to create "the finest and most beautiful system of public parks and boulevards of any city in America." This

| Limits and Regulations | | Protection |
|---|---|---|
| • Limit building permits<br>• Urban growth boundaries<br>• Green belts around cities<br>• Public review of new development | | • Preserve existing open space<br>• Buy new open space<br>• Buy development rights that prohibit certain types of development on land parcels |
| **Zoning** | | **Taxes** |
| • Encourage mixed use<br>• Concentrate development along mass transportation routes<br>• Promote high-density cluster housing developments | | • Tax land, not buildings<br>• Tax land on value of actual use (such as forest and agriculture) instead of highest value as developed land |
| **Planning** | | **Tax Breaks** |
| • Ecological land-use planning<br>• Environmental impact analysis<br>• Integrated regional planning<br>• State and national planning | | • For owners agreeing legally to not allow certain types of development (conservation easements)<br>• For cleaning up and developing abandoned urban sites (brownfields) |
| | | **Revitalization and New Growth** |
| | | • Revitalize existing towns and cities<br>• Build well-planned new towns |

**Figure 25-20** *Smart growth tools* used to prevent and control urban growth and sprawl.

goal has been achieved. Today the city has 170 parks spaced so most homes in Minneapolis are within six blocks of a green space. A 2000 study by the nonprofit Trust for Public Land rated Minneapolis, Minnesota, Cincinnati, Ohio, and Boston, Massachusetts, as having the country's best urban park systems.

As newer cities expand, they can develop large or medium-size parks. Even older cities can create small or medium-size parks or open spaces by **(1)** removing buildings and streets, **(2)** planting trees and grass, and **(3)** establishing ponds, wetlands, and lakes in areas where buildings have been abandoned.

Another approach is to **(1)** buy land for use as parks and other forms of community open space and to protect environmentally sensitive land or surrounding farmland from being developed or **(2)** purchase *development rights* that prohibit certain types of development on environmentally sensitive land. Such purchases can be made by **(1)** private groups such as the Nature Conservancy (Solutions, p. 623), **(2)** local nonprofit, tax-exempt charitable organizations (such as land trusts),

and **(3)** government agencies through taxes or bond referendums.

Some cities provide open space and control urban growth by surrounding a large city with a *greenbelt* (Figure 25-21): an open area used for recreation, sustainable forestry, or other nondestructive uses. Satellite towns can be built outside the belt. Ideally, the outlying towns and the central city are linked by an extensive public transport system. Many cities in western Europe and Canadian cities such as Toronto and Vancouver have used this approach.

Another approach to preserving open space outside a city is to set up an *urban growth boundary:* a line surrounding a city beyond which new development is not allowed. This is required for all communities in the states of Washington, Tennessee, and Oregon (Solutions, p. 683).

Since World War II, the typical approach to suburban housing development in the United States has been to bulldoze a tract of woods or farmland and build rows of standard houses on standard-size lots (Figure 25-22, middle, p. 682). Many of these developments and their streets are named after the trees and wildlife they displaced (Oak Lane, Cedar Drive, Pheasant Run, Fox Fields).

In recent years, builders have increasingly used a new pattern, known as *cluster development,*

**Figure 25-21** Establishing a *greenbelt* around a large city can control urban growth and provide open space for recreation and other nondestructive uses. Satellite towns sometimes are built outside the belt. Highways or rail systems can be used to transport people around the periphery or into the central city.

Undeveloped land

Creek

Marsh

Typical housing development

Cluster housing development

Cluster

Creek

Cluster

Pond

**Figure 25-22** *Conventional and cluster housing developments* as they might appear if constructed on the same land area. With cluster development, houses, town houses, condominiums, and two- to six-story apartments are built on part of the tract. The rest, typically 30–50% of the area, is left as open space, parks, and cycling and walking paths.

in which high-density housing units are concentrated on one portion of a parcel, with the rest of the land (often 40–50%) used for commonly shared open space (Figure 25-22, bottom). When done properly, high-density cluster developments are a win-win solution for residents, developers, and the environment. Residents get **(1)** more open and recreational space, **(2)** aesthetically pleasing surroundings, and **(3)** lower heating and cooling costs because some walls are shared. Developers can cut their costs for site preparation, roads, utilities, and other forms of infrastructure by as much as 40% and sell units that have a higher market value.

Some cities have converted abandoned railroad rights-of-way and dry creek beds into bicycle, hiking, and jogging paths, often called *greenways*. More than 500 new greenway projects, developed largely by citizens' groups, are under way in the United States. Many German, Dutch, and Danish cities are connected by extensive networks of footpaths and bike paths.

## 25-5 SOLUTIONS: MAKING URBAN AREAS MORE LIVABLE AND SUSTAINABLE

**What Are the Pros and Cons of Building New Cities and Towns?**   Urban problems must be solved in existing cities. However, building new cities and towns could take some of the pressure off overpopulated and economically depressed urban areas and allow development of more environmentally sustainable cities.

Great Britain has built 16 new towns and is building 15 more. New towns have also been built in Singapore, Hong Kong, Japan, Finland, Sweden, France, the Netherlands, Venezuela, Brazil, New Zealand, the Philippines, and the United States. They are of three types: **(1)** *satellite towns,* located fairly close to an existing large city (Figure 25-21), **(2)** *freestanding new towns,* located far from any major city, and **(3)** *in-town new towns,* located within existing urban areas.

Typically, new towns are designed for populations of 20,000–100,000 people (Case Study, p. 683). Some of the more successful new towns have been funded and developed by a partnership between the public and private sectors.

A new town called Las Colinas, Texas, has been built 8 kilometers (5 miles) from the Dallas–Fort Worth Airport on land that was once a ranch. The community is built around an urban center and a lake, with water taxis to transport people across it. The town is laced with greenbelts and open spaces to separate high-rise office buildings, warehouses, and residential buildings. People working in high-rise buildings park their cars outside the core and take a computer-controlled personal transit system to their offices. New or rebuilt smaller-scale village communities have been created in **(1)** Gainesville, Florida, **(2)** Harbor Town, Tennessee (developed on an island in the Mississippi River, 5 minutes from downtown Memphis), **(3)** Laguna West, California (a middle-class development on the far fringes of suburban Sacramento), **(4)** Valencia, California, and **(5)** Eco-Village, New York (a potentially sustainable village being developed near Ithaca, New York).

New towns and more environmentally sustainable communities offer many benefits for those who can afford to live in such places. But some critics are concerned that most of these communities do not provide affordable housing for the poor and for many middle-class families.

**How Can We Make Cities More Sustainable and More Desirable Places to Live?**   According to most environmentalists and urban planners, increased urbanization and urban density are better than spreading people out over the countryside, which

## Land-Use Planning in Oregon

**SOLUTIONS**

Since the mid-1970s, Oregon has had a comprehensive statewide land-use planning process based on three principles:

**1.** *Permanently zone all rural land in Oregon as forest, agricultural, or urban land.*

**2.** *Draw an urban growth line around each community in the state, with no urban development allowed outside the boundary.*

**3.** *Place control over land-use planning in state hands through the Land Conservation and Development Commission.*

Not surprisingly, this last principle has been the most controversial. It is based on the idea that public good takes precedence over private property rights. It is a well-established principle in most European countries that is generally opposed in the United States.

However, Oregon's plan has worked because it is not designed to "just say no" to development. Instead, it encourages certain kinds of development, such as dense urban development that helps prevent destruction of croplands, wetlands, and biodiversity in the surrounding area.

Because of the plan, **(1)** most of the state's rural areas remain undeveloped, and **(2)** the state and many of its cities are consistently rated among the best places in the United States to live.

Since 1973, Portland, Oregon, has been using *smart growth* to control sprawl and reduce auto use by **(1)** establishing an urban growth boundary around Portland and 23 nearby cities, **(2)** creating large areas of green space, including removing a six-lane expressway to make room for a downtown riverfront park, **(3)** developing an efficient mass transportation system, **(4)** using zoning to encourage high-density development along major transit lines (with 85% of all new building

to be within a 5-minute walk from a transit stop), **(5)** allowing mixed development of offices, shops, and residences in the same area and retail stores on the street level of every parking garage and office building, and **(6)** placing a ceiling on the number of downtown parking spaces.

These policies have helped **(1)** create 30,000 new inner-city jobs, **(2)** double the number of people working downtown since 1975, and **(3)** attract almost $1 billion in private investment.

However, developers are now jumping over the growth boundary and creating urban sprawl on land beyond that is within easy commuting distance of Portland. Growth is occurring to the south in Salem, Oregon, and to the north across the state line in Vancouver, Washington.

### Critical Thinking

How would you improve on Oregon's land-use planning system?

would destroy more of the planet's biodiversity. To these analysts, the primary problem is not urbanization but our failure to make most cities more sustainable and livable.

Over the next few decades, they call for us to make new and existing urban areas more self-reliant, sustainable, and enjoyable places to live through good ecological design (Guest Essay, p. 684).

## Tapiola, Finland

**CASE STUDY**

Tapiola, Finland, a satellite new town not far from Helsinki, is internationally acclaimed for its ecological design, beauty, and high quality of life for its residents. Designed in 1951, it is located in a beautiful setting along the shores of the Gulf of Finland.

It is being built gradually in seven sections, with an ultimate projected population of 80,000. Today many of its more than 50,000 residents work in Helsinki, but its long-range goal is industrial and commercial independence.

Tapiola is divided into several villages separated by greenbelts. Each village consists of several neighborhoods clustered around a shopping and cultural center that can be reached on foot. Playgrounds and parks radiate from this center, and walkways lead to the various residential neighborhoods.

Each neighborhood has a social center and contains a mix of about 20% high-rise apartments and 80% single-family houses nestled among lush evergreen forests and rocky hills. Housing is not segregated by income. Because housing is clustered, more land is available for

open space, recreation areas, and parks.

Industrial buildings and factories, with strict pollution controls, are located away from residential areas and screened by vegetation to reduce noise and visual pollution, but they are close enough so people can walk or bicycle to work. Finland plans to build six more new satellite towns around Helsinki.

### Critical Thinking

What might be some drawbacks to living in a new town such as Tapiola? Would you like to live in such a town? Explain.

In a more environmentally sustainable city, called an *ecocity* or *green city,* the demands on the earth's resources are reduced by mimicking the circular metabolism of nature (Figure 3-21, p. 61). In such an ecocity, the emphasis is on **(1)** preventing pollution and reducing waste, **(2)** using energy and matter resources efficiently (Section 16-2, p. 383, and Solutions, p. 533), **(3)** recycling and reusing at least 60% of all municipal solid waste, **(4)** using solar and other locally available renewable energy resources (Figure 25-1), **(5)** encouraging biodiversity, **(6)** using composting to help create soil, and **(7)** using solar-powered living machines (Figure 19-1, p. 483) and wastewater gardens (Figure 19-19, p. 506) to treat sewage.

An ecocity is a people-oriented city, not a car-oriented city. Its residents are able to **(1)** walk or bike to most places, including work, and **(2)** use low-polluting mass transit (Solutions, p. 678).

An ecocity **(1)** takes advantage of locally available renewable energy sources and **(2)** requires that all buildings, vehicles, and appliances meet high energy-efficiency standards. Trees and plants adapted to the local climate and soils are planted throughout to **(1)** provide shade and beauty, **(2)** reduce pollution, noise, and soil erosion, and **(3)** supply wildlife habitats. Small organic gardens and a variety of plants adapted to local climate conditions (Figure 14-21, p. 332) often replace monoculture grass lawns.

Abandoned lots and industrial sites (brownfields) and polluted creeks and rivers are cleaned up and restored. Nearby forests, grasslands, wetlands, and farms are preserved instead of being devoured by urban sprawl. Much of an ecocity's food comes from **(1)** nearby organic farms, **(2)** solar greenhouses, **(3)** community gardens, and **(4)** small gardens on rooftops, in yards, and in window boxes. People designing and

## The Ecological Design Arts

**GUEST ESSAY**

*David W. Orr*

*David W. Orr is professor of environmental studies at Oberlin College in Ohio and one of the nation's most respected environmental educators. He is author of numerous environmental articles and three books, including* Ecological Literacy *and* Earth in Mind. *He is education editor for* Conservation Biology *and a member of the editorial advisory board of* Orion Nature Quarterly. *With help from students, faculty, and townspeople, he used ecological design to build an innovative environmental studies building at Oberlin (Figure 16-24, p. 399).*

If *Homo sapiens sapiens* entered its industrial civilization in an intergalactic design competition, it would be tossed out in the qualifying round. It does not fit. It will not last. The scale is wrong, and even its defenders admit that it's not very pretty. The most glaring design failures of industrial and technologically driven societies are the loss of diversity of all kinds, impending climate change, pollution, and soil erosion.

Of course, industrial civilization was not designed at all; it was mostly imposed by single-minded individuals, armed with one doctrine of human progress or another, each requiring a homogenization of nature and society. These individuals for the most part had no knowledge of ecological design arts.

Good ecological design incorporates understanding about how nature works [Solutions, p. 201] into the ways we design, build, and live in just about anything that directly or indirectly uses energy or materials or governs their use.

When human artifacts and systems are well designed, they are in harmony with the ecological patterns in which they are embedded. When poorly designed, they undermine those larger patterns, creating pollution, higher costs, and social stress.

Good ecological design has certain common characteristics, including correct scale, simplicity, efficient use of resources, a close fit between means and ends, durability, redundancy, and resilience. These characteristics often are place-specific, or, in John Todd's words, "elegant solutions predicated on the uniqueness of place."

Good design also solves more than one problem at a time and promotes human competence, efficient and frugal resource use, and sound regional economies. Where good design becomes part of the social fabric at all levels, unanticipated positive side effects multiply. When people fail to design with ecological competence, unwanted side effects and disasters multiply.

The pollution, violence, social decay, and waste all around us indicate that we have designed things badly, for, I think, three primary reasons. *First,* as long as land and energy were cheap and the world was relatively empty, we did not need to master the discipline of good design. The result was **(1)** sprawling cities, **(2)** wasteful economies, **(3)** waste dumped into the environment, **(4)** bigger and less efficient automobiles and buildings, and **(5)** conversion of entire forests into junk mail and Kleenex—all in the name of economic growth and convenience.

*Second,* design intelligence fails when greed, narrow self-interest, and individualism take over. Good design is a cooperative community process requiring people who share common values and goals that bring them together and hold them together, as has been done in Curitiba, Brazil [Solutions, p. 678], and Chattanooga, Tennessee [p. 685]. Most American cities, with their extremes of poverty and opulence, are products of people who be-living in ecocities take seriously the advice Lewis Mumford gave more than three decades ago: "Forget the damned motor car and build cities for lovers and friends."

The ecocity is not a futuristic dream. Examples of cities that have attempted to become more environmentally sustainable and livable include (1) Curitiba, Brazil (Solutions, p. 678), (2) Waitakere City, New Zealand, (3) Tapiola, Finland (Case Study, p. 683), (4) Portland, Oregon (Solutions, p. 683), (5) Davis, California (p. 660), and (6) Chattanooga, Tennessee.

**Case Study: Chattanooga, Tennessee** In the 1950s, Chattanooga was known as one of the dirtiest cities in the United States. Its air was so polluted that people sometimes had to turn on their headlights in the middle of the day, and the U.S. Environmental Protection Agency warned that when women walked outside, their nylon stockings were likely to disintegrate. The Tennessee River, flowing through the city's industrial wasteland, bubbled with toxic waste.

In less than two decades, Chattanooga has transformed itself from one of the most polluted cities in the United States to one of its most livable cities. Efforts began in 1984 when civic leaders used town meetings as part of a *Vision 2000* process. It was built around a 20-week series of community meetings that brought together thousands of citizens from all walks of life to build a consensus about what the city could be like at the turn of the century. Groups of citizens and civic leaders (1) identified the city's main problems, (2) set goals, and (3) brainstormed thousands of ideas for dealing with these problems.

To help achieve the overall goal of more sustainable development, city officials and 1,700 citizens spent more than 5 months shaping the results of the Vision

lieve they have little in common with one another. Greed, suspicion, and fear undermine good community and good design alike.

*Third*, poor design results from poorly equipped minds. Only people who understand harmony, patterns, and systems can do good design. Industrial cleverness, on the contrary, is evident mostly in the minutiae of things, not in their totality or their overall harmony. Good design requires a breadth of view that causes people to ask how human artifacts and purposes fit within a particular culture and place. It also requires ecological intelligence, by which I mean an intimate familiarity with how nature works [Solutions, p. 201].

An example of good ecological design is found in John Todd's living machines, which are carefully orchestrated ensembles of plants, aquatic animals, technology, solar energy, and high-tech materials to purify wastewater, but without the expense, energy use, and chemical hazards of conventional sewage treatment technology. Todd's living machines resemble greenhouses filled with plants and aquatic animals [Figure 19-1, p. 483]. Wastewater enters at one end and purified water leaves at the other. In between, an ensemble of organisms driven by sunlight use and remove nutrients, break down toxins, and incorporate heavy metals in plant tissues.

Ecological design standards also apply to the making of public policy. For example, the Clean Air Act of 1970 required car manufacturers to install catalytic converters to remove air pollutants. Two decades later, emissions per vehicle are down substantially, but because more cars are on the road, air quality is about the same—an example of inadequate ecological design. A sounder design approach to transportation would (1) create better access to housing, schools, jobs, stores, and recreation areas, (2) build better public transit systems, (3) restore and improve railroads, and (4) create bike trails and walkways.

An education in the ecological design arts would foster the ability to see things in their ecological context, integrating firsthand experience and practical competence with theoretical knowledge about how nature works. It would equip people to build households, institutions, farms, communities, corporations, and economies that (1) do not emit carbon dioxide or other greenhouse gases, (2) operate on renewable energy, (3) preserve biological diversity, (4) recycle material and organic wastes, and (5) promote sustainable local and regional economies.

The outline of a curriculum in ecological design arts can be found in recent work in ecological restoration, ecological engineering, solar design, landscape architecture, sustainable agriculture, sustainable forestry, energy efficiency, ecological economics, and least-cost, end-use analysis. A program in ecological design would weave these and similar elements together around actual design objectives that aim to make students smarter about systems and about how specific things and processes fit in their ecological context. With such an education we can develop the habits of mind, analytical skills, and practical competence needed to help sustain the earth for us and other species.

**Critical Thinking**

1. Does your school offer courses or a curriculum in ecological design? If not, suggest some reasons why it does not.

2. Use Orr's three principles of good ecological design to evaluate how well your campus is designed. Suggest ways to improve its design.

2000 process into 34 specific goals and 223 projects. The city launched a number of combined public and private partnerships for green development, generating **(1)** a total investment of $739 million (two-thirds of it from private investors), **(2)** 1,300 new permanent jobs, and **(3)** 7,800 temporary construction jobs.

By 1995, the city had met most of its original goals, including **(1)** encouraging zero-emission industries to locate in Chattanooga, **(2)** renovating existing low-income housing and building new low-income rental units, **(3)** building the nation's largest freshwater aquarium, which became the centerpiece for the city's downtown renewal, **(4)** replacing all its diesel buses with a fleet of quiet, nonpolluting electric buses, made by a new local firm, **(5)** developing an 8-kilometer-long (5-mile-long) riverfront park, which is being extended 35 kilometers (22 miles) along both sides of the Tennessee River and now draws more than 1 million visitors per year, and **(6)** launching an innovative recycling program (after citizen activists and environmentalists blocked construction of a new garbage incinerator).

In 1993, the community began the process again in *Revision 2000.* More than 2,600 participants identified 27 additional goals and more than 120 recommendations for further improvements. One of these goals calls for transforming a blighted, mostly abandoned industrial area (brownfield) in South Chattanooga into an environmentally advanced, mixed community of residences, retail stores, and zero-emission industries so employees can live near their workplaces.

This new zero-waste ecoindustrial park, modeled after the one in Kalundborg, Denmark (Figure 21-5, p. 532), will have underground tunnels linking some 30 industrial buildings to share heating, cooling, and water supplies and to use the waste matter and energy of some enterprises as resources for others. For example, excess heat generated by metal foundries will be used to warm water used at a nearby chicken-processing plant. Biomass waste from this plant will be converted to ethanol for use as a fuel in another facility. By-products from the ethanol plant will then be used as nutrients for a tree nursery, greenhouse, and fish farm. The new ecoindustrial area will also have an ecology center that will use a living machine (Figure 19-1, p. 483) to treat sewage, wastewater, and contaminated soils.

These accomplishments show what citizens, environmentalists, and business leaders can do when they work together to develop and achieve common goals. However, the city still faces serious environmental problems. One is the controversy over how to handle at least 11 Superfund toxic waste sites on the once heavily industrialized Chattanooga Creek, where many African American communities are located.

According to many environmentalists, urban planners, and economists, urban areas that fail to become more ecologically sustainable over the next few decades are inviting economic depression and increased unemployment, pollution, and social tension.

*A sustainable world will be powered by the sun; constructed from materials that circulate repeatedly; made mobile by trains, buses, and bicycles; populated at sustainable levels; and centered around just, equitable, and tight-knit communities.*

GARY GARDNER

## REVIEW QUESTIONS

**1.** Define the boldfaced terms in this chapter.

**2.** Describe how Davis, California, has been designed to be a more ecologically sustainable city.

**3.** Distinguish between **(a)** an *urban area* and a *rural area,* **(b)** a *village* and a *city,* and **(c)** *degree of urbanization* and *urban growth.*

**4.** List factors that *push* people and *pull* people to migrate from rural areas to urban areas.

**5.** What are five major trends in urbanization and urban growth? What percentage of the population lives in urban areas in **(a)** the world, **(b)** developed countries, and **(c)** developing countries?

**6.** Summarize the major urban problems of Mexico City.

**7.** Summarize the major problems of the urban poor.

**8.** What four shifts in the U.S. population have taken place since 1800? What percentage of the U.S. population lives in **(a)** urban areas and **(b)** suburban areas?

**9.** List four pieces of *good news* and four pieces of *bad news* about urban problems in the United States.

**10.** What is *urban sprawl?* List six factors that have promoted urban sprawl in the United States. List the major harmful effects of urban sprawl.

**11.** Describe three major spatial patterns of urban development. What is a *megalopolis?*

**12.** List seven environmental benefits of urbanization. List nine environmentally harmful effects of urbanization.

**13.** List four ways in which crime decreases environmental quality.

**14.** Describe the major resource and environmental problems of urban areas relating to **(a)** trees and plants, **(b)** food production, **(c)** microclimate (urban heat islands), **(d)** water supply and flooding, **(e)** pollution, **(f)** noise, **(g)** beneficial and harmful effects on human health, **(h)** loss of rural cropland, fertile soil, forests, wetlands, and wildlife habitats as cities expand, and **(i)** poverty and social problems.

**15.** What are four ways cities can grow more of their food? What is an *urban heat island?* List four ways to save money and counteract the urban heat island effect. What are five ways to reduce noise pollution?

**16.** How do transportation systems affect urban development? What are two basic types of cities in terms of population density and transportation systems?

**17.** What are the pros and cons of motor vehicles? List seven ways to reduce dependence on the automobile. List four factors promoting dependence on the automobile in the United States.

**18.** List the pros and cons of **(a)** motor scooters, **(b)** bicycles, **(c)** heavy- and light-rail systems within urban areas **(d)** high-speed trains between urban areas, and **(e)** bus systems. List factors that have discouraged use of mass transit in the United States.

**19.** Describe how Curitiba, Brazil, has become a global model of a more environmentally sustainable and livable city.

**20.** Distinguish between *conventional land-use planning* and *ecological land-use planning*. List four factors hindering the use of ecological land-use planning. Describe the cycle that leads to uncontrolled urban growth and sprawl.

**21.** Describe how geographic information system (GIS) technology can be used in land-use planning.

**22.** What is *zoning,* and what are its pros and cons?

**23.** What is *smart growth?* List ten tools cities can use to promote smart growth.

**24.** Describe how the state of Oregon and the city of Portland, Oregon, have used smart growth to help prevent urban sprawl.

**25.** List five ways to preserve open space. Distinguish among *development rights, greenbelts, urban growth boundaries, cluster development*, and *greenways*.

**26.** How can new towns and cities be used to help solve urban problems? Describe the new town known as Tapiola, Finland.

**27.** Describe the major characteristics of a more sustainable *ecocity* or *green city*. Briefly describe the progress that Chattanooga, Tennessee, has made in becoming an ecocity.

## CRITICAL THINKING

**1.** Do you prefer living in a rural, suburban, small town, or urban environment? Describe the ideal environment in which you would like to live, and list the environmental pros and cons of living in such a place.

**2.** Why is the rate of urbanization **(a)** so high in South America (79%) and **(b)** so low in Africa (33%; Figure 25-2)?

**3.** Do you believe the United States (or the country where you live) should develop a comprehensive and integrated mass transit system over the next 20 years, including building an efficient rapid-rail network for travel within and between its major cities? How would you pay for such a system?

**4.** Do you believe the approach to land-use planning used in Oregon (Solutions, p. 683) should be used in the state or area where you live? Explain your position.

**5.** In 2002, some developers in the United States claimed that affluent people going into existing older neighborhoods, tearing down existing houses, and putting up mega-mansions (typically three times as big and costing three times as much as the old house) were helping reduce urban sprawl. They claim this is a form of smart growth that **(1)** does not eat up farmland and open space, **(2)** reduces the need for new roads, schools, police, and other services because these homes are built in neighborhoods with such services, **(3)** lessens traffic congestion by keeping people who work in cities closer to their work, **(4)** encourages walking and biking to nearby stores, schools, and parks, **(5)** breathes new life into older neighborhoods, **(6)** can increase the market value of existing older homes, **(7)** creates mixed-income neighborhoods instead of concentrating wealth in newer suburbs, and **(8)** adds to the urban tax base. Opponents agree with some of these anti-sprawl benefits but contend that this approach **(1)** destroys many existing and often historic homes, **(2)** yields huge homes that are out of scale with the neighborhood character, **(3)** can pit the rich against the middle class, and **(4)** drives out many middle-class homeowners who cannot afford their usually higher property taxes. They favor restoring, renovating, and adding on to existing homes. But many well-heeled homebuyers do not want to own or renovate existing houses that are obsolete and do not meet their wants. What is your position on this issue? Explain.

**6.** In June 1996, representatives from the world's countries met in Istanbul, Turkey, at the Second UN Conference on Human Settlements (nicknamed the City Summit). One of the areas of controversy was whether housing is a universal *right* (a position supported by most developing countries) or just a *need* (supported by the United States and several other developed countries). What is your position on this issue? Defend your choice.

**7.** Some analysts suggest phasing out federal, state, and government subsidies that encourage sprawl from building roads, single-family housing, and large malls and superstores. These would be replaced with subsides that encourage walking and bicycle paths, multifamily housing, high-density residential development, and development with a mix of housing, shops, and offices (mixed-use development). Do you support this approach? Explain.

**8.** Congratulations! You are in charge of the world. List the five most important features of your urban policy.

## PROJECTS

**1.** Consult local officials to determine how land use is decided in your community. What roles do citizens play in this process?

**2.** For a class or group project, try to borrow one or more decibel meters from your school's physics or engineering department (or from a local electronics repair shop). Make a survey of sound pressure levels at various times of day and at several locations. Plot the results on a map. Also, measure sound levels in a room with a sound system and from earphones at several different volume settings. If possible, measure sound levels at an indoor concert, a club, and inside and outside a boom car at various distances from the speakers. Correlate your findings with those in Figure 25-12, p. 670.

**3.** As a class project, **(a)** evaluate land use and land-use planning by your school, **(b)** draw up an improved plan based on ecological principles, and **(c)** submit the plan to school officials.

**4.** As a class project, use the following criteria to rate your city on a green index from 0 to 10. Are existing trees protected and new ones planted throughout the city? Do you have parks to enjoy? Can you swim in any nearby lakes and rivers? What is the quality of your water and air? Is there an effective noise pollution reduction program? Does your city have a recycling program, a composting program, and a hazardous waste collection program, with the goal of reducing the current solid waste output by at least 60%? Is there an effective mass transit system? Are there bicycle paths? Are all buildings required to meet high energy-efficiency standards? How much of the energy is obtained from locally available renewable resources? Are environmental regulations for existing industry tough enough and enforced well enough to protect citizens? Do local officials look carefully at an industry's environmental record and plans before encouraging it to locate in your city or county? Is ecological planning used to make land-use decisions? Are city officials actively planning to improve the quality of life for all of its citizens? If so, what is their plan?

**5.** Use the library or the Internet to find bibliographic information about *John Kenneth Galbraith* and *Gary Gardner,* whose quotes appear at the beginning and end of this chapter.

**6.** Make a concept map of this chapter's major ideas, using the section heads and subheads and the key terms (in boldface). Look on the website for this book for information about making concept maps.

## INTERNET STUDY RESOURCES AND RESOURCES FOR FURTHER READING AND RESEARCH

The website for this book contains helpful study aids and many ideas for further reading and research. Log on to

www.info.brookscole.com/miller13

and click on the Chapter-by-Chapter area. Choose Chapter 25 and select a resource:

- Flash Cards allows you to test your mastery of the Terms and Concepts to Remember for this chapter.

- Tutorial Quizzes provides a multiple-choice practice quiz.

- Student Guide to InfoTrac will lead you to Critical Thinking Projects that use InfoTrac College Edition as a research tool.

- References lists the major books and articles consulted in writing this chapter.

- Hypercontents takes you to an extensive list of sites with news, research, and images related to individual sections of the chapter.

## INFOTRAC COLLEGE EDITION

Improve your skills with InfoTrac College Edition, a searchable online database of articles from more than 700 periodicals. Log on to

http://www.infotrac-college.com

or access InfoTrac through the website for this book. Try to find the following articles:

**1.** McHarg, I. L. 1997. Natural factors in planning. *Journal of Soil and Water Conservation* 52: 13. *Keywords:* "natural factors" and "ecological planning." An outstanding article on the details of ecological land use planning.

**2.** Sheehan, M. O. 2002. What will it take to halt SPRAWL? *World Watch* 15: 12. *Keyword:* "halt sprawl." Urban sprawl is more than a frustrating commute and rapid development. The implications of sprawl can be far-reaching and most undesirable.

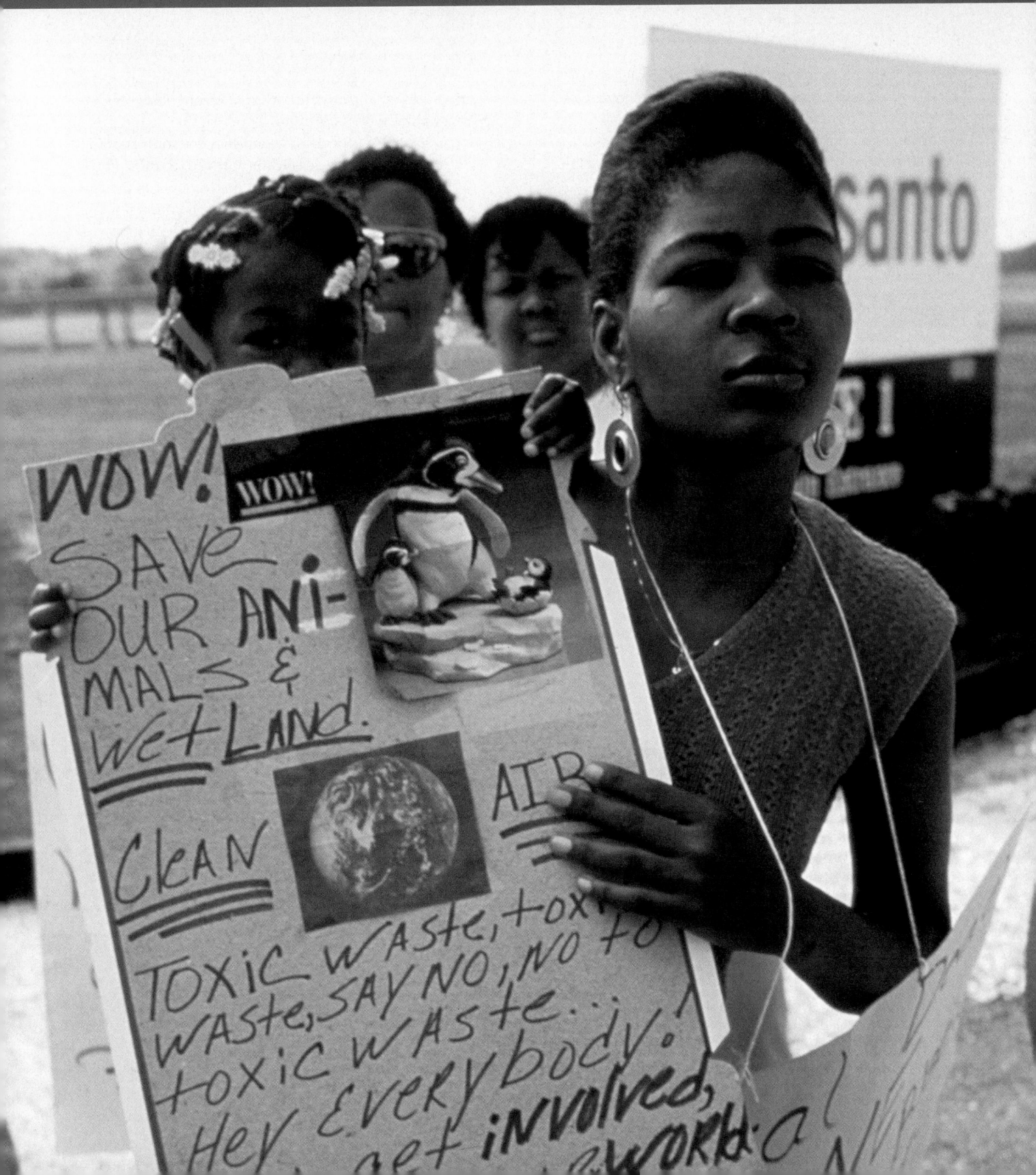

# PART VI

## ENVIRONMENT AND SOCIETY

*When it is asked how much it will cost to protect the environment, one more question should be asked: How much will it cost our civilization if we do not?*

GAYLORD NELSON

# 26 ECONOMICS, ENVIRONMENT, AND SUSTAINABILITY

## How Important Are Natural Resources?

*Natural resources*, or *natural capital* (Guest Essay, p. 16), include the earth's air, energy, water, soil, wildlife, biodiversity, and minerals and nature's dilution, waste disposal, pest control, and recycling services that support all life and economies (Figure 4-34, p. 92, and Figure 26-1).

Economic systems transform natural resources into *goods* such as houses, food, household items, highways, and cities, and *services* such as health and education.

*Conventional economists* believe (1) we can use our ingenuity and technology to develop a substitute for any scarce resource, and (2) depletion and degradation of natural resources will not limit future economic growth.

*Ecological economists* disagree. They believe (1) there are no substitutes for many natural resources, such as air, water, fertile soil, and biodiversity, and (2) some forms of economic growth deplete and degrade the quantity and quality of these

irreplaceable forms of natural capital (Guest Essay, p. 16).

Ecological economists believe over the next few decades we need to unite ecology and economics by modifying our economic systems to (1) mimic the four principles of sustainability derived from observing how nature works (Solutions, p. 201), (2) encourage earth-sustaining forms of economic development, and (3) discourage earth-degrading forms of economic growth.

They believe carrying out this *environmental economic revolution* can (1) greatly increase profits for earth-sustaining business, (2) provide more jobs by reversing the trend of substituting machines for labor, (3) use and waste much less material and energy by greatly increasing resource productivity (Solutions, p. 533), (4) prevent or at least slow depletion and degradation of the earth's natural capital, (5) reduce taxes on income and wealth by increasing taxes on pollution and waste, and (6) free up financial resources and human creativity for improving environmental quality and human health, reducing poverty and other social ills, and restoring damaged ecosystems.

Production of energy-efficient fuel-cell cars

Underground $CO_2$ storage using abandoned oil wells

High speed trains

Forest conservation

No-till cultivation

Deep sea $CO_2$ storage

Solar cell fields

Bicycling

Communities of passive solar homes

Cluster housing development

Wind farms

Landfill

Water conservation

Recycling plant

Recycling, reuse, and composting

**Figure 26-1** Some components of environmentally sustainable economic development favored by ecological economists. Such systems would put more emphasis on conserving and sustaining the air, water, soil, biodiversity, and other natural resources that sustain all life and all economies.

*Converting the economy of the 21st century into one that is environmentally sustainable represents the greatest investment opportunity in history.*

LESTER R. BROWN AND CHRISTOPHER FLAVIN

This chapter addresses the following questions:

- What are the different types of economic systems, and what types of resources support them?

- How can we monitor economic and environmental progress?

- How can we use economics to help control pollution and manage resources?

- What are the pros and cons of using regulations and market forces to improve environmental quality?

- How does poverty reduce environmental quality? How can we reduce poverty?

- How can we shift to more environmentally sustainable economies over the next few decades?

## 26-1 ECONOMIC RESOURCES AND SYSTEMS AND ENVIRONMENTAL PROBLEMS

**What Supports and Drives Economies?** An **economy** is a system of production, distribution, and consumption of goods and services that satisfies people's wants or needs. In an economy, individuals, businesses, and governments make **economic decisions** about **(1)** what goods and services to produce, **(2)** how to produce them, **(3)** how much to produce, and **(4)** how to distribute them.

The kinds of resources (or capital) that produce goods and services in an economy are called **economic resources.** They fall into four groups:

- **Natural resources,** or **natural capital:** goods and services produced by the earth's natural processes, which support all economies and all life (Guest Essay, p. 16, and Figure 4-34, p. 92). There are no substitutes for many of these natural resources and the natural income they provide.

- **Human resources:** people's physical and mental talents that provide labor, innovation, culture, and organization.

- **Financial resources:** cash, investments, and monetary institutions used to support the use of natural resources and human resources to provide goods and services.

- **Manufactured resources:** items made from natural resources with the help of human and financial resources. This type of capital includes tools, machinery, equipment, factories, and transportation and distribution facilities used to provide goods and services.

**What Are the Major Types of Economic Systems?** Two major types of economic systems are command and market. In a **pure command economic system,** the government makes all *economic decisions* about **(1)** what and how much goods and services are produced, **(2)** how they are produced, and **(3)** for whom they are produced.

Market economic systems can be divided into two types: pure free market and capitalist market. In a **pure free-market economic system,** which so far exists only in theory,

- All economic decisions are made in *markets,* in which buyers (demanders) and sellers (suppliers) of economic goods freely interact without any government or other interference.

- All buying and selling is based on *pure competition,* in which no seller or buyer can control or manipulate the market.

- All economic decisions are governed solely by the competitive interactions of **(1)** *demand* (the amount of a good or service that people want), **(2)** *supply* (the amount of a good or service that is available), and **(3)** *price* (the market cost of a good or service). If all factors are constant except price, supply, and demand, the supply and demand curves for a particular good or service intersect at the **market price equilibrium point:** the price at which sellers are willing to sell and buyers are willing to buy a certain quantity of a good or service (Figure 26-2). Changes

**Figure 26-2** Supply, demand, and market equilibrium for oil to produce gasoline in a pure market system. If all factors except price, supply, and demand are held fixed, market equilibrium occurs at the point at which the demand and supply curves intersect. This is the price at which sellers are willing to sell and buyers are willing to pay for a particular good or service.

in supply and demand in the competitive market-place can shift demand curves (Figure 26-3) and supply curves (Figure 26-4) to new market equilibrium points. In effect, if supply is lower than demand, prices rise, and if the supply is greater than demand, prices fall.

- All sellers and buyers have full access to the market and enough information about the beneficial and harmful aspects of economic goods to make informed decisions.

- Prices reflect all harmful costs to society and the environment (*full-cost pricing*).

The **capitalist market economic systems** found in the real world are designed to subvert many of the theoretical conditions of a truly free market. Here are the basic operating rules for a company operating in the world's capitalist market economies:

- Drive out all competition and gain monopolistic control of market prices on a global scale.

- Lobby for unrestricted *global free trade* that allows anything to be manufactured anywhere in the world and sold anywhere else.

- Lobby for **(1)** government subsidies, tax breaks, or regulations that give a company's products a market

advantage over their competitors and **(2)** governments to bail them out if they make bad investments.

- Withhold information about dangers posed by products and deny consumers access to information that would allow them to make informed choices.

- Maximize profits by passing harmful costs resulting from production and sale of goods and services on to the public, the environment, and in some cases future generations.

- A company's primary obligation is to produce the highest profit for the owners or stockholders whose financial capital the company is using to do business.

Both command and market economic systems have an enormous impact on the environment. However, they have different views about **(1)** what causes pollution and environmental degradation and **(2)** how to reduce these harmful effects (Figure 26-5).

**Why Have Governments Intervened in Market Economic Systems?** Governments have intervened in economies to

- Help level the economic playing field by preventing a single seller or buyer (monopoly) or a single group of sellers or buyers (oligopoly) from dominat-

**Figure 26-3** An increase in demand for gasoline because of **(1)** more drivers, **(2)** a switch to less fuel-efficient cars, **(3)** more disposable income for travel, or **(4)** decreased use of mass transit shifts the demand curve to the right and establishes a different market equilibrium point. Similarly, if the reverse of one or more of these factors decreases demand, the demand curve shifts to the left and creates a different market equilibrium point.

**Figure 26-4** A decrease in the supply of gasoline because **(1)** the costs of finding, extracting, and refining crude oil increase or **(2)** existing oil deposits are economically depleted shifts the supply curve to the left and creates a different market equilibrium point. If the gasoline supply increases, however, the supply curve shifts to the right and creates a different market equilibrium point.

| Type of Economic System | Cause of Environmental Pollution and Degradation | Solution |
|---|---|---|
| Command | Economic activity (flow of matter and energy resources) | Regulate economic activity |
| Market | Too little economic incentive to care for the environment | Put a price on harmful environmental activities so marketplace can respond |

**Figure 26-5** Command and market economic systems differ on **(1)** what causes pollution and environmental degradation and **(2)** how we should deal with these problems.

ing the market and thus controlling supply or demand and price.

- Help ensure economic stability by trying to control boom-and-bust economic cycles that occur in market systems.

- Provide basic services such as national security, education, and health care.

- Provide an economic safety net for people who because of health, age, and other factors cannot work and meet their basic needs.

- Protect people from fraud, trespass, theft, and bodily harm.

- Protect the health and safety of workers and consumers.

- Help compensate owners for large-scale destruction of their assets by floods, earthquakes, hurricanes, and other natural disasters.

- Protect common property resources such as the atmosphere, open oceans, and ozone layer (Connections, p. 11).

- Prevent or reduce pollution and depletion of natural resources.

- Manage public land resources (p. 597).

**What Are the Pros and Cons of a Global Market Economy?** Since 1950 and especially since 1970 (p. 7), the world has moved rapidly toward an global capitalist economy **(1)** dominated by large transnational corporations and **(2)** governed by global economic institutions such as the World Bank, International Monetary Fund, and the World Trade Organization (WTO). In 1995, most of the world's national governments granted unprecedented global economic powers to the WTO to establish and enforce rules for the free flow of economic goods and services between countries.

Some see a global market economy run by the WTO as a way to bring economic prosperity to everyone. Others see it as a way to make the rich much richer at the expense of workers, local communities, democratic governments, and the environment.

Proponents say that the WTO will **(1)** stimulate economic growth in all countries, **(2)** help bring economic prosperity to everyone, **(3)** allow consumers to buy more things at lower prices through economic competition, and **(4)** raise environmental and health standards in developing countries.

Critics contend that the underlying goal of the WTO is to **(1)** weaken the power of nation-states and democratic governments to interfere in the marketplace, **(2)** move toward a global capitalist market economy in which large transnational corporations dominate the global marketplace, **(3)** create a homogenized global economy in which global corporations sell the same goods and services in the same way everywhere, with little or no regard for local customs, tastes, or cultural or religious differences (standardized mass consumption), and **(4)** override any economic, environmental, and social policy decisions of the world's nation-states and democratic governments that interfere with the interests of the world's transnational corporations. Today, for example, 50 of the top 100 economies in the world are transnational corporations.

**How Do Conventional and Ecological Economists Differ in Their View of Market-Based Economic Systems?** *Conventional economists* often depict a market-based economic system as a circular flow of economic goods and money between households and businesses operating essentially independently of the earth's life-support systems or natural resources (Figure 26-6, p. 694). They **(1)** assume the environment is a subsystem of the economic system, **(2)** consider the earth's natural resources important but not vital because of our ability to find substitutes for scarce resources and ecosystem services, and **(3)** believe because of human ingenuity that depletion and degradation of natural resources will not limit future economic growth.

*Ecological economists* (Guest Essay, p. 698) disagree with this view. They **(1)** view economic systems as subsystems of the environment, **(2)** consider the earth's natural resources vital because they support all life and economic systems (Figure 26-7, p. 694, and Guest Essay, p. 16), **(3)** believe conventional economic growth eventually is unsustainable because it depletes or degrades the natural resources on which economic systems depend, and **(4)** are devoted to integrating ecology ("nature's household") with economics ("humanity's household").

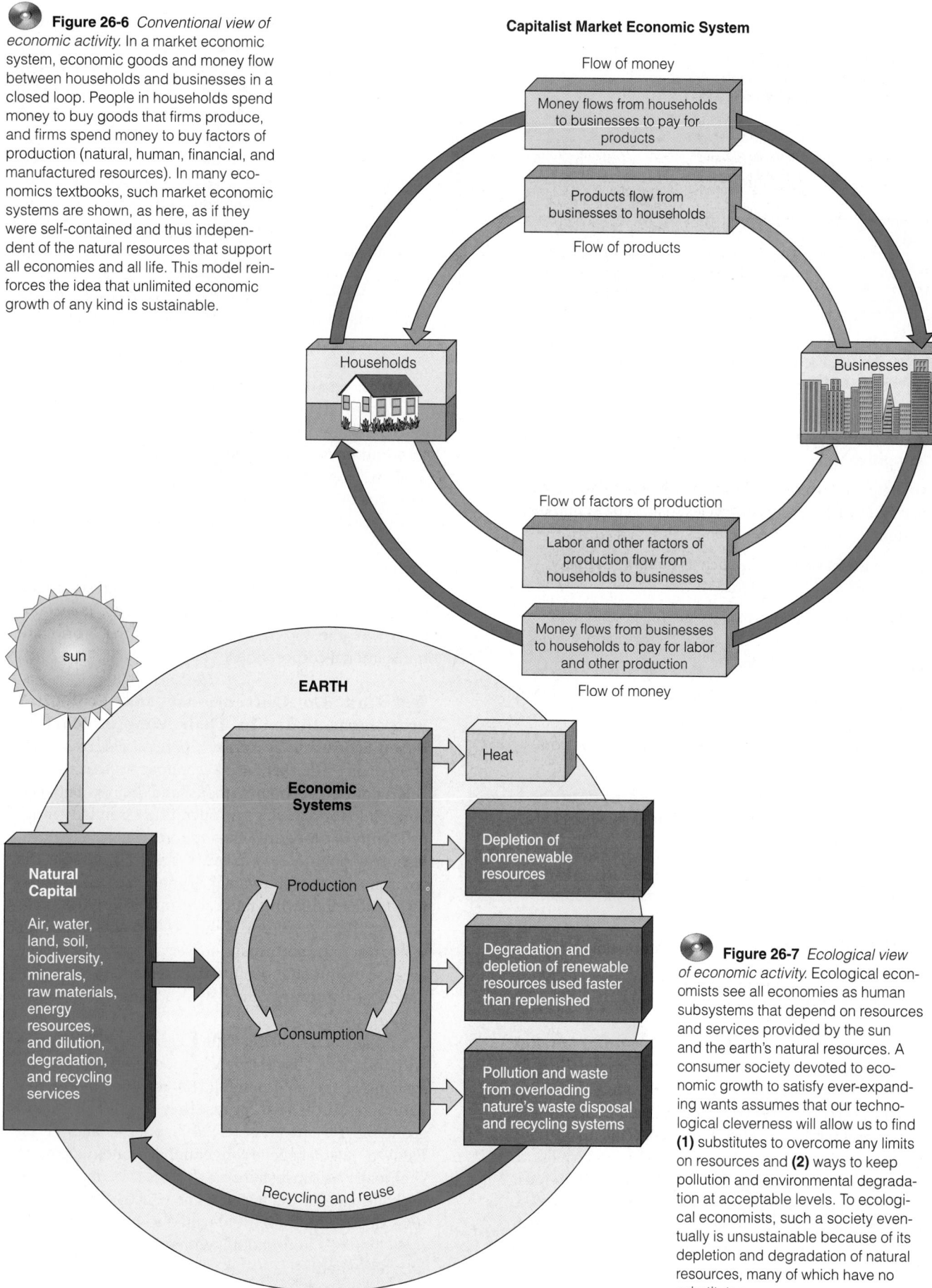

**Figure 26-6** *Conventional view of economic activity.* In a market economic system, economic goods and money flow between households and businesses in a closed loop. People in households spend money to buy goods that firms produce, and firms spend money to buy factors of production (natural, human, financial, and manufactured resources). In many economics textbooks, such market economic systems are shown, as here, as if they were self-contained and thus independent of the natural resources that support all economies and all life. This model reinforces the idea that unlimited economic growth of any kind is sustainable.

**Capitalist Market Economic System**

Flow of money

Money flows from households to businesses to pay for products

Products flow from businesses to households

Flow of products

Households

Businesses

Flow of factors of production

Labor and other factors of production flow from households to businesses

Money flows from businesses to households to pay for labor and other production

Flow of money

sun

**EARTH**

Heat

**Economic Systems**

Production

Consumption

Depletion of nonrenewable resources

Degradation and depletion of renewable resources used faster than replenished

Pollution and waste from overloading nature's waste disposal and recycling systems

**Natural Capital**

Air, water, land, soil, biodiversity, minerals, raw materials, energy resources, and dilution, degradation, and recycling services

Recycling and reuse

**Figure 26-7** *Ecological view of economic activity.* Ecological economists see all economies as human subsystems that depend on resources and services provided by the sun and the earth's natural resources. A consumer society devoted to economic growth to satisfy ever-expanding wants assumes that our technological cleverness will allow us to find **(1)** substitutes to overcome any limits on resources and **(2)** ways to keep pollution and environmental degradation at acceptable levels. To ecological economists, such a society eventually is unsustainable because of its depletion and degradation of natural resources, many of which have no substitutes.

Ecological economists distinguish between **(1)** unsustainable economic growth and **(2)** environmentally sustainable economic development (Figure 26-8). They call for making a shift from our current economy based on unlimited economic growth to a more *environmentally sustainable economy,* or *eco-economy.* This new type of economy would be based on **environmentally sustainable economic development,** which involves increasing the *quality* of goods and services without depleting or degrading the quality of natural resources to unsustainable levels for current and future generations (Figure 26-8).

An eco-economy mimics the processes that sustain the earth's natural systems (Solutions, p. 201) by

- *Using renewable solar energy as the primary source of energy.* This requires a shift from nonrenewable and polluting fossil fuels to a *solar–hydrogen economy* (Section 16-7, p. 405) powered mostly by renewable energy from **(1)** wind, **(2)** flowing water, **(3)** solar cells, **(4)** fuel cells powered by hydrogen, and **(5)** heat from within the earth (geothermal energy).

- *Replenishing nutrients, disposing of wastes, and preventing pollution by recycling and reusing chemicals and material items.* In this mimicry of the earth's chemical cycling systems (Section 4-6, p. 82), **(1)** 60–80% of an economy's solid and hazardous waste would be reused, recycled, or composted, **(2)** the waste of one industry would become a raw material for another industry (Figure 21-5, p. 532), and **(3)** recycling and reuse industries would replace most extraction industries such as mining and harvesting trees to make paper.

- *Not depleting or degrading the earth's net primary productivity* that through photosynthesis supplies the biomass used as a food source for all organisms (Figure 4-25, p. 81). Doing this means using more sustainable forms of agriculture (Figure 13-36, p. 308), forestry (p. 605), and ways to harvest and use of aquatic resources (Chapter 24, p. 634).

- *Living off ecological income by not exceeding the sustainable yields of forests, rangelands, fisheries, croplands, and other ecosystems that support all economies.*

- *Preserving biodiversity that* **(1)** helps sustain ecosystems and economies and **(2)** serves as a source of adaptations to changing environmental conditions.

- *Stabilizing population growth and discouraging harmful forms of resource consumption because in nature*

**Figure 26-8** Comparison of unsustainable economic growth and environmentally sustainable economic development.

| Characteristic | Unsustainable Economic Growth | Environmentally Sustainable Economic Development |
|---|---|---|
| Production emphasis | Quantity | Quality |
| Natural resources | Not very important | Very important |
| Resource productivity | Inefficient (high waste) | Efficient (low waste) |
| Resource throughput | High | Low |
| Resource type emphasized | Nonrenewable | Renewable |
| Resource fate | Matter discarded | Matter recycled, reused, or composted |
| Pollution control | Cleanup (output reduction) | Prevention (input reduction) |
| Guiding principles | Risk–benefit analysis | Prevention and precaution |

*there are always limits to population growth and resource consumption.*

Making this shift involves

- Using ecological indicators to monitor economic and ecological health (*environmental accounting*).

- Having the market prices of all goods and services include their harmful environmental effects (*full-cost pricing*).

- Shifting government subsidies to **(1)** reward environmentally sustainable forms of economic development and **(2)** discourage environmentally harmful forms of economic growth.

- Shifting taxes to tax pollution and waste instead of income and wealth.

- Using eco-labeling to identify products produced by environmentally sound methods.

Ecological economists urge developing countries to **(1)** leapfrog to environmentally sustainable economic development based on low pollution and low waste instead of following the pollute-first-and-clean-up-later economic path of developed countries and **(2)** emphasize resource-saving, labor-intensive *appropriate technology* (Solutions, p. 696).

## Appropriate Technology

In his 1973 classic book *Small Is Beautiful: Economics As If People Mattered*, the late E. F. Schumacher described principles for developing more environmentally sustainable economies and societies. One of his proposals was for developing countries to make greater use of what he called *appropriate technology*, which has the following characteristics:

- Human labor is favored over automation.

- Machines are small to medium-sized and easy to understand and repair.

- Production is decentralized, and whenever possible factories use local resources and renewable resources to produce products mostly for local consumption.

- Factories **(1)** use energy and materials efficiently, **(2)** produce little pollution and wastes, and **(3)** do not disrupt the local culture.

- Management stresses meaningful work by allowing workers to perform a variety of tasks instead of a single production-line task.

Examples of appropriate technology include **(1)** simple stoves for use in rural villages (Individuals Matter, p. 620), **(2)** passive solar heating, **(3)** small wind turbines, **(4)** solar cells, **(5)** conventional and electric bicycles, **(6)** wastewater gardens (Figure 19-19, p. 506), **(7)** drip irrigation systems (Solutions, p. 333), **(8)** small-scale water purification systems (Individuals Matter, p. 508, and **(9)** compost bins.

Appropriate technology is not a panacea. However, it is an important tool that can be used to **(1)** provide jobs, **(2)** produce more environmentally sustainable products, and **(3)** benefit local economies, especially in developing countries.

### Critical Thinking

**1.** What are some disadvantages of appropriate technology?

**2.** What types of goods might be made by appropriate technology for use in your local community?

## 26-2 MONITORING ECONOMIC AND ENVIRONMENTAL PROGRESS

**Are GNI and GDP Useful Measures of Economic and Environmental Health and Human Well-Being?** *Gross national income* (GNI), *gross domestic product* (GDP), and *per capita GNI and GDP* indicators (p. 4) provide a standardized method for comparing the economic outputs of nations. Economists who developed these indicators many decades ago never intended them to be used as measures of economic health, environmental health, or human well-being. However, most governments and business leaders use them for such purposes.

GNI and GDP indicators are poor measures of economic health, environmental health, and human well-being for several reasons:

- *GNI and GDP hide the harmful environmental and social effects of producing goods and services.* Pollution, crime, sickness, and death are counted as positive gains in the GDP or GNI. Thus the GNI increases for a country with rising cancer and crime rates and increasingly polluted air and water because money is spent to deal with these problems. In other words, these harmful effects are counted as benefits that are added to these indicators instead of as costs that should be subtracted.

- *GNI and GDP do not include the depletion and degradation of natural resources or assets on which all economies depend.* A country can be headed toward ecological bankruptcy, exhausting its mineral resources, eroding its soils, cutting down its forests, destroying its wetlands and estuaries, and depleting its wildlife and fisheries. At the same time, it can have a rapidly rising GNI and GDP, at least for a while, until its ecological debts come due when the country has lost most of its environmental assets and the income from these assets.

- *GNI and GDP do not include many beneficial transactions that meet basic needs in which no money changes hands.* Examples are the **(1)** labor we put into volunteer work, **(2)** health care and child care we give loved ones, **(3)** food we grow for ourselves, and **(4)** cooking, cleaning, and repairs we do for ourselves.

- *GNI and GDP hide the enormous waste of natural and human resources because they measure only money spent, not value received.* According to Paul Hawken (Guest Essay, p. 16) and Amory Lovins (Guest Essay, p. 384), at least $2 trillion of the roughly $9 trillion spent every year in the United States provides consumers with no value. For example, money, time, and resources spent sitting in traffic jams produce zero value for drivers and cost the United States about $100 billion a year in lost productivity. Another $200 billion a year spent on energy is wasted because the United States does not use energy as efficiently as other developed countries such as Japan.

- *GNI and GDP tell us nothing about income distribution and economic justice.* They do not reveal how resources, income, or the harmful effects of economic growth (pollution, waste dumps, and land degradation) are distributed among the people in a country. The United

Nations Children's Fund (UNICEF) suggests that countries should be ranked not by average per capita GNI or GDP but by average or median income of the poorest 40% of their people.

**Solutions: Can Environmental Accounting Help?** Ecological economists believe GNI and GDP indicators should be supplemented with widely used and publicized *environmental indicators* that give a more realistic picture of environmental health, human welfare, and economic health.

Basically, such indicators would (1) subtract from the GDP and GNI things that lead to a lower quality of life and depletion of natural resources and (2) add to the GNI and GDP things that enhance environmental quality and human well-being but are currently being left out.

One such indicator is the *genuine progress indicator (GPI)*. This indicator, developed by Redefining Progress, evaluates economic output by (1) subtracting expenses that do not improve environmental quality and human well-being from the GDP and (2) adding services that improve environmental quality and human well-being not currently included in the GDP. Figure 26-9 compares the total and per capita values of the GDP and GPI for the United States between 1950 and 1998 and shows a steady decline in both GPI indicators since 1980.

For example, suppose the demand for water causes us to exceed the sustainable yield of aquifers with the water table dropping and wells going dry (Figure 14-16, p. 326, and Case Study, p. 327). For a *con-ventional economist* guided by increasing economic growth as measured by GNI, the solution is to drill existing water wells deeper and drill new wells. By contrast, an *ecological economist* would (1) stop drilling new or deeper wells once the water table starts falling, (2) use water more efficiently (Section 14-7, p. 328), and (3) slow population growth to reduce the per capita use of water.

This and other environmental indicators are far from perfect and include many crude estimates. However, without such indicators, we do not (1) know much about what is happening to people, the environment, and the planet's natural resource base or (2) have an effective way to measure what policies work. In effect, according to ecological economists, we are trying to guide national and global economies through treacherous economic and environmental waters at ever-increasing speeds using faulty radar.

## 26-3 HARMFUL EXTERNAL COSTS AND FULL-COST PRICING

**What Are Internal and External Costs?** All economic goods and services have both internal and external costs. For example, the price a consumer pays for a car reflects the costs of the factory, raw materials, labor, marketing, and shipping, as well as a markup to allow the car company and its dealers some profits. After a car is purchased, the buyer must pay for gasoline, maintenance, and repair. All these

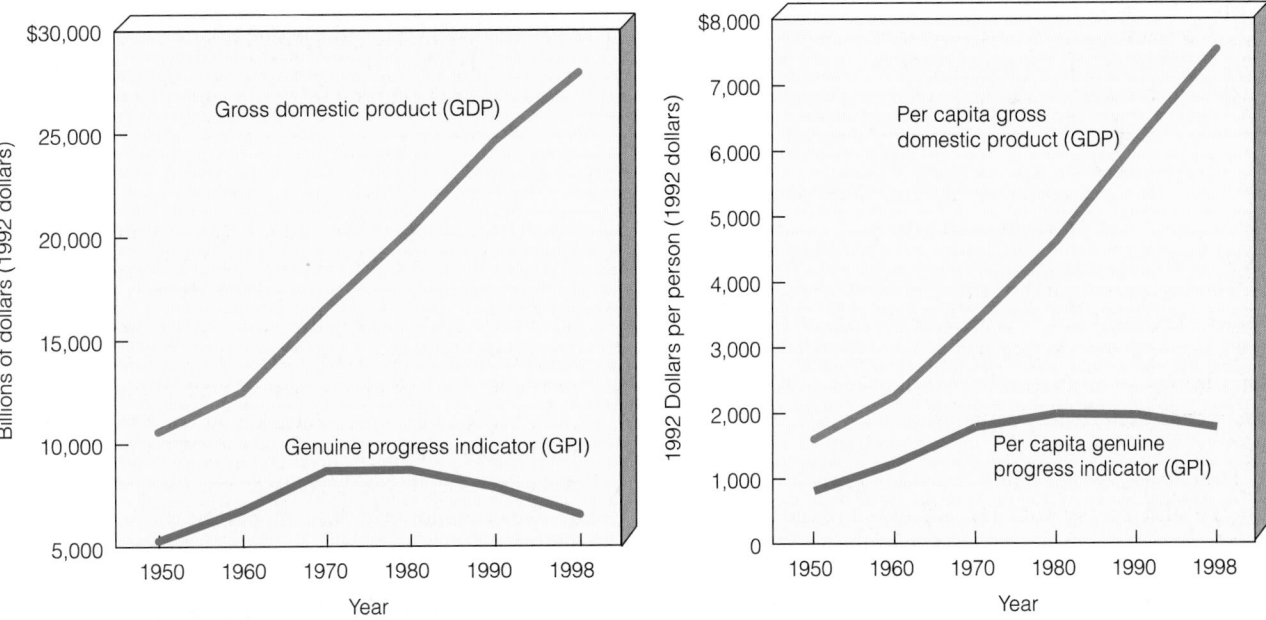

**Figure 26-9** Comparison of the gross domestic product (GDP) and genuine progress indicator (GPI, left) and the per capita values for these indicators (right) in the United States between 1950 and 1998. (Data from Clifford Cobb, Mary Sue Goodman, and Mathis Wackernagel)

*Herman E. Daly*

*Herman E. Daly is senior research scholar at the School of Public Affairs, University of Maryland. Between 1989 and 1993, he was senior economist at the Environmental Department of the World Bank. Before joining the World Bank he was Alumni Professor of Economics at Louisiana State University. He is founder of the emerging field of ecological economics and cofounder and associate editor of the* Journal of Ecological Economics. *Daly has written many articles and several books, including* Steady-State Economics *(2nd ed., 1991),* Beyond Growth: The Economics of Sustainable Development *(1996),* Ecological Economics and the Ecology of Economics: Essays in Criticism *(2000), and, with coauthor John Cobb Jr.,* For the Common Good: Redirecting the Economy Towards Community, the Environment, and a Sustainable Future *(1994). He is considered one of the foremost thinkers in ecological economics.*

A steady-state economic system is characterized by balanced, opposing forces that maintain a constant stock of physical wealth and people through a system of dynamic interactions and feedback loops. A low rate of flow or throughput of matter and energy resources maintains this wealth and population size at some desirable and sustainable level.

In such systems, emphasis is on increasing the quality of goods and services without depleting or degrading natural resources to unsustainable levels for current and future generations. In other words, *sustainable economic development* is development without growth in resource throughput and depletion and degradation of natural resources [Figure 26-8].

The worldview underlying conventional economics is that an economy is a system that is essentially isolated from the natural world and involves a circular exchange of goods and services between businesses and households [Figure 26-6]. This model ignores the origin of natural resources flowing into the system and the fate of wastes flowing out of the system. It is as if a biologist had a model of an animal that contained a circulatory system but had no digestive system that tied it firmly to the environment at both ends.

The steady-state or ecological economic view recognizes that economic systems are not isolated from the natural world but are fully dependent on ecosystems for the natural goods and services they provide [Figure 26-7].

Throughput is roughly equivalent to GNI, the annual flow of new production of goods and services. It is the cost of maintaining the stocks of final goods and services by continually importing high-quality matter and energy resources from the environment and exporting waste matter and low-quality heat energy back to the environment [Figure 3-20, p. 60]. The ultimate cost of continually increasing throughput in an economic system is the loss of ecosystem services as more irreplaceable natural capital is converted to manufactured capital.

The reasoning just given suggests that the gross national income should be called the *gross national cost* (*GNC*). We should minimize it, subject to maintaining stocks of essential items. For example, if we can maintain a desired, sufficient stock of cars with a lower throughput of iron, coal, petroleum, and other resources, we are better off, not worse. To maximize GNI throughput for its own sake is absurd. Physical and ecological limits to the volume of throughput suggest that sooner or later a steady-state economy will be necessary.

Another problem with conventional economic theory is that it assumes that manufactured capital based on human ingenuity can be substituted for natural capital. In fact, however, manufactured capital loses its economic value without an input of natural capital. What good are more fishing boats without fish, more chain saws and

direct and indirect costs, which are paid for by the seller and the buyer of an economic good, are called **internal costs.**

Making, distributing, and using any economic good or service also involve external costs or benefits not included in the market price. For example, if a car dealer builds an aesthetically pleasing showroom, it is an **external benefit** to people who enjoy the sight at no cost.

However, extracting and processing raw materials to make and propel cars **(1)** depletes nonrenewable energy and mineral resources, **(2)** produces solid and hazardous wastes, **(3)** disturbs land, **(4)** pollutes the air and water, **(5)** contributes to global climate change, and **(6)** reduces biodiversity. These harmful effects are **external costs** passed on to the public, the environment, and in some cases future generations.

Because these harmful costs are not included in the market price, people do not connect them with car ownership. Still, everyone pays these hidden costs sooner or later, in the form of **(1)** poorer health, **(2)** higher costs for health care and health insurance, and **(3)** higher taxes for pollution control. For example, in the United States, gasoline cost about $1.40 per gallon (37¢ per liter) in 2002. However, when you add all the external costs of pollution, health, insurance, and other social costs, American consumers are paying $5–7 per gallon ($1.30–1.90 per liter). Most vehicle owners are unaware they are paying these hidden costs and do not associate them with driving. Thus the world's current pricing system does not provide consumers with accurate information about the environmental impacts of the products and services they buy in the marketplace.

sawmills without forests, more water pumps without aquifers, and more crop-harvesting machines without fertile soil?

Humankind is facing a historic juncture. For the first time, the limits to increased prosperity will increasingly be limited by lack of natural capital as a growing number of consumers use more of the world's natural resources to produce more manufactured goods.

The greatest challenges facing us today are

- For physical and biological scientists to define more clearly the limits and interactions within ecosystems and the biosphere (which determine the feasible levels of the steady state) and to develop technologies more in conformity with such limits

- For social scientists to design institutions that will bring about the transition to a steady-state or environmentally sustainable economy and permit its continuance

- For philosophers, theologians, and educators to stress the neglected traditions of stewardship and distributive justice that exist in our cultural and religious heritage.

This last item is of paramount importance because the ethical and political problem of sharing a fixed amount of resources and goods is much greater than that of sharing a growing amount. Indeed, this has been the primary reason for giving top priority to economic growth. If the pie is always growing, it is said there will always be crumbs—and the hope of a slice—for the poor. This avoids the moral question of a more equitable distribution of the world's resources and wealth.

The kinds of economic institutions needed to make this transition follow directly from the definition of a steady-state economy.

- An institution for maintaining a constant population size within the limits of available resources. For example, economic incentives can be used to encourage each woman or couple to have no more than a certain number of children, or each woman or couple could be given a marketable license to have a certain number of children, as the late economist Kenneth Boulding suggested.

- An institution for maintaining a constant stock of physical wealth and for limiting resource throughput. For example, the government could set and auction off transferable annual depletion quotas for key resources.

- An institution for limiting inequalities in the distribution of the constant physical wealth among the constant population in a steady-state economy. For example, there might be minimum and maximum limits on personal income and maximum limits on personal wealth. One formula for helping achieve a fairer distribution of wealth might be that high-income people should make only about 10 times as much as low-income people. This would give high-income people an incentive to raise the incomes of low-income people because it would be the only way they could increase their incomes. Another way to distribute income is to tax the haves and transfer the money to the have-nots.

Many such institutions could be imagined. The problem is to achieve the necessary global and societal (macro) control with the least sacrifice of freedom at the individual (micro) level.

### Critical Thinking

**1.** What are the pros and cons of establishing institutions for maintaining population size and resource throughput to avoid depleting and degrading natural resources?

**2.** What are the pros and cons of establishing minimum and maximum limits on personal income? Do you favor doing this? Explain.

**Should We Shift to Full-Cost Pricing?** For most economists, the solution to the harmful costs of goods and services is to include or internalize such costs in the market prices of goods and services. *Internalizing external costs* will not occur unless it is required by government regulation. As long as businesses receive subsidies and tax breaks for extracting and using virgin resources and are not taxed for the pollutants they produce, few will volunteer to reduce short-term profits by becoming more environmentally responsible.

Assume you own a company and believe it is wrong to subject your workers to hazardous conditions and to pollute the environment beyond what natural processes can handle. Suppose you voluntarily improve safety conditions for your workers and install pollution controls, but your competitors do not. Then your product will cost more to produce than similar products produced by your competitors, and you will be at a competitive disadvantage. Your profits will decline and you may eventually go bankrupt and have to lay off your employees.

Ways to deal with the problem of harmful external costs is for the government to **(1)** levy taxes, **(2)** pass laws and develop regulations, **(3)** provide subsidies, or **(4)** use other strategies that encourage or force producers to include all or most of these costs in the market prices of their economic goods and services. Then the market price would be the **full cost** of these goods and services: internal costs plus short- and long-term external costs.

Internalizing the external costs of pollution and environmental degradation would make **(1)** preventing pollution more profitable than cleaning it up and **(2)** waste reduction, recycling, and reuse more profitable than burying or burning most of the waste we produce. Making this shift requires government action because few companies will intentionally increase their cost of doing business unless their competitors must do so as well.

The *bad news* is that when external costs are internalized, the market prices for most goods and services would rise. However, the *good news* is that total price people pay would be about the same because the hidden external costs related to each product would be included in its market price. In addition, full-cost pricing provides consumers with information needed to make informed economic decisions about the effects of their purchases and lifestyles on the planet's life-support systems and on human health.

However, as external costs are internalized, economists and environmentalists warn that governments need to **(1)** reduce income, payroll, and other taxes on wages and profits and **(2)** withdraw subsidies formerly used to hide and pay for these external costs. Otherwise, consumers will face higher market prices without tax relief—a politically unacceptable policy guaranteed to fail.

Some more *good news* is that some goods and services would cost less because internalizing external costs encourages producers to **(1)** find ways to cut costs by inventing more resource-efficient and less-polluting methods of production and **(2)** offer more environmentally beneficial (or *green*) products. Jobs would be lost in environmentally harmful businesses, but at least as many and probably more jobs would be created in environmentally beneficial businesses. If a shift to full-cost pricing took place over several decades, most current environmentally harmful businesses would have time to transform themselves into profitable environmentally beneficial businesses.

**What Is Holding Back the Shift to Full-Cost Pricing?** Full-cost pricing seems to make a lot of sense. Why is it not used more widely? There are several reasons:

- Many producers of harmful and wasteful goods would have to charge so much they could not stay in business.

- Huge government subsidies distort the marketplace and hide many of the harmful environmental and social costs of producing and using some goods and services.

- Producers would have to give up government subsidies and tax breaks that have helped hide the harmful external costs of their goods and services and distort the marketplace. Studies by Norman Myers (Guest Essay, p. 108) and other analysts estimate that governments around the globe spend about

$2 trillion per year to help subsidize **(1)** habitat-destroying road transportation ($780 billion), **(2)** unsustainable agriculture ($510 billion), **(3)** use of nonrenewable fossil fuels and nuclear energy that discourage energy conservation and development of less harmful renewable energy alternatives ($510 billion), **(4)** water projects and groundwater depletion that discourage water conservation ($230 billion), **(5)** unsustainable forestry ($92 billion), and **(6)** overfishing ($25 billion). Economists estimate that eliminating these environmentally harmful (perverse) subsidies and replacing them with environmentally beneficial subsidies would probably cost taxpayers about one-sixth as much.

- The prices of harmful but desirable goods and services would rise.

- It is hard to put a price tag on many harmful environmental and health costs.

- Many business interests, political leaders, and consumers are unaware they are paying these costs in ways not connected to the market prices of goods and services.

## 26-4 THE ECONOMICS OF POLLUTION CONTROL AND RESOURCE MANAGEMENT

**How Much Are We Prepared to Pay to Control Pollution?** The cleanup cost for removing specific pollutant gases or wastewater being discharged into the environment rises with each additional unit of pollutant that is removed. As Figure 26-10 shows, a large percentage of the pollutants emitted by a smokestack or wastewater discharge can be removed fairly cheaply.

However, as more and more pollutants are removed, the cost to remove each additional unit of pollution rises sharply. Beyond a certain point, the cleanup costs exceed the harmful costs of pollution. The *breakeven point* is the level of pollution control at which the harmful costs to society and the costs of cleanup are equal. Pollution control beyond this level costs more than it is worth, and not controlling pollution to this level causes environmental harm we can afford to avoid.

To find the breakeven level, economists plot two curves: **(1)** a curve of the estimated economic costs of cleaning up pollution and **(2)** a curve of the estimated harmful external costs of pollution to society. They then add the two curves together to get a third curve showing the total costs. The lowest point on this third curve is the breakeven point, or the *optimum level of pollution* (Figure 26-11).

Figure 26-10 The cost of removing each additional unit of pollution rises. Cleaning up a certain amount of pollution is affordable, but at some point the cost of pollution control is greater than the harmful costs of the pollution to society.

On a graph, determining the optimum value of pollution looks neat and simple, but there are problems with this approach:

- Ecological economists, health scientists, and business leaders often disagree in their estimates of the harmful costs of pollution, and such costs are difficult to determine.

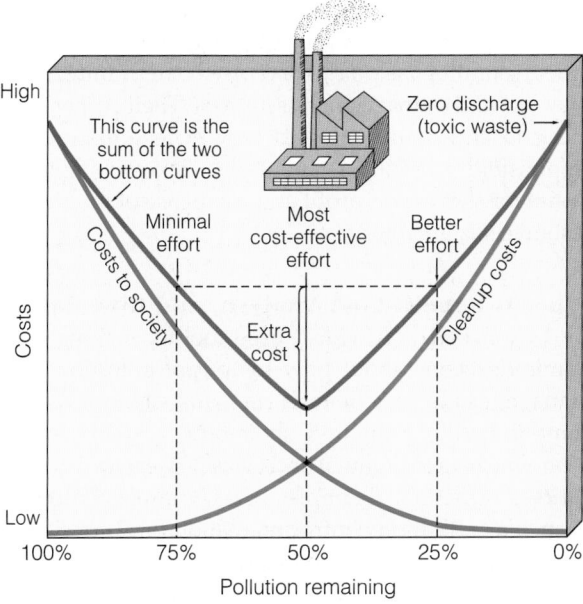

Figure 26-11 Finding the optimum level of pollution. This graph shows the optimum level at 50%, but the actual level varies depending on the pollutant.

- Some critics raise *environmental justice* questions about who benefits and who suffers from allowing optimum levels of pollution. The levels may be optimum for an entire country or an area. However, this is not the case for the people who live near or downwind or downriver from a polluting power plant, incinerator, or factory and are exposed to high levels of pollution.

- Assigning monetary values to things such as lost lives, forests, wetlands, and ecological services is difficult and controversial. But assigning little or no value to such things means they will not be counted in determining optimum pollution levels.

Some analysts point out that we should not be unduly influenced by curves showing the sharply increasing costs of improving pollution control (Figure 26-10). The reason is that stricter regulations and higher pollution control costs can stimulate business to (1) find cheaper ways to control pollution or (2) redesign manufacturing processes to sharply reduce or eliminate pollution.

For example, in the 1970s, the U.S. chemical industry predicted that controlling benzene emissions would cost $350,000 per plant. Shortly after these predictions were made, however, the companies developed a process that substituted other chemicals for benzene and almost eliminated control costs.

**How Can We Assign Monetary Values to Resources and Pollution Costs?** Three ways used to estimate the monetary value of resources that cannot be priced by conventional means are to determine

- *Mitigation costs:* the costs of offsetting damages. For example, how much would it cost to protect a forest from cutting, move an endangered species to a new habitat, or restore a statue damaged by air pollution?

- *Willingness to pay:* using a survey to determine how much people would be willing to pay to keep a particular species from becoming extinct, a particular forest from being cut down, or a specific river or beach from being polluted.

- *Maintenance and protection costs:* how much it would cost to maintain and protect the quality of various natural resources.

There are also problems in assessing the costs of pollution. Economists identify three types of costs associated with pollution:

- *Direct costs* that a polluting company incurs when it has to add pollution control equipment or clean up an oil spill or toxic waste dump.

- *Indirect costs* incurred by local, federal, and state governments in regulating pollution and in damages to local economies from reductions in tourism, jobs, and revenues from fishing and other activities curtailed because of pollution.

- *Repercussion costs,* in which a polluting industry can have an unfavorable image that causes consumers to boycott or reduce their purchases of the company's products.

**What Economic Factors Affect How a Natural Resource Is Used or Managed?**  Economic factors influencing how a resource is used or managed are **(1)** *discount rates,* **(2)** *time preferences,* **(3)** *opportunity costs,* **(4)** *government subsidies and tax breaks,* **(5)** *taxes,* and **(6)** *ethics.* The **discount rate** is an estimate of a resource's future economic value compared to its present value. The size of the discount rate (usually given as a percentage) is a primary factor affecting how a resource such as a forest or fishery is used or managed.

At a zero discount rate, for example, a stand of redwood trees worth $1 million today will still be worth $1 million 50 years from now. However, most businesses, the U.S. Office of Management and Budget, and the World Bank typically use a 10% annual discount rate to evaluate how resources should be used. At this rate, the stand of redwood trees will be worth only $10,000 in 50 years. With this discount rate, it makes sense from an economic standpoint to cut these trees down as quickly as possible and invest the money in something else.

Proponents of high (5–10%) discount rates argue that **(1)** inflation will reduce the value of their future earnings, **(2)** innovation or changes in consumer preferences could make a product or service obsolete, and **(3)** without a high discount rate, they can make more money by investing their capital in some other venture.

Critics point out that high discount rates encourage such rapid exploitation of resources for immediate payoffs that sustainable use of most renewable natural resources is virtually impossible. These critics believe **(1)** a 0% or even a negative discount rate should be used to protect unique and scarce resources, and **(2)** discount rates of 1–3% would make it profitable to use other nonrenewable and renewable resources more sustainably or slowly.

*Time preference* is a measure of how willing one is to postpone some current income for the possibility of greater income in the future. For example, farmers have two options in deciding how to manage the soil on their land:

- A *depletion strategy,* in which artificial fertilizers, irrigation, and pesticides are used to achieve high yields and profits for a short period until soil fertility is depleted or degraded and aquifers are depleted or polluted (Case Study, p. 327).

- A *conservation strategy,* in which investments are made in techniques to conserve topsoil and maintain fertility (Section 10-7, p. 222) and reduce waste of irrigation water (Section 14-7, p. 328) and thus sustain profits in the future

*Opportunity cost* is the cost from not putting money in something that could give a higher yield. For example, forest owners and farmers who spend money on using a conservation strategy to harvest crops and trees on a long-term sustainable basis might have the opportunity to make more money by investing their money in the stock market or another business venture.

*Government subsidies and tax breaks* can strongly influence how resources are used. Resource depletion and degradation are accelerated by **(1)** giving mining, oil, and coal companies depletion allowances and tax breaks for getting minerals and oil out of the ground, **(2)** subsidizing the cost of irrigation water for farmers, **(3)** providing subsidies and low-cost loans for buying fishing boats (Connections, p. 305), and **(4)** subsidizing livestock grazing on public land. Resource conservation can be encouraged, however, by **(1)** withdrawing such resource-depletion subsidies and tax breaks or **(2)** giving resource users subsidies and tax breaks for practicing resource conservation and not selling farmland, ranchland, and forestland to developers.

*High taxes* on raw materials, pollution, and manufactured goods can be used to discourage resource depletion and degradation, and *low taxes* on resource conservation can encourage use of this strategy. Of course, the reverse is also true.

Economic return is not always the determining factor in how resources are used or managed. In some cases, farmers and owners of forests, wetlands, and other resources use *ethical concerns* in determining how they use and manage such resources. Their respect for the land and nature or what they believe to be their responsibility to future generations can override their desire for short-term profit at the expense of long-term resource sustainability.

**What Is Benefit-Cost Analysis, and How Can It Be Improved?**  A widely used tool for making economic decisions about how to control pollution and manage resources is **benefit-cost analysis.** It involves comparing the estimated short-term and long-term economic benefits (gains) and costs (losses) for various courses of action. Examples are **(1)** implementing a particular pollution control regulation or **(2)** deciding whether a dam should be built, a wetland filled, or a forest cleared.

However, such analyses **(1)** have some serious limitations, **(2)** usually are very rough approximations, and **(3)** can be manipulated easily. There are controversies over **(1)** assigning discount rates, **(2)** determining who benefits and who is harmed, and **(3)** putting estimated price tags on human life, good health, clean air and water, wilderness, and various forms of natural resources.

One problem with benefit-cost analysis is determining *who benefits and who is harmed.* In the United States, an estimated **(1)** 100,000 people die prematurely each year because of exposure to hazardous chemicals and other safety hazards at work, and **(2)** an additional 400,000 are seriously injured by such exposure. In many other countries (especially developing countries), the situation is much worse. Is this a necessary or an unnecessary cost of doing business?

Another problem is that *many things we value cannot easily be reduced to dollars and cents.* We can put estimated price tags on human life, good health, clean air and water, pollution and accidents that are prevented, wilderness, an endangered species, and various forms of natural capital. However, the dollar values that different people assign to such things vary widely because of different assumptions, discount rates, and value judgments. This leads to a wide range of projected benefits and costs.

Because estimates of benefits and costs are so variable, *figures can be weighted easily to achieve the outcome desired by proponents or opponents of a proposed project or environmental regulation.* For example, one U.S. industry-sponsored benefit-cost study estimated that compliance with a standard to protect U.S. workers from vinyl chloride would cost $65–90 billion; in fact, less than $1 billion was actually needed to comply with the standard.

Critics also point out that benefit-cost analyses

- Typically fail to evaluate alternative ways to **(1)** control or prevent a particular form of pollution, **(2)** manage a certain resource, or **(3)** find alternative uses or a substitute for a resource.

- Are too imprecise—often varying by a factor of 1,000—to use as the *primary way* to make decisions about environmental regulations and resources. To these critics, using this tool is somewhat like trying to detect a car speeding at 160 kilometers per hour (100 miles per hour) with a radar device so unreliable that at best it can tell us only that the car's speed is somewhere between 8 kph (5 mph) and 8,000 kph (5,000 mph).

To minimize possible abuses, environmentalists and economists advocate the following guidelines for all benefit-cost analyses: **(1)** Use uniform standards, **(2)** state all assumptions, **(3)** evaluate the reliability of all data inputs as high, medium, or low, **(4)** make projections using low, medium, and high discount rates, **(5)** show the estimated range of costs and benefits based on various sets of assumptions, **(6)** estimate the short- and long-term benefits and costs to all affected population groups, and **(7)** evaluate and compare all alternative courses of action.

## 26-5 USING REGULATIONS AND MARKET FORCES TO IMPROVE ENVIRONMENTAL QUALITY

**What Are the Pros and Cons of Using Regulations to Improve Environmental Quality?** Most economists agree that government intervention in the marketplace is needed to control or prevent pollution and reduce resource waste. Such government action can take the form of regulation, the use of market forces, or some combination of these approaches.

*Regulation* is a *command-and-control* approach. It involves enacting and enforcing laws and establishing regulations that **(1)** set pollution standards, **(2)** regulate harmful activities, **(3)** ban the release of toxic chemicals into the environment, and **(4)** require that certain irreplaceable or slowly replenished resources be protected from unsustainable use.

Both environmentalists and business leaders agree that *innovation-friendly regulations* can encourage companies to **(1)** find innovative ways to prevent pollution and improve resource productivity (which reduce costs) and **(2)** develop innovative products and industrial processes (which can increase profits and competitiveness in national and international markets).

Business leaders and many environmentalists also agree that some pollution control regulations are too costly and discourage innovation by **(1)** concentrating on cleanup instead of prevention, **(2)** being too prescriptive (for example, by mandating specific technologies), **(3)** setting compliance deadlines that are too short to allow companies to find innovative solutions, and **(4)** discouraging risk taking and experimentation.

Consider the difference between pollution regulation of the pulp and paper industries in the United States and in Sweden. In the 1970s, strict regulations in the United States with short compliance deadlines forced U.S. companies to adopt the best available but costly end-of-pipe pollution treatment systems.

By contrast, in Sweden the government started out with slightly less strict standards and longer compliance deadlines but clearly indicated that tougher standards would follow. This more flexible and innovation-friendly approach **(1)** gave companies time to focus on redesigning the production process itself instead of relying mostly on waste treatment and **(2)** spurred them to look for innovative ways to prevent pollution and improve resource productivity to meet stricter future standards. The Swedish companies were able to develop innovative pulping processes and chlorine-free bleaching processes that **(1)** met the emission standards, **(2)** lowered operating costs, and (3) give them a competitive advantage in international markets.

An innovation-friendly regulatory process

- *Emphasizes pollution control and waste reduction.*

- *Requires industry and environmental interests to participate in developing realistic standards and timetables.*

- *Sets goals but frees industries to meet such goals in any way that works.*

- *Sets standards strict enough to promote real innovation.*

- *Establishes well-defined deadlines that allow companies enough time to innovate.*

- *Uses market incentives such as emission and resource-use charges and tradable pollution and resource-use permits to encourage compliance and innovation.*

**How Can Economic Incentives Be Used to Improve Environmental Quality and Reduce Resource Waste?** *Market forces* can help improve environmental quality and reduce resource waste, mostly by encouraging the internalization of external costs by using (1) *economic incentives* (rewards) or (2) *economic disincentives* (punishments). This is based on a fundamental principle of the marketplace in today's capitalist market economic systems: *What we reward (mostly by government subsidies and tax breaks) we tend to get more of, and what we discourage (mostly by governmental regulations and taxes) we tend to get less of.*

One way to put this principle into practice is to (1) *phase in government subsidies and tax breaks that encourage environmentally beneficial behavior and* (2) *phase out government subsidies and tax breaks that encourage environmentally harmful behavior.* The problem is that doing this involves political decisions that often are opposed successfully by powerful economic interests.

Another approach is to use *product or eco-labeling programs* to (1) encourage companies to develop green products and services and (2) help consumers select the most environmentally sustainable products and services. Eco-labeling programs have been developed in Europe, Japan, Canada, and the United States (for example, the *Green Seal* labeling program that has certified more than 300 products). They are also being used increasingly to (1) identify fish caught by sustainable methods (certified by the newly created Marine Stewardship Council) and (2) certify timber produced and harvested by sustainable methods (evaluated by organizations such as the Forestry Stewardship Council; Solutions, p. 606).

**How Can We Use Economic Disincentives to Improve Environmental Quality and Reduce Resource Waste?** Economic *disincentive* approaches include the following:

- *Using green taxes or effluent fees* to help internalize many of the harmful environmental costs of production and consumption. Taxes can be levied on each unit of (1) pollution discharged into the air or water, (2) hazardous or nuclear waste produced, (3) virgin resources used, and (4) fossil fuel used. Economists point out that such *green taxes* work if (1) they reduce or replace income, payroll, or other taxes, and (2) the poor and middle class are given a safety net to reduce the regressive nature of consumption taxes on essentials such as food, fuel, and housing. In other words, to be politically acceptable, environmental taxes must be seen as a *tax-shifting* instead of a *tax-burden* approach (Solutions, p. 705).

- *Charging user fees* that cover all or most costs for activities such as (1) extracting lumber and minerals from public lands, (2) using water provided by government-financed projects, and (3) using public lands for livestock grazing.

- *Requiring businesses to post a pollution-prevention bond* when they plan to develop a new mine, plant, incinerator, landfill, or development and before they introduce a new chemical or new technology. After a set length of time, the deposit (with interest) would be returned, minus actual or estimated environmental costs. This approach is similar to the performance bonds that contractors are often required to post for major construction projects.

**What Are the Pros and Cons of Using Tradable Pollution and Resource-Use Rights?** Another market approach is for the government to *grant tradable pollution and resource-use rights.* For example, the government can (1) set a total limit on emissions of a pollutant or use of a resource such as a fishery and (2) use permits to allocate or auction the total limit among manufacturers or users.

Permit holders not using their entire allocation can (1) use it as a credit against future expansion, (2) use it in another part of their operation, or (3) sell it to other companies. Tradable rights can also be established among countries to help (1) preserve biodiversity and (2) reduce emissions of greenhouse gases and other pollutants with harmful regional (or global) effects.

Some environmentalists support tradable pollution rights as an improvement over the current regulatory approach. Ecological economist Herman Daly (Guest Essay, p. 698) likes the idea of issuing tradable pollution permits because it requires society to confront the political and ethical problems of (1) how much total pollution is acceptable and (2) how the distribution of rights to pollute should be distributed (fair distribution).

Some environmentalists oppose allowing companies to buy and trade rights to pollute because it

**SOLUTIONS**

According to a number of economists, important goals of a more sustainable economic system are to **(1)** tax labor, income, and wealth less and **(2)** tax throughput of matter and energy resources more. The tax structure in most countries encourages businesses to increase productivity by substituting manufactured capital (machines) and throughput (energy and materials) for workers (human capital).

To many analysts such a tax system is backward. It **(1)** discourages what we want *more of* (jobs, income, and profit-driven innovation), **(2)** encourages what we want *less of* (pollution and resource depletion and degradation), and **(3)** leads to tremendous waste of natural and human capital. Such tax systems remain primarily because of political resistance to change and the political power of businesses that profit from them.

Shifting more of the tax burden from wages and profits to pollution and waste **(1)** decreases depletion and degradation of natural capital, **(2)** improves environmental quality by making polluters and resource depleters and degraders pay for the harm they cause (full-cost pricing), **(3)** stimulates resource productivity (Solutions, p. 533) by encouraging pollution prevention, waste reduction, and creativity in solving environmental problems (to avoid paying pollution taxes), **(4)** rewards recycling and reuse instead of use of non-renewable virgin resources, **(5)** uses the marketplace, rather than regulations, to help protect the environment, **(6)** reduces unemployment, and **(7)** allows cuts in highly resented and often regressive income, payroll, and sales taxes.

Such a tax shift would have to be phased in over a 15- to 20-year period. This would allow businesses to plan for the future and depreciate existing capital investments over their useful lives.

Because such consumption taxes place a larger burden than income taxes on the poor, governments would need to provide an economic safety net for poor and lower-middle-class people.

Europe is far ahead of the United States in this tax shifting process, largely because of the efforts of Ernst von Weizäcker who pioneered this concept. Trial versions of such tax shifts are taking place in Germany, Sweden, Great Britain, Norway, Denmark, Italy, France, Spain, and the Netherlands. Environmentally harmful activities now taxed in various European countries include coal mining, tree cutting, landfilling, water use, electricity sales, vehicle ownership, carbon emissions, and sulfur dioxide emissions. Currently, such environmental taxes make up only 3% of the world's taxes but these initial results are encouraging.

If Europe and other countries continue moving toward this type of tax shift over the next two decades, their labor costs will be lowered and their resource productivity will increase. To remain competitive in the global marketplace, the United States and other countries may be forced to follow.

### Critical Thinking

What are some disadvantages of making such a tax shift for you and for the country where you live? Do you favor making such a shift in what is taxed? Explain.

---

- Allows the wealthiest companies to continue polluting and thereby excludes smaller companies from the market.

- Tends to concentrate pollutants at the dirtiest plants and thus jeopardizes the health of people downwind or downstream from the plant.

- Creates an incentive for fraud because **(1)** most pollution control regulations are based on self-reporting of pollution outputs, and **(2)** government monitoring and enforcement of such outputs are inadequate.

- Does not work unless the limits on pollution or resource use are set low enough to encourage innovation.

- Has no built-in incentives to continue reducing overall pollution and resource use unless the system requires gradual decrease in the total pollution or resource use allowed (which is rarely the case).

**Should We Rely Mostly on Regulations or Market Approaches?** Most analysts would answer that both regulations and market approaches are appropriate, depending on the situation. Table 26-1 (p. 706) shows that each of the major approaches discussed in this section has advantages and disadvantages.

Currently, in the United States private industry and local, state, and federal governments spend about $130 billion a year to comply with federal environmental regulations (compared to about $55 billion in 1972). Studies estimate that greater reliance on a variety of market-based policies could cut these expenditures by one-third to one-half.

**In What Ways Has Environmental Management Changed?** Figure 26-12 shows the evolution of several phases of environmental management, with the long-term goal of achieving more environmentally sustainable economies and societies.

**Table 26-1 Economic Solutions to Pollution and Resource Use**

| Solution | Internalizes External Costs | Innovation | International Competitiveness | Administrative Costs | Increases Government Revenue |
|---|---|---|---|---|---|
| **Regulation** | Partially | Can encourage | Decreased* | High | No |
| **Subsidies** | No | Can encourage | Increased | Low | No |
| **Withdrawing harmful subsidies** | Yes | Can encourage | Decreased* | Low | Yes |
| **Tradable rights** | Yes | Encourages | Decreased* | Low | Yes |
| **Green taxes** | Yes | Encourages | Decreased* | Low | Yes |
| **User fees** | Yes | Can encourage | Decreased* | Low | Yes |
| **Pollution-prevention bonds** | Yes | Encourages | Decreased* | Low | No |

*Unless more cost-effective and productive technologies are developed.

The period between 1970 and 1985 can be viewed as the *resistance-to-change management era.* In the 1970s, **(1)** many companies and government environmental regulators developed an adversarial approach in which companies resented and actively resisted environmental regulations, and **(2)** government regulators thought they had to prescribe ways for reluctant companies to clean up their pollution emissions. At this stage, most companies dealt with environmental regulations by **(1)** hiring outside environmental consultants, who usually favored end-of-pipe pollution control solutions, **(2)** using lawyers to oppose or find legal loopholes in the regulations, and **(3)** lobbying elected officials to have environmental laws and regulations overthrown or weakened.

By 1985, most company managers accepted environmental regulations and continued to rely mostly on pollution control. However, they placed little emphasis on trying to find innovative solutions to pollution and resource waste problems because they believed them to be too costly.

In the 1990s, a growing number of company managers began to realize that environmental improvement is an economic and competitive opportunity instead of a cost to be resisted. This was the beginning of the *innovation management era* that environmental and business visionaries project will go through several phases over the next 40–50 years (Figure 26-12, right).

These phases include implementing

- *Total quality management,* with an emphasis on preventing pollution and more recently on greatly improving resource productivity (Solutions, p. 533).

- *Life cycle management* based on assuming environmental stewardship of a product throughout its entire life cycle. After products are sold or leased to customers, companies are responsible for maintaining them and taking them back for repair, upgrading, recycling, or remanufacturing (Individuals Matter, p. 534).

- A switch from selling products (such as heating and air conditioning equipment) to *selling services* (such as heating and cooling) (p. 533).

**Resistance-to-Change Management**

| Phase 1 | Phase 2 |
|---|---|
| Pollution control and confrontation | Acceptance without innovation |

**Innovation-Directed Management**

| Phase 3 | Phase 4 | Phase 5 | Phase 6 |
|---|---|---|---|
| Total quality management | Life cycle management | Process design management | Total life quality management |
| Pollution prevention and increased resource productivity | Product stewardship and selling services instead of things | Clean technology | Ecoindustrial webs, environmentally sustainable economies and societies |

**Figure 26-12** Evolving eras of environmental management.

- *Process design management* to achieve cleaner production (Guest Essay, p. 536) by totally redesigning existing manufacturing processes or developing new ones with the goals of **(1)** eliminating or sharply reducing pollution and resource waste and **(2)** decreasing production, waste management, product liability, and pollution compliance costs.

- *Total life quality management* in which many companies become involved in *eco-industrial networks* (Figure 21-5, p. 532) where they exchange resources and wastes in industrial webs not unlike the food webs found in nature.

These changes in environmental management involve a shift from achieving economic growth by producing more stuff to using information and knowledge to increase resource productivity by **(1)** avoiding waste, **(2)** miniaturizing things (bigger is not better), **(3)** replacing chemical plants with green plants capable of producing chemicals we need, and **(4)** learning how to do more with less. According to Robert B. Shapiro, CEO of Monsanto, "If economic development means using more stuff, then those who argue that growth and environmental sustainability are incompatible are right. And if we grow by using more stuff, I'm afraid we'd better start looking for a new planet." Accomplishing such goals requires improving environmental management in business (Spotlight, right).

## 26-6 REDUCING POVERTY TO IMPROVE ENVIRONMENTAL QUALITY AND HUMAN WELL-BEING

**What Is the Relationship Between Poverty and Environmental Problems?**   Poverty usually is defined as the inability to meet one's basic economic needs. The World Bank defines **(1)** *acute poverty* as trying to live on an income of roughly $1 per day and **(2)** *poverty* as trying to live on less than $3 a day.

Poverty has a number of harmful health and environmental effects. It **(1)** causes premature deaths and preventable health problems (Figure 11-17, p. 247, and Figure 11-18, p. 248), **(2)** tends to increase birth rates because the poor have more children to help them grow food or work and to take care of them in their old age, and **(3)** often pushes poor people to use renewable resources unsustainably to survive. For example, a major factor causing deforestation in developing countries is hundreds of millions of poor farmers who are driven to feed their families by slashing and burning patches of forest to grow crops at an unsustainable rate (Connections, p. 616).

**Is Economic Growth the Solution to Reducing Poverty?**   Most economists believe a growing economy is the best way to help the poor because such

## What Is Good Environmental Management?

**SPOTLIGHT**

According to business leaders and business management analysts, key practices in good corporate environmental management are these:

- Providing leadership, beginning with the board of directors.

- Giving a clear statement of the company's environmental principles and objectives, which have full backing of the board.

- Involving employees, environmental groups, customers, and members of local communities in developing and evaluating the business's environmental policies, strategies for improvement, and progress.

- Making the improvement of environmental quality and worker safety and health a major priority for every employee.

- Conducting an annual cradle-to-grave environmental audit of all operations and products, including a detailed strategy for making improvements, and disseminating the results to employees, stockholders, and the public. Currently, some U.S. companies shun environmental audits because they fear lawsuits or prosecution by state and federal environmental agencies. However, several states have passed laws protecting the results of a company's voluntary environmental audit as privileged information.

- Helping customers safely distribute, store, use, and dispose of or recycle company products.

- Recognizing that carrying out these policies is the best way to **(1)** encourage innovation, **(2)** expand markets, **(3)** improve profit margins, **(4)** develop happy and loyal customers, **(5)** attract and keep the best qualified employees, and **(6)** help sustain companies and the economy.

### Critical Thinking

Why have many companies not instituted the environmental management principles listed here? What could be done to change this situation?

growth **(1)** creates more jobs, **(2)** enables more of the increased wealth to reach workers, and **(3)** provides greater tax revenues that can be used to help the poor help themselves.

Some *good news* is that the percentage of people in developing countries suffering from acute poverty (living on less than $1 per day) fell from 29% in 1990 to 23% in 2000. Also, the World Bank and other international monetary agencies hope to reduce the rate of acute poverty to 14.5% by 2015.

The *bad new* is that

- About one of every five people on the planet are trying to survive on the equivalent of $1 a day and one of every two are struggling to live on less than $3 a day.

- The world's desperately poor cannot wait until 2015 to have their numbers hopefully cut in half.

- Rich countries and individuals could essentially eliminate poverty within a decade by sharing more of their wealth.

However, since 1960, most of the benefits of global economic growth as measured by income have flowed up to the rich rather than down to the poor. This has made the top one-fifth of the world's people much richer and the bottom one-fifth poorer in terms of total real income and real per capita GNI (adjusted for inflation; Figure 26-13). Since 1980, growth of this *wealth gap* has increased. According to Ismail Serageldin, the planet's richest three people have more wealth than the combined GDP of the world's 47 poorest countries. Kevin Phillips reports that the average pay of CEOs in the United States increased between 1990 and 2000 from 85 to 531 times that of the average worker.

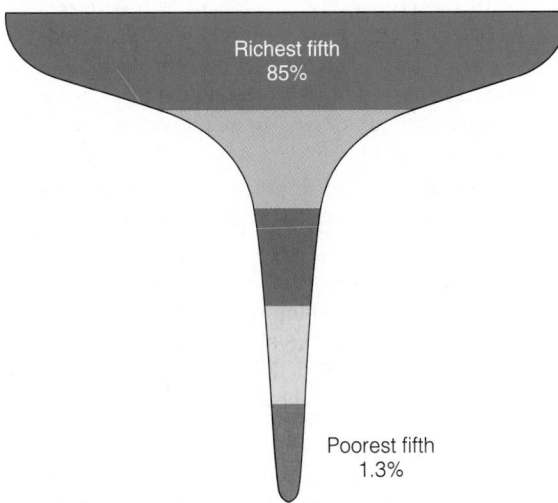

**Figure 26-13** Data on the *global distribution of income* show that most of the world's income has flowed up, with the richest 20% of the world's population receiving more of the world's income than all of the remaining 80%. Each horizontal band in this diagram represents one-fifth of the world's population. This upward flow of global income has accelerated since 1960 and especially since 1980. This trend can increase environmental degradation by **(1)** increasing average per capita consumption by the richest 20% of the population and **(2)** causing the poorest 20% of the world's people to use renewable resources faster than they are replenished to survive. (Data from UN Development Programme and Ismail Serageldin, 2002, "World Poverty and Hunger—The Challenge for Science," *Science* 296: 54–58)

- In 1992, at the Rio Earth Summit meeting, developed countries agreed to contribute 0.7% of their GNI annually as economic development assistance to developing countries. Between 1992 and 2000, four countries—Denmark, the Netherlands, Sweden, and Norway—exceeded this goal by contributing 0.8–1.1% of their GNIs for development assistance. However, average development assistance by the top 15 donor countries dropped from 0.33% to 0.22% of their GNI between 1992 and 2000. The United States, the world's richest country, was at the bottom of the list, devoting only 0.1% of its GNI to development assistance in 2000—half of what it gave in 1992.

- Government studies also show that current forms of economic growth have not led to large increases in jobs for the unemployed and underemployed poor. According to the United Nations Development Programme, worldwide more than 1 billion willing workers are involuntarily unemployed (150 million) or underemployed (900 million). A major reason for this is that since 1980, most economic systems have been increasing productivity by replacing human capital (which is an abundant resource, especially in developing countries) with manufactured capital (machines). If emphasis shifts to increasing resource productivity (Solutions, p. 533), economists project an increase in jobs because this takes more labor and less natural capital, and environmental quality will improve.

- The world's developing countries owe $2.6 trillion to **(1)** commercial banks and private lenders in developed countries (62% of the debt), **(2)** governments of developed countries (21% of the debt), and **(3)** international lending agencies such as the International Monetary Fund and the World Bank (17% of the debt). For many of the poorest countries paying the interest on their debt hinders their economic development and causes unnecessary suffering for the poor because of a lack of funds for providing basic social services.

Studies show that canceling the debts of the poorest countries will not bankrupt or harm the credit of international lending agencies, which have huge cash reserves and have already written these debts off as uncollectible.

**How Can We Reduce Poverty?** Analysts point out that reducing poverty requires the governments of most developing countries to make policy changes. Two examples are **(1)** shifting more of the national budget to help the rural and urban poor work their way out of poverty and **(2)** giving villages, villagers, and the urban poor title to common lands and to crops and trees they plant on them.

Analysts also urge developed countries and the wealthy in developing countries to help reduce poverty. Several ways to do this have been suggested:

- *Forgive* **(1)** *at least 60% of the $2.6 trillion debt (up ten-fold from $0.25 trillion in 1970) that developing countries owe to developed countries and international lending agencies and* **(2)** *all of the $422 billion debt of the poorest and most heavily indebted poor countries if the money is spent on meeting basic human needs.* Currently, developing countries pay almost $300 billion per year in interest to developed countries to service this debt.

- *Increase nonmilitary government and private aid to developing countries from developed countries, with the aid going directly to the poor to help them become more self-reliant.* To many economic analysts, providing foreign aid is a better way to stimulate economic development than loans. This was demonstrated by the use of foreign aid from the United States to rebuild the economies of European nations after World War II.

- *Encourage banks and other organizations to make small loans to poor people wanting to increase their income* (Solutions, below).

- *Require international lending agencies to use standard environmental and social impact analysis to evaluate any proposed development project before it is funded.* Some analysts believe no project should be supported unless **(1)** its net environmental impact (using full-cost accounting) is favorable, **(2)** most of its benefits go to the poorest 40% of the people affected, and **(3)** the local people it affects are involved in planning and executing the project.

- *Carefully monitor all projects, and halt funding if environmental safeguards are not followed.*

- *Help developing countries increase resource productivity* (Solutions, p. 533) *as a way to provide more jobs and income and reduce pollution and resource waste.* According to Robert B. Shapiro, CEO of Monsanto, "If emerging economies have to relive the entire industrial revolution with all its waste, its energy use, and its pollution, I think it's all over."

- *Establish policies that encourage both developed countries and developing countries to stabilize their populations.*

**How Much Will It Cost?** According to the United Nations Development Programme (UNDP), it will cost about $40 billion a year to provide universal access to basic services such as education, health, nutrition, family planning, reproductive health, safe water, and sanitation. The UNDP notes that this is less than 0.1% of the world's annual income.

---

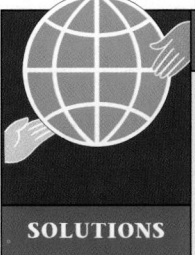

## Microloans to the Poor

**SOLUTIONS**

Most of the world's poor desperately want to earn more, become more self-reliant, and have a better life. However, they have no credit record and few if any assets to use for collateral to secure a loan to buy seeds and fertilizer for farming or tools and materials for a small business.

During the last 27 years, the growing use of an innovative tool called *microlending* or *microfinance* has helped deal with this problem by providing the poor with small-scale loans and other financial services. For example, since economist Muhammad Yunus started it in 1976, the Grameen (Village) Bank in Bangladesh has provided more than $2 billion in microloans (varying from $50 to $500) to 2.3 million mostly poor, rural, and landless women in 40,000 villages. About 94% of the loans are to women (who make up 70% of the world's poor) who start their own small businesses as sewers, weavers, book-binders, peanut fryers, or vendors.

To stimulate repayment and provide support, the Grameen Bank organizes microborrowers into five-member "solidarity" groups. If one member of the group misses a weekly payment or defaults on the loan, the other members of the group must make the payments.

The Grameen Bank's experience has shown that microlending is both successful and profitable. For example, **(1)** less than 3% of microloan repayments to the Grameen Bank are late, and **(2)** the repayment rate on its loans is an astounding 95%, compared with a repayment rate of conventional loans by commercial banks of only 30%.

About half of Grameen's borrowers move above the poverty line within 5 years, and domestic violence, divorce, and birth rates are lower among borrowers. Microloans to the poor by the Grameen Bank are being used to **(1)** develop day-care centers, health clinics, reforestation projects, drinking water supply projects, literacy programs, and group insurance programs and **(2)** bring solar and wind micropower systems to rural villages.

Grameen's model has inspired the development of microcredit projects in more than 58 countries that have reached 36 million people (including dependents). In 1997, some 2,500 representatives of microlending organizations from 113 countries met at a Microcredit Summit in Washington, D.C., and adopted a goal of reaching 100 million of the world's poorest people by 2005.

### Critical Thinking

Why do you think there has been little use of microloans by international development and lending agencies such as the World Bank and the International Monetary Fund? How might this situation be changed?

This expenditure for providing everyone with basic services is only a fraction of the almost $800 billion per year devoted to military spending and the $50 billion spent on cigarettes each year in Europe. For example, providing

- Universal basic health and nutrition would cost about $10 billion per year—much less than the $17 billion spent each year on pet foods in the United States and Europe.

- Universal access to sanitation and safe drinking water would cost about $12 billion per year—about what Americans and Europeans spend each year on perfumes.

## 26-7 MAKING THE TRANSITION TO MORE ENVIRONMENTALLY SUSTAINABLE ECONOMIES

**How Can We Make Working with the Earth Profitable? Greening Business** Figure 26-14 lists principles that Paul Hawken (Guest Essay, p. 16) and several other business leaders and economists have suggested for making the transition from environmentally unsustainable to more environmentally sustainable economies (Figure 26-8) over the next several decades. Hawken's simple golden rule for operating such eco-economies is this: *"Leave the world better than you found it, take no more than you need, try not to harm life or the environment, and make amends if you do."*

As we make the transition to more environmentally sustainable economies during this century, **(1)** some environmentally harmful businesses will decline and become *sunset businesses,* and **(2)** other more environmentally sustainable, or *eco-friendly, businesses* will grow in importance (Figure 26-15). Forward-looking owners and investors in sunset businesses will use their profits and capital to invest in emerging eco-friendly businesses.

**Case Study: How Are Germany, Denmark, and the Netherlands Working to Achieve a More Environmentally Sustainable Economy?** Germany (Case Study, p. 712), Denmark, and the Netherlands are working to make their economies more environmentally sustainable.

**Economics**

Reward (subsidize) earth-sustaining behavior

Penalize (tax and do not subsidize) earth-degrading behavior

Tax pollution and waste instead of wages and profits

Use full-cost pricing

Sell more services instead of more things

Do not deplete natural capital

Live off income from natural capital

Reduce poverty

**Environmentally Sustainable Economy (Eco-Economy)**

**Resource Use and Pollution**

Reduce resource use and waste by refusing, reducing, reusing, and recycling

Improve energy efficiency

Rely more on renewable solar and geothermal energy

Shift from a carbon based (fossil fuel) economy to a solar–hydrogen based economy

**Ecology and Population**

Mimic nature

Preserve biodiversity

Repair ecological damage

Stabilize population by reducing fertility

**Figure 26-14** Major principles for shifting to more environmentally sustainable economies or eco-economies during this century.

Some *good news* is that Denmark is a leader in making the transition to an eco-economy. It **(1)** has banned the construction of coal-burning power plants, **(2)** gets 15% of its energy from renewable wind and is the world's leader in producing wind turbines, **(3)** uses the bicycle for 32% of the urban trips in Copenhagen, **(4)** banned the use of nonrefillable beverage containers, and **(5)** has stabilized its population. However, some *bad news* is that in 2002 a newly elected government began undermining some of these efforts.

In 1989, the Netherlands (a tiny country with about 16 million people) began implementing a National Environmental Policy Plan (or Green Plan) as a result of widespread public alarm over declining environmental quality. The goal of this plan is to slash production of many types of pollution by 70–90% and achieve the world's first environmentally sustainable economy by 2010.

The government identified eight major areas for improvement: **(1)** climate change, **(2)** acid deposition, **(3)** eutrophication, **(4)** toxic chemicals, **(5)** waste disposal, **(6)** groundwater depletion, **(7)** unsustainable

**Sunset Businesses**

Coal mining

Oil production

Nuclear power

Energy-wasting motor vehicles

Mining

Throwaway products

Clearcut logging

Paper production

Conventional pesticide production

Unsustainable farming

Water well drilling

Conventional economics

Conventional engineering, design, and architecture

Business travel

**Environmentally Sustainable Economy (Eco-Economy)**

**Eco-Friendly Business**

| | |
|---|---|
| Solar cell production | Soil conservation |
| Hydrogen production | Water conservation |
| Fuel-cell production | Pollution prevention |
| Wind turbine production | Ecoindustrial design |
| Wind farm construction | Biodiversity management and protection |
| Geothermal energy production | |
| | Ecological restoration |
| Production of energy-efficient fuel-cell cars, trucks, and buses | Disease prevention |
| | Environmental engineering, design, and architecture |
| Conventional and electric bicycle production | |
| | Ecocity urban design |
| Light-rail construction | Environmental science |
| Sustainable agriculture | Environmental education |
| Integrated pest management | Ecological economics |
| Aquaculture | Environmental accounting |
| Recycling, reuse, and composting | Teleconferencing |

**Figure 26-15** The projected decline of environmentally harmful, or *sunset*, businesses and rise of more environmentally sustainable, or *eco-friendly*, businesses during this century. As this transition takes place, jobs will decrease in sunset businesses (left) and increase in eco-friendly businesses (right). (Data from Lester R. Brown, Earth Policy Institute)

use of renewable and nonrenewable resources, and **(8)** local nuisances (mostly noise and odor pollution).

The government **(1)** formed target groups, consisting of major industrial, government, and citizens' groups for each of the eight areas and **(2)** asked each group to develop a voluntary agreement on establishing targets and timetables for drastically reducing pollution. Each group was free to pursue whatever policies or technologies it wanted. However, if a group could not agree, the government would impose **(1)** its own targets and timetables and **(2)** stiff penalties for industries not meeting certain pollution reduction goals.

The government identified four general themes for each group to focus on: **(1)** implementing life cycle management, which makes companies responsible for the remains of their products after users are through with them (a goal that increased the design of products that can be reused or recycled), **(2)** improving energy efficiency (Section 16-2, p. 383), with the government committing $385 million per year to energy conserva-

tion programs, **(3)** inventing new or improved more sustainable technologies, supported by a government program to help develop such technologies, and **(4)** improving public awareness through a massive government-sponsored public education program.

Many of the country's leading industrialists like the Green Plan because

■ They can make investments in pollution prevention and pollution control with less financial risk because they have a high degree of certainty about long-term environmental policy.

■ They are free to deal with the problems in ways that make the most sense for their businesses. This has encouraged cooperation between environmentalists and industrial leaders.

■ Industrial leaders have learned that creating more efficient and environmentally sound products and processes can often reduce costs and increase profits as such innovations are sold at home and abroad.

## How Is Germany Investing in the Future and the Earth?

German political and business leaders see sales of environmental protection goods and services—already more than $600 billion per year—as a major source of new markets and future income because environmental standards and concerns are expected to rise everywhere.

Mostly because of stricter air pollution regulations, German companies have **(1)** developed some of the world's cleanest and most efficient gas turbines and **(2)** invented the world's first steel mill that uses no coal to make steel. Germany sells these and other improved environmental technologies globally.

However, Germany continues to heavily subsidize its coal-mining industry, which increases environmental degradation and pollution and adds large amounts of carbon dioxide to the atmosphere. According to environmental expert Norman Myers (Guest Essay, p. 108), these subsidies are so high that the German government would

save money by closing all of its coal mines and sending the miners home on full pay for the rest of their lives. This approach is in sharp contrast to that in China, which since 1993 **(1)** has reduced its coal subsidies by 73% and **(2)** imposed a tax on the burning of high-sulfur coals.

In 1977, the German government started the Blue Angel *eco-labeling* program to inform consumers about products that cause the least environmental harm. Most international companies use the German market to test and evaluate green products.

Germany has also revolutionized the recycling business. German car companies are required to pick up and recycle all domestic cars they make. Bar-coded parts enable disassembly plants to dismantle an auto for recycling in 20 minutes. Such *take-back* requirements are being extended to almost all products to reduce use of energy and virgin raw materials. Germany plans to sell its newly developed recycling technologies to other countries.

The German government has also supported research and development aimed at making Germany the world's leader in solar-cell technology (p. 398) and hydrogen fuel (Section 16-7, p. 405), which it expects to provide a rapidly increasing share of the world's energy.

Finally, Germany provides about $1 billion per year in green foreign aid to developing countries. Much of the aid is designed to stimulate demand for German technologies such as solar-powered lights, solar cells, and wind-powered water pumps.

### Critical Thinking

What major steps (if any) are the government and businesses in the country where you live taking to make the transition to a more environmentally sustainable economy? What three major things could you do to help promote such a shift in your country and in your local community?

---

Is the plan working? The news is mixed but encouraging. Many of the target groups are meeting their goals on schedule, and some have even exceeded them. A huge amount of environmental research by the government and private sector has taken place. This has led to **(1)** an increase in organic agriculture, **(2)** greater reliance on bicycles in some cities, and **(3)** more ecologically sound new housing developments.

However, there have been some setbacks:

- Some of the more ambitious goals such as decreasing $CO_2$ levels may have to be revised downward or even abandoned.

- Some environmentalists who strongly support the plan are not happy with **(1)** the compromises they have had to make and **(2)** the mild backlash in some industry circles against an energy tax to reduce $CO_2$ emissions.

Despite its shortcomings, the Netherlands plan is the first attempt by any country to **(1)** foster a national debate on the issue of environmental sustainability and **(2)** encourage innovative solutions to environmental problems.

**Can We Make the Transition to a More Environmentally Sustainable Economy?** Even if people believe an environmentally sustainable economy is desirable, is it possible to make such a drastic change in the way we think and act? Some environmentalists, economists, and business leaders (Individuals Matter, p. 534) say **(1)** it is not only possible but imperative, and **(2)** it can be done over the next 40–50 years.

According to Paul Hawken, this new approach to economic thinking and actions recognizes that most business leaders are not evil, earth-degrading ogres. Instead, they are trapped in a system that by design rewards them (with the highest profits and salaries and best chances for promotion) for maximizing short-term profits for owners and investors, regardless of the harmful short- and long-term environmental and social impacts.

Hawken argues that environmentally sustainable economies throughout the world would free business leaders, workers, and investors from this ethical dilemma. In such economies, they would be financially compensated and respected for **(1)** doing socially and ecologically responsible work, **(2)** improving environ-

## Jobs and the Environment

Environmental protection is a major growth industry that creates new jobs. According to Worldwatch Institute estimates, annual sales of global ecotechnology industries are $600 billion—on a par with the global car industry—and these industries employ about 11 million people. In 2000, the environmental industry in the United States employed nearly 1.4 million people and generated annual revenues of more than $185 billion.

Studies by the EPA show that environmental laws create far more jobs than have been lost. Indeed, the U.S. Clean Air and Clean Water Acts have created more than 300,000 jobs in pollution control.

A congressional study concluded that investing $115 billion per year in solar energy and in improving energy efficiency in the United States would **(1)** eliminate about 1 million jobs in oil, gas, coal, and electricity production but **(2)** create 2 million other new jobs. Investing the money saved by reducing energy waste could create another 2 million jobs.

Shifting to more environmentally sustainable economies over the next several decades would create a host of new jobs in eco-friendly industries and services (Figure 26-15, right). However, jobs would be lost in **(1)** ecologically harmful industries such as mining, logging, and fossil fuels (Figure 26-15, left) and **(2)** in regions and communities dependent on such sunset industries.

Ways suggested by various analysts to ease this transition include **(1)** providing tax breaks to make it more profitable for companies to keep or hire more workers instead of replacing them with machines, **(2)** using incentives to encourage location of new, eco-friendly industries in hard-hit communities, **(3)** helping such areas diversify their economic bases, and **(4)** providing income and retraining assistance for workers displaced from environmentally harmful businesses (a *Superfund for Workers*).

### Critical Thinking

What major things (if any) have the national and local governments of the country where you live done to stimulate the growth of environmental jobs? What major things (if any) have these governments done to discourage the growth of environmental jobs?

more business leaders, elected officials, and voters to begin changing current government systems of economic rewards and penalties.

Here are three pieces of *great news*:

- Making the shift to more environmentally sustainable economies could be an extremely profitable enterprise that will **(1)** create many jobs, **(2)** greatly improve environmental quality, and **(3)** sharply reduce poverty.

- We have most of the technologies needed to implement this economic shift.

- Governments would not have to spend more money. Such a shift would be revenue neutral if governments **(1)** shifted environmentally harmful subsidies to environmentally beneficial enterprises and **(2)** taxed pollution and resource waste instead of wages and income (Solutions, p . 705).

Forward-looking investors, corporate executives (Individuals Matter, p. 534), and political leaders recognize that *the environmental revolution is also an economic revolution.*

*I'm fascinated with the concept of distinctions that transform people. Once you learn certain things—once you learn to ride a bike, say—your life has changed forever. You cannot unlearn it. For me sustainability is one of those distinctions. Once you get it, it changes how you think. It becomes automatic and is a part of who you are.*

ROBERT B. SHAPIRO

## REVIEW QUESTIONS

**1.** Define the bold-faced terms in this chapter.

**2.** Describe how conventional economists and ecological economists disagree on the importance of natural resources in sustaining economies.

**3.** Distinguish among *natural, human, financial,* and *manufactured resources* used in an economic system.

**4.** Distinguish among *pure command, pure free-market,* and *capitalist market* economic systems.

**5.** List ten reasons why governments intervene in economic systems.

**6.** List the pros and cons of a global market economy.

**7.** Distinguish between *economic growth* and *environmentally sustainable economic development.* What are three characteristics of environmentally sustainable economic development?

**8.** Explain how conventional economists and ecological economists differ in their view of market-based economic systems. Describe Herman Daly's concept of the *steady-state economy.*

**9.** List the major characteristics of and give three examples of *appropriate technology.*

mental quality, and **(3)** still making hefty profits for owners and stockholders. Making this shift should also create jobs (Connections, above).

*The problem in making this shift is not economics but politics.* It involves the difficult task of convincing

**10.** List five reasons why GNI and GDP are not useful measures of economic health, environmental health, or human well-being. Describe an environmental indicator that could be used to provide such information.

**11.** Distinguish between *internal costs* and *external costs,* and give an example of each. What is *full-cost pricing,* and what are the pros and cons of using this approach to internalize external environmental costs? List six reasons why full-cost pricing has not been widely used.

**12.** How do economists determine the *optimum level of pollution* for a particular chemical? What are the pros and cons of using this approach?

**13.** Distinguish among using *mitigation, willingness to pay,* and *maintenance and protection cost methods* to estimate the monetary value of natural resources.

**14.** Distinguish among *direct, indirect,* and *repercussion costs* associated with pollution.

**15.** Distinguish among the use of *discount rates, time preferences, opportunity costs, government subsidies and tax breaks,* and *taxes* in managing natural resources.

**16.** What is *benefit-cost analysis?* What are the pros and cons of using this tool to evaluate alternative courses of action in controlling pollution and managing natural resources? List seven ways to improve benefit-cost analysis.

**17.** What are the pros and cons of using regulations to improve environmental quality? List six characteristics of *innovation-friendly regulations.*

**18.** Describe two types of *economic incentives* (rewards) that can be used to improve environmental quality and reduce resource waste. List the pros and cons of each type.

**19.** Describe two types of *economic disincentives* (punishments) that can be used to improve environmental quality and reduce resource waste. List the pros and cons of each type.

**20.** What are the pros and cons of using tradable pollution and resource-use rights to reduce pollution and resource waste?

**21.** List six phases or eras in the evolution of environmental management, and describe each phase.

**22.** List seven principles of good environmental management.

**23.** What is *poverty,* and what are its harmful health and environmental effects?

**24.** List two ways in which the governments of developing countries can reduce poverty. List seven ways in which governments of developed countries can help reduce poverty. What are *microloans,* and how are they being used to reduce poverty?

**25.** List sixteen principles for shifting to more environmentally sustainable economies over the next several decades.

**26.** Distinguish between projected *sunset* and *eco-friendly* businesses and give three examples of each type. Describe the projected relationship between jobs and the shift to more eco-friendly business during this century.

**27.** Describe attempts to develop more environmentally sustainable economies in **(a)** Germany, **(b)** Denmark, and **(c)** the Netherlands.

**28.** List three great pieces of news about making the shift to more environmentally sustainable economies over the next several decades. Explain why the environmental revolution is also an economic revolution.

## CRITICAL THINKING

**1.** The primary goal of current economic systems is to maximize economic growth by producing and consuming more and more economic goods. Do you agree with that goal? Explain. What are the alternatives?

**2.** According to one definition, *sustainable development* involves meeting the needs of the present human generation without compromising the ability of future generations to meet their needs. What do you believe are the needs used in this definition? Compare this definition with the definition of environmentally sustainable development given on page 15 and in Figure 26-8, p. 695.

**3.** Suppose that over the next 20 years the current harmful environmental and health costs of goods and services are internalized so their market prices reflect their total costs. What harmful and beneficial effects might this have on **(a)** your lifestyle and **(b)** any child you might have?

**4.** Do you believe we should establish optimum levels or zero-discharge levels for toxic chemicals we release into the environment? Explain.

**5.** Do you agree or disagree with the proposals that various analysts have made for sharply reducing poverty as discussed on pages 708–709? Explain.

**6.** Explain why you agree or disagree with each of the major principles listed in Figure 26-14, p. 710, for shifting to more environmentally sustainable economies during this century.

**7.** What are the major pros and cons of shifting from our current economy to a more environmentally sustainable economy over the next 40–50 years?

## PROJECTS

**1.** List all the goods you use, and then identify those that meet your basic needs and those that satisfy your wants. Identify any economic wants you **(a)** would be willing to give up, **(b)** you believe you should give up but are unwilling to give up, and **(c)** you hope to give up in the future. Relate the results of this analysis to your personal impact on the environment. Compare your results with those of your classmates.

**2.** Use the library or the Internet to find bibliographic information about *Gaylord Nelson, Lester R. Brown, Christopher Flavin,* and *Robert B. Shapiro,* whose quotes appear at the beginning and end of this chapter.

**3.** Make a concept map of this chapter's major ideas, using the section heads and subheads and the key terms (in boldface type). Look on the website for this book for information about making concept maps.

## INTERNET STUDY RESOURCES AND RESOURCES FOR FURTHER READING AND RESEARCH

The website for this book contains helpful study aids and many ideas for further reading and research. Log on to

www.info.brookscole.com/miller13

and click on the Chapter-by-Chapter area. Choose Chapter 26 and select a resource:

- Flash Cards allows you to test your mastery of the Terms and Concepts to Remember for this chapter.

- Tutorial Quizzes provides a multiple-choice practice quiz.

- Student Guide to InfoTrac will lead you to Critical Thinking Projects that use InfoTrac College Edition as a research tool.

- References lists the major books and articles consulted in writing this chapter.

- Hypercontents takes you to an extensive list of sites with news, research, and images related to individual sections of the chapter.

## INFOTRAC COLLEGE EDITION

Improve your skills with InfoTrac College Edition, a searchable online database of articles from more than 700 periodicals. Log on to

http://www.infotrac-college.com

or access InfoTrac through the website for this book. Try to find the following articles:

**1.** Holly, C. 2001. Study shows green taxes can benefit economy. *Energy Daily* 29: 4. *Keyword:* "green taxes." These days it seems that when people start talking about taxes and regulations to benefit the environment, they are met with dire predictions of economic catastrophe. But is this really the case?

**2.** Costanza, R. 2001. Visions, values, valuation, and the need for an ecological economics. *BioScience* 51: 459. *Keyword:* "ecological economics." This article looks deeply at how we view the world and how we view ourselves in it.

# 27 POLITICS, ENVIRONMENT, AND SUSTAINABILITY

## Rescuing a River

In the 1960s, Marion Stoddart (Figure 27-1) moved to Groton, Massachusetts, on the Nashua River, then considered one of the nation's filthiest rivers. For decades, industries and towns along the river had used it as a dump. Dead fish bobbed on its waves, and at times the water was red, green, or blue from pigments discharged by paper mills.

Instead of thinking nothing could be done, she committed herself to restoring the Nashua and establishing public parklands along its banks.

She did not start by filing lawsuits or organizing demonstrations. Instead she created a careful cleanup plan and approached state officials with it in 1962. They laughed, but she was not deterred and began practicing the most time-honored skill of politics: one-on-one persuasion. She identified the power brokers in the riverside communities and began to educate them, win them over, and get them to cooperate in cleaning up the river.

She also got the state to ban open dumping in the river. When promised federal matching funds for building the treatment plant failed to materialize, Stoddart gathered 13,000 signatures on a petition sent to President Richard Nixon. The funds arrived in a hurry.

Stoddart's next success was getting a federal grant to beautify the river. She hired high school dropouts to clear away mounds of debris. When the river cleanup was completed, she persuaded communities along the river to create some 2,400 hectares (6,000 acres) of riverside park and woodlands along both banks.

Now, four decades later, the Nashua is still clean. Several new water treatment plants have been built, and a citizens' group founded by Stoddart keeps watch on water quality. The river supports many kinds of fish and other wildlife, and its waters are used for canoeing and other kinds of recreation. The project is considered a model for other states and is testimony to what a committed individual can do to bring about change from the bottom up by getting people to work together.

For her efforts, the UN Environment Programme named Stoddart an outstanding worldwide worker for the environment. However, she might say the blue and canoeable Nashua itself is her best reward.

**Politics** is the process by which individuals and groups try to influence or control the policies and actions of governments at the local, state, national, or international levels. Politics is concerned with **(1)** who has power over the distribution of resources and **(2)** who gets what, when, and how. Thus it plays a significant role in **(1)** regulating and influencing economic decisions (Chapter 26) and **(2)** persuading people to work together toward a common goal, as Marion Stoddart did.

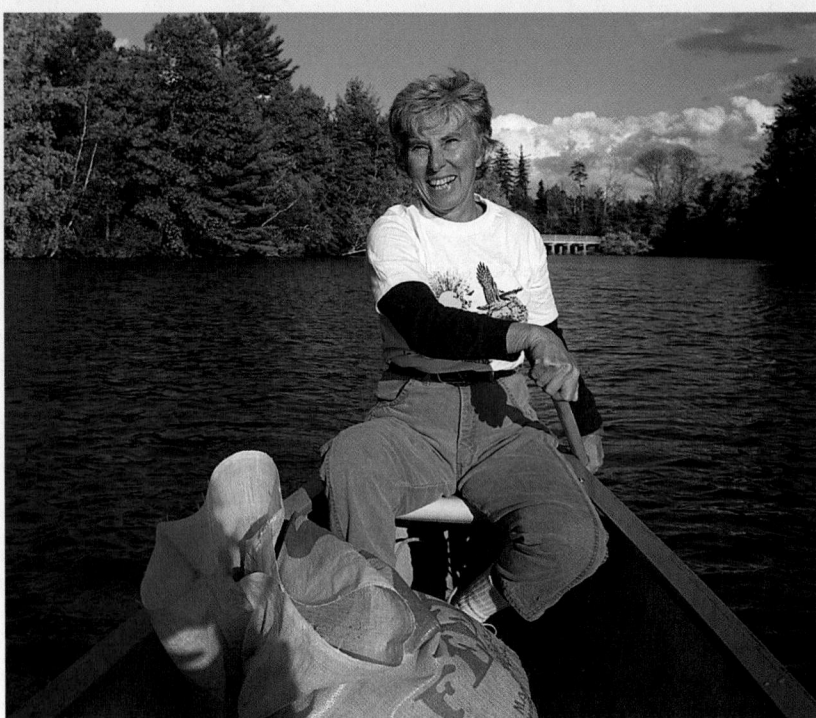

**Figure 27-1** Marion Stoddart canoeing on the Nashua River near Groton, Massachusetts. She spent more than two decades spearheading successful efforts to have this river cleaned up.

*Politics is the art of making good decisions on insufficient evidence.*

LORD KENNET

This chapter addresses the following questions:

- How do democracies work, and what factors hinder the ability of democracies to deal with environmental problems?

- What are guidelines for making environmental policy? How can people affect such decisions?

- How is environmental policy made in the United States, and how can such policy decisions be improved?

- What are the major types and roles of environmental groups and anti-environmental groups? How can we evaluate the claims of these opposing forces?

- What types of global environmental policies exist, and how might they be improved?

## 27-1 POLITICS AND ENVIRONMENTAL POLICY

**What Is a Democracy, and How Do Democratic Governments Work?** **Democracy** is government by the people through elected officials and representatives. In a *constitutional democracy*, a constitution (1) provides the basis of government authority, (2) limits government power by mandating free elections, and (3) guarantees freely expressed public opinion.

Political institutions in constitutional democracies are designed to allow gradual change to ensure economic and political stability. In the United States, for example, rapid and destabilizing change is curbed by the system of checks and balances that distributes power among the three branches of government—*legislative, executive,* and *judicial*—and among federal, state, and local governments.

In passing laws, developing budgets, and formulating regulations, elected and appointed government officials must deal with pressure from many competing *special-interest groups*. Each group advocates (1) passing laws, providing subsidies, and establishing regulations favorable to its cause and (2) weakening or repealing unfavorable laws, subsidies, and regulations.

Some special-interest groups (such as corporations) are *profit-making organizations,* and others are *nonprofit nongovernment organizations (NGOs)*. Examples of NGOs are (1) educational institutions, (2) labor unions, and (3) mainstream and grassroots environmental organizations.

Most political decisions made by democratic governments result from bargaining, accommodation, and compromise between leaders of competing *elites,* or power brokers. The primary goal of government by competing elites is to maintain the overall economic and political stability of the system (status quo) by making only gradual or *incremental* change.

**What Factors Hinder the Ability of Democracies to Deal with Environmental Problems?** The deliberately stable design of democracies is desirable but has several related disadvantages for dealing with environmental problems:

- Emphasis is on reacting to short-term environmental problems in isolation from one another instead of acting to prevent them from occurring in the future. However, many important environmental problems such as climate change, biodiversity loss, and long-lived hazardous waste (1) have long-range effects, (2) are related to one another, and (3) require integrated long-term solutions emphasizing prevention.

- Because elections are held every few years, most politicians focus on short-term individual problems rather than on the more complex, time-consuming, and often politically unrewarding job of finding integrated solutions to long-term problems.

- Children, unborn generations, and wild species do not vote, and most politicians will no longer be in office when any harmful long-term effects from environmental problems appear. Thus no powerful political constituency exists for the future or for long-term environmental sustainability.

- Whether they like it or not, most elected officials must spend much of their time raising money to get reelected.

## 27-2 DEVELOPING AND INFLUENCING ENVIRONMENTAL POLICY

**What Principles Can Be Used as Guidelines in Making Environmental Policy Decisions?** Analysts have suggested that legislators and individuals evaluating existing or proposed environmental policy should be guided by several principles:

- *The humility principle:* Recognize and accept that we have a limited capacity to manage nature because our understanding of nature and of the consequences of our actions is quite limited.

- *The reversibility principle:* Try not to do something that cannot be reversed later if the decision turns out to be wrong. For example, ecologists believe the current large-scale destruction and degradation of forests, wetlands, wild species, and other components of the earth's biodiversity is unwise because much of it could be irreversible on a human time scale.

- *The precautionary principle:* When much evidence indicates that an activity raises threats of harm to human health or the environment, take precautionary measures to prevent or reduce such harm even if some of the cause-and-effect relationships are not fully established scientifically. In such cases, it is better to be safe than sorry.

- *The prevention principle:* Whenever possible, make decisions that help prevent a problem from occurring or becoming worse.

- *The integrative principle:* Make decisions that involve integrated solutions to environmental and other problems.

- *The environmental justice principle:* Establish environmental policy so no group of people bears an unfair share of the harmful environmental risks from (1) industrial, municipal, and commercial operations or (2) the execution of environmental laws, regulations, and policies. The EPA defines **environmental justice** as "the fair treatment and meaningful involvement of all people regardless of race, color, national origin, or income with respect to the development, implementation, and enforcement of environmental laws, regulations, and policies."

**How Can Individuals Affect Environmental Policy?** A major theme of this book is that *individuals matter.* History shows that significant change usually comes from the *bottom up* when individuals join with others to bring about change. Without grassroots political action by millions of individual citizens and organized groups, the air you breathe and the water you drink today would be much more polluted, and much more of the earth's biodiversity would have disappeared.

Individuals can influence and change government policies in constitutional democracies by

- Running for office (especially local offices).

- Trying to get appointed to local planning and zoning boards and environmental commissions that study and make recommendations to elected officials.

- Making their views known by appearing at hearings before local planning and zoning boards, environmental commissions, and public meetings of elected officials.

- Voting for candidates and ballot measures.

- Contributing money and time to candidates seeking office.

- Writing, faxing, e-mailing, calling, or meeting with elected representatives, asking them to (1) pass or oppose certain laws, (2) establish certain policies, and (3) fund various programs.

- Forming or joining nongovernmental organizations (NGOs) that lobby elected and regulatory officials to support a particular position (photo on p. 689).

- Working to reform the rules governing the financing of election campaigns (Solutions, p. 721). According to most political analysts, *campaign financing* is the biggest problem that keeps elected officials from being more responsive to the environmental and other needs and problems of ordinary citizens.

- Using education and persuasion to convert elected officials and other citizens to a particular position (p. 716).

- Exposing fraud, waste, and illegal activities in government (whistle-blowing).

**What Is Environmental Leadership?** It is important to distinguish among leaders, rulers, and managers:

- A *leader* is a person other people follow voluntarily because of his or her vision, credibility, or charisma.

- A *ruler* is a person who has enough power to make people follow against their will.

- A *manager* is a person who knows how to organize things, get things done, pay attention to detail, and delegate responsibility. Some leaders and rulers can also be good managers and vice versa.

Individuals can provide leadership on environmental (or other) issues by

- *Leading by example,* using one's lifestyle to show others that change is possible and beneficial.

- *Working within existing economic and political systems to bring about environmental improvement.* People can influence political decisions by campaigning and voting for candidates and by communicating with elected officials. They can also work within the system by choosing environmental careers (Individuals Matter, p. 724). See the website material for this chapter for information on how to communicate with elected officials.

- *Proposing and working for better solutions to environmental problems.* Leadership is more than being against something; it also involves (1) coming up with better ways to accomplish various goals and (2) getting people to work together to achieve such goals.

## 27-3 CASE STUDY: ENVIRONMENTAL POLICY IN THE UNITED STATES

**What Are the Three Branches of Government in the United States?** The federal government of the United States consists of three separate but inter-connected branches: legislative, executive, and judicial.

■ The *legislative branch* is the Congress, composed of the House of Representatives and the Senate. Its goal is to approve and oversee government policy by **(1)** passing laws that establish a government

agency or instruct an existing agency to take on new tasks or programs and **(2)** overseeing the functioning and funding of various agencies of the executive branch concerned with carrying out government policies.

■ The *executive branch* consists of a chief executive, the president, who with his or her staff oversees the various agencies authorized by Congress to carry out government policies such as environmental policy (Figure 27-2). The president also **(1)** proposes annual budgets, legislation, and appointees for executive

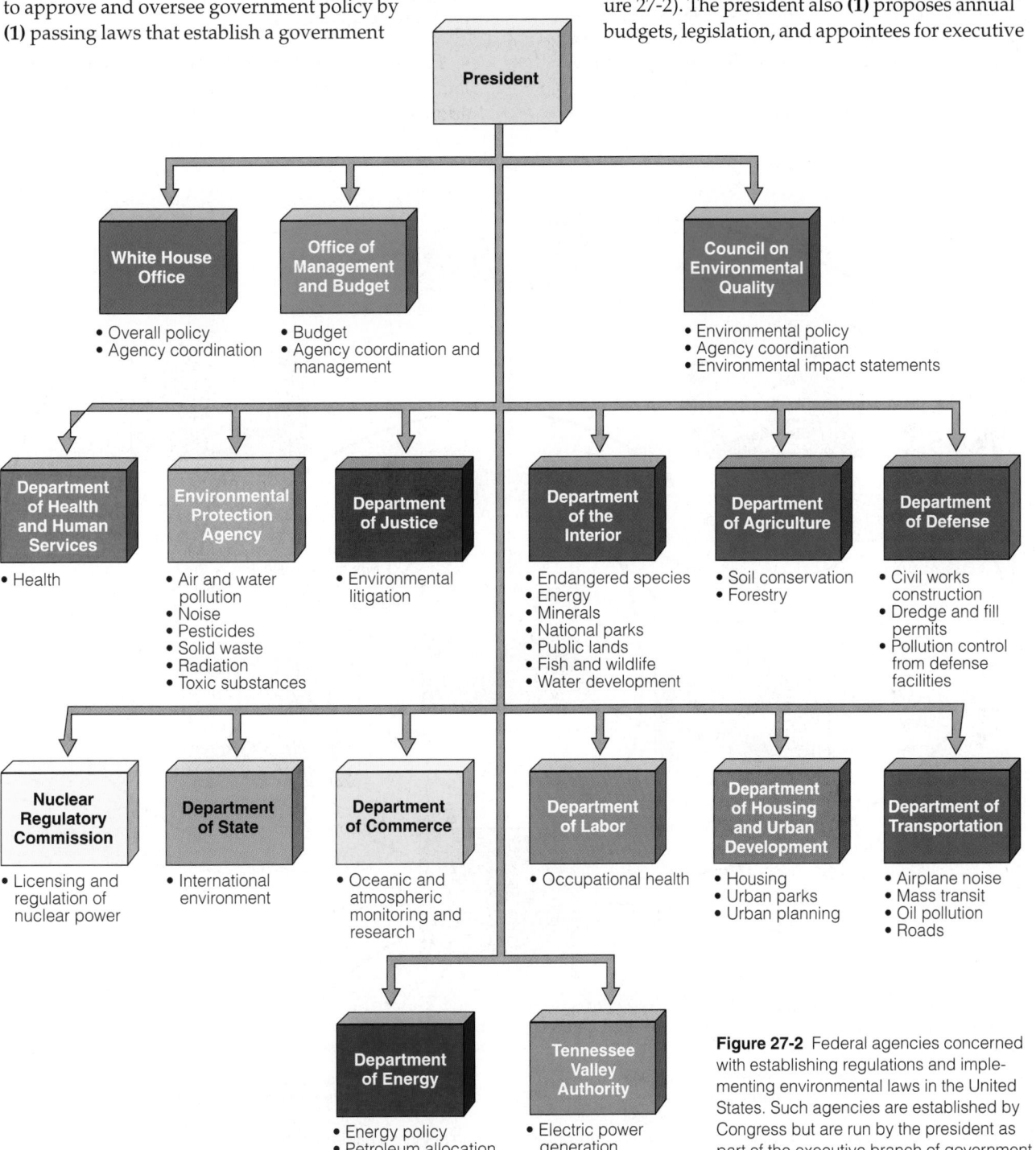

**Figure 27-2** Federal agencies concerned with establishing regulations and implementing environmental laws in the United States. Such agencies are established by Congress but are run by the president as part of the executive branch of government.

positions that must be approved by Congress and **(2)** tries to persuade Congress and the public to support his or her policy proposals.

- The *judicial branch* consists of a complex and layered series of courts at the local, state, and federal levels (Supreme Court). These courts enforce and interpret different categories of laws such as constitutional law, administrative law, and laws passed by legislative bodies (statutory laws).

The major function of the federal government in the United States is to develop and implement *policy* for dealing with various issues. This policy is composed of various **(1)** *laws* passed by the legislative branch, **(2)** *regulations* instituted by the executive

branch to put laws into effect (Figure 27-2), and **(3)** *funding* to implement and enforce the laws and regulations. Figure 27-3 is a greatly simplified overview of how individuals and lobbyists for and against a particular environmental law interact with the three branches of government in the United States.

**How Is Environmental Policy Made in the United States?** Several steps are involved in establishing federal environmental policy (or any other policy) in the United States:

- Persuade lawmakers that an environmental problem exists and the government has a responsibility to address it.

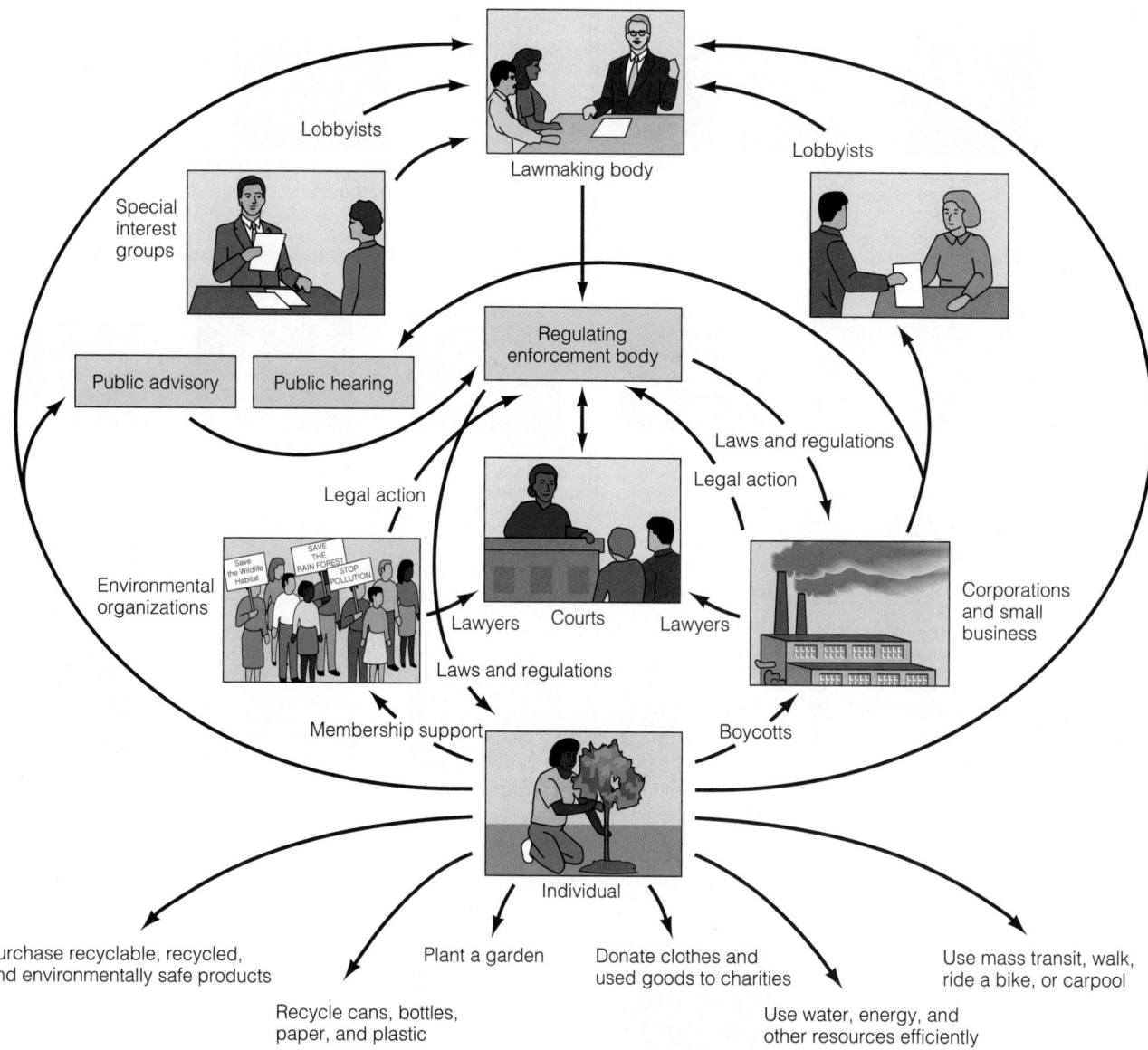

**Figure 27-3** Greatly simplified overview of how individuals and lobbyists for and against a particular environmental law interact with the legislative, executive, and judicial branches of government in the United States. The bottom of this diagram also shows some ways in which individuals can bring about environmental change through their own lifestyles. See the website for this book for details on contacting elected representatives.

# Election Finance Reform*

**SOLUTIONS**

In the United States, the candidates raising the most money win about 90% of federal, state, and local elections. Unless they are wealthy and willing to spend their own money, candidates can get this kind of money only from wealthy individuals and corporations.

Most analysts and about 80% of citizens polled agree that the U.S. political system is based more on money than on citizens' votes—one reason so many Americans do not bother to vote. For example, voter turnout for federal elections in the United States dropped from 74% in 1900 to 49% in 2000. According to social analyst Paul H. Ray, survey upon survey shows that over 70% of U.S. voters are unhappy with the country's election system and politicians. Many people who do vote often feel they are simply choosing the lesser of two evils.

This explains why a growing number of analysts of all political persuasions see drastic *election finance reform* as the single most important way to reduce the influence of special-interest money in local, state, and federal elections in the United States. They urge American citizens to focus their efforts on this crucial issue as the key to making government more responsive to ordinary people on environmental and other matters.

One suggestion for reducing undue influence by powerful special interests would be to let the people (taxpayers) *alone* finance all federal, state, and local election campaigns, with low spending limits. Candi-

dates could use their own money because it would be unconstitutional to forbid such use. However, they could not accept direct or indirect donations from any other individuals, groups, or parties, *with absolutely no exceptions.*

Once elected, officials could not **(1)** use free mailing, staff employees, or other privileges to aid their election campaigns and **(2)** accept donations or any kind of direct or indirect financial aid from any individual, corporation, political party, or interest group for their future election campaigns or for any other reason that could even remotely influence their votes on legislation.

Violators of this new *Public Funding Elections Act* would be barred from the campaign or removed from office. Anyone making illegal donations would be subject to large fines and possible jail sentences.

Having all elections financed entirely by public funds would cost each U.S. taxpayer only about $5–10 per year (as part of their income taxes) for all federal elections and a much smaller amount for state and local elections.

With such a reform, elected officials could spend their time governing instead of raising money and catering to powerful special interests. Office seekers would not need to be wealthy. Special-interest groups would be heard because of the validity of their ideas, not the size of their pocketbooks.

Proponents of this reform contend this is an issue that ordinary people of all political persuasions could work together on. From this fundamental political reform, other political, economic, and environmental reforms could flow.

The problem is getting members of Congress (and state legislatures) to pass an effective and constitutionally acceptable plan that would put them on equal financial footing

with their challengers and thus could decrease their chances of getting reelected.

Supporters of public financing of all elections argue that the way out of this dilemma is to **(1)** find and elect candidates who pledge to bring about this fundamental political reform, and **(2)** vote them out of office if they do not. They believe many of the people who have given up exercising their right to vote because of the undue financial influence of special-interest groups could be persuaded to participate in such efforts.

They envision the formation of a voting coalition consisting of **(1)** active voters of all political persuasions who are fed up with the lack of serious election finance reform and **(2)** concerned citizens who have stopped voting because they believe powerful money interests have taken over the election process.

Some steps have been taken to reform election financing. Thanks to the work of many citizens candidates running for office in four states—Arizona, Maine, Massachusetts, and Vermont—have the option of rejecting all private campaign contributions and qualifying for full public financing of their campaigns within certain spending limits. In 2002, the U.S. Congress passed a Campaign Finance Law that supporters say took an important but tiny step toward election finance reform

## Critical Thinking

**1.** Do you agree or disagree with this approach to election reform? Explain. What role would you take in bringing about or opposing such a reform?

**2.** Why might the mainstream environmental groups in the United States not support such a reform? Should they?

*For an in-depth analysis of this issue, see Moti Nissani, "Brass-Tacks Ecology," *The Trumpeter* 14, no. 3 (Summer 1997), pp. 143–48, and Chapter 10 in Moti Nissani, *Lives in the Balance: The Cold War and American Politics, 1945–1991* (Carson City, Nev.: Dowser, 1992).

- Try to influence how laws are written and to pass laws to deal with the problem. Converting a bill into a law is a complex process (Figure 27-4, p. 722). Most environmental bills are evaluated by as many as ten

committees in the House of Representatives and the Senate. Effective proposals often are weakened by this fragmentation and by lobbying from groups opposing the law. Nonetheless, since the 1970s, a number of

**Figure 27-4** How a bill introduced into the U.S. House of Representatives becomes a law. Individual citizens and lobbying groups (Figure 27-3) can influence **(1)** how the bill is written before it is introduced and **(2)** what happens to it at every stage of this complex process. Once a bill is signed into law, it goes to appropriations committees in both houses for agreement on how much funding it receives. Without adequate funding, a law cannot be implemented. Continued intervention by individuals and lobbying groups can be very important at this stage.

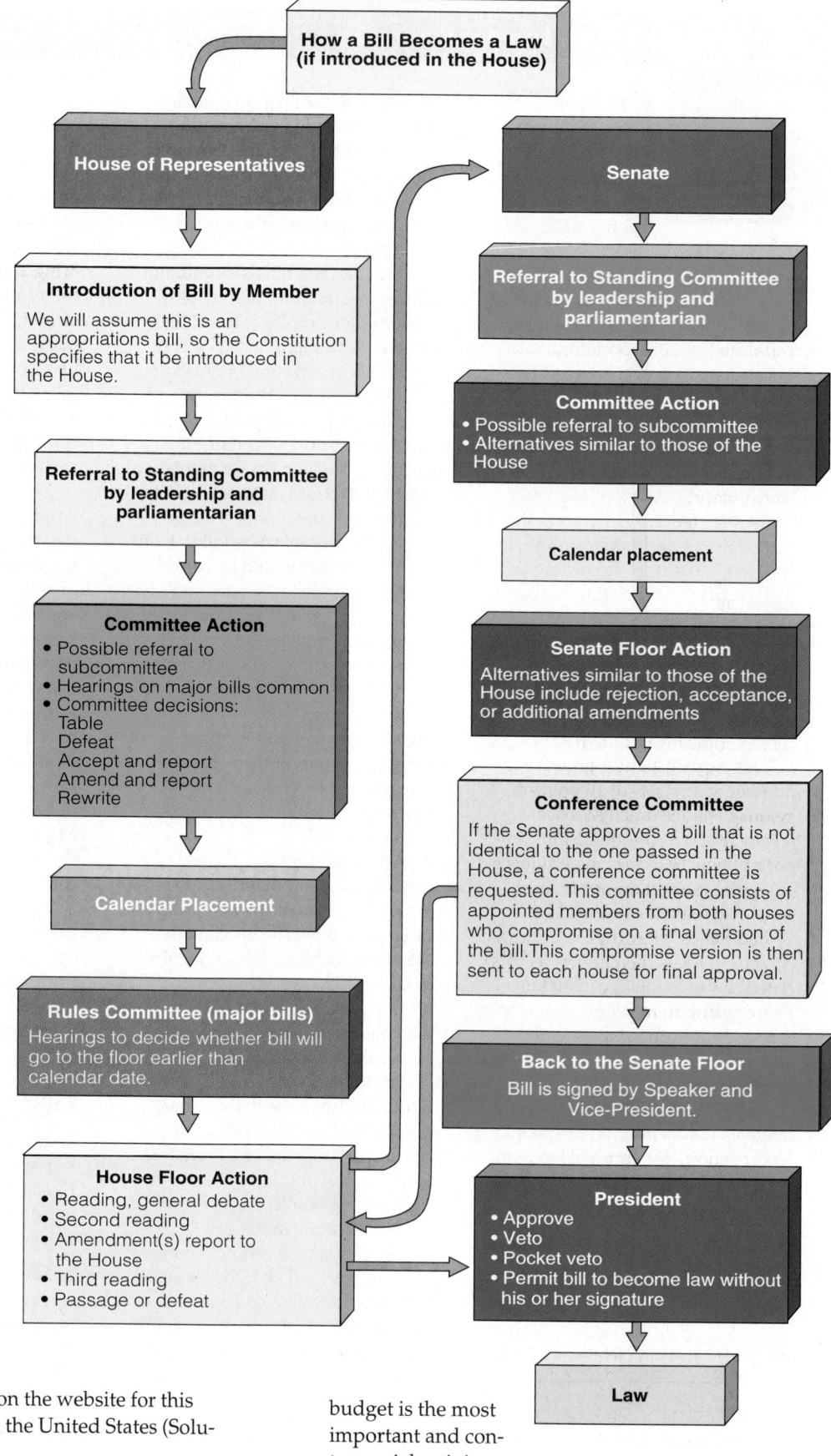

environmental laws (see list on the website for this chapter) have been passed in the United States (Solutions, p. 724).

■  Appropriate enough funds to implement and enforce each law. Indeed, developing and adopting a budget is the most important and controversial activity of the executive and legislative branches. Developing a budget involves answering two key questions:

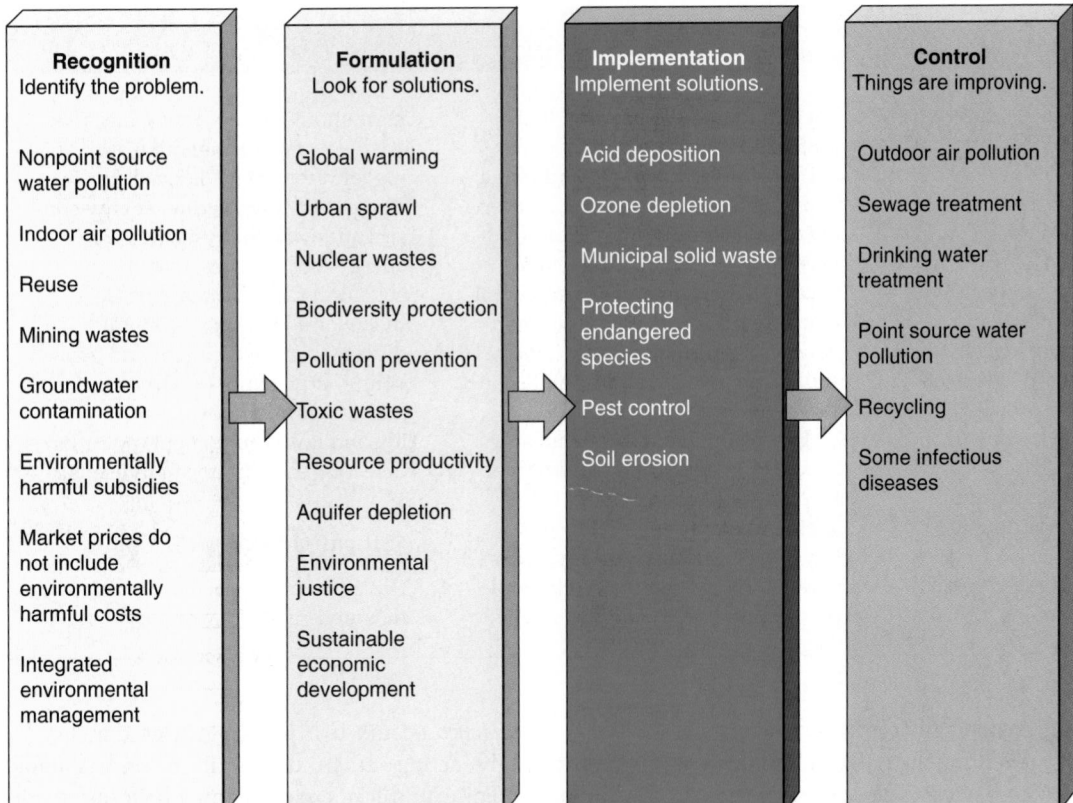

| Recognition<br>Identify the problem. | Formulation<br>Look for solutions. | Implementation<br>Implement solutions. | Control<br>Things are improving. |
|---|---|---|---|
| Nonpoint source water pollution | Global warming | Acid deposition | Outdoor air pollution |
| Indoor air pollution | Urban sprawl | Ozone depletion | Sewage treatment |
| Reuse | Nuclear wastes | Municipal solid waste | Drinking water treatment |
| Mining wastes | Biodiversity protection | Protecting endangered species | Point source water pollution |
| Groundwater contamination | Pollution prevention | Pest control | Recycling |
| Environmentally harmful subsidies | Toxic wastes | Soil erosion | Some infectious diseases |
| Market prices do not include environmentally harmful costs | Resource productivity | | |
| Integrated environmental management | Aquifer depletion | | |
| | Environmental justice | | |
| | Sustainable economic development | | |

**Figure 27-5** General position of several major environmental problems in the policy life cycle in most developed countries.

(1) What programs will be funded, and (2) how much money will be used to address each problem?

■ Have the appropriate government department or agency (Figure 27-2) draw up regulations for implementing each law. Groups try to influence how the regulations are written and enforced and sometimes challenge the final regulations in court.

■ Implement and enforce the approved regulations. Proponents or affected groups may take the agency to court for failing to implement and enforce the regulations or for enforcing them too rigidly.

According to social scientists, the development of public policy in democracies often goes through a *policy life cycle* consisting of four stages: **(1)** recognition, **(2)** formulation, **(3)** implementation, and **(4)** control. Figure 27-5 shows the general position of several major environmental problems in the policy life cycle in the United States and most other developed countries.

## 27-4 ENVIRONMENTAL LAW

**What Is the Difference Between Statutory and Common Laws?** Almost every major environmental regulation is challenged in court by industries, environmental organizations, individuals, or groups of individuals. In any court case **(1)** the **plaintiff** is the party bringing the charge, and **(2)** the **defendant** is the party being charged.

Environmental lawsuits involve statutory laws and common laws. **Statutory laws** are those developed and passed by legislative bodies such as federal and state governments. **Common law** is a body of unwritten rules and principles derived from thousands of past legal decisions. It is based on evaluation of what is reasonable behavior in attempting to balance competing social interests.

**What Is the Difference Between Nuisance and Negligence?** Many common law cases are settled using the legal principles of *nuisance* and *negligence*. A *nuisance* occurs when someone uses his or her property in a way that causes annoyance or injury to others. For example, a home owner may bring a nuisance suit against a nearby factory because of the noise it generates.

In such a *civil suit*, the plaintiff seeks to collect damages for injuries to health or for economic loss, to have the court issue a permanent injunction against any further wrongful action, or both. An individual or a clearly identified group may bring such suits. A *class action suit* is a civil suit filed by a group, often a public interest or environmental group, on behalf of a larger number of citizens who allege similar damages but who need not be listed and represented individually.

Using the principles of common law, the court may side with the plaintiff if it finds the loss of sleep, health problems, or other damage from the noise is greater than the cost of preventing the risk by eliminating or reducing the noise or having to close the factory. Often the court tries to find a reasonable or balanced solution to the problem. For example, it may order the factory to reduce the noise to certain levels or eliminate the noise during certain periods such as at night.

*Negligence* occurs if a person causes damage by knowingly acting in an unlawful or unreasonable manner. For example, a company may be found negligent if it fails to handle hazardous waste in a way required by a statutory law. A court may also find a company negligent if it fails to do something a reasonable person would do, such as testing waste for certain harmful chemicals before dumping it into a sewer, landfill, or river.

Generally, negligence is harder to prove than nuisance. For example, a company may be found not guilty because it argues it did not know that its wastes were harmful and therefore did not act in a negligent or unreasonable manner.

There is much legal controversy over whether federal and state governments must compensate corporations and individuals when government laws or regulations affect the use or financial value of their private property (Case Study, below).

**What Factors Hinder the Effectiveness of Environmental Lawsuits?** Several factors limit the effectiveness of environmental lawsuits:

■ Permission to file a damage suit is granted only if the harm to an individual plaintiff is clearly unique or different enough to be distinguished from that to

## The Regulatory Takings Controversy

**CASE STUDY**

An important controversy over government action affects the use of *private* land. It involves the difficult political and legal issue of whether federal and state governments must compensate private property owners when government laws or regulations **(1)** limit how the owners can use their property or **(2)** decrease its financial value.

The Fifth Amendment of the U.S. Constitution gives the government the power, known as *eminent domain,* to force a citizen to sell property needed for a public good. For example, suppose the government needs your land for a road. It can legally take your land, but must reimburse you based on the land's fair market value.

The current controversy is over whether the Constitution requires the government to compensate you if instead of taking your property (a *physical taking*) it reduces its value by not allowing you to do certain things with it (a *regulatory taking*). For example, you might not be allowed to **(1)** build on some or all of your property because it is a wetland protected by law or **(2)** harvest trees on all or part of your land because it is a habitat for an endangered species.

Regulatory takings is a complicated and highly controversial private property issue. Most people favor compensation for any losses in value or use of their property because of government regulation. The problem is that requiring government compensation for regulatory takings would cost so much money that it could

■ Cripple the financial ability of state and federal governments to protect the public good by enforcing existing environmental, land-use, health, and safety laws.

■ Hinder passage of any new environmental land-use, environmental, health, and safety laws because of lack of funding.

■ Undermine the long-standing rule of U.S. law that landowners must not use their land in any way that creates a public or private nuisance (in other words, harms neighbors or the public). Indeed, the purpose of most government land-use, environmental, health, zoning, and safety regulations is to protect the community from harmful actions by individual property owners.

Critics of government compensation for regulatory takings also point out that

■ Most of the government compensation would go to the 5% of nation's largest private landowners (mostly timber and mining companies, agribusinesses, energy companies, and developers) who own almost three-quarters of the country's privately owned land.

■ The value of property owned by ordinary citizens could decrease because of increased pollution and environmental degradation resulting from less funding available for environmental regulation.

The controversy over regulatory takings is a continuation of the classic conflict over two types of freedoms: **(1)** the right to be protected by law from the damaging actions of others and **(2)** the right to do as one pleases without undue government interference. Achieving a balance between these conflicting types of individual rights is a difficult problem that governments have been wrestling with for centuries.

To most analysts, regulatory takings is one of the most important and far-reaching legal, political, economic, and environmental issues facing the citizens of the United States. Since 1991, members of Congress have attached regulatory takings amendments to a variety of major pieces of legislation. If passed, the U.S Supreme Court would determine the constitutionality of such laws.

### Critical Thinking

**1.** Describe and list the pros and cons of the issue of *regulatory takings* in the United States.

**2.** Should individuals and corporations be compensated financially if they are prevented **(a)** from using land they own or **(b)** from extracting resources from land they own because the land is classified by state or federal government as protected wetlands or habitats for endangered or threatened wildlife species? Explain.

the general public. For example, you could not sue the U.S. Department of the Interior for actions leading to the commercialization of a wilderness area because the harm to you could not be separated from that to the general public. However, if the government damaged property you own, you would have grounds to sue.

- Bringing any lawsuit is expensive.

- Public interest law firms cannot recover attorneys' fees unless Congress has specifically authorized such recovery in the laws the firms seek to have enforced. By contrast, corporations can reduce their taxes by deducting their legal expenses and in effect have the public pay for part of their legal fees. In other words, the legal playing field is uneven and in financial terms is stacked against individuals and groups of private citizens.

- To stop a nuisance or to collect damages from a nuisance or act of negligence, plaintiffs must prove they have been harmed in some significant way and the defendant caused the harm. This process is often very complex and costly. Suppose a company (the defendant) is charged with harming individuals by polluting a river. If hundreds of other industries and cities dump waste into that river, establishing that the defendant is the culprit is very difficult and entails expensive investigation, scientific research, and expert testimony. In addition, it is hard to establish that a particular chemical is what caused the plaintiffs to come down with a disease such as cancer.

- The *statue of limitations* limits the length of time within which a plaintiff can sue after a particular event in most states. In such states, this statute makes it essentially impossible for victims of cancer, which may take 10–20 years to develop, to file or win a negligence suit.

- The court (or series of courts if the case is appealed) may take years to reach a decision. During that time a defendant may continue the allegedly damaging action unless the court issues a temporary injunction against the action until the case is decided.

- Plaintiffs sometimes abuse the system by bringing frivolous suits that delay and run up the costs of projects. In recent years, some corporations and developers have begun filing lawsuits for damages against citizen activists (Spotlight, at right).

Because of such difficulties, an increasing number of environmental lawsuits are being settled out of court. Some are settled privately and others by *mediation,* in which a neutral party tries to resolve the dispute in a way that is acceptable to both parties. Mediation is much less costly and time consuming and may bring about a more satisfactory resolution of a dispute than going to court. But a settlement drawn up by

## SPOTLIGHT

## SLAPPs: Intimidating Environmental Activists

In recent years, some corporations and developers have begun filing *strategic lawsuits against public participation (SLAPPs)* against individuals and activist environmental groups.* Such suits have two goals: **(1)** to use up the time and financial resources of private citizens and environmental groups and **(2)** to deter citizens from becoming involved.

SLAPPs range from $100,000 to $100 million but average $9 million per suit. Judges who recognize them for what they are throw out about 90% of the SLAPPs that go to court. However, individuals and groups hit with SLAPPs must spend much money on lawyers and typically spend 1–3 years defending themselves.

Most SLAPPs are not meant to be won. Instead, they are intended to intimidate individual citizens and activist groups so they will not exercise their democratic rights. Once fear and rising defense costs shake the victim of a SLAPP, the plaintiff often offers a voluntary dismissal, provided the citizen or group agrees never to discuss the case or oppose the plaintiff again.

Some citizen activists have fought back with countersuits and have been awarded damages. For example, a Missouri woman who was sued for criticizing a medical waste incinerator won an $86.5 million judgment against the incinerator's owner.

Even after paying such awards, corporations and developers generally save money by filing such suits. Unlike the people they are suing, these businesses can count such legal and insurance liability costs as a business expense and write them off on their taxes. In other words, they get all taxpayers to pay much of the cost of such lawsuits against a few taxpayers who are exercising their rights as citizens.

### Critical Thinking

Are you in favor of SLAPPs? Explain. If not, what do you think should be done to discourage such tactics?

---

*Free information on SLAPPs can be obtained from the SLAPP Resource Center, University of Denver College of Law, 1900 Olive St., Denver, CO 80220; 303-871-6266.

mediation is not legally binding. Thus months of expensive mediation can result in an agreement that polluters may ignore.

Despite many obstacles, proponents of environmental law have accomplished a great deal since the

1960s. In the United States, more than 20,000 attorneys in 100 public interest law firms and groups now specialize partly or entirely in environmental and consumer law. In addition, many other lawyers and scientific experts participate in environmental and consumer lawsuits as needed.

**How Can We Level the Legal Playing Field for Ordinary Citizens?** Reforms suggested for making the legal playing field more level for citizens suffering environmental damage include the following:

- Allowing citizens to sue violators of environmental laws for triple damages.

- Awarding citizens their attorney fees in successful lawsuits.

- Establishing rules and procedures for identifying frivolous SLAPP suits (Spotlight, p. 726) so cases without factual or legal merit could be dismissed within a few weeks rather than years.

- Raising fines for violators of environmental laws and punishing more violators with jail sentences. Polls indicate that 84% of Americans consider damaging the environment a serious crime.

## 27-5 ENVIRONMENTAL AND ANTI-ENVIRONMENTAL GROUPS AND CLAIMS

**What Are the Roles of Mainstream Environmental Groups?** The spearhead of the global conservation and environmental movement consists of more than 30,000 NGOs working at the international, national, state, and local levels. More than 3,000 international NGOs work on environmental issues. They include mainstream groups such as the Worldwide Fund for Nature (nearly 5 million members), Greenpeace (2.5 million members), World Wildlife Fund (1.2 million members), the Nature Conservancy (Solutions, p. 623; 1.1 million members), Conservation International, and the Wildlife Conservation Society.

Using e-mail and the Internet, environmental NGOs have organized themselves into an array of powerful international networks. Examples include the Pesticide Action, Climate Action, International Rivers, Women's Environment and Development, and Biodiversity Action Networks.

These international organizations and networks (1) monitor the environmental activities of governments, corporations, and international agencies such as the United Nations, World Bank, International Monetary Fund, and the World Trade Organization (WTO) and (2) push for improved environmental performance by such organizations and by governments.

In the United States, more than 8 million citizens belong to at least 10,000 NGOs dealing with environmental issues at the international, national, state, and local levels. Some of these environmental organizations are multimillion-dollar *mainstream* groups, led by chief executive officers and staffed by expert lawyers, scientists, and economists. In the United States, mainstream environmental groups are active primarily at the national level and to a lesser extent at the state level; sometimes they form coalitions to work together on issues.

Some mainstream organizations such as the Sierra Club provide funds for local activists and projects. Some groups focus much of their efforts on specific issues, such as (1) population (Population Connection), (2) protecting habitats (local land trusts, Wilderness Society, and Nature Conservancy; Solutions, p. 623), and (3) wildlife conservation (National Audubon Society, National Wildlife Federation, and the World Wildlife Fund). Other organizations concentrate on education and research (Worldwatch Institute, Rocky Mountain Institute, Population Reference Bureau, and World Resources Institute). Still other groups provide information, training, and assistance to localities and grassroots organizations (Center for Health, Environment, and Justice and the Institute for Local Self-Reliance).

Mainstream groups work within the political system. Many of these NGOs have been major forces in (1) persuading the U.S. Congress to pass and strengthen environmental laws (see the list on the website for this chapter) and (2) fighting off attempts to weaken or repeal such laws.

However, mainstream environmental groups must guard against (1) being subverted by the political system they work to improve and (2) losing touch with ordinary people and nature in the insulated atmosphere of national and state capitals. For example, the ten largest U.S. mainstream environmental organizations—the "Group of 10"—rely heavily on corporate donations, and many of them have corporate executives as board members, trustees, or council members. Proponents of this corporate involvement argue that it is a way to raise much needed funds and influence industry. However, critics of this policy believe it is a way for corporations to influence environmental organizations.

Instead of acting as adversaries, some industries and environmental groups have worked together to find solutions to environmental problems. For example, the Environmental Defense Fund has worked with (1) McDonald's to redesign its packaging system to eliminate its polyethylene-foam clamshell hamburger containers, (2) General Motors to remove high-pollution cars from the road, and (3) nine multinational

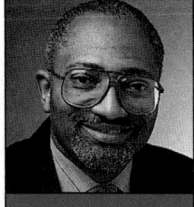
# Environmental Justice for All

*Robert D. Bullard*

*Robert D. Bullard is professor of sociology and director of the Environmental Justice Resource Center at Clark Atlanta University. For more than a decade, he has conducted research in the areas of urban land use, housing, community development, industrial facility siting, and environmental justice. He is the author of four books and more than three dozen articles, monographs, and scholarly papers that address concerns about environmental justice. His book* Dumping in Dixie: Race, Class, and Environmental Quality, *2nd ed. (Westview Press, 1994) has become a standard text in the field. Other books are* Confronting Environmental Racism *(South End Press, 1993) and* Unequal Protection: Environmental Justice and Communities of Color *(Sierra Club Books, 1994).*

Despite widespread media coverage and volumes written on the U.S. environmental movement, environmentalism and social justice have seldom been linked. Nevertheless, an environmental revolution has been taking shape in the United States that combines the environmental and social justice movements into one framework.

People of color (African-Americans, Latinos, Asians, Pacific Islanders, and Native Americans), working-class people, and poor people in the United States suffer disproportionately from industrial toxins, dirty air and drinking water, unsafe work conditions, and the location of noxious facilities such as municipal landfills, incinerators, and toxic-waste dumps.

The *environmental justice* movement attempts to dismantle **(1)** exclusionary zoning ordinances, **(2)** discriminatory land-use practices, **(3)** differential enforcement of environmental regulations, **(4)** disparate siting of risky technologies, and **(5)** the dumping of toxic waste on the poor and people of color in the United States and in developing countries.

Despite the government's attempts to level the playing field, all communities are not created equal when it comes to resolving environmental and public health concerns. More than 300,000 farm workers (more than 90% of whom are people of color) and their children are poisoned by pesticides sprayed on crops in the United States. Some 3–4 million children (many of them African-Americans or Latinos living in the inner city) are poisoned by lead-based paint in old buildings, lead-soldered pipes and water mains, lead-tainted soil contaminated by industry, and air pollutants from smelters.

All communities do not bear the same burden or reap the same benefits from industrial expansion. This is true in the case of the mostly African-American Emelle, Alabama (home of the nation's largest hazardous-waste landfill), Navajo lands in Arizona where uranium is mined, and the 2,000 factories, known as *maquiladores*, located just across the U.S. border in Mexico.

corporations (including Canadian aluminum company Alcan and the Mexican oil company Pemex) to set targets for reducing their $CO_2$ emissions. Also, the World Wildlife Fund and the Center for Energy and Climate Solutions have worked to help several multinational corporations (including Nike and Johnson & Johnson) reduce their $CO_2$ emissions through fuel switching and improving energy efficiency.

Some environmental groups have shifted some of their resources away from demonstrating and litigating to publicizing research on innovative solutions to environmental problems. For example, to promote the use of chlorine-free paper, Greenpeace Germany **(1)** printed a magazine using such paper and **(2)** encouraged readers to demand that magazine publishers switch to chlorine-free paper. Shortly thereafter, several major magazines made such a shift.

**What Are the Roles of Grassroots Environmental Groups?** The base of the environmental movement in the United States and throughout the world consists of thousands of grassroots citizens' groups organized to improve environmental quality, often at the local level. According to political analyst Konrad von Moltke, "There isn't a government in the world that would have done anything for the environment if it weren't for the citizen groups."

These groups carry out a number of environmental roles such as

- Preventing environmental harm to their members and their local communities by opposing projects such as landfills, waste incinerators, nuclear waste dumps, clear-cutting of forests, and harmful development projects.

- Getting government officials to take action because they have been victims of environmental harm or of environmental injustice because of the unequal distribution of environmental risks (Guest Essay, above, and photo, p. 689).

- Forming land trusts and other local organizations to **(1)** save wetlands, forests, farmland, and ranchland from development, **(2)** restore degraded rivers (p. 716) and wetlands, and **(3)** convert abandoned urban lots into community gardens and parks.

- Forming coalitions of workers and environmentalists to improve worker safety and health.

Nationally, 60% of African-Americans and 50% of Latinos live in communities with at least one uncontrolled toxic-waste site. Three of the five largest hazardous-waste landfills are located in communities that are predominantly African-American or Latino.

Environmental justice does not stop at the U.S. border. Environmental injustices exist from the *favelas* of Rio de Janeiro, Brazil, to the shantytowns of Johannesburg, South Africa. Members of the environmental justice movement are also questioning the wasteful and unsustainable development models being exported to the developing world.

Grassroots leaders are demanding justice. Residents of communities such as West Dallas and Texarkana (Texas), West Harlem (New York), Rosebud (South Dakota), Kettleman City (California), and Sunrise, Lions, and Wallace (Louisiana) see their struggle for environmental justice as a life-and-death matter. Unfortunately, their stories of environmental racism are not broadcast into the nation's living rooms during the nightly news, nor are they splashed across the front pages of national newspapers and magazines. To a large extent, the communities that are the victims of environmental injustice remain invisible to the larger society.

The environmental justice movement is led, planned, and to a large extent funded by people who are not part of the established environmental community or the "Big 10" environmental organizations. Most environmental justice groups are small and operate with resources generated from the local community.

For too long these groups and their leaders have been invisible and their stories muted. This is changing as these grassroots groups are forcing their issues onto the nation's environmental agenda.

The United States has a long way to go in achieving environmental justice for all its citizens. The membership of decision-making boards and commissions still does not reflect the racial, ethnic, and cultural diversity of the country, and token inclusion of people of color on boards and commissions does not necessarily mean that their voices will be heard or their cultures respected. The ultimate goal of any inclusion strategy should be to democratize the decision-making process and empower disenfranchised people to speak and do for themselves.

### Critical Thinking

**1.** How would you define environmental injustice? Can you identify any examples of environmental injustice in your community?

**2.** Have you been a victim of environmental injustice? Compare your answers with those of other members of your class.

---

- Setting up Internet service providers and networks to **(1)** improve environmental education and health, **(2)** provide individuals and NGOs with information on toxic releases and other environmentally harmful activities by local industries, and **(3)** publicize successful environmental projects.

- Working to make colleges and public schools more environmentally sustainable (Individuals Matter, p. 732)

The late John W. Gardner, former cabinet official and founder of Common Cause, summarized the basic rules for effective political action by grassroots organizations:

- *Have a full-time continuing organization.*

- *Limit the number of targets and hit them hard.* Groups dilute their effectiveness by taking on too many issues.

- *Organize for action, not just for study, discussion, or education.*

- *Form alliances with other organizations on a particular issue.*

- *Communicate your positions in an accurate, concise, and moving way.*

- *Persuade and use positive reinforcement.*

- *Concentrate efforts mostly at the state and local levels.*

**How Successful Have Environmental Groups Been?** Opponents sometimes portray the environmental movement in the United States (and elsewhere) as a well-organized and well-funded effort to bring about fundamental changes in how we perceive and act in the world. In truth, what is called the environmental movement has not really been a movement at all.

Instead, it has consisted of a hodgepodge of efforts on many fronts without overall direction and coherence. During the past 32 years, a variety of environmental groups have **(1)** raised understanding of environmental issues by the general public and some business leaders (Individuals Matter, p. 534), **(2)** gained public support for passage of an array of environmental and resource-use laws in the United States (see the list on the website for this chapter) and other developed countries, and **(3)** helped individuals deal with a number of local environmental problems (Guest Essay, p. 530).

Polls show that three-fourths of the U.S. public are strong supporters of environmental laws and regulations and do not want them weakened. However, polls also show that less than 10% of the U.S. public views the environment as one of the nation's most pressing problems. As a result, environmental concerns often do not get transferred to the ballot box. As one political scientist put it, "Environmental concerns are like the Everglades, a mile wide but only a few inches deep."

On one hand, the diversity of environmental groups and concerns is a strength because they analyze and provide a range of possible solutions to the complex environmental problems we face in a largely unpredictable world. On the other hand, it is a weakness because it has not led to deep convictions and environmental concerns on the part of most of the public.

This diversity has also allowed a well-organized and well-funded anti-environmental movement to develop an array of tactics (summarized on the website for this book) for undermining much of the improvement in environmental understanding and support for environmental concerns. Indeed, since 1980, mainline environmental groups in the United States have spent most of their time and money trying to prevent existing environmental laws and regulations from being weakened or repealed.

One problem is that many environmentalists have concentrated mostly on making the public aware of environmental bad news. However, history shows that bearers of bad news are not received well, and anti-environmentalists have used this to undermine environmental concerns.

History also shows that people are moved to bring about change mostly by an inspiring, positive vision of what the world could be like that provides them with a sense of hope for the future. So far, environmentalists with a variety of beliefs and goals have not worked together to develop broad, compelling, coherent, and positive visions that can be used as a road map for a more sustainable future for humans and other species.

**What Are the Goals of the Anti-Environmental Movement in the United States?** Despite general public approval, there is strong opposition to many environmental proposals by the following groups:

- Leaders of some corporations and people in positions of economic and political power who see environmental laws and regulations as threats to their wealth and power.

- Citizens who see environmental laws and regulations as threats to their private property rights (Case Study, p. 725) and jobs.

- Some state and local government officials who (1) are tired of having to implement federal environmental laws and regulations without federal funding (unfunded mandates) or (2) disagree with certain federal environmental regulations.

Since 1980, businesses, individuals, and grassroots groups in the United States have mounted a strong campaign to (1) weaken or repeal existing environmental laws and regulations, (2) change the way in which public lands are used (p. 597), and (3) destroy the reputation and effectiveness of the environmental movement. Some of the tactics used by this anti-environmental movement are listed on the website for this book.

**Why Are Most Environmental Issues Controversial?** As you have seen throughout this book, many environmental issues are very controversial. A key reason for such controversy is that these are important scientific, political, economic, social, and ethical issues that will not go away and must be dealt with.

One problem is that the focus of environmental issues has shifted to more complex and controversial environmental problems that (1) are harder to understand and solve and (2) have long-range harmful effects instead of easily visible short-term effects. Examples are (1) climate change, (2) ozone depletion, (3) biodiversity protection, (4) nonpoint water pollution (such as runoff from farms and lawns), and (5) protection of unseen groundwater. Explaining such complex issues to the public and mobilizing support for often controversial, long-range solutions to such problems are difficult (Guest Essay, p. 734).

Polarization and distortion of opposing views on environmental issues often lead to deadlock. Some people on both sides of such issues are working to mediate such disputes by getting each side to (1) listen to one another's concerns, (2) try to find areas of agreement, and (3) work together to find solutions, as is being done in the Netherlands (p. 710). For example, both environmentalists and anti-environmentalists agree that some environmental regulations in the United States go too far or are unjustly enforced, and they could work together to improve environmental laws and regulations (Solutions, p. 736).

Because of the importance of these issues, analysts urge us to try to understand both sides of these issues and decide what should be done. In doing this, we need to

- Gather and carefully evaluate the evidence for each position by using the techniques of critical thinking (Guest Essay, p. 42).

- Distinguish between frontier and consensus science (p. 44) when claims are made.

- Identify the consensus of most scientists in the particular field involved and not give equal weight to a small minority of scientists in such fields or those working outside these fields who disagree with the current consensus view.

- Become better informed about the relative degree of potential harm posed by various risks and try to rank risks as best we can (Figure 11-15, p. 246; Figure 11-17, p. 247; and Figure 11-18, p. 248).

- Support the use of pollution prevention and precautionary principles to deal with potentially serious problems for which we have inadequate scientific information.

## 27-6 GLOBAL ENVIRONMENTAL POLICY

**Should We Expand the Concept of National and Global Security?** Countries are legitimately concerned with *military security* and *economic security.* However, ecologists point out that (1) all economies are supported by natural resources (Figure 26-7, p. 694, and Guest Essay, p. 16), and (2) many environmental problems do not recognize political boundaries. Thus military and economic security also depend on national and global environmental security.

According to environmental expert Norman Myers (Guest Essay, p. 108),

*If a nation's environmental foundations are degraded or depleted, its economy may well decline, its social fabric deteriorate, and its political structure become destabilized as growing numbers of people seek to sustain themselves from declining resource stocks. Thus, national security is no longer about fighting forces and weaponry alone. It relates increasingly to watersheds, croplands, forests, genetic resources, climate, and other factors that, taken together, are as crucial to a nation's security as are military factors.*

Examples of conflicts arising from environmental shortages include

- Clashes between nations over declining fishery stocks.
- Disputes over access to shared water supplies (p. 312).
- Clashes over deforestation when water-absorbing tree cover removed by one nation leads to extensive flooding of downstream communities in other nations (Connections, p. 335).

Proponents call for all countries to (1) make environmental security a major focus of diplomacy and government policy at all levels and (2) have a council of advisers made up of highly qualified experts in environmental, economic, and military security who integrate all three security concerns in making major decisions.

**What Progress Has Been Made in Developing International Environmental Cooperation and Policy?** Here is some *good news*:

- Since the 1972 UN Conference on the Human Environment in Stockholm, Sweden, some progress has been made in addressing environmental issues at the global level.

- Today, 115 nations have environmental protection agencies, and there are over 500 international environmental treaties and agreements between various countries related to the environment. More than 300 of these agreements have been developed since the 1972 Stockholm conference.. They address issues such as endangered species, ozone depletion, ocean pollution, climate change, ozone layer depletion, biodiversity, and hazardous waste export. The 1972 conference also created the UN Environment Programme (UNEP) to negotiate environmental treaties and to help monitor and implement them.

- In June 1992, the second UN Conference on the Human Environment, known as the *Rio Earth Summit,* was held in Rio de Janeiro, Brazil. More than 100 heads of state, thousands of officials, and more than 1,400 accredited NGOs from 178 nations met to develop plans to address environmental issues. The major official results included (1) an *Earth Charter,* a nonbinding statement of broad principles for guiding environmental policy that commits countries that sign it to pursue sustainable development and work toward eradicating poverty, (2) *Agenda 21,* a nonbinding detailed action plan to guide countries toward sustainable development and protection of the global environment during the 21st century, (3) a *forestry agreement* that is a broad, nonbinding statement of principles of forest management and protection, (4) a *convention on climate change* that requires countries to use their best efforts to reduce their emissions of greenhouse gases, (5) a *convention on protecting biodiversity* that calls for countries to develop strategies for the conservation and sustainable use of biological diversity, and (6) the *UN Commission on Sustainable Development,* composed of high-level government representatives charged with carrying out and overseeing the implementation of these agreements.

Here is some *bad news*:

- Most environmentalists were disappointed with the Rio Earth Summit because its accomplishments consisted of nonbinding agreements without sufficient incentives or funding for their implementation.

## Environmental Action on Campuses

Since 1988, there has been a boom in environmental awareness on college campuses and some public schools across the United States. Much of this momentum began in 1989, when the Student Environmental Action Coalition (SEAC), then at the University of North Carolina at Chapel Hill (UNC), held the first national student environmental conference on the UNC campus.

SEAC groups are active on 700 campuses, and the National Wildlife Federation's Campus Ecology Program (launched in 1989) has groups on about 600 campuses.* Most student environmental groups work with members of the faculty and administration to bring about environmental improvements on their own campuses and in their local communities.

Many of these groups focus on making environmental audits of their campuses or schools. Then they use the data gathered to pro-

pose changes that will make their campuses or schools more ecologically sustainable, usually saving them money in the process.**

Such audits have resulted in numerous improvements. For example, Morris A. Pierce, a graduate student at the University of Rochester in New York, developed an energy management plan adopted by that school's board of trustees. Under this plan, a capital investment of $33 million is projected to save the university $60 million over 20 years. Students have also induced almost 80% of universities and colleges in the United States to develop recycling programs.

At Bowdin College in Maine, chemistry professor Dana Mayo and student Caroline Foote developed the concept of *microscale experiments*, in which smaller amounts of chemicals are used. This has reduced toxic wastes and saved the chemistry department

more than $34,000. Today more than 50% of all undergraduates in chemistry in the United States use such microscale techniques, as do universities in a growing number of other countries.

Students at Oberlin College in Ohio helped design a new sustainable environmental studies building (Figure 16-24, p. 399). At Northland College in Wisconsin, students helped design a "green" dorm that features passive solar design, furniture from a sustainable forest, and waterless (composting) toilets based on use of a living machine (Figure 19-1, p. 483).

A 1997 report by the National Wildlife Foundation's Campus Ecology Program found that 23 student-researched and student-motivated projects had saved the participating universities and colleges $16.3 million. According to this study, implementing similar programs in the nation's 3,700 universities and colleges could (1) help improve environmental quality and environmental education and (2) lead to a savings of more than $27.6 billion. Such student-spurred environmental activities and research studies are spreading to universities in at least 42 other countries.

---

*See *Ecodemia: Campus Environmental Stewardship at the Turn of the 21st Century* (Washington, D.C.: National Wildlife Federation, 1995) and the *Campus Environmental Yearbook*, published annually by the National Wildlife Federation.

**Details for conducting such audits are found in April Smith and the Student Environmental Action Coalition, *Campus Ecology: A Guide to Assessing Environmental Quality and Creating Strategies for Change* (Los Angeles, Calif.: Living Planet Press, 1993), and Jane Heinze-Fry, *Green Lives, Green Campuses*, available free on the website for this textbook.

---

- According to analysts, most international environmental treaties and agreements lack clear criteria for monitoring and measuring their effectiveness.

- There is a lack of funding for the UNEP, which was set up in 1972 to help negotiate, monitor, and implement environmental treaties. The UNEP annual budget is about $100 million, compared to (1) an almost $8 billion annual budget for the U.S. Environmental Protection Agency, (2) the U.S. military budget of over $300 billion per year, and (3) global military expenditures of more than $750 billion per year.

- According to analyses by the United Nations, by 2000 there was little improvement in the major environmental problems discussed at the Rio summit.

Here is some *encouraging news.* There is hope for greater progress in the slowly moving arena of international cooperation because

- The Rio Earth Summit gave the world a forum for discussing and seeking solutions to environmental problems. This led to general agreement on some key principles, which with enough political pressure from citizens and NGOs could be implemented or improved.

- Paralleling the official meeting was a Global Forum that brought together 20,000 concerned citizens and activists from more than 1,400 NGOs in 178 countries. These people outnumbered the conference's official representatives by at least two to one. These NGOs (1) worked behind the scenes to influence official policy, (2) formulated their own agendas and treaties for environmental sustainability, (3) learned from one another, (4) developed a series of new global networks (such as the Climate Action Network and the Third World Network), alliances, and projects, and (5) developed key goals (Solutions, p. 737).

- In the long run, these newly formed networks and alliances may play the greatest role in helping **(1)** monitor, support, and implement the commitments and plans developed by the 1992 conference, **(2)** set the agenda for the third UN Conference on the Human Environment at Johannesburg, South Africa, in 2002, and **(3)** formulate environmental goals (Solutions, p. 737).

## Is Encouraging Global Free Trade Environmentally Helpful or Harmful?

Like it or not, we are in an age of rapid economic, political, and social globalization (p. 7). Countries (or, more accurately, transnational corporations) involved in international trade want to eliminate trade barriers that prevent the free flow of goods and services from one place to another.

On April 15, 1994, representatives of 120 nations signed the Uruguay Round of the General Agreement on Tariffs and Trade (GATT). This is a revised version of the 1948 GATT convention, which attempted to lower tariff barriers to world trade between member nations. The new GATT established a World Trade Organization (WTO) and gave it the status of a major international organization (similar to the United Nations and the World Bank). The WTO, which came into existence in 1995, is charged with **(1)** enforcing the new GATT rules of world trade and **(2)** settling any disputes about these rules between nations.

Currently, the WTO has 140 member countries (nations that are not members can be frozen out of international trade). Representatives of the Quad Countries—the United States, Canada, Japan, and the European Union—determine most WTO policy. WTO officials consist mostly of trade experts and corporate lawyers, representing primarily the interests of transnational corporations.

The member countries have granted the WTO unprecedented power to **(1)** govern world trade and **(2)** make binding decisions about whether environmental, health, and worker safety laws and regulations by its member countries are illegal because they restrict trade as defined by WTO rules.

WTO member countries must follow 700 pages of GATT rules for international trade. Any member country can charge another member country with violating one of the trade rules. When this occurs,

- The case is decided by a tribunal of three anonymous WTO judges, usually corporate lawyers with no particular expertise in the issues being decided. There are no conflict-of-interest restraints on tribunal members, and no information about their possible conflicts of interest is available to the public.

- All cases are **(1)** decided in secret at unannounced times and places and **(2)** fully insulated from ordinary citizens, the press, representatives of state and local governments, and groups and experts concerned with environmental protection, health, safety, and worker issues. Only official government representatives of the countries involved can submit documents or appear before the tribunal. This **(1)** weakens the ability of the governments of poor developing countries without the necessary government experts to present their case and **(2)** insulates tribunal members (who usually have little expertise in the issues they are deciding) from information and advice by people and organizations with relevant information.

- All documents, transcripts, and details of the proceedings are kept secret, and only the results are announced. Governments involved in a case can release information about what they submitted to the tribunal, but all other details of the deliberations of the tribunal members are kept secret.

- Decisions are binding worldwide and can be appealed only to another tribunal of judges within the WTO. A final panel ruling can be appealed to the entire WTO but can be overturned only by consensus of all WTO members. This is virtually impossible because the winning country is unlikely to vote to overturn a ruling in its favor.

- Any country (or part of a country) that violates a ruling of WTO panels has four choices: **(1)** Amend its laws to comply with WTO rules, **(2)** pay annual compensation to the winning country, **(3)** pay high tariffs imposed on the disputed goods by the WTO, or **(4)** find itself shunned and locked out of global commerce.

According to critics, the powerful WTO is **(1)** radically undemocratic because it is not subject to elected representatives, freedom of information, and public review and comment and **(2)** designed primarily to serve the interests and needs of transnational corporations, not the citizens of countries their decisions affect. They view it as a *financially based, corporate-centered* and *trade-driven* trend that can lead to environmental unsustainability in contrast to an *ecologically based, people-centered,* and *earth-centered* trend they believe is the key to environmental sustainability.

Proponents argue that this significant transfer of power from nations to the WTO is necessary and beneficial because

- Globalization of trade is inevitable and we have to guide it.

- Reducing global trade barriers will benefit developing countries, whose products often are at a competitive disadvantage in the global marketplace because of trade barriers erected by developed countries.

## Covering the Environment

*Andrew C. Revkin*

**GUEST ESSAY**

*Andrew (Andy) C. Revkin, currently an environmental reporter for the* New York Times, *has written about the environment and science since 1982. He is author of two widely acclaimed environmental books:* The Burning Season: The Murder of Chico Mendes and the Fight for the Amazon Basin Forest *(Plume Paperback, 1994), which was the basis of the Emmy-winning HBO film of the same name, and* Global Warming: Understanding the Forecast *(Abbeville Press, 1992). He was formerly a senior editor of* Discover *magazine and senior writer at* Science Digest. *He has won more than half a dozen national writing awards, including the Robert F. Kennedy award for* The Burning Season *and the American Association for the Advancement of Science/Westinghouse Science Journalism Award. He has taught a course on environment and energy reporting at the Columbia University Graduate School of Journalism.*

When I traveled to Brazil in 1989 to write a biography of Chico Mendes, the slain leader of the movement to save the Amazon rain forest, Chico's friends were at first very suspicious. "Why should we talk to you?" they asked me. "How do we know you are going to tell the truth?"

They said they were skeptical because, shortly after the murder, dozens of journalists had flown in for a day or two and then left. As a result, many of the articles or television reports were simplistic or inaccurate. Only after I had stayed for months did people open up. And only then did the complexities of the story of the invasion of the rain forest and the struggle to defend it start to make a little sense.

I was very lucky. For the first time in my career, I had the luxury of being able to spend substantial time on the story. Most often, a reporter has a few hours, or maybe a few days, or—rarely—a week or two to figure out how to explain a complicated subject in an interesting and accurate way.

The lack of time affects journalists covering everything from war to sports. Something that is news today does not stay news for very long. But for a writer covering the environment, other factors combine with deadline pressure to make the challenge of effective communication particularly difficult.

First, there is the complexity and unfamiliarity of science. A baseball writer or a political writer can assume at least some basic knowledge on the reader's part of the rules of the game. But when writing about the deterioration of a diffuse layer of ozone high in the atmosphere that helps block harmful ultraviolet radiation, the writer must explain almost every step. It is no easy task to fit in all the essential ideas while still telling a story that does not cause readers to flip to the comics or movie reviews.

Making the task more difficult is the widespread lack of understanding of some of the most basic scientific concepts—not just among readers, but also among the editors who decide what stories make front pages or evening broadcasts. Recently, a biology professor at Oberlin College, Michael Zimmerman, designed a survey to gauge the basic scientific literacy of Americans. He decided to send a little scientific quiz to the managing editors of the nation's 1,563 daily newspapers. He was not trying to pick on the editors. He just figured that they represented a decent cross-section of educated America.

The results of the survey were disquieting, to say the least. When asked whether it were true or false that "dinosaurs and humans lived contemporaneously," only 51% of the editors disagreed strongly with the statement. Thirty-seven percent either agreed or had no opinion on the matter. That means a big chunk of our newspapers are being edited by people who subscribe, at least tacitly, to what amounts to the "Flintstones Theory" of evolution.

Another impediment to good environmental reporting is something one of my journalism professors used

---

- Reducing global trade barriers can stimulate economic growth in all countries by allowing consumers to buy more things at lower prices.

- Globalization of trade will raise the environmental and health standards of developing countries.

- Globalization of trade may involve some sacrifices, but in the long run the economic benefits will outweigh the costs.

Many environmental groups, and those concerned with consumer protection and worker health and safety, agree that global trade barriers are needed to help level the economic playing field for nations involved in international trade. However, they are strongly opposed to WTO rules that weaken **(1)** environmental protection and protection for consumers and workers and **(2)** the power of governments to interfere in the marketplace in the interests of their citizens. They contend that current WTO rules will

- **(1)** *Increase the economic and political power of transnational corporations and* **(2)** *decrease the power of small businesses, citizens, and democratically elected governments.*

- *Eliminate many jobs and lower wages in developed countries and eventually in developing countries.* Transnational companies are increasingly **(1)** moving to call "the MEGO factor," with the acronym standing for "my eyes glaze over." Editors are bombarded with so much information every day that they become numb to its significance. If a reporter asks to write an update on toxic chemicals in a river or the latest findings on climate change, at many papers, magazines, and television networks, the response is likely to be along the lines of, "Haven't we done that story?" Nothing causes an editor's eyes to glaze faster than a complicated, subtle topic.

Another impediment to effective environmental journalism is the endless appetite for the sound bite or snappy quote. Journalists often try to create balance in a story by quoting a yea-sayer and a nay-sayer. As one journalist put it, echoing a famous law of physics, "For every Ph.D., there is an equal and opposite Ph.D." This is a quick and easy way of establishing that the reporter has no bias. The problem is that the loudest voices on an issue often are the most suspect. Scientists who can deliver well-honed sound bites may have been spending more time in front of microphones than microscopes. Too often, such stories confuse instead of inform.

Finally, there is the need for articles to be timely, to have a "news peg" to hang on, in journalistic parlance. In stark contrast to traditional news events, most environmental problems develop in a creeping, almost imperceptible fashion.

In the 1980s, networks and many national publications gave top billing to a report on risks to children from Alar, a pesticide used on apple crops. Apple growers in the Northwest were nearly bankrupted as apple juice sales plummeted. Soon it became clear that the threat was drastically overstated, and most apples were not even treated with the compound. This kind of reactive reporting can end up confusing readers and creating an air of cynical skepticism about environmental threats.

One result, according to many scientists and health experts, is that the public has become overly fearful of such things as toxic dumps and does not take seriously such threats to humanity's future as the continuing growth in concentrations of greenhouse gases in the atmosphere. We fret about parts per billion of certain synthetic chemicals in food while happily heading to the beach for a new dose of ultraviolet radiation—and increasingly getting there in fleets of gas-guzzling Blazers and Broncos and thus contributing to global warming.

Many journalists have worked long and hard to overcome some of these impediments to coverage of environmental issues. Editors are becoming more informed. Reporters have created a Society of Environmental Journalists, which is fostering a daily debate on the Internet and in its newsletter on ways to do a better job. The result is a steady improvement in the national debate on environmental and resource use issues.

Ultimately, though, part of the responsibility rests with readers as well as writers. Consumers of news on television or in the print media become better informed when they treat reports with a skeptical eye and seek a variety of sources. Just as good journalism results when a reporter seeks a multiplicity of sources for a story, good citizenship results when people seek to understand an issue by relying on more than one medium for their information—magazines, newspapers, television reports, books, the Internet, and more.

### Critical Thinking

**1.** Do your eyes generally glaze over when you read a newspaper or magazine story covering some complex environmental issue such as ozone depletion, global warming, biodiversity, or environmental economics?

**2.** How well do you meet your responsibility as a consumer of information to seek a variety of sources on key environmental issues? Have you become skeptical of environmental stories? Why? Have you become too skeptical of such stories by assuming almost all of them are suspect?

their operations throughout the world in search of cheap labor and natural resources and **(2)** substituting machines for human labor in manufacturing and service industries. This is likely to **(1)** eliminate many manufacturing and service jobs in developed countries, **(2)** drag the wages of those with jobs down to the lowest global common denominator, and **(3)** require most people lucky enough to find a job to work without job security or benefits. Eventually, jobs in developing countries will also be lost as businesses cut costs by substituting machines for human labor. The result is *jobless economic growth* and increased fear and insecurity among the world's workers. These critics say it does consumers little good to have access to cheaper products if they lose their jobs, get paid less for their work, and face higher taxes to cover the social cost of increased unemployment.

■ *Weaken environmental and health and safety standards in developed countries.* Countries are free to adopt environmental, health, and other laws that affect products or manufacturing processes within their borders but cannot impose such rules on products imported from other countries.

WTO rulings have found that the following government laws or regulations are illegal barriers to free international trade:

## Improving Environmental Laws and Regulations

Environmentalists agree that **(1)** some government laws and regulations go too far, and **(2)** bureaucrats sometimes develop and impose ridiculous and excessively costly regulations. They also agree that one of the functions of government is to steer a course toward a desired goal, such as improving environmental quality.

This is often accomplished by **(1)** establishing laws and regulations with general goals and guidelines, **(2)** allowing the marketplace and local governments leeway in finding the best ways to meet these goals, and **(3)** carefully monitoring progress.

Environmentalists argue that the solution is to stop regulatory abuse, not throw out or seriously weaken the body of laws and regulations that help protect the public good.

According to environmental economist William Ashworth,

*If we wish to make progress, it will do us no good to replace one failed system with another that failed just as badly. Government regulation, after all, did not fall out of the sky; it was erected, piece by piece, as an attempt to deal with the damage caused by unrestrained property rights and the unregulated free-market system. . . . We do not need to deconstruct regulation, but to reconstruct it.*

To accomplish this, a growing number of analysts urge environmentalists to take a hard look at existing environmental laws and regulations. Which laws (or parts of laws) have worked, and why? Which ones have failed, and why? Which government bureaucracies concerned with developing and enforcing environmental and resource regulations have abused their power or have not been responsive enough to the needs of ordinary people? How can such abuses be corrected? What existing environmental laws (or parts of laws) and regulations should be repealed or modified?

How can a balanced program of regulation and market-based ap-

proaches (Table 26-1, p. 706) be used to achieve environmental goals? What environmental problems lend themselves to market-based approaches (free-market environmentalism), and which ones do not? How can pollution prevention, waste reduction, and the precautionary principle become guidelines for environmental legislation and regulation? What is the minimum amount of environmental legislation and regulation needed?

These are important issues that environmentalists, business leaders, elected officials, and government regulators need to address with a cooperative, problem-solving spirit.

### Critical Thinking

Analyze a particular environmental law in the United States or in the country where you live to come up with ways in which it could be improved. Develop a strategy for bringing about such changes.

---

- U.S. laws banning imports of tuna caught by methods not designed to prevent dolphins from drowning in tuna nets. Congress weakened the law.

- European Union (EU) laws banning U.S. imports of beef treated with growth hormones suspected of causing cancer and hormone disruption (Connections, p. 235) because it was based on inadequate risk assessment. When the EU disregarded the ruling, the WTO ordered the EU to pay the United States $117 million in compensatory tariffs. To critics this is a particularly worrisome decision because almost everyone agrees that the EU enacted this ban as a precautionary measure to protect consumers, not as a trade barrier to protect its domestic cattle industry.

- In a pending case, an EU law requiring imports of genetically modified food (Figure 13-17, p. 292) from the United States or other countries to carry identifying labels to protect consumers' right to know about the possible health and environmental impact of products they purchase. The EU contends that such labeling requirements are a prudent and precautionary response to a new technology that has potentially seri-

ous health and ecological effects still clouded by many scientific uncertainties.

- EPA regulations requiring that gasoline imported into the United States be formulated in a way that reduces air pollution. The EPA weakened its standards.

- Japan's use of stricter limits on pesticide residues in imported agricultural products than those of other countries such as the United States. Japan reluctantly agreed to force its consumers to ingest more pesticides than their government considered safe.

Here are a few WTO rules or omissions of principles that critics say affect the ability of national, state, and local governments to protect the environment, the health of its citizens, and worker health and safety:

- Governments cannot set standards for how imported products are produced or harvested. This means, for example, that government purchasing policies cannot **(1)** discriminate against materials produced by child labor or slave labor, **(2)** require that items be manufactured from recycled materials or use cleaner production methods, or **(3)** require fish-harvesting methods that help protect other species such as dolphins or turtles.

■ National, state, or local governments cannot ban products from countries recognized as violating universally recognized human rights such as using torture and murder to suppress political opposition or using slave labor.

■ Current WTO rules do not acknowledge the rights of countries to take action to protect the atmosphere, the oceans, and other parts of the global commons. There is concern that some provisions of international treaties to protect biodiversity and the ozone layer and reduce the threats of global warming might be ruled as illegal under WTO rules.

■ All national, state, or local environmental, health, and safety laws and regulations must be based on globally accepted scientific evidence and risk analysis showing there is a worldwide scientific consensus on the danger. Otherwise, they are considered to be trade barriers that exceed the international standards set by corporations through the WTO. Because of the inherent scientific and other uncertainties in determining health risks (Section 11-5, p. 245) and carrying out risk analysis (Section 11-2, p. 229), this is an almost impossible standard to meet. In other words, any chemical, product, or technology traded internationally is assumed to be harmless unless it can be proven harmful by extensive scientific research and by risk analysis, which involve many uncertainties and provide opportunities for manipulation and legal challenges. In other words, the burden of proof falls on those trying to prevent pollution instead of the polluters (Figure 27-6). The effect of this rule is that a chemical, product, or technology cannot be banned on the basis of the pollution prevention or precautionary principles, which are two of the foundations of modern environmental protection.

**Figure 27-6** Burden of proof under pollution control and pollution prevention and precautionary systems.

## Goals of Global and National Environmental NGOs

Currently, there are more than 3,000 NGOs operating across international borders. Some key goals of many of these global and national environmental NGOs are to

■ Pressure powerful international organizations such as the World Bank, International Monetary Fund, and World Trade Organization to **(1)** give the public more information about their often secret meetings, policies, and deliberations and **(2)** allow more input from NGOs concerned with environment, public health, and worker health and safety issues into their policies and decisions and be more responsive to these issues.

■ Pressure the United Nations to create a new assembly within its overall body in which the views of the people of the world could be more directly represented than under the current system. Such a body could be similar to the directly elected European Forum.

■ Exert pressure for upgrading the UNEP into a World Environment Organization (WEO) on a par with the WTO that would oversee and integrate global environmental policies.

**Critical Thinking**

Do you agree or disagree with each of these goals? Explain.

■ National laws covering packaging, recycling, and eco-labeling of items involved in international markets are illegal barriers to trade. This rule effectively cancels the third mainstay of modern environmental protection: *consumers' right to know* about the safety and content of products through labeling.

If allowed to stand, environmentalists contend the last three WTO rules just described will force us back to an earlier and less effective era of using end-of-pipe pollution cleanup based on uncertain and easily manipulated risk assessment and as the primary way for dealing with pollution (Section 11-5, p. 245 and Guest Essay, p. 536).

On a more positive side, nations may be able to use the WTO to reduce environmentally harmful subsidies that distort the economic playing field. However, this would also prevent using subsidies to reward companies producing environmentally beneficial goods and services.

Critics of the latest version of GATT call for it to be improved (Solutions, p. 738).

## Improving Trade Agreements

**SOLUTIONS**

Critics of current trade agreements would rewrite and correct what they believe are serious weaknesses in GATT and turn it into GAST: the *General Agreement for Sustainable Trade*. They offer the following suggestions for doing this:

- Judging GATT or any trade agreement primarily on how it benefits the environment, workers, and the poorest 40% of humanity and changing WTO rules as needed to meet these goals.

- Setting minimum environmental, consumer protection, and worker health and safety standards for all participating countries.

- Requiring all panels or bodies setting and enforcing WTO rules to have environmental, labor, consumer, and health representatives from developed countries and developing countries alike.

- Opening all discussions and findings of any GATT panel or other WTO body to **(1)** global public scrutiny and **(2)** inputs from experts on the issues involved. Critics argue that by closing its doors to the public, the WTO **(1)** denies itself important information that could help it make better decisions about public health, worker safety, and the environment and **(2)** loses public support.

- Incorporating the precautionary and pollution prevention principles into WTO rules.

- Protecting the rights of consumers to know about the health and environmental impact of imported products they purchase by allowing eco-labeling programs.

- Recognizing the right of countries to use trade measures to protect the global commons.

- Allowing countries to require that items be manufactured totally or partially from recycled materials.

- Allowing national, state, or local governments to restrict imports of products from countries shown by international investigation to **(1)** use child or slave labor or **(2)** violate universally recognized human rights.

- Allowing international environmental agreements and treaties to prevail when they conflict with WTO rules or the rules of any other trade agreement.

Unless citizens and NGOs exert intense pressure on legislators, critics warn that such safeguards will not be incorporated into GATT and international trade agreements.

### Critical Thinking

Explain why you agree or disagree with each of the suggestions in this box. If you agree with all or most of these proposals, how could they be implemented?

---

**Can We Develop More Environmentally Sustainable Political and Economic Systems in the Next Few Decades?** Environmentalists call for people from all political persuasions and walks of life to work together to develop a positive vision for making the transition to environmentally sustainable societies throughout the world.

Two major goals would be **(1)** promoting the development of creative experiments at local levels, such as the one in Curitiba, Brazil (Solutions, p. 678), that could be spread to other areas over the next few decades and **(2)** getting citizens, business leaders, and elected officials to cooperate in trying to find and implement innovative solutions to local, national, and global environmental, economic, and social problems.

Proponents recognize that making such a cultural shift over the next 40–50 years will be controversial, and like all significant change it will not be predictable, orderly, or painless.

According to business leader Paul Hawken (Guest Essay, p. 16), making this change means

*Thinking big and long into the future. It also means doing something now. It means electing people who really want to make things work (Solutions, p. 721), and who can imagine a better world. It means writing to companies and telling them what you think. It*

*means never forgetting that the cash register is the daily voting booth in democratic capitalism.*

In working with the earth we should be guided by historian Arnold Toynbee's observation, "If you make the world ever so little better, you will have done splendidly, and your life will have been worthwhile," and by George Bernard Shaw's reminder that "indifference is the essence of inhumanity."

*As the wagon driver said when they came to a long, hard hill, "Them that's going on with us, get out and push. Them that ain't, get out of the way."*

ROBERT FULGHUM

## REVIEW QUESTIONS

**1.** Define the boldfaced terms in this chapter.

**2.** Explain how Marion Stoddart's actions in cleaning up a river illustrate the importance of individual political action.

**3.** What is *politics*? What is a *democracy*?

**4.** List four factors that hinder the ability of democracies to deal with environmental problems.

**5.** List six principles that can be used as guidelines in making environmental policy decisions.

**6.** List ten ways in which individuals can influence the environmental policies of local, state, and federal governments.

**7.** Distinguish among *leaders, rulers,* and *managers.* Describe three types of environmental leadership.

**8.** Describe the role of each of the three branches of the federal government in the United States.

**9.** Describe the five steps used to develop federal environmental policy in the United States.

**10.** Describe the four phases of a *policy life cycle.*

**11.** List five types of federal environmental laws in the United States and five principles used to establish regulations for implementing such laws.

**12.** Describe and evaluate the pros and cons of using only public funds to finance all election campaigns in the United States.

**13.** Distinguish between **(a)** *plaintiffs* and *defendants,* **(b)** *statutory law* and *common law,* and **(c)** *nuisance* and *negligence.* List seven factors that hinder the effectiveness of environmental law in the United States.

**14.** Describe the regulatory takings issue.

**15.** What are SLAPPs, and how are they used?

**16.** List three ways to level the legal playing field for ordinary citizens suffering from environmental damage.

**17.** Describe the key roles of mainstream and grassroots environmental groups. List seven rules for effective political action by grassroots organizations.

**18.** What is *environmental justice*? What types of environmental injustice did Robert Bullard describe in his Guest Essay on page 728?

**19.** Describe some of the environmentally beneficial activities that have been carried out by high school and college students.

**20.** Describe three major accomplishments of environmental groups over the past 30 years. What are the major strengths and weaknesses of the diverse array of groups involved in bringing about environmental improvement?

**21.** List three reasons why some people oppose environmental reform. List three main goals of the anti-environmental movement in the United States.

**22.** Describe the problems environmental journalists face in explaining environmental issues to the public as discussed by Andrew Revkin in his Guest Essay on page 734.

**23.** Why are any environmental issues controversial? List five ways to evaluate the conflicting claims of environmentalists and anti-environmentalists.

**24.** Describe ways in which environmentalists could work to improve environmental laws and regulations.

**25.** Distinguish among environmental, economic, and military security. Explain the importance of making environmental security a key priority of governments.

**26.** List six pieces of *good* or *encouraging news* and four pieces of *bad news* about progress in developing international cooperation and policy on environmental issues.

**27.** What is the World Trade Organization (WTO)? Describe the procedure it uses to determine whether a member nation of this group has violated one of its international trade rules.

**28.** List the major pros and cons of the international GATT treaty as enforced by the WTO.

**29.** List ten measures critics have suggested for improving the GATT treaty as administered by the World Trade Organization.

## CRITICAL THINKING

**1.** What are the greatest strengths and weaknesses of the system of government in your country with respect to **(a)** protecting the environment and **(b)** ensuring environmental justice for all? What three major changes, if any, would you make in this system?

**2.** Explain why you agree or disagree with the six principles some analysts believe should be used in making environmental policy decisions listed on pages 717–718.

**3.** Rate the last four presidents of the United States (or leaders of the country where you live) on a scale of 1–10 in terms of their ability to act as a **(a)** leader and **(b)** manager.

**4.** Suppose a presidential candidate ran on a platform calling for the federal government to phase in a tax on gasoline so that, over 5–10 years, the price of gasoline would rise to $5–7 a gallon (as is the case in Japan and most western European nations). The candidate argues that this tax increase is necessary to encourage oil and gasoline conservation, reduce air pollution, slow global warming, and enhance future economic, environmental, and military security. The candidate also says the tax revenue should be used to **(1)** reduce income taxes on the poor and middle class by an amount roughly equal to the increase in gasoline taxes and **(2)** reduce taxes on wages and profits (Solutions, p. 705). Would you vote for this candidate who wants to triple the price of gasoline? Explain.

**5.** What are the pros and cons of using only public funds to finance all election campaigns? Explain why you support or oppose such an idea.

**6.** Explain why you agree or disagree with each of the four solutions given on page 727 for leveling the legal playing field for citizens who have suffered environmental harm. Try to have an environmental lawyer and a corporate lawyer discuss their views.

**7.** Do you agree or disagree with the position that we need to place much more emphasis on environmental security? Should we treat it with the same degree of seriousness, analysis, and funding as we do economic security and military security, or should environmental security have higher or lower priority? Defend your answers.

**8.** Explain why you agree or disagree with the charge that the current rules of the World Trade Organization weaken the ability of governments to protect the environment, the health of their citizens, and the health and safety of their workers.

**9.** Congratulations! You are in charge of formulating environmental policy in the country where you live. List the three most important components of your policy. Compare your views with those of other members of your class and see if you can agree on a consensus policy.

## PROJECTS

**1.** A 1990 national survey by the Roper Organization found that even though 78% of Americans believe a major national effort is needed for environmental improvement (ranking it fourth among national priorities), only 22% were making significant efforts to improve the environment. The poll identified five categories of citizens: **(1)** *true-blue greens* (11%), who are involved in a wide range of environmental activities, **(2)** *greenback greens* (11%), who do not have time to be involved but are willing to pay more for a cleaner environment, **(3)** *grousers* (24%), who are not involved in environmental action, mainly because they do not see why they should be if everybody else is not involved, **(4)** *sprouts* (26%), who are concerned but do not believe individual action will make much difference, and **(5)** *basic browns* (28%), who strongly oppose the environmental movement. To which category do you belong? As a class, conduct a similar poll on your campus.

**2.** Have each member of your class select a particular environmental law, and evaluate the law in terms of **(a)** its use of or failure to use the principles listed on page 717–718 and **(b)** the role that environmental organizations and citizen actions played in its development. Compare the results of these analyses.

**3.** Have each member of your class select a particular environmental legal case and evaluate its outcome in terms of the six limiting factors discussed on page 726. Compare the results of these analyses.

**4.** What student environmental groups (if any) are active at your school? How many people actively participate in these groups? What environmentally beneficial things have they done? What actions (if any) taken by such groups do you disagree with? Why?

**5.** Try to interview **(a)** a lobbyist for an industry seeking to keep a specific environmental law from being strengthened, **(b)** a lobbyist for an environmental group seeking to strengthen the law, **(c)** an EPA official supporting strengthening the law, and **(d)** an elected representative who must make a decision about the law. Compare their views and perspectives, and come to a conclusion about what should be done.

**6.** Have each member of your class use the library or the Internet to learn about and evaluate the effectiveness of a different major environmental group.

**7.** Have each member of your class use the library or the Internet to learn about and evaluate a different decision

made by the World Trade Organization in determining whether a member nation violated one of its international trade rules.

**8.** Use the library or the Internet to find bibliographic information about *Lord Kennet* and *Robert Fulghum,* whose quotes appear at the beginning and end of this chapter.

**9.** Make a concept map of this chapter's major ideas, using the section heads and subheads and the key terms (in boldface type). Look at the the website for this book for information about making concept maps.

### INTERNET STUDY RESOURCES AND RESOURCES FOR FURTHER READING AND RESEARCH

The website for this book contains helpful study aids and many ideas for further reading and research. Log on to

**www.info.brookscole.com/miller13**

and click on the Chapter-by-Chapter area. Choose Chapter 27 and select a resource:

- "Flash Cards" allows you to test your mastery of the Terms and Concepts to Remember for this chapter.

- "Tutorial Quizzes" provides a multiple-choice practice quiz.

- "Student Guide to InfoTrac" will lead you to Critical Thinking Projects that use InfoTrac College Edition as a research tool.

- "References" lists the major books and articles consulted in writing this chapter.

- "Hypercontents" takes you to an extensive list of sites with news, research, and images related to individual sections of the chapter.

### INFOTRAC COLLEGE EDITION

Improve your skills with InfoTrac College Edition, a searchable online database of articles from more than 700 periodicals. Log on to

**http://www.infotrac-college.com**

or access InfoTrac through the website for this book. Try to find the following articles:

**1.** Harris, A. 2001. States' anti-SLAPP measures meet resistance from business. (Brief article) *Daily Business Review* 76: A11. *Keyword:* "anti-SLAPP." SLAPP lawsuits allow businesses to curtail environmental activists effectively. Some states are trying to curb the use of SLAPPs, but the challenges are great.

**2.** Hattam, J. 2001. Wise Use Movement, R.I.P? (Brief article) *Sierra* 86: p. 20. *Keyword:* "Wise Use Movement." Although "Wise Use Movement" sounds like the name of a reasonable group, the group's agenda is far from environmentally responsible. However, its days seem to be numbered.

## Biosphere 2: A Lesson in Humility

In 1991, eight scientists (four men and four women) were sealed into Biosphere 2, a $200 million facility designed to be a self-sustaining life-support system (Figure 28-1)

The project, financed with private capital, was designed to **(1)** provide information and experience in designing self-sustaining stations in space or on the moon or other planets and **(2)** increase our understanding of the earth's life-support system: Biosphere 1.

The 1.3-hectare (3.2-acre) closed and sealed system was built in the desert near Tucson, Arizona. It had a variety of ecosystems, each built from scratch. They included a tropical rain forest, lakes, a desert, streams, freshwater and saltwater wetlands, and a mini-ocean with a coral reef.

The system was designed to mimic the earth's natural chemical recycling systems. Water evaporated from its ocean and other aquatic systems condensed to provide rainfall over the tropical rain forest. This water then trickled through soil filters into the marshes and the ocean to provide fresh water for the crew and the facility's ecosystems before being evaporated again.

The facility was stocked with more than 4,000 species of organisms selected to maintain life-support functions. The crew was to get their food from **(1)** intensive organic farming, **(2)** raising a few goats and chickens, and **(3)** fish farming in ponds and tanks. Sunlight and external natural gas-powered generators provided energy.

The Biospherians were supposed to be isolated for 2 years and to **(1)** raise their own food, **(2)** breathe air recirculated by plants, and **(3)** drink water cleansed by natural nutrient-cycling processes. From the beginning they encountered numerous unexpected problems.

The life-support system began unraveling. Large amounts of oxygen disappeared mysteriously. Additional oxygen had to be pumped in from the outside to keep the Biospherians from suffocating.

The nitrogen and carbon cycling systems also failed to function properly. Levels of nitrous oxide rose high enough to threaten the occupants with brain damage and had to be controlled by outside intervention. Carbon dioxide skyrocketed to levels that threatened to poison the humans and spurred the growth of weedy vines that choked out food crops. Plant nutrients leached from the soil and polluted the water systems.

Disruption of the facility's chemical cycling systems and leaks in the seals from the outside disrupted populations of the system's life-forms. Tropical birds disappeared after the first freeze. An Arizona ant species got into the enclosure, proliferated, and killed off most of the system's introduced insect species. After the majority of the introduced insect species became extinct, the facility was overrun with cockroaches and katydids. All together, 19 of the Biosphere's 25 small animal species became extinct. Before the 2-year period was up, all plant-pollinating insects became extinct, thereby dooming to extinction most of the plant species.

Despite many problems, all of the facility's waste and wastewater was recycled, and the Biospherians were able to produce 80% of their food supply.

Scientists Joel Cohen and David Tilman, who evaluated the project, concluded, "No one yet knows how to engineer systems that provide humans with life-supporting services that natural ecosystems provide for free." In other words, an expenditure of $200 million failed to maintain a life-support system for eight people. The earth—Biosphere 1—does this every day for 6.2 billion people and millions of other species at no cost. If we had to pay for these services at the same annual cost of $12.5 million per person in Biosphere 2, the total bill for the earth's 6.2 billion people would be 1,900 times the annual world national product.

Today Columbia University uses this world's largest ecological laboratory—renamed the Lamont-Doherty Earth Observatory—to carry out climate and ecological research.

**Figure 28-1** *Biosphere 2*, constructed near Tucson, Arizona, was designed to be a self-sustaining life-support system for eight people sealed into the facility in 1991. The experiment failed because of a breakdown in its nutrient cycling systems.

*The main ingredients of an environmental ethic are caring about the planet and all of its inhabitants, allowing unselfishness to control the immediate self-interest that harms others, and living each day so as to leave the lightest possible footprints on the planet.*

ROBERT CAHN

This chapter addresses the following questions:

- What human-centered environmental worldviews guide most industrial societies?
- What are some life-centered and earth-centered environmental worldviews?
- What ethical guidelines might be used to help us work with the earth?
- How can we live more sustainably?

## 28-1 ENVIRONMENTAL WORLDVIEWS IN INDUSTRIAL SOCIETIES

**What Is an Environmental Worldview?** There are conflicting views about how serious our environmental problems are and what we should do about them. These conflicts arise mostly out of differing **environmental worldviews: (1)** how people think the world works, **(2)** what they think their role in the world should be, and **(3)** what they believe is right and wrong environmental behavior (**environmental ethics**).

People with widely differing environmental worldviews can take the same data, be logically consistent, and arrive at quite different conclusions because they start with different assumptions and values.

The many different types of environmental worldviews are summarized in Figure 28-2. Most can be divided into two groups according to whether they are **(1)** *individual centered* (atomistic) or **(2)** *earth centered* (holistic). Atomistic environmental worldviews tend to be *human centered* (anthropocentric) or *life centered* (biocentric, with the primary focus on individual species or individual organisms). Holistic or ecocentric environmental worldviews focus on sustaining the earth's **(1)** natural systems (ecosystems), **(2)** life-forms (biodiversity), and **(3)** life-support systems (biosphere) for all species.

**What Is the Difference Between Instrumental and Intrinsic Values?** What we value largely determines how we act. Environmental philosophers normally divide values into two types:

- **Instrumental**, or **utilitarian:** a value something has because of its usefulness to us or to the biosphere. For example, the concept of preserving natural capital and biodiversity because they sustain life and support economies is an instrumental value based mostly on the usefulness of these natural goods and services to us.

- **Intrinsic**, or **inherent value:** the value something has just because it exists, regardless of whether it has any instrumental value to us. There is controversy over whether nonhuman forms of life and nature as a whole have intrinsic value.

The view that a wild species, a biotic community ecosystem, biodiversity, or the biosphere has value only because of its usefulness to us is called an **anthropocentric** (human-centered) instrumental value. According to an *anthropocentric worldview*, **(1)** humans have intrinsic value, **(2)** the rest of nature has instrumental value, and **(3)** we are in charge of the earth.

In contrast, the view that these forms of life are valuable simply because they exist, independently of their use to human beings, is called a **biocentric** (life-centered) intrinsic value. According to a *biocentric*

**Figure 28-2** General types of environmental worldviews. (Diagram developed by Jane Heinze-Fry)

*worldview,* **(1)** all species and ecosystems and the biosphere have both intrinsic and instrumental value, **(2)** we are just one of many species, and **(3)** we have an ethical responsibility not to impair the long-term sustainability and adaptability of the earth's natural systems for all life.

**What Are the Major Human-Centered Environmental Worldviews?** Most people in today's industrial consumer societies have a **planetary management worldview,** which has become increasingly common during the past 50 years. According to this human-centered environmental worldview, human beings, as the planet's most important and dominant species, can and should manage the planet mostly for their own benefit. Other species and parts of nature are seen as having only *instrumental value* based on how useful they are to us.

Figure 28-3 (left) summarizes the four major beliefs or assumptions of this one version of this worldview. All or most aspects of this worldview are widely supported because it is said to be the primary driving force behind the major improvements in the human condition since the beginning of the industrial revolution.

There are several variations of this environmental worldview:

- The *no-problem school.* We can solve any environmental, population, or resource problems with more economic growth and development, better management, and better technology.

- The *free-market school.* The best way to manage the planet for human benefit is through a free-market

global economy with minimal government interference and regulations. Free-market advocates would convert all public property resources to private property resources and let the global marketplace, governed by pure free-market competition (p. 691), decide essentially everything.

- The *responsible planetary management school.* We have serious environmental problems, but we can sustain our species with a mixture of market-based competition, better technology, and some government intervention that **(1)** promotes environmentally sustainable forms of economic development, **(2)** protects environmental quality and private property rights, and **(3)** protects and manages public and common property resources. People holding this view follow the pragmatic principle of *enlightened self-interest:* Better earth care is better self-care.

- The *spaceship-earth school.* The earth is seen as a spaceship: a complex machine that we can understand, dominate, change, and manage to prevent environmental overload and provide a good life for everyone. This view developed as a result of photographs taken from space showing the earth as a finite planet or island "floating" in space (Figure 5-1, p. 95). This powerful image led many people to see that the earth is our only home and we had better treat it right.

- The *stewardship school.* We have an ethical responsibility to be caring and responsible managers, or stewards, of the earth. According to this view, we can and should make the world a better place for our species and other species through love, care, compassion, knowledge, and technology.

**Figure 28-3** Comparison of two opposing environmental worldviews.

## 28-2 LIFE-CENTERED ENVIRON-MENTAL WORLDVIEWS

**Can We Manage the Planet?** Some people believe any human-centered worldview will eventually fail because it wrongly assumes we now have (or can gain) enough knowledge to become effective managers, or stewards, of the earth.

According to these analysts, the unregulated global free-market approach will not work because it **(1)** is based on increased losses of natural capital (Figure 4-34, p. 92, and Figure 26-7, p. 694) that support all life and economies and **(2)** focuses on short-term economic benefits regardless of the harmful long-term environmental and social consequences.

The image of the earth as an island or spaceship in space has played an important role in raising global environmental awareness. However, critics argue that thinking of the earth as a spaceship that we should and can manage is an oversimplified and misleading way to view an incredibly complex and ever-changing planet, as the failure of Biosphere 2 demonstrated (p. 741). For example, these critics point out that we do not even know how many species live on the earth, much less what their roles are and how they interact with one another and their nonliving environment. We have only an inkling of what goes on in a handful of soil, a meadow, a patch of forest, a pond, or any other part of the earth.

As biologist David Ehrenfeld puts it, "In no important instance have we been able to demonstrate comprehensive successful management of the world, nor do we understand it well enough to manage it even in theory." Environmental educator David Orr (Guest Essay, p. 684) says we are losing rather than gaining the knowledge and wisdom needed to adapt creatively to continually changing environmental conditions: "On balance, I think, we are becoming more ignorant because we are losing cultural knowledge about how to inhabit our places on the planet sustainably, while impoverishing the genetic knowledge accumulated through millions of years of evolution."

Even if we had enough knowledge and wisdom to manage spaceship earth, some critics see this approach as requiring us to give up individual freedom to survive. Life on spaceship earth under a comprehensive system of planetary management or world government might be much like the regimented life of astronauts in their capsule. The astronauts have almost no individual freedom with essentially all of their actions dictated by a central command (ground control).

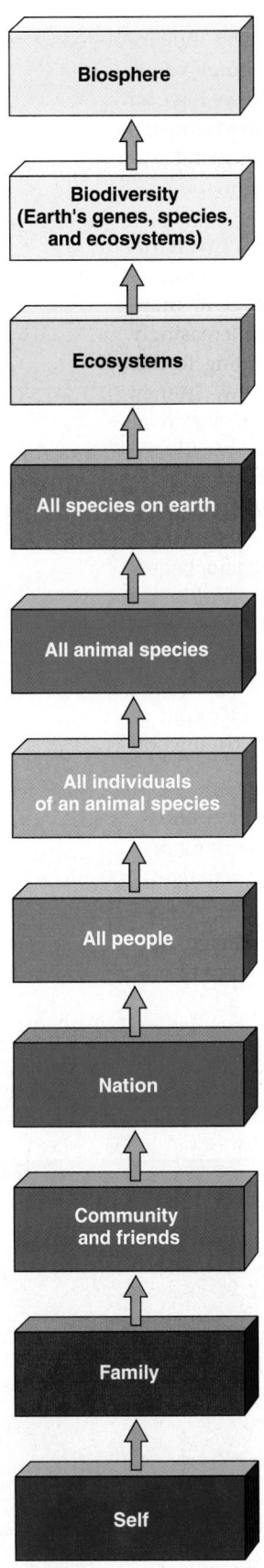

**Figure 28-4** Levels of ethical concern. People disagree over how far we should extend our ethical concerns on this scale.

### What Are Some Major Biocentric and Ecocentric Worldviews?

People disagree over how far we should extend our ethical concerns for various forms or levels of life (Figure 28-4). Critics of human-centered environmental worldviews believe such worldviews should be expanded to recognize the *inherent* or *intrinsic value* of all forms of life regardless of their potential or actual use to us.

Another source of conflict between human-centered and life-centered worldviews results from whether emphasis should be on short-term or long-term values. Because of the nature of major environmental problems, many analysts believe they need to be dealt with in terms of both the short-term and long-term future.

Most people with a life-centered (biocentric) worldview believe we have an ethical responsibility not to cause the premature extinction of a species because of our activities. Most people give protection of a species priority over protection of an individual member of a species because each species is a unique storehouse of genetic information that **(1)** should be respected and protected because it exists (intrinsic value), **(2)** is a potential economic good for human use (instrumental value), and **(3)** is capable through evolution and speciation of adapting to changing environmental conditions. In this sense, **(1)** individuals are temporary representatives of a species, and **(2)** the premature extinction of a species can be regarded as killing future generations of a species and eliminating its possibility for future evolutionary adaptation or speciation.

Trying to decide whether all or only some species should be protected from premature extinction resulting from human activities is a difficult and controversial ethical problem. It is hard to know where to draw the line and be ethically consistent. For example,

- Should all species be protected from premature extinction because of their intrinsic value, or should only certain ones be preserved because of their known or potential instrumental value to us or to their ecosystems?

- Should all insect and bacterial species be protected, or should we attempt to exterminate those that eat our crops, harm us, or transmit disease organisms?

- Should we emphasize protecting keystone species (pp. 165 and 172) in ecosystems over other species that play lesser ecological roles?

Others believe we must go beyond this biocentric worldview, which focuses on species and individual organisms. They believe we have an ethical responsibility not to degrade the earth's systems (ecosystems), life-forms (biodiversity), and life-support systems (biosphere) for this and future generations of humans

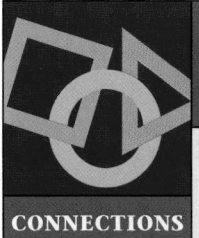

## Why Should We Care About Future Generations?

**CONNECTIONS**

Some people believe our only ethical obligation is to the present human generation. They ask, "What has the future done for me?" or believe we cannot know enough about the condition of the earth for future generations to be concerned about it.

According to biologist David W. Ehrenfeld, caring about future generations enough not to degrade the earth's life-support systems is important because it gives future generations more options for dealing with the problems they will face. He points out that if our ancestors had left for us the ecological degradation we appear to be leaving our descendants, our options for enjoyment—perhaps even for survival—would be quite limited.

In response to the question, "What can future generations do for us?" Ehrenfeld gives the following answer: "They give us a reason for treating our ecological home respectfully, so that our lives as well as theirs will be enriched."

According to this view, as we use the earth's natural resources we **(1)** are borrowing from the earth and from future generations and **(2)** have an ethical responsibility to leave the earth in as good as or better condition than it is now for future generations. In thinking about our responsibility toward future generations, some analysts believe we should consider the wisdom given to us in the 18th century by the Iroquois Confederation of Native Americans: *In our every deliberation, we must consider the impact of our decisions on the next seven generations.*

### Critical Thinking

What obligations, if any, concerning the environment do you have to future generations? To how many future generations do you have responsibilities? Be honest about your feelings.

(Connections, below) and other forms of life based on their intrinsic and instrumental values. In other words, they have an *earth-centered*, or *ecocentric*, environmental worldview, devoted to preserving the earth's biodiversity and the functioning of its life-support systems (Figure 28-4) for all forms of life.

Why should we care about the earth's biodiversity? According to the late environmentalist and systems expert Donella Meadows,

> *Biodiversity contains the accumulated wisdom of nature and the key to its future. If you wanted to destroy a society, you would burn its libraries and kill its intellectuals. You would destroy its knowledge. Nature's knowledge is contained in the DNA within living cells. The variety of genetic information is the driving engine of evolution and the source of adaptability.*

According to the ecocentric worldview, we are part of, not apart from, the community of life and the ecological processes that sustain all life. Aldo Leopold (Section 2-5, p. 36) summed up this idea in 1948: "All ethics rest upon a single premise: that the individual is a member of a community of interdependent parts."

There are many life-centered and earth-centered environmental worldviews, and several of them overlap in some of their beliefs. Figure 28-3 (right) summarizes the four major beliefs or assumptions of the **environmental wisdom worldview,** which are the opposite of those making up the planetary management worldview (Figure 28-3, left). A related ecocentric environmental worldview is the *deep ecology worldview* (Spotlight, p. 746).

Others say we do not need to be biocentrists or ecocentrists to value life or the earth. They point out that human-centered stewardship and planetary management environmental worldviews also call for us to value individuals, species, and the earth's life-support systems as part of our responsibility as the earth's caretakers.

**What Is the Ecofeminist Environmental Worldview?** The term *ecofeminism*, coined in 1974 by French writer Françoise d'Eaubonne, includes a spectrum of views on the relationships of women to the earth and to male-dominated societies (patriarchies). Most ecofeminists agree that we need a life-centered or earth-centered environmental worldview. However, they believe a main cause of our environmental problems is not just human centeredness, but specifically male centeredness (*androcentrism*).

Many ecofeminists argue that the rise of male-dominated societies and environmental worldviews since the advent of agriculture is primarily responsible for our violence against nature (and for the oppression of women and minorities as well). To such ecofeminists, this led to a shift from an image of nature as a nurturing mother to a foe to be conquered.

## Deep Ecology

Deep ecology consists of the following ecocentric beliefs developed in 1972 by Norwegian philosopher Arne Naess, in conjunction with philosopher George Sessions and sociologist Bill Devall:

- Each nonhuman form of life on the earth has inherent value that is independent of its value to humans.

- The fundamental interdependence, richness, and diversity of lifeforms contribute to the flourishing of human and nonhuman life on earth.

- Humans have no right to reduce this interdependence, richness, and diversity except to satisfy vital needs.

- Present human interference with the nonhuman world is excessive, and the situation is worsening rapidly.

- Because of the damage caused by human interference in the non-human world, it would be better for humans, and much better for nonhumans, if there were a substantial decrease in the human population.

- Basic economic, technological, and ideological policies must therefore be changed.

- The ideological change is mainly that of appreciating *life quality* (involving situations of inherent value) rather than adhering to an ever-higher material standard of living.

- Those who subscribe to these points have an obligation directly or indirectly to try to implement the necessary changes.

Naess has also described some lifestyle guidelines compatible with the basic beliefs of deep ecology. They include (1) appreciating all forms of life, (2) protecting or restoring local ecosystems, (3) consuming less, (4) emphasizing satisfying vital needs rather than desires, (5) attempting to live *in* nature and promote community, (6) appreciating ethnic and cultural differences, (7) working to improve the standard of living for the world's poor, (8) working to eliminate injustice toward fellow humans or other species, and (9) acting nonviolently.

Deep ecology is not an ecoreligion, nor is it antireligious or anti-human, as some of its critics have claimed. Instead, it is a set of beliefs designed to have us think more deeply about (1) the inherent value of all life on the earth and (2) our obligations toward both human and nonhuman life.

### Critical Thinking

**1.** Which, if any, of the eight basic beliefs of the deep ecology environmental worldview do you agree with? Explain.

**2.** List five major changes that would occur in your life if you and most people lived by the beliefs of deep ecology.

---

As evidence of male domination, ecofeminists note that women earn less than 10% of all wages, own less than 1% of all property, and in most societies have far fewer rights than men. These analysts argue that to become primary players in the male power-and-domination game, most women are forced to emphasize the characteristics deemed masculine and become "honorary men."

Some ecofeminists suggest that oppression by men has driven women closer to nature and made them more compassionate and nurturing. As oppressed members of society, they argue, women have more experience in (1) dealing with interpersonal conflicts, (2) bringing people together, (3) acting as caregivers, and (4) identifying emotionally with injustice, pain, and suffering.

Ecofeminists argue that women should be (1) given the same rights as men, (2) allowed to have their views heard and respected, and (3) treated as equal partners. They do not want just a fair share of the patriarchal pie; they want to work with men to bake an entirely new pie that (1) helps heal the rift between humans and nature and (2) ends oppression based on sex, race, class, and cultural and religious beliefs. In doing this, they do not want to be given token roles or co-opted into the male power game.

Ecofeminists are not alone in calling for us to encourage the rise of *life-centered people* who emphasize the best human characteristics: gentleness, caring, compassion, nonviolence, cooperation, and love.

**What Is the Social Ecology Worldview?** According to activist and philosopher Murray Bookchin, the ecological crisis we currently face results from (1) the power of our hierarchical and authoritarian social, economic, and political structures and (2) the various technologies used to dominate people and nature. In other words, our current environmental situation has been created by industrialized societies driven by the conventional planetary management environmental worldview (Figure 28-3, left).

To deal with the ecological problems we face, Bookchin believes we must adopt a *social ecology environmental worldview.* It is built around creating (1) better versions of democratic communities, (2) new forms of environmentally sustainable production, and (3) types of appropriate technology that are smaller in scale, consume fewer resources and less earth capital, and do not cause environmental degradation of local ecological regions (Solutions, p. 696).

**Are There Really Physical and Biological Limits to Human Economic Growth?** The planetary management and environmental wisdom worldviews (and related versions of these two types of worldviews) differ over whether there are physical and biological limits to economic growth, beyond which both ecological and economic collapse is likely to occur. This argument over limits has been going on since Thomas Malthus published his book *The Principles of Political Economy* in 1836, with each side insisting it is right at least in the long term.

In 2000, conservation biologist Carlos Davidson (with a background in economics) proposed a way to **(1)** bridge the gap between these two opposing viewpoints and **(2)** help motivate the political changes needed to halt or slow the spread of environmental degradation.

He disagrees with the view of some economists that technology will allow continuing economic growth without causing serious environmental damage. However, he also disagrees with the concept that continuing economic growth based on consuming and degrading natural capital will lead to ecological and economic crashes.

Instead of crashes, he suggests we use the metaphor of the gradual unraveling of some of the threads in a woven *tapestry* to describe the effects of environmental degradation. He views nature as an incredibly diverse and interwoven tapestry of threads consisting of a variety of patterns (biomes, aquatic systems, and ecosystems). As environmental degradation removes threads from different parts of the biosphere, nature's tapestry in these areas becomes worn and tattered.

Clearly, if too many of the threads are removed, the tapestry can be destroyed. However, Davidson contends that as threads are pulled from various parts of the tapestry, local losses of ecological function and occasional local and regional tears occur rather than overall collapse. Global problems such as climate change, ozone depletion, and biodiversity loss may be exceptions to this analogy. However, even with these problems, some areas of the tapestry are damaged more than other areas.

Davidson agrees with the views of ecologists and environmentalists that degradation in parts of the earth's ecological tapestry is occurring, spreading, and must be prevented. He supports doing this by using the pollution prevention and precautionary principles to protect areas of the biosphere from further damage.

However, he believes using catastrophe metaphors such as "ecological collapse" and "going over a cliff" can hinder achievement of these important goals. He argues that repeated predictions of catastrophe, like the boy who cries wolf, initially motivate people's concern. However, when the threats turn out to be less severe than predicted, people tend to ignore future warnings. As a result, they are not politically motivated to **(1)** prevent more tears in nature's tapestry and **(2)** look more deeply at the economic, political, and social forces responsible for environmental degradation.

Biologist Kevin S. McCann at McGill University in Montreal, Canada, believes the tapestry metaphor is misleading because it assumes nature is in a static equilibrium state when in fact it undergoes constant dynamic change. He points out that tearing nature's fabric sends "waves of dynamic change through an ecosystem, and the waves get bigger as biological diversity declines."

## 28-3 SOLUTIONS: LIVING MORE SUSTAINABLY

**How Should We Evaluate Sustainability Proposals?** *Sustainability* has become a buzzword that means different things to different people. Environmental leader Lester Brown has this simple test for any sustainability proposal: "Does this policy or action lower carbon emissions? Does it reduce the generation of toxic wastes? Does it slow population growth? Does it increase the earth's tree cover? Does it cut emissions of ozone-depleting chemicals? Does it reduce pollution? Does it reduce radioactive waste generation? Does it lead to less soil erosion? Does it protect the planet's biodiversity?"

Additional questions also help us evaluate sustainability proposals. Does it deplete or degrade the earth's natural capital? Does it require getting most of our energy from current sunlight instead of ancient sunlight stored as fossil fuels? Does it promote full-cost pricing of goods and services (p. 699)? Does it diminish human cultural diversity? Does it reduce poverty, hunger, and disease? Does it prevent pollution? Does it reduce resource waste? Does it save energy? Does it transfer the most resource-efficient and environmentally benign technologies to developing countries? Does it keep wealth in the local community? What are its true costs, and who pays? Does it enhance environmental and economic justice for all?

**Solutions: What Are Some Ethical Guidelines for Working with the Earth?** Ethicists and philosophers have developed ethical guidelines for living more sustainably on the earth. Anyone can use such guidelines, regardless of their environmental worldview.

### Biosphere and Ecosystems

- We should try to understand and work with the rest of nature to help sustain the natural capital, biodiversity, and adaptability of the earth's life-support systems.

- When we alter nature to meet our needs or wants, we should choose methods that do the least possible short- and long-term environmental harm. This ethical concept of *ahimsa,* or avoiding unnecessary harm, is a key element of Hinduism, Buddhism, and Janism.

### Species and Cultures

- No wild species should become prematurely extinct because of our actions.

- The best ways to protect species and individuals of species are to **(1)** protect the places where they live, **(2)** help restore biological habitats we have degraded, and **(3)** control the accidental or deliberate introduction of nonnative species into aquatic and terrestrial systems.

## Envisioning a Sustainable Society

**GUEST ESSAY**

*Lester W. Milbrath*

*Lester W. Milbrath is director of the Research Program in Environment and Society and professor emeritus of political science and sociology at the State University of New York at Buffalo. During his distinguished career he has served as director of the Environmental Studies Center at SUNY/ Buffalo (1976–87) and taught at Northwestern University, Duke University, the University of Tennessee, National Taiwan University in Taipei, and Aarhus University in Denmark. He has also been a visiting research scholar at the Australian National University and at Mannheim University in Germany. His research has focused on the relationships among science, society, and citizen participation in environmental policy decisions, with emphasis on environmental perceptions, beliefs, attitudes, and values. He has written numerous articles and books. His book* Envisioning a Sustainable Society: Learning Our Way Out *(1989) summarizes a lifetime of studying our environmental predicament. It is considered one of the best analyses of what we can do to learn how to work with the earth. His most recent book is* Learning to Think Environmentally While There Is Still Time *(1995).*

Try this thought experiment: Imagine that, suddenly, all the humans disappeared, but all the buildings, roads, shopping malls, factories, automobiles, and other artifacts of modern civilization were left behind. What then? After three or four centuries, buildings would have crumbled, vehicles would have rusted and fallen apart, and plants would have recolonized fields, roads, parking lots, even buildings. Water, air, and soil would gradually clear up; some endangered species would flourish. Nature would thrive splendidly without us.

That mental experiment makes it clear that we do not have an environmental crisis; we have a crisis of civilization. Here are some of civilization's most crucial problems: **(1)** Humans are reproducing at such high rates that world population could rise to 9 billion by 2050, **(2)** resource depletion and waste generation could easily triple or even quadruple over that period, **(3)** waste discharges are already beginning to change the way the biosphere works, and **(4)** climate change and ozone loss are likely to reduce the productivity and structure of ecosystems just

when large numbers of new humans will be looking for sustenance and will destroy the confidence people need to invest in the future.

Without intending to, we have created a civilization that appears to be headed for destruction. Either we learn to control our growth in population and in economic activity, or nature will use death to control it for us.

Present-day society is not capable of producing a solution because it is disabled by the values our leaders constantly trumpet: economic growth, jobs, consumption, competitiveness, power, and domination. Societies pursuing these goals cannot avoid depleting their resources, degrading nature, poisoning life with wastes, and upsetting biospheric systems. *We have no choice but to change, and resisting change will make us victims of change.* Not to decide is to decide.

How do we transform to a sustainable society? My answer, which I believe is the only answer, is that *we must learn our way.* Nature, and the imperatives of its laws, will be our most powerful teacher [Solutions, p. 201] as we learn our way to a new society. Most crucially, we must learn how to think about values.

Life in a viable ecosystem must become the core value of a sustainable society; that means all life, not just human life. Ecosystems function splendidly without humans, but human society would not exist without viable ecosystems. People seeking life quality need a well-functioning society living in well-functioning ecosystems.

A sustainable society would affirm love as a primary value and extend it not only to those near and dear but to people in other lands, to future generations, and to other species. A sustainable society emphasizes partnership rather than domination, cooperation over competition, love over power. A sustainable society affirms justice and security as primary values.

A sustainable society would encourage self-realization—helping people to become all they are capable of being, rather than spending and consuming—as the key to a fulfilling life. A sustainable society would make long-lasting products to be cherished and conserved. People would learn a love of beauty and simplicity.

A sustainable society would use both planning and markets as basic and supplementary information sys-

- No human culture should become extinct because of our actions.

### Individual Responsibility

- We should not inflict unnecessary suffering or pain on any animal we raise or hunt for food or use for scientific or other purposes.

- We should leave the earth in as good as or better condition than we found it.

- We should use no more of the earth's resources than we need.

- We should work with the earth to help heal ecological wounds we have inflicted.

In March 2000, the Earth Charter was finalized. More than 100,000 people in 51 countries and 25 global leaders in environment, business, politics, religion, and education took part in creating this charter. It is a document creating an ethical and moral framework to

tems. Markets fail us because they can neither anticipate the future nor make moral choices between objects and between policies. Markets also cannot provide public goods such as schools, parks, and environmental protection, which are just as important for life quality as private goods.

A sustainable society would continue further development of science and technology because we need practical creative solutions that are both environmentally sound and economically feasible. However, we should recognize that those who control science and technology could use them to dominate all other creatures; we must learn to develop social controls of science and technology to make our society more sustainable. We should not allow the deployment of powerful new technologies that can induce sweeping changes in economic patterns, lifestyles, governance, and social values without careful forethought regarding their long-term impacts.

Conscious social learning would become the dynamic of social change in a sustainable society, not only to deal with pressing problems but also to realize a vision of a good society. Meaningful and lasting social change occurs when nearly everyone learns the necessity of change and the value of working toward it.

Ecological thinking is different from most thinking that guides modern society. For example, the following key maxims derived from the law of conservation and matter [p. 55], the laws of energy or thermodynamics [Section 3-7, p. 59], and the workings of ecosystems [Chapters 4–10 and Solutions, p. 201] are routinely violated in contemporary thinking and discourse: **(1)** *Everything must go somewhere (there is no away)*, **(2)** *energy should not be wasted because all use of energy produces disorder in the environment*, **(3)** *we can never do just one thing (everything is connected)*, and **(4)** *we must constantly ask, "And then what?"*

Every schoolchild and every adult should learn these simple truths; we need to reaffirm the tradition that knowledge of nature's workings and a respect for all life are basic to a true education. We should require such environmental education of all students, just as we now require every student to study history.

Ecological thinking recognizes that a proper understanding of the world requires people to learn how to think holistically, systematically, and futuristically. Because everything is connected to everything else, we must learn to anticipate second-, third-, and higher-order consequences for any contemplated major societal action.

A society learning to be sustainable would redesign government to maximize its ability to learn. It would require that people who govern listen to citizens, not only to keep the process open for public participation but also to cultivate mutual learning between officials and citizens.

A sustainable society would strive for an effective system of planetary politics because our health and welfare are vitally affected by how people, businesses, and governments in other lands behave. It would nurture planetwide social learning.

Learning our way to a new society cannot occur until enough people become aware of the need for major societal change. As long as contemporary society is working reasonably well and leaders keep telling us that society is on the right track, most people will not listen to a message urging significant change. For that reason, urgently needed change probably will be delayed, and conditions on our planet are likely to get worse before they can get better. Nature will be our most powerful teacher, especially when biospheric systems no longer work the way they used to. In times of great system turbulence, social learning can be extraordinarily swift.

Our species has a special gift: the ability to recall the past and foresee the future. Once we have a vision of the future, every decision becomes a moral decision. Even the decision not to act becomes a moral judgment. Those who understand what is happening to the only home for us and other species are not free to shrink from the responsibility to help make the transition to a more sustainable society.

### Critical Thinking

**1.** Do you agree or disagree that we can only learn our way to a sustainable society? Explain.

**2.** Do you think we will learn our way to a sustainable society? Explain. What role, if any, do you intend to play in this process?

guide the conduct of people and nations to each other and to the earth. Here are its four guiding principles:

- Respect earth and life in all its diversity.

- Care for life with understanding, love, and compassion.

- Build societies that are free, just, participatory, sustainable, and peaceful.

- Secure earth's bounty and beauty for present and future generations.

The moral rules of most of the world's religions and ethical systems boil down to a few simple ones. Do not lie. Do not cheat. Do not steal. Do not hurt people. Do not hurt the earth that sustains us. Help each other out. Do not do to someone else what you would not want done to yourself.

**Solutions: How Can We Implement Earth Education?** Most environmentalists believe that learning how to live more sustainably takes a foundation of environmental or earth education that relies heavily on an interdisciplinary and holistic approach to learning (Guest Essay, p. 748). According to its proponents, the most important goals of such an education are these:

- *Develop respect or reverence for all life.*

- *Understand as much as we can about how the earth works and sustains itself, and use such knowledge* (Solutions, p. 201) *to guide our lives, communities, and societies.*

- *Use critical thinking skills* (Guest Essay, p. 42) *to become seekers of environmental wisdom instead of vessels of environmental information.*

- *Understand and evaluate our environmental worldview and see this as a lifelong process* (Individuals Matter, at right).

- *Learn how to evaluate the beneficial and harmful consequences of our choices of lifestyle and profession on the earth, today and in the future.*

- *Use critical thinking skills to evaluate advertising that encourages us to buy more and more things.* As humorist Will Rogers said, "Too many people spend money they haven't earned to buy things they don't want, to impress people they don't like." David Orr points out, "Our children, consumers-in-training, can identify more than a thousand corporate logos but only a dozen or so plants and animals native to their region." Each year U.S. corporations spend more than $150 billion on advertising, far more than is spent on all secondary education in the country.

- *Foster a desire to make the world a better place and act on this desire.* As David Orr (Guest Essay, p. 684) puts

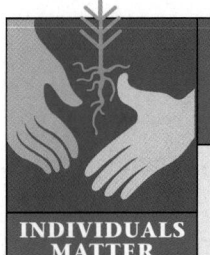

## Mindquake: Evaluating Our Environmental Worldview

**INDIVIDUALS MATTER**

Questioning and perhaps changing our environmental worldview can be difficult and threatening. It can set off a cultural *mindquake* that involves examining many of our most basic beliefs. However, once we change our worldview, it no longer makes sense for us to do things in the old ways. If enough people do this and put their beliefs into action (probably no more than 10% of the population), then tremendous cultural change, once considered impossible, can take place rapidly.

Most environmentalists urge us to think about what our basic environmental beliefs are and why we have them. They believe evaluating our beliefs, and being open to the possibility of changing them, should be one of our most important lifelong activities.

As this book emphasizes, many environmental issues are filled with controversy and uncertainty. A clearly right or wrong path is not easy to discover and usually is strongly influenced by our environmental worldview. As philosopher Georg Hegel pointed out nearly two centuries ago, tragedy is not the conflict between right and wrong, but the conflict between right and right.

### Critical Thinking

What are the basic beliefs of your environmental worldview?

it, education should help students "make the leap from 'I know' to 'I care' to 'I'll do something.'"

According to environmental educator Mitchell Thomashow, four basic questions should be at the heart of environmental education:

- Where do the things I consume come from?

- What do I know about the place where I live?

- How am I connected to the earth and other living things?

- What is my purpose and responsibility as a human being?

How we answer these questions determines our *ecological identity.*

In addition to formal education, some analysts believe we need to experience nature directly to help us learn to walk more lightly on the earth (Connections, p. 751). Noel Perrin (Guest Essay, p. 752) summarizes some actions various colleges and universities have taken to promote environmental sustainability.

**How Can We Live More Simply?** Many analysts urge us to *learn how to live more simply.* Seeking happiness through the pursuit of material things is considered folly by almost every major religion and philosophy. But modern advertising incessantly urges us to buy more and more things.

Some affluent people in developed countries are adopting a lifestyle of *voluntary simplicity,* doing and enjoying more with less by learning to live more simply. Voluntary simplicity is based on Mahatma Gandhi's *principle of enoughness:* "The earth provides enough to satisfy every person's need but not every person's greed. . . . When we take more than we need, we are simply taking from each other, borrowing from the future, or destroying the environment and other species."

Implementing this principle means asking oneself, "How much is enough?" This is not easy because people in affluent societies are conditioned to want more

and more, and they often think of such wants as vital needs (Spotlight, p. 754).

Voluntary simplicity begins by asking a series of questions before buying anything: **(1)** Do I really need this? **(2)** Can I buy it secondhand (reuse)? **(3)** Can I borrow, rent, lease, or share it? **(4)** Can I build it myself?

The decision to buy something triggers another set of questions: **(1)** Is the product produced in an environmentally sustainable manner? **(2)** Did the workers producing it get fair wages for their work, and did they have safe and healthful working conditions? **(3)** Is it designed to last as long as possible? **(4)** Is it easy to repair, upgrade, reuse, and recycle?

Choosing voluntary simplicity means **(1)** spending less time working for money, **(2)** leading lives less driven to accumulate stuff, and **(3)** spending more time living. Instead of seeing this choice as a sacrifice, those practicing voluntary simplicity view it as a more satisfying, meaningful, and sustainable way to live.

According to surveys by the Trends Research Institute, an estimated 12–15% of adult Americans are participating in this social trend, and this trend is increasing.

---

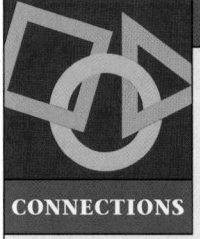

**CONNECTIONS**

## Learning from the Earth

Formal environmental education is important, but many earth thinkers believe it is not enough. They urge us to take the time to escape the cultural and technological body armor we use to insulate ourselves from nature and to experience nature directly.

They suggest we kindle a sense of awe, wonder, mystery, and humility within us by standing under the stars, sitting in a forest, taking in the majesty and power of an ocean, or experiencing a stream, lake, coral reef, or other part of nature.

We might pick up a handful of soil and try to sense the teeming microscopic life in it that keeps us alive. We might look at a tree, mountain, rock, or bee and try to sense how they are a part of us and we a part of them as interdependent participants in the earth's life-sustaining recycling processes.

Earth thinker Michael J. Cohen suggests we recognize who we really are by saying,

*I am a desire for water, air, food, love, warmth, beauty, freedom, sensations, life, community, place, and spirit in the natural world. . . . I have two mothers: my human mother and my planet mother, Earth. The planet is my womb of life.*

Many psychologists believe that consciously or unconsciously we spend much of our lives in a search for roots: something to anchor us in a bewildering and frightening sea of change. As philosopher Simone Weil observed, "To be rooted is perhaps the most important and least recognized need of the human soul."

Earth philosophers say that to be rooted, each of us needs to find a *sense of place:* a stream, a mountain, a yard, a neighborhood lot, or any piece of the earth we feel at one with as a place we know, experience emotionally, and love. It can be a place where we live or a place we occasionally visit and experience in our inner being. When we become part of a place, it becomes a part of

us. Then we are driven to defend it from harm and to help heal its wounds.

To many earth thinkers, emotionally experiencing our connectedness with the earth leads us to recognize that the healing of the earth and the healing of the human spirit are one and the same. They call for us to discover and tap into what Aldo Leopold calls "the green fire that burns in our hearts" and use this as a force for respecting and working with the earth and with one another.

### Critical Thinking

Some analysts believe learning environmental wisdom by experiencing the earth and forming an emotional bond with its life-forms and processes is unscientific, mystical poppycock based on a romanticized view of nature. They believe better scientific understanding of how the earth works and improved technology are the only ways to achieve sustainability. Do you agree or disagree? Explain.

---

## Green Colleges

*Noel Perrin*

*Noel Perrin is an adjunct professor of environmental studies at Dartmouth College. He has owned three electric cars over the past 11 years, and currently drives a gasoline-electric hybrid.*

**GUEST ESSAY**

About 1,100 American colleges and universities run at least a token environmental studies program, and many hundreds of these programs offer well-designed and useful courses.

But only a drastically smaller number practice even a portion of what they preach. The one exception is recycling. Nearly every institution that offers so much as one lonely environmental studies course also does a little half-hearted recycling. Paper and glass, usually.

There are, I'm glad to say, some glorious exceptions to these rather crude observations. How many? Nobody knows. But it is possible to make an educated guess. I believe there are somewhere close to a hundred colleges and universities that are leading the United States toward a more sustainable future. If our culture adjusts in time, these hundred will have been one of the reasons why. Here is a sampling of what the hundred do. I give them in no special order.

- **Michigan State University:** Many colleges and universities purchase recycled paper. Well, somewhat recycled. If you look closely, the recycled content (post-consumer) turns out to be 30%, 20%, maybe just 10%. Michigan State does strikingly better. The university's aim is to buy only paper made from 100% post-consumer pulp. Not every office within the university cooperates in this effort. But the majority do. As far as I know, only the University of Buffalo has so far joined Michigan State in shooting for 100%.

- **Channnel Islands** is a new subsidiary of California State University. When it inherited its campus, it got 45 gasoline powered service vehicles thrown in as a part of the deal. There has been modest growth: The University now owns 48 service vehicles. But the mix is quite different. The current fleet includes: 1 propane-powered dump truck, 6 compressed natural gas vehicles, 26 electric vehicles, and finally 15 relics from the past—the last 15 gas vehicles.

- **Marlboro College** in Vermont is "in the process of taking up the majority of the pavement that wends through the central campus, greening it over, and making the central campus a car-free zone."

- Wisconsin's **Northland College** may not be the only institution to have both solar panels and a windmill on top of its newest dormitory, but it probably is the only one to have installed composting toilets. (There are conventional flush ones nearby, but the college says the composters get the most use.)

- At Ohio's **Oberlin College,** students and faculty participated in designing a more sustainable environmental studies building.

- New York's **Cornell University** recently completed what I think to be the largest green project yet done in this country. Cost: $60 million. First purpose: to eliminate conventional air conditioning on the Cornell campus while keeping 3.5 million square feet of space cool and comfortable all summer. Second purpose: radical reduction of Cornell-caused pollution. The project, completed

---

We should not confuse voluntary simplicity by those who have more than they need with the *forced simplicity* of the poor, who do not have enough to meet their basic needs for food, clothing, shelter, clean water and air, and good health.

After a lifetime of studying the growth and decline of the world's human civilizations, historian Arnold Toynbee summarized the true measure of a civilization's growth in what he called the *law of progressive simplification:* "True growth occurs as civilizations transfer an increasing proportion of energy and attention from the material side of life to the nonmaterial side and thereby develop their culture, capacity for compassion, sense of community, and strength of democracy."

### Is a Cultural Shift Beginning to Take Place in the United States?

Researchers Paul Ray and Sherry Anderson have been gathering and analyzing survey data indicating cultural patterns and beliefs in the United States. Using surveys, they have identified three major cultural groupings in the United States:

- *Moderns* (about 45% of the adult U.S. population), who **(1)** actively seek materialism and the drive to acquire money and property, **(2)** take a cynical view of idealism and caring, **(3)** accept some form of the planetary management worldview (Figure 28-3, left), and **(4)** tend to be pro big business.

- *Traditionals* (about 19% of the adult U.S. population), who believe in **(1)** family, church, and community, **(2)** helping others, **(3)** having caring relationships, and **(4)** working to create a better society. Many are pro-environment and anti–big business. They tend to be older, poorer, and less educated than most other people in the United States.

- *Cultural Creatives* or *New Progressives* (about 36% of the adult U.S. population and 45% of voters) who have a strong commitment to **(1)** family, **(2)** community, **(3)** the environment, **(4)** education, **(5)** equality, **(6)** perin the year 2000, has been a striking success. The new system, which uses the cold deep waters of Lake Cayuga, takes only one-fifth as much electricity to run as did the old system. There is essentially no pollution at all, except that caused by the generation of a 20 percent electricity load.

- At North Carolina's **Catawba College** students have found ways to recycle 98% of the construction debris from the college's newly built Center for the Environment.

- Kentucky's **Berea College** is building what it calls Ecovillage: 32 units of housing intended primarily for married students. Among the plans for Ecovillage: reduce energy use by 75%, reduce per capita water use by 75%, and convert sewage to swimmable quality water.

- **Duke University** in North Carolina collects 17 kinds of recyclables from 630 locations. A permanent work force of six, assisted by a dozen work-study students does the collecting.

- **Tulane University** in Louisiana has developed the usual programs in recycling, composting, and energy efficiency that one expects from a green college. But what sets Tulane apart is the Environmental Law Clinic. Three law fellows who are practicing attorneys back up third-year law students staffing the clinic. The clinic does legal work for environmental organizations across Louisiana. "It most likely has had a greater environmental impact than all our other efforts combined," says Elizabeth Davey, Tulane's first-ever environmental coordinator.

- At New York's **Vassar College** the VASSAR Greens, a student-founded, student-run organization with about 150 members, is the principal engine of change. The Greens staff an education committee, a composting committee, a recycling committee, and a sustainability committee.

- **Hampshire College** in Massachusetts is one of at least 20 rural and liberal arts colleges that have established organic farms. But it probably has the biggest and most ambitious project. Hampshire's Farm Center includes 2.6 square kilometers (1 square mile) of fields and woodlands. The center grows 4 hectares (10 acres) of organic vegetables and berries, has an herb garden, offers classes in organic gardening, and has a student-run food co-op.

- **University of California, Davis** is a bicyclist's paradise. There are 14 miles of bike paths on campus, and another 45 miles of bike paths in the small city of Davis [p. 660]. Bike commuting, like clean air, is routine. What happens on rainy days? "A surprising number continue to bike," says David Takemoto-Weerts, coordinator of the university's bicycle program. There are also buses.

- New Jersey's **Princeton University** generates about 11 metric tons (12 tons) a month of edible food waste. This food is not only edible, it gets eaten. Pigs eat it. Princeton has been supplying a local piggery with top quality pig rations since 1995. There is no cost to the piggery and no charge to Princeton. On green campuses that is how it should be.

### Critical Thinking

**1.** On a scale of 1 to 10, what environmental rating would you give to your school?

**2.** List the three most important things needed to improve your school's environmental rating.

sonal growth and spiritual development, **(7)** helping other people, **(8)** living in harmony with the earth, and **(9)** making a contribution to society. They have an optimistic outlook and are open to change and different beliefs and points of view. However, they reject the **(1)** hedonism, materialism, and cynicism of the moderns and **(2)** intolerance of the religious right. According to various surveys, Cultural Creatives are crafting a new environmental and spiritual worldview and a new agenda to help solve the environmental and social problems the United States faces.

These surveys indicate that the environmental beliefs of Moderns are beginning to weaken and to shift more to some of the environmental views of the Cultural Creatives. Evidence of this shift comes from surveys indicating that **(1)** 87% of adult Americans believe we need to treat the planet as a living system, **(2)** 83% say we need to rebuild our neighborhoods and small communities, **(3)** 82% say we should be stewards over nature and protect it, **(4)** 75% believe humans are part of nature, not its ruler, **(5)** 68% want to return to a simpler life with less emphasis on consumption and wealth, and **(6)** 63% believe the government should shut down industries that keep polluting the air.

These surveys suggest a shift in values away from some of the beliefs of the planetary management environmental worldview (Figure 28-3, left) toward some of the beliefs of the environmental wisdom environmental worldview (Figure 28-3, right). The real test of such a shift in values is **(1)** whether it is accompanied by changes in human behavior and **(2)** whether an existing or new political party can mobilize these people into an effective force for political change.

**How Can We Move Beyond Blame, Guilt, and Denial to Responsibility?** When we first encounter an environmental problem, our initial response often is to find someone or something to blame: greedy industrialists, uncaring politicians, environmentalists, and people with misguided worldviews or beliefs. It is

## What Are Our Basic Needs?

Obviously, each of us has a basic need for enough food, clean air, clean water, shelter, and clothing to keep us alive and in good health. According to various psychologists and other social scientists, each of us also has other basic needs:

- A secure and meaningful livelihood to provide our basic material needs

- Good physical and mental health

- The opportunity to learn and give expression to our intellectual, mechanical, and artistic talents

- A nurturing family and friends and a peaceful and secure community that help us develop our capacity for caring and loving relationships while giving us the freedom to make personal choices

- A clean and healthy environment that is vibrant with biological and cultural diversity

- A sense of belonging to and caring for a particular place and community (Connections, p. 751)

- An assurance that our children and grandchildren will have access to these same basic needs

A difficult but fundamental question is asking how much of the stuff we are all urged to buy helps us meet these basic needs. Indeed, psychologists point out that many people buy things in the hope or belief they will make up for not having some of the basic needs listed here.

### Critical Thinking

**1.** What basic needs, if any, would you add to or remove from the list given here?

**2.** Which of the basic needs listed here (or additional ones you would add) do you feel are being met? What are your plans for trying to fulfill any of your unfulfilled needs? Relate these plans to your environmental worldview.

the fault of such villains, and we are the victims. This response can lead to despair, denial, and inaction because we feel powerless to stop or influence these forces.

There are also many complex and interconnected environmental problems and conflicting views about their seriousness and possible solutions. As a result, we feel overwhelmed and wonder whether there is any way out—another emotion leading to denial and inaction.

Upon closer examination we may realize we all make some direct or indirect contributions to the environmental problems we face. As Pogo said, "We have met the enemy and it is us." We do not want to feel guilty or bad about all of the things we are not doing, so we avoid thinking about them—another path to denial and inaction.

How do we move beyond blame, fear, denial, and guilt to more responsible environmental actions in our daily lives? Analysts have suggested several ways to do this:

- Recognize and avoid common mental traps that lead to denial, indifference, and inaction. These traps include **(1)** *gloom-and-doom pessimism* (it is hopeless), **(2)** *blind technological optimism* (science and technofixes will save us), **(3)** *fatalism* (we have no control over our actions and the future), **(4)** *extrapolation to infinity* (if I cannot change the entire world quickly, I will not try to change any of it), **(5)** *paralysis by analysis* (searching for the perfect worldview, philosophy, solutions, and scientific information before doing anything), and **(6)** *faith in simple, easy answers.*

- Understand that no one can even come close to doing all of the things people suggest (or we know we should be doing) to work with the earth. Try to determine what things you do have the greatest environmental impact, and concentrate on them. Focus on what you feel strongly about and you can do something about. Rejoice in the good things you have done, and continually expand your efforts to make the earth a better place.

- Keep your empowering feelings of hope slightly ahead of your immobilizing feelings of despair.

- Do not use guilt and fear to motivate other people to work with the earth and other people. We need to nurture, reassure, understand, and care for one another.

- Recognize there is no single correct or best solution to the environmental problems we face. Indeed, one of nature's most important lessons (from evolution) is that preserving diversity or a rainbow of flexible and adaptable solutions to our problems is the best way to adapt to earth's largely unpredictable, ever-changing conditions.

- Have fun and take time to enjoy life. Laugh every day and enjoy nature, beauty, friendship, and love.

**What Are the Major Components of the Environmental Revolution?** The *environmental revolution* that many environmentalists call for us to bring about during this century would have several components:

- An *efficiency revolution* that involves not wasting matter and energy resources

- A *solar-hydrogen revolution* [Section 16-7, p. 405] based on decreasing our dependence on carbon-based nonrenewable fossil fuels and increasing our dependence on forms of renewable solar energy that can be used to produce hydrogren fuel from water.

- A *pollution prevention revolution* that reduces pollution and environmental degradation from harmful chemicals by (1) keeping them from being released into the environment by recycling or reusing them within industrial processes, (2) trying to find less polluting substitutes, or (3) or not producing them at all.

- A *biodiversity protection revolution* devoted to sustaining the genes, species, ecosystems, and ecological processes that make up the earth's biodiversity.

- A *sufficiency revolution.* This involves (1) trying to meet the basic needs of all people on the planet and (2) asking how many material things we really need to have a decent and meaningful life (Spotlight, p. 754).

- A *demographic revolution* based on reducing fertility to bring the size and growth rate of the human population into balance with the earth's ability to support humans and other species without serious environmental degradation.

- An *economic and political revolution* in which we use economic systems to reward environmentally beneficial behavior and discourage environmentally harmful behavior (Section 26-7, p. 710).

Opponents of such a cultural change like to paint environmentalists as messengers of gloom, doom, and hopelessness. However, *the real message of environmentalism is not gloom and doom, fear, and catastrophe but hope and a positive vision of the future.* This is an empowering message of challenge and adventure as we struggle to find better and more responsible ways to live on this planet.

In this book, we have seen that there is a lot of good environmental news, at least for most people in developed countries. We should rejoice in our environmental accomplishments, but the real question is *where do we go from here?* How do we transfer the environmental advances of the past 35 years to developing countries? How, during this century, do we make a new cultural transition to more environmentally sustainable societies based on learning from and working with nature (Solutions, p. 201, and Guest Essay, p. 748)?

As you have learned in this book, we have an incredible array of technological and economic solutions to the environmental problems and we face. The challenge is to implement such solutions by converting our environmental wisdom and beliefs into political action.

This requires us to become involved in making the world a better place. This means recognizing that a major lesson of our brief history on this marvelous planet is that *individuals matter.* Virtually all of the environmental progress we have made during the last few decades occurred because individuals banded together to insist that we can do better.

It is an incredibly exciting time to be alive as we struggle to enter into a new relationship with the earth that keeps us all alive and supports our economies. Jump in and get involved in guiding this new wave of cultural change.

Envision the earth's life-sustaining processes as a beautiful and diverse web of interrelationships—a kaleidoscope of patterns, rhythms, and connections whose very complexity and multitude of possibilities remind us that cooperation, sharing, honesty, humility, compassion, and love should be the guidelines for our behavior toward one another and the earth.

*When there is no dream, the people perish.*
PROVERBS 29:18

## REVIEW QUESTIONS

**1.** Define the boldfaced terms in this chapter.

**2.** Describe the Biosphere 2 experiment and the lessons it taught us.

**3.** Distinguish between (a) *environmental worldviews* and *environmental ethics,* (b) *instrumental values* and *intrinsic values,* and (c) *anthropocentric instrumental values* and *biocentric intrinsic values.*

**4.** What are the four major beliefs of the *planetary management environmental worldview?* Describe the (a) *no-problem,* (b) *free-market,* (c) *responsible planetary management,* (d) *spaceship-earth,* and (e) *stewardship* variations of the planetary management worldview.

**5.** Explain why some analysts believe planetary management worldviews will not work.

**6.** Give two reasons for caring about future generations.

**7.** What are (a) the four major beliefs of the *environmental wisdom worldview* and (b) the eight major beliefs of the *deep ecology environmental worldview?*

**8.** Summarize the major beliefs of the (a) *ecofeminist* and (b) *social ecology* environmental worldviews.

**9.** Describe Carlos Davidson's tapestry metaphor as it relates to environmental degradation.

**10.** Describe ways to evaluate sustainability proposals.

**11.** List nine ethical guidelines for living more sustainably.

**12.** List the four guiding principles of the Earth Charter.

**13.** Describe Lester W. Milbrath's viewpoint in the Guest Essay on page 748.

**14.** List seven guidelines of environmental or earth education and four questions that should be answered to determine one's *ecological identity*.

**15.** Explain why some analysts believe it is important to learn more about the earth from direct experience.

**16.** What is *voluntary simplicity*?

**17.** Distinguish among *Moderns, Traditionals,* and *Cultural Creatives* as major cultural groups in the United States.

**18.** List seven basic needs beyond our basic physical needs.

**19.** List six ways to move beyond blame, guilt, and denial and become more environmentally responsible. Describe six mental traps that can lead to denial, indifference, and inaction about environmental (and other) problems.

**20.** What are seven major components of an environmental revolution that most environmentalists believe we should bring about during this century?

## CRITICAL THINKING

**1.** Some analysts argue that the problems with Biosphere 2 resulted mostly from inadequate design, and a better team of scientists and engineers could make it work. Explain why you agree or disagree with this view. Were the lessons learned from this experiment worth its $200 million cost? Explain.

**2.** This chapter has summarized a number of different environmental worldviews. Analyze these worldviews and find the beliefs you agree with to describe your own environmental worldview. Which of your beliefs were added or modified as a result of taking this course?

**3.** Theologian Thomas Berry calls the industrial consumer society built on the human-centered, planetary management environmental worldview the "supreme pathology of all history." He says, "We can break the mountains apart; we can drain the rivers and flood the valleys. We can turn the most luxuriant forests into throwaway paper products. We can tear apart the great grass cover of the western plains, and pour toxic chemicals into the soil and pesticides onto the fields, until the soil is dead and blows away in the wind. We can pollute the air with acids, the rivers with sewage, the seas with oil. . . . We can invent computers capable of processing ten million calculations per second. And why? To increase the volume and speed with which we move natural resources through the consumer economy to the junk pile or the waste heap. . . . If, in these activities, the topography of the planet is damaged, if the environment is made inhospitable for a multitude of living species, then so be it. We are, supposedly, creating a technological wonderworld. . . . But our supposed progress . . . is bringing us to a wasteworld instead of a wonderworld." Explain why you agree or disagree with this assessment.

**4.** List the pros and cons of viewing nature as a tapestry for helping prevent environmental degradation. Are you for or against using this approach? Explain.

**5.** Do you agree with the cartoon character Pogo that "we have met the enemy and he is us"? Explain. Criticize this statement from the viewpoint of the poor. Criticize it from the viewpoint that many large corporations are big polluters and resource depleters and degraders.

**6.** Try to answer the following fundamental ecological questions about the corner of the world you inhabit: Where does your water come from? Where does the energy you use come from? What kinds of soils are under your feet? What types of wildlife are your neighbors? Where does your food come from? Where does your waste go?

**7.** Would you classify yourself as a *Modern, Traditional,* or *Cultural Creative* (p. 752)? Compare your answer with those of your classmates.

**8.** **(a)** Would you accept employment on a project that you knew would degrade or destroy a wild habitat? Explain. **(b)** If you were granted three wishes, what would they be? **(c)** Could you live without an automobile? Explain. **(d)** Could you live without TV? Explain. **(e)** If you won $100 million in a lottery, how would you spend the money?

**9.** How do you feel about **(a)** carving huge faces of people in mountains, **(b)** carving your initials into a tree, **(c)** driving an off-road motorized vehicle in a desert, grassland, or forest, **(d)** using throwaway paper towels, tissues, napkins, and plates, **(e)** wearing furs, **(f)** hunting for recreation, **(g)** fishing for recreation, and **(h)** having tropical fish, birds, snakes, or other wild animals as pets?

**10.** Explain why you agree or disagree with the following ideas: **(a)** everyone has the right to have as many children as they want, **(b)** each member of the human species has a right to use as many resources as they want, and **(c)** individuals should have the right to do anything they want with land they own. Relate your answers to the beliefs of your environmental worldview that you described in question 2.

**11.** Would you or do you use the principle of voluntary simplicity in your life? How?

**12.** Which (if any) of the ethical guidelines on pages 748–749 do you disagree with? Explain. Can you suggest any additional ethical guidelines for working with the earth?

**13.** Review your experience with the mental traps described on page 754. Which of these traps have you fallen into? Were you aware you had been ensnared by any of these mental traps? Do you plan to free yourself from these traps? How?

## PROJECTS

**1.** Use a combination of the major existing societal, economic, and environmental trends, possible new trends, and your imagination to construct three different scenarios of what the world might be like in 2060. Identify the scenario you favor, and outline a strategy for achieving this alternative future. Compare your scenarios and strategies with those of your classmates.

**2.** Make an environmental audit of your school. What proportion of each of the major types of matter resources it uses are recycled, reused, or composted? What priority does your school give to buying recycled materials? How much does your school emphasize energy efficiency, use of renewable forms of solar energy, and environmental design in developing new buildings and renovating existing ones? Does it use ecologically sound planning in deciding how its grounds and buildings are managed and used? Does your school limit the use of toxic chemicals in its buildings and on its grounds? What proportion of its food purchases comes from nearby farmers? What proportion of the food it purchases is grown by sustainable agriculture?

**3.** Does your school's curriculum provide *all* graduates with the basic elements of ecological literacy? To what extent are the funds in its financial endowments invested in enterprises that are working to develop or encourage environmental sustainability? Over the past 20 years, what important roles have its graduates played in making the world a better and more sustainable place to live? Using such information, rate your school on a 1–10 scale in terms of its contributions to environmental awareness and sustainability. Develop a detailed plan illustrating how your school could become better at achieving such goals, and present this information to school officials, alumni, parents, and financial backers.

**4.** If you knew you were going to die and had an opportunity to address everyone in the world for 5 minutes, what would you say? Write out your 5-minute speech and compare it with those of other members of your class.

**5.** Write an essay in which you identify key environmental experiences that have influenced your life and thus helped form your current ecological identity. Examples may include **(a)** fond childhood memories of special places where you connected with the earth through emotional experiences, **(b)** places you knew and cherished that have been polluted, developed, or destroyed, **(c)** key events that forced you to think about environmental values or worldviews, **(d)** people or educational experiences that influenced your understanding and concern about environmental problems and challenges, and **(e)** direct experience and contemplation of wild places. Share your experiences with other members of your class.

**6.** Use the library or the Internet to find bibliographic information about *Robert Cahn*, whose quote is found at the beginning of this chapter.

**7.** Make a concept map of this chapter's major ideas, using the section heads and subheads and the key terms (in boldface type). Look on the website for this book for information about making concept maps.

## INTERNET STUDY RESOURCES AND RESOURCES FOR FURTHER READING AND RESEARCH

The website for this book contains helpful study aids and many ideas for further reading and research. Log on to

www.info.brookscole.com/miller13

and click on the Chapter-by-Chapter area. Choose Chapter 28 and select a resource:

- Flash Cards allows you to test your mastery of the Terms and Concepts to Remember for this chapter.

- Tutorial Quizzes provides a multiple-choice practice quiz.

- Student Guide to InfoTrac will lead you to Critical Thinking Projects that use InfoTrac College Edition as a research tool.

- References lists the major books and articles consulted in writing this chapter.

- Hypercontents takes you to an extensive list of sites with news, research, and images related to individual sections of the chapter.

## INFOTRAC COLLEGE EDITION

Improve your skills with InfoTrac College Edition, a searchable online database of articles from more than 700 periodicals. Log on to

http://www.infotrac-college.com

or access InfoTrac through the website for this book. Try to find the following articles:

**1.** Ehrlich, P. R. 2002. Human natures, nature conservation, and environmental ethics. *BioScience* 52: 31. *Keywords:* "human natures" and "environmental ethics." Scientists well understand the environmental problems faced by humans today, but the general population is not well informed. Therefore, the focus in environmental studies is changing toward behavior and psychology in an effort to improve human responses to environmental degradation.

**2.** Maughan, E. and P. Reason. 2001. A cooperative inquiry into deep ecology. *ReVision* 23: 18. *Keyword:* "deep ecology." A prestigious business school in Great Britain teaches more than basic economics. Students are exposed to the real world of ecology, environment, and human relationships.

# UNITS OF MEASURE

## LENGTH

### Metric

1 kilometer (km) = 1,000 meters (m)
1 meter (m) = 100 centimeters (cm)
1 meter (m) = 1,000 millimeters (mm)
1 centimeter (cm) = 0.01 meter (m)
1 millimeter (mm) = 0.001 meter (m)

### English

1 foot (ft) = 12 inches (in)
1 yard (yd) = 3 feet (ft)
1 mile (mi) = 5,280 feet (ft)
1 nautical mile = 1.15 miles

### Metric–English

1 kilometer (km) = 0.621 mile (mi)
1 meter (m) = 39.4 inches (in)
1 inch (in) = 2.54 centimeters (cm)
1 foot (ft) = 0.305 meter (m)
1 yard (yd) = 0.914 meter (m)
1 nautical mile = 1.85 kilometers (km)

## AREA

### Metric

1 square kilometer ($km^2$) = 1,000,000 square meters ($m^2$)
1 square meter ($m^2$) = 1,000,000 square millimeters ($mm^2$)
1 hectare (ha) = 10,000 square meters ($m^2$)
1 hectare (ha) = 0.01 square kilometer ($km^2$)

### English

1 square foot ($ft^2$) = 144 square inches ($in^2$)
1 square yard ($yd^2$) = 9 square feet ($ft^2$)
1 square mile ($mi^2$) = 27,880,000 square feet ($ft^2$)
1 acre (ac) = 43,560 square feet ($ft^2$)

### Metric–English

1 hectare (ha) = 2.471 acres (ac)
1 square kilometer ($km^2$) = 0.386 square mile ($mi^2$)
1 square meter ($m^2$) = 1.196 square yards ($yd^2$)
1 square meter ($m^2$) = 10.76 square feet ($ft^2$)
1 square centimeter ($cm^2$) = 0.155 square inch ($in^2$)

## VOLUME

### Metric

1 cubic kilometer ($km^3$) = 1,000,000,000 cubic meters ($m^3$)
1 cubic meter ($m^3$) = 1,000,000 cubic centimeters ($cm^3$)
1 liter (L) = 1,000 milliliters (mL) = 1,000 cubic centimeters ($cm^3$)
1 milliliter (mL) = 0.001 liter (L)
1 milliliter (mL) = 1 cubic centimeter ($cm^3$)

### English

1 gallon (gal) = 4 quarts (qt)
1 quart (qt) = 2 pints (pt)

### Metric–English

1 liter (L) = 0.265 gallon (gal)
1 liter (L) = 1.06 quarts (qt)
1 liter (L) = 0.0353 cubic foot ($ft^3$)
1 cubic meter ($m^3$) = 35.3 cubic feet ($ft^3$)
1 cubic meter ($m^3$) = 1.30 cubic yards ($yd^3$)
1 cubic kilometer ($km^3$) = 0.24 cubic mile ($mi^3$)
1 barrel (bbl) = 159 liters (L)
1 barrel (bbl) = 42 U.S. gallons (gal)

## MASS

### Metric

1 kilogram (kg) = 1,000 grams (g)
1 gram (g) = 1,000 milligrams (mg)
1 gram (g) = 1,000,000 micrograms (μg)
1 milligram (mg) = 0.001 gram (g)
1 microgram ($\mu$g) = 0.000001 gram (g)
1 metric ton (mt) = 1,000 kilograms (kg)

### English

1 ton (t) = 2,000 pounds (lb)
1 pound (lb) = 16 ounces (oz)

### Metric–English

1 metric ton (mt) = 2,200 pounds (lb) = 1.1 tons (t)
1 kilogram (kg) = 2.20 pounds (lb)
1 pound (lb) = 454 grams (g)
1 gram (g) = 0.035 ounce (oz)

## ENERGY AND POWER

### Metric

1 kilojoule (kJ) = 1,000 joules (J)
1 kilocalorie (kcal) = 1,000 calories (cal)
1 calorie (cal) = 4,184 joules (J)

### Metric–English

1 kilojoule (kJ) = 0.949 British thermal unit (Btu)
1 kilojoule (kJ) = 0.000278 kilowatt-hour (kW-h)
1 kilocalorie (kcal) = 3.97 British thermal units (Btu)
1 kilocalorie (kcal) = 0.00116 kilowatt-hour (kW-h)
1 kilowatt-hour (kW-h) = 860 kilocalories (kcal)
1 kilowatt-hour (kW-h) = 3,400 British thermal units (Btu)
1 quad (Q) = 1,050,000,000,000,000 kilojoules (kJ)
1 quad (Q) = 2,930,000,000,000 kilowatt-hours (kW-h)

## TEMPERATURE CONVERSIONS

Fahrenheit($°F$) to Celsius($°C$):
$$°C = (°F - 32.0) \div 1.80$$
Celsius($°C$) to Fahrenheit($°F$):
$$°F = (°C \times 1.80) + 32.0$$

# SOME BASIC CHEMISTRY

**How Can Elements Be Arranged in the Periodic Table According to Their Chemical Properties?** Chemists have developed a way to classify the elements according to their chemical behavior, in what is called the *periodic table of elements* (Figure 1). Each of the horizontal rows in the table is called a *period*. Each vertical column lists elements with similar chemical properties and is called a *group*.

The partial periodic table in Figure 1 shows how the elements can be classified as *metals, nonmetals,* and *metalloids*. Most of the elements found to the left and at the bottom of the table are *metals,* which usually conduct electricity and heat and are shiny. Examples are sodium (Na), calcium (Ca), aluminum (Al), iron (Fe), lead (Pb), and mercury (Hg). Atoms of such metals achieve a more stable state by losing one or more of their electrons to form positively charged ions such as $Na^+$, $Ca^{2+}$, and $Al^{3+}$.

*Nonmetals,* found in the upper right of the table, do not conduct electricity very well and usually are not shiny. Examples are hydrogen (H),* carbon (C), nitrogen (N), oxygen (O), phosphorus (P), sulfur (S), chlorine (Cl), and fluorine (F). Atoms of some nonmetals such as chlorine, oxygen, and sulfur tend to gain one or more electrons lost by metallic atoms to form negatively charged ions such as $O^{2-}$, $S^{2-}$, and $Cl^-$. Atoms of nonmetals can also combine with one another to form molecules in which they share one or more pairs of their electrons.

The elements arranged in a diagonal staircase pattern between the metals and nonmetals have a mixture of metallic and nonmetallic properties and are called *metalloids*. Figure 1 also identifies the ele-

---

*Hydrogen, a nonmetal, is placed by itself above the center of the table because it does not fit very well into any of the groups.

ments required as *nutrients* for all or some forms of life and elements that are moderately or highly toxic to all or most forms of life. Six nonmetallic elements—carbon (C) oxygen (O), hydrogen (H), nitrogen (N), sulfur (S), and phosphorus (P)—make up about 99% of the atoms of all living things.

**What Are Ionic and Covalent Bonds?** Sodium chloride (NaCl) consists of a three-dimensional network of oppositely charged *ions* ($Na^+$ and $Cl^-$) held together by the forces of attraction between opposite charges (Figure 2). The strong forces of attraction between such oppositely charged ions are called *ionic bonds*. Because ionic compounds consist of ions formed from atoms of metallic (positive ions) and nonmetallic (negative ions) elements, they can be described as *metal-nonmetal compounds*.

Figure 3 shows the chemical formulas and shapes of the molecules for several

**Figure 1** Abbreviated *periodic table of elements*. Elements in the same vertical column, called a *group,* have similar chemical properties. To simplify matters at this introductory level, only 72 of the 115 known elements are shown.

common covalent compounds, formed when atoms of one or more nonmetallic elements (Figure 1) combine with one another. The bonds between the atoms in such molecules are called *covalent bonds* and form when the atoms in the molecule share one or more pairs of their electrons. Because they are formed from atoms of nonmetallic elements, molecular or covalent compounds can be described as *nonmetal-nonmetal compounds*.

**What Are Hydrogen Bonds?** Ionic and covalent bonds form between the ions or atoms *within* a compound. There are also weaker forces of attraction *between* the molecules of covalent compounds (such as water) resulting from an unequal sharing of electrons by two atoms.

For example, an oxygen atom has a much greater attraction for electrons than does a hydrogen atom. Thus, in a water molecule, the electrons shared between the oxygen atom and its two hydrogen atoms are pulled closer to the oxygen atom, but not actually transferred to the oxygen atom. As a result, the oxygen atom in a water molecule has a slightly negative partial charge, and its two hydrogen atoms have a slightly positive partial charge (Figure 4, p. A-4, top).

The slightly positive hydrogen atoms in one water molecule are then attracted to the slightly negative oxygen atoms in another water molecule. These forces of attraction *between* water molecules are called *hydrogen bonds* (Figure 4, p. A-4, top). Hydrogen bonds also form between other covalent molecules or portions of such molecules containing hydrogen and nonmetallic atoms with a strong ability to attract electrons.

**What Are Nucleic Acids?** *Nucleic acids* are made by linking hundreds to thousands of four different types of monomers, called *nucleotides*. Each nucleotide consists of **(1)** a phosphate group, **(2)** a sugar molecule containing five carbon atoms (deoxyribose in DNA molecules and ribose in RNA molecules), and **(3)** one of four different nucleotide bases (represented by A, G, C, and T, the first letter in each of their names) (Figure 5, p. A-4).

In the cells of living organisms, these nucleotide units combine in different numbers and sequences to form *nucleic acids* such as various types of DNA and RNA. Hydrogen bonds formed between parts of the four nucleotides in DNA hold two DNA strands together like a spiral staircase, forming a double helix (Figure 6, p. A-4). DNA molecules can unwind and replicate themselves.

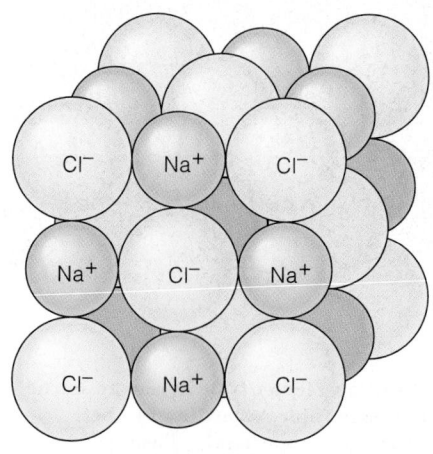

**Figure 2** A solid crystal of an *ionic compound* such as sodium chloride consists of a three-dimensional array of opposite charged ions held together by *ionic bonds* resulting from the strong forces of attraction between opposite electrical charges. They are formed when an electron is transferred from a metallic atom such as sodium (Na) to a nonmetallic element such as chlorine (Cl). Such compounds tend to exist as solids at normal room temperature and atmospheric pressure.

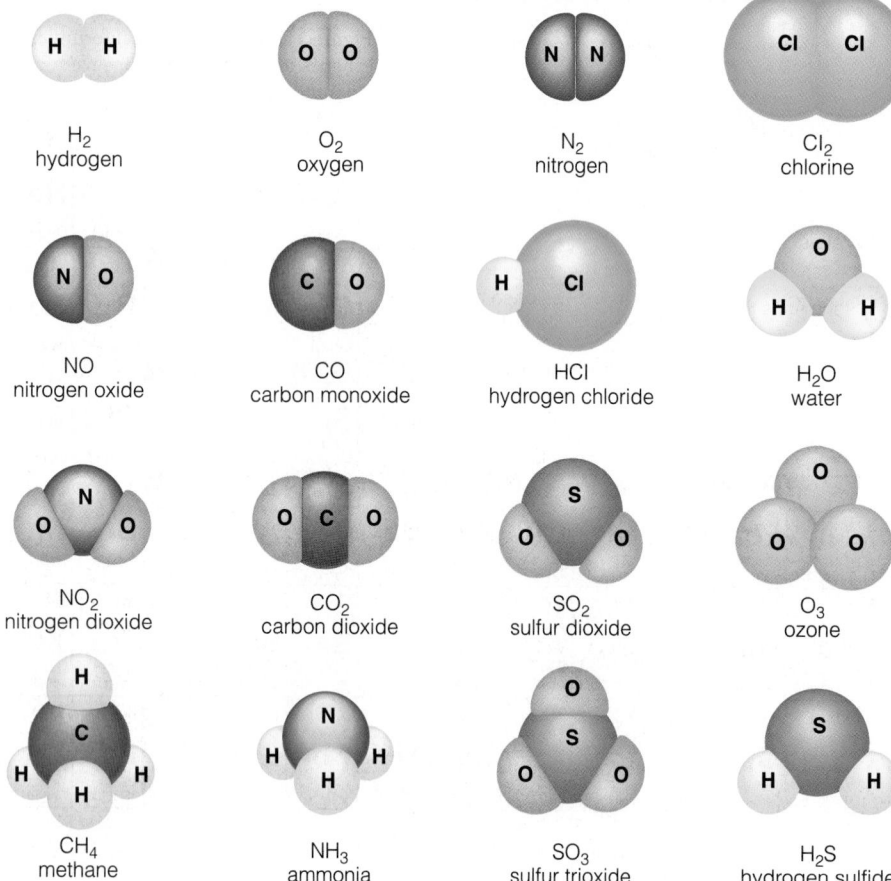

**Figure 3** Chemical formulas and shapes for some molecular compounds formed when atoms of one or more nonmetallic elements combine with one another. The bonds between the atoms in such molecules are called *covalent bonds*. Molecular compounds tend to exist as gases or liquids at normal room temperature and atmospheric pressure.

**Figure 4** *Hydrogen bonds.* Slightly unequal sharing of electrons in the water molecule creates a molecule with a slightly negatively charged end and a slightly positively charged end. Because of this electrical polarity, hydrogen atoms of one water molecule are attracted to oxygen atoms of another water molecule. These forces of attraction *between* water molecules are called *hydrogen bonds.*

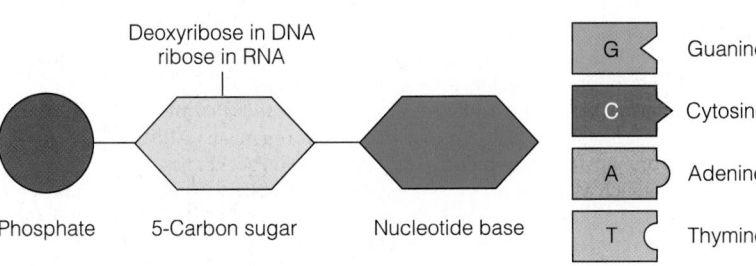

**Figure 5** Generalized structure of nucleotide molecules linked in various numbers and sequences to form large nucleic acid molecules such as various types of DNA (deoxyribose nucleic acid) and RNA (ribose nucleic acid). In DNA the 5-carbon sugar in each nucleotide is deoxyribose; in RNA it is ribose. The four basic nucleotides used to make various forms of DNA molecules differ in the types of nucleotide bases they contain—guanine (G), cytosine (C), adenine (A), and thymine (T).

**Figure 6** Portion of the double helix of a DNA molecule. The helix is composed of two spiral (helical) strands of nucleotides, each containing a unit of phosphate (P), deoxyribose (S), and one of four nucleotide bases: guanine (G), cytosine (C), adenine (A), and thymine (T). The two strands are held together by hydrogen bonds formed between various pairs of the nucleotide bases. Guanine (G) bonds with cytosine (C), and adenine (A) with thymine (T).

# CLASSIFYING AND NAMING SPECIES

**How Can Species Be Classified?** Biologists classify species into different *kingdoms,* on the basis of similarities and differences in characteristics such as their **(1)** modes of nutrition, **(2)** cell structure, **(3)** appearance, and **(4)** developmental features.

In this book, the earth's organisms are classified into six kingdoms: *eubacteria, archaebacteria, protists, fungi, plants,* and *animals.* Most bacteria, fungi, and protists are *microorganisms:* organisms so small they cannot be seen with the naked eye.

*Eubacteria* consist of all single-celled prokaryotic (Figure 4-3, left, p. 67) bacteria except archaebacteria. Examples are various cyanobacteria and bacteria such as *Staphylococcus* and *Streptococcus.*

*Archaebacteria* are single-celled bacteria that are evolutionarily closer to eukaryotic cells than to eubacteria. Examples are **(1)** methanogens that live in anaerobic sediments of lakes and swamps and in animal guts, **(2)** halophiles that live in extremely salty water, and **(3)** thermophiles that live in hot springs, hydrothermal vents, and acidic soil.

*Protists (Protista)* are mostly single-celled eukaryotic organisms such as diatoms, dinoflagellates, amoebas, golden brown and yellow-green algae, and protozoans. Some protists cause human diseases such as malaria and sleeping sickness.

*Fungi* are mostly many-celled, sometimes microscopic, eukaryotic organisms such as mushrooms, molds, mildews, and yeasts. Many fungi are decomposers. Other fungi kill various plants and cause huge losses of crops and valuable trees.

*Plants (Plantae)* are mostly many-celled eukaryotic organisms such as red, brown, and green algae and mosses, ferns, and flowering plants (whose flowers produce seeds that perpetuate the species). Some plants such as corn and marigolds are *annuals,* which complete their life cycles in one growing season; others are *perennials,* which can live for more than 2 years, such as roses, grapes, elms, and magnolias.

*Animals (Animalia)* are also many-celled eukaryotic organisms. Most, called *invertebrates,* have no backbones. They include sponges, jellyfish, worms, arthropods (insects, shrimp, and spiders), mollusks (snails, clams, and octopuses), and echinoderms (sea urchins and sea stars). Insects play roles that are vital to our existence (p. 64). *Vertebrates* (animals with backbones and a brain protected by skull bones) include fishes (sharks and tuna), amphibians (frogs and salamanders), reptiles (crocodiles and snakes), birds (eagles and robins), and mammals (bats, elephants, whales, and humans).

**How Are Species Named?** Within each kingdom, biologists have created subcategories based on anatomical, physiological, and behavioral characteristics. Kingdoms are divided into *phyla,* which are divided into subgroups called *classes.* Classes are subdivided into *orders,* which are further divided into *families.* Families consist of *genera* (singular, *genus*), and each genus contains one or more *species.* Note that the word *species* is both singular and plural. Figure 1 shows this detailed taxonomic classification for the current human species.

Most people call a species by its common name, such as robin or grizzly bear. Biologists use scientific names (derived from Latin) consisting of two parts (printed in italics or underlined) to describe a species. The first word is the capitalized name (or abbreviation) for the genus to which the organism belongs. This is followed by a lowercase name that distinguishes the species from other members of the same genus. For example, the scientific name of the robin is *Turdus migratorius* (Latin for "migratory thrush"), and the grizzly bear goes by the scientific name *Ursus horribilis* (Latin for "horrible bear").

**Animalia** Many-celled eukaryotic organisms

**Chordata** Animals with notochord (a long rod of stiffened tissue), nerve cord, and a pharynx (a muscular tube used in feeding, respiration, or both)

**Vertebrata** Spinal cord enclosed in a backbone of cartilage or bone; and skull bones that protect the brain

**Mammalia** Animals whose young are nourished by milk produced by mammary glands of females; and that have hair or fur and warm blood

**Primates** Animals that live in trees or are descended from tree dwellers

**Hominidae** Upright animals with two-legged locomotion and binocular vision

*Homo* Upright animals with large brain, language, and extended parental care of young

*sapiens* Animals with sparse body hair, high forehead, and large brain

*sapiens sapiens* Animals capable of sophisticated cultural evolution

Kingdom
Phylum
Subphylum
Class
Order
Family
Genus
Species
Species

**Figure 1** Taxonomic classification of the latest human species, *Homo sapiens sapiens.*

# GLOSSARY

**abiotic** Nonliving. Compare *biotic*.

**absolute humidity** Amount of water vapor found in a certain mass of air (usually expressed as grams of water per kilogram of air). Compare *relative humidity*.

**acclimation** Adjustment to slowly changing new conditions. Compare *threshold effect*.

**accuracy** Extent to which a measurement agrees with the accepted or correct value for that quantity, based on careful measurements by many people. Compare *precision*.

**acid** See *acid solution*.

**acid deposition** The falling of acids and acid-forming compounds from the atmosphere to the earth's surface. Acid deposition is commonly known as *acid rain*, a term that refers only to wet deposition of droplets of acids and acid-forming compounds.

**acid rain** See *acid deposition*.

**acid solution** Any water solution that has more hydrogen ions ($H^+$) than hydroxide ions ($OH^-$); any water solution with a pH less than 7. Compare *basic solution, neutral solution*.

**active solar heating system** System that uses solar collectors to capture energy from the sun and store it as heat for space heating and water heating. Liquid or air pumped through the collectors transfers the captured heat to a storage system such as an insulated water tank or rock bed. Pumps or fans then distribute the stored heat or hot water throughout a dwelling as needed. Compare *passive solar heating system*.

**adaptation** Any genetically controlled structural, physiological, or behavioral characteristic that helps an organism survive and reproduce under a given set of environmental conditions. It usually results from a beneficial mutation. See *biological evolution, differential reproduction, mutation, natural selection*.

**adaptive management** Flexible management that views attempts to solve problems as experiments, analyzes failures to see what went wrong, and tries to modify and improve an approach before abandoning it. Because of the inherent unpredictability of complex systems, it often uses the precautionary principle as a management tool. See *precautionary principle*.

**adaptive radiation** Process in which numerous new species evolve to fill vacant and new ecological niches in changed environments, usually after a mass extinction or mass depletion. Typically, this takes millions of years.

**adaptive trait** See *adaptation*.

**advanced sewage treatment** Specialized chemical and physical processes that reduce the amount of specific pollutants left in wastewater after primary and secondary sewage treatment. This type of treatment usually is expensive. See also *primary sewage treatment, secondary sewage treatment*.

**aerobic respiration** Complex process that occurs in the cells of most living organisms, in which nutrient organic molecules such as glucose ($C_6H_{12}O_6$) combine with oxygen ($O_2$) and produce carbon dioxide ($CO_2$), water ($H_2O$), and energy. Compare *photosynthesis*.

**age structure** Percentage of the population (or number of people of each sex) at each age level in a population.

**agricultural revolution** Gradual shift from small, mobile hunting and gathering bands to settled agricultural communities in which people survived by learning how to breed and raise wild animals and to cultivate wild plants near where they lived. It began 10,000–12,000 years ago. Compare *environmental revolution, hunter–gatherers, industrial revolution, information and globalization revolution*.

**agroforestry** Planting trees and crops together.

**air pollution** One or more chemicals in high enough concentrations in the air to **(1)** harm humans, other animals, vegetation, or materials or **(2)** alter climate. Excess heat and noise are also considered forms of air pollution. Such chemicals or physical conditions are called air pollutants. See *primary pollutant, secondary pollutant*.

**albedo** Ability of a surface to reflect light.

**alien species** See *nonnative species*.

**allele** Slightly different molecular form found in a particular gene.

**alley cropping** Planting of crops in strips with rows of trees or shrubs on each side.

**alpha particle** Positively charged matter, consisting of two neutrons and two protons, that is emitted as a form of radioactivity from the nuclei of some radioisotopes. See also *beta particle, gamma rays*.

**altitude** Height above sea level. Compare *latitude*.

**anaerobic respiration** Form of cellular respiration in which some decomposers get the energy they need through the breakdown of glucose (or other nutrients) in the absence of oxygen. Compare *aerobic respiration*.

**ancient forest** See *old-growth forest*.

**animal manure** Dung and urine of animals used as a form of organic fertilizer. Compare *green manure*.

**animals** Eukaryotic, multicelled organisms such as sponges, jellyfishes, arthropods (insects, shrimp, lobsters), mollusks (snails, clams, oysters, octopuses), fish, amphibians (frogs, toads, salamanders), reptiles (turtles, lizards, alligators, crocodiles, snakes), birds, and mammals (kangaroos, bats, cats, rabbits, elephants, whales, porpoises, monkeys, apes, humans). See *carnivores, herbivores, omnivores*.

**annual** Plant that grows, sets seed, and dies in one growing season. Compare *perennial*.

**anthropocentric** Human-centered. Compare *biocentric*.

**appropriate technology** Forms of technology that are small scale, efficient, and labor intensive and that use locally available resources to produce goods that benefit local communities.

**aquaculture** Growing and harvesting of fish and shellfish for human use in freshwater ponds, irrigation ditches, and lakes, or in cages or fenced-in areas of coastal lagoons and estuaries. See *fish farming, fish ranching*.

**aquatic** Pertaining to water. Compare *terrestrial*.

**aquatic life zone** Marine and freshwater portions of the biosphere. Examples include freshwater life zones (such as lakes and streams) and ocean or marine life zones (such as estuaries, coastlines, coral reefs, and the deep ocean).

**aquifer** Porous, water-saturated layers of sand, gravel, or bedrock that can yield an economically significant amount of water.

**arable land** Land that can be cultivated to grow crops.

**area strip mining** Type of surface mining used where the terrain is flat. An earthmover strips away the overburden, and a power shovel digs a cut to remove the mineral deposit. After removal of the mineral, the trench is filled with overburden, and a new cut is made parallel to the previous one. The process is repeated over the entire site. Compare *dredging, mountaintop removal, open-pit mining, subsurface mining*.

**arid** Dry. A desert or other area with an arid climate that has little precipitation.

**artificial selection** Process by which humans select one or more desirable genetic traits in the population of a plant or animal and then use *selective breeding* to end up with populations of the species containing large numbers of individuals with the desired traits. Compare *genetic engineering, natural selection*.

**asexual reproduction** Reproduction in which a mother cell divides to produce two identical daughter cells that are clones of the mother cell. This type of reproduction is common in single-celled organisms. Compare *sexual reproduction*.

**atmosphere** Whole mass of air surrounding the earth. See *stratosphere, troposphere*.

**atom** Minute unit made of subatomic particles that is the basic building block of all chemical elements and all matter; the smallest unit of an element that can exist and still have the unique characteristics of that element. Compare *ion, molecule*.

**atomic number** Number of protons in the nucleus of an atom. Compare *mass number*.

**autotroph** See *producer*.

**background extinction** Normal extinction of various species as a result of changes in local environmental conditions. Compare *mass depletion, mass extinction*.

**bacteria** Prokaryotic, one-celled organisms. Some transmit diseases. Most act as decomposers and get the nutrients they need by breaking down complex organic compounds in the tissues of living or dead organisms into simpler inorganic nutrient compounds.

**barrier islands** Long, thin, low offshore islands of sediment that generally run parallel to the shore along some coasts.

**basic solution**   Water solution with more hydroxide ions ($OH^-$) than hydrogen ions ($H^+$); water solution with a pH greater than 7. Compare *acid solution, neutral solution.*

**benefit–cost analysis**   Estimates and comparison of short-term and long-term benefits (gains) and costs (losses) from an economic decision.

**benthos**   Bottom-dwelling organisms. Compare *decomposer, nekton, plankton.*

**beta particle**   Swiftly moving electron emitted by the nucleus of a radioactive isotope. See also *alpha particle, gamma rays.*

**bioaccumulation**   An increase in the concentration of a chemical in specific organs or tissues at a level higher than would normally be expected. Compare *biomagnification.*

**biocentric**   Life centered. Compare *anthropocentric.*

**biodegradable**   Capable of being broken down by decomposers.

**biodegradable pollutant**   Material that can be broken down into simpler substances (elements and compounds) by bacteria or other decomposers. Paper and most organic wastes such as animal manure are biodegradable but can take decades to biodegrade in modern landfills. Compare *degradable pollutant, nondegradable pollutant, slowly degradable pollutant.*

**biodiversity**   Variety of different species (*species diversity*), genetic variability among individuals within each species (*genetic diversity*), variety of ecosystems (*ecological diversity*), and functions such as energy flow and matter cycling needed for the survival of species and biological communities (*functional diversity*).

**biofuel**   Gas or liquid fuel (such as ethyl alcohol) made from plant material (biomass).

**biogeochemical cycle**   Natural processes that recycle nutrients in various chemical forms from the nonliving environment to living organisms and then back to the nonliving environment. Examples are the carbon, oxygen, nitrogen, phosphorus, sulfur, and hydrologic cycles.

**bioinformatics**   Applied science of managing, analyzing, and communicating biological information.

**biological amplification**   See *biomagnification.*

**biological community**   See *community.*

**biological diversity**   See *biodiversity.*

**biological evolution**   Change in the genetic makeup of a population of a species in successive generations. If continued long enough, it can lead to the formation of a new species. Note that populations—not individuals—evolve. See also *adaptation, differential reproduction, natural selection, theory of evolution.*

**biological oxygen demand (BOD)**   Amount of dissolved oxygen needed by aerobic decomposers to break down the organic materials in a given volume of water at a certain temperature over a specified time period. See *dissolved oxygen content.*

**biological pest control**   Control of pest populations by natural predators, parasites, or disease-causing bacteria and viruses (pathogens).

**biomagnification**   Increase in concentration of DDT, PCBs, and other slowly degradable, fat-soluble chemicals in organisms at successively higher trophic levels of a food chain or web. Compare *bioaccumulation.*

**biomass**   Organic matter produced by plants and other photosynthetic producers; total dry weight of all living organisms that can be supported at each trophic level in a food chain or web; dry weight of all organic matter in plants and animals

in an ecosystem; plant materials and animal wastes used as fuel.

**biome**   Terrestrial regions inhabited by certain types of life, especially vegetation. Examples are various types of deserts, grasslands, and forests.

**biosphere**   Zone of earth where life is found. It consists of parts of the atmosphere (the troposphere), hydrosphere (mostly surface water and groundwater), and lithosphere (mostly soil and surface rocks and sediments on the bottoms of oceans and other bodies of water) where life is found. Sometimes called the *ecosphere.*

**biotic**   Living organisms. Compare *abiotic.*

**biotic potential**   Maximum rate at which the population of a given species can increase when there are no limits on its rate of growth. See *environmental resistance.*

**birth rate**   See *crude birth rate.*

**bitumen**   Gooey, black, high-sulfur, heavy oil extracted from tar sand and then upgraded to synthetic fuel oil. See *tar sand.*

**breeder nuclear fission reactor**   Nuclear fission reactor that produces more nuclear fuel than it consumes by converting nonfissionable uranium-238 into fissionable plutonium-239.

**broadleaf deciduous plants**   Plants such as oak and maple trees that survive drought and cold by shedding their leaves and becoming dormant. Compare *broadleaf evergreen plants, coniferous evergreen plants.*

**broadleaf evergreen plants**   Plants that keep most of their broad leaves year round. Examples are the trees found in the canopies of tropical rain forests. Compare *broadleaf deciduous plants, coniferous evergreen plants.*

**buffer**   Substance that can react with hydrogen ions in a solution and thus hold the acidity or pH of a solution fairly constant. See *pH.*

**calorie**   Unit of energy; amount of energy needed to raise the temperature of 1 gram of water 1°C (unit on Celsius temperature scale). See also *kilocalorie.*

**cancer**   Group of more than 120 different diseases, one for each type of cell in the human body. Each type of cancer produces a tumor in which cells multiply uncontrollably and invade surrounding tissue. See *carcinogen, metastasis.*

**capitalism**   See *capitalist market economic system.* Compare *pure command economic system, pure free-market economic system.*

**capitalist market economic system**   Economic system built around controlling market prices of goods and services, global free trade, and maximizing profits for the owners or stockholders whose financial capital the company is using to do business. Compare *pure command economic system, pure free-market economic system.*

**carbon cycle**   Cyclic movement of carbon in different chemical forms from the environment to organisms and then back to the environment.

**carcinogen**   Chemicals, ionizing radiation, and viruses that cause or promote the development of cancer. See *cancer.* Compare *mutagen, teratogen.* See *cancer.*

**carnivore**   Animal that feeds on other animals. Compare *herbivore, omnivore.*

**carrying capacity (K)**   Maximum population of a particular species that a given habitat can support over a given period of time. See *dieback.*

**cell**   Smallest living unit of an organism. Each cell is encased in an outer membrane or wall and contains genetic material (DNA) and other parts to perform its life function. Organisms such as bacteria consist of only one cell, but most of the

organisms we are familiar with contain many cells. See *eukaryotic cell, prokaryotic cell.*

**centrally planned economy**   See *pure command economic system.*

**CFCs**   See *chlorofluorocarbons.*

**chain reaction**   Multiple nuclear fissions, taking place within a certain mass of a fissionable isotope, that release an enormous amount of energy in a short time. See *nuclear fission.*

**chemical**   One of the millions of different elements and compounds found naturally and synthesized by humans. See *compound, element.*

**chemical change**   Interaction between chemicals in which there is a change in the chemical composition of the elements or compounds involved. Compare *nuclear change, physical change.*

**chemical evolution**   Formation of the earth and its early crust and atmosphere, evolution of the biological molecules necessary for life, and evolution of systems of chemical reactions needed to produce the first living cells. These processes are believed to have occurred about 1 billion years before biological evolution. Compare *biological evolution.*

**chemical formula**   Shorthand way to show the number of atoms (or ions) in the basic structural unit of a compound. Examples are $H_2O$, $NaCl$, and $C_6H_{12}O_6$.

**chemical reaction**   See *chemical change.*

**chemosynthesis**   Process in which certain organisms (mostly specialized bacteria) extract inorganic compounds from their environment and convert them into organic nutrient compounds without the presence of sunlight. Compare *photosynthesis.*

**chlorinated hydrocarbon**   Organic compound made up of atoms of carbon, hydrogen, and chlorine. Examples are DDT and PCBs.

**chlorofluorocarbons (CFCs)**   Organic compounds made up of atoms of carbon, chlorine, and fluorine. An example is Freon-12 ($CCl_2F_2$), used as a refrigerant in refrigerators and air conditioners and in making plastics such as Styrofoam. Gaseous CFCs can deplete the ozone layer when they slowly rise into the stratosphere and their chlorine atoms react with ozone molecules.

**chromosome**   Grouping of various genes and associated proteins in plant and animal cells that carry certain types of genetic information. See *genes.*

**city**   Large group of people with a variety of specialized occupations who live in a specific area and depend on a flow of resources from other areas to meet most of their needs and wants.  See *rural area, urban area.* Compare *village.*

**civil suit**   Lawsuit in which a plaintiff seeks to (1) collect damages for injuries or for economic loss or (2) have the court issue a permanent injunction against further wrongful action. Compare *class action suit.*

**class action suit**   Civil lawsuit in which a group files a suit on behalf of a larger number of citizens who allege similar damages but who need not be listed and represented individually. Compare *civil suit.*

**clear-cutting**   Method of timber harvesting in which all trees in a forested area are removed in a single cutting. Compare, *seed-tree cutting, selective cutting, shelterwood cutting, strip cutting.*

**climate**   Physical properties of the troposphere of an area based on analysis of its weather records over a long period (at least 30 years). The two main factors determining an area's climate are *temperature,* with its seasonal variations, and the amount and distribution of *precipitation.* Compare *weather.*

**climax community**  See *mature community.*

**closed system**  System in which energy but not matter is exchanged between the system and its environment. Compare *open system.*

**coal**  Solid, combustible mixture of organic compounds with 30–98% carbon by weight, mixed with various amounts of water and small amounts of sulfur and nitrogen compounds. It forms in several stages as the remains of plants are subjected to heat and pressure over millions of years.

**coal gasification**  Conversion of solid coal to synthetic natural gas (SNG).

**coal liquefaction**  Conversion of solid coal to a liquid hydrocarbon fuel such as synthetic gasoline or methanol.

**coastal wetland**  Land along a coastline, extending inland from an estuary, that is covered with salt water all or part of the year. Examples are marshes, bays, lagoons, tidal flats, and mangrove swamps. Compare *inland wetland.*

**coastal zone**  Warm, nutrient-rich, shallow part of the ocean that extends from the high-tide mark on land to the edge of a shelflike extension of continental land masses known as the continental shelf. Compare *open sea.*

**coevolution**  Evolution in which two or more species interact and exert selective pressures on each other that can lead each species to undergo various adaptations. See *evolution, natural selection.*

**cogeneration**  Production of two useful forms of energy, such as high-temperature heat or steam and electricity, from the same fuel source.

**cold front**  Leading edge of an advancing mass of cold air. Compare *warm front.*

**commensalism**  Interaction between organisms of different species in which one type of organism benefits and the other type is neither helped nor harmed to any great degree. Compare *mutualism.*

**commercial extinction**  Depletion of the population of a wild species used as a resource to a level at which it is no longer profitable to harvest the species.

**commercial inorganic fertilizer**  Commercially prepared mixture of plant nutrients such as nitrates, phosphates, and potassium applied to the soil to restore fertility and increase crop yields. Compare *organic fertilizer.*

**common law**  Body of unwritten rules and principles derived from thousands of past legal decisions. It is based on evaluation of what is reasonable behavior in attempting to balance competing social interests. Compare *statutory law.*

**common-property resource**  Resource that people normally are free to use; each user can deplete or degrade the available supply. Most are renewable and owned by no one. Examples are clean air, fish in parts of the ocean not under the control of a coastal country, migratory birds, gases of the lower atmosphere, and the ozone content of the upper atmosphere (stratosphere). See *tragedy of the commons.*

**community**  Populations of all species living and interacting in an area at a particular time.

**community development**  See *ecological succession.*

**competition**  Two or more individual organisms of a single species (*intraspecific competition*) or two or more individuals of different species (*interspecific competition*) attempting to use the same scarce resources in the same ecosystem.

**competitive exclusion principle**  No two species can occupy exactly the same fundamental niche indefinitely in a habitat where there is not enough of a particular resource to meet the needs of both species. See *ecological niche, fundamental niche, realized niche.*

**compost**  Partially decomposed organic plant and animal matter used as a soil conditioner or fertilizer.

**compound**  Combination of atoms, or oppositely charged ions, of two or more different elements held together by attractive forces called chemical bonds. Compare *element.*

**concentration**  Amount of a chemical in a particular volume or weight of air, water, soil, or other medium.

**condensation nuclei**  Tiny particles on which droplets of water vapor can collect.

**coniferous evergreen plants**  Cone-bearing plants (such as spruces, pines, and firs) that keep some of their narrow, pointed leaves (needles) all year. Compare *broadleaf deciduous plants, broadleaf evergreen plants.*

**coniferous trees**  Cone-bearing trees, mostly evergreens, that have needle-shaped or scalelike leaves. They produce wood known commercially as softwood. Compare *deciduous plants.*

**consensus science**  Scientific data, models, theories, and laws that are widely accepted by scientists considered experts in the area of study. These results of science are very reliable. Compare *frontier science.*

**conservation**  Sensible and careful use of natural resources by humans. People with this view are called *conservationists.*

**conservation biologist**  Biologist who investigates human impacts on the diversity of life found on the earth (biodiversity) and develops practical plans for preserving such biodiversity. Compare *conservationist, ecologist, environmentalist, environmental scientist, preservationist, restorationist.*

**conservation biology**  Multidisciplinary science created to deal with the crisis of maintaining the genes, species, communities, and ecosystems that make up earth's biological diversity. Its goals are to investigate human impacts on biodiversity and to develop practical approaches to preserving biodiversity.

**conservationist**  Person concerned with using natural areas and wildlife in ways that sustain them for current and future generations of humans and other forms of life. Compare *conservation biologist, ecologist, environmentalist, environmental scientist, preservationist, restorationist.*

**conservation-tillage farming**  Crop cultivation in which the soil is disturbed little (minimum-tillage farming) or not at all (no-till farming) to reduce soil erosion, lower labor costs, and save energy. Compare *conventional-tillage farming.*

**constancy**  Ability of a living system, such as a population, to maintain a certain size. Compare *inertia, resilience.* See *homeostasis.*

**consumer**  Organism that cannot synthesize the organic nutrients it needs and gets its organic nutrients by feeding on the tissues of producers or of other consumers; generally divided into *primary consumers* (herbivores), *secondary consumers* (carnivores), *tertiary* (higher-level) *consumers, omnivores,* and *detritivores* (decomposers and detritus feeders). In economics, one who uses economic goods.

**contour farming**  Plowing and planting across the changing slope of land, rather than in straight lines, to help retain water and reduce soil erosion.

**contour strip mining**  Form of surface mining used on hilly or mountainous terrain. A power shovel cuts a series of terraces into the side of a hill. An earthmover removes the overburden, and a power shovel extracts the coal, with the overburden from each new terrace dumped onto the one below. Compare *area strip mining, dredging, mountaintop removal, open-pit mining, subsurface mining.*

**controlled burning**  Deliberately set, carefully controlled surface fires that reduce flammable litter and decrease the chances of damaging crown fires. See *ground fire, surface fire.*

**conventional-tillage farming**  Crop cultivation method in which a planting surface is made by plowing land, breaking up the exposed soil, and then smoothing the surface. Compare *conservation-tillage farming.*

**convergent plate boundary**  Area where earth's lithospheric plates are pushed together. See *subduction zone.* Compare *divergent plate boundary, transform fault.*

**coral reef**  Formation produced by massive colonies containing billions of tiny coral animals, called polyps, that secrete a stony substance (calcium carbonate) around themselves for protection. When the corals die, their empty outer skeletons form layers and cause the reef to grow. They are found in the coastal zones of warm tropical and subtropical oceans.

**core**  Inner zone of the earth. It consists of a solid inner core and a liquid outer core. Compare *crust, mantle.*

**corridors**  Long areas of land that connect habitat that would otherwise become fragmented.

**cost-benefit analysis**  See *benefit-cost nalysis.*

**critical mass**  Amount of fissionable nuclei needed to sustain a nuclear fission chain reaction.

**crop rotation**  Planting a field, or an area of a field, with different crops from year to year to reduce soil nutrient depletion. A plant such as corn, tobacco, or cotton, which removes large amounts of nitrogen from the soil, is planted one year. The next year a legume such as soybeans, which adds nitrogen to the soil, is planted.

**crown fire**  Extremely hot forest fire that burns ground vegetation and treetops. Compare *controlled burning, ground fire, surface fire.*

**crude birth rate**  Annual number of live births per 1,000 people in the population of a geographic area at the midpoint of a given year. Compare *crude death rate.*

**crude death rate**  Annual number of deaths per 1,000 people in the population of a geographic area at the midpoint of a given year. Compare *crude birth rate.*

**crude oil**  Gooey liquid consisting mostly of hydrocarbon compounds and small amounts of compounds containing oxygen, sulfur, and nitrogen. Extracted from underground accumulations, it is sent to oil refineries, where it is converted to heating oil, diesel fuel, gasoline, tar, and other materials.

**crust**  Solid outer zone of the earth. It consists of oceanic crust and continental crust. Compare *core, mantle.*

**cultural eutrophication**  Overnourishment of aquatic ecosystems with plant nutrients (mostly nitrates and phosphates) because of human activities such as agriculture, urbanization, and discharges from industrial plants and sewage treatment plants. See *eutrophication.*

**cyanobacteria**  Single-celled, prokaryotic, microscopic organisms. Before being reclassified as monera, they were called blue-green algae.

**DDT**  Dichlorodiphenyltrichloroethane, a chlorinated hydrocarbon that has been widely used as a pesticide but is now banned in some countries.

**death rate**  See *crude death rate*.

**debt-for-nature swap**  Agreement in which a certain amount of foreign debt is canceled in exchange for local currency investments that will improve natural resource management or protect certain areas in the debtor country from harmful development.

**deciduous plants**  Trees, such as oaks and maples, and other plants that survive during dry seasons or cold seasons by shedding their leaves. Compare *coniferous trees, succulent plants*.

**decomposer**  Organism that digests parts of dead organisms and cast-off fragments and wastes of living organisms by breaking down the complex organic molecules in those materials into simpler inorganic compounds and then absorbing the soluble nutrients. Producers return most of these chemicals to the soil and water for reuse. Decomposers consist of various bacteria and fungi. Compare *consumer, detritivore, producer*.

**deductive reasoning**  Using logic to arrive at a specific conclusion based on a generalization or premise. It goes from the general to the specific. Compare *inductive reasoning*.

**defendant**  The individual, group of individuals, corporation, or government agency being charged in a lawsuit. Compare *plaintiff*.

**deforestation**  Removal of trees from a forested area without adequate replanting.

**degradable pollutant**  Potentially polluting chemical that is broken down completely or reduced to acceptable levels by natural physical, chemical, and biological processes. Compare *biodegradable pollutant, nondegradable pollutant, slowly degradable pollutant*.

**degree of urbanization**  Percentage of the population in the world, or a country, living in areas with a population of more than 2,500 people (higher in some countries). Compare *urban growth*.

**democracy**  Government by the people through their elected officials and appointed representatives. In a *constitutional democracy*, a constitution provides the basis of government authority and puts restraints on government power through free elections and freely expressed public opinion.

**demographic transition**  Hypothesis that countries, as they become industrialized, have declines in death rates followed by declines in birth rates.

**depletion time**  Time it takes to use a certain fraction, usually 80%, of the known or estimated supply of a nonrenewable resource at an assumed rate of use. Finding and extracting the remaining 20% usually costs more than it is worth.

**desalination**  Purification of salt water or brackish (slightly salty) water by removal of dissolved salts.

**desert**  Biome in which evaporation exceeds precipitation and the average amount of precipitation is less than 25 centimeters (10 inches) a year. Such areas have little vegetation or have widely spaced, mostly low vegetation. Compare *forest, grassland*.

**desertification**  Conversion of rangeland, rainfed cropland, or irrigated cropland to desertlike land, with a drop in agricultural productivity of 10% or more. It usually is caused by a combination of overgrazing, soil erosion, prolonged drought, and climate change.

**detritivore**  Consumer organism that feeds on detritus, parts of dead organisms, and cast-off fragments and wastes of living organisms. The two principal types are *detritus feeders* and *decomposers*.

**detritus**  Parts of dead organisms and cast-off fragments and wastes of living organisms.

**detritus feeder**  Organism that extracts nutrients from fragments of dead organisms and their cast-off parts and organic wastes. Examples are earthworms, termites, and crabs. Compare *decomposer*.

**deuterium (D; hydrogen-2)**  Isotope of the element hydrogen, with a nucleus containing one proton and one neutron and a mass number of 2.

**developed country**  Country that is highly industrialized and has a high per capita GNP. Compare *developing country*.

**developing country**  Country that has low to moderate industrialization and low to moderate per capita GNP. Most are located in Africa, Asia, and Latin America. Compare *developed country*.

**dew point**  Temperature at which condensation occurs for a given amount of water vapor.

**dieback**  Sharp reduction in the population of a species when its numbers exceed the carrying capacity of its habitat. See *carrying capacity*.

**differential reproduction**  Phenomenon in which individuals with adaptive genetic traits produce more living offspring than do individuals without such traits. See *natural selection*.

**dioxins**  Family of 75 different chlorinated hydrocarbon compounds formed as unwanted by-products in chemical reactions involving chlorine and hydrocarbons, usually at high temperatures.

**discount rate**  The economic value a resource will have in the future compared with its present value.

**dissolved oxygen (DO) content**  Amount of oxygen gas ($O_2$) dissolved in a given volume of water at a particular temperature and pressure, often expressed as a concentration in parts of oxygen per million parts of water. See *biological oxygen demand*.

**disturbance**  A discrete event that disrupts an ecosystem or community. Examples of *natural disturbances* include fires, hurricanes, tornadoes, droughts, and floods. Examples of *human-caused disturbances* include deforestation, overgrazing, and plowing.

**divergent plate boundary**  Area where earth's lithospheric plates move apart in opposite directions. Compare *convergent plate boundary, transform fault*.

**DNA (deoxyribonucleic acid)**  Large molecules in the cells of organisms that carry genetic information in living organisms.

**domesticated species**  Wild species tamed or genetically altered by crossbreeding for use by humans for food (cattle, sheep, and food crops), pets (dogs and cats), or enjoyment (animals in zoos and plants in gardens). Compare *wild species*.

**dose**  The amount of a potentially harmful substance an individual ingests, inhales, or absorbs through the skin. See *dose-response curve, median lethal dose*. Compare *response*.

**dose-response curve**  Plot of data showing effects of various doses of a toxic agent on a group of test organisms. See *dose, median lethal dose, response*.

**doubling time**  Time it takes (usually in years) for the quantity of something growing exponentially to double. It can be calculated by dividing the annual percentage growth rate into 70. See *rule of 70*.

**drainage basin**  See *watershed*.

**dredge spoils**  Materials scraped from the bottoms of harbors and streams to maintain shipping channels. High levels of toxic substances that have settled out of the water often contaminate these materials. See *dredging*.

**dredging**  Type of surface mining in which chain buckets and draglines scrape up sand, gravel, and other surface deposits covered with water. It is also used to remove sediment from streams and harbors to maintain shipping channels. See *dredge spoils*. Compare *area strip mining, contour strip mining, mountaintop removal, open-pit mining, subsurface mining*.

**drift-net fishing**  Catching fish in huge nets that drift in the water.

**drought**  Condition in which an area does not get enough water because of (1) lower-than-normal precipitation or (2) higher-than-normal temperatures that increase evaporation.

**dust dome**  Dome of heated air that surrounds an urban area and traps pollutants, especially suspended particulate matter. See also *urban heat island*.

**dust plume**  Elongation of a dust dome by winds that can spread a city's pollutants hundreds of kilometers downwind.

**early successional plant species**  Plant species found in the early stages of succession that (1) grow close to the ground, (2) can establish large populations quickly under harsh conditions, and (3) have short lives. Compare *late successional plant species, midsuccessional plant species*.

**earth capital**  See *natural resources*.

**earthquake**  Shaking of the ground resulting from the fracturing and displacement of rock, which produces a fault, or from subsequent movement along the fault.

**earth resources**  See *natural resources*.

**ecological diversity**  Variety of forests, deserts, grasslands, oceans, streams, lakes, and other biological communities interacting with one another and with their nonliving environment. See *biodiversity*. Compare *functional diversity, genetic diversity, species diversity*.

**ecological efficiency**  Percentage of energy transferred from one trophic level to another in a food chain or web.

**ecological footprint**  Measure of the ecological impact of the (1) consumption of food, wood products, and other resources, (2) use of buildings, roads, garbage dumps, and other things that consume land space, and (3) destruction of the forests needed to absorb the $CO_2$ produced by burning fossil fuels.

**ecological land-use planning**  Method for deciding how land should be used; development of an integrated model that considers geological, ecological, health, and social variables.

**ecological niche**  Total way of life or role of a species in an ecosystem. It includes all physical, chemical, and biological conditions a species needs to live and reproduce in an ecosystem. See *fundamental niche, realized niche*.

**ecological population density**  Number of individuals of a population per unit area of habitat. Compare *population density*.

**ecological restoration**  Deliberate alteration of a degraded habitat or ecosystem to restore as much of its ecological structure and function as possible.

**ecological succession**  Process in which communities of plant and animal species in a particular area are replaced over time by a series of different and often more complex communities. See *primary succession, secondary succession*.

**ecologist**  Biological scientist who studies relationships between living organisms and their environment. Compare *conservation biologist, conservationist, environmentalist, environmental scientist, preservationist, restorationist*.

**ecology**  Study of the interactions of living organisms with one another and with their nonliving environment of matter and energy; study of the structure and functions of nature.

**economic decision** Deciding (1) what goods and services to produce, (2) how to produce them, (3) how much to produce, and (4) how to distribute them to people.

**economic depletion** Exhaustion of 80% of the estimated supply of a nonrenewable resource. Finding, extracting, and processing the remaining 20% usually costs more than it is worth; may also apply to the depletion of a renewable resource, such as a fish or tree species.

**economic development** Improvement of living standards by economic growth. Compare *economic growth, environmentally sustainable economic development*.

**economic growth** Increase in the capacity to provide people with goods and services produced by an economy; an increase in GNI. Compare *economic development, environmentally sustainable economic development, sustainable economic development*.

**economic resources** Natural resources, capital goods, and labor used in an economy to produce material goods and services. See *natural resources*.

**economic system** Method that a group of people uses to choose (1) what goods and services to produce, (2) how to produce them, (3) how much to produce, and (4) how to distribute them to people. See *capitalist market economic system, pure command economic system, pure free-market economic system*.

**economic threshold** Point at which the economic loss caused by pest damage outweighs the cost of applying a pesticide.

**economy** System of production, distribution, and consumption of economic goods.

**ecosphere** See *biosphere*.

**ecosystem** Community of different species interacting with one another and with the chemical and physical factors making up its nonliving environment.

**ecosystem services** Natural services or natural capital that support life on the earth and are essential to the quality of human life and the functioning of the world's economies. See *natural resources*.

**ecotone** Transitional zone in which one type of ecosystem tends to merge with another ecosystem. See *edge effect*.

**edge effect** Existence of a greater number of species and a higher population density in a transition zone (ecotone) between two ecosystems than in either adjacent ecosystem. See *ecotone*.

**electromagnetic radiation** Forms of kinetic energy traveling as electromagnetic waves. Examples are radio waves, TV signals, microwaves, infrared radiation, visible light, ultraviolet radiation, X rays, and gamma rays. Compare *ionizing radiation, nonionizing radiation*.

**electron (e)** Tiny particle moving around outside the nucleus of an atom. Each electron has one unit of negative charge and almost no mass. Compare *neutron, proton*.

**element** Chemical, such as hydrogen (H), iron (Fe), sodium (Na), carbon (C), nitrogen (N), or oxygen (O), whose distinctly different atoms serve as the basic building blocks of all matter. There are 92 naturally occurring elements. Another 23 have been made in laboratories. Two or more elements combine to form compounds that make up most of the world's matter. Compare *compound*.

**endangered species** Wild species with so few individual survivors that the species could soon become extinct in all or most of its natural range. Compare *threatened species*.

**endemic species** Species that is found in only one area. Such species are especially vulnerable to extinction.

**energy** Capacity to do work by performing mechanical, physical, chemical, or electrical tasks or to cause a heat transfer between two objects at different temperatures.

**energy efficiency** Percentage of the total energy input that does useful work and is not converted into low-quality, usually useless heat in an energy conversion system or process. See *energy quality, net energy*. Compare *material efficiency*.

**energy productivity** See *energy efficiency*.

**energy quality** Ability of a form of energy to do useful work. High-temperature heat and the chemical energy in fossil fuels and nuclear fuels are concentrated high-quality energy. Low-quality energy such as low-temperature heat is dispersed or diluted and cannot do much useful work. See *high-quality energy, low-quality energy*.

**environment** All external conditions and factors, living and nonliving (chemicals and energy), that affect an organism or other specified system during its lifetime.

**environmental degradation** Depletion or destruction of a potentially renewable resource such as soil, grassland, forest, or wildlife that is used faster than it is naturally replenished. If such use continues, the resource becomes nonrenewable (on a human time scale) or nonexistent (extinct). See also *sustainable yield*.

**environmental ethics** Our beliefs about what is right or wrong environmental behavior.

**environmentalist** Person concerned about the impact of people on environmental quality who believes some human actions are degrading parts of the earth's life-support systems for humans and many other forms of life. Compare *conservation biologist, conservationist, ecologist, environmental scientist, preservationist, restorationist*.

**environmental justice** Fair treatment and meaningful involvement of all people regardless of race, color, sex, national origin, or income with respect to the development, implementation, and enforcement of environmental laws, regulations, and policies.

**environmentally sustainable economic development** Development that (1) *encourages* environmentally sustainable forms of economic growth that meet the basic needs of the current generations of humans and other species without preventing future generations of humans and other species from meeting their basic needs and (2) *discourages* environmentally harmful and unsustainable forms of economic growth. It is the economic component of an *environmentally sustainable society*. Compare *economic development, economic growth*.

**environmentally sustainable society** Society that satisfies the basic needs of its people without depleting or degrading its natural resources and thereby preventing current and future generations of humans and other species from meeting their basic needs.

**environmental movement** Efforts by citizens (mostly at the grassroots level) to demand that political leaders enact laws and develop policies to (1) curtail pollution, (2) clean up polluted environments, and (3) protect pristine areas and species from environmental degradation.

**environmental resistance** All the limiting factors that act together to limit the growth of a population. See *biotic potential, limiting factor*.

**environmental revolution** Cultural change involving halting population growth and altering lifestyles, political and economic systems, and the way we treat the environment so we can help sustain the earth for ourselves and other species. This involves working with the rest of nature by learning more about how nature sustains itself. See *en-*

*vironmental wisdom worldview*. Compare *agricultural revolution, hunter–gatherers, industrial revolution, information and globalization revolution*.

**environmental science** Study of how we and other species interact with one another and with the nonliving environment (matter and energy). It is a physical and social science that integrates knowledge from a wide range of disciplines, including physics, chemistry, biology (especially ecology), geology, geography, resource technology and engineering, resource conservation and management, demography (the study of population dynamics), economics, politics, sociology, psychology, and ethics.

**environmental scientist** Scientist who uses information from the physical sciences and social sciences to (1) understand how the earth works, (2) learn how humans interact with the earth, and (3) develop solutions to environmental problems. Compare *conservation biologist, conservationist, ecologist, preservationist, restorationist*.

**environmental wisdom worldview** Beliefs that (1) nature exists for all the earth's species, not just for us, and we are not in charge of the rest of nature; (2) there is not always more, and it is not all for us; (3) some forms of economic growth are beneficial and some are harmful, and our goals should be to design economic and political systems that encourage earth-sustaining forms of growth and discourage or prohibit earth-degrading forms; and (4) our success depends on learning to cooperate with one another and with the rest of nature instead of trying to dominate and manage earth's life-support systems primarily for our own use. Compare *frontier environmental worldview, planetary management worldview, spaceship-earth worldview*.

**environmental worldview** How people think the world works, what they think their role in the world should be, and what they believe is right and wrong environmental behavior (environmental ethics).

**EPA** U.S. Environmental Protection Agency; responsible for managing federal efforts to control air and water pollution, radiation and pesticide hazards, environmental research, hazardous waste, and solid waste disposal.

**epidemiology** Study of the patterns of disease or other harmful effects from exposure to toxic chemicals or disease organisms within defined groups of people to find out why some people get sick and some do not.

**epiphyte** Plant that uses its roots to attach itself to branches high in trees, especially in tropical forests.

**erosion** Process or group of processes by which loose or consolidated earth materials are dissolved, loosened, or worn away and removed from one place and deposited in another. See *weathering*.

**estuary** Partially enclosed coastal area at the mouth of a river where its fresh water, carrying fertile silt and runoff from the land, mixes with salty seawater.

**eukaryotic cell** Cell containing a *nucleus*, a region of genetic material surrounded by a membrane. Membranes also enclose several of the other internal parts found in a eukaryotic cell. Compare *prokaryotic cell*.

**euphotic zone** Upper layer of a body of water through which sunlight can penetrate and support photosynthesis.

**eutrophication** Physical, chemical, and biological changes that take place after a lake, estuary, or slow-flowing stream receives inputs of plant nutrients—mostly nitrates and phosphates—from natural erosion and runoff from the surrounding land basin. See *cultural eutrophication*.

**eutrophic lake** Lake with a large or excessive supply of plant nutrients, mostly nitrates and phosphates. Compare *mesotrophic lake, oligotrophic lake.*

**evaporation** Conversion of a liquid into a gas.

**even-aged management** Method of forest management in which trees, sometimes of a single species in a given stand, are maintained at about the same age and size and are harvested all at once. Compare *uneven-aged management.*

**evergreen plants** Plants that keep some of their leaves or needles throughout the year. Examples are ferns and cone-bearing trees (conifers) such as firs, spruces, pines, redwoods, and sequoias. Compare *deciduous plants, succulent plants.*

**evolution** See *biological evolution.*

**exhaustible resource** See *nonrenewable resource.*

**exotic species** See *nonnative species.*

**experiment** Procedure a scientist uses to study some phenomenon under known conditions. Scientists conduct some experiments in the laboratory and others in nature. The resulting scientific data or facts must be verified or confirmed by repeated observations and measurements, ideally by several different investigators.

**exploitation competition** Situation in which two competing species have equal access to a specific resource but differ in how quickly or efficiently they exploit it. See *interference competition, interspecific competition.*

**exponential growth** Growth in which some quantity, such as population size or economic output, increases by a fixed percentage of the whole in a given time period; when the increase in quantity over time is plotted, this type of growth yields a curve shaped like the letter *J*. Compare *linear growth.*

**external benefit** Beneficial social effect of producing and using an economic good that is not included in the market price of the good. Compare *external cost, full cost.*

**external cost** Harmful environmental or social effect of producing and using an economic good that is not included in the market price of the good. Compare *external benefit, full cost, internal cost.*

**externalities** Social benefits ("goods") and social costs ("bads") not included in the market price of an economic good. See *external benefit, external cost.* Compare *full cost, internal cost.*

**extinction** Complete disappearance of a species from the earth. This happens when a species cannot adapt and successfully reproduce under new environmental conditions or when it evolves into one or more new species. See *endangered species, mass depletion, mass extinction, threatened species.* Compare *speciation.*

**family planning** Providing information, clinical services, and contraceptives to help people choose the number and spacing of children they want to have.

**famine** Widespread malnutrition and starvation in a particular area because of a shortage of food, usually caused by drought, war, flood, earthquake, or other catastrophic events that disrupt food production and distribution.

**feedback loop** Circuit of sensing, evaluating, and reacting to changes in environmental conditions as a result of information fed back into a system; it occurs when one change leads to some other change, which eventually reinforces or slows the original change. See *negative feedback loop, positive feedback loop.*

**feedlot** Confined outdoor or indoor space used to raise hundreds to thousands of domesticated livestock. Compare *rangeland.*

**fermentation** See *anaerobic respiration.*

**fertilizer** Substance that adds inorganic or organic plant nutrients to soil and improves its ability to grow crops, trees, or other vegetation. See *commercial inorganic fertilizer, organic fertilizer.*

**financial resources** Cash, investments, and monetary institutions used to support the use of natural resources and human resources to provide economic goods and services. Compare *human resources, manufactured resources, natural resources.*

**first law of energy** See *first law of thermodynamics.*

**first law of thermodynamics** In any physical or chemical change, no detectable amount of energy is created or destroyed, but in these processes energy can be changed from one form to another; you cannot get more energy out of something than you put in; in terms of energy quantity, you cannot get something for nothing (there is no free lunch). This law does not apply to nuclear changes, in which energy can be produced from small amounts of matter. See also *second law of thermodynamics.*

**fishery** Concentrations of particular aquatic species suitable for commercial harvesting in a given ocean area or inland body of water.

**fish farming** Form of aquaculture in which fish are cultivated in a controlled pond or other environment and harvested when they reach the desired size. See also *fish ranching.*

**fish ranching** Form of aquaculture in which members of a fish species such as salmon are held in captivity for the first few years of their lives, released, and then harvested as adults when they return from the ocean to their freshwater birthplace to spawn. See also *fish farming.*

**fissionable isotope** Isotope that can split apart when hit by a neutron at the right speed and thus undergo nuclear fission. Examples are uranium-235 and plutonium-239. See *nuclear fission.*

**floodplain** Flat valley floor next to a stream channel. For legal purposes, the term often applies to any low area that has the potential for flooding, including certain coastal areas.

**flows** See *throughputs.*

**flyway** Generally fixed route along which waterfowl migrate from one area to another at certain seasons of the year.

**food chain** Series of organisms in which each eats or decomposes the preceding one. Compare *food web.*

**food web** Complex network of many interconnected food chains and feeding relationships. Compare *food chain.*

**forest** Biome with enough average annual precipitation (at least 76 centimeters, or 30 inches) to support growth of various tree species and smaller forms of vegetation. Compare *desert, grassland.*

**fossil fuel** Products of partial or complete decomposition of plants and animals that occur as crude oil, coal, natural gas, or heavy oils as a result of exposure to heat and pressure in the earth's crust over millions of years. See *coal, crude oil, natural gas.*

**fossils** Skeletons, bones, shells, body parts, leaves, seeds, or impressions of such items that provide recognizable evidence of organisms that lived long ago.

**free-access resource** See *common-property resource.*

**Freons** See *chlorofluorocarbons.*

**freshwater life zones** Aquatic systems where water with a dissolved salt concentration of less than 1% by volume accumulates on or flows through the surfaces of terrestrial biomes. Examples are (1) *standing* (lentic) bodies of fresh water such as lakes, ponds, and inland wetlands and (2) *flowing* (lotic) systems such as streams and rivers. Compare *biome.*

**front** The boundary between two air masses with different temperatures and densities. See *cold front, warm front.*

**frontier environmental worldview** Viewing undeveloped land as a hostile wilderness to be conquered (cleared, planted) and exploited for its resources as quickly as possible. Compare *environmental wisdom worldview, planetary management worldview, spaceship-earth worldview.*

**frontier science** Preliminary scientific data, hypotheses, and models that have not been widely tested and accepted. Compare *consensus science.*

**full cost** Cost of a good when its internal costs and its estimated short- and long-term external costs are included in its market price. Compare *external cost, internal cost.*

**functional diversity** Biological and chemical processes or functions such as energy flow and matter cycling needed for the survival of species and biological communities. See *biodiversity, ecological diversity, genetic diversity, species diversity.*

**fundamental niche** The full potential range of the physical, chemical, and biological factors a species can use if there is no competition from other species. See *ecological niche.* Compare *realized niche.*

**fungi** Eukaryotic, mostly multicellular organisms such as mushrooms, molds, and yeasts. As decomposers, they get the nutrients they need by secreting enzymes that speed up the breakdown of organic matter in the tissue of other living or dead organisms. Then they absorb the resulting nutrients.

**fungicide** Chemical that kills fungi.

**Gaia hypothesis** Hypothesis that the earth is alive and can be considered a system that operates and changes by feedback of information between its living and nonliving components.

**game species** Type of wild animal that people hunt or fish for, for sport and recreation and sometimes for food.

**gamma rays** Form of ionizing electromagnetic radiation with a high energy content emitted by some radioisotopes. They readily penetrate body tissues. See also *alpha particle, beta particle.*

**gangue** Waste or undesired material in an ore. See *ore.*

**gap analysis** Scientific method used to determine how adequately native plant and animal species and the existing network of conservation lands protects natural communities. Species and communities not adequately represented in existing conservation lands constitute conservation gaps. The idea is to identify these gaps and then eliminate them by establishing new reserves or changing land management practices.

**GDP** See *gross domestic product.*

**gene flow** Movement of genes between populations, which can lead to changes in the genetic composition of local populations.

**gene mutation** See *mutation.*

**gene pool** Sum total of all genes found in the individuals of the population of a particular species.

**generalist species** Species with a broad ecological niche. They can live in many different places, eat a variety of foods, and tolerate a wide range of environmental conditions. Examples are flies, cockroaches, mice, rats, and human beings. Compare *specialist species*.

**genes**   Coded units of information about specific traits that are passed on from parents to offspring during reproduction. They consist of segments of DNA molecules found in chromosomes.

**gene splicing**   See *genetic engineering*.

**genetic adaptation**   Changes in the genetic makeup of organisms of a species that allow the species to reproduce and gain a competitive advantage under changed environmental conditions. See *differential reproduction, evolution, mutation, natural selection*.

**genetically modified organism (GMO)**   Organism whose genetic makeup has been modified by genetic engineering.

**genetic diversity**   Variability in the genetic makeup among individuals within a single species. See *biodiversity*. Compare *ecological diversity, functional diversity, species diversity*.

**genetic engineering**   Insertion of an alien gene into an organism to give it a new and usually beneficial genetic trait. Compare *artificial selection, natural selection*.

**genome**   Complete set of genetic information for an organism.

**geographic isolation**   Separation of populations of a species for long times into different areas.

**geology**   Study of the earth's dynamic history. Geologists study and analyze rocks and the features and processes of the earth's interior and surface.

**geothermal energy**   Heat transferred from the earth's underground concentrations of **(1)** dry steam (steam with no water droplets), **(2)** wet steam (a mixture of steam and water droplets), or **(3)** hot water trapped in fractured or porous rock.

**globalization**   Broad process of global social, economic, and environmental change that leads to an increasingly similar and integrated world. See *information and globalization revolution*.

**global warming**   Warming of the earth's atmosphere because of increases in the concentrations of one or more greenhouse gases primarily as a result of human activities. See *greenhouse effect, greenhouse gases*.

**GNI**   See *gross national income*.

**GNP**   See *gross national product*.

**grassland**   Biome found in regions where moderate annual average precipitation (25–76 centimeters, or 10–30 inches) is enough to support the growth of grass and small plants but not enough to support large stands of trees. Compare *desert, forest*.

**greenhouse effect**   Natural effect that releases heat in the atmosphere (troposphere) near the earth's surface. Water vapor, carbon dioxide, ozone, and several other gases in the lower atmosphere (troposphere) absorb some of the infrared radiation (heat) radiated by the earth's surface. This causes their molecules to vibrate and transform the absorbed energy into longer-wavelength infrared radiation (heat) in the troposphere. If the atmospheric concentrations of these greenhouse gases rise and they are not removed by other natural processes, the average temperature of the lower atmosphere will increase gradually. Compare *global warming*.

**greenhouse gases**   Gases in the earth's lower atmosphere (troposphere) that cause the greenhouse effect. Examples are carbon dioxide, chlorofluorocarbons, ozone, methane, water vapor, and nitrous oxide.

**green manure**   Freshly cut or still-growing green vegetation that is plowed into the soil to increase

the organic matter and humus available to support crop growth. Compare *animal manure*.

**green revolution**   Popular term for introduction of scientifically bred or selected varieties of grain (rice, wheat, maize) that, with high enough inputs of fertilizer and water, can greatly increase crop yields.

**gross domestic product (GDP)**   Total market value in current dollars of all goods and services produced *within a country*, usually during a year. Compare *gross national product, gross world product*.

**gross national income (GNI)**   Total market value in current dollars of all goods and services produced *within* and *outside* a country during a year plus net income earned abroad by a country's citizens. Formerly called *gross national product*. Compare *gross domestic product, gross world product*.

**gross national income in purchasing power parity (GNI PPP)**   Market value of the GNI in terms of the goods and services it would buy in the United States. This is a better way to compare the standards of living among countries.

**gross national product (GNP)**   See *gross national income*.

**gross primary productivity (GPP)**   Rate at which an ecosystem's producers capture and store a given amount of chemical energy as biomass in a given length of time. Compare *net primary productivity*.

**gross world product (GWP)**   Market value in current dollars of all goods and services produced in the world each year. Compare *gross domestic product, gross national income*.

**ground fire**   Fire that burns decayed leaves or peat deep below the ground surface. Compare *crown fire, surface fire*.

**groundwater**   Water that sinks into the soil and is stored in slowly flowing and slowly renewed underground reservoirs called aquifers; underground water in the zone of saturation, below the water table. Compare *runoff, surface water*.

**gully reclamation**   Restoring land suffering from gully erosion by seeding gullies with quick-growing plants, building small dams to collect silt and gradually fill in the channels, and building channels to divert water away from the gully.

**habitat**   Place or type of place where an organism or population of organisms lives. Compare *ecological niche*.

**habitat fragmentation**   Breakup of a habitat into smaller pieces, usually as a result of human activities.

**half-life**   Time needed for one-half of the nuclei in a radioisotope to emit its radiation. Each radioisotope has a characteristic half-life, which may range from a few millionths of a second to several billion years. See *radioisotope*.

**hazard**   Something that can cause injury, disease, economic loss, or environmental damage. See also *risk*.

**hazardous chemical**   Chemical that can cause harm because it **(1)** is flammable or explosive, **(2)** can irritate or damage the skin or lungs (such as strong acidic or alkaline substances), or **(3)** can cause allergic reactions of the immune system (allergens). See also *toxic chemical*.

**hazardous waste**   Any solid, liquid, or containerized gas that **(1)** can catch fire easily, **(2)** is corrosive to skin tissue or metals, **(3)** is unstable and can explode or release toxic fumes, or **(4)** has harmful concentrations of one or more toxic materials that can leach out. See also *toxic waste*.

**heat**   Total kinetic energy of all the randomly moving atoms, ions, or molecules within a given

substance, excluding the overall motion of the whole object. Heat always flows spontaneously from a hot sample of matter to a colder sample of matter. This is one way to state the second law of thermodynamics. Compare *temperature*.

**herbicide**   Chemical that kills a plant or inhibits its growth.

**herbivore**   Plant-eating organism. Examples are deer, sheep, grasshoppers, and zooplankton. Compare *carnivore, omnivore*.

**heterotroph**   See *consumer*.

**high**   Air mass with a high pressure. Compare *low*.

**high-input agriculture**   See *industrialized agriculture*.

**high-quality energy**   Energy that is concentrated and has great ability to perform useful work. Examples are high-temperature heat and the energy in electricity, coal, oil, gasoline, sunlight, and nuclei of uranium-235. Compare *low-quality energy*.

**high-quality matter**   Matter that is concentrated and contains a high concentration of a useful resource. Compare *low-quality matter*.

**high-throughput economy**   Situation in most advanced industrialized countries, in which ever-increasing economic growth is sustained by maximizing the rate at which matter and energy resources are used, with little emphasis on pollution prevention, recycling, reuse, reduction of unnecessary waste, and other forms of resource conservation. Compare *low-throughput economy, matter-recycling economy*.

**high-waste society**   See *high-throughput economy*.

**homeostasis**   Maintenance of favorable internal conditions in a system despite fluctuations in external conditions. See *constancy, inertia, resilience*.

**host**   Plant or animal on which a parasite feeds.

**human capital**   See *human resources*.

**human resources**   Physical and mental talents of people used to produce, distribute, and sell an economic good. Compare *financial resources, manufactured resources, natural resources*.

**humus**   Slightly soluble residue of undigested or partially decomposed organic material in topsoil. This material helps retain water and water-soluble nutrients, which can be taken up by plant roots.

**hunter–gatherers**   People who get their food by gathering edible wild plants and other materials and by hunting wild animals and fish. Compare *agricultural revolution, environmental revolution, industrial revolution, information and globalization revolution*.

**hydrocarbon**   Organic compound of hydrogen and carbon atoms. The simplest hydrocarbon is methane ($CH_4$), the major component of natural gas.

**hydroelectric power plant**   Structure in which the energy of falling or flowing water spins a turbine generator to produce electricity.

**hydrologic cycle**   Biogeochemical cycle that collects, purifies, and distributes the earth's fixed supply of water from the environment to living organisms and then back to the environment.

**hydropower**   Electrical energy produced by falling or flowing water. See *hydroelectric power plant*.

**hydrosphere**   The earth's **(1)** liquid water (oceans, lakes, other bodies of surface water, and underground water), **(2)** frozen water (polar ice caps, floating ice caps, and ice in soil, known as permafrost), and **(3)** small amounts of water vapor in the atmosphere. See also *hydrologic cycle*.

**identified resources**   Deposits of a particular mineral-bearing material of which the location, quantity, and quality are known or have been estimated from direct geological evidence and measurements. Compare *undiscovered resources.*

**igneous rock**   Rock formed when molten rock material (magma) wells up from the earth's interior, cools, and solidifies into rock masses. Compare *metamorphic rock, sedimentary rock.* See *rock cycle.*

**immature community**   Community at an early stage of ecological succession. It usually has a low number of species and ecological niches and cannot capture and use energy and cycle critical nutrients as efficiently as more complex, mature communities. Compare *mature community.*

**immigrant species**   See *nonnative species.*

**immigration**   Migration of people into a country or area to take up permanent residence.

**indicator species**   Species that serve as early warnings that a community or ecosystem is being degraded. Compare *keystone species, native species, nonnative species.*

**inductive reasoning**   Using observations and facts to arrive at generalizations or hypotheses. It goes from the specific to the general and is widely used in science. Compare *deductive reasoning.*

**industrialized agriculture**   Using large inputs of energy from fossil fuels (especially oil and natural gas), water, fertilizer, and pesticides to produce large quantities of crops and livestock for domestic and foreign sale. Compare *subsistence farming.*

**industrial revolution**   Use of new sources of energy from fossil fuels and later from nuclear fuels, and use of new technologies, to grow food and manufacture products. Compare *agricultural revolution, environmental revolution, hunter–gatherers, information and globalization revolution.*

**industrial smog**   Type of air pollution consisting mostly of a mixture of sulfur dioxide, suspended droplets of sulfuric acid formed from some of the sulfur dioxide, and a variety of suspended solid particles. Compare *photochemical smog.*

**inertia**   Ability of a living system to resist being disturbed or altered. Compare *constancy, resilience.*

**infant mortality rate**   Number of babies out of every 1,000 born each year that die before their first birthday.

**infiltration**   Downward movement of water through soil.

**information and globalization revolution**   Use of new technologies such as the telephone, radio, television, computers, the Internet, automated databases, and remote sensing satellites to enable people to have increasingly rapid access to much more information on a global scale. Compare *agricultural revolution, environmental revolution, hunter–gatherers, industrial revolution.*

**inherent value**   See *intrinsic value.*

**inland wetland**   Land away from the coast, such as a swamp, marsh, or bog, that is covered all or part of the time with fresh water. Compare *coastal wetland.*

**inorganic compounds**   All compounds not classified as organic compounds. See *organic compounds.*

**inorganic fertilizer**   See *commercial inorganic fertilizer.*

**input**   Matter, energy, or information entering a system. Compare *output, throughput.*

**input pollution control**   See *pollution prevention.*

**insecticide**   Chemical that kills insects.

**instrumental value**   Value of an organism, species, ecosystem, or the earth's biodiversity based on its usefulness to us. Compare *intrinsic value.*

**integrated pest management (IPM)**   Combined use of biological, chemical, and cultivation methods in proper sequence and timing to keep the size of a pest population below the size that causes economically unacceptable loss of a crop or livestock animal.

**intercropping**   Growing two or more different crops at the same time on a plot. For example, a carbohydrate-rich grain that depletes soil nitrogen and a protein-rich legume that adds nitrogen to the soil may be intercropped. Compare *monoculture, polyculture, polyvarietal cultivation.*

**interference competition**   Situation in which one species limits access of another species to a resource, regardless of whether the resource is abundant or scarce. See *exploitation competition, interspecific competition.*

**intermediate goods**   See *manufactured resources.*

**internal cost**   Direct cost paid by the producer and the buyer of an economic good. Compare *external benefit, external cost, full cost.*

**interplanting**   Simultaneously growing a variety of crops on the same plot. See *agroforestry, intercropping, polyculture, polyvarietal cultivation.*

**interspecific competition**   Members of two or more species trying to use the same limited resources in an ecosystem. See *competition, competitive exclusion principle, intraspecific competition.*

**intertidal zone**   Area of shoreline between low and high tides.

**intraspecific competition**   Two or more organisms of a single species trying to use the same limited resources in an ecosystem. See *competition, interspecific competition.*

**intrinsic rate of increase (r)**   Rate at which a population could grow if it had unlimited resources. Compare *environmental resistance.*

**intrinsic value**   Value of an organism, species, ecosystem, or the earth's biodiversity based on its existence, regardless of whether it has any usefulness to us. Compare *instrumental value.*

**inversion**   See *temperature inversion.*

**invertebrates**   Animals that have no backbones. Compare *vertebrates.*

**ion**   Atom or group of atoms with one or more positive (+) or negative (−) electrical charges. Compare *atom, molecule.*

**ionizing radiation**   Fast-moving alpha or beta particles or high-energy radiation (gamma rays) emitted by radioisotopes. They have enough energy to dislodge one or more electrons from atoms they hit, forming charged ions in tissue that can react with and damage living tissue. Compare *nonionizing radiation.*

**isotopes**   Two or more forms of a chemical element that have the same number of protons but different mass numbers because they have different numbers of neutrons in their nuclei.

**J-shaped curve**   Curve with a shape similar to that of the letter *J;* can represent prolonged exponential growth. See *exponential growth.*

**kerogen**   Solid, waxy mixture of hydrocarbons found in oil shale rock. Heating the rock to high temperatures causes the kerogen to vaporize. The vapor is condensed, purified, and then sent to a refinery to produce gasoline, heating oil, and other products. See also *oil shale, shale oil.*

**keystone species**   Species that play roles affecting many other organisms in an ecosystem. Compare *indicator species, native species, nonnative species.*

**kilocalorie (kcal)**   Unit of energy equal to 1,000 calories. See *calorie.*

**kilowatt (kW)**   Unit of electrical power equal to 1,000 watts. See *watt.*

**kinetic energy**   Energy that matter has because of its mass and speed or velocity. Compare *potential energy.*

**K-selected species**   Species that produce a few, often fairly large offspring but invest a great deal of time and energy to ensure that most of those offspring reach reproductive age. Compare *r-selected species.*

**K-strategists**   See *K-selected species.*

**kwashiorkor**   Type of malnutrition that occurs in infants and very young children when they are weaned from mother's milk to a starchy diet low in protein. See *marasmus, malnutrition.*

**lake**   Large natural body of standing fresh water formed when water from precipitation, land runoff, or groundwater flow fills a depression in the earth created by (1) glaciation, (2) earth movement, (3) volcanic activity, or (4) a giant meteorite. See *eutrophic lake, mesotrophic lake, oligotrophic lake.*

**land classification**   Method for reducing soil erosion that identifies easily erodible land that should not be planted in crops or cleared of vegetation.

**landfill**   See *sanitary landfill.*

**land-use planning**   Process for deciding the best present and future use of each parcel of land in an area. See *ecological land-use planning.*

**late successional plant species**   Mostly trees that can tolerate shade and form a fairly stable complex forest community. Compare *early successional plant species, midsuccessional plant species.*

**latitude**   Distance from the equator. Compare *altitude.*

**law of conservation of energy**   See *first law of thermodynamics.*

**law of conservation of matter**   In any physical or chemical change, matter is neither created nor destroyed but merely changed from one form to another; in physical and chemical changes, existing atoms are rearranged into different spatial patterns (physical changes) or different combinations (chemical changes).

**law of tolerance**   Existence, abundance, and distribution of a species in an ecosystem are determined by whether the levels of one or more physical or chemical factors fall within the range tolerated by the species. See *threshold effect.*

**LD$_{50}$**   See *median lethal dose.*

**LDC**   See *developing country.*

**leaching**   Process in which various chemicals in upper layers of soil are dissolved and carried to lower layers and, in some cases, to groundwater.

**less developed country (LDC)**   See *developing country.*

**life cycle cost**   Initial cost plus lifetime operating costs of an economic good. Compare *full cost.*

**life expectancy**   Average number of years a newborn infant can be expected to live.

**limiting factor**   Single factor that limits the growth, abundance, or distribution of the population of a species in an ecosystem. See *limiting factor principle.*

**limiting factor principle**   Too much or too little of any abiotic factor can limit or prevent growth of a population of a species in an ecosystem, even if all other factors are at or near the optimum range of tolerance for the species. See *range of tolerance.*

**linear growth** Growth in which a quantity increases by some fixed amount during each unit of time. Compare *exponential growth*.

**liquefied natural gas (LNG)** Natural gas converted to liquid form by cooling to a very low temperature.

**liquefied petroleum gas (LPG)** Mixture of liquefied propane ($C_3H_8$) and butane ($C_4H_{10}$) gas removed from natural gas and used as a fuel.

**lithosphere** Outer shell of the earth, composed of the crust and the rigid, outermost part of the mantle outside the asthenosphere; material found in earth's plates. See *crust, mantle*.

**loams** Soils containing a mixture of clay, sand, silt, and humus. Good for growing most crops.

**logistic growth** Pattern in which exponential population growth occurs when the population is small, and population growth decreases steadily with time as the population approaches the carrying capacity. See *S-shaped curve*. Compare *J-shaped curve*.

**low-input agriculture** See *sustainable agriculture*.

**low** Air mass with a low pressure. Compare *high*.

**low-quality energy** Energy that is dispersed and has little ability to do useful work. An example is low-temperature heat. Compare *high-quality energy*.

**low-quality matter** Matter that is dilute or dispersed or contains a low concentration of a useful resource. Compare *high-quality matter*.

**low-throughput economy** Economy based on working with nature by (1) recycling and reusing discarded matter, (2) preventing pollution, (3) conserving matter and energy resources by reducing unnecessary waste and use, (4) not degrading renewable resources, (5) building things that are easy to recycle, reuse, and repair, (6) not allowing population size to exceed the carrying capacity of the environment, and (7) preserving biodiversity. See *environmental worldview*. Compare *high-throughput economy, matter-recycling economy*.

**low-waste society** See *low-throughput economy*.

**LPG** See *liquefied petroleum gas*.

**macroevolution** Long-term, large-scale evolutionary changes among groups of species. Compare *microevolution*.

**macronutrients** Chemical elements that organisms need in large amounts to live, grow, or reproduce. Examples are carbon, oxygen, hydrogen, nitrogen, phosphorus, sulfur, potassium, calcium, magnesium, and iron. Compare *micronutrients*.

**magma** Molten rock below the earth's surface.

**malnutrition** Faulty nutrition, caused by a diet that does not supply an individual with enough protein, essential fats, vitamins, minerals, and other nutrients needed for good health. See *Kawashiorkor, maramus*. Compare *overnutrition, undernutrition*.

**mangrove swamps** Swamps found on the coastlines in warm tropical climates. They are dominated by mangrove trees, any of about 55 species of trees and shrubs that can live partly submerged in the salty environment of coastal swamps.

**mantle** Zone of the earth's interior between its core and its crust. See *lithosphere*. Compare *core, crust*.

**manufactured capital** See *manufactured resources*.

**manufactured resources** Manufactured items made from natural resources and used to produce and distribute economic goods and services bought by consumers. These include tools, machinery, equipment, factory buildings, and trans-

portation and distribution facilities. Compare *financial resources, human resources, natural resources*.

**manure** See *animal manure, green manure*.

**marasmus** Nutritional deficiency disease caused by a diet that does not have enough calories and protein to maintain good health. See *kwashiorkor, malnutrition*.

**market equilibrium** See *market price equilibrium point*.

**mass** Amount of material in an object.

**mass depletion** Period of species loss in which extinction rates are much higher than normal but not high enough to classify as a mass extinction. Compare *background, extinction, mass extinction*.

**mass extinction** Catastrophic, widespread, often global event in which major groups of species are wiped out over a short time compared with normal (background) extinctions. Compare *background extinction, mass depletion*.

**mass number** Sum of the number of neutrons (n) and the number of protons (p) in the nucleus of an atom. It gives the approximate mass of that atom. Compare *atomic number*.

**mass transit** Buses, trains, trolleys, and other forms of transportation that carry large numbers of people.

**material efficiency** Total amount of material needed to produce each unit of goods or services. Also called *resource productivity*. Compare *energy efficiency*.

**matter** Anything that has mass (the amount of material in an object) and takes up space. On the earth, where gravity is present, we weigh an object to determine its mass.

**matter quality** Measure of how useful a matter resource is, based on its availability and concentration. See *high-quality matter, low-quality matter*.

**matter-recycling economy** Economy that emphasizes recycling the maximum amount of all resources that can be recycled. The goal is to allow economic growth to continue without depleting matter resources and without producing excessive pollution and environmental degradation. Compare *high-throughput economy, low-throughput economy*.

**mature community** Fairly stable, self-sustaining community in an advanced stage of ecological succession; usually has a diverse array of species and ecological niches; captures and uses energy and cycles critical chemicals more efficiently than simpler, immature communities. Compare *immature community*.

**maximum sustainable yield** See *sustainable yield*.

**MDC** See *developed country*.

**median lethal dose (LD$_{50}$)** Amount of a toxic material per unit of body weight of test animals that kills half the test population in a certain time.

**megacity** City with 10 million or more people.

**meltdown** Melting of the core of a nuclear reactor.

**mesosphere** Third layer of the atmosphere; found above the stratosphere. Compare *stratosphere, troposphere*.

**mesotrophic lake** Lake with a moderate supply of plant nutrients. Compare *eutrophic lake, oligotrophic lake*.

**metabolism** Ability of a living cell or organism to capture and transform matter and energy from its environment to supply its needs for survival, growth, and reproduction.

**metamorphic rock** Rock produced when a preexisting rock is subjected to high temperatures (which may cause it to melt partially), high pressures, chemically active fluids, or a combination of these agents. See *rock cycle*. Compare *igneous rock, sedimentary rock*.

**metastasis** Spread of malignant (cancerous) cells from a tumor to other parts of the body. See *cancer*.

**metropolitan area** See *urban area*.

**microclimates** Local climatic conditions that differ from the general climate of a region. Various topographic features of the earth's surface such as mountains and cities typically create them.

**microevolution** Small genetic changes a population undergoes. Compare *macroevolution*.

**micronutrients** Chemical elements organisms need in small or even trace amounts to live, grow, or reproduce. Examples are sodium, zinc, copper, chlorine, and iodine. Compare *macronutrients*.

**microorganisms** Organisms such as bacteria that are so small they can be seen only by using a microscope.

**micropower systems** Systems of small-scale decentralized units that generate 1–10,000 kilowatts of electricity. Examples include (1) microturbines, (2) fuel cells, and (3) household solar panels and solar roofs.

**midsuccessional plant species** Grasses and low shrubs that are less hardy than early successional plant species. Compare *early successional plant species, late successional plant species*.

**mineral** Any naturally occurring inorganic substance found in the earth's crust as a crystalline solid. See *mineral resource*.

**mineral resource** Concentration of naturally occurring solid, liquid, or gaseous material in or on the earth's crust in a form and amount such that extracting and converting it into useful materials or items is currently or potentially profitable. Mineral resources are classified as *metallic* (such as iron and tin ores) or *nonmetallic* (such as fossil fuels, sand, and salt).

**minimum dynamic area (MDA)** Minimum area of suitable habitat needed to maintain the minimum viable population. See *minimum viable population*.

**minimum-tillage farming** See *conservation-tillage farming*.

**minimum viable population (MVP)** Estimate of the smallest number of individuals necessary to ensure the survival of a population in a region for a specified time period, typically ranging from decades to 100 years.

**mixture** Combination of one or more elements and compounds.

**model** Approximate representation or simulation of a system being studied.

**molecule** Combination of two or more atoms of the same chemical element (such as $O_2$) or different chemical elements (such as $H_2O$) held together by chemical bonds. Compare *atom, ion*.

**monera** See *bacteria, cyanobacteria*.

**monoculture** Cultivation of a single crop, usually on a large area of land. Compare *polyculture, polyvarietal cultivation*.

**more developed country (MDC)** See *developed country*.

**mountaintop removal** Type of surface mining that uses explosives, massive shovels, and even larger machinery called draglines to remove the top of a mountain to expose seams of coal underneath a mountain. Compare *area strip mining, contour strip mining*.

**multiple use** Use of an ecosystem such as a forest for a variety of purposes such as timber harvesting, wildlife habitat, watershed protection, and recreation. Compare *sustainable yield.*

**municipal solid waste** Solid materials discarded by homes and businesses in or near urban areas. See *solid waste.*

**mutagen** Chemical or form of radiation that causes inheritable changes (mutations) in the DNA molecules in the genes found in chromosomes. See *carcinogen, mutation, teratogen.*

**mutation** Random change in DNA molecules making up genes that can yield changes in anatomy, physiology, or behavior in offspring. See *mutagen.*

**mutualism** Type of species interaction in which both participating species generally benefit. Compare *commensalism.*

**native species** Species that normally live and thrive in a particular ecosystem. Compare *indicator species, keystone species, nonnative species.*

**natural capital** See *natural resources.*

**natural gas** Underground deposits of gases consisting of 50–90% by weight methane gas ($CH_4$) and small amounts of heavier gaseous hydrocarbon compounds such as propane ($C_3H_8$) and butane ($C_4H_{10}$).

**natural greenhouse effect** Heat buildup in the troposphere because of the presence of certain gases, called greenhouse gases. Without this effect, the earth would be nearly as cold as Mars, and life as we know it could not exist. Compare *global warming.*

**natural ionizing radiation** Ionizing radiation in the environment from natural sources. See *ionizing radiation.*

**natural law** See *scientific law.*

**natural radioactive decay** Nuclear change in which unstable nuclei of atoms spontaneously shoot out particles (usually alpha or beta particles) or energy (gamma rays) at a fixed rate.

**natural rate of extinction** See *background extinction.*

**natural recharge** Natural replenishment of an aquifer by precipitation, which percolates downward through soil and rock. See *recharge area.*

**natural resources** The earth's natural materials and processes that sustain other species and us. Compare *financial resources, human resources, manufactured resources.*

**natural selection** Process by which a particular beneficial gene (or set of genes) is reproduced in succeeding generations more than other genes. The result of natural selection is a population that contains a greater proportion of organisms better adapted to certain environmental conditions. See *adaptation, biological evolution, differential reproduction, mutation.*

**negative feedback loop** Situation in which a change in a certain direction provides information that causes a system to change less in that direction. Compare *positive feedback loop.*

**nekton** Strongly swimming organisms found in aquatic systems. Compare *benthos, plankton.*

**net energy** Total amount of useful energy available from an energy resource or energy system over its lifetime, minus the amount of energy (1) used (the first law of thermodynamics), (2) automatically wasted (the second law of thermodynamics), and (3) unnecessarily wasted in finding, processing, concentrating, and transporting it to users.

**net primary productivity (NPP)** Rate at which all the plants in an ecosystem produce net useful chemical energy; equal to the difference between the rate at which the plants in an ecosystem produce useful chemical energy (gross primary productivity) and the rate at which they use some of that energy through cellular respiration. Compare *gross primary productivity.*

**neutral solution** Water solution containing an equal number of hydrogen ions ($H^+$) and hydroxide ions ($OH^-$); water solution with a pH of 7. Compare *acid solution, basic solution.*

**neutron (n)** Elementary particle in the nuclei of all atoms (except hydrogen-1). It has a relative mass of 1 and no electric charge. Compare *electron, proton.*

**niche** See *ecological niche.*

**nitrogen cycle** Cyclic movement of nitrogen in different chemical forms from the environment to organisms and then back to the environment.

**nitrogen fixation** Conversion of atmospheric nitrogen gas into forms useful to plants by lightning, bacteria, and cyanobacteria; part of the nitrogen cycle.

**noise pollution** Any unwanted, disturbing, or harmful sound that (1) impairs or interferes with hearing, (2) causes stress, (3) hampers concentration and work efficiency, or (4) causes accidents.

**nondegradable pollutant** Material that is not broken down by natural processes. Examples are the toxic elements lead and mercury. Compare *biodegradable pollutant, degradable pollutant, slowly degradable pollutant.*

**nonionizing radiation** Forms of radiant energy such as radio waves, microwaves, infrared light, and ordinary light that do not have enough energy to cause ionization of atoms in living tissue. Compare *ionizing radiation.*

**nonnative species** Species that migrate into an ecosystem or are deliberately or accidentally introduced into an ecosystem by humans. Compare *native species.*

**nonpersistent pollutant** See *degradable pollutant.*

**nonpoint source** Large or dispersed land areas such as cropfields, streets, and lawns that discharge pollutants into the environment over a large area. Compare *point source.*

**nonrenewable resource** Resource that exists in a fixed amount (stock) in various places in the earth's crust and has the potential for renewal by geological, physical, and chemical processes taking place over hundreds of millions to billions of years. Examples are copper, aluminum, coal, and oil. We classify these resources as exhaustible because we are extracting and using them at a much faster rate than they were formed. Compare *renewable resource.*

**nontransmissible disease** Disease that is not caused by living organisms and does not spread from one person to another. Examples are most cancers, diabetes, cardiovascular disease, and malnutrition. Compare *transmissible disease.*

**no-till farming** See *conservation-tillage farming.*

**nuclear change** Process in which nuclei of certain isotopes spontaneously change, or are forced to change, into one or more different isotopes. The three principal types of nuclear change are natural radioactivity, nuclear fission, and nuclear fusion. Compare *chemical change, physical change.*

**nuclear energy** Energy released when atomic nuclei undergo a nuclear reaction such as the spontaneous emission of radioactivity, nuclear fission, or nuclear fusion.

**nuclear fission** Nuclear change in which the nuclei of certain isotopes with large mass numbers (such as uranium-235 and plutonium-239) are split apart into lighter nuclei when struck by a neutron. This process releases more neutrons and a large amount of energy. Compare *nuclear fusion.*

**nuclear fusion** Nuclear change in which two nuclei of isotopes of elements with a low mass number (such as hydrogen-2 and hydrogen-3) are forced together at extremely high temperatures until they fuse to form a heavier nucleus (such as helium-4). This process releases a large amount of energy. Compare *nuclear fission.*

**nucleus** Extremely tiny center of an atom, making up most of the atom's mass. It contains one or more positively charged protons and one or more neutrons with no electrical charge (except for a hydrogen-1 atom, which has one proton and no neutrons in its nucleus).

**nutrient** Any food, element, or compound an organism must take in to live, grow, or reproduce.

**nutrient cycle** See *biogeochemical cycle.*

**oil** See *crude oil.*

**oil shale** Fine-grained rock containing various amounts of kerogen, a solid, waxy mixture of hydrocarbon compounds. Heating the rock to high temperatures converts the kerogen into a vapor that can be condensed to form a slow-flowing heavy oil called shale oil. See *kerogen, shale oil.*

**old-growth forest** Virgin and old, second-growth forests containing trees that are often hundreds, sometimes thousands, of years old. Examples include forests of Douglas fir, western hemlock, giant sequoia, and coastal redwoods in the western United States. Compare *second-growth forest, tree plantation.*

**oligotrophic lake** Lake with a low supply of plant nutrients. Compare *eutrophic lake, mesotrophic lake.*

**omnivore** Animal that can use both plants and other animals as food sources. Examples are pigs, rats, cockroaches, and people. Compare *carnivore, herbivore.*

**open-pit mining** Removing minerals such as gravel, sand, and metal ores by digging them out of the earth's surface and leaving an open pit. Compare *area strip mining, contour strip mining, dredging, mountaintop removal, subsurface mining.*

**open sea** Part of an ocean that is beyond the continental shelf. Compare *coastal zone.*

**open system** System, such as a living organism, in which both matter and energy are exchanged between the system and the environment. Compare *closed system.*

**ore** Part of a metal-yielding material that can be economically and legally extracted at a given time. An ore typically contains two parts: the ore mineral, which contains the desired metal, and waste mineral material (gangue).

**organic compounds** Compounds containing carbon atoms combined with each other and with atoms of one or more other elements such as hydrogen, oxygen, nitrogen, sulfur, phosphorus, chlorine, and fluorine. All other compounds are called *inorganic compounds.*

**organic farming** Producing crops and livestock naturally by using organic fertilizer (manure, legumes, compost) and natural pest control (bugs that eat harmful bugs, plants that repel bugs, and environmental controls such as crop rotation) instead of using commercial inorganic fertilizers and synthetic pesticides and herbicides. See *sustainable agriculture.*

**organic fertilizer** Organic material such as animal manure, green manure, and compost, applied to cropland as a source of plant nutrients. Compare *commercial inorganic fertilizer.*

**organism** Any form of life.

**other resources** Identified and undiscovered resources not classified as reserves. Compare *identified resources, reserves, undiscovered resources*.

**output** Matter, energy, or information leaving a system. Compare *input, throughput*.

**output pollution control** See *pollution cleanup*.

**overburden** Layer of soil and rock overlying a mineral deposit. Surface mining removes this layer.

**overfishing** Harvesting so many fish of a species, especially immature fish, that not enough breeding stock is left to replenish the species, such that it is not profitable to harvest them.

**overgrazing** Destruction of vegetation when too many grazing animals feed too long and exceed the carrying capacity of a rangeland or pasture area.

**overnutrition** Diet so high in calories, saturated (animal) fats, salt, sugar, and processed foods and so low in vegetables and fruits that the consumer runs high risks of diabetes, hypertension, heart disease, and other health hazards. Compare *malnutrition, undernutrition*.

**oxygen-demanding wastes** Organic materials that are usually biodegraded by aerobic (oxygen-consuming) bacteria if there is enough dissolved oxygen in the water. See also *biological oxygen demand*.

**ozone depletion** Decrease in concentration of ozone ($O_3$) in the stratosphere. See *ozone layer*.

**ozone layer** Layer of gaseous ozone ($O_3$) in the stratosphere that protects life on earth by filtering out most harmful ultraviolet radiation from the sun.

**PANs** Peroxyacyl nitrates. Group of chemicals found in photochemical smog.

**parasite** Consumer organism that lives on or in and feeds on a living plant or animal, known as the host, over an extended period of time. The parasite draws nourishment from and gradually weakens its host; it may or may not kill the host. See *parasitism*.

**parasitism** Interaction between species in which one organism, called the parasite, preys on another organism, called the host, by living on or in the host. See *host, parasite*.

**parts per billion (ppb)** Number of parts of a chemical found in 1 billion parts of a particular gas, liquid, or solid.

**parts per million (ppm)** Number of parts of a chemical found in 1 million parts of a particular gas, liquid, or solid.

**parts per trillion (ppt)** Number of parts of a chemical found in 1 trillion parts of a particular gas, liquid, or solid.

**passive solar heating system** System that captures sunlight directly within a structure and converts it into low-temperature heat for space heating or for heating water for domestic use without the use of mechanical devices. Compare *active solar heating system*.

**pasture** Managed grassland or enclosed meadow that usually is planted with domesticated grasses or other forage to be grazed by livestock. Compare *feedlot, rangeland*.

**pathogen** Organism that produces disease.

**PCBs** See *polychlorinated biphenyls*.

**per capita GNI** Annual gross national income (GNI) of a country divided by its total population. See *gross national income*.

**per capita GNI in purchasing power parity (per capita GNI PPP)** The GNI PPP divided by the total population at midyear. This is a better

way to compare people's economic welfare among countries.

**per capita GNP** See *per capita GNI*.

**percolation** Passage of a liquid through the spaces of a porous material such as soil.

**perennial** Plant that can live for more than 2 years. Compare *annual*.

**permafrost** Perennially frozen layer of the soil that forms when the water there freezes. It is found in arctic tundra.

**permeability** Degree to which underground rock and soil pores are interconnected and thus a measure of the degree to which water can flow freely from one pore to another. Compare *porosity*.

**perpetual resource** Essentially inexhaustible resource on a human time scale. Solar energy is an example. See *renewable resource*. Compare *nonrenewable resource, renewable resource*.

**persistence** How long a pollutant stays in the air, water, soil, or body. See also *inertia*.

**persistent pollutant** See *slowly degradable pollutant*.

**pest** Unwanted organism that directly or indirectly interferes with human activities.

**pesticide** Any chemical designed to kill or inhibit the growth of an organism that people consider undesirable. See *fungicide, herbicide, insecticide*.

**petrochemicals** Chemicals obtained by refining (distilling) crude oil. They are used as raw materials in manufacturing most industrial chemicals, fertilizers, pesticides, plastics, synthetic fibers, paints, medicines, and many other products.

**petroleum** See *crude oil*.

**pH** Numeric value that indicates the relative acidity or alkalinity of a substance on a scale of 0–14, with the neutral point at 7. Acid solutions have pH values lower than 7, and basic or alkaline solutions have pH values greater than 7.

**phosphorus cycle** Cyclic movement of phosphorus in different chemical forms from the environment to organisms and then back to the environment.

**photochemical smog** Complex mixture of air pollutants produced in the lower atmosphere by the reaction of hydrocarbons and nitrogen oxides under the influence of sunlight. Especially harmful components include ozone, peroxyacyl nitrates (PANs), and various aldehydes. Compare *industrial smog*.

**photosynthesis** Complex process that takes place in cells of green plants. Radiant energy from the sun is used to combine carbon dioxide ($CO_2$) and water ($H_2O$) to produce oxygen ($O_2$) and carbohydrates (such as glucose, $C_6H_{12}O_6$) and other nutrient molecules. Compare *aerobic respiration, chemosynthesis*.

**photovoltaic cell (solar cell)** Device which converts radiant (solar) energy directly into electrical energy.

**physical change** Process that alters one or more physical properties of an element or a compound without altering its chemical composition. Examples are changing the size and shape of a sample of matter (crushing ice and cutting aluminum foil) and changing a sample of matter from one physical state to another (boiling and freezing water). Compare *chemical change, nuclear change*.

**phytoplankton** Small, drifting plants, mostly algae and bacteria, found in aquatic ecosystems. Compare *plankton, zooplankton*.

**pioneer community** First integrated set of plants, animals, and decomposers found in an area undergoing primary ecological succession. See *immature community, mature community*.

**pioneer species** First hardy species, often microbes, mosses, and lichens that begin colonizing a site as the first stage of ecological succession. See *ecological succession, pioneer community*.

**plaintiff** The individual, group of individuals, corporation, or government agency bringing the charges in a lawsuit. Compare *defendant*.

**planetary management worldview** Beliefs that (1) we are the planet's most important species; (2) there are always more resources, and they are all for us; (3) all economic growth is good, more economic growth is better, and the potential for economic growth is limitless; and (4) our success depends on how well we can understand, control, and manage the earth's life-support systems for our own benefit. See *spaceship-earth worldview*. Compare *environmental wisdom worldview*.

**plankton** Small plant organisms (phytoplankton) and animal organisms (zooplankton) that float in aquatic ecosystems.

**plantation agriculture** Growing specialized crops such as bananas, coffee, and cacao in tropical developing countries, primarily for sale to developed countries.

**plants (plantae)** Eukaryotic, mostly multicellular organisms such as algae (red, blue, and green), mosses, ferns, flowers, cacti, grasses, beans, wheat, rice, and trees. These organisms use photosynthesis to produce organic nutrients for themselves and for other organisms feeding on them. Water and other inorganic nutrients are obtained from the soil for terrestrial plants and from the water for aquatic plants.

**plasma** An ionized gas consisting of electrically conductive ions and electrons. It is known as a fourth state of matter.

**plates** See *tectonic plates*.

**plate tectonics** Theory of geophysical processes that explains the movements of lithospheric plates and the processes that occur at their boundaries. See *lithosphere, tectonic plates*.

**point source** Single identifiable source that discharges pollutants into the environment. Examples are the (1) smokestack of a power plant or an industrial plant, (2) drainpipe of a meat-packing plant, (3) chimney of a house, or (4) exhaust pipe of an automobile. Compare *nonpoint source*.

**poison** Chemical that in one dose kills exactly 50% of the animals (usually rats and mice) in a test population (usually 60 to 200 animals) within a 14-day period. See *median lethal dose*.

**politics** Process through which individuals and groups try to influence or control government policies and actions that affect the local, state, national, and international communities.

**pollutant** Particular chemical or form of energy that can adversely affect the health, survival, or activities of humans or other living organisms. See *pollution*.

**pollution** Undesirable change in the physical, chemical, or biological characteristics of air, water, soil, or food that can adversely affect the health, survival, or activities of humans or other living organisms.

**pollution cleanup** Device or process that removes or reduces the level of a pollutant after it has been produced or has entered the environment. Examples are automobile emission control devices and sewage treatment plants. Compare *pollution prevention*.

**pollution prevention** Device or process that **(1)** prevents a potential pollutant from forming or entering the environment or **(2)** sharply reduces the amount entering the environment. Compare *pollution cleanup*.

**polychlorinated biphenyls (PCBs)** Group of 209 different toxic, oily, synthetic chlorinated hydrocarbon compounds that can be biologically amplified in food chains and webs.

**polyculture** Complex form of intercropping in which a large number of different plants maturing at different times are planted together. See also *intercropping*. Compare *monoculture, polyvarietal cultivation*.

**polyvarietal cultivation** Planting a plot of land with several varieties of the same crop. Compare *intercropping, monoculture, polyculture*.

**population** Group of individual organisms of the same species living in a particular area.

**population change** Increase or decrease in the size of a population. It is equal to (Births + Immigration) − (Deaths + Emigration).

**population density** Number of organisms in a particular population found in a specified area or volume.

**population dispersion** General pattern in which the members of a population are arranged throughout its habitat.

**population distribution** Variation of population density over a particular geographic area. For example, a country has a high population density in its urban areas and a much lower population density in rural areas.

**population dynamics** Major abiotic and biotic factors that tend to increase or decrease the population size and age and sex composition of a species.

**population size** Number of individuals making up a population's gene pool.

**population viability analysis (PVA)** Use of mathematical models to estimate a population's risk of extinction. See *minimum viable population*.

**porosity** Percentage of space in rock or soil occupied by voids, whether the voids are isolated or connected. Compare *permeability*.

**positive feedback loop** Situation in which a change in a certain direction provides information that causes a system to change further in the same direction. Compare *negative feedback loop*.

**potential energy** Energy stored in an object because of its position or the position of its parts. Compare *kinetic energy*.

**poverty** Inability to meet basic needs for food, clothing, and shelter.

**ppb** See *parts per billion*.

**ppm** See *parts per million*.

**ppt** See *parts per trillion*.

**precautionary principle** When there is scientific uncertainty about potentially serious harm from chemicals or technologies, decision makers should act to prevent harm to humans and the environment. See *pollution prevention*.

**precipitation** Water in the form of rain, sleet, hail, and snow that falls from the atmosphere onto the land and bodies of water.

**precision** Measure of reproducibility, or how closely a series of measurements of the same quantity agree with one another. Compare *accuracy*.

**predation** Situation in which an organism of one species (the predator) captures and feeds on parts or all of an organism of another species (the prey).

**predator** Organism that captures and feeds on parts or all of an organism of another species (the prey).

**predator–prey relationship** Interaction between two organisms of different species in which one organism, called the *predator*, captures and feeds on parts or all of another organism, called the *prey*.

**preservationist** Person concerned primarily with setting aside or protecting undisturbed natural areas from harmful human activities. Compare *conservation biologist, conservationist, ecologist, environmentalist, environmental scientist, restorationist*.

**prey** Organism that is captured and serves as a source of food for an organism of another species (the predator).

**primary consumer** Organism that feeds on all or part of plants (herbivore) or on other producers. Compare *detritivore, omnivore, secondary consumer*.

**primary pollutant** Chemical that has been added directly to the air by natural events or human activities and occurs in a harmful concentration. Compare *secondary pollutant*.

**primary productivity** See *gross primary productivity, net primary productivity*.

**primary sewage treatment** Mechanical sewage treatment in which large solids are filtered out by screens and suspended solids settle out as sludge in a sedimentation tank. Compare *advanced sewage treatment, secondary sewage treatment*.

**primary succession** Ecological succession in a bare area that has never been occupied by a community of organisms. See *ecological succession*. Compare *secondary succession*.

**prior appropriation** Legal principle by which the first user of water from a stream establishes a legal right to continued use of the amount originally withdrawn. Compare *riparian rights*.

**probability** Mathematical statement about how likely it is that something will happen.

**producer** Organism that uses solar energy (green plant) or chemical energy (some bacteria) to manufacture the organic compounds it needs as nutrients from simple inorganic compounds obtained from its environment. Compare *consumer, decomposer*.

**prokaryotic cell** Cell that does not have a distinct nucleus. Other internal parts are also not enclosed by membranes. Compare *eukaryotic cell*.

**protists (protista)** Eukaryotic, mostly single-celled organisms such as diatoms, amoebas, some algae (golden brown and yellow-green), protozoans, and slime molds. Some protists produce their own organic nutrients through photosynthesis. Others are decomposers and some feed on bacteria, other protists, or cells of multicellular organisms.

**proton (p)** Positively charged particle in the nuclei of all atoms. Each proton has a relative mass of 1 and a single positive charge. Compare *electron, neutron*.

**pure capitalism** See *pure free-market economic system*.

**pure command economic system** System in which all economic decisions are made by the government or some other central authority. Compare *capitalist market economic system, pure free-market economic system*.

**pure free-market economic system** System in which all economic decisions are made in the market, where buyers and sellers of economic goods interact freely, with no government or other interference. Compare *capitalist market economic system, pure command economic system*.

**pyramid of biomass** Diagram representing the biomass, or total dry weight of all living organisms, that can be supported at each trophic level in a food chain or food web. See *pyramid of energy flow, pyramid of numbers*.

**pyramid of energy flow** Diagram representing the flow of energy through each trophic level in a food chain or food web. With each energy transfer, only a small part (typically 10%) of the usable energy entering one trophic level is transferred to the organisms at the next trophic level. Compare *pyramid of biomass, pyramid of numbers*.

**pyramid of numbers** Diagram representing the number of organisms of a particular type that can be supported at each trophic level from a given input of solar energy at the producer trophic level in a food chain or food web. Compare *pyramid of biomass, pyramid of energy flow*.

**radiation** Fast-moving particles (particulate radiation) or waves of energy (electromagnetic radiation). See *alpha particle, beta particle, gamma rays*.

**radiation temperature inversion** Temperature inversion that typically occurs at night in which a layer of warm air lies atop a layer of cooler air nearer the ground as the air near the ground cools faster than the air above it. As the sun rises and warms the earth's surface, the inversion normally disappears by noon and disperses the pollutants built up during the night. See *temperature inversion*. Compare *subsidence temperature inversion*.

**radioactive decay** Change of a radioisotope to a different isotope by the emission of radioactivity.

**radioactive isotope** See *radioisotope*.

**radioactive waste** Waste products of nuclear power plants, research, medicine, weapon production, or other processes involving nuclear reactions. See *radioactivity*.

**radioactivity** Nuclear change in which unstable nuclei of atoms spontaneously shoot out "chunks" of mass, energy, or both at a fixed rate. The three principal types of radioactivity are gamma rays and fast-moving alpha particles and beta particles.

**radioisotope** Isotope of an atom that spontaneously emits one or more types of radioactivity (alpha particles, beta particles, gamma rays).

**rain shadow effect** Low precipitation on the far side (leeward side) of a mountain when prevailing winds flow up and over a high mountain or range of high mountains. This creates semiarid and arid conditions on the leeward side of a high mountain range.

**rangeland** Land that supplies forage or vegetation (grasses, grasslike plants, and shrubs) for grazing and browsing animals and is not intensively managed. Compare *feedlot, pasture*.

**range of tolerance** Range of chemical and physical conditions that must be maintained for populations of a particular species to stay alive and grow, develop, and function normally. See *law of tolerance*.

**rare species** Species that **(1)** has naturally small numbers of individuals, often because of limited geographic ranges or low population densities, or **(2)** has been locally depleted by human activities.

**realized niche** Parts of the fundamental niche of a species that are actually used by that species. See *ecological niche, fundamental niche*.

**recharge area** Any area of land allowing water to pass through it and into an aquifer. See *aquifer, natural recharge*.

**recycling** Collecting and reprocessing a resource so it can be made into new products. An example is collecting aluminum cans, melting them down, and using the aluminum to make new cans or other aluminum products. Compare *reuse*.

**reforestation**   Renewal of trees and other types of vegetation on land where trees have been removed; can be done naturally by seeds from nearby trees or artificially by planting seeds or seedlings.

**relative humidity**   Amount of water vapor in a certain mass of air, expressed as a percentage of the maximum amount it could hold at that temperature. Compare *absolute humidity*.

**reliable runoff**   Surface runoff of water that generally can be counted on as a stable source of water from year to year. See *runoff*.

**renewable resource**   Resource that can be replenished rapidly (hours to several decades) through natural processes. Examples are trees in forests, grasses in grasslands, wild animals, fresh surface water in lakes and streams, most groundwater, fresh air, and fertile soil. If such a resource is used faster than it is replenished, it can be depleted and converted into a nonrenewable resource. Compare *nonrenewable resource* and *perpetual resource*. See also *environmental degradation*.

**replacement-level fertility**   Number of children a couple must have to replace them. The average for a country or the world usually is slightly higher than 2 children per couple (2.1 in the United States and 2.5 in some developing countries) because some children die before reaching their reproductive years. See also *total fertility rate*.

**reproduction**   Production of offspring by one or more parents.

**reproductive isolation**   Long-term geographic separation of members of a particular sexually reproducing species.

**reproductive potential**   See *biotic potential*.

**reserves**   Resources that have been identified and from which a usable mineral can be extracted profitably at present prices with current mining technology. See *identified resources, undiscovered resources*.

**reserve-to-production ratio**   Number of years reserves of a particular nonrenewable mineral will last at current annual production rates. See *reserves*.

**resilience**   Ability of a living system to restore itself to original condition after being exposed to an outside disturbance that is not too drastic. See *constancy, inertia*.

**resource**   Anything obtained from the living and nonliving environment to meet human needs and wants. The term can also be applied to other species.

**resource partitioning**   Process of dividing up resources in an ecosystem so species with similar needs (overlapping ecological niches) use the same scarce resources at different times, in different ways, or in different places. See *ecological niche, fundamental niche, realized niche*.

**resource productivity**   See *material efficiency*.

**respiration**   See *aerobic respiration*.

**response**   Amount of health damage caused by exposure to a certain dose of a harmful substance or form of radiation. See *dose, dose-response curve, median lethal dose*.

**restoration ecology**   Research and scientific study devoted to restoring, repairing, and reconstructing damaged ecosystems.

**restorationist**   Scientist or other person devoted to the partial or complete restoration of natural areas that have been degraded by human activities. Compare *conservation biologist, conservationist, ecologist, environmental scientist, preservationist*.

**reuse**   Using a product over and over again in the same form. An example is collecting, washing,

and refilling glass beverage bottles. Compare *recycling*.

**riparian rights**   System of water law that gives anyone whose land adjoins a flowing stream the right to use water from the stream, as long as some is left for downstream users. Compare *prior appropriation*.

**riparian zones**   Thin strips and patches of vegetation that surround streams. They are very important habitats and resources for wildlife.

**risk**   Probability that something undesirable will result from deliberate or accidental exposure to a hazard. See *risk analysis, risk assessment, risk-benefit analysis, risk management*.

**risk analysis**   Identifying hazards, evaluating the nature and severity of risks (*risk assessment*), using this and other information to determine options and make decisions about reducing or eliminating risks (*risk management*), and communicating information about risks to decision makers and the public (*risk communication*).

**risk assessment**   Process of gathering data and making assumptions to estimate short- and long-term harmful effects on human health or the environment from exposure to hazards associated with the use of a particular product or technology. See *risk-benefit analysis*.

**risk-benefit analysis**   Estimate of the short- and long-term risks and benefits of using a particular product or technology. See *risk assessment*.

**risk communication**   Communicating information about risks to decision makers and the public. See *risk, risk analysis, risk-benefit analysis*.

**risk management**   Using risk assessment and other information to determine options and make decisions about reducing or eliminating risks. See *risk, risk analysis, risk-benefit analysis, risk communication*.

**rock**   Any material that makes up a large, natural, continuous part of earth's crust. See *igneous rock, metamorphic rock, mineral, sedimentary rock*.

**rock cycle**   Largest and slowest of the earth's cycles, consisting of geologic, physical, and chemical processes that form and modify rocks and soil in the earth's crust over millions of years.

**r-selected species**   Species that reproduce early in their life span and produce large numbers of usually small and short-lived offspring in a short period of time. Compare *K-selected species*.

**r-strategists**   See *r-selected species*.

**rule of 70**   Doubling time (in years) = 70/percentage growth rate. See *doubling time, exponential growth*.

**ruminants**   Grazing animals with complex digestive systems that enable them to convert grass and other roughage into meat and milk.

**runoff**   Fresh water from precipitation and melting ice that flows on the earth's surface into nearby streams, lakes, wetlands, and reservoirs. See *reliable runoff, surface runoff, surface water*. Compare *groundwater*.

**rural area**   Geographic area in the United States with a population of less than 2,500. The number of people used in this definition may vary in different countries. Compare *urban area*.

**salinity**   Amount of various salts dissolved in a given volume of water.

**salinization**   Accumulation of salts in soil that can eventually make the soil unable to support plant growth.

**saltwater intrusion**   Movement of salt water into freshwater aquifers in coastal and inland areas as groundwater is withdrawn faster than it is recharged by precipitation.

**sanitary landfill**   Waste disposal site on land in which waste is spread in thin layers, compacted, and covered with a fresh layer of clay or plastic foam each day.

**scavenger**   Organism that feeds on dead organisms that were killed by other organisms or died naturally. Examples are vultures, flies, and crows. Compare *detritivore*.

**science**   Attempts to discover order in nature and use that knowledge to make predictions about what should happen in nature. See *consensus science, frontier science, scientific data, scientific hypothesis, scientific law, scientific methods, scientific model, scientific theory*.

**scientific data**   Facts obtained by making observations and measurements. Compare *scientific hypothesis, scientific law, scientific methods, scientific model, scientific theory*.

**scientific hypothesis**   Educated guess that attempts to explain a scientific law or certain scientific observations. Compare *scientific data, scientific law, scientific methods, scientific model, scientific theory*.

**scientific law**   Description of what scientists find happening in nature repeatedly in the same way, without known exception. See *first law of thermodynamics, law of conservation of matter, second law of thermodynamics*. Compare *scientific data, scientific hypothesis, scientific methods, scientific model, scientific theory*.

**scientific methods**   Ways that scientists gather data and formulate and test scientific hypotheses, models, theories, and laws. See *scientific data, scientific hypothesis, scientific law, scientific model, scientific theory*.

**scientific model**   Simulation of complex processes and systems. Many are mathematical models that are run and tested using computers.

**scientific theory**   Well-tested and widely accepted scientific hypothesis. Compare *scientific data, scientific hypothesis, scientific law, scientific methods, scientific model*.

**secondary consumer**   Organism that feeds only on primary consumers. Compare *detritivore, omnivore, primary consumer*.

**secondary pollutant**   Harmful chemical formed in the atmosphere when a primary air pollutant reacts with normal air components or other air pollutants. Compare *primary pollutant*.

**secondary sewage treatment**   Second step in most waste treatment systems in which aerobic bacteria break down up to 90% of degradable, oxygen-demanding organic wastes in wastewater. This usually involves bringing sewage and bacteria together in trickling filters or in the activated sludge process. Compare *advanced sewage treatment, primary sewage treatment*.

**secondary succession**   Ecological succession in an area in which natural vegetation has been removed or destroyed but the soil is not destroyed. See *ecological succession*. Compare *primary succession*.

**second-growth forest**   Stands of trees resulting from secondary ecological succession. Compare *old-growth forest, tree plantation*.

**second law of thermodynamics**   In any conversion of heat energy to useful work, some of the initial energy input is always degraded to a lower-quality, more dispersed, less useful energy, usually low-temperature heat that flows into the environment; you cannot break even in terms of energy quality. See *first law of thermodynamics*.

**sedimentary rock**   Rock that forms from the accumulated products of erosion and in some cases from the compacted shells, skeletons, and other remains of dead organisms. Compare *igneous rock, metamorphic rock.* See *rock cycle.*

**seed-tree cutting**   Removal of nearly all trees on a site in one cutting, with a few seed-producing trees left uniformly distributed to regenerate the forest. Compare *clear-cutting, selective cutting, shelterwood cutting, strip cutting.*

**selective cutting**   Cutting of intermediate-aged, mature, or diseased trees in an uneven-aged forest stand, either singly or in small groups. This encourages the growth of younger trees and maintains an uneven-aged stand. Compare *clear-cutting, seed-tree cutting, shelterwood cutting, strip cutting.*

**septic tank**   Underground tank for treating wastewater from a home in rural and suburban areas. Bacteria in the tank decompose organic wastes, and the sludge settles to the bottom of the tank. The effluent flows out of the tank into the ground through a field of drainpipes.

**sexual reproduction**   Reproduction in organisms that produce offspring by combining sex cells, or *gametes* (such as ovum and sperm), from both parents. This produces offspring that have combinations of traits from their parents. Compare *asexual reproduction.*

**shale oil**   Slow-flowing, dark brown, heavy oil obtained when kerogen in oil shale is vaporized at high temperatures and then condensed. Shale oil can be refined to yield gasoline, heating oil, and other petroleum products. See *kerogen, oil shale.*

**shelterbelt**   See *windbreak.*

**shelterwood cutting**   Removal of mature, marketable trees in an area in a series of partial cuttings to allow regeneration of a new stand under the partial shade of older trees, which are later removed. Typically, this is done by making two or three cuts over a decade. Compare *clear-cutting, seed-tree cutting, selective cutting, strip cutting.*

**shifting cultivation**   Clearing a plot of ground in a forest, especially in tropical areas, and planting crops on it for a few years (typically 2–5 years) until the soil is depleted of nutrients or the plot has been invaded by a dense growth of vegetation from the surrounding forest. Then a new plot is cleared and the process is repeated. The abandoned plot cannot successfully grow crops for 10–30 years. See also *slash-and-burn cultivation.*

**slash-and-burn cultivation**   Cutting down trees and other vegetation in a patch of forest, leaving the cut vegetation on the ground to dry, and then burning it. The ashes that are left add nutrients to the nutrient-poor soils found in most tropical forest areas. Crops are planted between tree stumps. Plots must be abandoned after a few years (typically 2–5 years) because of loss of soil fertility or invasion of vegetation from the surrounding forest. See also *shifting cultivation.*

**slowly degradable pollutant**   Material that is slowly broken down into simpler chemicals or reduced to acceptable levels by natural physical, chemical, and biological processes. Compare *biodegradable pollutant, degradable pollutant, nondegradable pollutant.*

**sludge**   Gooey mixture of toxic chemicals, infectious agents, and settled solids removed from wastewater at a sewage treatment plant.

**smart growth**   Form of urban planning that recognizes urban growth will occur but uses zoning laws and an array of other tools to **(1)** prevent sprawl, **(2)** direct growth to certain areas, **(3)** protect ecologically sensitive and important lands and waterways, and **(4)** develop urban areas that are more environmentally sustainable and more enjoyable places to live.

**smelting**   Process in which a desired metal is separated from the other elements in an ore mineral.

**smog**   Originally a combination of smoke and fog but now used to describe other mixtures of pollutants in the atmosphere. See *industrial smog, photochemical smog.*

**soil**   Complex mixture of inorganic minerals (clay, silt, pebbles, and sand), decaying organic matter, water, air, and living organisms.

**soil conservation**   Methods used to reduce soil erosion, prevent depletion of soil nutrients, and restore nutrients already lost by erosion, leaching, and excessive crop harvesting.

**soil erosion**   Movement of soil components, especially topsoil, from one place to another, usually by wind, flowing water, or both. This natural process can be greatly accelerated by human activities that remove vegetation from soil.

**soil horizons**   Horizontal zones that make up a particular mature soil. Each horizon has a distinct texture and composition that vary with different types of soils. See *soil profile.*

**soil permeability**   Rate at which water and air move from upper to lower soil layers. Compare *porosity.*

**soil porosity**   See *porosity.*

**soil profile**   Cross-sectional view of the horizons in a soil. See *soil horizon.*

**soil structure**   How the particles that make up a soil are organized and clumped together. See also *soil permeability, soil texture.*

**soil texture**   Relative amounts of the different types and sizes of mineral particles in a sample of soil.

**solar capital**   Solar energy from the sun reaching the earth. Compare *natural resources.*

**solar cell**   See *photovoltaic cell.*

**solar collector**   Device for collecting radiant energy from the sun and converting it into heat. See *active solar heating system, passive solar heating system.*

**solar energy**   Direct radiant energy from the sun and a number of indirect forms of energy produced by the direct input. Principal indirect forms of solar energy include wind, falling and flowing water (hydropower), and biomass (solar energy converted into chemical energy stored in the chemical bonds of organic compounds in trees and other plants).

**solid waste**   Any unwanted or discarded material that is not a liquid or a gas. See *municipal solid waste.*

**spaceship-earth worldview**   View of the earth as a spaceship: a machine we can understand, control, and change at will by using advanced technology. See *planetary management worldview.* Compare *environmental wisdom worldview.*

**specialist species**   Species with a narrow ecological niche. They may be able to **(1)** live in only one type of habitat, **(2)** tolerate only a narrow range of climatic and other environmental conditions, or **(3)** use only one type or a few types of food. Compare *generalist species.*

**speciation**   Formation of two species from one species because of divergent natural selection in response to changes in environmental conditions; usually takes thousands of years. Compare *extinction.*

**species**   Group of organisms that resemble one another in appearance, behavior, chemical makeup and processes, and genetic structure. Organisms that reproduce sexually are classified as members of the same species only if they can actu-

ally or potentially interbreed with one another and produce fertile offspring.

**species diversity**   Number of different species and their relative abundances in a given area. See *biodiversity.* Compare *ecological diversity, genetic diversity.*

**species equilibrium model**   See *theory of island biogeography.*

**spoils**   Unwanted rock and other waste materials produced when a material is removed from the earth's surface or subsurface by mining, dredging, quarrying, and excavation.

**S-shaped curve**   Leveling off of an exponential, *J*-shaped curve when a rapidly growing population exceeds the carrying capacity of its environment and ceases to grow.

**stability**   Ability of a living system to withstand or recover from externally imposed changes or stresses. See *constancy, inertia, resilience.*

**statutory law**   Law developed and passed by legislative bodies such as federal and state governments. Compare *common law.*

**stewardship**   View that because of our superior intellect and power or because of our religious beliefs, we have an ethical responsibility to manage and care for domesticated plants and animals and the rest of nature. Compare *environmental wisdom worldview, planetary management worldview.*

**storage area**   Place within a system where energy, matter, or information can accumulate for various lengths of time before being released. Compare *input, output, throughput.*

**stratosphere**   Second layer of the atmosphere, extending about 17–48 kilometers (11–30 miles) above the earth's surface. It contains small amounts of gaseous ozone ($O_3$), which filters out about 95% of the incoming harmful ultraviolet (UV) radiation emitted by the sun. Compare *troposphere.*

**stream**   Flowing body of surface water. Examples are creeks and rivers.

**strip cropping**   Planting regular crops and close-growing plants, such as hay or nitrogen-fixing legumes, in alternating rows or bands to help reduce depletion of soil nutrients.

**strip cutting**   Variation of clear-cutting in which a strip of trees is clear-cut along the contour of the land, with the corridor narrow enough to allow natural regeneration within a few years. After regeneration, another strip is cut above the first, and so on. Compare *clear-cutting, seed-tree cutting, selective cutting, shelterwood cutting.*

**strip mining**   Form of surface mining in which bulldozers, power shovels, or stripping wheels remove large chunks of the earth's surface in strips. See *area strip mining, contour strip mining, surface mining.* Compare *subsurface mining.*

**subatomic particles**   Extremely small particles—electrons, protons, and neutrons—that make up the internal structure of atoms.

**subduction zone**   Area in which oceanic lithosphere is carried downward (subducted) under the island arc or continent at a convergent plate boundary. A trench ordinarily forms at the boundary between the two converging plates. See *convergent plate boundary.*

**subsidence**   Slow or rapid sinking of part of the earth's crust that is not slope related.

**subsidence temperature inversion**   Inversion of normal air temperature layers when a large mass of warm air moves into a region at a high altitude and floats over a mass of colder air near the ground. This keeps the air over a city stagnant and prevents vertical mixing and dispersion of air pollutants. See *temperature inversion.* Compare *radiation temperature inversion.*

**subsistence farming** Supplementing solar energy with energy from human labor and draft animals to produce enough food to feed oneself and family members; in good years there may be enough food left over to sell or put aside for hard times. Compare *industrialized agriculture*.

**subsurface mining** Extraction of a metal ore or fuel resource such as coal from a deep underground deposit. Compare *surface mining*.

**succession** See *ecological succession, primary succession, secondary succession*.

**succulent plants** Plants, such as desert cacti, that survive in dry climates by having no leaves, thus reducing the loss of scarce water. They store water and use sunlight to produce the food they need in the thick, fleshy tissue of their green stems and branches. Compare *deciduous plants, evergreen plants*.

**sulfur cycle** Cyclic movement of sulfur in different chemical forms from the environment to organisms and then back to the environment.

**superinsulated house** House that is heavily insulated and extremely airtight. Typically, active or passive solar collectors are used to heat water, and an air-to-air heat exchanger is used to prevent buildup of excessive moisture and indoor air pollutants.

**surface fire** Forest fire that burns only undergrowth and leaf litter on the forest floor. See *controlled burning*. Compare *crown fire, ground fire*.

**surface mining** Removing soil, subsoil, and other strata and then extracting a mineral deposit found fairly close to the earth's surface. See *area strip mining, contour strip mining, mountaintop removal, open-pit mining*. Compare *subsurface mining*.

**surface runoff** Water flowing off the land into bodies of surface water. See *reliable runoff*.

**surface water** Precipitation that does not infiltrate the ground or return to the atmosphere by evaporation or transpiration. See *runoff*. Compare *groundwater*.

**survivorship curve** Graph showing the number of survivors in different age groups for a particular species.

**sustainability** Ability of a system to survive for some specified (finite) time.

**sustainable agriculture** Method of growing crops and raising livestock based on organic fertilizers, soil conservation, water conservation, biological pest control, and minimal use of nonrenewable fossil fuel energy.

**sustainable development** See *environmentally sustainable economic development*.

**sustainable living** Taking no more potentially renewable resources from the natural world than can be replenished naturally and not overloading the capacity of the environment to cleanse and renew itself by natural processes.

**sustainable society** A society that manages its economy and population size without doing irreparable environmental harm by overloading the planet's ability to absorb environmental insults, replenish its resources, and sustain human and other forms of life over a specified period, usually hundreds to thousands of years. During this period, it satisfies the needs of its people without depleting natural resources and thereby jeopardizing the prospects of current and future generations of humans and other species.

**sustainable yield (sustained yield)** Highest rate at which a potentially renewable resource can be used without reducing its available supply throughout the world or in a particular area. See also *environmental degradation*.

**symbiosis** Any intimate relationship or association between members of two or more species. See *symbiotic relationship*.

**symbiotic relationship** Species interaction in which two kinds of organisms live together in an intimate association. Members of the participating species may be harmed by, benefit from, or be unaffected by the interaction. See *commensalism, interspecific competition, mutualism, parasitism, predation*.

**synergistic interaction** Interaction of two or more factors or processes so the combined effect is greater than the sum of their separate effects.

**synergy** See *synergistic interaction*.

**synfuels** Synthetic gaseous and liquid fuels produced from solid coal or sources other than natural gas or crude oil.

**synthetic natural gas (SNG)** Gaseous fuel containing mostly methane produced from solid coal.

**system** Set of components that function and interact in some regular and theoretically predictable manner.

**tailings** Rock and other waste materials removed as impurities when waste mineral material is separated from the metal in an ore.

**tar sand** Deposit of a mixture of clay, sand, water, and varying amounts of a tarlike heavy oil known as bitumen. Bitumen can be extracted from tar sand by heating. It is then purified and upgraded to synthetic crude oil. See *bitumen*.

**tectonic plates** Various-sized areas of the earth's lithosphere that move slowly around with the mantle's flowing asthenosphere. Most earthquakes and volcanoes occur around the boundaries of these plates. See *lithosphere, plate tectonics*.

**temperature** Measure of the average speed of motion of the atoms, ions, or molecules in a substance or combination of substances at a given moment. Compare *heat*.

**temperature inversion** Layer of dense, cool air trapped under a layer of less dense, warm air. This prevents upward-flowing air currents from developing. In a prolonged inversion, air pollution in the trapped layer may build up to harmful levels. See *radiation temperature inversion, subsidence temperature inversion*.

**teratogen** Chemical, ionizing agent, or virus that causes birth defects. Compare *carcinogen, mutagen*.

**terracing** Planting crops on a long, steep slope that has been converted into a series of broad, nearly level terraces with short vertical drops from one to another that run along the contour of the land to retain water and reduce soil erosion.

**terrestrial** Pertaining to land. Compare *aquatic*.

**territoriality** Process in which organisms patrol or mark an area around their home, nesting, or major feeding site and defend it against members of their own species.

**tertiary (higher-level) consumers** Animals that feed on animal-eating animals. They feed at high trophic levels in food chains and webs. Examples are hawks, lions, bass, and sharks. Compare *detritivore, primary consumer, secondary consumer*.

**tertiary sewage treatment** See *advanced sewage treatment*.

**theory of evolution** Widely accepted scientific idea that all life-forms developed from earlier life forms. Although this theory conflicts with the creation stories of many religions, it is the way biologists explain how life has changed over the past 3.6–3.8 billion years and why it is so diverse today.

**theory of island biogeography** The number of species found on an island is determined by a balance between two factors: the (1) *immigration rate* (of species new to the island) from other inhabited areas and (2) *extinction rate* (of species established on the island). The model predicts that at some point the rates of immigration and extinction will reach an equilibrium point that determines the island's average number of different species (species diversity).

**thermal inversion** See *temperature inversion*.

**thermocline** Zone of gradual temperature decrease between warm surface water and colder deep water in a lake, reservoir, or ocean.

**threatened species** Wild species that is still abundant in its natural range but likely to become endangered because of a decline in numbers. Compare *endangered species*.

**threshold effect** Harmful or fatal effect of a small change in environmental conditions that exceeds the limit of tolerance of an organism or population of a species. See *law of tolerance*.

**throughput** Rate of flow of matter, energy, or information through a system. Compare *input, output*.

**throwaway society** See *high-throughput economy*.

**time delay** Time lag between the input of a stimulus into a system and the response to the stimulus.

**tolerance limits** Minimum and maximum limits for physical conditions (such as temperature) and concentrations of chemical substances beyond which no members of a particular species can survive. See *law of tolerance*.

**total fertility rate (TFR)** Estimate of the average number of children who will be born alive to a woman during her lifetime if she passes through all her childbearing years (ages 15–44) conforming to age-specific fertility rates of a given year. In simpler terms, it is an estimate of the average number of children a woman will have during her childbearing years.

**totally planned economy** See *pure command economic system*.

**toxic chemical** Chemical that is fatal to humans in low doses or fatal to more than 50% of test animals at stated concentrations. Most are neurotoxins, which attack nerve cells. See *carcinogen, hazardous chemical, mutagen, teratogen*.

**toxicity** Measure of how harmful a substance is.

**toxicology** Study of the adverse effects of chemicals on health.

**toxic waste** Form of hazardous waste that causes death or serious injury (such as burns, respiratory diseases, cancers, or genetic mutations). See *hazardous waste*.

**traditional intensive agriculture** Producing enough food for a farm family's survival and perhaps a surplus that can be sold. This type of agriculture uses higher inputs of labor, fertilizer, and water than traditional subsistence agriculture. See *traditional subsistence agriculture*. Compare *industrialized agriculture*.

**traditional subsistence agriculture** Production of enough crops or livestock for a farm family's survival and, in good years, a surplus to sell or put aside for hard times. Compare *industrialized agriculture, traditional intensive agriculture*.

**tragedy of the commons** Depletion or degradation of a potentially renewable resource to which people have free and unmanaged access. An example is the depletion of commercially desirable fish species in the open ocean beyond areas controlled by coastal countries. See *common-property resource*.

**transform fault** Area where the earth's lithospheric plates move in opposite but parallel directions along a fracture (fault) in the lithosphere. Compare *convergent plate boundary, divergent plate boundary.*

**transmissible disease** Disease caused by living organisms (such as bacteria, viruses, and parasitic worms) that can spread from one person to another by air, water, food, or body fluids (or in some cases by insects or other organisms). Compare *nontransmissible disease.*

**transpiration** Process in which water (1) is absorbed by the root systems of plants, (2) moves up through the plants, (3) passes through pores (stomata) in their leaves or other parts, and (4) evaporates into the atmosphere as water vapor.

**tree farm** See *tree plantation.*

**tree plantation** Site planted with one or only a few tree species in an even-aged stand. When the stand matures it is usually harvested by clear-cutting and then replanted. These plantations normally are used to grow rapidly growing tree species for fuelwood, timber, or pulpwood. See *even-aged management.* Compare *old-growth forest, second-growth forest, uneven-aged management.*

**trophic level** All organisms that are the same number of energy transfers away from the original source of energy (for example, sunlight) that enters an ecosystem. For example, all producers belong to the first trophic level, and all herbivores belong to the second trophic level in a food chain or a food web.

**troposphere** Innermost layer of the atmosphere. It contains about 75% of the mass of earth's air and extends about 17 kilometers (11 miles) above sea level. Compare *stratosphere.*

**true cost** See *full cost.*

**undergrazing** Reduction of the net primary productivity of grassland vegetation and grass cover from absence of grazing for long periods (at least 5 years). Compare *overgrazing.*

**undernutrition** Consuming insufficient food to meet one's minimum daily energy needs for a long enough time to cause harmful effects. Compare *malnutrition, overnutrition.*

**undiscovered resources** Potential supplies of a particular mineral resource, believed to exist because of geologic knowledge and theory, although specific locations, quality, and amounts are unknown. Compare *identified resources, reserves.*

**uneven-aged management** Method of forest management in which trees of different species in a given stand are maintained at many ages and sizes to permit continuous natural regeneration. Compare *even-aged management.*

**upwelling** Movement of nutrient-rich bottom water to the ocean's surface. This can occur far from shore but usually occurs along certain steep coastal areas where the surface layer of ocean water is pushed away from shore and replaced by cold, nutrient-rich bottom water.

**urban area** Geographic area with a population of 2,500 or more. The number of people used in this definition may vary, with some countries setting the minimum number of people at 10,000–50,000.

**urban growth** Rate of growth of an urban population. Compare *degree of urbanization.*

**urban heat island** Buildup of heat in the atmosphere above an urban area. The large concentration of cars, buildings, factories, and other heat-producing activities produces this heat.

**urbanization** See *degree of urbanization.*

**urban sprawl** Growth of low-density development on the edges of cities and towns. See *smart growth.*

**utilitarian value** See *instrumental value.*

**vertebrates** Animals that have backbones. Compare *invertebrates.*

**village** Group of rural households linked together by custom, culture, and family ties, usually surviving by harvesting local natural resources for food, fuel, and other basic needs. Compare *city.* See *rural area, urban area.*

**volcano** Vent or fissure in the earth's surface through which magma, liquid lava, and gases are released into the environment.

**warm front** Boundary between an advancing warm air mass and the cooler one it is replacing. Because warm air is less dense than cool air, an advancing warm front rises over a mass of cool air. Compare *cold front.*

**water cycle** See *hydrologic cycle.*

**waterlogging** Saturation of soil with irrigation water or excessive precipitation so the water table rises close to the surface.

**water pollution** Any physical or chemical change in surface water or groundwater that can harm living organisms or make water unfit for certain uses.

**watershed** Land area that delivers water, sediment, and dissolved substances via small streams to a major stream (river).

**water table** Upper surface of the zone of saturation, in which all available pores in the soil and rock in the earth's crust are filled with water.

**watt** Unit of power, or rate at which electrical work is done. See *kilowatt.*

**weather** Short-term changes in the temperature, barometric pressure, humidity, precipitation, sunshine, cloud cover, wind direction and speed, and other conditions in the troposphere at a given place and time. Compare *climate.*

**weathering** Physical and chemical processes in which solid rock exposed at earth's surface is changed to separate solid particles and dissolved material, which can then be moved to another place as sediment. See *erosion.*

**wetland** Land covered all or part of the time with salt water or fresh water, excluding streams, lakes, and the open ocean. See *coastal wetland, inland wetland.*

**wilderness** Area where the earth and its community of life have not been seriously disturbed by humans and where humans are only temporary visitors.

**wildlife** All free, undomesticated species. Sometimes the term is used to describe only free, undomesticated *animal* species.

**wildlife management** Manipulation of populations of wild species (especially game species) and their habitats for (1) human benefit, (2) the welfare of other species, and (3) the preservation of threatened and endangered wildlife species.

**wildlife resources** Wildlife species that have actual or potential economic value to people.

**wild species** Species found in the natural environment. Compare *domesticated species.*

**windbreak** Row of trees or hedges planted to partially block wind flow and reduce soil erosion on cultivated land.

**wind farm** Cluster of small to medium-sized wind turbines in a windy area to capture wind energy and convert it into electrical energy.

**worldview** How people think the world works and what they think their role in the world should be. See *environmental wisdom worldview, planetary management worldview, spaceship-earth worldview.*

**zero population growth (ZPG)** State in which the birth rate (plus immigration) equals the death rate (plus emigration) so the population of a geographic area is no longer increasing.

**zone of aeration** Zone in soil that is not saturated with water and lies above the water table. See *water table, zone of saturation.*

**zone of saturation** Area where all available pores in soil and rock in the earth's crust are filled by water. See *water table, zone of aeration.*

**zoning** Regulating how various parcels of land can be used.

**zooplankton** Animal plankton. Small floating herbivores that feed on plant plankton (phytoplankton). Compare *phytoplankton.*

# INDEX

A-55 fuel, 406
Abiotic decrease factors, 192
Abiotic ecosystem components, 71, 73
Abiotic factors, 73, 74
Abiotic growth factors, 192
Abortions
    availability of, 261
    family planning and, 270
Aboveground buildings, hazardous waste storage
    in, 546
Absolute humidity, 83
Absorption chiller, 384
Abt Associates report, 442
Abyssal zone, 148, 153
Accidentally introduced species, 576. *See also*
    Nonnative species
Accidents
    motor vehicle, 673
    release of toxic chemicals due to, 528–529
Accounting, improper, 17
Acetaldehyde, 228
Acid deposition, 87, 88
    areas affected by, 428–430
    effects of, 430–432
    reducing, 433–434
    regional outdoor air pollution from, 428–434
Acidic bogs, 139
Acid mine drainage, 344
Acid-producing chemicals
Acid rain, 87, 428. *See also* Acid deposition
Acids, 48
    water and, 313
Acid shock, 431
Acid wastes, 527
    export of, 430
Acquired immune deficiency syndrome (AIDS),
    237, 238–240. *See also* AIDS-related diseases
Action strategies, 43
Activated charcoal nanofibers, storing hydrogen
    on, 408
Activated sludge process, 504
Active solar heating systems, 394, 395, 396
Activism, 530–531
Acute effects of toxic chemicals, 230
Acute poverty, 7, 707. *See also* Poverty
Acute respiratory infections, 237
Acute toxicity tests, 232
Adam Joseph Lewis Center for Environmental
    Studies, 399
Adaptations, 101, 103
    ecological niches and, 103–104
    evolution and, 100–103
    limits on, 104
Adaptive ecological management, 626–627
Adaptive radiations, 106, 564–566
Adaptive traits, 101, 103
Addams, Jane, 28
Adélie penguins, 463
Adenine (A), A4
Advanced industrial societies, 25
Advanced light-water reactors (ALWRs), 375
Advanced sewage treatment, 505
Aepyornis, 563
Aeration, zone of, 314
Aerobic respiration, 74, 85, 99
Aerosol pollutants, 457

Aerosols, global warming and, 459
Aesthetic biodiversity value, 570
Aesthetics, effects of urban sprawl on, 666
Africa
    AIDS in, 239–240
    atmospheric warming in, 464
African Americans, environmental justice for,
    728–729
African bees, 169–170
African elephant, 565, 573
African honeybee, 576
African savannas, 128
    grazing animals of, 130
African veldt, 132
Aftershocks, 210–211
Age distribution, of populations, 191
Age of Ecology, 446
Age of genetic engineering, 290
Age of Oil, 359
Age structure, 263
    population growth and, 263–264
Age structure diagrams, 263
    projections using, 264–266
Agenda 21, 731
Aging, global, 266
Agribusiness, 281
Agricultural land, 80–81
Agricultural nutrient management, 500
Agricultural policy, 307–308
Agricultural products, pesticide residues in, 736
Agricultural revolution, 22–23
    consequences of, 24
Agricultural systems, inputs to, 280
Agricultural wastes, runoff of, 498
Agriculture. *See also* Sustainable agriculture
    atmospheric warming and, 461
    ecological approach to, 277
    industrialization of, 281–283
    nonpoint pollution from, 486
    traditional, 279, 280
Agrodiversity, low-input, 284
Agroforestry, 223, 284
*Ahimsa* concept, 748
A horizon, 212, 213
AIDS. *See* Acquired immune deficiency syndrome
    (AIDS)
AIDS-related diseases, 239
Air, 418, 419–420. *See also* Atmosphere
    effects of urban sprawl on, 666
Air circulation, global, 118
Air conditioners
    absorption chillers as, 384
    solar-powered evaporative, 395
Airplanes, emissions from, 459
Air pollutants
    common, 422
    major classes of, 420
Air pollution, 6. *See also* Clean air; Indoor air pol-
    lution; Regional outdoor air pollution; Smog
    from coal burning, 364
    effects of, 437–439, 459
    effects of food production on, 288
    effects of ozone thinning on, 475
    forests and, 608
    history of, 423
    hydrogen gas and, 405

    in Mexico City, 663
    from motor vehicles, 673
    indoor, 422, 438
    lichens and, 418
    outdoor, 420–422, 438
    premature deaths from, 437–438
    preventing and reducing, 439–444
    in Thailand, 254
Air pollution laws, 439
    improving, 440–441
Air properties, climate and, 117
Alar, 735
Alaska
    deer population in, 193
    oil and gas development in, 360
    oil reserves in, 358
Alaska National Interest Lands Conservation Act
    of 1980, 34, 360
Albedo, 457, 459
Alcock, James, 612
Algae, producing hydrogen from, 408
Algal blooms, 146, 634
Alien species, 169. *See also* Nonnative species
Alkalinity, 48
Alkaloids, cancer and, 570
Alleles, 100
Allen, George, 507
Alley cropping, 223, 224, 284
Alligator farms, 587
Alligators, 173
All-India Women's Conference, 620
Alpha particles, 56, 57
Alpine tundra, 134
Alternative assessment, 249
Altitude, generalized effects of, 123–125
Aluminum ions (Al$^{3+}$), 431
Amazon basin, 612, 663
Amazon.com, 393
Amazon park system, 621
American bison, near extinction of, 21
American Bison Society, 21
American Council for an Energy-Efficient
    Economy (ACEEE), 386, 392
American Council on Science and Health (ACSH),
    515
American Public Transit System, 677
Americium-241, 373
Ames, Bruce, 515
Amino acids, origin of life and, 97
Ammonia (NH$_3$), 477, A3
    in earth's atmosphere, 97
Ammonification, 87
Ammonium ions (NH$_4^+$), 48
Ammonium sulfate [(NH$_4$)$_2$SO$_4$], 89
Amphibians, decline of, 170–171
Amu Darya River, 319
Anaconda, Montana, mining and smelting waste
    in, 527
Anaerobic bacteria, 87
    in lakes, 490
Anaerobic respiration, 75, 99
Anderson, Ray, 533, 534
Anderson, Sherry, 752
Androcentrism, 745
Anecdotal information, 43
Anemia, 287

Angel Island, carrying capacity of, 272
Animal biodiversity, atmospheric warming and, 460, 461
Animal manure, 225. *See also* Manure
Animal protein, converting grain into, 298
Animals
  classifying, A5
  desert, 126–128
  domestication of, 24
  dry grassland, 130
  as a food resource, 278
  global extinction of, 2
  moist grassland, 130
  soil and, 212–215
  survival rights of, 571
Animal welfare groups, 232
*Anopheles* mosquitoes, 243, 244, 514
Antarctica
  food web in, 78
  global warming and, 463
  mining moratorium in, 35
  ozone depletion above, 34, 474–475
Antarctic ice shelf, disintegration of, 453–454
Anthropocentric instrumental value, 742
Anthropocentric worldview, 742
Anti-environmental bills, 34
Anti-environmental coalition, 33–34
Anti-environmental groups, 35
Anti-environmental movement, goals of, 730
Antibiotics, 237
  bacterial resistance to, 238–239
  biodiversity and, 569–570
  microbes and, 65
Antiquities Act of 1906, 26, 27, 32, 34
Ants, species diversity of, 167
Aphids, ladybug beetle control of, 521
*Apollo* mission, 30
Appliances
  energy-efficient, 392
  recycling, 540
  turning off, 392
Appropriate technology, in environmental economics, 695, 696
Aquaculture, 305–307, 651
  advantages and disadvantages of, 307
  new trends in, 307
Aquaculture ponds, 306
Aquariums
  preserving endangered species in, 587–588
  public, 587–588, 643
Aquatic biodiversity, 635–659. *See also* Marine biodiversity
  human impacts on, 637–639
  importance of, 635–637
  loss in Lake Victoria, 634
Aquatic ecosystems, 80. *See also* Aquatic life zones
  biodiversity in, 144–164
  effects of acid deposition on, 430–431
  mercury in, 549, 550
  phosphate in, 88
  pollution threats to, 639
  sustainability of, 162–163
Aquatic food chain, polychlorinated biphenyls in, 490
Aquatic life zones, 70, 71, 73, 148
  kinds of organisms in, 145
  life-limiting factors in, 146–147
  sustainability of, 162–163
  types of, 145
Aquatic organisms
  effects of chemicals on, 501–502
  key characteristics of, 145–146
Aquatic plants, analyzing, 485
Aquifer depletion, 324
  areas of, 326
Aquifers, 83, 314–315
  contaminated, 495
  overpumping, 326
  tropical deforestation and, 616
Aquifer subsidence, 324, 326
Arabian oryx, 565, 587
Aral Sea water transfer disaster, 324–325
Archaebacteria, A5

Arctic, ozone loss over, 475
Arctic fox, evolution of, 105
Arctic National Wildlife Refuge (ANWR), 586
  oil and gas development in, 360
Arctic soils, 125
Arctic temperatures, global warming and, 452–453
Arctic tundra, 123, 124, 128, 129, 132–134
  wet, 160
Area, units of, A1
Area strip mining, 341, 342, 363
Argentina fire ant, 576, 578
Arid areas, undergrazing in, 298
Arizona, Biosphere experiments in, 741
Árnason, Bragi, 409
Arrhenius, Svante, 27, 448
Arsenic (As)
  from mining and smelting, 527
  in drinking water, 495, 496–497
  in groundwater, 493, 495, 496–497
Arsenic-producing companies, 497
Artificial ecosystems, creating, 629
Artificial plasma, 50–51
Artificial selection, 100, 101
Asbestos, 434, 435, 436–437
Asbestosis, 436
Asexual reproduction, 66, 195
Ashworth, William, 736
Asia
  acid deposition in, 430
  air pollution in, 425
  atmospheric warming in, 464
  kudzu vine from, 577
  pollution from, 110
  species decline in, 165
Asian elephant, 573
Asian long-horned beetle, 576, 578
Asian swamp eel, 639
Asian tiger mosquitoes, 576, 578
Assimilation, 87
Asthenosphere, 68, 204, 205, 208, 211
Asthma, 437
Aswan High Dam, 312, 321
Athabasca Tar Sands, 361
Atlantic white-sided dolphin, 644
Atmosphere, 68. *See also* Air entries
  chemical makeup of, 120
  earth's original, 96–97, 99
  heat "trapping" and "reradiation" by, 448
  maintaining, 97
  structure of, 419–420
  transfer of energy by convection in, 117, 118
Atmospheric climate models, 454, 456
Atmospheric pressure, 112
Atmospheric temperatures, earth's reflectivity and, 457
Atmospheric warming. *See also* Global warming
  possible effects of, 460–464
  regional variations in, 464
Atomic bomb, 58
Atomic Energy Act of 1954, 29
Atomic Energy Commission (AEC), 366
Atomic mass, 48
Atomic number, 48
Atomistic environmental worldviews, 742
Atoms, 47, 54
  building blocks of, 47–48
Atrazine, 519
Attached organisms, 153
Attitude and value strategies, 43
Audubon Society, 27, 590, 727
Australian flatback turtle, 642
Autoclaves, 543–544
Automobile companies
  emission reductions by, 470
  versus mass-transit systems, 677
Automobile subsidies, 672
Automobile use. *See also* Cars; Motor vehicles
  alternatives to, 674–675
  reducing, 672–674
Autotrophs, 74
Average precipitation, 115, 124
Average temperature, 115, 124
*Azadirachta indica*, 569

Baby-boom period, 259, 264–265
Baby-bust generation, 265
Bachman's warbler, 574
Background extinction, 106
Bacon, Francis, 201
Bacteria, 65
  in aquatic life zones, 145
  in bottled water, 509
  classifying, A5
  controlling, 522
  in drinking water, 485
  increased immunity of, 238–239
  in Mexico City air, 663
  mining with, 349
  nitrogen cycle and, 86–87
  origin of life and, 99
  as pathogens, 237
  phosphorus cycle and, 87
  sewage treatment with, 504
  in soils, 213–214
  symbiosis with, 178
  tuberculosis caused by, 241
Bacterial decay, in streams, 486–487
Baghouse filter, 442
Baird's beaked whale, 644
Balakrishnan, Lalita, 620
Balanced chemical equations, 54
Balance of nature, 184
Baleen whales, 149, 643, 645. *See also* Cetaceans
Baltic Marine Protection Commission, 499
Baltic Sea, pollutants in, 497, 499
Banana spiders, 512
Bangladesh
  floodplains in, 335
  microloans in, 709
  water purification in, 508
Bannerman's turaco, 564
Bark beetles, 606
Barnett, Tim, 458
Barrier beaches, 150–151
  organisms living in, 151
Barrier islands, 152, 153
Barrios, 662
Basal cell carcinoma, 476, 478
Basel Convention on Hazardous Waste, 547
Bases, 48
  water and, 313
Basic needs, of humans, 754
Basic services, cost of universal access to, 709–710
Bathyal zone, 148, 153
Bats, 172, 564
  vulnerability to extinction, 567
Baykalsk, 654
Beach erosion, 647–648
Beaches. *See also* Barrier beaches; Rocky shores; Sandy beaches; Sandy shores
  eroding of, 638
  oil-polluted, 502
Beach pollution, 497, 498
Beachsaver modules, in limiting beach erosion, 648
Beaver dams, 172
Beavers, 589
Beckke, Paul, 457
Bedrock, 212, 214
Beech trees, atmospheric warming and, 462
Beef production, industrialized approach to, 297
Bees, using to detect toxic pollutants, 553
Beluga whale, 644
Bender, Judith, 508
Beneficial effects
  harmful effects versus, 46
  of global warming, 460
  of ozone, 420
  of pesticides, 514–516
Benefit–cost analysis, 245, 702–703. *See also* Cost–benefit analysis
Bennett, Hugh, 219
Benthic ocean region, 157, 635
Benthos, 145
Benz, Karl, 673
Benzo–pyrene, 434

Bequests, as nonuse biodiversity value, 570
Berea College, as green college, 753
Berger, John, 630
Berry, Wendell, 628
Beta particles, 56, 57
Betz, Robert, 629–630
Bhopal, India, pesticide plant disaster in, 34, 528, 529
B horizon, 212, 214
Bicarbonate ions (HCO$_3^a$), 85–86
Bichnell's thrush, 574
Bicycles, 674–675
    electric, 389
Bighead carp, 306
Bike-and-ride systems, 674
Bike paths, 674
Bills, introduction of, 722
Bioaccumulation, 230, 231
Biocentric intrinsic value, 742
Biocentric worldview, 742, 744–745
Biocides, 513. See also Insecticides; Pesticides
Biocultural restoration, 630
Biodegradable pollutants, 55
Biodegradable wastes, using composting to recycle, 539
Biodegradation, 74
    natural, 486–487, 488
Biodiversity, 76, 110, 201. See also Aquatic biodiversity; Terrestrial biodiversity
    in aquatic systems, 144–164
    atmospheric warming and, 460, 461
    of coral reefs, 153
    effects of food production on, 288
    effects of speciation and extinction on, 106–107
    effects of urban sprawl on, 666
    factors affecting, 561
    freshwater, 637
    human impacts on, 561–563
    importance of, 568–571
    instrumental values of, 569–570
    intrinsic value of, 571
    islands of, 141
    in Lake Baikal, 654
    loss of, 292, 563
    mapping, 631
    necessity of, 198
    preserving, 199, 622
    range of, 142, 167–168
    time to rebuild, 568
    total economic value of, 570
    urbanization and, 668
Biodiversity centers, endangered, 625–626
Biodiversity hot spots, 568, 583, 624–626
Biodiversity layers, in forests, 601
Biodiversity protection revolution, 755
Biodiversity reserves, global system of, 621–622
Bioengineered pathogens, 291
Biofiltration, 149
Biofuels, 403, 404
Biogas, 404
Biogas digesters, 404–405
Biogeochemical cycles, 82
Biogeography, 110
Bioinformatics, 199
    biodiversity and, 582
Bioinvaders, 639
Biological community, 68
Biological evolution, 96, 100. See also Evolution
Biological extinction, 563. See also Extinction(s)
Biological hazards, 229, 236–245
Biological indicator species, 553
Biological information databases, 624. See also Bioinformatics; Computer entries
Biologically diverse environments, degradation of, 568
Biological oxygen demand (BOD), 485
Biological pest control, 520–521
Biological principles, 61
Biological zones, in the open sea, 153–155
Biolysis, 405
Biomagnification, 230, 231, 490
Biomass, 77, 351. See also Solid biomass
    producing energy from, 403–405

Biomass plantations, 404
Biomass production, 80–81, 82
    consumer species and, 81–82
Biomass storage, 79–80
Biomass waste, 686
Biome map, 123
    climate map versus, 141–142
Biomes, 110, 122–125. See also Ecosystems
    characteristics of, 142
    desert, 125–128
    global air circulation and, 118
    habitat disturbance in various, 574
    major, 70
    map of earth's, 123
    mountain, 141
Biomimicry, 532
Biomining, 349
Biophilia, 572
Bioprospecting, 570
Bioremediation, 542
Biosphere, 66, 67, 68
    carbon cycling in, 84–86
    ecosystems and, 748
Biosphere 1, 741
Biosphere 2, 741
Biosphere reserves, 626
Bioterrorism, spread of disease via, 242
Biotic change, 184
Biotic decrease factors, 192
Biotic ecosystem components, 71
Biotic growth factors, 192
Biotic potential, 191, 192
Bird feeding niches, in coastal wetlands, 152–153
Birds. See also Migrating birds
    as biological indicators, 170–171
    endangered, 463
    exotic, 581
    species diversity of, 167
Birth control methods, 254
    availability of, 261
    effectiveness rates of, 261
Birth rates, 255
    economic development and, 267–270
    economic rewards/penalties and, 271
    empowerment of women and, 270
    factors affecting, 259–261
    family planning and, 270
    reducing, 267
    U.S., 259
Bison, near extinction of, 21
Bitumen, 361
Black-capped vireo, 574
Black-footed ferret, 564, 581
Black lace cactus, 574
Black rhinoceros, 564, 573
Black smokers, 340
Black turtle, 642
Blast zone, of volcanic eruptions, 203
BLM. See Bureau of Land Management (BLM)
Bloom, Arnold, 459
Blue Angel program, 555, 712
"Blue baby syndrome," 495
Bluefin tuna, 304
Blue revolution, 335
Blue Sky program, 441
Blue whale, 565, 645
    near extinction of, 643
Boar, 576
Body temperature, feedback loops controlling, 45
Bogs, 160
Bole, 601, 605
Boll weevil, 516
    geographic range of, 515
Bombs, "dirty," 373–374
Book publishing, electronic versus paper, 393
Bookchin, Murray, 746
Boreal ecosystem, 140
Boreal forests, 134, 139, 598, 599
    climate graph for, 136
Botanical desert, 591
Botanical gardens, 586–587
Botanicals, 515, 522
Botkin, Daniel B., 188

Bottled water, 509
Bottlenose dolphin, 644
Bottles, refillable, 534–535
Bottom habitats, 638. See also Benthic ocean region
Bottom trawling, 156
Bottom-up change, 718
Bottom-up control hypothesis, 194–195
Bottom-up food web dynamics, 635
"Bottom-up" reasoning, 43
Boulding, Kenneth, 699
Bounceback period, from extinctions, 108–109
Boundary conditions, in climate models, 456
Bowash, 667, 668
Bowhead whale, 645
Bowling, Mike, 357
Brain cancer, childhood, 519
Braungart, Michael, 533
Brazil, 663, 734
    national parks in, 621
"Breakbone fever," 242
Breakeven point, 700
Breast milk, contaminated, 536
Breeder nuclear fission reactors, 376
Breezes, sea and land, 122. See also Air currents
Brewer, Peter, 468
British Royal Society, 44
Broadleaf deciduous plants, 125
Broadleaf evergreen plants, 125
Broad niches, 103–104
Broad-spectrum agents, 514
Broad-spectrum insecticides, 516–517
Bromine compounds, 474
Bronchitis, 437
Bronx Zoo, 588
Brower, David, 31, 32, 627
Brown, Lester R., 15, 226, 274, 377, 691, 747
Brown-air smog, 423
Brownfields, 553–554
Brown tides, 498
Brown tree snake, 576, 578
Brownwell, Kelly, 287
Browsing, 128
Bryde's whale, 646
Bubonic plague, 194
Buffer zone concept, 502, 624
    in biosphere reserve, 626
Building-block molecules of proteins, 97
Buildings
    in Curitiba, Brazil, 678
    energy efficiency of, 391, 392
    influence on smog, 426
    radon gas in, 435–436
    saving energy in, 389–393
Build-it-yourself system, in Curitiba, Brazil, 678–679
Bullard, Robert D., 728–729
Bullet trains, 675, 676
Bureau of Land Management (BLM), 31, 299, 595
Burkholder, JoAnn M., 487, 489
Burning
    controlled, 629
    of wastes, 543–544
Buses, 675, 676
    automobile manufacturers versus, 677
    in Curitiba, Brazil, 678
    fuel-cell systems for, 408
Bush administration, 470–471. See also Bush, George W.
    cleanup costs and, 554
    EPA budget and, 509
    EPA standards and, 497
    forest management under, 610–611
Bush, George H. W., 34
Bush, George W., 35–36, 497. See also Bush administration
    Kyoto Treaty and, 469
Bushmeat, 580
Businesses
    greening, 710
    reducing water waste in, 331
Butte, Montana, mining and smelting waste in, 527
Butterfly, 565

Bycatch, 302, 304
  reducing, 651

Cactus, 564, 565
Cahn, Robert, 741
Calcium carbonate ($CaCO_3$), 428–429
Calcium ions ($Ca^{2+}$), 48
California, emission reductions by, 470
California Air Resources Board, 440
California condor, 564
California gnatcatcher, 574
California Water Project, 323
Callender, Jim, 652
Camouflage, 177–178
Campaign financing problem, 718
Campus Ecology Program, 732
Campuses, environmental groups on, 732, 752–753
Canada
  emission reductions by, 470
  oil deposits in, 361
  reusable containers in, 535
Canada geese, 589
Cancer. See also Carcinogens; Lung cancer; Skin
    cancers
  from air pollution, 438
  indoor pollutants and, 435
  pesticides and, 515
  from water pollution, 495, 496–497
Candidate conservation agreements, 584
Cannibalism, on Easter Island, 40
Canopy layer, in forests, 134, 601
Cap-and-trade market approach, 441
Capital, 3
  protecting, 4
Capitalism, natural, 16–17
Capitalist market economic systems, 692, 694
  global, 693
Captive breeding, 587
Carbohydrates
  complex, 50
  simple, 49
Carbon (C), 48
Carbonate compounds, 86
Carbonate ions ($CO_3^{2-}$), 85–86, 146
Carbon-based compounds, 49
Carbon cycle, 84–86
  human activities and, 86
Carbon dioxide ($CO_2$), 54, 84–85, 425, A3
  dissolved, 146
  as greenhouse gas, 448–450
  global warming and, 450, 451
  sequestering, 467–469
  tropospheric, 448
Carbon dioxide emissions, 358–359, 365, 387–388,
    391, 440–441, 449, 450, 465
  decreasing, 471–472
  top ten nations for, 451
Carbon dioxide levels, photosynthesis and, 459
Carbon fuels, 467
Carbonic acid ($H_2CO_3$), 468
Carbon monoxide (CO), 425, 434, A3
  as criteria air pollutant, 422
  tracking, 421
Carbon oxides, 420
Carbon taxes, 465
Carbon tetrachloride ($CCl_4$)
  as greenhouse gas, 449
  as ozone-depleting compound, 473
Car-centered cities, 671
Carcinogens, 234. See also Cancer
  dioxin compounds as, 552
  pesticides as, 518, 519
Cardinale, Bradley, 185
Careers, environmental, 624
Car emissions, 432. See also Cars
Car-free areas, 672
Caribou herds, 132
Carnivores, 74, 77, 79
  behavior of, 177
Carnivorous fish, farming of, 307
Carolina parakeet, 581
Carpet manufacturing, 534
Carpets, leasing, 533, 534
Carrier air conditioning equipment, 533–534

Carrying capacity (K), 191, 272–273
  population size and, 192–193
Cars. See also Automobile entries; Motor vehicles
  in Curitiba, Brazil, 678
  electric, 384
  energy-efficient, 381
  fuel cells in, 387–388, 408
  fuel efficiency of, 385–386, 440
  hybrid-electric, 386–387
  pollution levels inside, 435
  subcompact, 386
  superefficient, 386
Car-sharing network, 672–673
Carson, Rachel, 29, 30, 33, 163, 446, 514
Carter, Jimmy, 32
  Love Canal cleanup and, 525
Case reports, 232
Cash crops, tropical deforestation and, 616
Catalyzed chlorine cycle, 474
Catastrophic ecosystem changes, 183
Catawba College, as green college, 753
Catawba College Center for the Environment, 399
Caterpillars, 521
  malaria elimination and, 200
Catfish, 307
Cathranthus roseus, 569
Cattle. See Livestock entries
Cattle ranching, tropical deforestation and, 615
CCC. See Civilian Conservation Corps (CCC)
Cell membrane, 67
Cells, 50, 65
  mutations in, 100
Center for Energy and Climate Solutions, 728
Center for Health, Environment, and Justice, 727
Center for Plant Conservation, 586–587
Center for Strategic and International
    Studies, 373
Center-pivot low-pressure sprinklers, 330
Centers for Disease Control and Prevention, 508,
    548, 550
  on bacterial antibiotic resistance, 239
  on smoking, 228
Central American countries, 663
Central Arizona Project, 323
Centralized power system, 410, 411
Centralized recycling, 537
Central receiver system, 396. See also Power tower
Ceramics, 349
Cerulean warbler, 574
Cesium-137, 373
Cetaceans, 643, 644–645
CFCs. See Chlorofluorocarbons (CFCs)
Chain reaction, 58
Change, potential for, 18
Channel Islands, as green college, 752
Chaotic events, 47
Chaotic population behavior, 194
Chaparral, 123, 124, 134
Charcoal nanofibers, storing hydrogen on, 408
Charcoal production, 618
Charter forest, 611
Chateaubriand, François-Auguste-René de, 595
Chattanooga, Tennessee, transformation of,
    685–686
Chauffagistes, 533
Chemical change, 54
Chemical cycles, 82
  interfering with, 199
Chemical elements. See Elements
Chemical equations, 54
Chemical evolution, 96–97
Chemical fertilizers, 46
Chemical forms of matter, 47
Chemical formula, 48
Chemical hazards, 229, 233–236
Chemical industry, 701
Chemical interactions, of toxic chemicals, 230
Chemical methods of oil cleanup, 502
Chemical nutrients, recycling, 92
Chemical reaction, 54
Chemicals. See also Toxic chemicals
  harmful effects of, 235–236
  toxicity of, 231
  as water pollutants, 484

Chemical warfare, 178
Chemical weathering, 209
Chemosynthesis, 74, 154, 340
Chernobyl nuclear disaster, 34, 57, 338, 367, 374,
    376, 418
Chesapeake Bay, 500
  oyster population in, 501
Chesapeake Bay Foundation, 500
Chesapeake Bay Program, 500
Children
  cost of raising and educating, 260
  in the labor force, 259
  limiting numbers of, 699
  malnourished, 8, 288
  saving in developing countries, 289
China, 325
  contaminated drinking water in, 507
  deforestation in, 616
  feeding the population of, 293
  fish polyculture in, 306
  industrialization of, 15
  Kyoto Treaty and, 470
  pollution from, 110
  population in, 256, 271–274
  reducing urban sprawl in, 680
  soil erosion in, 217–218, 219
  Three Gorges Dam project in, 320–321
  water prices in, 331
Chlorinated hydrocarbon compounds, 49, 551
Chlorination, in advanced sewage treatment, 505
Chlorine ($Cl_2$), 48, A3
  ban on, 493
  exposure to, 551
  hydrogen peroxide versus, 530, 541
  in paper making, 540–541
Chlorine compounds, 473–474, 551
Chlorine dioxide ($ClO_2$), in paper making, 540–541
Chlorofluorocarbons (CFCs), 35, 49, 199, 472–473
  as greenhouse gases, 449
  substitutes for, 477
Chloroform, 434
Cholera, 508
C horizon, 212, 214
Christy, Ann, 545
Chromated copper arsenate (CCA), 497
Chromosomes, 50
  genetic information in, 100
Chronic effect, of toxic chemicals, 230
Chronic undernourishment, 285
Chulhas, 620
Cichlids, in Lake Victoria, 634
Ciecerone, Ralph, 477
Cigarette smoke, 435
  hazards of, 228
Cilia, 437
Cinchona ledogeriana, 569
Circle of poison, 518
CITES. See Convention on International Trade in
    Endangered Species (CITES)
Cities. See also Ecocities; Megacities; New cities;
    Urbanization
  compact, 671
  microclimates of, 121–122
  migration to and from, 664
  sustainable, 660–686
Citizens, leveling the legal playing field for, 727.
    See also Individuals
Citizens' Clearinghouse for Hazardous Wastes,
    530
Citrus-based solvents, 479
Civic pride, in Curitiba, Brazil, 679
Civilian Conservation Corps (CCC), 28
Civilian Conservation Service, 29
Civilization, crisis of, 748–749
Civil suit, 723
Clarke, Arthur C., 526
Clark Fork Foundation, 527
Class action suit, 723
Classes, A5
Classification of species, A5
Clay, in soil, 215, 216
Clean air, in Curitiba, Brazil, 678
Clean Air Act of 1956 (England), 423
Clean Air Act of 1963, 423

Clean Air Act of 1970, 31, 423, 433, 439, 685, 724
    amendments to, 35, 423
Clean Air Act of 1977, 439
Clean Air Act of 1990, 439, 440, 441
Clean Air Act standards, 364
Clean production systems, 537
Clean Water Act of 1972, 503, 505, 724
Clean Water Act of 1977, 31
Clear-cutting, 603, 604
    forest fires and, 608
Clear sky cap-and-trade program, 441
Cleveland, Ohio, oil pollution in, 30
Climate, 70, 110, 115–122. *See also* Climate change;
    Global climate
    biomes and, 122
    defined, 115
    effect of air pollution on, 459
    effect of oceans on, 457–458
    effect of urban sprawl on, 666
    effect of water vapor content and clouds on,
        458–459
    global air circulation and, 115–118
    ocean currents and, 118–120
    vegetation and, 124
Climate change
    dealing with, 464–469
    economic consequences of reducing the threat
        of, 466
    effects of, 454–456, 486
    as environmental issue, 2
    forests and, 608
    future, 454–456
    human activities and, 448–454
    past, 447–448
    reducing the threat of, 465–466
    role in extinction, 582
    speed of, 460
Climate graphs, for forests, 136
Climate map, biome map versus, 141–142. *See also*
    Global climate zones; Weather maps
Climate models, benefits of, 456
Climate types, 117
Climate zones, maps of, 116, 117
Climax community, 184
Clinton, Bill, 34–35
Cloning, 587
Closed-loop recycling, 535
*Closing Circle, The* (Commoner), 31
Clothes dryers, 393
Clouds, effect on climate, 458–459
Cloud seeding, 328
Clownfish, 179
Clumped population dispersal pattern, 191
Cluster development, 681–682
CO₂ emissions. *See* Carbon dioxide emissions
Coal, 363–365
    as nonrenewable energy source, 350
    sulfur-containing, 89
Coal-burning power plants, 428, 449
    efficiency of, 382
    pollution control for, 442
Coal deposits, locations of, 356
Coal formation, stages in, 363
Coal gasification, 364–365, 405
Coal liquefaction, 365
Coal mining methods, 342
Coal reserves, 363–364
Coal use, 350–351
Coastal areas. *See also* Beach entries
    atmospheric warming and, 461
    effect of pollutants on, 496–500
Coastal chaparral, 70
Coastal coniferous forests, 139
Coastal developments, 156, 639, 640
Coastal management, integrated, 500, 647
Coastal waters, protecting, 502
Coastal wetlands, 148–149, 155, 651. *See also*
    Wetlands
    bird feeding niches in, 152–153
Coastal zone, 147, 148
Coastal Zone Management Act of 1972, 31
Coastal zoning, 647
Coastline home losses, 647
Cobalt-60, 373

Coburn, Theo, 35
Cockroaches, success of, 105
Coevolution, 103, 513
Coffee growing, 618
Cogeneration systems, 384
Cohen, Joel, 741
Cohen, Michael J., 419, 751
Cold deserts, 125, 126
Cold frames, 390
Cold front, 111–112
Coliform bacteria count, in drinking water, 485.
    *See also Escherichia coli*
Colinvaux, Paul A., 447
Colorado, Summitville gold mine debacle in, 345
Colorado River, 320, 322, 323
Colorado River basin, 320, 322, 323
Columbia River Basin, managing, 656–657
Comanagement, of coastal fishing communities,
    650
Combined-cycle natural gas systems, 362
Combined heat and power (CHP) systems, 384
Command-and-control approach, 703
Commensalism, 172, 179–180
Commercial energy, 350
    use of, 351, 353
Commercial extinction, 304, 639
Commercial fishing industry, 301, 302, 303, 304
Commercial hunting, of blue whales, 643
Commercial inorganic fertilizers, 225–226
Commercial logging. *See* Logging
Common carp, 306
Common dolphin, 644
Commoner, Barry, 30, 31
Common law, 723
    groundwater use and, 329
Common pigeon, 576
Common-property resources, 11
Communication indicators of globalization, 7–8
Communities, 66, 67–68
    differences among, 166
    ecological design for, 684–685
    insects in biological, 64
Community ecology, 165, 166–189
Community structure, 166–169
Commuters, 677
    in Curitiba, Brazil, 678
    motor vehicles and, 673
Compact cities, 671
Compact fluorescent lightbulbs, energy-efficiency
    of, 392
Comparative risk analysis, 229, 245, 246. *See also*
    Risk entries
Compensation, for government taking of private
    property, 725
Competition
    adaptations that reduce or avoid, 174–175
    amphibian decline and, 170, 171
    interspecific, 173–174
Competitive exclusion principle, 174
Competitor species, 196–198
Complex carbohydrates, 50
Complex systems
    models of, 45
    time delays and, 46
Compost, 225, 539
Compounds, 47, A2–A4
    atoms and ions in, 48–49
Comprehensive Environmental Response,
    Compensation, and Liability Act of 1980,
    32, 552–553
Compressed gas storage tanks, 407
Computer models, 24, 91
    of climate changes, 454
    of weather, 111
Computers, in bioinformatics, 582
Concentration, 48
    of pollutants, 55
Concentric circle city, 666, 667
Condensation, 82
Condensation nuclei, 83
Condensation trails (contrails), 459
Condor, 564
Conduction, 52, 53
Cone of depression, 326

Confined aquifer, 315
Conflicts, as consequence of agricultural revolu-
    tion, 24
Coniferous evergreen plants, 125
Coniferous forests, 70, 124
    coastal, 139
    evergreen, 139
    soil in, 215
Consensus science, 43, 44
Conservation, 109
    profitable, 631
Conservation biology, 3, 198–199
Conservation concession, 617
Conservation easements, 598, 617
Conservation era of U.S. history, 25, 26–29
Conservation events, 1930–1960, 29
Conservation gaps, 624
Conservation International (CI), 617, 727
    studies by, 6
Conservationists, 3, 32
    early, 26
Conservation movement, 36
    in the United States, 26–28
Conservation of matter, law of, 54, 55
Conservation Reserve Program (CRP), 223
Conservation reserves, 223
Conservation strategy, 702
Conservation-tillage farming, 222
    advantages and disadvantages of, 223
Consolidated metropolitan areas, 665
Constancy, 185
Constant loss curves, 198
Constitutional democracy, 717
Consultative Group on International Agricultural
    Research, 218
Consumer information, about fish harvesting, 651
Consumer Product Safety Act of 1972, 31
Consumer species, 72, 74, 76
    biomass production and, 81–82
Consumption, reducing, 529
Consumptive water use, 316
Containers, refillable, 534–535
Contaminated water, deaths from, 508
Continental crust, 204, 206
Continental drift, 105, 106, 205–206
Continental shelf, 147, 148
Contour farming, 222, 224
Contour strip mining, 341, 342, 363
Control, in policy life cycles, 723
Control group, 43, 232
Controlled experiments, 43, 44, 232
Controlled nuclear fusion, 58
Control rods, of nuclear reactor, 365
Control system, 90
Convection, 52, 53
    atmospheric, 117, 118
Convection cells, 118, 205
Conventional economists, 693, 694
    ecological economists versus, 693–695, 697,
        698–699
    environmental conceptions of, 690
Conventional housing development, 682
Conventional land-use planning, 676
Conventional natural gas, 362
Conventional-tillage farming, 222
Convention on Biological Diversity (CBD), 582
Convention on climate change, 731
Convention on International Trade in Endangered
    Species (CITES), 31, 581, 582, 641, 646
Convention on protecting biodiversity, 731
Convergent plate boundaries, 207, 208
Conway, Gordon, 308
Cooking, via solar energy, 397
Coolant, nuclear reactor, 366
Cooling, low-temperature, 384
Cooling services, 533–534
Copper mining, 349
Coral, 155
Coral bleaching, 144, 155
Coral reefs, 144, 152–153, 154, 635
    damage to, 561
    major threats to, 155
    threats to, 638
Corbett, Judy, 660

Corbett, Michael, 660
Core
    of earth, 204, 205, 206
    of a nuclear reactor, 365
Core areas, in biosphere reserve, 624, 626
Cormorant birds, 589
Cornell University, as green college, 752–753
Corporate Average Fuel Economy (CAFE) stan-
        dards, 385, 386
Corporations
    in capitalist marketing systems, 692
    Kyoto Treaty and, 470
    land ownership by, 725
    SLAPP lawsuits by, 726, 727
    as special-interest groups, 717
Cosmetic spraying, of crops, 520
Cosmic ray hypothesis, 457
Costa Rica
    parks in, 622
    tropical dry forest in, 630
Costanza, Robert, 571
Cost–benefit analysis, 247. *See also* Benefit–cost
        analysis
Cotton top tamarin, 76
Council on Environmental Quality, 719
Countries
    most biodiverse, 625
    most populous, 257
Coupled positive and negative feedback loops, 45
Covalent bonds/compounds, 49, A2, A3
Cree Indian saying, 559
Crime, environmental benefits of reducing, 671
Crime rates, 671
Crisis of civilization, 748–749
Criteria air pollutants, table of, 422
Critical habitat, 583
Critical mass, 57–58
Critical thinking, science and, 41–44
*Critical Thinking and Environmental Studies: A Be-
        ginner's Guide* (Heinze-Fry & Miller), 42–43
Crop damage, reducing, 522–523
Crop diversity, 284
Crop dusting, 517
Cropland
    in China, 293
    expansion of, 295
    services provided by, 281
Croplands system, 278
Crop losses, synthetic pesticides and, 517
Crop production
    increasing, 289–296
    Ogallala aquifer and, 327
Crop productivity, loss in, 219
Crop residue recycling, 298
Crop residues, burning, 404
Crop rotation, 225
Crops, air pollution damage to, 438–439. *See also*
        Agriculture; Farming
Crop seed varieties, 291
Crop spraying, 520
Crop strains, genetically improved, 289–290
Crop varieties, green revolution, 292
Crop yield research, 284
Crop yields, 292
Crossbreeding, 289–290
    traditional, 290
Crosson, Pierre, 220
Crown fires, 607, 608
Crude birth rate, 255
    changes in, 262
    in China, 274
Crude death rate, 255
    changes in, 262
Crude oil, 354–355
    recovery from exposure to, 502
    refining, 355
Crude petroleum, 501
Crust, of earth, 68, 204, 205
Cruzen, Paul, 35
*Cryptosporidium* outbreak, 508
Cultivation. *See* Agriculture; Farming
Cultivation practices, pest control and, 520
Cultural carrying capacity, 267, 272–273
Cultural changes, environment and, 22–25

Cultural Creatives, cultural shift among, 752–753
Cultural diversity, 76
Cultural eutrophication, 157, 226, 490
    in the Great Lakes, 491–492
    of lakes, 654–655
    preventing or reducing, 490–491
Cultural extinction, in tropical forests 613, 614
Cultural hazards, 229
Cultural shift, 752–753
Cultures, avoiding harm to, 748–749
Curitiba, Brazil, as environmental showcase,
        678–679
Cuvier's beaked whale, 644
Cuyahoga River
    cleanup of, 487–488
    oil pollution in, 30
Cyanide heap leaching, 345
Cyanobacteria, 87, 508, A5
    origin of life and, 99
Cyclic population fluctuations, 194
Cyclodextrin, 542
Cyclones, 113
Cyclone separator, 442
Cypress swamp, 162
Cytosine (C), A4

Daly, Herman E., 698–699, 704
Damaged ecosystems, rehabilitating and
        restoring, 628–629
Dam removal, salmon restoration and, 656–657
Dams
    building, 334
    environmental consequences of, 400
    tropical deforestation and, 616
    using, 318–321
Daniel, Pauly, 649
Dartmouth College, as green college, 752
Dartmouth Medical School report, 496
Darwin, Charles, 96, 191
Data, scientific, 41
Data analysis, 91
Davidson, Carlos, 747
Davidson, Eric, 46
Davis, California
    ecocity concept in, 660
    green college at, 753
DDE, in the Great Lakes, 493
D–D (deuterium–deuterium) fusion reaction,
        58, 376
DDT (dichlorodiphenyltrichloroethane), 29, 33, 55,
        231, 513, 518
Death rates, 255
    effects of a rise in, 266–267
    factors affecting, 261–263
Deaths
    causes of, 228, 247
    from infectious diseases, 245
    from motor vehicle accidents, 673
Death Valley National Monument, 620
d'Eaubonne, Françoise, 745
Debt, of developing countries, 708, 709
Debt-for-nature swaps, 616–617
Decentralized power system, 411
Deceptive behavior, avoiding predation via, 177
Deceptive looks, avoiding predation via, 177
Decibel-A (dbA) sound pressure units, 670
Deciduous forests, 70, 123, 124
    soil in, 215
    temperate, 136, 137–139
    tropical, 137
Deciduous plants, broadleaf, 125
Decision making, in traditional and sustainable
        societies, 17
Decomposers, 72, 74, 75–76, 79
    in aquatic life zones, 145
    sea-bottom, 153
Decomposition boreal forest, 139
Decorative plants, role in extinction, 581–582
Deductive reasoning, 44
Deep ecology, 745, 746
Deep-ocean floor habitat, 635
Deep-ocean heat absorption, 458
Deep-sea mining, 638
Deep-well disposal, 545

Deer population, 589
Defendant, 723
Defenders of Wildlife, 589
Deferred grazing, 300–301
Deforestation, 90, 333
    species decline via, 165
    tropical, 612–619
Degradable pollutants, 55
Degradable wastes
    in groundwater, 493
    stream breakdown of, 487, 488
Degradation. *See also* Environmental degradation
    role in extinction, 572–573
    of tropical forests, 612, 614–616
Degraded ecosystems, restoring and rehabilitat-
        ing, 629
Degree of isolation, 168
Deliberately introduced species, 575–577. *See also*
        Nonnative species
Demand, in economic decisions, 691–692
Democracies, 717
Demographically divided world, 263–264
Demographic data
    comparison of, 260
    for India and China, 271
Demographic indicators, comparison of, 264
Demographic revolution, 755
Demographic transition, 259, 269
Demographic trap, 269
Denitrification, 87. *See also* Nitrogen ($N_2$)
Denmark
    environmentally sustainable economy in,
        710–712
    industrial ecosystem in, 532
Density, population, 191
Density-dependent population controls, 193
Density-independent population controls, 193
Depletion allowances, 346
Depletion curves, for nonrenewable resources, 346
Depletion strategy, 702
Depletion time, 346
Deposit feeders, 153
Depression, Great, 28
Desalination, 328
Desert animals and plants, 125, 126–128
Desert biomes, 125–128
Desert ecosystem, temperate, 127
Desertification, 220–221
    causes and consequences of, 221
    world map of, 220
Deserts, 70, 123, 124
    annual temperature in, 126
    human impacts on, 128
    major types of, 125
    map of earth's, 126
Desert soil, 215
Desiccation, 317
Design revolution, 533
Destructive earthquakes, 210
Detoxification of wastes, 542
Detritivores (detritus feeders), 74, 75, 77, 79
Detritus, 74
Deuterium, 48. *See also* D–D (deuterium–
        deuterium) fusion reaction; D–T
        (deuterium–tritium) fusion reaction
Devall, Bill, 746
Developed countries, 5–6. *See also* Developing
        countries
    environmental impact in, 12, 13
    flooding in, 332–334
    freshwater supplies in, 318
    urban growth in, 662
Developers, land-use planning and, 680. *See also*
        Development
Developing countries, 6
    agricultural aid to, 309
    aid to, 709
    coastal pollutants in, 497
    death rates in, 269
    debt of, 708, 709
    drinking water in, 507
    economic growth of, 10
    emission reductions by, 469
    energy sources in, 351

environmental impact in, 12, 13
exporting hazardous waste to, 547
flooding in, 334
freshwater supplies in, 318
fuelwood crisis in, 617–618
improving health care in, 244
indoor air pollution in, 443
infectious diseases in, 244, 245
poverty in, 707–708
reducing water pollution in, 509–510
saving children in, 289
technology transfer to, 466
undernutrition and malnutrition in, 285–286
urban population in, 661–662
Development
  sustainable economic, 698
  waterway, 657
Development rights, 681
Devices, efficiencies of, 381–382
Devil's Hole pupfish, 564
Dew point, 83
Diarrheal diseases, 237
Dichlorodifluoromethane ($CCl_2F_2$), 472, 473
Dichlorovos, 519
Dieback, 192, 193
Dieldrin, versus malaria, 200
Diet, healthiest, 287. See also Food entries;
  Nutrients
Differential reproduction, 101
Digitalis purpurea, 569
Dimethyl sulfide (DMS), 88, 89
Dioxins, 34, 531, 541, 551–552
Direct costs, 701
Directional natural selection, 101–102
Direct solar energy systems, 394
Dirty dozen list of chemicals, 555
"Dirty" radioactive bombs, 373–374
Discharge area, 315
Discharge trading policy, 503
Discontinuities, 47
Discount rate, 702
Disease. See also Diseases; Epidemic diseases;
    Infectious diseases
  amphibian decline and, 170, 171
  flooding and, 486
Disease-causing organisms
  killing, 508
  strengthening populations of, 199
Diseases. See also Disease
  insect-transmitted, 514–515
  pesticide-related, 518
  water-related, 484–485
Dispersion, of populations, 191
Dissolved oxygen (DO) content, 74
  in aquatic life zones, 146
  of water, 485
Distillation, 328
Distributed receiver system, 396
Disturbances, 183–184
Disturbed land, natural restoration of, 181
Divergence (divergent evolution), 104–105
Divergent plate boundaries, 207, 208
Diversifying natural selection, 102, 103
Diversity. See Biodiversity; Cultural diversity;
    Ecological diversity; Functional diversity;
    Genetic diversity; Human cultural diversity;
    Species diversity
DMS. See Dimethyl sulfide (DMS)
DNA (deoxyribose nucleic acid), 50, 100, A3–A4
  from coral, 155
  in cells, 67
  structure of, A4
DNA testing, commercial whaling and, 646
DO content. See Dissolved oxygen (DO) content
Doctrine of riparian rights, 329
Document services, 533
Dodo, 563
Doll, Richard, 515
Domestication, of animals, 24
Donora, Pennsylvania, air pollution disaster at, 29,
    423, 427
Dorr, Ann, 339
Dose, 230
Dose-response curve, 231, 232, 233

Double helix, A3–A4
Doubling time, 4
Doubly green revolution, 308
Dow Chemical, 534
Downcycling, 535
Drainage basin, 159, 314
Drainage systems, in limiting beach erosion, 648
Dredge spoils, 501
Dredging, 341, 342
Drift-net fishing, 302
Drilling technologies, 355
Drinking water. See also Bottled water
  chlorine in, 551
  contamination of, 488
  pollutants in, 493
  purification of, 508
  quality of, 507–510
  standards for, 497
Drip irrigation systems, 330–331, 333
Driscoll, Charles T., 432
DRiWATER(r), 333
Drought, 317
  amphibian decline and, 170, 171
  Dust Bowl and, 219
Dry cleaning, 530
Dry climate, 317
Dry deposition, 428
Dry thorn scrub, animals of, 130
D–T (deuterium–tritium) fusion reaction,
    58, 376
Du Pont Corporation, 534
Dubos, René, 3
Ducks Unlimited, 590
Duke University, as green college, 753
Dunes, primary and secondary, 152
Dung beetles, 172
Dung burning, 618
Durant, Will, 204
Durham, Jimmie, 25
Durian fruits, 165
Dusky seaside sparrow, 563
Dust, wind-borne, 110
Dust Bowl, 219
Dying from Dioxin (Gibbs), 530

Early conservation era, 26–29
Early loss curves, 198
Early successional species, 181, 182, 589
Earth, 95. See also Global entries; Planet; World
    entries
  biological evolution of, 98
  changes in reflectivity of, 457
  chemical and biological evolution of, 96, 99
  economic value of biodiversity of, 570, 571
  emergence of life on, 96, 99
  energy flow to and from, 69
  ethical guidelines for working with,
      747–750
  green future for, 446
  implementing education about, 750
  internal and external processes of, 205–209
  learning from, 751
  major biomes of, 123
  management of, 743–744
  natural resource depletion on, 186–187
  projected biodiversity status of, 562
  rotation of, 116
  structure of, 68, 204
  temperature increase of, 457
  working with, 18
Earth-centered environmental worldview, 745
Earth Charter, 731, 749–750
Earth Day, 30, 31, 35
Earth Island Institute, 31, 32
Earth Policy Institute, 325
Earthquake hazards, reducing, 211
Earthquake ratings, 210
Earthquakes, 210–211
  map of North American, 211
Earthquake sites, 206–207
Earth Sanctuaries, Ltd., 629
Earth's crust, 68, 204
  major features of, 205
Earth-sheltered housing, 446

Earth's life-support systems, 14, 68–70
Earth's surface, uneven heating of, 115
Earth tubes, 395
Easter Island, 40, 45, 192
Eastern gamma grass, 277
Ebola, 237–238
Echo-boom generation, 259, 265
Ecocentric environmental worldviews, 742,
    744–745
Ecocities, 660, 684–685
Eco-economy, 695
Ecofeminist worldview, 745–746
Ecofriendly businesses, 710
Ecoindustrial networks, 707
Ecoindustrial revolution, 531–533
Ecolabeling programs, 555, 695, 704, 712, 737
Ecological benefits, of forests, 609–610
Ecological design arts, 684–685. See also Green
    design
Ecological diversity, 76
Ecological economists, 693–695, 697, 698–699
  environmental conceptions of, 690
Ecological efficiency, 77
Ecological extinction, 563
Ecological footprint, 10
Ecological identity, 750
Ecological land-use planning, 676–677
  six steps in, 680
Ecological management, adaptive, 626–627
Ecological niches, 103–104
  re-creating, 629
Ecological restoration, 628–631
  purpose of, 630
Ecological services, 570
  economic value of, 571
Ecological Society of America, 27
Ecological stability, 184–187
Ecological succession, 180–184
  effect of disturbances on, 183–184
  species replacement in, 182–183
  stages of, 182
Ecological thinking, 749
Ecologists, 3
Ecology, 3, 30, 64
  deep, 746
  goal of, 68
  nature of, 65–68
  of coral reefs, 144
Ecology of Commerce, The (Hawken), 534
Ecomark program, 555
Economic benefits, of forests, 609
Economic decisions, 691–692
Economic development, 5–7
  birth rates and, 267–270
  environmentally sustainable, 15–18, 695,
      698–699
Economic disincentives, 704
Economic drivers, 691
Economic effects, of soil erosion, 218
Economic goods, biodiversity and, 569–570
Economic growth, 4–5, 14, 15
  of China, 15
  in Middle East, 312
  physical and biological limits to, 747
  poverty and, 707–708
Economic incentives, environmental quality
    and, 704
Economic indicators of globalization, 7
Economic justice, 696–697
Economic output, global increase in, 2, 5
Economic penalties, 15
Economic progress, monitoring, 696–697
Economic resources, 691. See also Resources
  environmental problems and, 691–695
Economic revolution, 755
Economic rewards/penalties, 15
  birth rates and, 271
  changing, 713
Economic systems
  developing environmentally sustainable,
      738
  types of, 691–692
Economic threshold, pesticides and, 520
Economically depleted minerals, 346

Economically depleted resources, 9
Economics
  ecological services and, 571
  effect on mineral resource supplies, 346–348
  fishery management and, 651
  of pollution control, 700–703
  role in energy resource use, 412–413
Economies (economy)
  acid deposition and, 430
  environmentally sustainable, 710–713
  steady-state, 698–699
  urban sprawl and, 666
Economists
  conventional versus ecological, 690, 693–695,
    697, 698–699
  environmental conceptions of, 690
Eco-ranching, 599
Ecoreligion, 746
Eco-roofs, 390–391
Ecosystem approach, 594
Ecosystem damage, preventing, 630
Ecosystem diversity, preserving, 568
Ecosystem models, 91
Ecosystems, 64–94. See also Damaged ecosystems;
    Degraded ecosystems
  biosphere and, 748
  boundaries of, 71
  changes affecting, 183
  human impacts on, 199–201
  learning about, 89–92
  major components of, 71, 73–74, 75
  matter cycling in, 82–89
  matter waste in, 76
  nonequilibrium state of, 622
  preserving, 568–569
  primary productivity of, 80–82
  priorities for protecting, 630–631
  response to change by, 180
  types of, 81
Ecosystem services, 92
  human disturbances and, 185
Ecosystem stability, species diversity and, 185
Ecosystem sustainability, 92
Ecotones, 71, 123, 166
Eco-tourism, 570
Ecuador, reusable containers in, 535
Edge effects, 166
Education
  in Curitiba, Brazil, 678
  in ecological design arts, 684–685
Efficiency
  ecological, 77
  energy, 59
Efficiency revolution, 754
Effluent fees, 704
Egg pulling, 587
Egypt, Nile River damming and, 312, 321
Ehrenfeld, David W., 744, 745
Ehrlich, Ann, 309
Ehrlich, Paul, 30, 309
Einstein, Albert, 44, 555
Eisenhower, Dwight D., 366
Eisley, Loren, 145
Ejecta, 211
Ekman spiral, 118
El-Ashry, Mohamed, 328, 414
Election finance reform, 721
Electric bicycles, 674
Electric cars, 384, 386–387
Electric motors
  efficient, 384
  energy-wasting, 384–385
Electricity
  as an alternative to natural gas, 406
  cost of, 392
  in Curitiba, Brazil, 678
  geothermal, 410
  global production of, 351
  in passive solar design, 390
  plasma and, 542
  producing from heat stored in water, 401
  producing from moving water, 400–401
  producing from nuclear power, 367
  producing from tides and waves, 401

producing from wind, 401–403
producing with solar cells, 398–400
sources of, 385
using solar energy to generate, 396–397
Electrolysis, 405
Electromagnetic radiation spectrum, 52
Electronic waste (e-waste), 526
Electrons, 47
  in plasma, 50
Electrostatic precipitator, 442
Elements, 47
  periodic table of, A2
Elephants, 172, 565, 573
  protecting from extinction, 580–581
Elk herds, 589
El Niño-Southern Oscillation (ENSO), 119–120,
    121, 305
  global climatic effects of, 120
El Segunda blue butterfly, 565
Emergency action strategy, for biodiversity,
    624–626
Emergent layer, in forests, 601
Emerson, Ralph Waldo, 513
Eminent domain, 725
Emission credits, 466–467
Emissions, dioxin, 552. See also Carbon dioxide
    emissions
Emissions trading, 441, 442
Emphysema, 437, 438
Employment, environment and, 713. See also
    Careers
Endangered and threatened species list, 583
Endangered plants, refuges for, 586
Endangered species, 563, 564–565. See also
    Threatened species
  alligators as, 173
  black market demand for, 580
  flying foxes as, 165
  marine, 640–643
  protecting all, 585
Endangered Species Act (ESA) of 1973, 30,
    583–584, 584–585, 594, 641, 724
  accomplishments of, 586
Endangered Species laws, 582–583
Endemic species, 572, 612
Endocrine system, chemical harm to, 234–235
End-of-pipe pollution controls, 537
Energy. See also Energy efficiency (productivity)
  from chemical reactions, 54
  daily use per person, 350
  effects of urban sprawl on, 666
  forms and quality of, 51–54
  net, 382, 383
  origin of life and, 97
  producing from biomass, 403–405
  types of, 349–352
  units of, A1
Energy changes, laws governing, 59–60
Energy conservation, research on, 35
Energy content, 52
Energy conversion devices, efficiencies of, 381–382
Energy efficiency (productivity), 59, 381–383
  improving, 383–393, 465
  net, 382, 383, 391
Energy efficiency revolution, 380
Energy flow pyramids, 77–79
Energy flows, interfering with, 199
Energy policies, 353
Energy Policy and Conservation Act of 1975, 31
Energy prices, 413
Energy quality, 53–54, 59
Energy research and development funds, 377
Energy resources, 9, 339
  decision making about, 353
  economics and, 412–413
  evaluating, 349–354
  quality of, 53
  sustainable, 412–413
Energy-saving devices, 390
Energy-saving measures, 384–385
Energy taxes, 465
Energy waste, 381
  reducing, 382, 393
English units, A1

Enhanced greenhouse effect, 450
Enoughness principle, 751
Environment, 3
  crime reduction and, 671
  cultural change and, 22–25
  employment and, 713
  poverty and, 8
Environmental accounting, 695, 697
Environmental activism, 530–531
Environmental careers, 624
Environmental conditions, adaptation and, 104
Environmental damage warning, 13
Environmental decade, 31
Environmental Defense Fund, 30, 727
Environmental degradation, 9. See also
    Degradation
  as consequence of agricultural revolution, 24
  economics and, 695
  internalizing external costs of, 699–700
Environmental disturbances, 183–184
Environmental economic revolution, 690
Environmental education, in Curitiba, Brazil, 678
Environmental effects, of globalization, 8
Environmental era of U.S. history, 25, 29–36
Environmental ethics, 14, 742
Environmental events (1930–1960), 29
Environmental factors, as hazards, 229
Environmental groups, 730
  grassroots, 728–729
  mainstream, 727–728
  success of, 729–730
Environmental history, 21–38
  of the United States, 25–36
Environmental impacts, of using mineral re-
    sources, 343–346
Environmental indicator species, 575, 697
Environmental injustice, 555. See also Environ-
    mental justice
Environmental Insurance Resolution Fund, 554
Environmentalism, 536
Environmental issues, 2–20
  controversial nature of, 730–731
  described, 2
Environmentalists, 3
Environmental justice, 701, 718
  poverty and, 728–729
Environmental laws, 624, 723–727. See also Laws;
    Regulations
  federal agencies concerned with, 719
Environmental lawsuits, hindrances to the effec-
    tiveness of, 725–727
Environmental leadership, 718
Environmentally beneficial technologies, 12
Environmentally harmful technologies, 12
Environmentally sustainable economic develop-
    ment, 15–18, 695, 698–699
Environmentally sustainable economies, transi-
    tioning to, 710–713
Environmentally sustainable political systems, 738
Environmentally sustainable society, 4, 748–749
Environmental management, 705–707
Environmental movement, 33, 36
  beginning of, 29
Environmental networks, international, 727
Environmental pessimists, 14, 16
Environmental policy. See also Global environ-
    mental policy
  developing and influencing, 717–718
  guidelines for, 717–718
  individuals and, 718
  politics and, 716, 717
  in the United States, 719–723
Environmental Policy Act of 1969, 30
"Environmental president," 34
Environmental problems, 12–13
  economic resources and, 691–695
  seriousness of, 13–14
  working for solutions to, 718
Environmental programs, 28–29
Environmental progress, monitoring, 696–697
Environmental protection agencies, 731
Environmental Protection Agency (EPA), 30, 36,
    485, 513–514, 719
  drinking water standards of, 497

emission standards by, 439
    Love Canal cleanup and, 525
    pesticide banning by, 518–519
    radon surveys by, 436
    studies by, 434, 435
    National Surface Water Survey (NSWS) of, 431
Environmental quality
    economic disincentives and incentives and, 704
    improving, 36, 703–707, 707–710
Environmental refugees, 317, 338
Environmental Research Foundation, 536
Environmental resistance, 191
Environmental revolution, 15–16
    components of, 754–755
Environmental science, 3, 47
Environmental scientists, 3
Environmental shortages, conflicts arising from, 731
Environmental showcase
    Curitiba, Brazil as, 678–679
    Tapiola, Finland as, 683
Environmental stress, effects of, 200
Environmental studies programs, 35
    critical thinking in, 42–43
Environmental surprises, anticipating, 47
Environmental threshold, 47
Environmental wisdom worldview, 14–15, 745
Environmental Working Group, on mercury-contaminated fish, 550
Environmental worldviews, 750
    biocentric and ecocentric, 744–745
    clash of, 14–15
    ecofeminist, 745–746
    human-centered, 743
    life-centered, 743–744
    in industrial societies, 742–743
    social ecology, 746–747
EPA. *See* Environmental Protection Agency (EPA)
E-paper, 535
Epicenter, 210
Epidemic disease
    amphibian decline and, 170, 171
    tuberculosis as, 241
Epidemiological studies, 232
Epilimnion, 157
Epiphytes, 179
Equatorial upwellings, 119
Erosion, 132, 208. *See also* Soil erosion
    beach, 647–648
    in Madagascar, 148
    mining and, 343
    by streams, 159–160
Eruptions, ecological impact of, 203
*Escherichia coli*, 508, 522
Essentially nontoxic substances, 232
Estuaries, 147–148, 149
    oil-polluted, 502
Estuarine zone, 148
Estuary habitat, 635
Ethanol, 405, 406
    liquid, 404
Ethics
    of corporations, 692
    guidelines for, 747–750
    in resource use, 702
Ethiopia, Nile River damming and, 312, 321
Eubacteria, A5
Eucalyptus trees, 619
Eukaryotic cell
    origin of life and, 99
    structure of, 67
Eukaryotic organisms, 65
Euphotic zone, 146, 148, 153
Eurasian ruffe, 576, 655
Europe
    atmospheric warming in, 464
    private versus public property rights in, 683
    reducing urban sprawl in, 680
    tax-shifting approach in, 705
European red mite, geographic range of, 515
European starling, 576
European Union (EU), 394
    environmental laws in, 736
European wild boar (pig), 576, 577

Eutrophication, 157, 158, 490
Evaporation, 82
Evaporite mineral deposits, 340
Even-aged forest management, 601
Everglades National Park, 620, 652–653
Evergreen coniferous forests, 139
    components and interactions in, 140
Evergreen plants
    broadleaf, 125
    coniferous, 125
*Evernia* lichen, 418
Evolution, 96–100, 100–103
    misconceptions about, 104
Exclusive economic zones (EEZs), 646, 649
Executive branch, 719–720
Existence
    as nonuse biodiversity value, 570
    what sustains, 3–4
Exotic plant and pet market
    role in extinction, 581–582
    trading in, 581–582
Exotic species, 169
Experimental group, 43, 232
Experimental system, 90
Exploitation competition, 174
Exponential age, living in, 2, 5
Exponential growth, defined, 2
Exponential population growth, 5, 192, 193, 255
External benefit, 698
External costs, 697–698
    internalizing, 699–700
External processes, 208
    of earth, 209
Extinction(s), 105–106, 198. *See also* Commercial extinction; Premature extinctions
    of amphibians, 170–171
    of blue whale, 643
    bounceback period after, 108–109
    effect on biodiversity, 106–107
    as environmental issue, 2
    from habitat loss and degradation, 572–574
    from hunting and poaching, 579–581
    nonnative species and, 574–579
    premature, 560
    protecting wild species from, 582–588
Extinction-prone species, characteristics of, 566
Extinction rates, 563–567
    effects of human activities on, 567–568
    global, 561–562
Extinction spasms, 564, 567
Extreme weather, atmospheric warming and, 461, 462–463
Extremely toxic substances, 232
*Exxon Valdez* oil spill, 34, 360, 502

Facilitation, 183
Failsafe systems, 247–248
Fair trade labeling, 618
Falkenmark, Malin, 317
Fall overturn, 157
False killer whale, 644
Families, in classification, A5
Family planning, 270
    access to, 274
FAO. *See* United Nations Food and Agriculture Organization (FAO)
FAO international treaty, 291
Farm Act of 1985, 223
Farmers, 24
    in reducing greenhouse gases, 468
Farmers Home Administration, 223
Farming. *See also* Agriculture
    endangered species and, 587
    soil conservation in, 222–226
    tropical deforestation and, 616
Farm profits, pesticides and, 515
Farm subsidies, 307–308
Fat-soluble toxins, 230
Fault, 210
Favelas, 729
Fecal coliform bacteria test, 485
Fecal snow, 662–663

Federal Environmental Pesticide Control Act of 1972, 31
Federal Food, Drug, and Cosmetic Act of 1938, 29, 724
Federal Insecticide, Fungicide, and Rodenticide Act (FIFRA) of 1947, 29, 518
Federal Land Policy and Management Act of 1978, 31
Federal resource conservation policy, 29
Federal Water Pollution Control Act of 1972, 503, 724
Federation of American Scientists, 373
Feedback loops, 45, 456
Feeding level, 76
Feed-lots, 297
Fens, 160
Feral cats, 577
Feral pigs, 576, 577
Fermentation, 75, 99
Fermenters, 99
Fermi National Accelerator Laboratory, 629–630
Ferret, 564, 581
Fertility, effects of reduced, 266–267
Fertility rates, 263, 264, 265, 270. *See also* Total fertility rate (TFR)
    changes in, 259
    factors affecting, 259–261
    global, 257–259
Fertilizer
    inorganic, 225–226
    organic, 225
    sludge as, 506
Fertilizer runoff, 492
    reducing, 502
Fetuses
    exposure to mercury, 550
    lead damage to, 547
Fiberglass, as a carcinogen, 435
Field ecosystem, components of, 72
Field research, 89–90
Filter feeders, 149, 154
Filter-feeding mussels, 485
Filtration, in advanced sewage treatment, 505
Financial resources, 691
Fine particles
    health dangers from, 440
    in suspended particulate matter, 426
Finland, 683
Fin whale, 645
Fire ant, 576, 578
Fires. *See* Forest fires
First decade of the environment, 30
First-generation pesticides, 513
First green revolution, 281
First law of thermodynamics, 59
Fish
    catching and raising, 301–307
    freshwater, 637
    in the Great Lakes, 493
    harvesting, 301–302, 302–304, 304–307
    major commercially harvested types of, 302
    marine, 636
    mercury-contaminated, 549–550
    toxic, 503
Fish catch, worldwide, 304
Fisheries, 301
    controlling access to, 649–650
    marine, 649–651
Fishery regulations, 650–651
Fish farming, 305
Fishing
    methods of, 301–302, 303
    tragedy of the commons and, 305
Fishing subsidies, 305, 651
Fish-killing microbes, 489
Fish kills, 488, 491
Fish polyculture, 306
Fish ranching, 305
Fish stocks, depletion of, 304
Fitness, 104
Flavin, Christopher, 691

Flesh flower, 76
Flood control levees, 160, 638
Flooding
  causes and effects of, 332–334
  deforestation and, 616
  spread of disease via, 242–243, 486
Flood insurance subsidies, federal, 647
Flood irrigation methods, 330
Floodplains, 160, 332
  in Bangladesh, 335
Floodplain zone, 159, 160
Flood-prone areas, identifying and managing, 334–335
Flood risks, reducing, 334–335
Floor layer, in forests, 601
Florida, alligators in, 173
Florida Bay, 653
Florida Everglades, restoring, 652–653. See also Everglades National Park
Florida Keys, 653
Florida manatee, 564
Florida panther, 564
Florida scrub jay, 574
Flowing systems, 156
Flow of matter and energy, 75
Flows, system, 45
Flu, 237, 238
Fluidized-bed coal combustion, 364
Fluorescent lamps, 392
  compact, 392
  efficiency of, 382
Fluoride ion (F⁻)
  in drinking water, 495
  in groundwater, 493, 495
Flying foxes, 165
Flyways, 590
Focus of an earthquake, 210
Food. See also Diet; Foods; Nutrients
  dioxins in, 552
  effects of ozone thinning on, 475
  for human consumption, 82
  fossil fuel energy required for production of, 280
  genetically modified, 290
Food chains, 76–77
Food distribution, 287–288
Food intake, average daily, 287
Food irradiation, 522
Food prices, 284, 307
Food production, 278–280
  agricultural policy and, 307–308
  global, 6
  increase in, 284–285
  major environmental effects of, 288–289
  major types of, 278–279
  urbanization and, 668
  in the United States, 281–283
Food Quality Protection Art (FQPA) of 1996, 519–520
Food resources, 277–311
Foods. See also Food
  new, 292–293
  organic, 308
  pesticide residues in, 518
Food supplies, pesticides and, 515
Food web, 77
  Antarctic, 78
  dynamics of, 635
Forbes magazine, on nuclear power mismanagement, 374
Forced simplicity, 751
Ford, William, 388
"Forecaring" principle, 187
Forest area, net change in, 605
Forest biomes, 134–141
Forest depletion
  as consequence of agricultural revolution, 24
  during frontier era, 26
Forest fires
  forest ecosystems and, 607–608
  suppression of, 608
  tropical deforestation and, 616
Forest health, 34
Forest management, 598–608
  major types of, 600–602

Forest Reserve Act of 1891, 26, 27
Forest reserves, 26
Forestry agreement, 731
Forests. See also National forests
  air pollution damage to, 438
  atmospheric warming and, 461, 462
  building roads into, 602
  degradation of, 604
  destruction of, 562
  effects of acid deposition on, 431–432
  effects of ozone thinning on, 475
  fate of, 604–605
  fires and, 607–608
  frontier, 630
  human impacts on, 141
  major types of, 134, 598–600
  pathogens and insects in, 606–607
  pollution and climate change threats to, 608
  services provided by, 600
  sustainable management of, 605–606
  in the United States, 609–612
  use of wastewater to grow, 507
  world distribution of, 136, 600
Forest service timber-cutting program, 610
Forest Stewardship Council (FSC), 606
Formaldehyde, 434
  exposure to, 435
Formosan termite, 576, 578, 579
Fossil fuel economies, 405
Fossil fuels, 85, 412, 448
  burning, 443–444
  gases from, 6–7
  global consumption of, 351
  global warming and, 465
  nonrenewable, 23, 352
  taxes on, 413
Fossil record, 99, 106
Fossils, 97–99
Foxglove, 569
Fracture zone, 208
France
  breeder reactors in, 376
  energy planning in, 385
"Frankenfood," 290
Franklin, Benjamin, 12, 335
Fraser, William, 463
Free-access resources, 11
Free-market approach, 412–413
Free-market economic system, 691
Free markets, 692
Free-market school, 743, 744
Free trade, illegal barriers to, 735–736
Freeman, David, 369
Freestanding new towns, 682
Freezing, of water, 313
French, Hilary F., 444
Freons, 472
Fresh water. See also Rivers; Streams
  in Antarctic ice shield, 453
  availability of, 314
  in Greenland ice shield, 454
  use of, 315–316
Freshwater biodiversity, 637
Freshwater ecosystem, components of, 72
Freshwater fisheries, managing and sustaining, 657
Freshwater habitat loss, 638
Freshwater inland wetlands, 160
Freshwater lakes
  life zones in, 156–157
  pollution of, 489–493
Freshwater life zones, 70, 145, 156–162
Freshwater marsh, 162
Freshwater rivers, 159–160
Freshwater shortages, 317–318
Freshwater solar ponds, 401
Freshwater species, extinction of, 638
Freshwater streams, pollution of, 486–488
Freshwater supplies, increasing, 318
Freshwater systems
  ecological and economic services provided by, 157
  human impacts on, 160–162
Friends of the Earth, 32

Frivolous lawsuits, 726
Frogs
  decline of, 170–171
  life cycle of, 171
Frontier, closing of, 26, 27
Frontier environmental worldview, 25–26
Frontier era of U.S. history, 25–26
Frontier forests, 598–600
Frontier science, 43, 44
Fronts, 111–112
Frost wedging, 208
Fuel-cell cars, 387–388
Fuel cells, 380
  cost of, 409
  efficiency of, 382
  role in the solar–hydrogen revolution, 408–409
Fuel economies, 388
Fuel-efficiency standards, 440
Fuels, producing from solid biomass, 404–405
Fuelwood crisis, 617–619
Fuelwood planting projects, 619
Fuentes, Carlos, 663
Fulghum, Robert, 738
Full-cost pricing, 692, 695, 699–700
Fumigants, 514
Functional diversity, 76
Fundamental land, 680
Fundamental niche, 103, 173, 175
Fungi, 65, 179
  classifying, A5
Fungicides, 513, 514
Furans, 551
Future generations, 745
Future of Life, The (Wilson), 630–631

Gadgil, Ashok J., 508
Galatis, George, 369
Galbraith, John Kenneth, 661
Game animals, wild, 166
Game management programs, 588
Gamma radiation, 56
  for pest control, 522
Ganges River, 319
Gangue, 344
Gannett, Allison, 389
Gap analysis, 624
Garbage, 526
Gardner, Gary, 686
Gardner, John W., 729
Gas development, in the Arctic National Wildlife Refuge, 360
Gases, 50. See also Natural gas
Gas mileage standards, 33, 36
Gasohol, 405
Gasoline, 28
  alternatives to, 406
  chemical energy available in, 59
  leaded, 548
  real cost of, 388
  reformulated, 406
Gasoline engine emissions, 440
Gasoline engines, efficiency of, 382
Gasoline prices, 386
Gasoline tax
  increases in, 674
  revenue from U.S., 677
Gause, G. F., 174
Gearheart, Robert, 507
Gender equality, 270
Gene banks, 586
Gene pool, 100
Genera (genus), A5
General Agreement for Sustainable Trade (GAST), 738
General Agreement on Tariffs and Trade (GATT), 733, 738
General circulation models (GCMs), 454, 456
Generalist species, 103
  cockroaches as, 105
General Mining Law of 1872, 345, 347, 597
Generation X, 265
Generation Y, 265
Gene revolutions, 290
Genes, 50

Gene splicing, 290
Genetically improved crop strains, 289–290
  advantages and disadvantages of, 292
Genetically modified food (GMF), 290, 736
Genetically modified organisms (GMOs), 290
Genetic damage, from ionizing radiation, 57
Genetic diversity, 67, 68, 76
Genetic engineering, 107, 290–292
  pest control and, 520, 521
Genetic information, 50
  from species, 570
Genetic plant library, shrinkage of, 295
Genetic variability, 100
Gene transfer, in bacteria, 238–239
Genuine progress indicator (GPI), 697
Geographic ecology, 141–142
Geographic information systems (GISs), 90, 91,
  676. See also GIS maps
  in Curitiba, Brazil, 679
Geographic isolation, 104
Geologic processes, 204
  within earth's interior, 205
  on the earth's surface, 208–209
Geologic resources, 339–379
Geology, 203–227
Georgia Power Company model, 389
Geothermal energy, 95, 409–410
  as nonrenewable energy source, 350
Geothermal reservoirs, 410
Germany
  Blue Angel program in, 555, 712
  environmentally sustainable economy in,
    710–712
  recycling and waste reduction in, 540
  reusable containers in, 535
"Germs," 65
Geysers, The, 410
Ghost bat, 564
Giant pandas, 104, 565
Giant toad, 576
Gibbs, Lois Marie, 525, 530–531
GIS maps, 624
GISs. See Geographic information systems
  (GISs)
Glacial periods
  Antarctic ice shield during, 453–454
  Greenland ice shield during, 454
Glass microspheres, storing hydrogen in, 408
Gleck, Peter H., 319
Global aging, 266
Global air circulation
  climate and, 115–118
  models of, 454
Global biodiversity, human impacts on,
  561–563
Global Biological Information Facility, 582
Global capitalist economy, 693
Global carbon cycle, 84–85, 458
Global climate, warmer, 460–464
Global climate change, as environmental
  issue, 2
Global Climate Coalition, 470
Global climate zones, maps of, 116, 117
Global cooling, 447
Global cooperation, 478, 479
Global Coral Reef Monitoring Network, 156
Global environmental policy, 731–738
Global extinction rate, 561–562
Global fertility rates, 257–259
Global fisheries, managing, 650–651
Global food production, increase in, 278, 281
Global Forum, 732
Global free trade, 692
  encouraging, 733–737
Globalization, 7–8
Global life expectancy, 261
Global market economy, pros and cons of, 693
Global oil reserves, 357
Global population growth, cutting, 274
Global seafood harvest, 307
Global security, 731
Global soil erosion, 217–219
Global solar energy, availability of, 396
Global temperature, variations in, 449

Global trade barriers, 734
Global warming, 7, 35, 36, 86, 120, 242, 294, 305,
  447, 448–452, 455–456. See also Atmospheric
  warming
  Antarctic ice shelf and, 453–454
  aquatic systems and, 639
  beneficial effects of, 460
  coral reefs and, 153
  effects of ozone thinning on, 475
  effects on food production, 289
  effects on water pollution, 486
  energy efficiency and, 465
  forest fires and, 608
  human-caused, 455, 457, 458
  major characteristics of, 451
  ocean currents and, 458
  options concerning, 464–465
  ozone depletion and, 479
  preparing for, 471–472
  reduction of species populations by, 463
  slowing, 467–469
  using the Internet to reduce, 393
  warning signs of, 450, 452–453
Global Water Policy Project, 503
Global water withdrawal, 315–316
Global wind power industry, 402
Glyphosate, 519
Gold mines
  Lake Victoria and, 634
  environmental effects of, 345
Golden Age of Conservation, 26
Golden-cheeked warbler, 574
Golden eagles, 589
Golden lion tamarin, 565
Golden rice, 287
Gorilla, 565
  as bushmeat, 580
Government. See also Democratic governments
  branches of, 719–720
  increasing role of, 26, 27
  major function of, 720
Government agricultural policy, 307–308
Government subsidies, 465–466, 614, 700, 702, 704
  for corporations, 692
Grade, of an ore, 345–346
Gradual ecosystem changes, 183
Grain area per person, average, 295
Grain import wars, 312
Grain production, 284, 285
Grain yields, 292
Grameen (Village) Bank, 709
Grand Canyon, 26, 620
Grass carp, 306
Grasses, rangeland, 297
Grasshoppers
  geographic range of, 515
Grasslands, 70, 123, 124, 128–134
  human impacts on, 134
  temperature and precipitation variations in,
    129
  world distribution of, 129
Grassland soil, 215
Grassroots action, 555–556, 718
Grassroots environmental groups, 35, 728–729
Gravel, in soil, 215, 216
Gravimeter, 341
Gravity, 69
  atmospheric pressure and, 112
Gravity flow irrigation systems, 330
Gray-air smog, 425
Gray fox, arctic fox and, 105
Gray water, 331
Gray whale, 645, 646
Gray wolf, 564, 594
Grazing, 128
  deferred, 300–301
  effects of, 297
Grazing animals, in the African savanna, 130
Grazing fees, 598
Grazing interests, 597–598
Great auk, 563
Great Barrier Reef Marine Park, 647
Great Depression, 28

Great earthquakes, 210
Great Lakes
  cultural eutrophication of, 654–655
  nonnative invaders in, 655–656
  pollution in, 491–493
  water quality problems of, 492
Great Lakes basin, 492
Great Lakes cleanup, EPA funding for, 493
Great Lakes pollution control program, 492
Great Plains, 219, 220
Great Smoky Mountains National Park, 620
Green algae, producing hydrogen from, 408
Green Belt movement, 619, 681
Green cities, 660, 684–685
Green colleges, 752–753
Green design, 398
  three principles of, 684–685
Greenhouse effect, 70, 86, 121, 448, 450. See also
  Enhanced greenhouse effect
  chemical makeup of atmosphere and, 120
Greenhouse gas emissions, 479
  reducing, 469–472
  soil conservation and, 468
  using the marketplace to reduce, 466–467
Greenhouse gases, 70, 120, 448–450
  accumulation of, 455
  from human activities, 449
  hydropower and, 400
  reducing, 440–441
Green job market, 624
Green Label program, 555
Greenland ice sheet, melting of, 453, 454
Green manure, 225
Greenpeace, 727
Greenpeace Germany, 728
Green Plan, 711–712
Green products, 700
Green revolutions
  crop yield increase during, 282
  expanding, 292
  food production by, 281–284
Green Seal labeling, 555, 704
Green taxes, 704, 706
Green tides, 498
Green turtle, 642
Greenways, 682
Grizzly bear, 565
Grocery bags, least-damaging, 535
Groins, in limiting beach erosion, 648
Gross domestic product (GDP), 4
  as a measure of economic and environmental
    health, 696–697
Gross national cost (GNC), 698
Gross national income (GNI), 4
  as a measure of economic and environmental
    health, 696–697
Gross national income in purchasing power parity
  (GNI PPP), 4
Gross national product (GNP), 4
Gross primary productivity (GPP), 80–82
  satellite data on, 81
Gross warming potential (GWP), 468
Gross world product (GWP), 4
Ground fires, 607
Groundfishes, harvest of, 305
Groundwater, 314–315
  contaminated, 325, 525
  landfill contamination of, 545
  mining, 327
  pesticide contamination of, 520
  protecting, 495
  tapping and withdrawing, 324–325
Groundwater deficits, in China, 293
Groundwater depletion, 84
  preventing or slowing, 326–328
Groundwater pollution, 493–495
Groundwater storage areas, 82–83
Groundwater studies, 493–495
Groundwater system, 315
Groundwater testing, 552
Groundwater use, common law and, 329
"Group of 10," 727
Guanacaste National Park, 630
Guanine (G), A4

Gulf of Mexico, 500
Gully erosion, 217
Gully reclamation, 225
GWP. *See* Gross world product (GWP)
Gypsy moth, 576, 606
    distribution of, 607
    geographic range of, 515

Habitat, 67, 103
    population size and, 198
Habitat conservation plans (HCPs), 584
Habitat corridors, 624
Habitat degradation, fish harvests and, 304–307
Habitat fragmentation, 199, 568, 573–574
    amphibian decline and, 170
    species decline and, 170–171
Habitat islands, 169, 573, 622
Habitat loss
    amphibian decline and, 170, 171
    freshwater, 638
    marine, 638
    role in extinction, 572–573
Habitat management, 589
Habitat modifications, by keystone species, 172
Habitat patch dynamics, 624
Hadley cells, 118
Half-life, 56
Halogen lightbulbs, 392
Halons
    as greenhouse gases, 449
    as ozone-depleting compounds, 473
Hamilton, Alice, 28
Hamshire College, as green college, 753
Harbor porpoise, 644
Hardin, Garrett, 30, 272–273
Hardrock mineral mining, 347
Harmful alga blooms (HABs), 498
Harmful effects
    beneficial effects versus, 46
    of pesticides, 516–518
Harvesting trees, 602–604
Hawken, Paul G., 16–17, 51, 533, 696, 710, 738, 712
Hawksbill sea turtle, 565, 642
Hazardous air pollutants (HAPs), 420
Hazardous chemicals, 233
Hazardous materials, common household, 527
Hazardous waste, 526–528
    biological detoxification of, 542
    burning, 543–544
    chemical detoxification of, 542
    exporting, 547
    from plastic production, 541
    incineration of, 548
    land disposal of, 545–547
    liquid, 494–495
    plasma-torch detoxification of, 542
    things considered not to be, 527–528
Hazardous waste dump sites
    cleanup of, 553
    identifying, 552
Hazardous waste regulation, 552–554
Hazardous waste shipments, accidents involving, 546–547
Hazards, major types of, 229
HBFCs, as ozone-depleting compounds, 473
Health
    atmospheric warming and, 461, 463–464
    effects of acid deposition on, 430
    effects of ozone thinning on, 475–476
    effects of urban sprawl on, 666
    groundwater contamination and, 493, 496–497
    indoor air pollution and, 444
    in Mexico City, 663
    particulate air pollution and, 440
    pesticides and, 514, 515, 518
    pollutants and, 422
    sludge fertilizer and, 506
    urbanization and, 669
Health Effects Institute, 440
Heat, 52. *See also* Energy entries; Temperature entries
    earth's internal, 205–206
    energy and, 51, 53
    plasma and, 542

in thermodynamics, 59, 60, 61
    water and, 313
    as water pollutant, 484
Heating
    low-temperature, 384
    solar, 393–400
Heat islands, 670–671
Heat stored in water, producing electricity from, 401
Heat transfer, 53
Heavy crude oil, 354
Heavy oils, 359–361
Heavy-rail systems, 675
Hegel, Georg, 750
Heinze-Fry, Jane, 42–43
Heliostats, 396
Helium (He), 477
Helsinki Commission, 499
Helsinki Convention, 499
Hemingway, Ernest, 22
Hemlock woolly adelgid, 606–607
Henslow's sparrow, 574
Hepatitis B, 237
    edible vaccine for, 242
Herbicides, 513, 514, 519. *See also* Pesticides
Herbivores, 74, 77, 79, 138
    behavior of, 177
    in grasslands, 128
    in rain forests, 135
    small, 132
    in tropical forest rivers, 161
Heritable traits, 101
Hetch Hetchy Valley, 26–27, 32
Heterotrophs, 74
Hexachlorobutadiene, as ozone-depleting compound, 473
Hidden costs, of gasoline, 388
Higher-level consumers, 74
High grading, 602–604
High-input agriculture, 278
High-input monocultures, 281
High-level radioactive waste, 370–372
High-pressure air mass (high), 112
High-quality energy, 53, 353
    one-way flow of, 68–69
High-quality matter, 51
High seas, 649
High-temperature heat, 396–397
High-throughput (high-waste) economies, 60
High tide, 148
Highwall, 342
High-waste approach to waste management, 529
High-waste society, 526
Highwater, Jamake, 25
Highways, gasoline tax and, 677
Hirschorn, Joel, 250
HIV. *See* Human immunodeficiency virus (HIV)
HIV/AIDS epidemic, 266
HIV-infected people, distribution of, 239–240
Holistic environmental worldviews, 742
Home pesticide products, 513–514
Home-building, nonwood, 611
Homes, reducing water waste in, 331
Homestead Act of 1862, 25
*Homo habilis*, evolution of, 98
*Homo sapiens sapiens*, 22
    evolution of, 98
Hong Kong, mass transit in, 675
Hoof-and-mouth disease, 297
Hooker Chemicals and Plastics, 525
Hoover Dam, 29
Hoover, Herbert, 28
Hormonally active agents (HAAs), 234, 235
Hormone blockers, 234, 235
Hormone mimics, 234, 235
Hormones, 234–235
    pest control and, 521–522
Hormone-treated beef, 736
Horseradish, purifying water using, 508
Hosts, 178
Hot dry-rock zones, 410
Hot spots. *See* Biodiversity hot spots
Hot water, geothermal energy from, 409, 410
Hot water insect spray, 522

House heating, net energy efficiencies for, 391
Household chemicals, 506
Household hazardous materials, 527
Houses
    earth-sheltered, 446
    in ecocities, 660
    heating via solar energy, 394–395
    naturally cool, 395
    passive solar design for, 390
    saving energy in, 389–393
    strawbale, 389–390
    superinsulated, 389
    waste heat from, 383
Hubbard-Brook Experimental Forest, 90, 432
Huckins, Olga, 33
Hughes Aircraft, ozone-saving discovery at, 479
Hughes, Jennifer, 568
Human activities. *See also* Human impacts
    alligators endangered by, 173
    carbon cycle and, 86
    effect on extinction rates, 566
    effect on global biodiversity, 561–562
    effect on the Chesapeake Bay, 500
    effects on extinction rates, 567–568
    extinction of passenger pigeon from, 560
    as a force in extinction, 107, 108–109
    future generations and, 745
    global warming and, 120, 455
    impact on freshwater systems, 160–162
    impacts on marine systems, 155–156
    in national parks, 620
    nitrogen cycle and, 87
    phosphorus cycle and, 88
    pollution from, 10
    sulfur cycle and, 88–89
    water cycle and, 84
Human beings
    basic needs of, 754
    damage to, 536–537
    efficiency of, 382
Human-caused ecosystem changes, 183
Human-centered worldviews, 742, 743
Human cultural diversity, 76
Human culture sphere, 14
Humane Society, 589
Human health, effects of food production on, 288
Human immunodeficiency virus (HIV), 240
Human impacts. *See also* Human activities
    deep ecology and, 746
    on aquatic biodiversity, 637–639
    on biodiversity, 561–563
    on deserts, 128
    on forests, 141
    on grasslands, 134
    on Madagascar, 612–613
Human population, 254–276
    factors affecting size of, 255–263
Human productivity, 17
Human reproduction rate, 748–749. *See also* Population
Human resources, 691
Human sociocultural system, 14
Human well-being, reducing poverty to improve, 707–710
Humboldt Bay, 507
Humidity, 83
Humility principle, 717
Humpback chub, 565
Humpback whale, 645
Humus, 213
    in soil, 215, 216
Hunger, 240, 242. *See also* Starvation
    poverty and, 318
Hunters, producing game animals and birds for, 588
Hunting. *See also* Sport hunting
    amphibian decline and, 170, 171
    of blue whales, 643
    extinction threats from, 579–581
    species decline via, 165
Hunting-and-gathering societies, 22
Hurricane Brett, 114
Hurricane damage, in North Carolina, 487

Hurricane Floyd, 487
Hurricanes, 113–114
 spread of disease via, 242
Hybrid-electric cars, 386–387
Hybrid gas-electric engine, 387
Hydrilla, 576, 655
Hydrocarbons (HCs), 49, 476–477
 chlorinated, 505
 volatile organic, 501–502
Hydrochlorofluorocarbons (HCFCs), 477
 as greenhouse gases, 449
Hydrofluorocarbons (HFCs), 477
 as greenhouse gases, 449
Hydrogen (H$_2$), 48, A3
 as fuel, 380, 386–389
 liquid, 407
 in periodic table, A2
 producing from green algae, 408
 pros and cons of using as an energy resource, 409
 reforming, 405
 replacing oil with, 405–407
 storing, 407–408
 in water, 54
Hydrogen bonds, 49, 313, A3, A4
Hydrogen chloride (HCl), A3
 in earth's atmosphere, 97
 as ozone-depleting compound, 473
Hydrogen cities, 409
Hydrogen economies, 405–407
Hydrogen energy system, 407
Hydrogen fuel storage, 388
Hydrogen ions (H$^+$), 48
Hydrogen isotopes, 48
Hydrogen peroxide (H$_2$O$_2$)
 chlorine versus, 530, 541
 purifying water using, 508
Hydrogen-powered fuel cells, 408–409
Hydrogen sulfide (H$_2$S), 88, 89, A3
 in earth's atmosphere, 97
Hydrogen utility districts, 409
Hydrologic cycle, 82, 83, 314. *See also* Water cycle
 mountains in, 141
Hydropower, advantages and disadvantages of, 401
Hydropower plants, 400–401
Hydrosphere, 68
Hydrothermal processes, 340
Hydrothermal vents, 97
Hypolimnion, 157
Hypotheses, scientific, 41

Ice, in Arctic Sea, 452
Ice albedo feedback system, positive, 457
Icebergs, towing, 328
Iceland
 as a hydrogen economy, 408–409
 whaling by, 646
Identified coal reserves, 363
Identified global oil reserves, 357
Identified resources, 339
Igneous rock, 209, 210
Illinois, tall-grass prairie restoration in, 629–630
Illinois bundleflower, 277
Immigration. *See also* Migration
 amphibian decline and, 170
 push and pull factors related to, 661
 to the United States, 268
Immune system, chemical harm to, 234–235
Immunization, 240–241
Imported oil, reducing dependence on, 358
Imported sand, in limiting beach erosion, 648
Incandescent lightbulbs
 efficiency of, 382
 energy-efficient, 392
Incinerators, 543–544
Income distribution, 696–697, 708
India
 drinking water in, 507
 slowing population growth in, 271–274
Indian elephant, 573
Indian Ocean, air pollution over, 430
Indian tiger, 573
Indicator species, 170–171, 485

Indigenous cultures, 613–614
Indirect costs, 701
Indirect solar energy systems, 394
Individuals
 ecology and, 755
 emission reductions by, 471–472
 lobbying by, 720
 political pressure by, 509–510
Individuals matter theme, 718
Individual transfer quotas (ITQs), 649, 650
Indonesia, integrated pest management in, 522
Indoor air pollution, 422, 434–437, 438
 preventing, 444
 reducing, 443
Inductive reasoning, 43–44
Indus River, 319
Industrial ecology, 532
Industrial ecosystem, 532
Industrial forestry, 601
Industrialization, of China, 15
Industrialized agriculture, 278, 279, 280
Industrial plants, 449
 release of toxic chemicals from, 528–529
*Industrial Poisons in the United States* (Hamilton), 28
Industrial revolution, 22, 23–24
 air pollution during, 423
 global warming and, 448–449
Industrial smog, 423, 425–428
Industrial societies
 advanced, 25
 environmental worldviews in, 742–743
Industrial stage of demographic transition, 269
Industrial waste
 ocean dumping of, 500–501
 stream pollution from, 488
 treatment of, 492
Industrial waste ponds, 494
Industry
 reducing water waste in, 331
 saving energy in, 384–385
Inertia, 185
Infant mortality, 6, 260, 261, 262–263
Infections, viral, 240–241
Infectious agents, as water pollutants, 484, 485
Infectious diseases, 8. *See also* Diseases
 global death rate from, 245
 malnutrition and, 8
 reducing incidence of, 244–245
 spread of, 241–243
Influenza, 237, 238
Information
 indicators of globalization, 7–8
 as utilitarian biodiversity value, 570
Information and globalization revolution, 22, 24–25
Information technologies, 24–25
Infrared radiation, 69, 70
Inherent value, 742
Inhibition, 183
Initial conditions, in climate models, 456
Inland wetlands, 160, 651
Inner core, of earth, 204, 206
Innovation-friendly regulations, 703, 704
Innovation management era, 706
Inorganic chemicals, 50, 97
 as water pollutants, 484
Inorganic fertilizers, 225–226
Input pollution control, 11
Inputs, system, 45
Insect birth control, 521
Insect-eating warblers, resource partitioning among, 175
Insecticides, 513, 514. *See also* Pesticides
 broad-spectrum, 516–517
 in cut flowers, 514
Insect pests, eliminating, 390
Insects
 controlling with spiders, 512
 ecological role of, 64
 tree damage by, 606–607
Insect species, edible, 292
Insect spray, hot-water, 522
Insect vectors, 242

Insignificant earthquakes, 210
*In situ* mining, 349
In-town new towns, 682
Institute for Local Self-Reliance, 727
Instrumental values, 742–743, 744
Insulation, 395
Insurance spraying, of crops, 520
Integrated coastal management, 500, 647
Integrated pest management (IPM), 522–523
Integrative principle, 718
Intensive agriculture, traditional, 279
Intercropping, 284
Interface Corporation, 534
Interference competition, 174
Interglacial periods, 447–448
Intergovernmental Panel on Climate Change (IPCC), 454–455. *See also* IPCC 2001 report
Intermediate disturbance hypothesis, 184, 622
Internal combustion engines, efficiency of, 382
Internal costs, 697–698
Internal processes, of earth, 205
International agreements, 478–479
International Atomic Energy Agency (IAEA), 374
International Bottled Water Association (IBWA) testing requirements, 509
International Center for Technology Assessment, 388
International environmental policy, developing, 731–733
International Food Policy Research Institute, 289
International migration, 267
International trade, GATT rules for, 733. *See also* Trade entries
International treaties, 582. *See also* Treaties
International Treaty on Persistent Organic Pollutants of 2000, 35
International Whaling Commission (IWC), 643–644, 645–646
Internet use, to save energy, 393
Interplanting, 284
Interspecific competition, 172, 173–174
Intertidal zone, 149–151
Intraspecific competition, 172
Intrinsic rate of increase (r), 191
Intrinsic value, 742–743, 744
 of biodiversity, 571
 of wilderness, 627
Invader species, 579, 580. *See also* Nonnative species
 killing with nitrogen gas, 580
Invertebrates, classifying, A5
Iodine deficiency, 287
Ionic bonds, 49, A2
Ionic compounds, 48, 49, A3
Ionizing radiation, 52, 370
 effects of, 57
 exposure to, 57
 types of, 56
Ions, 47, 48
 in plasma, 50
IPCC. *See* U.N. International Panel on Climate Change (IPCC)
IPCC 2001 report, 462–463, 463–464, 464–465
Iraq, irrigation in, 312
Iridium-192, 373
Iron deficiency, 287
Iroquois Confederation of Native Americans, 417, 745
Irrigated land, 293–294
Irrigation, 24. *See also* Drip irrigation; Water entries
 from the Aral Sea, 324–325
 from the Colorado River, 322
 large-scale, 294–295
 in the Middle East, 312, 321
 water waste in, 330–331
Irrigation technologies, low-cost, 331
Irrigation water
 government-subsidized, 329
 soil degradation by, 221–222
Irruption, 194
Island arcs, 208
Island biogeography, 168–169, 567, 572, 622

Islands, number of species on, 168–169. *See also* Heat islands
Islands of biodiversity, 141
Island states, atmospheric warming in, 464
Isle Royale
  moose and wolf interactions on, 197
  primary ecological succession on, 180
  sulfur dioxide pollution on, 418
Isolation, degree of, 168
Isotopes, 48
Israel, irrigation in, 330–331
Ivory trade, 580–581

Jackson, Wes, 277
Jacobson, Mark, 459
Jacops, Stanley, 453
James Bay Watershed Transfer Project, 323–324
Janzen, Daniel, 630
Japan
  kudzu vine from, 577
  whaling by, 645, 646
Japanese beetle, 576
Jennings, Daniel, 512
Jobs. *See* Employment
Jordan Basin, 312
Judicial branch, 720
Junk food advertising, 287
Junk mail, 526
Justice. *See* Environmental injustice; Environmental justice

Kalundborg, Denmark industrial ecosystem, 532
Kansas prairie, perennial crops on, 277
Kazakhstan
  Aral Sea water transfer disaster and, 325
  natural gas reserves in, 362
Kelp, 190
Kemp's ridley turtle, 642
Kenaf, 611–612
Kennebac River, 319
Kenya, 634
  Green Belt movement in, 619
Kerogen, 359
Keystone resources, protection of, 585
Keystone species, 165, 172, 567, 594, 635
  alligators as, 173
  sea otters as, 190
Killer bees, 169–170, 576
Killer whales, 644
  sea otter predation by, 190
Kinetic energy, 51
Kingdoms, A5
Kirtland's warbler, 463, 565, 574
Kissimmee River, 652, 653
Knowlton cactus, 565
Krebs, Charles J., 195
Krill, as whale food, 643, 645
K-selected species, 195, 196–198
Kudzu vine, introduction into the United States, 577
Kwashiorkor, 285
Kyoto treaty, 35, 36, 364, 469–471

Labeling, 704. *See also* Eco-labeling
Laboratory experiments, 90–91
  toxicity and, 232–233
Lacandon Maya Indians, agroforestry among, 618
Lacey Act of 1900, 27, 582
Ladybug beetles, pest control via, 521
Lake Baikal, 654
Lake Erie, pollution of, 30, 491–492
Lake habitats, 635
Lake Karachay, 372
Lake Merrit wildlife refuge, 27
Lake Nasser reservoir, 312, 321
Lake Okeechobee, 652, 653
Lakes
  effect of plant nutrients on, 157
  freshwater 156, 157
  greatest environmental threats to, 654–655
  pollution of, 489–493
  protecting, sustaining, and restoring, 654–657
  temperate, 157
Lake Victoria, 634

Lake Washington, 654
Lamprey, 576
Land. *See also* Public lands; Rangeland
  classification of, 225, 294
  climate and life on, 122–125
  effects of urban sprawl on, 666
  protecting from exploitation, 621
  restoring degraded, 629
Land abuse, 37
Land area, human disturbance of, 7
Land breezes, 122
Land conservation, 623
Land Conservation and Development Commission, in Oregon, 683
Land cultivation, 294–296. *See also* Agriculture; Farming
Land ecosystems, 80
Land ethics, 36–37
Landfill methane, using for heating, 549
Landfills. *See also* Secure hazardous waste landfills
  for radioactive waste disposal, 370
  sanitary, 544–545
  sludge in, 506
  toxic, 545
Landfill space, saving, 538
Landforms, external processes and, 209
Land Institute, 277
Land leasing, for wind power production, 403
Land-ocean hemisphere, 147
Landowners, protection of endangered species by, 583
Landslides, after earthquakes, 210
Land use, 595–598
  in Curitiba, Brazil, 678–679
  motor vehicles and, 673
  for producing electricity, 400
  urbanization and, 668
  zoning in, 677
Land-use ethic, 597
Land-use planning
  ecological, 680
  in Oregon, 683
  urban, 676–682
Land zones, 71
La Niña, 120, 121
Large marine systems management approach, 649
Large-scale hydropower, 400
Las Colinas, Texas, 682
Las Vegas
  impure water crisis in, 508
  urban sprawl in, 665
  water shortages in, 334
Late loss curves, 198
Lateral recharge, 315
Late successional species, 181, 182, 589
Latin America
  atmospheric warming in, 464
  countries of, 663
  environmental justice for, 729
Latinos, environmental justice for, 728–729
Latitude
  effect on species diversity, 167
  generalized effects of, 123, 124
Lava, 211
Law of conservation of energy, 59
Law of conservation of matter, 54, 55, 60
Law of progressive simplification, 752
Law of the Sea Treaty, 348
Law of tolerance, 73
Lawrence Berkeley National Laboratory, 392
Laws, 720. *See also* Environmental laws; Legislation; Regulations
  air-pollution, 440–441
  bills becoming, 722
  bottle-recycling, 31
  endangered species, 582–583
  environmental, 624, 723–727, 736
  forest management, 610–611
  hazardous-waste, 527–528
  on the high seas, 649
  influencing, 721–722
  national and international, 641
  for recycling and reuse, 539–540
  of thermodynamics, 59–60, 61

water, 329
  for water pollution control, 487
LD$_{50}$. *See* Median lethal dose (LD$_{50}$)
Leachate, 544, 545
Leaching, 215
Lead (Pb)
  as criteria air pollutant, 422
  dangers of, 547–548
  in groundwater, 493
  reducing exposure to, 548–549
Lead-Based Paint Poisoning Act of 1973, 31
Leaded gasoline, 548
Leader, 718
Lead exposure, 547–548
Leading by example, 718
Leatherback turtle, 642
Leave No Trace (LNT) wilderness ethic, 628
Lee, G. Fred, 545
Legal approach to protecting wild species, 582–586
Legal playing field, leveling, 727
Legislation. *See also* Clean Air Act entries; Laws; Regulations
  air pollution, 439
  pollution control, 443
Legislative branch, 719
Length, units of, A1
Lentic bodies of fresh water, 156
Leopold, Aldo, 14, 29, 32, 278, 446, 561, 597, 631, 745
  concept of land ethics of, 36–37
Lerner, Jaime, 679
Lethal mutations, 100
Levees, building, 334
Levin, Donald, 568
Levin, Philip, 568
Levitus, Sydney, 458
Lichens, 178
  as air pollution alarms, 418
Lichter, John, 459
Life, deep ecology and, 746
Life-centered environmental worldviews, 742, 743–747
Life-centered people, 746
Life cycle cost, 382
Life cycle cost analysis, 393
Life cycle management, 706
Life expectancies, 198, 250, 261
  global, 6
Life forms. *See* Organisms
*Life in the Woods* (Thoreau), 26
Life on earth, 95
  evolution of, 98, 99
  origins of, 96–100
  what sustains, 68–69
Life quality, 746
Lifestyle guidelines, deep ecology and, 746
Lifestyle risks, 246
Life table, 198
Life zones, freshwater, 156–162
Lightbulbs, 59
  efficiency of, 382, 392
Lighting, high-efficiency, 385
Light-rail systems, 675
  automobile manufacturers versus, 677
  in the United States, 677
Light-water reactors (LWRs), 365, 366
Likens, Gene, 433
Limestone, as carbonate reservoir, 86
Liming, 434
Limiting factor, 73–74, 87
*Limits to Growth*, 31
Limnetic zone, 156
Linberg, Steve, 545
Linderman, Chuck, 410
Liquefaction of rock, after earthquakes, 210
Liquefied natural gas (LNG), 362
Liquefied petroleum gas (LPG), 362, 384
Liquid hazardous wastes, deep-well disposal of, 545
Liquids, 50
  water as, 313

Literacy survey, 734
Lithosphere, 68, 204, 205, 211
Lithospheric plates
    types of boundaries between, 208
    world map of, 207
Littoral zone, 156
Livestock
    public rangeland and, 598
    raising, 296
Livestock diseases, 297
Livestock grazing, damage to riparian zones, 300
Livestock production, 298, 299
Livestock rotation, 301
Living, simple, 751–752
Living machines, 483, 507
Living organisms
    adaptability of, 536–537
    effects of air pollution on, 437–439
Living sustainably, 4
Living Technologies, 483
Loams, 215–216
Lobbying, 720
    by corporations, 692
Local extinction, 563, 568
Local outdoor air pollution, 428
Local population losses, 568
Loggerhead turtle, 642
Logging
    commercial, 36, 614
    in national forests, 610
    protecting forests from, 604
    tropical deforestation and, 614
Logging interests, 597–598
Logging roads, 602, 614
Logistic growth curve, 197
Logistic population growth, 192, 193
Loire River basin, 319
London, killer smogs in, 29
London Dumping Convention of 1972, 501
Longlining, 302
Longwall coal mining, 342
Lord Kennet, 717
Los Angeles, smog in, 425
Los Angeles basin, temperature inversions in, 427–428
Lotic systems, 156
*Love Canal: My Story* (Gibbs), 530
Love Canal, New York, toxic wastes in, 31, 32, 525, 530–531
Lovins, Amory B., 31, 51, 380, 381, 384–385, 393, 465, 533, 696
Lovins, Hunter, 380, 533
Low-emissivity (low-E) windows, 391
Low-energy precision application (LEPA) sprin-
    klers, 330
Lower-grade ores, mining, 348
Low-income countries, 6
Low-input agriculture, 308
Low-input agrodiversity, 284
Low-level radioactive waste, 369–370
Low-pressure air mass (low), 112–113
Low-quality energy, 53
Low-quality matter, 51
Low-temperature nuclear fusion, 376
Low-throughput (low-waste) economy, 61
Low tide, 148
Low-waste approach to waste management, 529
Low-waste society, achieving, 555–556
Lung cancer, 437
    from asbestos exposure, 436
    from radon, 435–436
Lungs, air pollution and, 437, 438
Lyman, Edwin, 375–376
Lynx-hare cycle, 194–195

Maathai, Wangari, 619
MacArthur, Robert H., 168, 169, 175, 195
Macroevolution, 100
Macronutrients, 285
Madagascar
    biological diversity threatened in, 612–613
    erosion in, 148
Mad cow disease, 297
Maden, John, 655

Magma, 211, 410
    ore formation from, 339–340
Magnetometer, 341
Magnitude of an earthquake, 210
Mainstream environmental groups, 727
Maintenance/protection costs, 701
Major earthquakes, 210
Malaria, 200, 237, 244, 514
    life cycle of, 243
    worldwide distribution of, 243
Malnutrition, 8, 240, 242, 266, 285. *See also*
    Starvation; Undernutrition
    poverty and, 318
    seriousness of, 285–286
Malthus, Thomas, 747
Mammoth Cave, 620
Mammoth wildrye, 277
Man and Biosphere (MAB) Programme, 626
*Man and Nature* (Marsh), 26
Manatee, 564
Manganese nodules, 340
Mangrove forests, 149
    in Bangladesh, 335
    clearing of, 638
    human impacts on, 155
Mantle, 204, 205
Mantle plumes, 205
Manufactured resources, 691
Manufacturing processes, redesigning, 529,
    530–531
Manure
    animal, 225
    burning, 404
    green, 225
    from livestock production, 299
    runoff and infiltration of, 502
Manuscript preparation, electronic versus paper,
    393
Maquiladores, 728
Marasmus, 285
Marginal land, 294
Marine biodiversity, 636. *See also* Aquatic
    biodiversity
    patterns of, 635
    protecting and sustaining, 640–648
Marine depth, effect on species diversity, 167.
    *See also* Water depth
Marine ecosystems, 85–86
    pharmaceuticals from, 636
Marine fisheries, managing and sustaining,
    649–651
Marine habitat loss, 638
Marine habitats, protecting, 651
Marine hot spots, 631
Marine life zones, 70, 145
Marine Mammal Protection Act of 1972, 31
Marine mammals
    effect of sewage dumping on, 501
    endangered, 641
Marine protected areas (MPAs), 646
Marine Protection, Research, and Sanctuaries Act
    of 1972, 31
Marine reserve studies, 646–647
Marine sanctuaries, protected, 646–647
Marine species, endangered, 640–643
Marine systems
    ecological and economic services provided by,
    147
    human impacts on, 155–156
Marine toad, 576
Market approaches, relying on, 705
Market economic systems
    differing views of, 693–695
    government intervention in, 692–693
Market forces, 704
    using to improve environmental quality,
    703–707
Marketplace, in reducing greenhouse gas
    emissions, 466–467
Market price equilibrium point, 691–692
Markets, 691
    economic decisions in, 691–692
    sustainable living and, 748–749
Markey, Ed, 368–369

Marlboro College, as green college, 752
Marriage, average age at, 260
Mars, 95
Marsh, George Perkins, 26, 39
Marshall, Robert, 32
Marshall Plan, 266
Marshes, 160
Mass, units of, A1
Mass-burn incinerators, 543
Mass depletions, 106, 107
    human-caused, 108–109
Mass extinctions, 106, 107, 564, 567
    human-caused, 108–109
Mass number, 48
Mass production techniques, 24
Mass transit, 671, 679
    automobile manufacturers versus, 677
    in Curitiba, Brazil, 678
    gasoline tax and, 677
    in Singapore, 672
    in the United States, 677
Mass transit rail systems, 675
Material efficiency, 51
Material flow economy, 533. *See also* High-
    throughput (high-waste) economies
Material resources, types of, 9
Materials, effects of air pollutants on, 439
Materials-recovery facilities (MRFs), 537, 538
Materials revolution, 349
Mathematical climate models, 454, 456
Mathematical models, 45
Mather, Stephen T., 27–28
Matter
    cycling of, 69, 82–89
    defined, 47
    forms, structure, and quality of, 47–51
    law of conservation of, 54, 55
    organization of, 66
    recycling of, 60–61, 75
    states of, 50–51
Matter and energy flow, 75
Matter-recycling economy, 60–61
Mature community, 184
Maximilian sunflower, 277
Maximum contaminant levels, 508
Maximum sustained yield (MSY), 588, 649
Mayak, plutonium production facility explosion
    at, 372
Mayo, Dana, 732
McCann, Kevin S., 747
McGinn, Anne Platt, 556, 657
Mead, Margaret, 18, 480
Meadows, Donella, 745
Measles, 237
Meat production, 296–301
    crop residue recycling and, 298
    environmental consequences of, 297–298, 299
Mechanical methods of oil cleanup, 502
Mechanical weathering, 208
Median lethal dose ($LD_{50}$), 231
    table of, 232
Mediation, 726
Medical wastes, 543–544
Medicines, derivation of, 569–570
Mediterranean climate, 134
Mediterranean fruit fly (medfly), 521
Megacities, 661, 662
Megalopolises, 666–668
Megareserves, 622
"MEGO (my eyes glaze over) factor," 735
Melanocytes, 476
Melanoma, malignant, 476, 478
Melis, Tasios, 408
Mellon, Margaret, 239
Membrane-based technologies, in advanced
    sewage treatment, 505
Menander, 92
Mendes, Chico, 734
Menominee nation, lumber harvesting by, 606
Mental models, 45
Merchant fleet, sewage dumping by, 501
Mercury (Hg)
    reducing exposure to, 550–551
    threat from, 549–550

Mercury emissions, 550–551
Mesothelioma, 436
Mesotrophic lakes, 157, 158
Metabolic reserve, 296, 297
Metal hydride compounds, 388
  solid, 408
Metallic mineral resources, 9, 339
Metalloids, in periodic table, A2
Metal-nonmetal compounds, A2
Metal resources, life cycle of, 344
Metals, in periodic table, A2
Metamorphic rock, 210
Metastasis, 234
Meteorologists, 111
Methane (CH₄), 407, A3
  in atmosphere, 97
  as greenhouse gas, 449, 450
  from landfill, 549
Methane emissions, 459
Methane hydrates, 362, 459
Methane production, 299
Methanol, 405, 406
  liquid, 404
Methyl bromide (CH₃Br), as ozone-depleting
    compound, 473
Methyl chloroform, as ozone-depleting
    compound, 473
Methylene chloride, 434
Methyl isocyanate (MIC) gas, at Bhopal, India, 528
Metric units, A1
Metropolitan areas, 661
Mexico City
  polluted environments in, 662–664
  urban growth in, 664
Michigan State University, as green college, 752
Microbes. See also Microorganisms
  fish-killing, 489
  mining with, 349
  sewage treatment with, 504
  uses of, 65
Microbotanicals, 515, 522
Microclimates
  creation of, 121–122
  urbanization and, 670–671
Microevolution, 100
  coevolution and, 103
  role of natural selection in, 101, 102
Microfiltration, in advanced sewage treatment, 505
Microfinance, 709
Microlivestock, 292
Microloans, 709
Micronutrient deficiencies, 286–287
Micronutrients, 285
Microorganisms, 65, 571. See also Microbes
Micropower, decentralized, 410–412
Micropower systems, 410–412
Microscale experiments, 732
Microturbines, 412
Microwave ovens, 393
Middle Ages, air pollution during, 423
Middle East, grain import wars in, 312
Middle-income, moderately developed countries,
  6
Midgley, Thomas, Jr., 472
Midsuccessional species, 181, 182, 589
Migrating birds, plight of, 575
Migration. See also Immigration
  to and from cities and rural areas, 664
  population size and, 267
  spread of disease via, 241–242
Migratory Bird Act of 1918, 27
Migratory Bird Hunting and Conservation Stamp
    Act of 1934, 590
Migratory waterfowl, managing populations of,
  590
Milbrath, Lester W., 748–749
Military dumps, 553
Millennials, 265
Miller, G. Tyler, 42
Miller, Stanley, 97
Millstone Unit 3 reactor, 371
Milwaukee, impure water crisis in, 508
Mimicry, 177, 178

Mindquake, 750
Mineral deposits, in the United States, 597
Mineral formation, from sedimentary and weath-
    ering processes, 340
Mineral resources, 9, 209–210, 339–340
  environmental impacts of using, 343–346
  exploring for, 348
  nonrenewable, 349
  supplies of, 346–349
Mineral resource supplies, effect of economics on,
  346–348
Minimum dynamic area (MDA), 567
Minimum-tillage farming, 222
Minimum viable population (MVP), 192, 566–567,
  587
Mining
  environmental impacts of, 343–346
  of lower-grade ores, 348
  with microbes, 349
  of oceans, 348
  on public lands, 348
  tropical deforestation and, 616
Mining and smelting wastes, 527
Mining companies, in the United States, 346–347
Mining interests, 597–598
Mining methods, 341, 342
  destructive, 345
Minke whale, 645, 646
Minnesota Mining and Manufacturing Company
    (3M)
  Pollution Prevention Pays (3P) program,
    532–533
Mitigation approach, 630
Mitigation banking policy, 651
Mitigation costs, 701
Mixtures, 47
Mobile sources of air pollution, 420, 421
Models. See also Computer models
  of complex systems, 45
  for hypothesis testing, 41, 43
  of systems, 44–47, 91
Moderate desertification, 220
Moderately restricted-use lands, 595–596
Moderately toxic substances, 232
Moderator, of nuclear reactor, 365–366
Modern monoculture, 277
Moderns, cultural shift among, 752
Mojave desert tortoise, 565
Molecular compounds, 49
Molecules, 47
  shapes of, A2–A4
Molina, Mario, 31, 35, 472
Moltke, Konrad von, 728
Monarch butterflies, 67
Money, decisions based on, 531, 720. See also
    Economics
Monocultures, 132, 199, 278
  developing and planting, 281, 513
  modern, 277
  high-input, 281
Monomers, 49–50
Monsoon forests, tropical, 137
Montague, Peter, 506, 536–537
Montana, mining and smelting waste in, 527
Montreal Protocol, 34, 477–478
Moose, 589
  on Isle Royale, 197
Mopani, 292
Mosaics, biomes as, 123, 166, 184
Mosquitoes, malaria and, 243, 244. See also Anophe-
    les mosquitoes; Asian tiger mosquitoes
Mosses, acid-loving, 431
Motor scooters, 674
Motor vehicles. See also Automobile entries; Cars;
    Sport utility vehicles (SUVs)
  advantages and disadvantages of, 673
  efficiency of, 470
  fuel efficiency of, 385–386
  photochemical smog and, 424
  pros and cons of, 672
  recycling of, 540
  reducing emissions from, 442–443
Mount Pinatubo, 110, 211

Mount St. Helens, 203, 211
Mountain biomes, 141
Mountain gorilla, 565
Mountain lions, 589
Mountains, influence on smog, 426
Mountaintop removal, 342
Muddy-boots biology, 89
Muir, John, 26, 27, 29, 32, 142, 627
Müller, Paul, 513
Multilateral drilling, 355
Multiple cropping, 281
Multiple-nuclei city, 666, 667
Multiple use, 26
Multiple-use lands, 595
Multispecies management approach, 649
Multivariable analysis, 43
Mumford, Lewis, 673, 685
Municipal groundwater, contamination of, 494
Municipal recycling programs, 538
Municipal solid waste (MSW), 526
  recycling, 537
Mushroom spores, 225
Muskegs, 139
Mutagens, 100, 233
Mutations, 233
  evolution of life and, 100
Mutualism, 165, 172, 178–179
Mycorrhizae fungi, 179, 225
Myers, Norman, 108–109, 289, 568, 626, 700, 712,
  731
Mysterious Island, The (Verne), 405
Mysticetes, 645. See also Cetaceans

Naess, Arne, 746
Naming, of species, A5
Nanofibers, storing hydrogen on, 408
Nanofiltration, in advanced sewage treatment, 505
Narrow niches, 103–104
Narrow-spectrum agents, 514
Narwhal, 644
Nash, Roderick, 628
Nashua River, cleanup of, 716
National Acid Precipitation Assessment Program
    (NAPAP), 432
National ambient air quality standards (NAAQS),
  439
National Biodiversity Institute (INBio), 622
National Bison Range, 21
National Center for Ecological Analysis and Syn-
    thesis, 646–647
National Energy Act, 724
National Environmental Education Act of 1990, 35
National Environmental Policy Act of 1970, 31, 724
National Fish and Wildlife Foundation, 304
National forest reserves, 26
National Forest Management Act of 1976, 31
National forests, 609–610
  management of, 610–611
National Forest System, 595
National Gap Analysis Program (GAP), 624
National Marine Fisheries Service (NMFS), 583
National parks
  managing and sustaining, 619–621
  threats to, 620–621
National Parks and Conservation Association, 621
National Park Service, 27
National Park Service Act of 1916, 27
National Park System, 26, 27, 32, 596
National People of Color summit, 35
National Priorities List (NPL), 552, 553, 554
National Resource Lands, 595
National Resources Conservation Service, 219, 225
National Resources Defense Council (NRDC), 386
National security, 731
National Surface Water Survey (NSWS), 431
National Toxicology Program, 552
National Wild and Scenic Rivers Act of 1968, 657
National Wild and Scenic Rivers System, 657
National Wilderness Preservation System, 596
National Wilderness System, 30, 32
National Wildlife Federation, 727, 732
National Wildlife Refuge System, 29, 586,
  595–596

Native Americans, 745
    bison and, 21
    environmental justice for, 728–729
    view of wilderness among, 25
Native species, 169
Natural capital, 3, 16–17, 92, 690, 691
*Natural Capitalism* (Hawken, Lovins, and Lovins), 533
Natural chemicals, 231
Natural ecosystems. *See also* Ecosystems
    changes to, 183
    human modification of, 199
    simplifying, 199
Natural enemies, defined, 513
Natural floodplain, flooding in, 332
Natural gas, 351, 362–363, 434
    compressed, 406
    as nonrenewable energy source, 350
Natural gas deposits, locations of, 356
Natural greenhouse effect, 70, 86, 120, 447–448
Natural hazards, 210–212
Natural law, 42
Natural organic compounds, 49
Natural plasma, 50
Natural radioactivity, 55–57
Natural recharge, 315
Natural regulation principle, 621
Natural resources, 3, 691
    depletion of, 186–187, 696
    economic factors affecting, 702
    importance of, 690
Natural Resources Conservation Service, 29, 219
Natural Resources Defense Council (NRDC), 31, 508, 509
    report by, 470
Natural sciences, 3
Natural selection
    role in microevolution, 101
    types of, 101–103
Natural soil erosion, 217
Natural systems, protecting, 185–187. *See also* Ecosystems
Nature
    balance of, 184, 200
    building blocks of, 47
    in ecological design arts, 685
    learning about, 42–43, 199–201
    minimizing damage to, 200
    recreational pleasure provided by, 570
    sustainable living with, 748–749
    valuing, 569
Nature Conservancy, 29, 572, 583, 590, 623, 681, 727
Nature reserves, 621–628
    design of, 623–624
    establishing and managing, 621–623, 624–626
Nature-technology partnership, 418
Neem tree, 569, 614
Negative feedback loop, 45, 456
Negligence, legal principle of, 723–725, 726
Nekton, 145
Nelson, Gaylord, 30
Nelson, Mark, 506
Nematocides, 513
Nepal, 390
Nervous system, chemical harm to, 234–235
Net energy, 353–354, 382, 383
Net energy efficiency, 382, 383, 391
Net energy ratio, 353, 354
Netherlands, environmentally sustainable economy in, 710–712
Net primary productivity (NPP), 80, 81, 82, 147, 278, 695
    destroying, 199
Neurotoxins, 234
    from fish-killing microbes, 489
Neutral solutions, 48
Neutrons, 47
New cities, pros and cons of building, 682
Newell, Roger, 501
Newfoundland cod fishery, 304
New Guinea, species diversity on, 169
New Orleans, Formosan termite in, 579

New progressives, cultural shift among, 752–753
New York City
    air pollution deaths in, 30
    air pollution in, 423
    harbor water cleanup in, 488
    motor vehicles in, 673
New York State, Love Canal cleanup in, 525
New Zealand, managing fisheries by, 650
Niche, 103. *See also* Ecological niches
Niche overlap, 173–174
Niche specialization, 175
Niche structure, 166
Nicotine, 228
Nicotine sulfate, 513
Nigeria, birth rate in, 264
Nile delta basin, 321
Nile perch, 634
Nile River, 634
    irrigation water from, 312
1960s, environmental history of, 29–30
1970s, environmental history of, 30–32
1980s, environmental history of, 32–34
1990s, environmental history of, 34–36
Nitrate ions ($NO_3^-$), 48
    in groundwater, 495
    bans on, 490–491
Nitric oxide (NO), 87, 423
Nitrification, 87
Nitrite ions ($NO_2^-$), 495
Nitrogen ($N_2$), 47, A3
    in aquatic life zones, 146
    in earth's atmosphere, 97
    microbes that convert, 65
    killing invader species using, 580
Nitrogen compounds, 87
Nitrogen cycle, 86–87
    human activities and, 87
Nitrogen dioxide ($NO_2$), 87, 423, A3
    as criteria air pollutant, 422
Nitrogen fixation, 87, 178
Nitrogen oxide emissions, 432, 433, 440
Nitrogen oxides, 420, 428, 434, A3
Nitrous oxide ($N_2O$), 87
    as greenhouse gas, 449, 450
Nixon, Richard M., 30, 31, 716
No-problem school, 743
No-regrets strategy, 465, 468–469
No-till cultivation, 222, 468
Noise Control Act of 1976, 31
Noise levels, chart of, 670
Noise pollution, 669–670
Nomadic herding, 279, 280, 296, 298
Nondegradable plastics, 541
Nondegradable pollutants, 55
Nondegradable wastes, in groundwater, 493
Nonequilibrium state, of ecosystems, 622
Nongovernment organizations (NGOs), 717, 718, 727
    goals of environmental, 737
Nonimaging optical solar concentrator, 397
Non-ionizing radiation, 52
Nonmetallic mineral resources, 9, 339
Nonmetal-nonmetal compounds, A3
Nonmetals, in periodic table, A2
Nonnative aquatic organisms, killing, 580
Nonnative invaders
    in the Great Lakes, 655–656
    marine, 651
Nonnative species
    amphibian decline and, 170, 171
    in coastal waters, 639
    extinction threats from, 574–579
    introducing, 199
    in national parks, 620
    problems with, 169–170, 171
    reducing the threat from, 578–579
Nonpersistent pollutants, 55
Nonpoint sources of pollution, 10, 491, 486
    controlling, 502–503
Nonprofit organizations, as special-interest groups, 717
Nonrenewable energy resources, 10, 350, 352

Nonrenewable fossil fuels, 23, 352
Nonrenewable metallic resources, 10, 350
    finding and removing, 341–343
    substitutes for, 349
Nonrenewable resources, 9–10, 339
    depletion curves for, 346
Nonthreshold dose-response model, 233
Nontoxic substances, 232
Nontransmissible disease, 236
Nonuse biodiversity, 569, 570
Nonutilitarian biodiversity, 569, 570
Nordhaus, William, 466
Norse, Elliot, 156
North America
    atmospheric warming in, 464
    tornadoes and tropical cyclones in, 114
North American bison, near extinction of, 21
North Borneo, malaria in, 200
North Carolina
    fish-killing microbes in, 489
    hurricane damage in, 487
    secondary ecological succession in, 181
North China Plain, 325
Northern spotted owl, 564
Northland College, as green college, 752
Northwest Power Act of 1980, 656
Northwest Power Planning Council (NPPC), 656
Norway, whaling by, 645, 646
"Not in anyone's backyard" (NIABY) approach, 555
"Not in my backyard" (NIMBY) approach, 555
"Not on planet Earth" (NOPE) approach, 555
N-propyl bromide, as ozone-depleting compound, 473
Nuclear chain reaction, 58
Nuclear changes, 55–58
Nuclear Control Institute, 368
Nuclear energy, 365–377
Nuclear fission, 57–58
Nuclear fission reactor, 365–366
Nuclear fuel cycle, 367, 369–370, 375
Nuclear fusion, 58, 376–377
Nuclear options, 377
Nuclear plants, decommissioning of, 372–373
Nuclear power, 366–367
    costs of, 374–375
    electricity production from, 367
    future of, 377
    mismanagement of, 374
    pros and cons of, 367–369
Nuclear power generating capacity, global, 352
    locations of, 368
Nuclear power plants, 57, 351, 367
    accidents in, 29, 367, 374, 376
    as terrorist targets, 529
    efficiency of, 382, 383
    safety of, 367–369
    storage of radioactive wastes at, 371
Nuclear reactors, 58
    extending the life of, 373
    locations of, 368
    safe, 375–376
Nuclear Regulatory Commission (NRC), 367–368, 371, 719
Nuclear Waste Technical Review Board, 374
Nuclear weapons, spread of, 373
Nuclear weapon sites, 372
Nucleic acids, 50, A3–A4. *See also* DNA entries
    synthesis of, 97
*Nucleonics Week*, 375
Nucleotides, 100, A3, A4
Nucleus
    atomic, 47
    for condensation, 83
    of a cell, 50, 65, 67
Nuisance, legal principle of, 723–725, 726
Nutria, 576
Nutrient cycles, 82
    deforestation and, 90
Nutrient overload
    in lakes, 490
    principal sources of, 491

Nutrients. *See also* Diet; Food entries
  in aquatic life zones, 146
  in periodic table, A2
Nutritional deficiency diseases, 287
Nutritional mutualism, 178, 179

Oahu tree snail, 564
Oberlin College, 684
  environmental studies center at, 398, 399
  as green college, 752
Obesity, 287
Occupational Health and Safety Act of 1970, 31
Ocean bottom communities and habitats, 156
Ocean currents
  atmospheric warming and, 460–462
  climate and, 118–120
  effect of global warming on, 458
  formation of, 118
Ocean Dumping Act of 1972, 31
Ocean ecosystems, effects of oil on, 501–502
Ocean hemisphere, 147
Oceanic crust, 204, 206
Oceanic fisheries system, 278
Ocean life zones, 70, 148
Ocean oil pollution, 501–502
Ocean pollution, 496–502
Oceans. *See also* Aquatic entries; Marine entries;
    Open sea; Water entries
  burying radioactive wastes in, 371
  as carbon-storage reservoirs, 85–86
  distribution of, 145
  effect on climate, 457–458
  importance of, 147
  major life zones in, 148
  mining, 348
  pollutants dumped into, 500–501
  sequestering $CO_2$ in, 468
Ocean species, fossil fuel required for harvesting,
    303
Ocean thermal energy conversion (OTEC) plants,
    401
Odontocetes, 644. *See also* Cetaceans
Offboard hydrogen fuel storage, 388
Office buildings, waste heat from, 383–384
Office of Management and Budget, 719
Offshore drilling, 357
Ogallala aquifer, 325, 327
Ohio Valley, industrial plants in, 428
O horizon, 212, 213
Oil, 351. *See also* Petroleum
  effect on ocean ecosystems, 501–502
  history of, 359
  low-cost, 393
  as nonrenewable energy source, 350
  replacing with hydrogen, 405–407
Oil dependence, nuclear power and, 374
Oil deposits, locations of, 356
Oil development, in the Arctic National Wildlife
    Refuge, 360
Oil drilling, 354–355
Oil embargo, 30–31
Oil prices, 357
Oil refinery, 355
Oil reserves, 355
Oil resources, 354–361
Oil royalty payments, 358
Oil sand, 361
Oil shale, 361
Oil-soluble toxins, 230
Oil spills, cleaning up, 502
Oil supplies
  decline of, 357–359
  location of, 355–356
Old-growth forests, 185, 598–600, 609, 631
Oligotrophic lake, 157, 158
Olympic National Park, 620
Omnivores, 74
Onboard liquid reformer system, 387–388
One-way energy flow, 75
OPEC. *See* Organization of Petroleum Exporting
    Countries (OPEC)
OPEC oil embargo, 30–31
Open-access resource, 640
Open-pit mining, 341, 342

Open ranges, 296
Open sea, 147. *See also* Aquatic entries; Marine
    entries; Ocean entries
  biological zones in, 153–155
Open space, urban, 680–682
Opportunist species, 195–196
  following extinction, 109
Opportunity cost, 702
Optimum level of pollution, 700, 701
Optimum sustainable population, 267
Optimum sustained yield (OSY), 649
Options, as utilitarian biodiversity value, 570
Orders, A5
Ore, 339
Ore deposits, hydrothermal, 340
Ore formation, 339–340
  from sedimentary and weathering processes,
    340
Oregon
  bottle recycling law in, 31
  land-use planning in, 683
Ore mineral, 344
Organelles, 65
Organic chemicals, 49–50
  synthesis of, 97
  as water pollutants, 484
Organic farming, 308, 468
Organic fertilizer, 225
Organic foods, 308
Organic gardening, 390
Organic molecules, chemical evolution of,
    96–97, 99
Organisms, 65, 66
  environmental stress on, 200
  reproduction of, 66
  in soils, 212–215
Organization of Petroleum Exporting Countries
    (OPEC), 30, 355, 357, 359. *See also* OPEC
    oil embargo
Orr, David W., 398, 684–685, 744, 750
Oryx, 565
*Our Stolen Future* (Coburn), 35
Outdoor air pollution, 438
  reducing, 441–443
Outer core of earth, 204, 206
Output approach to controlling pollution, 11, 443
Outputs, system, 45
Overburden, 341
Overfishing, 304–307, 639, 649
Overgrazing
  Dust Bowl and, 219
  effects of, 297, 298
Overharvesting renewable resources, 199
Overhunting, amphibian decline and, 170, 171
Overnutrition, 287
Overpopulation, 267
Overpumping, 326
Overshoot, population, 192, 193
Oxpeckers, 179
OxyChem, 525
Oxygen ($O_2$), 47, A3. *See also* Ozone ($O_3$)
  dissolved, 146
  in earth's atmosphere, 97, 99
  in water, 54
Oxygen demand curve, 488
Oxygen-demanding wastes, as water pollutants,
    484, 485
Oxygen-depleted zones, 498–500
Oxygen depletion, in lakes, 490
Oxygen sag curve, 487, 488
Oysters, in Chesapeake Bay, 501
Ozone ($O_3$), 47, 419, A3. *See also* Ozone depletion;
    Photochemical ozone
  as criteria air pollutant, 422
  CFCs and, 472–473
  concentration of, 420, 440
  origin of earth's, 99
  seasonal thinning of, 474
Ozone-depleting chemicals (ODCs), 473–474, 476
  projected concentrations of, 479
Ozone depletion, 31, 34, 35, 474–475
  causes of, 472–473
  effects of, 475
  major characteristics of, 451

  reducing, 477–480
  stratosphere and, 472–476
Ozone hole, 474–475
Ozone layer
  chemical makeup of atmosphere and, 120
  protecting, 476–480
Ozone treaty, 479

Pacific salmon, 656–657
Pacific yew, 569
Packaging
  reduction of, 539–540
  unnecessary, 531
Packaging laws, 540
Padre Island National Seashore, 620
Paints, leaded, 548
Palmer, Margaret, 185
Pampas, 132
Pandas, 104, 565
Pangaea, 106
Panther, 564
Paper. *See also* E-paper; Paper production;
    Wastepaper
  recycling, 540–541
  tree-free, 611–612
Paper industry, pollution regulation of, 703–704
Paper mills, along Lake Baikal, 654
Paper parks, 620
Paper production, 540
  chlorine-free, 551
  as energy-intensive industry, 393
  from tree-free fibers, 611–612
Parabolic dish collectors, 396–397
Paracelsus, 230
Para-dichlorobenzene, 434
*Paramecium* species, competition among, 174
Parasites, 178
  controlling, 522
  in drinking water, 485
Parasitism, 172, 178
  amphibian decline and, 170, 171
Parent material, 212, 214
Parking space, paying for, 677
Parks. *See also* National parks
  Costa Rican, 622
  municipal, 680–681
Particulate air pollution, 440
Passenger pigeons, 560, 563
Passive heating, 380
Passive safety features, 375
Passive solar design, 390
Passive solar heating systems, 394–395, 396, 660
  efficiency of, 383
Pastoralists, 297
Pastures, 296
Patch dynamics, 624
Patenting of public lands, 347
Pathogens, 236
  bioengineered, 291
  introduction of, 242
  as water pollutants, 484, 485
Pauly, Daniel, 305
Pay-as-you-throw system, 539
Pebble bed modular reactor (PBMR), 375–376
Pelagic species, 302
Pelican Island refuge, 26, 27
Pension systems, 261
People of color, environmental justice for, 728–729
Peppered moths, microevolution in, 101
Per capita GNI, 4
Per capita GNI in purchasing power parity (per
    capita GNI PPP), 4–5
Per capita GNP, 4, 5, 7
Perchloroethylene (PERC), 530
Percolation, 82
  through soil, 214
Perennial crops, 293
Perennial polyculture, 277
Periodic table of the elements, 47, A2
Permafrost, 132
Peroxyacyl nitrates (PANs), 424
Perrin, Noel, 750, 752–753
Persian Gulf area, irrigation in, 312
Persian Gulf War, 35

Persistence, 185
  of chemicals, 230
  of pesticides, 514
  of pollutants, 55
Persistent organic pollutants (POPs), 35, 187, 518
Persistent organic pollutants (POPs) treaty, 555
Pest birth control, 521
Pest control
  biological, 520–521
  ecologically based, 523
  microbes and, 65
  natural, 513
  primary goal of, 520
  role in extinction, 581
  spiders in, 512
Pesticide concentrations, 435
Pesticide ingredients, EPA banning of, 518–519
Pesticide persistence, 514
Pesticide regulation, 519–520
Pesticide runoff, 488
  in Chesapeake Bay, 500
  reducing, 502
Pesticides. See also Herbicides; Insecticides; Pests
  benefits of, 514–516
  export of, 518
  genetic resistance to, 516
  groundwater contamination by, 494
  harmful effects of, 516–518, 547
  insects versus, 64
  migration of, 517
  natural, 513
  nonpoint land runoff of, 492
  regulation of, 518–520
  safety of, 515–516
  synthetic, 517
  types and uses of, 513–514
Pesticide subsidies, 523
Pesticide treadmill, 516
Pest-killing chemicals, searching for ideal, 516
Pests
  defined, 513
  geographic range of major, 515
  insects as, 64
  non-pesticide control of, 520–523
Pest species, strengthening populations of, 199
Pest strips, 519
Peto, Richard, 515
Petrochemicals, 355
Petroleum, 354–355. See also Oil entries
  crude and refined, 501
  sulfur-containing, 89
Petroleum production curves, 358
Pet trade, 581
Pfiesteria piscida outbreaks, 489
Pharmaceuticals, from marine ecosystems, 636
Phelan, James D., 32
Phenols, 508
Pheromones, pest control and, 521
Philippines, pollution from, 110
Phillips, Kevin, 708
Phillips, Peter, 508
Phosphate compounds, 87
Phosphate group, in nucleic acids, A4
Phosphate ions, 48, 87
Phosphates, bans on, 490–491
Phosphorus (P), in aquatic life zones, 146
Phosphorus cycle, 87–88
  human activities and, 88
Photochemical oxidants, 420, 424
Photochemical ozone, 419, 420, 423, 424
Photochemical reactions, 423
Photochemical smog, 423–428, 442
  formation of, 423–424
Photosynthesis, 69, 74, 85
  in aquatic life zones, 146
  $CO_2$ levels and, 459
  origin of life and, 99
Photosynthesizers, 99
Photovoltaic (PV) cells, 398. See also Solar cells
pH scale, 48, 49
pH values, of acid deposition in United States, 429
Phylum (phyla), A5
Physical change, 54
Physical hazards, 229

Physical states of matter, 50
Physical taking of private property, 725
Phytomonitoring, 542
Phytoplankton, 72, 74, 78, 82, 145, 153
Phytoremediation, 542
Picocurie, 436
Piedmont, secondary ecological succession in, 181
Pierce, Morris, A., 732
Pigeons, 576
Pilot whale, 644
Pimentel, David, 218, 229, 288, 405, 517, 575
Pinchot, Gifford, 26, 27, 32
Pine, Collins, 606
Pine barrens tree-frog, 565
Pink bollworm, geographic range of, 515
Pioneer species, 180
Place, sense of, 751
Placer deposits, 340
Plaintiff, 723
Planes, emissions from, 459
Planet, management of, 14, 555, 743–744. See also
    Earth entries; World entries
Planetary management worldview, 14, 743
Planetary sinks, 60
Plankton, sharks that feed on, 176
Plantation agriculture, 278–279
Plant biodiversity, atmospheric warming and,
    460, 461
Planting trees, reducing global warming by,
    467
Plant nutrients
  effect on lakes, 157
  as water pollutants, 484
Plants. See also Decorative plants
  in agricultural revolution, 24
  air pollution damage to, 438–439
  classifying, A5
  desert, 126–128
  differences in, 125
  effects of acid deposition on, 431–432
  endangered, 586
  exotic, 581–582
  as a food resource, 278
  genetically modifying, 291
  genetic library of, 295
  global extinction of, 2
  insects and, 64
  as "pollution sponges," 542
  rangeland, 296–297
  soil and, 212–215
Plant species
  health potential of, 569–570
  types, sizes, and stratification of, 166
Plasma, 50–51, 542
Plasma torches, 51
Plasma-torch hazardous waste detoxification,
    542
Plasmids, 239
Plasmodium, 243, 244
Plastic litter, in marine ecosystems, 641
Plastics, 349
  recycling, 541
Plate tectonics, 205–207
  mineral resources and, 339
"Please do not pollute" policy, 364
Plumbing pipes, 548
Plutonium-239, 370, 373, 376
  radioactive decay of, 56
Poaching. See also Ivory trade
  extinction threats from, 579–581
  protection from, 587
Point sources, 10
  of pollution, 491
  of water pollution, 486, 503–505, 509
Poison, 231
Polak, Paul, 331
Polar areas, atmospheric warming in, 464
Polar evergreen coniferous forests, climate graph
    for, 136
Polar forests, 134, 598. See also Polar forests
Polar grassland ecosystem, 123, 124, 128, 129,
    132–134
Polar vortex, 474, 475
Policy, 720

Policy life cycles, implementation in, 723
Political pressure, importance of, 509–510
Political revolution, 755
Political systems, developing environmentally
    sustainable, 738
Politicians, emission reductions and, 471
Politics, 716
  energy resource use and, 412–413
  environmental policy and, 716, 717
Pollination relationship, 178
Pollutants, 10
  in drinking water, 493
  harmful, 11, 55, 426–427
  recycling, 509
Pollutant sources, types of, 10–11
Pollutant transfer, 8
Polluter-pays principle, 552–553, 554
Pollution, 10–12. See also Air pollution; Tradable
    pollution; Water pollution
  amphibian decline and, 170, 171
  of aquatic systems, 639
  awareness of, 30
  from cyanide heap leaching, 345
  dealing with, 11–12
  economic solutions to, 706
  effect on species diversity, 167–168
  as environmental issue, 2
  external costs of, 699–700
  extinction and, 582
  forests and, 608
  internalizing external costs of, 699–700
  optimum level of, 700, 701
  reducing, 529–531, 536–537
  steps in preventing, 443–444
  urbanization and, 669
  using the marketplace to reduce, 441
Pollution cleanup, 11–12
Pollution control
  economics of, 700–703
  pollution reduction versus, 530–531, 536–537
  regulation of, 703–707
Pollution costs, monetary values of, 701–702
Pollution crisis, origin of life and, 99
Pollution prevention, 11–12, 28, 236, 530, 536
  integrated pest management and, 523
  key principles of, 555
Pollution-prevention bonds, 704, 706
Pollution Prevention Pays (3P) program, 532–533
Pollution prevention revolution, 755
Pollution rights, 441
Polychlorinated biphenyls (PCBs)
  biological magnification of, 490, 536
  in the Great Lakes, 493
Polyculture, 277, 278, 284, 292
Polyethylene terephthalate (PET) plastic, 534
Polymers, 49
Polynesians, on Easter Island, 40
Polyps, in coral reefs, 144
Polyvarietal cultivation, 284
Polyvinyl chloride (PVC) plastics
  chlorine in, 551
  lead-laden, 549
  recycling, 534
Ponds, pollution of, 489–493
Population. See also Human population;
    Population growth; Populations
  atmospheric warming and, 461
  average annual increase in, 256
  global increase in, 2, 5
  of world's urban areas, 662
Population age structure, 263–267
Population and Community Development
    Association (PCDA), 254
Population Bomb, The (Ehrlich), 30
Population change, 255
  average annual rate of, 256
Population change curves, 194
Population crisis, origin of life and, 99
Population decline, effects of, 266–267
Population decrease factors, 192
Population density, 191
Population dieback, 192
Population dynamics, 190, 191–194
Population fluctuations, 194

Population growth, 4, 5, 36, 285, 568. *See also*
    Population size
    age structure and, 263–264
    in Curitiba, Brazil, 679
    as environmental issue, 2, 5
    in India and China, 271–274
    limits on, 191–192, 201
    in Middle East, 312
    population density and, 193–194
    slowing, 267
Population growth curves, 193
Population growth factors, 192
Population overshoot, 192
Population projections, regional, 257
Population Reference Bureau, 727
Populations, 66, 67. *See also* Population
    genetic variability in, 100
    major characteristics of, 191
Population size
    carrying capacity and, 192–193
    factors that increase or decrease, 191–192
    influencing, 267–271
    migration and, 267
    role of predation in controlling, 194–195
Population structure, by age and sex, 264
Population viability analysis (PVA), 566
Porter, William, 589
Positive feedback loop, 45, 456, 457, 458
Postel, Sandra, 325, 329, 503
Postindustrial stage of demographic transition,
    269
Postreproductive age, 263
Potatoes, hepatitis B vaccine in, 242
Potential energy, 51
Poverty
    acute, 7, 707
    in Curitiba, Brazil, 678
    as environmental issue, 2
    environmental justice and, 728–729
    freshwater supplies and, 318
    harmful effects of, 8
    malnutrition and, 288
    reducing to improve environmental quality,
        707–710
    risks of death associated with, 245
    urbanization and, 662, 663, 671
Poverty-malnutrition-disease cycle, 286
Power, units of, A1
Power plants, decentralized, 377
Power tower, 396, 397
Prairie dog, 564
Prairie ecosystems, temperate tall-grass, 131
Prairie grassland, 70
Prairie potholes, 160, 162
Prairie restoration, 629–630
Prairies, 129
Precautionary principle, 186, 236, 555, 718
    hormone disrupters and, 235
    in marine management, 649
Precautionary strategies
    to preserve biodiversity, 568
    toward global warming, 464–465
Precipitation, 82. *See also* Acid deposition; Acid
        rain; Rain; Snow
    average, 115, 124
    average annual, 317
    in cyclones, 112–113
    in deserts, 125
    differences in, 314
    seasonal changes in, 115–116
    soils and, 214–215
Precipitation patterns
    atmospheric warming and, 462
    deforestation and, 616
Predation, 172
Predator–prey relationship, 176
Predators
    capture of prey by, 177
    eliminating from ecosystems, 199
    interaction of prey with, 176–177
    large, 139
    role in extinction, 581
Preindustrial stage of demographic transition,
    269

Premature death, 8
    from undernutrition and malnutrition, 286
Premature extinctions, 560, 562, 563, 567
    as environmental issue, 2
Prereproductive age, 263
Prescribed fires, 608
Preservationists, 3, 26, 27, 32
Pressure-treated lumber, 497
Pressurized water reactors, 365–366
Presuppression, of forest fires, 608
Prevailing surface winds, 117
Prevention approaches to reducing acid deposi-
        tion, 433
Prevention principle, 718
Prevention strategy, to avoid biodiversity loss, 624
Prey, interaction of predators with, 176–178. *See
        also* Predators
Price, in economic decisions, 691–692
Price-Anderson Act of 1957, 29, 366
Price controls, 308
Primary consumers, 74, 76, 77
Primary dunes, 152
Primary ecological succession, 180–181
Primary effects of earthquakes, 211
Primary pollutants, 420–421, 428
Primary productivity, 80–82
Primary recycling, 535
Primary sewage treatment, 504
Primary standard, for rating air pollution, 439
Primm, Stuart L., 107, 166, 568
Prince Edward Island, reusable containers in, 535
Princeton University, as green college, 753
Principle of enoughness, 751
*Principles of Political Economy, The* (Malthus), 747
Prior appropriation principle, 329
Private land, eminent domain over, 725
Private ownership, converting free-access
        resources to, 11
Private property rights, public good versus, 683
Probability, 229
Process design management, 707
Producers, 72, 74, 76, 77, 79
Production, cleaner, 531–534, 555
Productivity, energy, 59
Product labeling, 704
Products
    of chemical reactions, 54
    longer-lasting, 531
    recycling, 530–531
    risk associated with, 250
Product stewardship economy, 533
Pro-environmental coalition, 36
"Professor Hydrogen," 409
Profit
    decisions based on, 531
    maximizing, 692
Profit-making organizations, 717
Profundal zone, 157
Prokaryotic cell
    origin of life and, 99
    structure of, 67
Prokaryotic organisms, 65
Proof, scientific, 44
Property taxes, 676. *See also* Private property
        rights
Protected areas, 586, 587
    worldwide network of, 621
Protected marine sanctuaries, 646–647
Protectional mutualism, 178, 179
Protein deficiency, 285
Proteins, 50
    in cells, 67
    origin of life and, 97
Protists, classifying, A5
Protocells, 97
Protons, 47
Protozoa, 65
    classifying, A5
    in drinking water, 485
    malaria caused by, 243–244
    sewage treatment with, 504
Prudhoe Bay, 360
Public Funding Elections Act, 721
Public good, private property rights versus, 683

Public health, 27, 28, 29
Public Health Service Act of 1912, 27
Public lands, 595
    deterioration of, 36
    major types of, 595–596
    management of, 27, 31–32, 597–598
    mining on, 348
    patenting of, 347
    resource removal from, 28
    transfer of, 25
Public-pays approach, 554
Puget Sound, 654
Pull factors, in urban growth, 661
Pumped-storage hydropower, 400
Pure command economic system, 691
Pure free-market economic system, 691
Purple looselife, 576, 640
Purple sea urchin, 190
Purse-seine fishing, 302
Push factors, in urban growth, 661
Pygmy sperm whale, 644
Pyramid of biomass, 79–80
Pyramid of numbers, 80
Pyramids of energy flow, 77–79
    annual, 79
Pyrethrum, 513

Quagga mussel, 655

Rabies, 237
*Rachel's Environment and Health Biweekly*, 536
Radiation, 51, 53. *See also* Electromagnetic radia-
        tion spectrum; Gamma radiation; Infrared
        radiation; Ionizing radiation; Ultraviolet
        (UV) light (radiation)
Radiation-measuring equipment, 341
Radiation temperature inversions, 426, 427
Radioactive bombs, "dirty," 373–374
Radioactive isotopes (radioisotopes), 56
Radioactive materials, 420
    stolen or lost, 374
    as water pollutants, 484
Radioactive sites, contaminated, 372
Radioactive waste
    high-level, 370–372
    low-level, 369–370
    ocean dumping of, 501
    storing, 370–372, 374–375
Radioisotopes, safety of, 56
Radon-222, 434
    contamination by, 435–436
Radon testing, 436
*Rafflesia arnoldi*, 76
Rail systems, mass transit, 675
Rain, influence on smog, 425–426. *See also* Acid
        deposition; Acid rain; Precipitation
Rain forests, 123, 124
    flying foxes in, 165
    soils in, 294
    temperate, 139
Rain shadow effect, 121, 122
Ranchettes, 599
Ranching, on Forest Service land, 599
Randomness, of mutations, 100
Random population dispersal pattern, 191
Rangeland, 278, 296
    condition of, 298–299
    public, 598
    sustainable management of, 300–301
Rangeland plants, ecology of, 296–297
Range of tolerance, 73
Range site, carrying capacity of, 300
Rapa Nui, 40. *See also* Easter Island
Rapid-rail systems, 675, 676
*Rauvolfia serpentina*, 569
Ray, G. Carleton, 635
Ray, Paul H., 721, 752
Reactants, 54
Reagan, Ronald, 33
Realized niche, 103, 175
Reasoning, types of, 43–44
Recharge area, 315
Reclamation Act of 1902, 27
Recognition, in policy life cycles, 723

Recreation, as utilitarian biodiversity value, 570
Recreational benefits, of forests, 610
Recycling, 10, 535–540
  benefits of, 536
  centralized, 537
  in Curitiba, Brazil, 678
  economics of, 538–539
  hindrances to, 539–540
  types of, 535–537
Red-cockaded woodpeckers, 103
Red tides, 110, 498
Redwood sorrel, 179
Reefs, 144. See also Coral reefs
Rees, William, 10, 669
Refillable containers, 534–535
Refined oil (petroleum), 501
  recovery from exposure to, 502
Reforestation, neem tree and, 614
Refrigeration, efficient, 392–393
Regional outdoor air pollution, 428–434
Regolith, 212
Regulation, 706
  of free-access resources, 11
Regulations, 720. See also Laws
  air pollution, 439
  fishery, 650–651
  hazardous waste, 552–554
  improving environmental, 736
  innovation-friendly, 703, 704
  pesticide, 518–520
  pollution-control, 703–707
  relying on, 705
  using to improve environmental quality,
    703–707
  wetlands, 503
Regulatory taking of property, 725
Rehabilitation, of degraded ecosystems, 629
Reich, Peter, 284
Reid, Harry, 375
Relative humidity, 83
Reliable runoff, 314. See also Runoff
Reliable water supply, 315
Remote sensing, 90
Remote sensing satellites, 24
Renewable energy, 394
Renewable-energy revolution, 380
Renewable resources, 9
  overharvesting, 199
Renewable solar energy, 92
  indirect forms of, 350
Renewable wood, 23
Repercussion costs, 702
Replacement, of degraded ecosystems, 629
Replacement-level fertility, 257
Replogle, Michael, 673
Reproduction
  adaptation and, 104
  asexual and sexual, 66
  differential, 101
Reproduction patterns, of populations, 191
Reproductive age, 263
Reproductive isolation, 104–105
Reproductive patterns, 195–198
Reproductive time lag, 192
Reptiles, marine, 640–641, 642
Research, on global warming, 464
Research and development (R&D) spending
  and funding, 413
Research frontier
  aquatic biodiversity as, 635
  aquatic systems as, 147
Reserves, 339
  as habitat islands, 622
  principles for protecting, 622–623
Reserve-to-production ratio, 346
Reservoirs
  pollution of, 489–493
  using, 318–321
Residual deposits, 340
Resilience, 185
Resistance, to pesticides, 516
Resistance-to-change management era, 706
Resource Conservation and Recovery Act (RCRA)
  of 1976, 31, 552, 724

Resource consumption, four R's of, 446
Resource exchange webs, 532
Resource extraction, environmental limits to,
  345–346
Resource management, economics of, 700–703
Resource partitioning, 174–175
Resource productivity, 17, 51
  increasing, 533, 555
Resources, 9–10. See also Economic resources;
    Resource use
  common-property, 11
  consumption in China, 15
  free-access, 11
  monetary values of, 701–702
  open-access, 640
  wasting, 526–529
Resources Recovery Act of 1970, 31
Resource use
  economic solutions to, 706
  as environmental issue, 2
  urbanization and, 668
Resource-use rights, 704–705
Resource waste, economic incentives and
    disincentives to, 704
Respiration
  aerobic, 74
  anaerobic, 75
Respiratory system, air pollution and, 437
Response, 230
Responsibility
  individual, 749–750
  moving toward, 753–754
Responsible planetary management school, 743
Restoration, of degraded ecosystems, 629
Restorationists, 3
Restricted-use lands, 596
Reuse, 10, 534–535
  hindrances to, 539–540
Reverse osmosis, 328, 497
  in advanced sewage treatment, 505
Reversibility principle, 717–718
Revision 2000 process, 686
Revkin, Andrew C. "Andy," 734–735
Rey, Mark, 611
Rhine River, cleanup of, 488
Rhinoceros, 179, 564, 573
Rhizobium bacteria, 87, 178
Rice, strains of, 282
Rice cultivation, spread of disease via, 242
Richter scale, 210
Right whale, 645
Rignot, Eric, 453
Rill erosion, 217
Rio Earth Summit, 708, 731, 732
Rio Grande, 319
Riparian rights doctrine, 329
Riparian zones
  endangered, 300
  grazing on, 598
  preserving, 503
Risk, 229
  acceptable, 531
  estimating, 245
  greatest, 245–246
  life span and, 248
  perceiving, 249–250
Risk analysis, 245–250
  limitations of, 248–249
Risk assessment, 229, 245, 566
Risk communication, 245
Risk management, 229, 245, 249
River basins, stress on, 318. See also Amazon
    basin; Colorado River basin; Loire River
    basin; Yangtze River basin
Riverine forest, animals of, 130
River management, 319
Rivers. See also Streams; Wild rivers
  ecological services provided by, 318–319
  fragmentation of, 638
  freshwater, 159–160
  greatest environmental threats to, 656
  pollution of, 486–488
  protecting, sustaining, and restoring, 654–657
  threats to ecological services of, 487

River system habitats, 635
RNA (ribose nucleic acid), A3
Rock cycle, 210
Rock dove, 576
Rocks, 209–210
Rocky Mountain Institute, 380, 727
Rocky shores, 149–150
  organisms living in, 151
Rodenticides, 513
Rodricks, Joseph V., 235
Roland, Sherwood, 31
Romania, cyanide heap leaching in, 345
Roof gardens, 390–391
Roofing material, solar-cell, 398
Rooftop greenhouses, 443
Room-and-pillar mining, 342
Roosevelt, Franklin D., 28
Roosevelt, Theodore, 26, 27, 28, 253, 586, 627
Root-fuel plants, 619
Rosenblatt, Roger, 510
Rosenfield, Daniel, 426
Rosy periwinkle, 569
Rote learning, 43
Rotenone, 513
Roughage-based livestock feeding programs,
  298
Round goby, 655
Round Mountain Institute, Inc., 390
Round Mountain Organics, 390
Rowan, Rob, 155
Rowland, Sherwood, 35, 424, 472
Royal Botanical Gardens of England, 586
Royal Society of London, 14
Royalties
  on mined minerals, 347
  on oil, 358
r-selected species, 195–196
Ruckelshaus, William, 484
Rudd, Robert L., 523
Rule of 70, 4
Ruminants, 297
Runoff, 83, 156. See also Reliable runoff; Surface
    runoff
  shortage of, 316
Rural areas, 661
  migration to and from, 664
Russia. See also Soviet Union
  drinking water in, 507
  Lake Baikal in, 654
  natural gas reserves in, 362
  whaling by, 646
R-value, of insulation, 389

Saami people, Chernobyl nuclear disaster and,
  418
Sabah, malaria in, 200
Sacramento River, 323
Safe Drinking Water Act of 1974, 31, 508–509, 724
Safe harbor agreements, 584
Sagebrush rebellion, 31–32, 33
Sahara Desert, past rainfall in, 448
Saline solar ponds, 401
Salinity, 74
  of water, 145
Salinization, of soil, 221–222
Salmon, life cycles of, 306. See also Pacific
    salmon
Salmonella, 522
  in Mexico City, 663
Salmon ranching, 656
Salt cedar, 576
Salt marsh ecosystems, 150
  human impacts on, 155
  oil-polluted, 502
Saltwater intrusion, 328
  into aquifers, 325
  in drinking water, 495
Saltwater life zones, 145, 147–156
Salvage logging, 608
Samuelson, Robert, 673
San Juan Mountains, Summitville gold mine
    debacle in, 345
Sanctuary approach, to protecting wild species,
  586–588

Sand
in limiting beach erosion, 648
in soil, 215, 216
*Sand County Almanac, A* (Leopold), 29, 36
Sandia National Laboratories, 392
Sandor, Richard, 470
Sandy shores, 150–151
Sandy soils, 216
Sanitary landfills, 544–545
Santa Barbara, California, oil pollution at, 30
Satellite sensors, 90
Satellite towns, 682
Saturation, zone of, 314
Saudi Arabia, oil reserves in, 358. *See also*
Organization of Petroleum Exporting
Countries (OPEC)
Savannas, 123, 124, 128
Scavengers, 74
sea-bottom, 153
Scenic rivers, protecting and restoring, 657
Schaeffer, Eric, 442
Schlesinger, William H., 459
Schulenberg, Ray, 629
Schumacher, E. F., 571, 696
Science, critical thinking and, 41–44
Scientific Certification Systems (SCS), 606
Scientific data, 41
Scientific hypotheses, 41
Scientific law, 42
Scientific literacy survey, 734
Scientific methods, 42–43
Scientific proof, 44
Scientific results, validity of, 44
Scientific theory, 41–42
Scientists, role of, 41–43
Scientists' Statement on Global Climate
Disruption, 464–465
Scooters, electric, 389
Screwworm fly, 521
Scripps Institute of Oceanography, 430
Scrub, 70
animals of, 130
Scrub forests, 123, 124
tropical, 137
SCS. *See* Soil Conservation Service (SCS)
Sea and land breezes, 122
Sea anemone, 179
*Sea Around Us, The* (Carson), 33
Sea-grass meadows, human impacts on, 155
Sea ice volume, shrinking of, 452
Sea lamprey, 576
Sea level
atmospheric warming and, 460–462
changes in, 454, 458
projected rise in, 450, 461–462, 463, 464
Sea lions, 589
Seals, 190
endangerment of, 641
Sea otters, 190
Seared zone, of volcanic eruptions, 203
Seasonal changes, in temperate lakes, 157
Seasonal forests, tropical, 137
Seasonal wetlands, 160
Seasons, origin of, 116
Sea turtles, endangered, 641, 642. *See also* Turtles
Seawalls, limiting, 647, 648
Secondary consumers, 74, 76, 77
Secondary dunes, 152
Secondary ecological succession, 180, 181–182
Secondary effects of earthquakes, 211
Secondary pollutants, 421, 428
Secondary recycling, 535
Secondary sewage treatment, 504–505
Secondary standard, for rating air pollution, 439
Second-generation pesticides, 513
Second green revolution, 281
Second-growth forests, 600
Second law of thermodynamics, 42, 59, 60
effect on life, 59–60
Sector city, 666, 667
Secure hazardous waste landfills, 546
Sediment, as water pollutant, 484
Sedimentary precipitation, 340
Sedimentary rock, 209–210

Sedimentary sorting, 340
Seed banks, 586
Seed-tree cutting, 603, 604
Seismic surveys, 341
Sei whale, 645
Selective agents, 514
Selective breeding, 100
Selective cutting, of forests, 602–604
Semiconductors, in solar cells, 398
Semideserts, 123, 125, 126
Sense of place, 751
September 11 terrorist attacks, 371, 373. *See also*
World Trade Center towers
Septic tanks, 503, 504
Sequoia National Park, 620
Serageldin, Ismail, 708
Service flow businesses, 555
Service flow economy, 533–534
Services, selling, 531–534, 706
Severe desertification, 220
Sewage sludge, 501
uses of, 505–506
Sewage treatment
advanced, 505
natural, 483, 506–507
primary and secondary, 504–505
redesigning, 506
using wetlands, 507, 651
Sewage treatment plants, 505
for the Great Lakes, 492
malfunctioning, 488
Sewage treatment technologies, membrane-based, 505
Sewage walls, 507
Sewer system overflow, 503–504
Sex attractants, pest control and, 521
Sexually transmitted disease (STD), 238
Sexual reproduction, 66, 195
evolution of life and, 100
origin of life and, 99
Shale oil, 359–361
Shantytowns, 662, 663
in Curitiba, Brazil, 679
Shapiro, Robert B., 707, 709, 713
Sharks, benefits and ecological importance of, 176
Sharon Harris Nuclear Plant, 371
Shaw, George Bernard, 738
Sheet erosion, 217
Shellfish
harvesting, 301–302, 302–304
major commercially harvested types of, 302
Shelterbelts, 225
Shelterwood cutting, 603, 604
Shenandoah National Park, 629
Shifting cultivation, 22, 279, 280
Shipping containers, reusable, 535
Shiva, Vandana, 292
"Shoot, shovel, and shut up" solution to gray wolf
predation, 594
Shore upwelling, 119
Short-grass prairies, 129
Shrimp trawlers, sea turtles endangered by, 641
Shrubland, 123
temperate, 134
Siberia, Lake Baikal in, 654. *See also* Taiga
ecosystem
Siberian tiger, 565
Sick-building syndrome, 435
Sierra Club, 26, 27, 32, 589, 727
Sigmoid (S-shaped) population growth curve, 195, 196
*Silent Spring* (Carson), 29, 30, 33
Silicon Valley, underground tank leakage in, 494
Silt, in soil, 215, 216
Silver carp, 306
"Silver II" technology, 542
Simulation models. *See* Computer models
Singapore, motor vehicle use reduction in, 672
Single-variable analysis, 43
Skin, structure of, 476
Skin cancer, 476, 478
types of, 476
SLAPP (strategic lawsuits against public partici-
pation) suits, 726, 727

Slash-and-burn agriculture, 22, 612
Slavery, as consequence of agricultural revolution, 24
Slightly toxic substances, 232
Slime, purifying water using, 508
SLOSS (Single Large Or Several Small) debate, 623
Slowly degradable pollutants, 55
Sludge, 501
uses of, 505–506
Slums, 662
in Curitiba, Brazil, 679
*Small Is Beautiful: Economics As If People Mattered*
(Schumacher), 696
Small-scale hydropower, 400–401
Smart growth, 677–680
in Oregon, 683
Smart growth tools, 681
Smelting, 344
Smog. *See also* Air pollution
formation of, 425–426
photochemical and industrial, 423–428
Smokeless stoves, 620
Smokestacks, sequestering $CO_2$ from, 468
Smokey Bear educational campaign, 608
Smoking, 435, 436, 437
hazards of, 228
Snag, 601, 605
Snails, 564
microevolution in, 102
species diversity of, 167
Snake River, 656
Snow, influence on smog, 425–426. *See also*
Precipitation
Snow geese, 590
growing populations of, 591
Snow leopard, 564
Snow line, 141
Social ecology worldview, 746–747
Social impact analysis, 709
Social learning, 749
Social problems, urbanization and, 671
Social sciences, 3
Social Security taxes, 265
Sodium (Na), 48
Sodium borohydride, 388
Sodium chloride (NaCl), 49
structure of, A3
*Soft Energy Path, The* (Lovins), 31
Soil acidity, 215, 216
Soil alkalinity, 216
Soil chemistry, effects of acid deposition on,
431–432
Soil conservation, 222–226, 468
Soil Conservation Act of 1935, 29
Soil Conservation Service (SCS), 29, 219
Soil degradation, 221–222
Soil erosion, 83, 216–220. *See also* Erosion
causes of, 216–217
as consequence of agricultural revolution,
24
global, 217–219
reducing, 222–225
in the United States, 219–220
Soil Erosion Act of 1935, 219
Soil Erosion Service, 29
Soil fertility, maintaining and restoring, 225
Soil horizons, 213
Soil moisture detectors, 330
Soil permeability, 216, 217
Soil pH, 216
Soil porosity, 215, 216
Soil profiles, 212, 213, 215
Soil resources, 212–216
Soils, 180
acidic, 429
$CO_2$ absorption by, 459–460
colors of, 214
differences among, 215–216
effects of food production on, 288
formation of, 212
major layers in, 212–215
microbes in, 65
organisms in, 212–215
rain forest, 294

plant nutrient pathways in, 214
structure and texture of, 212, 215, 216
waterlogging of, 221, 222
Solar capital, 3, 92
Solar cells, 380
advantages and disadvantages of, 400
in carpet manufacturing, 534
design of, 399
producing electricity with, 398–400
Solar collectors, active, 395
Solar cookers, 397
Solar energy, 3–4, 9, 69–70, 201, 349–350. *See also* Sun
advantages and disadvantages of, 393–394, 398
in aquatic life zones, 146
atmospheric convection and, 117, 118
greenhouse effect and, 120, 121
for heat and electricity, 393–400
life on earth and, 95
in living systems, 59, 74
long-term variations in, 117
ocean currents and, 118
producing hydrogen using, 405–407
Solar heating, 393–400, 660
Solar–hydrogen economy, 695
Solar–hydrogen energy, 352, 406
Solar–hydrogen revolution, 380, 405–409, 755
role of fuel cells in, 408–409
Solar output, changes in, 457
Solar ovens, 619
Solar panels, 412
Solar ponds, saline and freshwater, 401
Solar power tower, 397. *See also* Power tower
Solar roofs, 412
Solar thermal plants, 396, 397
Solar thermal systems, 396
Solid biomass
advantages and disadvantages of burning, 404
burning, 403–404
producing fuels from, 404–405
Solids, 50
Solid waste, 526
burning, 543–544
centralized recycling of, 537
land disposal of, 544–545
separating for recycling, 537–538
Solid waste production, worldwide, 526
Solubility of toxic chemicals, 230
Solvent
citrus-based, 479
water as, 313
Somatic damage, from ionizing radiation, 57
Songbird species, ten most threatened, 574
Soot, global warming and, 459
Soulé, Michael, 570
Source separation approach to recycling, 538
Source zone, 159, 160
South America, countries of, 663
South American pampas, 132
Southern sea otter, 190
Soviet Union. *See also* Chernobyl nuclear disaster; Kazakhstan; Russia; Turkmenistan; Uzbekistan
radioactive contamination in former, 372
radioactive waste dumping by, 501
Spaceship-earth environmental worldview, 30, 743, 744
Spatial distribution of communities, 166
Special-interest groups, 717
election finance reform and, 721
Specialist species, 103–104
Speciation, 104. *See also* Species
effect on biodiversity, 106–107
following extinction, 109
Speciation crises, 568
Species 2000 global research project, 582
Species, 66–67, 95. *See also* Speciation
accidentally introduced, 578
avoiding harm to, 748–749
classifying and naming, A5
competition among, 173–174
deliberately introduced, 575–577

evolution of, 104–105
extinction of, 105–106, 563–568
generalist versus specialist, 103–104
general types of, 169–172
genetic information from, 570
interactions among, 103, 172–178
keystone, 165, 172, 173, 190, 567, 594, 635
number of, 67
origin and evolution of, 100
symbiotic interactions among, 178–180
Species-area relationship, 566
Species diversity, 76, 166. *See also* Biodiversity
ecosystem stability and, 185
effect of disturbances on, 183–184
factors affecting, 167
Species equilibrium model, 168–169
Species loss, aquatic, 637–638
Species-rich environments, 167–168
Sperm whale, 644
Spiders
dangerous, 512
in insect pest control, 512
Spoil banks, 342
Spoils, 342
Sponges, 149
Spores, 225
Sport hunting, 589–590
Sport utility vehicles (SUVs), 34, 385–386
Spotted owls, 103–104, 564
Sprague's pipit, 574
Sprawl
urban, 36, 664–666, 671, 673, 680, 681
using smart growth to control, 677–680
Spreading centers, 206
Spring overturn, 157
Sprinkler systems, 330–331
Spruce budworm, 606
Squamous cell carcinoma, 476, 478
Squatter settlements, 662, 663
in Curitiba, Brazil, 679
Squid, as sperm whale food, 644
Stability
ecological, 184–187
of populations, 194
Stabilizing natural selection, 102
Stahel, Walter, 533
Standing Bear, Luther, 25
Standing freshwater lakes, 156
Starvation, on Easter Island, 40. *See also* Malnutrition; Undernutrition
Stationary sources of air pollution, 420, 421
Statute of limitations, 726
Statutory laws, 723
Steady-state economy, 698–699
Steam, 477
dry and wet, 409–410
Steam turbines, efficiency of, 382
Steenland, Kyle, 552
Stegner, Wallace, 627
Steppes, 132
Stewardship, 699, 743
Stirling engines, 412
Stocker, Thomas F., 460
Stoddart, Marion, 716
Storage areas, system, 45
Stott, Philip, 612
Stoves, smokeless, 620
Stratification, of forests, 134–136, 137
Stratosphere, 68, 419–420
effects of decreased levels of ozone in, 475
Stratospheric ozone, depletion of, 472–476
Strawbale houses, 389–390
Streams. *See also* Freshwater entries; Rivers
erosion and, 208
freshwater, 159–160
pollution cleanup in, 487–488
pollution of, 486–488
species diversity in, 168
straightening and deepening, 334
threats to ecological services of, 487
Strip cropping, 223, 224
Strip cutting, 603, 604, 618
Strip mining, 363

Strong, Maurice, 352
Student Environmental Action Coalition (SEAC), 732
Styrene, 434
Subatomic particles, 47
Subduction zones, 206, 208
dumping radioactive wastes in, 371
Subphylum (subphyla), A5
Subsidence temperature inversion, 426
Subsidies, 706
Subsistence agriculture, traditional, 279
Subsoil, 212, 214
in forests, 601
Subspecies, A5
Subsurface mining, 341, 343
Subtropical forests, 598, 599
Suburban housing developments, 681
Suburbs, car-dependent, 679
Succession, predictability of, 184. *See also* Ecological succession
Succulent plants, 125
Sudan, Nile River damming and, 312
Suffering, alleviating, 16–17
Sufficiency revolution, 755
Sugars
in nucleic acids, A4
simple, 49
Sulfate ions, 48
Sulfate salts, 88, 89
Sulfur cycle, 88–89
Sulfur dioxide ($SO_2$), 88, 89, 425, 428, A3
as criteria air pollutant, 422
lichens as indicators of excess, 418
Sulfur dioxide emissions, 429, 433
Sulfur oxides, 420
Sulfur trioxide ($SO_3$), 88, 89, 425, A3
Sulfuric acid ($H_2SO_4$), 89, 425
Summitville gold mine, 345
Sun. *See also* Solar energy
in ecological view of economics, 694
electromagnetic spectrum of, 52
role in life on earth, 68, 69
as source of most of earth's energy, 349–350
Sunset businesses, 710, 711
Suntanning, 478
Superfund, 32, 34
improving, 554
Superfund Act of 1980, 552–553
Superfund for Workers, 713
Superfund sites, 345, 545
Superinsulated houses, 389
Superinsulating windows, 391
Superinsulation, 395
Supertoxic substances, 232
Supertrains, 675
Supply, in economic decisions, 691–692
Surface fires, 607
Surface impoundments, storing liquid hazardous wastes in, 546
Surface litter layer, 212, 213
Surface mining, 341
Surface Mining Control and Reclamation Act of 1977, 31, 343
Surface runoff, 83, 314
Surface water, 159, 314
Surface water pollution, preventing and reducing, 502–507
Surface winds, formation of, 117
"Survival of the fittest," 104
Survivorship curves, 198
Suspended particulate matter (SPM), 420, 426
as criteria air pollutant, 422
Sustainability, 201
of aquatic life zones, 162–163
Sustainability proposals, evaluating, 747
Sustainability revolution, 15–16
Sustainable agriculture, 308–309
in tropical forests, 618
Sustainable cities, 660–686
Sustainable cultivation, 22
Sustainable economic development, 698
Sustainable energy future, 413–414
Sustainable energy strategy, 412–413
Sustainable fisheries, 651

Sustainable forestry, in tropical forests, 618
Sustainable living, 3–4, 390, 748–749
    learning from nature, 199–201
Sustainable management, of forests, 605–606
Sustainable societies, decision making in, 17
Sustainable urban areas, 682–686
Sustainable water use, 335–336
Sustainable yield, 9, 26, 304
Sustainably grown timber, 606
Sustained yield, 610
SUVs. See Sport utility vehicles (SUVs)
Svensmark, Henrik, 457
Swallowtail butterfly, 565
Swamp pink, 565
Swamps, 160
Sweden
    hazardous waste burial in, 546
    paper industry regulation in, 703–704
Syllogism, 44
Symbiosis, 178
Symbiotic species interactions, 178–180
Symphonia, 564
Synergistic interactions, 46, 47, 230
Synergy, in complex systems, 46
Synfuels, 365
Synthetic chemicals, 234, 236
Synthetic natural gas (SNG), 364, 365
Synthetic organic compounds, 49
Syr Darya River, 319
Syria, irrigation in, 312
System modeling, 91
System optimization, 91
Systems
    defined, 44–45
    models and behavior of, 44–47
Systems analysis, 91–92
System simulation, 91
Systems measurement, 91

Taiga ecosystem, 139, 140
    climate graph for, 136
Tailings, 344
"Take-back" laws, 539–540, 712
Tall-grass prairies, 129
    restoration of, 629–630
Tamarisk, 576
Tamburri, Mario, 580
Tankless instant water heaters, 391
Tanzania, 634
Tapeworms, 178
Tapiola, Finland, as environmental showcase,
    683
Tar sands, 361
Tasmania, sheep population on, 193
Tassas, 284
Taxation. See also Carbon taxes; Energy taxes;
        Gasoline tax increases; Green taxes; Property
        taxes; Social Security taxes; Trash taxes
    high versus low, 702
    of fossil fuels, 413
Tax breaks, 702
    for corporations, 692
Tax-burden and tax-shifting approaches,
    704, 705
Taxus brevifolia, 569
Taylor, Rosamond, 307
Taylor Grazing Act of 1934, 29
TCDD, 232, 552
Technofixes, 469
    for ozone depletion, 477
Technological optimists, 14, 16–17
Technology
    impact of, 12, 16–17
    risk associated with, 246–248, 250
Technophilia, 572
Tectonic plates, 205, 206
    world map of, 207
Teenage pregnancy rate, 263
Television sets, incineration or landfill disposal
    of, 548–549
Temperate biomes, habitat degradation of, 572
Temperate deciduous forests, 137–139
    climate graph for, 136
    components and interactions in, 138

Temperate desert ecosystem, 125, 126 127
Temperate forests, 123, 134, 598, 599
    world map of, 136
Temperate grasslands, 123, 124, 128–132
Temperate lakes, seasonal changes in, 157
Temperate rain forests, 139
Temperate shrubland, 134
Temperate tall-grass prairie ecosystem, 131
Temperate zone lakes
    temperature layers in, 159
    zones of life in, 158
Temperature, 52. See also Heat
    in aquatic life zones, 146
    average, 115, 124
    in deserts, 126
    factors affecting change in, 457–460
    influence on smog, 426
    range of tolerance and, 73
    seasonal changes in, 115–116
Temperature conversions, A1
Temperature inversion, 426
Tennessee Valley Authority (TVA), 28, 719
Teratogens, 233
Terminator genes, 291
Termites, Formosan, 576, 578, 579
Terpenes, 477
Terra spacecraft, 421
Terracing, 222, 224
Terrestrial biodiversity, 594–631
Terrestrial ecosystems, 73
Territoriality, 172–173
Terrorism, 373
    release of toxic chemicals due to, 528–529
    versus nuclear plants and waste storage
        areas, 370
Tertiary consumers, 74, 77
Tetrachloroethylene, 434
Tetraethyl lead, 28
Thailand, slowing population growth in, 254
Thames River, cleanup of, 488
Theft of recyclables, 538
Theory, scientific, 41–42
Theory of evolution. See Evolution
Theory of island biogeography. See Island
        biogeography
Thermal cap, 120
Thermal pollution, 484
Thermal stratification, 157
Thermocline, 119, 157
Thermodynamics, laws of, 59, 60
Thermolysis, 405
Thinking strategies, 43
Thiobacillus ferroxidans, 349
Thomashow, Mitchell, 750
Thoreau, Henry David, 26
Threatened species, 563, 564–565. See also
        Endangered species
    alligators as, 173
    protecting all, 585
Three-factor model, 13
Three Gorges Dam, 320–321
Three Mile Island accident, 31, 367, 374
Threshold dose-response model, 233
Threshold level, 46
    of chemicals, 230
Throughput, 698, 699
    high, 60
    low, 61
    system, 45
Thunderheads, 112
Thymine (T), A4
Thyroid disrupters, 234, 235
"Tidal waves," 211
Tides, 148. See also Intertidal zone
    producing electricity from, 401
Tiger, 565, 573
    threats to, 580
Tiger mosquitoes, 576, 578
Tiger salamanders, 103
Tillinghast-Towers Perrin study, 436
Tilman, David, 185, 284, 741
Timber
    from national forests, 610
    sustainably grown, 606

Time delay, complex systems and, 46
Time preference, 702
Times Beach, Missouri, evacuation of, 34
Tissue culture techniques, advanced, 290
TNT, in "dirty" bombs, 373
Toads, 576
Todd, John, 483, 684, 685
Toilet systems, composting, 506
Toledo reactor, 368
Tolerance, 183
    range of, 73
Tolerance levels of pesticides, 518
Tool libraries, 535
Toothed whales, 643, 644. See also Cetaceans
Top-down control hypothesis, 194
Top-down food web dynamics, 635
Top-down reasoning, 44
Topography, microclimate creation and, 121–122
Top predator keystone species, 172
Topsoil, Dust Bowl and, 219
Topsoil erosion, 217
Topsoil layer, 212, 213
Tornadoes
    formation of, 112, 113
    in North America, 114
Total allowable catch (TAC), 650
Total fertility rate (TFR), 257, 258, 259. See also
        Fertility rates
Total life quality management, 707
Total quality management, 706
Tourism, wildlife, 570
Toxic chemicals, 229–230, 233, 344. See also Love
        Canal, New York; Persistent organic
        pollutants (POPs) treaty
    in the Great Lakes, 492
    in lakes and reservoirs, 490
    sensitivity to, 230
    trace levels of, 230–231
Toxicity, 229–230
    estimating, 232, 233
    laboratory experiments and, 232–233
Toxicity ratings, table of, 232
Toxicity studies, 233
Toxic industrial wastes, illegal dumping of, 503
Toxic materials
    buildup of, 536
    common household, 527
Toxicology, 229–233
Toxic pollutants, using bees to detect, 553
Toxic substances, defined, 232
Toxic Substances Control Act of 1976, 31, 724
Toxins, from fish-killing microbes, 489
Toynbee, Arnold, 738, 752
Trace levels of toxic chemicals, 230–231
Tradable pollution, 704–705
Tradable pollution rights, 704, 706
Trade, globalization of, 733–734. See also Global
        free trade
Trade agreements, improving, 738
Traditional agriculture, 279, 280
    growing techniques in, 284
Traditional intensive agriculture, 279, 280
Traditionals, cultural shift among, 752
Traditional subsistence agriculture, 279
Tragedy of the commons, 9, 11, 30
    commercial fishing and, 305
Trans-Alaska Pipeline System, 360
Transform faults, 207, 208
Transgenomics, 290
    in biosphere reserve, 626
Transitional stage, of demographic transition, 269
Transition zone, 71, 159, 160
Transmissible disease, 236–237. See also Disease
    spread of, 241–243
Transpiration, 82
Transportation
    $CO_2$ emissions and, 471–472
    saving energy in, 385–386
    urban development and, 671–675
Transportation tax deductions, 677
Trash collection, in Curitiba, Brazil, 678
Trash taxes, 531
Trawler fishing, 156, 301–302, 641
Trawling nets, 642

Treaties
    international, 582, 641, 646–647, 649, 731
    national, 641
Treberth, Kevan, 457
Tree diseases, 606–607
Tree-down zone, of volcanic eruptions, 203
Tree farms, 600
Tree-free fibers, making paper from, 611–612
Tree harvesting methods, 617
Tree plantations, 139, 600, 601, 604, 605–606, 609
Tree-removal zone, of volcanic eruptions, 203
Trees
    in Curitiba, Brazil, 678
    effects of acid deposition on, 431–432
    effects of air pollutants on, 432
    fast-growing, 619
    harvesting, 602–604, 611–612
    planting, 467
    urbanization and, 668
Trenches, oceanic, 208
Tribal era, of U.S. history, 25
Tribal peoples, 613–614
Trichinae, 522
1, 1, 1-Trichloroethane ($C_2H_3Cl_3$), 434
    as ozone-depleting compound, 473
Trichlorofluoromethane ($CCl_3F$), 472, 473
Trickling filters, 504
Tritium, 48. See also D–T (deuterium–tritium)
    fusion reaction
Trophic levels, 76, 79
Tropical cyclones, 113
    in North America, 114
Tropical deciduous forests, 137
Tropical deforestation, 612–619
    causes of, 614–616
    reducing, 616–617
Tropical deserts, 125
Tropical dry forest, ecological restoration of, 630
Tropical forest rivers, components and inter-
    actions in, 161
Tropical forests, 123, 124, 134, 598, 599. See also
    Tropical deforestation; Tropical rain forests
    clearing of, 616
    cultural extinction in, 613, 614
    degradation of, 616
    instrumental values of, 613
    sustainable agriculture and forestry in, 618
Tropical grasslands, 128, 129
Tropical monsoon forests, 137
Tropical plant species, health potential of, 569–570
Tropical rain forests, 134–137
    climate graph for, 136
    components and interactions in, 135
    plant and animal niches in, 137
    soil in, 215
    world map of, 136
Tropical scrub forests, 137
Tropical seasonal forests, 137
Troposphere, 68, 111, 419
    gray-air smog in, 425
    greenhouse effect and, 120
    warming of, 450
Tropospheric carbon dioxide, 448
Tropospheric heating effect, 448. See also
    Greenhouse effect
Trout species, 171
Tsetse fly, 294
Tsunamis, 211
Tuberculosis, global epidemic of, 241
Tube worms, species diversity of, 167
Tucson, water conservation in, 334. See also
    Biosphere 1; Biosphere 2
Tulane University, as green college, 753
Tundra, 123, 124, 128, 129, 132–134
    wet arctic, 160
Tuolumne River dam, 32
Turkey, irrigation in, 312
Turkmenistan, Aral Sea water transfer disaster
    and, 325
Turnell, Jack, 599
Turner, Ray, 479
Turtle exclusion devices (TEDs), 641, 642
Turtles, 565, 641, 642
TVA. See Tennessee Valley Authority (TVA)

Twenty-first century, environmental agenda for, 36
Two-cycle engines, regulation of emissions from,
    440
2001 State of the Bay Report, 500
Typhoons, 113–114

Uganda, 634
Ultrafiltration, in advanced sewage treatment, 505
Ultrafine particles
    health dangers from, 440
    in suspended particulate matter, 426
Ultraviolet (UV) light (radiation), 69, 419, 472.
    See also UV-A radiation; UV-B radiation
    amphibian decline and, 170, 171
    CFCs and, 472–473
    origin of life and, 97, 99
    in photochemical smog formation, 423
    purifying water with, 508
    skin cancer and, 476, 478
    water and, 313
Unconfined aquifer, 315
Uncontrolled nuclear fusion, 58
Unconventional natural gas, 362
Undergrazing, effects of, 297, 298
Underground coal mining, 342
Underground tanks, leaking of, 494
Undernutrition, 285–286. See also Malnutrition;
    Starvation
Understory layer, in forests, 601
Undiscovered resources, 339
Unemployment, 708. See also Employment
Uneven-aged forest management, 602
Unfunded mandates, 730
Unidentified coal reserves, 363
Uniform population dispersal pattern, 191
Union Carbide Bhopal pesticide plant disaster, 34,
    528, 529
Union of Concerned Scientists, 404
United Kingdom, hazardous waste landfills in,
    546
United Nations, world population projection by,
    258
United Nations Biological Diversity summit, 35
United Nations Biosphere Conference, 30
United Nations Center for Human Settlements,
    296
United Nations Children's Fund (UNICEF), 287
United Nations Commission on Sustainable
    Development, 731
United Nations Commission on Human Rights,
    555
United Nations Conference on Population and
    Development, 274
United Nations Conference on the Human
    Environment, 31, 731
United Nations Development Program (UNDP),
    709
United Nations Educational, Scientific, and
    Cultural Organization (UNESCO), 626
    Lake Baikal and, 654
United Nations Environment Program (UNEP),
    217, 466, 518, 646, 731, 732
United Nations Food and Agriculture
    Organization (FAO), 285, 304. See also FAO
    international treaty
United Nations Framework Convention on
    Climate Change, 469
United Nations International Panel on Climate
    Change (IPCC), 35
United Nations Law of the Sea, 646
United Nations Population Fund, 263
United States. See also Federal entries; Govern-
    ment entries; National entries; U.S. entries
    acid deposition in, 428–430, 432–433
    biodiversity hot spots in, 583
    biomass use in, 403–404
    birth rates in, 259
    coastal pollution in, 498
    common air pollutants in, 422
    cultural shift in, 752–753
    desalination plants in, 328
    election finance reform in, 721
    eminent domain policy in, 725
    energy consumption in, 351–352, 381

    energy industry subsidies by, 352–353
    energy waste in, 381
    environmental history of, 25–36
    environmental justice in, 728–729
    environmental laws in, 624
    environmental policy in, 719–723
    fertility rates in, 259
    flood-prone areas in, 334
    food production in, 281–283
    forest resources and management in, 609–612
    freshwater resources in, 316–317
    geographic range of pests in, 515
    gray wolf populations in, 594
    groundwater pollution in, 493–494, 495,
        496–497
    habitat disturbance in, 572
    hazardous waste regulation in, 552–554
    immigration to, 268
    industrialized agriculture in, 283
    kudzu vine in, 577
    Kyoto Treaty and, 469–471
    land use in, 283, 595–598
    major biomes of, 70
    major mineral deposits in, 597
    major urban problems in, 664–666
    mass transit in, 677
    mining industry subsidies by, 346–347
    motor vehicle accidents in, 673
    natural gas production decline in, 362–363
    nonnative species in, 574–575
    nuclear power in, 366–369, 377
    oil reserves of, 357
    oil use in, 356–357
    paper recycling in, 540
    pesticide regulation in, 518–520
    policymaking in, 720–723
    private versus public property rights in, 683
    purple loosestrife in, 640
    radioactive contamination in, 372
    rangeland in, 299
    real cost of gasoline in, 388
    recycling municipal solid waste in, 537
    rural-to-urban shift in, 664
    smoking in, 228
    soil erosion in, 219–220, 223
    solid waste produced by, 526
    species in, 562
    tax-shifting approach in, 705
    tornadoes in, 112, 114
    urban development in, 664, 680–682
    water rights in, 329
    water waste in, 328–329
    wetland protection in, 651
    wind power in, 402–403
    zebra mussel in, 655
Units of measure, A1
University campuses, environmental groups on,
    732, 752–753
University of California at Davis, as green college,
    753
Unpredictable events, 47
Upwellings, 118–119
Uranium (U), 48
Uranium-235 nucleus
Uranium isotopes, 48
Uranium ore, as nonrenewable energy source, 350
Uranium oxide fuel, 365
    fission of, 57
Urban areas, 661. See also Cities
    food growth in, 296
    major, 662
    photochemical smog in, 424–425
    sustainable, 682–686
    water in, 316, 317
Urban development (growth), 661–664, 680–682.
    See also Urbanization
    ecological aspects of, 682–686
    spatial patterns of, 666–667
    transportation and, 671–675
Urban growth boundary, 681
    in Oregon, 683
Urban heat islands, 670–671
Urban land-use planning, 676–682
    in Oregon, 683

Urban open space, preserving, 680–682
Urban poor, 662, 663. *See also* Poverty
Urban spatial structure, models of, 667
Urban sprawl, 36, 664–666, 667–668, 671
    motor vehicles and, 673
    reducing, 680, 681
Urbanization, 260, 661–668. *See also* Urban
        development (growth)
    advantages and disadvantages of, 668–671
    as consequence of agricultural revolution, 24
    flooding and, 332
    increasing, 294
    patterns of, 661–662
    in the United States, 664
Urey, Harold, 97
Uruguay Round of the General Agreement on
        Tariffs and Trade (GATT), 733
U.S. *See* United States
U.S. Department of Agriculture (USDA), 219, 719
    conservation reserve programs from, 223
U.S. Department of Commerce, 719
U.S. Department of Defense, 719
U.S. Department of Energy (DOE), 31, 32, 369, 372,
        374–375, 381, 719
    cleanup of nuclear waste sites of, 553
    energy-efficiency standards of, 392
U.S. Department of Health and Human Services,
        719
U.S. Department of Housing and Urban
        Development, 719
U.S. Department of Justice, 719
U.S. Department of Labor, 719
U.S. Department of State, 719
U.S. Department of the Interior, 719
U.S. Department of Transportation, 719
Use biodiversity, 569
Useful energy, 353
User fees, 704, 706
User-pays approach, 228, 672
U.S. Fish and Wildlife Service, 29
U.S. Food and Drug Administration (FDA), on
        mercury-contaminated fish, 550
U.S. Forest Service, 26, 27, 299
U.S. Geological Survey (USGS), 339, 494
U.S. House of Representatives, bills becoming
        laws in, 722
U.S. National Academy of Sciences, 14, 44, 370
    on harmful chemicals, 235–236
U.S. National Wilderness Preservation System, 628
*Usnea trichodea* lichen, 418
U.S. Park Service, 620
U.S. Wilderness Society, 627
Utah prairie dog, 564
Utilitarian biodiversity, 569
Utilitarian values, 742
UV-A radiation, 475, 478
UV-B radiation, 475–476, 478
UV light. *See* Ultraviolet (UV) light (radiation)
Uzbekistan, Aral Sea water transfer disaster and,
        325

Vaccines, 240–241
    for hepatitis B, 242
Values
    instrumental versus intrinsic, 742–743
    short-term versus long-term, 744
Variability of traits, 101
Vassar College, as green college, 753
Vectors, 236
    insect, 242
Vegetarian diet, 287
Vegetation
    buffer zones, 502
    overgrazing, 299
    wildlife management and, 588–589
Vegetation patches, 166, 184
Veldt, 132
Venus, 95
Verne, Jules, 405
Vertebrates, classifying, A5
Very toxic substances, 232
Village Homes, 660
"Village pharmacy" tree, 614
Villages, 661

Viral diseases
    spread of, 237–240
    treatment of, 240–241
Viravidaiya, Mechai, 254
Virgin forests, in the United States, 609
Viruses, 234, 237
    in coastal waters, 498
    in drinking water, 485
Visible light, 52, 69
Vision 2000 process, 685–686
Vitamin A deficiency, 286–287
Vitousek, Peter, 82
Volatile organic compounds (VOCs), 420, 439
    in drinking water, 495
Volcanic eruptions
    ecological impact of, 203
Volcanic islands, 208
Volcanoes, 211–212
Volcano hazards, reducing, 212
Volcano sites, 206–207
Volume, units of, A1
Voluntary emissions trading program, 441
Voluntary simplicity, 751
*Vorsorgeprinzip* principle, 187
Vulnerable species, 563

Wackernagel, Mathis, 10, 669
Warblers, 463, 565, 574
    insect-eating, 175
Ward, Barbara, 3
Warm front, 111
Warm-rock reservoir deposits, 410
Warmth services, 533
Warning coloration, 177, 178
Washing machines, ultrasonic wave, 491
Wasson, Kerstin, 580
Waste. *See also* Biodegradable wastes; Hazardous
        waste; Low-waste society
    detoxifying, 542
    hazardous, 526–528, 536
    issues related to, 531
    from mining and smelting, 527
    polyvinyl chloride, 534, 551
    postconsumer, 535, 541
    preconsumer, 541
    radioactive, 369–370
    reducing, 529–531, 536–537
    solid, 526
Waste disposal, 536, 537
Waste disposal firms, 547
Waste heat, 59, 60, 61
    using, 383–384
Waste management
    approaches to, 529, 536–537
    waste reduction versus, 530–531, 536–537
Wastepaper, recycling, 540–541
Waste-to-energy incinerators, 543
Waste treatment, advanced, 490
Wastewater, reusing, 509. *See also* Water waste
Wastewater garden system, 506
Wastewater treatment plants, 503–504
Water, 49, 477, A3. *See also* Aquatic entries;
        Bottled water; Drinking water; Freshwater
        entries; Marine entries; Ocean entries;
        Wetlands
    chemical analysis of, 485
    chemical equation for formation of, 54
    in Curitiba, Brazil, 678
    in desert ecosystems, 126–128
    in earth's atmosphere, 97
    effects of food production on, 288
    effects of urban sprawl on, 666
    efficient use of, 328–332
    grain import wars and, 312
    importance and properties of, 313–314
    oxygen-demanding wastes in, 484, 485, 488
    purifying with UV light, 508
    soil erosion by, 217
    zones in the downhill flow of, 159–160
Water budget, 314
Water cycle, 82–83. *See also* Hydrologic cycle
    human activities and, 84
Water depth, dissolved oxygen and carbon
        dioxide and, 146. *See also* Marine depth

Water distribution
    atmospheric warming and, 460
    in the Middle East, 312
Waterfowl
    managing populations of, 590
    protecting, 586
    refuges for, 590
Water heaters, 391–392
Water heating, via solar energy, 394–395
Water hyacinth, 576, 634
Water laws, 329
Water levels, in wetlands, 162
Waterlogging of soil, 221, 222
Water mining, 315, 325
Water pollution, 6, 483–511. *See also* Drinking
        water; Groundwater pollution; Ocean
        pollution; Surface water pollution
    from the Aral Sea water diversion project,
        324–325
    in the Baltic Sea, 499
    from coal burning, 364
    effect of climate change on, 486
    in freshwater lakes, 489–493
    in freshwater streams, 486–488
    point and nonpoint sources of, 486
    preventing, 510
    reducing, 503
    types and effects of, 484
Water Pollution Control Act of 1956, 29
Water pollution control laws, 487
Water prices, 329
Water properties, climate and, 117
Water purification systems, 509
Water quality
    improving, 487, 503
    measuring, 485
    modifying, 84
    renewal of, 83
Water Quality Act of 1987, 503
Water resources, 312–336
    access to, 317–318
    atmospheric warming and, 461
    supply, renewal, and use of, 314–317
    urbanization and, 668–669
Water rights, in the United States, 329
Water scarcity, 317
Watershed, 159, 314
    management of, 330
    reforesting, 503
Water shortages, 36, 314
Water-soluble toxins, 230
Water stress, 317
Water subsidy policies, 329
Water supplies, wildlife management and,
        588–589
Water table, 314
    lowering, 324–325
Water transfer, 322–324
Water use, sustainable, 294, 335–336
Water vapor, 83
    effect on climate, 458–459
    as greenhouse gas, 448
Water waste. *See also* Wastewater entries
    causes of, 329–330
    reducing, 328–329
Waterway development, 657
Water withdrawal, 315
Watts, Alan, 571
Wavelength, 52
Wave power, 401
Waves, 52
Wealth gap, 708
Weather, 70, 111–114
Weather breeder, troposphere as, 419
Weather extremes, 113. *See also* Extreme weather
    in North America, 114
Weathering, 208–209
    of rock, 340
Weather maps, 111
Weaver, Warren, 41
Weed killer, 519
Weeks Act of 1911, 27
Weizäcker, Ernst von, 705
West Nile virus, 237, 238

West Virginia spring salamander, 565
Wet deposition, 428
Wetlands. *See also* Coastal wetlands
    effect of pollutants on, 496–500
    freshwater inland, 160
    loss of, 162, 562, 638
    protecting, 651
    regulations concerning, 503
    restoring, 334, 652
    sustaining, 652
    using to treat sewage, 507, 651
Wet scrubber, 442
Weyer, Peter, 495
Whale Conservation and Protection Act of 1976, 641
Whales, 565. *See also* Cetaceans
Whaling, commercial, 643–646
Wheat production, worldwide, 284
Whelan, Elizabeth, 515
Whitcomb, Willard H., 512
White House Office, 719
White top pitcher plant, 565
WHO. *See* World Health Organization (WHO)
Whooping crane, 565
Wicks, Nancy, 390
Wild animals. *See also* Animals
    destruction of, 24
    hunting, 580
Wild boar, 576
Wilderness, 627
    preserving and managing, 627–628
    protecting, 26, 627
Wilderness Act of 1964, 29–30, 32, 627, 628, 724
Wilderness Preservation System, 628
Wilderness recovery areas, 628
Wilderness Society, 29, 32, 36, 621, 727
Wilderness species, 182, 589. *See also* Wildlife
    species; Wild species
Wild game animals, 166
Wildlands Project, The (TWP), 628
Wildlife. *See also* Wildlife species
    effects of ozone thinning on, 475
    pesticide harm to, 517
Wildlife Conservation Society, 727
Wildlife loss, energy resources and, 403
Wildlife management, 588–590
Wildlife refuges, 586
Wildlife Restoration Act of 1937, 588
Wildlife smuggling, 579
Wildlife species, types of, 588–589. *See also*
    Wilderness species; Wild species
Wildlife tourism, 570
Wildlife trade, illegal, 584
Wild plants, destruction of, 24. *See also* Plants
Wild rivers, protecting and restoring, 657
Wild species. *See also* Wilderness species; Wildlife
    species
    approaches to protecting, 586–588
    ecological services provided by, 570
    extinction of, 572
    nonutilitarian (nonuse) values of, 570

preserving, 568–569
protecting, 582–586
sustaining, 561–593
Wilkins, Mary, 446
Willingness to pay, 701
Wilson, Edward O., 65, 168, 169, 172, 195, 446, 562, 568, 571, 572, 591, 630
Win-win solutions, 580
Wind(s), 110. *See also* Surface winds
    influence on smog, 426
    lakes and, 157
    producing electricity from, 401–403
    soil erosion by, 217
    spread of disease via, 242
Windbreaks, 224, 225
Wind erosion, 132
Wind farms, 400, 402, 403
Windows
    energy-efficient, 395
    low-E (low-emissivity), 391
Wind power, advantages and disadvantages of, 403
Wind resources, 402–403
Wind turbines, 401, 402, 412, 433
Winged bean, 292
Wise-use movement, 32, 33–34
Wolves, 564, 594
    on Isle Royale, 197
Women
    educational and employment opportunities
      for, 260
    empowering, 270
Wood
    efficient use of, 611
    renewable, 23
Woodlands, 123
Work (in physics), 51
Workers, risk levels for, 246, 249. *See also*
    Employment
World. *See also* Earth entries; Planet
    biodiversity hot spots in, 625
    endangered marine animals in, 641
    forests of, 599, 604–605
    land use in, 595
    major urban areas of, 662
    management of, 743–744
World biodiversity status, 562
World Commission on Dams, 400
World Commission on Water in the 21st Century, 319, 507
World Conservation Union (IUCN), 628, 646
World crop production, increasing, 289–296
World Environment Organization (WEO), 737
World Health Organization (WHO), 422, 484
    campaign against malaria, 200
    on cigarette smoking, 228
    on poverty, 8
    on tuberculosis, 241
World Heritage Site, 654

World Life Conservation Society, 579
World Meteorological Organization (WMO) study, 479
World population, increase in, 2, 5. *See also*
    Population
World population projection, UN, 258
World Resources Institute (WRI), 160, 217, 325, 604, 727
World Trade Center towers, destruction of, 368, 529. *See also* September 11 terrorist attacks
World Trade Organization (WTO), 733, 734–735, 738
    criticisms against, 693
    environmental protection and, 736–737
Worldwatch Institute, 293, 297, 611, 727
Worldwide Fund for Nature, 727
World Wide Web, 24
World Wildlife Fund (WWF), 30, 156, 582, 727, 728
Worms
    controlling parasitic, 522
    in drinking water, 485
Wyoming, eco-ranching in, 599

Xeriscaping, 331, 332
Xerox Corporation, service flow economy at, 533

Yaneshé Indians, tree harvesting by, 618
Yangtze River, 320
    dam and reservoir project on, 321
Yangtze River basin, 616
Yellow River, 319
Yellowstone National Park, 27, 620
    fires in, 608
Yom Kippur War, 30
Yosemite National Park, 27
Young adult age structure, effects of a change in, 266
Yucca Mountain desert region, 374
Yunus, Muhammad, 709

Zahniser, Howard, 32
Zebra mussel, 576, 655
"Zebra mussel death ray," 655
Zero-discharge systems, 537
Zero-waste ecoindustrial park, 686
Zero waste goal, 534
Zimmerman, Michael, 734
Zion National Park, 621
Zone of aeration, 314
Zone of saturation, 314
Zoning. *See also* Land use; Land zoning
    in Oregon, 683
    using to control land use, 677
Zooplankton, 72, 78, 80, 145, 149, 153
Zoos, preserving endangered species in, 587–588
Zooxanthellae, 178
    in coral reefs, 144
Zorgoski, John, 495

# ENVIRONMENTAL SCIENCE: CONCEPTS AND CONNECTIONS

**Ecosystems** — studies interrelationships of

**Ecosystems**
- provide → Resources
- consist of → Communities, Matter Cycling
- function through → Energy Flow
- undergo → Change

**Communities**
- consist of → Populations
- consist of → Organisms
- consist of → Resources

**Matter Cycling**
- between → Nonliving (Abiotic) ↔ Living (Biotic)

**Nonliving (Abiotic)**
- includes → Physical Factors, Chemical Factors

**Living (Biotic)**
- includes → Producers, Consumers, Decomposers

**Energy Flow**
- primarily from → Sunlight

**Change**
- through → Population Dynamics, Succession, Evolution

**Resources**
- affect development of
- include → Matter Resources, Energy Resources

**Matter Resources**
- may be → Nonliving, Living

**Nonliving**
- may be → Nonrenewable, Potentially Renewable

**Nonrenewable**
- includes → Minerals

**Potentially Renewable**
- includes → Air, Water, Soil

**Living**
- are
- consist of → Land Systems (deserts, grasslands, forests), Aquatic Systems (oceans, lakes, streams, wetlands)
- provide → Ecosystem Services (nutrient cycling, pest control, waste purification, genetic material), Biodiversity (genes, species, ecosystems)

**Energy Resources**
- may be → Renewable (direct sun, wind, biomass, flowing water), Nonrenewable (fossil fuel, nuclear)

**Land Systems** → Food Resources

**Food Resources**
- include → Crops, Livestock, Fish

**Crops**
- depend on → Climate, Pest Control

**Pest Control**
- may be → Biological, Chemical (pesticides)

**Climate**
- primarily determined by

**Biodiversity**
- can sustain
- can decrease
- depletes
- affects

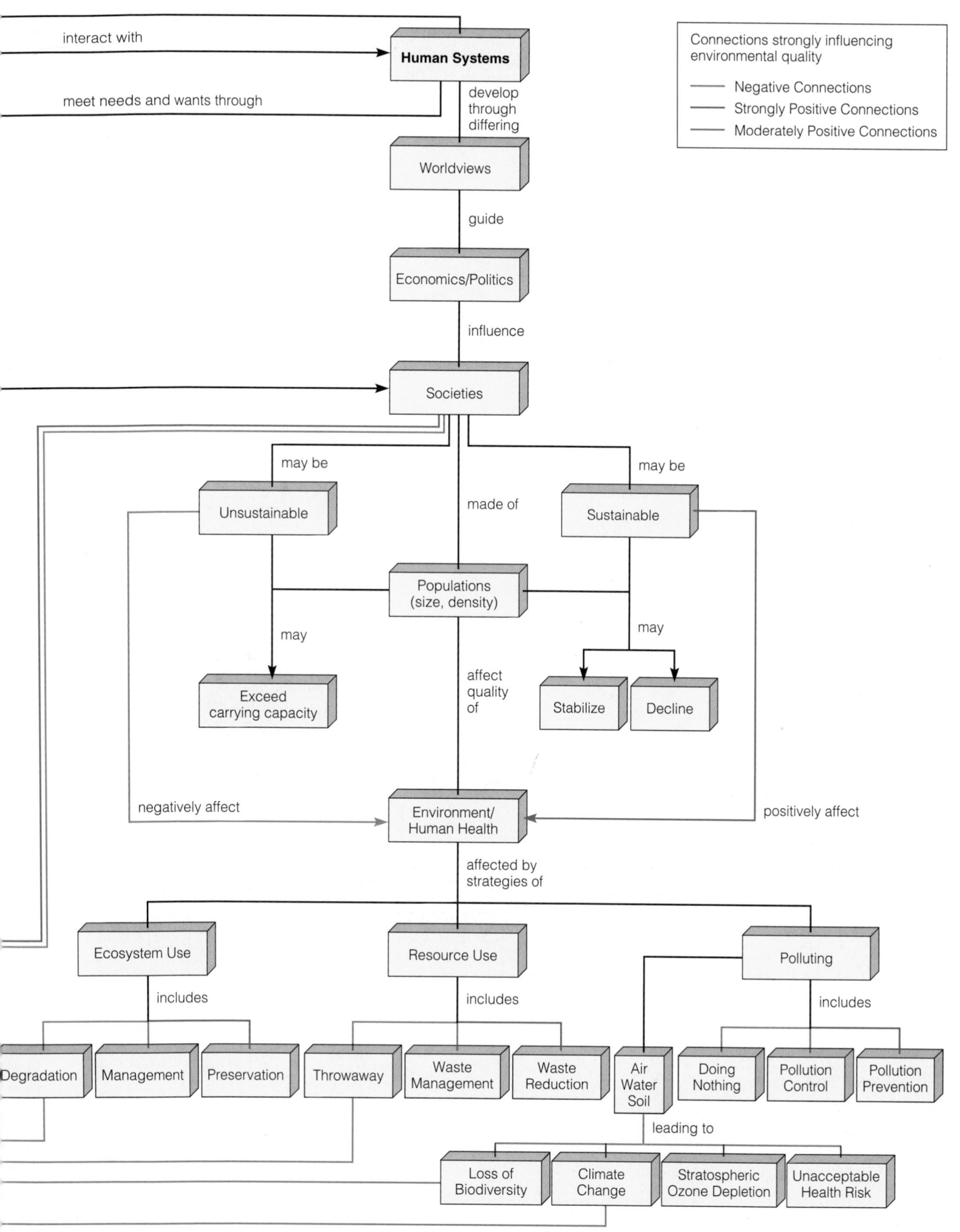

Developed by **Jane Heinze-Fry** with assistance from G. Tyler Miller, Jr.
(For assistance in creating your own concept maps, see the website for this book.)

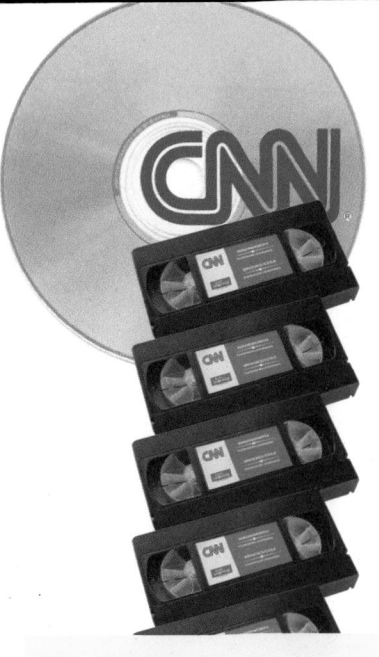

| ch. | description |
|---|---|
| 3 | Nuclear Medicine (2:26) |
| 4 | Agricultural Runoff and Water Quality (2:50) |
| 5 | Cockroaches |
| 5 | Biggest Mass Extinction (1:40) |
| 5 | Human Genome Project (1:46) |
| 5 | Creation vs. Evolution (2:21) |
| 6 | El Niño (1:54) |
| 7 | Sediment Kills Reefs (2:12) |
| 7 | Coral Reef Protection 2:06) |
| 7 | Artificial Reefs (2:37) |
| 8 | Fighting Foreign Fire Ants (3:18) |
| 8 | Sudden Oak Death (1:56) |
| 8 | Mutant Frogs (2:14) |
| 8 | Frogs as Indicator Species (2:19) |
| 9 | Studying Forest Elephants (3:08) |
| 11 | An Edible Vaccine (3:21) |
| 11 | Goodbye Guinea Worm ( 2:59) |
| 11 | World Smoking (2:04) |
| 11 | Smoking and Hearing Loss (2:02) |
| 11 | Obesity Epidemic (2:10) |
| 11 | Resistant Germ (2:42) |
| 11 | Smallpox Threat (5:12) |
| 11 | Anthrax Bioterror (3:04) |
| 11 | AIDS Update (2:10) |
| 11 | Power Lines and Cancer (2:05) |
| 11 | Passive Smoking Risks (1:59) |
| 11 | Electromagnetic Fields and Cancer (2:04) |
| 11 | Asbestos Threat (1:49) |
| 11 | Drug-Resistant Salmonella (1:44) |
| 11 | Emerging Infections (1:59) |
| 11 | Anti-Smoking Campaign (2:13) |
| 11 | PCB Health Hazards (2:07) |
| 12 | South African Malaria Epidemic (2:57) |
| 12 | Male Pill (2:11) |
| 12 | China's Environmental Effects (2:01) |
| 12 | Population Growth (2:07) |
| 13 | Speedy Flowers (2:56) |
| 13 | Unusual Kenyan Fish (3:14) |
| 13 | Bt Corn: A Threat to Monarchs? (2:13) |
| 13 | Transgenic Tobacco (2:00) |
| 13 | Genetic Crops (3:13) |

| ch. | description |
|---|---|
| 13 | Aquaculture (2:39) |
| 14 | Lost Beneath the Lake (3:05) |
| 14 | Water Conservation (1:55) |
| 15 | Radioactive Cleanup (2:20) |
| 15 | Recovery of Prince William Sound (2:59) |
| 15 | Legacy of Three Mile Island (1:49) |
| 15 | Arctic Wildlife Refuge Protection (2:58) |
| 15 | Britain Nuclear Plant Sabotage (2:11) |
| 15 | Ethanol Fueled Vehicles (2:18) |
| 15 | Chernobyl (2:56) |
| 15 | Nuclear Power Plant Safety (2:03) |
| 15 | Arctic National Wildlife Refuge (2:03) |
| 16 | Algal Fuel (2:00) |
| 16 | Wind Energy (2:26) |
| 16 | EPA Energy Stars (2:19) |
| 16 | Fuel Cell Revolution (2:04) |
| 16 | Fuel Cell Vehicles (1:46) |
| 16 | Renewable Energy (2:10) |
| 17 | Air Pollution Affects Health (1:51) |
| 17 | Airplane Pollution (2:03) |
| 17 | Mexico's Smoggy Problem (2:50) |
| 17 | Greening Sudbury (5:45) |
| 17 | Catalytic Converter Concerns (1:36) |
| 17 | Planning for Toxic Leaks (2:04) |
| 17 | Acid Rain in New York (2:00) |
| 17 | Acid Rain (2:07) |
| 17 | World Trade Center Air Pollution (3:13) |
| 17 | Ozone Pollution (1:44) |
| 18 | Ozone Healing (2: 03) |
| 18 | Arctic Warming (2:10) |
| 18 | Glacial Melting (2:06) |
| 18 | Forests and Global Warming (2:17) |
| 18 | Arctic Ozone Loss (1:48) |
| 18 | Maldives Climate Change (2:17) |
| 18 | Diminishing Ozone (1:49) |
| 18 | Global Warming (1:39) |
| 18 | Climate Changes (2:41) |
| 18 | Rising Global Temperatures (1:40) |
| 18 | Global Warming (2:16) |
| 19 | Controversial Water Quality (2:21) |
| 19 | Questioning Water Quality (3:04) |

| ch. | description |
|---|---|
| 19 | Agricultural Runoff and Water Quality (2:50) |
| 19 | Jet Ski Pollution (2:02) |
| 19 | Waste-Water Bioreactor (2:19) |
| 19 | Pfisteria: Killer Algae (6:37) |
| 19 | MTBE Concerns (1:17) |
| 19 | Yukon River Pollution (4:48) |
| 19 | River Pollution (1:58) |
| 19 | Lake Pollution (1:44) |
| 20 | Legacy of Agent Orange (2:47) |
| 20 | Polluted Breast Milk (1:58) |
| 21 | Trash Traders (4:12) |
| 21 | Landscaped Landfill (2:37) |
| 21 | Legacy of Love Canal (2:18) |
| 21 | Bees and Landmines (1:45) |
| 21 | Recycling in the U.S. (2:05) |
| 22 | Komodo Dragons (2:26) |
| 22 | Black Footed Ferrets (2:50) |
| 22 | Saving Guanacos (2:53) |
| 22 | Last of the Hartebeest (5:19) |
| 22 | Endangered Orangutans (4:18) |
| 22 | Tribal Whaling Resumes (1:50) |
| 22 | Saving the White Abalone (2:06) |
| 22 | Sea Turtles Vs Ebay (1:48) |
| 22 | Whaling (3:04) |
| 22 | Endangered Sea Turtles (1:45) |
| 23 | Fire in the Amazon (1:53) |
| 23 | Brazil's Ecotourism (2:43) |
| 23 | Logging Tierra Del Fuego (3:19) |
| 23 | Protecting Wildlife Reserves (3:16) |
| 23 | Illegal Logging (3:16) |
| 23 | Wildlife Refuge (2:21) |
| 23 | Deforestation (2:52) |
| 24 | Everglades Restoration (2:40) |
| 24 | Mercury in the Everglades (2:12) |
| 25 | Heat Islands (4:12) |
| 25 | Man-Made Weather (2:07) |
| 25 | Water-Cooled City (1:30) |
| 25 | Sprawl America (3:10) |
| 27 | Kyoto Protocol (2:18) |
| 27 | Clean Power Act (2:14) |